PEARSON ALWAYS LEARNING

Elayn Martin-Gay

Introductory Algebra

MAT 0028

Custom Revised Edition for Palm Beach State College

Taken from:
Introductory Algebra, Fourth Edition
by Elayn Martin-Gay

Prealgebra, Sixth Edition
by Elayn Martin-Gay

Cover Art: Courtesy of Palm Beach State College

Taken from:

Introductory Algebra, Fourth Edition
by Elayn Martin-Gay

Published by Prentice Hall
Upper Saddle River, New Jersey 07458

Prealgebra, Sixth Edition
by Elayn Martin-Gay

Published by Prentice Hall

This special edition published in cooperation with Pearson Learning Solutions.

Pearson Learning Solutions, 501 Boylston Street, Suite 900, Boston, MA 02116
A Pearson Education Company
www.pearsoned.com

Printed in the United States of America

4 5 6 7 8 9 10 V092 17 16 15 14 13

000200010271656446

SE

ISBN 10: 1-256-75642-3
ISBN 13: 978-1-256-75642-2

Contents

*Solutions to Selected Exercises are available in MyMathLab® under Tools for Success.

The content of this book is taken from *Introductory Algebra*, Fourth Edition, by Elayn Martin-Gay with the following exception. Sections 9.5-9.7 and their corresponding answers come from *Prealgebra*, Sixth Edition, by Elayn Martin-Gay.

Note to Students: The material included in this book has been specifically selected by your instructor. Some material that is not critical to your course has been eliminated, and the price of the book has been adjusted to reflect the content removed. The internal references (such as chapter, figure, and page numbers) in your text will reflect the numbers of their original sources, not this custom publication and so will not necessarily be consecutive.

Student Resources 714

These resources, located in the back of the text, give you a variety of tools conveniently located in one place to help you succeed in math.

A New Tool to Help You Succeed

Introducing Martin-Gay's New Student Organizer

The new **Student Organizer** guides you through three important parts of studying effectively–note-taking, practice, and homework.

It is designed to help you organize your learning materials and develop the study habits you need to be successful. The Student Organizer includes:

- How to prepare for class
- Space to take class-notes
- Step-by-step worked examples
- Your Turn exercises (modeled after the examples)
- Answers to the Your Turn exercises as well as worked-out solutions via references to the Martin-Gay text and videos
- Helpful hints and directions for completing homework assignments

A flexible design allows instructors to assign any or all parts of the Student Organizer.

The Student Organizer is available in a loose-leaf, notebook-ready format. It is also available for download in MyMathLab.

For more information, please go to

www.pearsonhighered.com/martingay

www.mypearsonstore.com (search Martin-Gay, Introductory Algebra, Fourth Edition)

your Martin-Gay MyMathLab course

Martin-Gay Video Resources

Interactive DVD Lecture Series

Active Learning at Your Pace

Designed for use on your computer or DVD player, these interactive videos include a 15–20 minute lecture for every section in the text as well as Concept Checks, Study Skills Builders, and a Practice Final Exam.

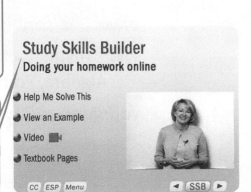

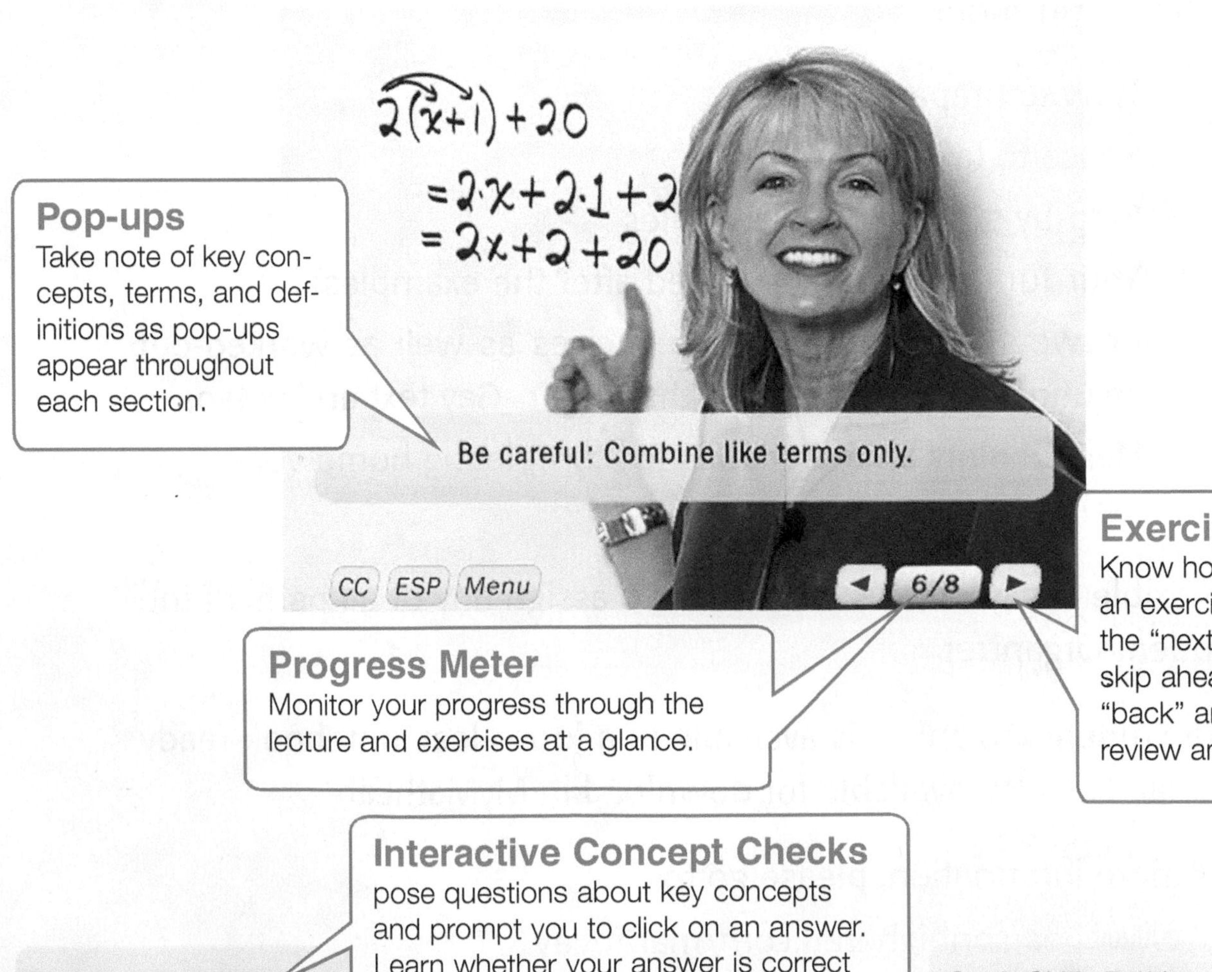

Pop-ups
Take note of key concepts, terms, and definitions as pop-ups appear throughout each section.
Be careful: Combine like terms only.
CC ESP Menu
6/8
Exercises
Know how to do an exercise? Click the "next" arrow to skip ahead or the "back" arrow to review an exercise.
Progress Meter
Monitor your progress through the lecture and exercises at a glance.
Interactive Concept Checks
pose questions about key concepts and prompt you to click on an answer. Learn whether your answer is correct and view the full solution.
Concept Check
Choose the pair of like terms.
A xy and -2yx
B 3x and 3y
C 4x and 3x²
Study Skills Builders
provide tips and suggestions to help you develop effective study habits.
Study Skills Builder
Doing your homework online
Help Me Solve This
View an Example
Video
Textbook Pages
SSB

to Help You Succeed

Chapter Test Prep Videos

Step-by-step solutions on video for all chapter tests exercises from the text. Available via:

- Interactive DVD Lecture Series
- MyMathLab
- YouTube (search MartinGayIntroAlg)

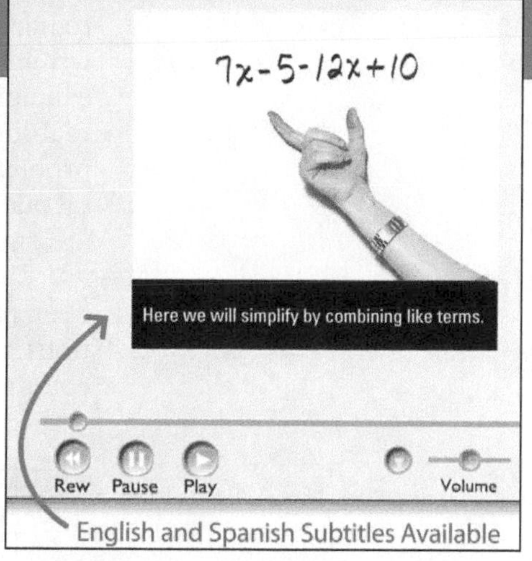

English and Spanish Subtitles Available

AlgebraPrep Apps for the iPhone™ and iPod Touch®

Your 24/7 Algebra Tutor—Anytime, Anywhere!

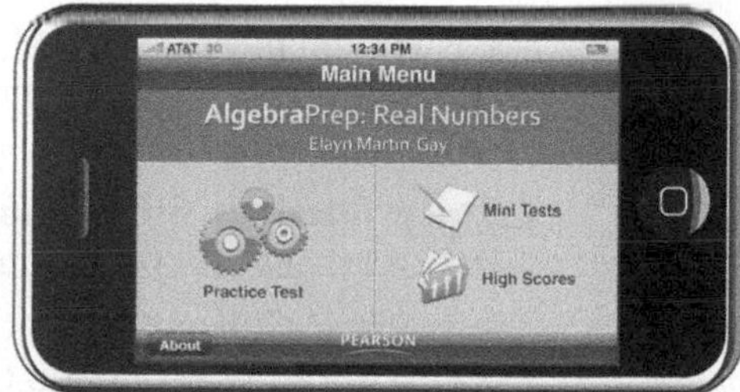

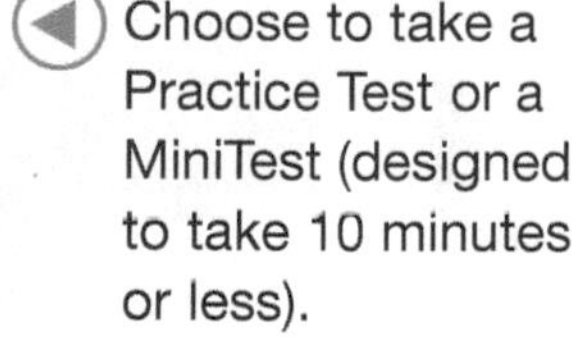
Choose to take a Practice Test or a MiniTest (designed to take 10 minutes or less).

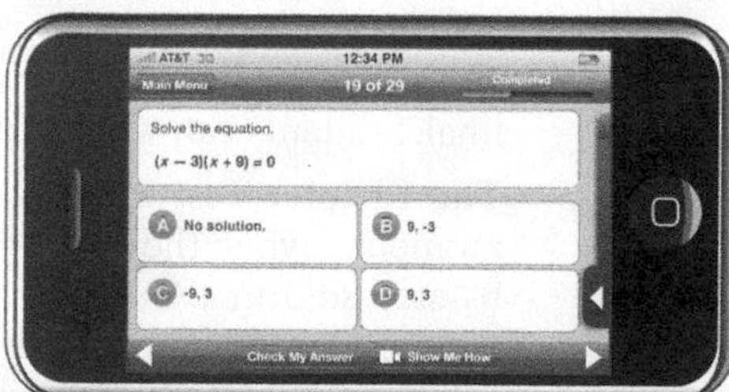

Practice Test exercises provide answer feedback to help you study and self-correct.

Step-by-step video solutions give you the guidance of an expert tutor whenever you need help.

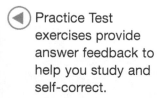

Preface

***Introductory Algebra,* Fourth Edition** was written to provide a solid foundation in algebra for students who might not have previous experience in algebra. Specific care was taken to make sure students have the most up-to-date relevant text preparation for their next mathematics course or for nonmathematical courses that require an understanding of algebraic fundamentals. I have tried to achieve this by writing a user-friendly text that is keyed to objectives and contains many worked-out examples. As suggested by AMATYC and the NCTM Standards (plus Addenda), real-life and real-data applications, data interpretation, conceptual understanding, problem solving, writing, cooperative learning, appropriate use of technology, mental mathematics, number sense, estimation, critical thinking, and geometric concepts are emphasized and integrated throughout the book.

The many factors that contributed to the success of the previous editions have been retained. In preparing the Fourth Edition, I considered comments and suggestions of colleagues, students, and many users of the prior edition throughout the country.

What's New in the Fourth Edition?

- The **Student Organizer** is designed by me to help students develop the study habits they need to be successful. This Organizer guides students through the three main components of studying effectively—note-taking, practice, and homework—and helps them develop the habits that will enable them to succeed in future courses. The Student Organizer can be packaged with the text in loose-leaf, notebook-ready format and is also available for download in MyMathLab.
- **Interactive DVD Lecture Series,** featuring your text author (Elayn Martin-Gay), provides students with active learning at their own pace. The new videos offer the following resources and more:

  A complete lecture for each section of the text highlights key examples and exercises from the text. New "pop-ups" reinforce key terms, definitions, and concepts.

  A new interface with menu navigation features allows students to quickly find and focus on the examples and exercises they need to review.

  Interactive Concept Check exercises measure students' understanding of key concepts and common trouble spots.

  The Interactive DVD Lecture Series also includes the following resources for test prep:

  The new Practice Final Exam helps students prepare for an end-of-course final. Students can watch full video solutions to each exercise.

  The Chapter Test Prep Videos help students during their most teachable moment—when they are preparing for a test. This innovation provides step-by-step solutions for the exercises found in each Chapter Test. The videos are captioned in English and Spanish. For the Fourth Edition, the chapter test prep videos are also available on YouTube™.
- **New Student Resources** section located in the back of the text, gives students a variety of tools that are conveniently located in one place to help them achieve success in math.
  - **Study Skills Builders** give students tips and suggestions on successful study habits and help them take responsibility for their learning. Assignable exercises check students' progress in improving their skills.
  - The **Bigger Picture—Study Guide Outline** covers key concepts of the course—simplifying expressions and solving equations and inequalities—to help students transition from thinking section-by-section to thinking about

how the material they are learning fits into mathematics as a whole. This outline provides a model for students on how to organize and develop their own study guide.

- The New **Practice Final Exam** helps students prepare for the end-of-the-course exam. Students can also watch the step-by-step solutions to all the Practice Final Exam exercises on the new Interactive DVD Lecture Series and in MyMathLab.
- **Answers to Selected Exercises** allows students to check their answers for all odd-numbered section exercises.

- **Guided application exercises** appear in many sections throughout the text, beginning with Section 2.4. These applications prompt students on how to set up the problem and get started with the solution process. These guided exercises will help students prepare to solve application exercises on their own.
- **Vocabulary and Readiness Check** exercises appear at the beginning of most exercise sets. These exercises quickly check a student's understanding of new vocabulary words so that forthcoming instructions in the problem sets will be clear. The **readiness** exercises center on a student's understanding of a concept that is necessary in order to continue with the exercise set. These exercises are also available for assignment in MyMathLab.
- **Enhanced emphasis on Study Skills** helps students develop good study habits and makes it more convenient for instructors to incorporate or assign study skills in their courses. The following changes have been made in the Fourth Edition:

  Section 1.1, Tips for Success in Mathematics, has been updated to include helpful hints for doing homework online in MyMathLab. Exercises pertaining to doing homework online in MyMathLab are now included in the exercise set for 1.1.

  The Study Skills Builders, formerly located at the end of select exercise sets, are now included in the new **Student Resources** section at the back of the book and organized by topic for ease of assignment. This section now also includes new Study Skills Builders on doing homework online in MyMathLab.
- All exercise sets have been reviewed and updated to ensure that even- and odd-numbered exercises are paired.
- **The Martin-Gay MyMathLab course** has been updated and revised, providing more exercise coverage and an expanded video program. There are section lectures for every section, students can also access at the specific objective level, and there are many more supporting watch clips at the exercise level to help students doing homework in MathXL. New readiness check exercises have been added so instructors can assess student preparation for class when assigning videos or reading of text sections. Suggested homework assignments have been premade for assignment at instructor's discretion.

Key Pedagogical Features

The following key features have been retained and/or updated for the Fourth Edition of the text:

Problem Solving Process This is formally introduced in Chapter 2 with a four-step process that is integrated throughout the text. The four steps are **Understand, Translate, Solve,** and **Interpret.** The repeated use of these steps in a variety of examples shows their wide applicability. Reinforcing the steps can increase students' comfort level and confidence in tackling problems.

Exercise Sets Revised and Updated The exercise sets have been carefully examined and extensively revised. Special focus was placed on making sure that even- and odd-numbered exercises are paired.

Examples Detailed step-by-step examples were added, deleted, replaced, or updated as needed. Many of these reflect real life. Additional instructional support is provided in the annotated examples.

Practice Exercises Throughout the text, each worked-out example has a parallel Practice Exercise. These invite students to be actively involved in the learning process. Students should try each Practice Exercise after finishing the corresponding example. Learning by doing will help students grasp ideas before moving on to other concepts. Answers to the Practice Exercises are provided at the bottom of each page.

Helpful Hints Helpful Hints contain practical advice on applying mathematical concepts. Strategically placed where students are most likely to need immediate reinforcement, Helpful Hints help students avoid common trouble areas and mistakes.

Concept Checks This feature allows students to gauge their grasp of an idea as it is being presented in the text. Concept Checks stress conceptual understanding at the point-of-use and help suppress misconceived notions before they start. Answers appear at the bottom of the page. Exercises related to Concept Checks are included in the exercise sets.

Mixed Practice Exercises Found in the section exercise sets, these require students to determine the problem type and strategy needed to solve it just as they would need to do on a test.

Integrated Reviews A unique, mid-chapter exercise set that helps students assimilate new skills and concepts that they have learned separately over several sections. These reviews provide yet another opportunity for students to work with "mixed" exercises as they master the topics.

Vocabulary Check Provides an opportunity for students to become more familiar with the use of mathematical terms as they strengthen their verbal skills. These appear at the end of each chapter before the Chapter Highlights. Vocabulary and Readiness exercises provide practice at the section level.

Chapter Highlights Found at the end of every chapter, these contain key definitions and concepts with examples to help students understand and retain what they have learned and help them organize their notes and study for tests.

Chapter Review The end of every chapter contains a comprehensive review of topics introduced in the chapter. The Chapter Review offers exercises keyed to every section in the chapter, as well as Mixed Review exercises that are not keyed to sections.

Chapter Test and Chapter Test Prep Video The Chapter Test is structured to include those problems that involve common student errors. The **Chapter Test Prep Videos** give students instant author access to a step-by-step video solution of each exercise in the Chapter Test.

Cumulative Review Follows every chapter in the text (except Chapters R and 1). Each odd-numbered exercise contained in the Cumulative Review is an earlier worked example in the text that is referenced in the back of the book along with the answer.

Writing Exercises These exercises occur in almost every exercise set and require students to provide a written response to explain concepts or justify their thinking.

Applications Real-world and real-data applications have been thoroughly updated and many new applications are included. These exercises occur in almost every exercise set and show the relevance of mathematics and help students gradually, and continuously develop their problem solving skills.

Review Exercises These exercises occur in each exercise set (except in Chapters R and 1) and are keyed to earlier sections. They review concepts learned earlier in the text that will be needed in the next section or chapter.

Exercise Set Resource Icons Located at the opening of each exercise set, these icons remind students of the resources available for extra practice and support:

See Student Resource descriptions page xvi for details on the individual resources available.

Exercise Icons These icons facilitate the assignment of specialized exercises and let students know what resources can support them.

DVD Video icon: exercise worked on the Interactive DVD Lecture Series.

△ Triangle icon: identifies exercises involving geometric concepts.

Pencil icon: indicates a written response is needed.

Calculator icon: optional exercises intended to be solved using a scientific or graphing calculator.

Group Activities Found at the end of each chapter, these activities are for individual or group completion and are usually hands-on or data-based activities that extend the concepts found in the chapter, allowing students to make decisions and interpretations and to think and write about algebra.

A Word about Textbook Design and Student Success

The design of developmental mathematics textbooks has become increasingly important. As students and instructors have told Pearson in focus groups and market research surveys, these textbooks cannot look "cluttered" or "busy." A "busy" design can distract a student from what is most important in the text. It can also heighten math anxiety.

As a result of the conversations and meetings we have had with students and instructors, we concluded the design of this text should be understated and focused on the most important pedagogical elements. Students and instructors helped us to identify the primary elements that are central to student success. These primary elements include:

- Exercise Sets
- Examples and Practice Problems
- Helpful Hints
- Rules, Property, and Definition boxes

As you will notice in this text, these primary features are the most prominent elements in the design. We have made every attempt to make sure these elements are the features the eye is drawn to. The remaining features, the secondary elements in the design, blend into the "fabric" or "grain" of the overall design. These secondary elements complement the primary elements without becoming distractions.

Pearson's thanks goes to all of the students and instructors (as noted by the author in Acknowledgments) who helped us develop the design of this text. At every step in the design process, their feedback proved valuable in helping us to make the right decisions. Thanks to your input, we're confident the design of this text will be both practical and engaging as it serves its educational and learning purposes.

Sincerely,

Paul Murphy

Editor-in-Chief

Developmental Mathematics

Optional: Calculator Exploration Boxes and Calculator Exercises The optional Calculator Explorations provide key strokes and exercises at appropriate points to give an opportunity for students to become familiar with these tools. Section exercises that are best completed by using a calculator are identified by 🖩 for ease of assignment.

Student and Instructor Resources

Student Resources

Student Organizer Guides students through the 3 main components of studying effectively—notetaking, practice, and homework. The organizer includes before-class preparation exercises, notetaking pages in a 2-column format for use in class, and examples paired with exercises for practice for each section. It is 3-hole punched.	**Student Solutions Manual** Provides complete worked-out solutions to • the odd numbered section exercises; all Practice Exercises; all exercises in the Integrated Reviews, Chapter Reviews, Chapter Tests, and Cumulative Reviews
Interactive DVD Lecture Series Provides students with active learning at their pace. The videos offer: • A complete lecture for each text section. The new interface allows easy navigation to examples and exercises students need to review • Interactive Concept Check exercises • Study Skills Builders • New Practice Final Exam • Chapter Test Prep Videos	**Chapter Test Prep Videos** • Step-by-step solutions to every exercise in each Chapter Practice Test. • Available in MyMathLab® and on YouTube, and in the Interactive DVD Lecture Series.

Instructor Resources

Annotated Instructor's Edition Contains all the content found in the student edition, plus the following: • Answers to exercises on the same text page • Teaching Tips throughout the text placed at key points.	**Instructor's Resource Manual with Tests and Mini-Lectures** • Mini lectures for each text section • Additional Practice worksheets for each section • Several forms of test per chapter—free response and multiple choice • Answers to all items **Instructor's Solutions Manual** **TestGen®** (Available for download from the IRC)
	Online Resources **MyMathLab®** (access code required) **MathXL®** (access code required)

Acknowledgments

There are many people who helped me develop this text, and I will attempt to thank some of them here. Cindy Trimble was *invaluable* for contributing to the overall accuracy of the text. Lisa Collette and Suellen Robinson were *invaluable* for their many suggestions and contributions during the development and writing of this Fourth Edition. Allison Campbell of Elm Street Publishing Services provided guidance throughout the production process.

A special thanks to my editor-in-chief, Paul Murphy, for all of his assistance, support, and contributions to this project. A very special thank you goes to my sponsoring editor, Mary Beckwith, for being there 24/7/365, as my students say. Last, my thanks to the staff at Pearson for all their support: Patty Bergin, Heather Scott, Michelle Renda, Adam Goldstein, Chris Hoag, and Greg Tobin.

I would like to thank the following rcviewers for their input and suggestions:

Sheila Anderson, *Housatonic Community College*
Tom Blackburn, *Northeastern Illinois University*
Gail Burkett, *Palm Beach State College*
James Butterbach, *Joliet Junior College*
Laura Dyer, *Southwestern Illinois College*
Sharon Edgemon, *Bakersfield College*
Hope Essien, *Olive-Harvey College*
Randa Kress, *Idaho State University*
Ted Lai, *Hudson Community College*
Nicole Lang, *North Hennepin Community College*
Lee LaRue, *Paris Junior College*
Jeri Lee, *Des Moines Area Community College*
Jean McArthur, *Joliet Junior College*
Michael Montano, *Riverside Community College*
Lisa J. Music, *Big Sandy Community and Technical College*
Linda Padilla, *Joliet Junior College*
Scott Perkins, *Lake Sumter Community College*
Marilyn Platt, *Gaston College*
Sandy Spears, *Jefferson Community College*
Ping Charlene Tintera, *Texas A & M University*
Jane Wampler, *Housatonic Community College*
Peter Zimmer, *West Chester University*

I would also like to thank the following dedicated group of instructors who participated in our focus groups, Martin-Gay Summits, and our design review for the series. Their feedback and insights have helped to strengthen this edition of the text. These instructors include:

Billie Anderson, *Tyler Junior College*
Cedric Atkins, *Mott Community College*
Andrea Barnett, *Tri-County Technical College*
Lois Beardon, *Schoolcraft College*
Michelle Beerman, *Pasco Hernando Community College*
Laurel Berry, *Bryant & Stratton College*
John Beyers, *University of Maryland*
Bob Brown, *Community College of Baltimore County–Essex*
Lisa Brown, *Community College of Baltimore County–Essex*
Sue Brown, *Guilford Technical Community College*
NeKeith Brown, *Richland College*
Gail Burkett, *Palm Beach State College*
Cheryl Cantwell, *Seminole Community College*
Jackie Cohen, *Augusta State College*
Julie Dewan, *Mohawk Valley Community College*
Janice Ervin, *Central Piedmont Community College*
Richard Fielding, *Southwestern College*
Cindy Gaddis, *Tyler Junior College*
Nita Graham, *St. Louis Community College*
Pauline Hall, *Iowa State College*
Elizabeth Hamman, *Cypress College*
Pat Hussey, *Triton College*
Dorothy Johnson, *Lorain County Community College*
Sonya Johnson, *Central Piedmont Community College*
Irene Jones, *Fullerton College*
Paul Jones, *University of Cincinnati*
Kathy Kopelousos, *Lewis and Clark Community College*
Nancy Lange, *Inver Hills Community College*
Judy Langer, *Westchester Community College*
Lisa Lindloff, *McLinnan Community College*

Sandy Lofstock, *St. Petersburg College*
Kathy Lovelle, *Westchester Community College*
Jamie Malek, *Florida State College*
Jean McArthur, *Joliet Junior College*
Kevin McCandless, *Evergreen Valley College*
Daniel Miller, *Niagara County Community College*
Marica Molle, *Metropolitan Community College*
Carol Murphy, *San Diego Miramar College*
Greg Nguyen, *Fullerton College*
Eric Ollila, *Jackson Community College*
Linda Padilla, *Joliet Junior College*
Davidson Pierre, *State College of Florida*
Marilyn Platt, *Gaston College*
Susan Poss, *Spartanburg Community College*
Natalie Rivera, *Estrella Mountain Community College*
Judy Roane, *Pearl River Community College*
Claudinna Rowley, *Montgomery Community College, Rockville*
Ena Salter, *Manatee Community College*
Carole Shapero, *Oakton Community College*
Janet Sibol, *Hillsborough Community College*
Anne Smallen, *Mohawk Valley Community College*
Barbara Stoner, *Reading Area Community College*
Jennifer Strehler, *Oakton Community College*
Ellen Stutes, *Louisiana State University Eunice*
Tanomo Taguchi, *Fullerton College*
MaryAnn Tuerk, *Elsin Community College*
Gwen Turbeville, *J. Sargeant Reynolds Community College*
Walter Wang, *Baruch College*
Leigh Ann Wheeler, *Greenville Technical Community College*
Valerie Wright, *Central Piedmont Community College*

A special thank you to those students who participated in our design review: Katherine Browne, Mike Bulfin, Nancy Canipe, Ashley Carpenter, Jeff Chojnachi, Roxanne Davis, Mike Dieter, Amy Dombrowski, Kay Herring, Todd Jaycox, Kaleena Levan, Matt Montgomery, Tony Plese, Abigail Polkinghorn, Harley Price, Eli Robinson, Avery Rosen, Robyn Schott, Cynthia Thomas, and Sherry Ward.

Elayn Martin-Gay

About the Author

Elayn Martin-Gay has taught mathematics at the University of New Orleans for more than 25 years. Her numerous teaching awards include the local University Alumni Association's Award for Excellence in Teaching, and Outstanding Developmental Educator at University of New Orleans, presented by the Louisiana Association of Developmental Educators.

Prior to writing textbooks, Elayn Martin-Gay developed an acclaimed series of lecture videos to support developmental mathematics students in their quest for success. These highly successful videos originally served as the foundation material for her texts. Today, the videos are specific to each book in the Martin-Gay series. The author has also created Chapter Test Prep Videos to help students during their most "teachable moment"—as they prepare for a test, along with Instructor-to-Instructor videos that provide teaching tips, hints, and suggestions for each developmental mathematics course, including basic mathematics, prealgebra, beginning algebra, and intermediate algebra. Her most recent innovations are the Algebra Prep Apps for the iPhone and iPod Touch. These Apps embrace the different learning styles, schedules, and paces of students and provide them with quality math tutoring.

Elayn is the author of 12 published textbooks as well as multimedia interactive mathematics, all specializing in developmental mathematics courses. She has participated as an author across the broadest range of educational materials: textbooks, videos, tutorial software, and courseware. This offers an opportunity of various combinations for an integrated teaching and learning package offering great consistency for the student.

Prealgebra Review

R

This optional review chapter covers basic topics and skills from prealgebra, such as fractions, decimals, and percents. Knowledge of these topics is needed for success in algebra.

Currently, there are more than 6000 movie theaters in the United States. The greatest recent growth of theaters has been with megaplexes (theaters containing 16 or more screens). The circle graph or pie chart below shows the fraction of movie screens by theater type. In Exercise 91, Exercise Set R.2, you will further explore these types of theaters and this circle graph.

Fraction of U.S. Screens by Theater Type

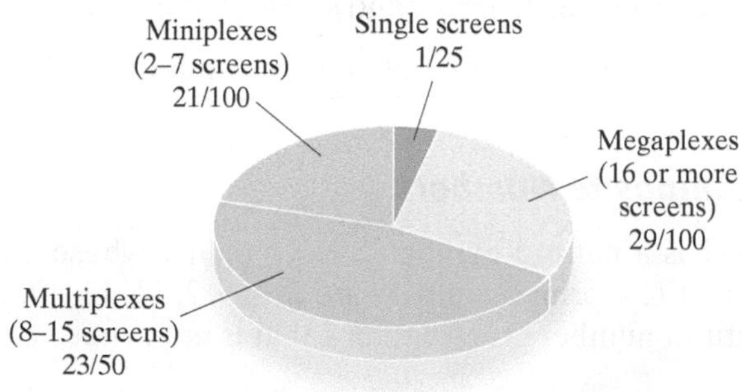

Source: Motion Picture Association of America

Sections

Check Your Progress

Objectives

A Write the Factors of a Number.

B Write the Prime Factorization of a Number.

C Find the LCM of a List of Numbers.

R.1 FACTORS AND THE LEAST COMMON MULTIPLE

Objective A Factoring Numbers

In arithmetic we factor numbers, and in algebra we factor expressions containing variables.

To **factor** means to write as a product.

Throughout this text, you will encounter the word *factor* often. Always remember that factoring means writing as a product.

Since $2 \cdot 3 = 6$, we say that 2 and 3 are **factors** of 6. Also, $2 \cdot 3$ is a **factorization** of 6.

PRACTICE 1

List the factors of 10.

Example 1 List the factors of 6.

Solution: First we write the different factorizations of 6.

$$6 = 1 \cdot 6, \quad 6 = 2 \cdot 3$$

The factors of 6 are 1, 2, 3, and 6.

Work Practice 1

PRACTICE 2

List the factors of 18.

Example 2 List the factors of 20.

Solution: $20 = 1 \cdot 20, \quad 20 = 2 \cdot 10, \quad 20 = 4 \cdot 5$

The factors of 20 are 1, 2, 4, 5, 10, and 20.

Work Practice 2

In this section, we will concentrate on **natural numbers** only. The natural numbers (also called counting numbers) are

Natural Numbers: 1, 2, 3, 4, 5, 6, 7, and so on

Every natural number except 1 is either a prime number or a composite number.

Prime and Composite Numbers

A **prime number** is a natural number greater than 1 whose only factors are 1 and itself. The first few prime numbers are 2, 3, 5, 7, 11, 13, 17, ... A **composite number** is a natural number greater than 1 that is not prime.

PRACTICE 3

Identify each number as prime or composite: 5, 16, 23, 42.

Example 3 Identify each number as prime or composite: 3, 28, 19, 35

Solution:

3 is a prime number. Its factors are 1 and 3 only.
28 is a composite number. Its factors are 1, 2, 4, 7, 14, and 28.
19 is a prime number. Its factors are 1 and 19 only.
35 is a composite number. Its factors are 1, 5, 7, and 35.

Work Practice 3

Answers

1. 1, 2, 5, 10 **2.** 1, 2, 3, 6, 9, 18
3. 5, 23 prime; 16, 42 composite

Objective B Writing Prime Factorizations

When a number is written as a product of primes, this product is called the **prime factorization** of the number. For example, the prime factorization of 12 is $2\cdot2\cdot3$ since

$$12 = 2\cdot2\cdot3$$

and all the factors are prime numbers.

Example 4 Write the prime factorization of 45.

Solution: We can begin by writing 45 as the product of two numbers, say 9 and 5.

$$45 = 9\cdot5$$

The number 5 is prime, but 9 is not. So we write 9 as $3\cdot3$.

$$\begin{aligned}45 &= 9\cdot5\\ &= 3\cdot3\cdot5\end{aligned}$$

Each factor is now a prime number, so the prime factorization of 45 is $3\cdot3\cdot5$.

Work Practice 4

PRACTICE 4

Write the prime factorization of 44.

Helpful Hint

Recall that order is not important when multiplying numbers. For example,

$$3\cdot3\cdot5 = 3\cdot5\cdot3 = 5\cdot3\cdot3 = 45$$

For this reason, any of the products shown can be called *the* prime factorization of 45, and we say that the prime factorization of a number is unique.

Example 5 Write the prime factorization of 80.

Solution: We first write 80 as a product of two numbers. We continue this process until all factors are prime.

$$\begin{aligned}80 &= 8\cdot10\\ &= 4\cdot2\cdot2\cdot5\\ &= 2\cdot2\cdot2\cdot2\cdot5\end{aligned}$$

All factors are now prime, so the prime factorization of 80 is

$2\cdot2\cdot2\cdot2\cdot5$.

Work Practice 5

PRACTICE 5

Write the prime factorization of 60.

✓**Concept Check** Suppose that you choose $80 = 4\cdot20$ as your first step in Example 5 and another student chooses $80 = 5\cdot16$. Will you both end up with the same prime factorization as in Example 5? Explain.

Answers

4. $2\cdot2\cdot11$ **5.** $2\cdot2\cdot3\cdot5$

✓ **Concept Check Answer**

yes; answers may vary

Helpful Hint

There are a few quick **divisibility tests** to determine if a number is divisible by the primes 2, 3, or 5.

A whole number is divisible by

- **2** if the ones digit is 0, 2, 4, 6, or 8.

↓

132 is divisible by 2

- **3** if the sum of the digits is divisible by 3.

144 is divisible by 3 since $1 + 4 + 4 = 9$ is divisible by 3

- **5** if the ones digit is 0 or 5.

↓

1115 is divisible by 5

When finding the prime factorization of larger numbers, you may want to use the procedure shown in Example 6.

PRACTICE 6

Write the prime factorization of 297.

Example 6 Write the prime factorization of 252.

Solution: Since the ones digit of 252 is 2, we know that 252 is divisible by 2.

$$2\overline{)252}\quad 126$$

126 is divisible by 2 also.

$$\begin{array}{r} 63 \\ 2\overline{)126} \\ 2\overline{)252} \end{array}$$

63 is not divisible by 2 but is divisible by 3. We divide 63 by 3 and continue in this same manner until the quotient is a prime number.

$$\begin{array}{r} 7 \\ 3\overline{)\ 21} \\ 3\overline{)\ 63} \\ 2\overline{)126} \\ 2\overline{)252} \end{array}$$

The prime factorization of 252 is $2 \cdot 2 \cdot 3 \cdot 3 \cdot 7$.

Work Practice 6

Objective C Finding the Least Common Multiple

A **multiple** of a number is the product of that number and any natural number. For example, the multiples of 3 are

$3 \cdot 1$	$3 \cdot 2$	$3 \cdot 3$	$3 \cdot 4$	$3 \cdot 5$	$3 \cdot 6$	$3 \cdot 7$	
3,	6,	9,	12,	15,	18,	21,	and so on.

The multiples of 2 are

$2 \cdot 1$	$2 \cdot 2$	$2 \cdot 3$	$2 \cdot 4$	$2 \cdot 5$	$2 \cdot 6$	$2 \cdot 7$	
2,	4,	6,	8,	10,	12,	14,	and so on.

Answer

6. $3 \cdot 3 \cdot 3 \cdot 11$

Notice that 2 and 3 have multiples that are common to both.

Multiples of 2: 2, 4, 6, 8, 10, 12, 14, 16, 18, and so on

Multiples of 3: 3, 6, 9, 12, 15, 18, 21, and so on

Common multiples of 2 and 3: 6, 12, 18, ...

The least or smallest common multiple of 2 and 3 is 6. The number 6 is called the **least common multiple** or **LCM** of 2 and 3. It is the smallest number that is a multiple of both 2 and 3.

The **least common multiple (LCM)** of a list of numbers is the smallest number that is a multiple of all the numbers in the list.

Finding the LCM by the method above can sometimes be time-consuming. Let's look at another method that uses prime factorization.

To find the LCM of 4 and 10, for example, we write the prime factorization of each.

$4 = 2 \cdot 2$
$10 = 2 \cdot 5$

If the LCM is to be a multiple of 4, it must contain the factors $2 \cdot 2$. If the LCM is to be a multiple of 10, it must contain the factors $2 \cdot 5$. Since we decide whether the LCM is a multiple of 4 and 10 separately, the LCM does not need to contain three factors of . The LCM only needs to contain a factor the greatest number of times that the factor appears in any **one** prime factorization.

$$\text{LCM} = \overbrace{2 \cdot 2}^{\text{The LCM is a multiple of 4.}} \cdot 5 = 20$$

The LCM is a multiple of 4.

The LCM is a multiple of 10.

The number 2 is a factor twice since that is the greatest number of times that 2 is a factor in either of the prime factorizations.

To Find the LCM of a List of Numbers

Step 1: Write the prime factorization of each number.

Step 2: Write the product containing each different prime factor (from Step 1) the greatest number of times that it appears in any one factorization. This product is the LCM.

Example 7 Find the LCM of 18 and 24.

Solution: First we write the prime factorization of each number.

$18 = 2 \cdot 3 \cdot 3$
$24 = 2 \cdot 2 \cdot 2 \cdot 3$

Now we write each factor the greatest number of times that it appears in any **one** prime factorization.

The greatest number of times that 2 appears is **3** times.
The greatest number of times that 3 appears is **2** times.

$$\text{LCM} = \underbrace{2 \cdot 2 \cdot 2}_{\text{2 is a factor 3 times.}} \cdot \underbrace{3 \cdot 3}_{\text{3 is a factor 2 times.}} = 72$$

Work Practice 7

PRACTICE 7

Find the LCM of 14 and 35.

Answer

7. 70

PRACTICE 8

Find the LCM of 5 and 9.

Example 8 Find the LCM of 11 and 10.

Solution: 11 is a prime number, so we simply rewrite it. Then we write the prime factorization of 10.

$$11 = 11$$
$$10 = 2 \cdot 5$$
$$\text{LCM} = 2 \cdot 5 \cdot 11 = 110$$

Work Practice 8

PRACTICE 9

Find the LCM of 4, 15, and 10.

Example 9 Find the LCM of 5, 6, and 12.

Solution:

$$5 = 5$$
$$6 = 2 \cdot 3$$
$$12 = 2 \cdot 2 \cdot 3$$
$$\text{LCM} = 2 \cdot 2 \cdot 3 \cdot 5 = 60.$$

Work Practice 9

Answers
8. 45 **9.** 60

Vocabulary and Readiness Check

Use the choices below to fill in each blank.

least common multiple	composite	multiple
prime factorization	prime	factor

1. The number 40 equals $2 \cdot 2 \cdot 2 \cdot 5$. Since each factor is prime, we call $2 \cdot 2 \cdot 2 \cdot 5$ the ________________ of 40.
2. A natural number, other than 1, that is not prime is called a(n) ________________ number.
3. A natural number that has exactly two different factors, 1 and itself, is called a(n) ________________ number.
4. The ________________ of a list of numbers is the smallest number that is a multiple of all the numbers in the list.
5. To ________________ means to write as a product.
6. A(n) ________________ of a number is the product of that number and any natural number.

R.1 Exercise Set

FOR EXTRA HELP

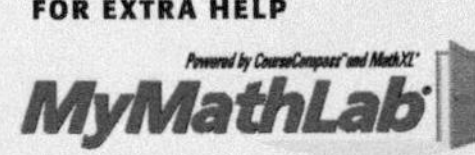

PRACTICE

WATCH

DOWNLOAD

READ

REVIEW

Objective A *List the factors of each number. See Examples 1 and 2.*

1. 9 **2.** 8 **3.** 24 **4.** 36 **5.** 42

6. 63 **7.** 80 **8.** 50 **9.** 19 **10.** 31

Identify each number as prime or composite. See Example 3.

11. 13 **12.** 21 **13.** 39 **14.** 53 **15.** 41

16. 51 **17.** 201 **18.** 307 **19.** 2065 **20.** 1798

Objective B *Write each prime factorization. See Examples 4 through 6.*

21. 18 **22.** 28 **23.** 20 **24.** 30

25. 56 **26.** 48 **27.** 81 **28.** 64

29. 300 **30.** 500 **31.** 588 **32.** 315

Multiple choice. Select the best choice to complete each statement.

33. The factors of 48 are

a. $2 \cdot 2 \cdot 2 \cdot 6$
b. $2 \cdot 2 \cdot 2 \cdot 3$
c. $2 \cdot 2 \cdot 2 \cdot 2 \cdot 3$
d. 1, 2, 3, 4, 6, 8, 12, 16, 24, 48

34. The prime factorization of 63 is

a. 1, 3, 7, 9, 63
b. 1, 3, 7, 9, 21, 63
c. $3 \cdot 3 \cdot 7$
d. 1, 3, 21, 63

Objective C *Find the LCM of each list of numbers. See Examples 7 through 9.*

35. 3, 4 **36.** 4, 5 **37.** 6, 14 **38.** 9, 15

39. 20, 30 **40.** 30, 40 **41.** 5, 7 **42.** 2, 11

43. 9, 12 **44.** 4, 18 **45.** 16, 20 **46.** 18, 30

47. 40, 90 **48.** 50, 70 **49.** 24, 36 **50.** 21, 28

51. 2, 8, 15 **52.** 3, 9, 20 **53.** 2, 3, 7 **54.** 3, 5, 7

55. 8, 24, 48 **56.** 9, 36, 72 **57.** 8, 18, 30 **58.** 4, 14, 35

Concept Extensions

59. Solve. See the concept check in the section.

a. Write the prime factorization of 40 using 2 and 20 as the first pair of factors.
b. Write the prime factorization of 40 using 4 and 10 as the first pair of factors.
c. Explain any similarities or differences found in parts a and b.

60. The LCM of 6 and 7 is 42. In general, describe when the LCM of two numbers is equal to their product.

61. Craig Campanella and Edie Hall both have night jobs. Craig has every fifth night off and Edie has every seventh night off. How often will they have the same night off?

62. Elizabeth Kaster and Lori Sypher are both publishing company representatives in Louisiana. Elizabeth spends a day in New Orleans every 35 days, and Lori spends a day in New Orleans every 20 days. How often are they in New Orleans on the same day?

Find the LCM of each pair of numbers.

63. 315, 504 **64.** 1000, 1125

R.2 FRACTIONS

Objectives

- **A** Discover Fraction Properties Having to do with 0 and 1.
- **B** Write Equivalent Fractions.
- **C** Write Fractions in Simplest Form.
- **D** Multiply and Divide Fractions.
- **E** Add and Subtract Fractions.
- **F** Perform Operations on Mixed Numbers.

A quotient of two numbers such as $\frac{2}{9}$ is called a **fraction.** The parts of a fraction are:

Fraction bar $\longrightarrow$ $\frac{2}{9}$ $\begin{matrix} \leftarrow \text{Numerator} \\ \leftarrow \text{Denominator} \end{matrix}$

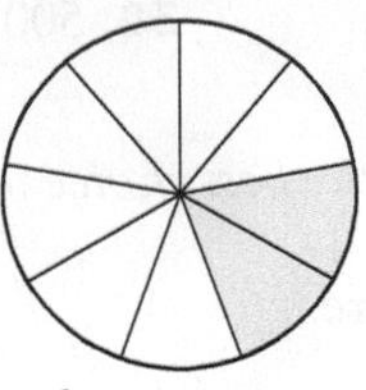

$\frac{2}{9}$ of the circle is shaded.

A fraction may be used to refer to part of a whole. For example, $\frac{2}{9}$ of the circle is shaded. The denominator 9 tells us how many equal parts the whole circle is divided into, and the numerator 2 tells us how many equal parts are shaded.

In this section, we will use numerators that are **whole numbers** and denominators that are nonzero whole numbers. The whole numbers consist of 0 and the natural numbers.

Whole Numbers: 0, 1, 2, 3, 4, 5, and so on

Objective A Discovering Fraction Properties with 0 and 1

Before we continue further, don't forget that the fraction bar indicates division. For example,

$$\frac{8}{4} = 8 \div 4 = 2 \quad \text{since} \quad 2 \cdot 4 = 8$$

Thus, we may simplify some fractions by recalling that the fraction bar means division.

$$\frac{6}{6} = 6 \div 6 = 1 \quad \text{and} \quad \frac{3}{1} = 3 \div 1 = 3$$

Examples Simplify by dividing the numerator by the denominator.

1. $\frac{3}{3} = 1$ Since $3 \div 3 = 1$.
2. $\frac{4}{2} = 2$ Since $4 \div 2 = 2$.
3. $\frac{7}{7} = 1$ Since $7 \div 7 = 1$.
4. $\frac{8}{1} = 8$ Since $8 \div 1 = 8$.
5. $\frac{0}{6} = 0$ Since $0 \cdot 6 = 0$.
6. $\frac{6}{0}$ is undefined because there is no number that when multiplied by 0 gives 6.

Work Practice 1–6

PRACTICE 1–6

Simplify by dividing the numerator by the denominator.

1. $\frac{4}{4}$ **2.** $\frac{9}{3}$ **3.** $\frac{10}{10}$

4. $\frac{5}{1}$ **5.** $\frac{0}{11}$ **6.** $\frac{11}{0}$

Answers

1. 1 **2.** 3 **3.** 1 **4.** 5 **5.** 0
6. undefined

From Examples 1 through 6, we can say the following:

Let a be any number other than 0.

$$\frac{a}{a} = 1, \quad \frac{0}{a} = 0,$$

$$\frac{a}{1} = a, \quad \frac{a}{0} \text{ is undefined}$$

Objective B Writing Equivalent Fractions

More than one fraction can be used to name the same part of a whole. Such fractions are called **equivalent fractions.**

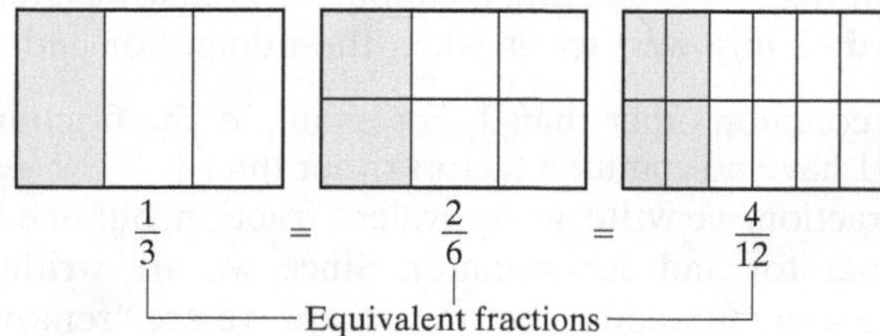

Equivalent Fractions

Fractions that represent the same portion of a whole are called **equivalent fractions.**

For example, let's write $\frac{1}{3}$ as an equivalent fraction with a denominator of 12. To do so, notice the denominator of 3, multiplied by 4, gives a denominator of 12. Thus let's multiply by 1 in the form of $\frac{4}{4}$.

$$\frac{1}{3} = \frac{1}{3} \cdot 1 = \frac{1}{3} \cdot \frac{4}{4} = \frac{1 \cdot 4}{3 \cdot 4} = \frac{4}{12}$$

$\frac{4}{4} = 1$

So $\frac{1}{3} = \frac{4}{12}$.

To Write an Equivalent Fraction

$$\frac{a}{b} = \frac{a}{b} \cdot \frac{c}{c} = \frac{a \cdot c}{b \cdot c}$$

Since $\frac{a}{b} = \frac{a}{b} \cdot 1$

where a, b, and c are nonzero numbers.

PRACTICE 7

Write $\frac{1}{4}$ as an equivalent fraction with a denominator of 20.

Example 7 Write $\frac{2}{5}$ as an equivalent fraction with a denominator of 15.

Solution: In the denominator, since $5 \cdot 3 = 15$, we multiply the fraction $\frac{2}{5}$ by 1 in the form of $\frac{3}{3}$.

$$\frac{2}{5} = \frac{2}{5} \cdot \frac{3}{3} = \frac{2 \cdot 3}{5 \cdot 3} = \frac{6}{15}$$

Then $\frac{2}{5}$ is equivalent to $\frac{6}{15}$. They both represent the same part of a whole.

Work Practice 7

Objective C Simplifying Fractions

A special equivalent fraction is one that is simplified or in lowest terms. A fraction is said to be **simplified** or in **lowest terms** when the numerator and the denominator have no factors in common other than 1. For example, the fraction $\frac{5}{11}$ is in lowest terms since 5 and 11 have no common factors other than 1.

To simplify a fraction, we write an equivalent fraction, but one with no common factors in the numerator and denominator. Since we are writing an equivalent fraction, we use the same method as before, except we are "removing" factors of 1 instead of "inserting" factors of 1.

To Write a Simplified, Equivalent Fraction

$$\frac{a \cdot c}{b \cdot c} = \frac{a}{b} \cdot \frac{c}{c} = \frac{a}{b}$$

Since $\frac{a}{b} \cdot 1 = \frac{a}{b}$

PRACTICE 8

Simplify: $\frac{20}{35}$

Example 8 Simplify: $\frac{42}{49}$

Solution: To help us see common factors in the numerator and denominator, or factors of 1, we write the numerator and the denominator as products of primes.

$$\frac{42}{49} = \frac{2 \cdot 3 \cdot 7}{7 \cdot 7} = \frac{2 \cdot 3}{7} \cdot \frac{7}{7} = \frac{2 \cdot 3}{7} = \frac{6}{7}$$

Work Practice 8

✓Concept Check Explain the error in the following steps.

a. $\frac{15}{55} = \frac{15}{55} = \frac{1}{5}$ b. $\frac{6}{7} = \frac{5+1}{5+2} = \frac{1}{2}$

PRACTICE 9–10

Simplify each fraction.

9. $\frac{7}{20}$ 10. $\frac{12}{40}$

Examples Simplify each fraction.

9. $\frac{11}{27} = \frac{11}{3 \cdot 3 \cdot 3}$ There are no common factors in the numerator and denominator other than 1, so $\frac{11}{27}$ is already simplified.

10. $\frac{88}{20} = \frac{2 \cdot 2 \cdot 2 \cdot 11}{2 \cdot 2 \cdot 5} = \frac{2}{2} \cdot \frac{2}{2} \cdot \frac{2 \cdot 11}{5} = \frac{22}{5}$

Work Practice 9–10

Answers

7. $\frac{5}{20}$ 8. $\frac{4}{7}$ 9. $\frac{7}{20}$ 10. $\frac{3}{10}$

✓ Concept Check Answer

a. $\frac{15}{55} = \frac{3 \cdot 5}{11 \cdot 5} = \frac{3}{11}$

b. $\frac{6}{7}$ can't be simplified

Below are two important notes about simplifying fractions.

Note 1: When simplifying, we can use a shortcut notation if desired. From Example 8,

$$\frac{42}{49} = \frac{2 \cdot 3 \cdot \overset{1}{\cancel{7}}}{7 \cdot \underset{1}{\cancel{7}}} = \frac{2 \cdot 3}{7} = \frac{6}{7}$$

Note 2: Also, feel free to save time if you immediately notice common factors. In Example 10, notice that the numerator and denominator of $\frac{88}{20}$ have a common factor of 4.

$$\frac{88}{20} = \frac{\overset{1}{\cancel{4}} \cdot 22}{\underset{1}{\cancel{4}} \cdot 5} = \frac{22}{5}$$

A **proper fraction** is a fraction whose numerator is less than its denominator. The fraction $\frac{22}{5}$ from Example 10 is called an improper fraction. An **improper fraction** is a fraction whose numerator is greater than or equal to its denominator.

The improper fraction $\frac{22}{5}$ may be written as the mixed number $4\frac{2}{5}$. Notice that a **mixed number** has a whole number part and a fraction part. We review operations on mixed numbers in objective F in this section. First, let's review operations on fractions.

Objective D Multiplying and Dividing Fractions

To multiply two fractions, we multiply numerator times numerator to obtain the numerator of the product. Then we multiply denominator times denominator to obtain the denominator of the product.

Multiplying Fractions

$$\frac{a}{b} \cdot \frac{c}{d} = \frac{a \cdot c}{b \cdot d} \quad \text{if } b \neq 0 \text{ and } d \neq 0$$

Helpful Hint The symbol "$\neq$" to the right means "is not equal to."

Example 11 Multiply: $\frac{2}{15} \cdot \frac{5}{13}$. Simplify the product if possible.

Solution: $\frac{2}{15} \cdot \frac{5}{13} = \frac{2 \cdot 5}{15 \cdot 13}$ Multiply numerators. Multiply denominators.

To simplify the product, we divide the numerator and the denominator by any common factors.

$$\frac{2}{15} \cdot \frac{5}{13} = \frac{2 \cdot \overset{1}{\cancel{5}}}{3 \cdot \underset{1}{\cancel{5}} \cdot 13} = \frac{2}{39}$$

Work Practice 11

PRACTICE 11

Multiply: $\frac{3}{4} \cdot \frac{8}{9}$. Simplify the product if possible.

Before we divide fractions, we first define **reciprocals.** Two numbers are reciprocals of each other if their product is 1.

The reciprocal of $\frac{2}{3}$ is $\frac{3}{2}$ because $\frac{2}{3} \cdot \frac{3}{2} = \frac{6}{6} = 1$.

The reciprocal of 5 is $\frac{1}{5}$ because $5 \cdot \frac{1}{5} = \frac{5}{1} \cdot \frac{1}{5} = \frac{5}{5} = 1$.

Answer

11. $\frac{2}{3}$

To divide fractions, we multiply the first fraction by the reciprocal of the second fraction. For example,

$$\frac{1}{2} \div \frac{5}{7} = \frac{1}{2} \cdot \frac{7}{5} = \frac{1 \cdot 7}{2 \cdot 5} = \frac{7}{10}$$

To divide, multiply by the reciprocal.

Dividing Fractions

$$\frac{a}{b} \div \frac{c}{d} = \frac{a}{b} \cdot \frac{d}{c}, \quad \text{if } b \neq 0, d \neq 0, \text{ and } c \neq 0$$

PRACTICE 12–14

Divide and simplify.

12. $\frac{2}{9} \div \frac{3}{4}$

13. $\frac{8}{11} \div 24$

14. $\frac{5}{4} \div \frac{15}{8}$

Examples Divide and simplify.

12. $\frac{4}{5} \div \frac{5}{16} = \frac{4}{5} \cdot \frac{16}{5} = \frac{4 \cdot 16}{5 \cdot 5} = \frac{64}{25}$ — The numerator and denominator have no common factors.

13. $\frac{7}{10} \div 14 = \frac{7}{10} \div \frac{14}{1} = \frac{7}{10} \cdot \frac{1}{14} = \frac{\overset{1}{\cancel{7}} \cdot 1}{2 \cdot 5 \cdot 2 \cdot \underset{1}{\cancel{7}}} = \frac{1}{20}$

14. $\frac{3}{8} \div \frac{3}{10} = \frac{3}{8} \cdot \frac{10}{3} = \frac{\overset{1}{\cancel{3}} \cdot \overset{1}{\cancel{2}} \cdot 5}{\underset{1}{\cancel{2}} \cdot 2 \cdot 2 \cdot \underset{1}{\cancel{3}}} = \frac{5}{4}$

Work Practice 12–14

Objective E Adding and Subtracting Fractions

To add or subtract fractions with the same denominator, we combine numerators and place the sum or difference over the common denominator.

Adding and Subtracting Fractions with the Same Denominator

$$\frac{a}{b} + \frac{c}{b} = \frac{a+c}{b}, \quad \text{if } b \neq 0$$

$$\frac{a}{b} - \frac{c}{b} = \frac{a-c}{b}, \quad \text{if } b \neq 0$$

PRACTICE 15–18

Add or subtract as indicated. Then simplify if possible.

15. $\frac{2}{11} + \frac{5}{11}$ **16.** $\frac{1}{8} + \frac{3}{8}$

17. $\frac{7}{6} - \frac{2}{6}$ **18.** $\frac{13}{10} - \frac{3}{10}$

Examples Add or subtract as indicated. Then simplify if possible.

15. $\frac{2}{7} + \frac{4}{7} = \frac{2+4}{7} = \frac{6}{7}$ ← Add numerators. ← Keep the common denominator.

16. $\frac{3}{10} + \frac{2}{10} = \frac{3+2}{10} = \frac{5}{10} = \frac{\overset{1}{\cancel{5}}}{2 \cdot \underset{1}{\cancel{5}}} = \frac{1}{2}$

17. $\frac{5}{3} - \frac{1}{3} = \frac{5-1}{3} = \frac{4}{3}$ ← Subtract numerators. ← Keep the common denominator.

18. $\frac{9}{7} - \frac{2}{7} = \frac{9-2}{7} = \frac{7}{7} = 1$

Work Practice 15–18

Answers

12. $\frac{8}{27}$ **13.** $\frac{1}{33}$ **14.** $\frac{2}{3}$ **15.** $\frac{7}{11}$ **16.** $\frac{1}{2}$ **17.** $\frac{5}{6}$ **18.** 1

To add or subtract with different denominators, we first write the fractions as **equivalent fractions** with the same denominator. We use the smallest or **least common denominator,** or **LCD.** The LCD is the same as the least common multiple of the denominators (see Section R.1).

Example 19 Add: $\frac{2}{5} + \frac{1}{4}$

Solution: We first must find the least common denominator before the fractions can be added. The least common multiple of the denominators 5 and 4 is 20. This is the LCD we will use.

We write both fractions as equivalent fractions with denominators of 20. Since

$$\frac{2}{5} = \frac{2}{5} \cdot 1 = \frac{2}{5} \cdot \frac{4}{4} = \frac{2 \cdot 4}{5 \cdot 4} = \frac{8}{20} \quad \text{and} \quad \frac{1}{4} = \frac{1}{4} \cdot 1 = \frac{1}{4} \cdot \frac{5}{5} = \frac{1 \cdot 5}{4 \cdot 5} = \frac{5}{20}$$

then

$$\frac{2}{5} + \frac{1}{4} = \frac{8}{20} + \frac{5}{20} = \frac{13}{20}$$

Work Practice 19

PRACTICE 19

Add: $\frac{3}{8} + \frac{1}{20}$

Example 20 Subtract and simplify: $\frac{19}{6} - \frac{23}{12}$

Solution: The LCD is 12. We write both fractions as equivalent fractions with denominators of 12.

$$\frac{19}{6} - \frac{23}{12} = \frac{19}{6} \cdot \frac{2}{2} - \frac{23}{12}$$

$$= \frac{19 \cdot 2}{6 \cdot 2} - \frac{23}{12}$$

$$= \frac{38}{12} - \frac{23}{12}$$

$$= \frac{15}{12} = \frac{\overset{1}{\cancel{3}} \cdot 5}{2 \cdot 2 \cdot \underset{1}{\cancel{3}}} = \frac{5}{4}$$

Work Practice 20

PRACTICE 20

Subtract and simplify: $\frac{8}{15} - \frac{1}{3}$

Objective F Performing Operations on Mixed Numbers

To perform operations on mixed numbers, first write each mixed number as an improper fraction. To recall how this is done, let's write $3\frac{1}{5}$ as an improper fraction.

$$3\frac{1}{5} = 3 + \frac{1}{5} = \frac{15}{5} + \frac{1}{5} = \frac{16}{5}$$

Because of the steps above, notice we can use a shortcut process for writing a mixed number as an improper fraction.

$$3\frac{1}{5} = \frac{5 \cdot 3 + 1}{5} = \frac{16}{5}$$

Answers

19. $\frac{17}{40}$ **20.** $\frac{1}{5}$

PRACTICE 21

Multiply: $5\frac{1}{6}\cdot 4\frac{2}{5}$

Example 21 Divide: $2\frac{1}{8} \div 1\frac{2}{3}$

Solution: First write each mixed number as an improper fraction.

$$2\frac{1}{8} = \frac{8\cdot 2 + 1}{8} = \frac{17}{8}; \quad 1\frac{2}{3} = \frac{3\cdot 1 + 2}{3} = \frac{5}{3}$$

Now divide as usual.

$$2\frac{1}{8} \div 1\frac{2}{3} = \frac{17}{8} \div \frac{5}{3} = \frac{17}{8}\cdot\frac{3}{5} = \frac{51}{40}$$

The fraction $\frac{51}{40}$ is improper. To write it as an equivalent mixed number, remember that the fraction bar means division, and divide.

$$\begin{array}{r} 1\frac{11}{40} \\ 40\overline{)51} \\ \underline{-40} \\ 11 \end{array}$$

Thus, the quotient is $\frac{51}{40}$ or $1\frac{11}{40}$.

Work Practice 21

As a general rule, if the original exercise contains mixed numbers, write the result as a mixed number, if possible.

PRACTICE 22

Add: $7\frac{3}{8} + 6\frac{3}{4}$

Example 22 Add: $2\frac{1}{8} + 1\frac{2}{3}$.

Solution: $2\frac{1}{8} + 1\frac{2}{3} = \frac{17}{8} + \frac{5}{3} = \frac{17\cdot 3}{8\cdot 3} + \frac{5\cdot 8}{3\cdot 8} = \frac{51}{24} + \frac{40}{24} = \frac{91}{24}$ or $3\frac{19}{24}$

Work Practice 22

When adding or subtracting larger mixed numbers, you might want to use the following method.

PRACTICE 23

Subtract: $76\frac{1}{12} - 35\frac{1}{4}$

Example 23 Subtract: $50\frac{1}{6} - 38\frac{1}{3}$

Solution:

$$\begin{array}{rcrcr} 50\frac{1}{6} & = & 50\frac{1}{6} & = & 49\frac{7}{6} \\ \underline{-38\frac{1}{3}} & = & \underline{-38\frac{2}{6}} & = & \underline{-38\frac{2}{6}} \\ & & & & 11\frac{5}{6} \end{array}$$

$50\frac{1}{6} = 49 + 1 + \frac{1}{6} = 49\frac{7}{6}$

Work Practice 23

Answers

21. $22\frac{11}{15}$ **22.** $14\frac{1}{8}$ **23.** $40\frac{5}{6}$

Vocabulary and Readiness Check

Use the choices below to fill in each blank.

improper	fraction	proper	reciprocals	mixed number	least common denominator (LCD)	$\frac{a \cdot d}{b \cdot c}$	$\frac{a \cdot c}{b \cdot d}$
equivalent	denominator	24	simplest form	numerator	$\frac{a - c}{b}$	$\frac{a + c}{b}$	

1. The number $\frac{17}{31}$ is called a(n) ______________. The number 31 is called its ______________ and 17 is called its ______________.

2. The fraction $\frac{8}{3}$ is called a(n) ______________ fraction, the fraction $\frac{3}{8}$ is called a(n) ______________ fraction, and $10\frac{3}{8}$ is called a(n) ______________.

3. In $\frac{11}{48}$, since 11 and 48 have no common factors other than 1, $\frac{11}{48}$ is in ______________.

4. Fractions that represent the same portion of a whole are called ______________ fractions.

5. To multiply two fractions, we write $\frac{a}{b} \cdot \frac{c}{d} =$ ______________.

6. Two numbers are ______________ of each other if their product is 1.

7. To divide two fractions, we write $\frac{a}{b} \div \frac{c}{d} =$ ______________.

8. $\frac{a}{b} + \frac{c}{b} =$ ______________ and $\frac{a}{b} - \frac{c}{b} =$ ______________.

9. The smallest positive number divisible by all the denominators of a list of fractions is called the ______________.

10. The LCD for $\frac{1}{6}$ and $\frac{5}{8}$ is ______________.

R.2 Exercise Set

FOR EXTRA HELP MyMathLab

Objective A *Simplify by dividing the numerator by the denominator. See Examples 1 through 6.*

1. $\frac{14}{14}$ **2.** $\frac{19}{19}$ **3.** $\frac{20}{2}$ **4.** $\frac{30}{5}$ **5.** $\frac{13}{1}$

6. $\frac{21}{1}$ **7.** $\frac{0}{9}$ **8.** $\frac{0}{15}$ **9.** $\frac{9}{0}$ **10.** $\frac{15}{0}$

Objective B *Write each fraction as an equivalent fraction with the given denominator. See Example 7.*

11. $\frac{7}{10}$ with a denominator of 30

12. $\frac{2}{3}$ with a denominator of 9

13. $\frac{2}{9}$ with a denominator of 18

14. $\frac{8}{7}$ with a denominator of 56

15. $\frac{4}{5}$ with a denominator of 20

16. $\frac{4}{5}$ with a denominator of 25

Objective C Simplify each fraction. See Examples 8 through 10.

17. $\frac{2}{4}$

18. $\frac{3}{6}$

19. $\frac{10}{15}$

20. $\frac{15}{20}$

21. $\frac{3}{7}$

22. $\frac{5}{9}$

23. $\frac{18}{30}$

24. $\frac{42}{45}$

25. $\frac{16}{20}$

26. $\frac{8}{40}$

27. $\frac{66}{48}$

28. $\frac{64}{24}$

29. $\frac{120}{244}$

30. $\frac{360}{700}$

31. $\frac{192}{264}$

32. $\frac{455}{525}$

Objectives D F **Mixed Practice** *Multiply or divide as indicated. See Examples 11 through 14 and 21.*

33. $\frac{1}{2} \cdot \frac{3}{4}$

34. $\frac{7}{11} \cdot \frac{3}{5}$

35. $\frac{2}{3} \cdot \frac{3}{4}$

36. $\frac{7}{8} \cdot \frac{3}{21}$

37. $\frac{1}{2} \div \frac{7}{12}$

38. $\frac{7}{12} \div \frac{1}{2}$

39. $\frac{3}{4} \div \frac{1}{20}$

40. $\frac{3}{5} \div \frac{9}{10}$

41. $5\frac{1}{9} \cdot 3\frac{2}{3}$

42. $2\frac{3}{4} \cdot 1\frac{7}{8}$

43. $8\frac{3}{5} \div 2\frac{9}{10}$

44. $1\frac{7}{8} \div 3\frac{8}{9}$

Objectives E F **Mixed Practice** *Add or subtract as indicated. See Examples 15 through 20, 22, and 23.*

45. $\frac{4}{5} + \frac{1}{5}$

46. $\frac{6}{7} + \frac{1}{7}$

47. $\frac{4}{15} - \frac{1}{12}$

48. $\frac{11}{12} - \frac{1}{16}$

49. $\frac{2}{3} + \frac{3}{7}$

50. $\frac{3}{4} + \frac{1}{6}$

51. $\frac{10}{3} - \frac{5}{21}$

52. $\frac{11}{7} - \frac{3}{35}$

53. $8\frac{1}{8} - 6\frac{3}{8}$

54. $5\frac{2}{5} - 3\frac{4}{5}$

55. $1\frac{1}{2} + 3\frac{2}{3}$

56. $7\frac{3}{20} + 2\frac{13}{15}$

Objectives D E F **Mixed Practice** *Perform the indicated operations. See Examples 11 through 23.*

57. $\frac{23}{105} + \frac{4}{105}$

58. $\frac{13}{132} + \frac{35}{132}$

59. $\frac{17}{21} - \frac{10}{21}$

60. $\frac{18}{35} - \frac{11}{35}$

61. $\frac{7}{10} \cdot \frac{5}{21}$

62. $\frac{3}{35} \cdot \frac{10}{63}$

63. $\frac{9}{20} \div 12$

64. $\frac{25}{36} \div 10$

65. $\frac{5}{22} - \frac{5}{33}$

66. $\frac{7}{15} - \frac{7}{25}$

67. $17\frac{2}{5} + 30\frac{2}{3}$

68. $26\frac{11}{20} + 40\frac{7}{10}$

69. $7\frac{2}{5} \div \frac{1}{5}$

70. $9\frac{5}{6} \div \frac{1}{6}$

71. $4\frac{2}{11} \cdot 2\frac{1}{2}$

72. $6\frac{6}{7} \cdot 3\frac{1}{2}$

73. $\frac{12}{5} - 1$

74. $2 - \frac{3}{8}$

75. $8\frac{11}{12} - 1\frac{5}{6}$

76. $4\frac{7}{8} - 2\frac{3}{16}$

Concept Extensions

Perform indicated operations.

77. $\frac{2}{3} - \frac{5}{9} + \frac{5}{6}$

78. $\frac{8}{11} - \frac{1}{4} + \frac{1}{2}$

For Exercises 79–82, determine whether the work is correct or incorrect. If incorrect, find the error and correct. See the Concept Check in this section.

79. $\frac{12}{24} = \frac{2 + 4 + 6}{2 + 4 + 6 + 12} = \frac{1}{12}$

80. $\frac{30}{60} = \frac{2 \cdot 3 \cdot 5}{2 \cdot 2 \cdot 3 \cdot 5} = \frac{1}{2}$

81. $\frac{2}{7} + \frac{9}{7} = \frac{11}{14}$

82. $\frac{16}{28} = \frac{2 \cdot 5 + 6 \cdot 1}{2 \cdot 5 + 6 \cdot 3} = \frac{1}{3}$

83. In your own words, describe how to divide fractions.

84. In your own words, describe how to add or subtract fractions.

Each circle below represents a whole, or 1. Determine the unknown part of the circle.

85.

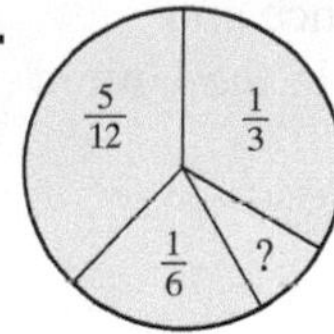

86.

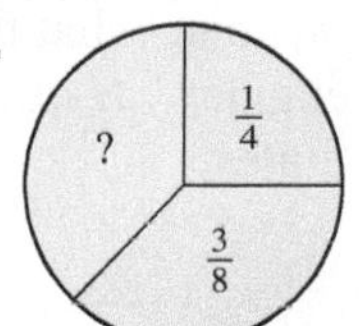

87.

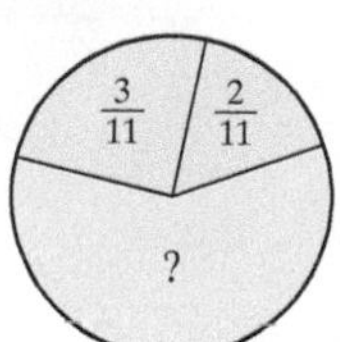

88.

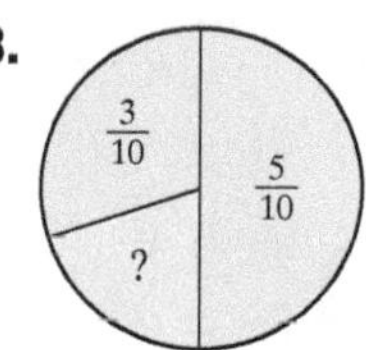

89. If Tucson's average rainfall is $11\frac{1}{4}$ inches and Yuma's is $3\frac{3}{5}$ inches, how much more rain, on the average, does Tucson get than Yuma?

90. A pair of crutches needs adjustment. One crutch is 43 inches and the other is $41\frac{5}{8}$ inches. Find how much the short crutch should be lengthened to make both crutches the same length.

91. Use the circle graph or pie chart below to answer the questions.

Fraction of U.S. Screens by Theater Type

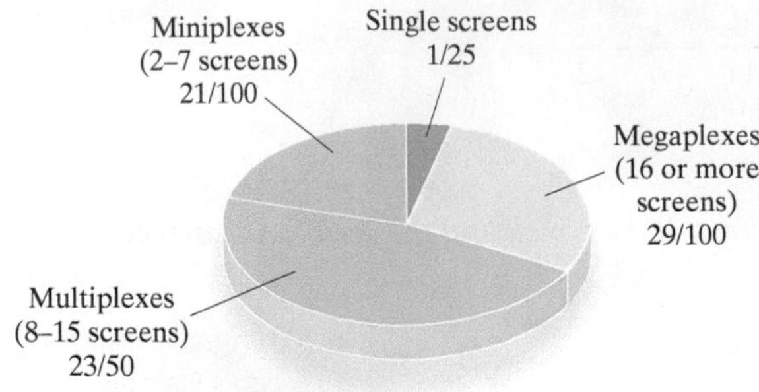

Source: Motion Picture Association of America

a. What fraction of U.S. movie screens are in miniplexes?

b. What fraction of U.S. movie screens are in single-screen theaters or multiplexes?

c. What theater type has the greatest fraction of screens?

d. What fraction of U.S. movie screens are in megaplexes or miniplexes?

92. The breakdown of science and engineering doctorate degrees awarded in the United States is summarized in the graph shown, called a circle graph or a pie chart. Use the graph to answer the questions. (*Source:* National Science Foundation)

Science and Engineering Doctorates Awarded, by Field of Study

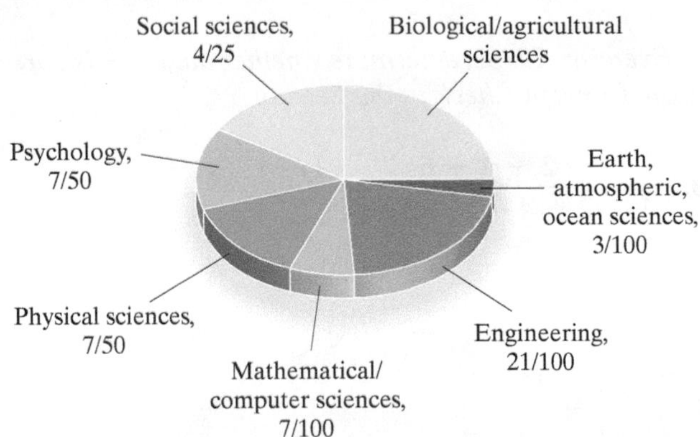

a. What fraction of science and engineering doctorates are awarded in the physical sciences?

b. Engineering doctorates make up what fraction of all science and engineering doctorates awarded in the United States?

c. Social sciences and psychology doctorates together make up what fraction of all science and engineering doctorates awarded in the United States?

d. What fraction of all science and engineering doctorates are awarded in the biological and agricultural sciences?

The area of a plane figure is a measure of the amount of surface of the figure. Find the area of each figure. (The area of a rectangle is the product of its length and width. The area of a triangle is $\frac{1}{2}$ the product of its base and height. Recall that area is measured in square units.)

△ **93.**

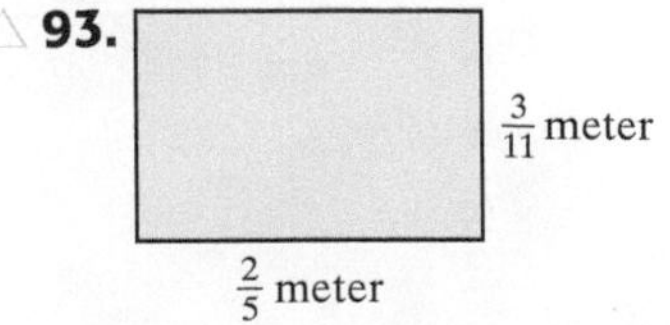

△ **94.**

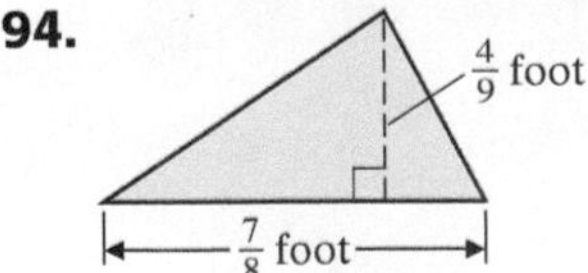

R.3 DECIMALS AND PERCENTS

Objectives

- **A** Write Decimals as Fractions.
- **B** Add, Subtract, Multiply, and Divide Decimals.
- **C** Round Decimals to a Given Decimal Place.
- **D** Write Fractions as Decimals.
- **E** Write Percents as Decimals and Decimals as Percents.

Objective A Writing Decimals as Fractions

Like fractional notation, **decimal notation** is used to denote a part of a whole. Below is a **place value chart** that shows the value of each place.

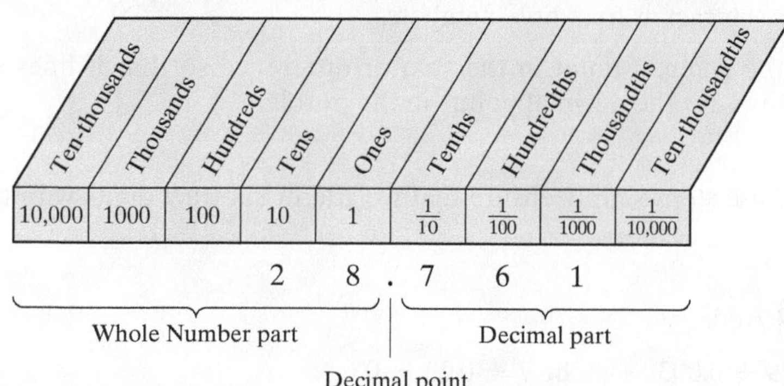

✓**Concept Check** Fill in the blank: In the number 52.634, the 3 is in the _____ place.

a. Tens **b.** Ones **c.** Tenths
d. Hundredths **e.** Thousandths

The next chart shows decimals written as fractions.

Decimal Form	Fractional Form
0.1	$\frac{1}{10}$ (tenths)
0.07	$\frac{7}{100}$ (hundredths)
2.31	$\frac{231}{100}$ (hundredths)
0.9862	$\frac{9862}{10,000}$ (ten-thousandths)

To write a decimal as a fraction, use place values.

Examples Write each decimal as a fraction. Do not simplify.

1. $0.37 = \frac{37}{100}$
2 decimal places, 2 zeros

2. $1.3 = \frac{13}{10}$
1 decimal place, 1 zero

3. $2.649 = \frac{2649}{1000}$
3 decimal places, 3 zeros

Work Practice 1–3

PRACTICE 1–3

Write each decimal as a fraction. Do not simplify.

1. 0.27 **2.** 5.1 **3.** 7.685

Answers

1. $\frac{27}{100}$ **2.** $\frac{51}{10}$ **3.** $\frac{7685}{1000}$

✓ **Concept Check Answer**

d

Objective B Adding, Subtracting, Multiplying, and Dividing Decimals

To **add** or **subtract** decimals, follow the steps below.

To Add or Subtract Decimals

Step 1: Write the decimals so that the decimal points line up vertically.

Step 2: Add or subtract as for whole numbers.

Step 3: Place the decimal point in the sum or difference so that it lines up vertically with the decimal points in the problem.

Notice that these steps simply ensure that we add or subtract digits with the same place value.

PRACTICE 4

Add.

a. 7.19 + 19.782 + 1.006

b. 12 + 0.79 + 0.03

Example 4 Add.

a. 5.87 + 23.279 + 0.003 **b.** 7 + 0.23 + 0.6

Solution:

a.
$$\begin{array}{r} 5.87 \\ 23.279 \\ +\ 0.003 \\ \hline 29.152 \end{array}$$

b.
$$\begin{array}{r} 7. \\ 0.23 \\ +0.6 \\ \hline 7.83 \end{array}$$

Work Practice 4

PRACTICE 5

Subtract.

a. 84.23 − 26.982

b. 90 − 0.19

Example 5 Subtract.

a. 32.15 − 11.237 **b.** 70 − 0.48

Solution:

a.
$$\begin{array}{r} \scriptstyle 1\ 11\ 4\ 10 \\ 3\not{2}.\not{1}\not{5}\not{0} \\ -\ 1\ 1.\ 2\ 3\ 7 \\ \hline 2\ 0.\ 9\ 1\ 3 \end{array}$$

b.
$$\begin{array}{r} \scriptstyle 6\ 9\ \ 9\ 10 \\ \not{7}\not{0}.\not{0}\not{0} \\ -\ \ 0.\ 4\ 8 \\ \hline 6\ 9.\ 5\ 2 \end{array}$$

Work Practice 5

Now let's study the following product of decimals. Notice the pattern in the decimal points.

$$\underbrace{0.03}_{\text{2 decimal places}} \times \underbrace{0.6}_{\text{1 decimal place}} = \frac{3}{100} \times \frac{6}{10} = \frac{18}{1000} \quad \text{or} \quad \underbrace{0.018}_{\text{3 decimal places}}$$

In general, to **multiply** decimals, follow the steps below.

To Multiply Decimals

Step 1: Multiply the decimals as though they are whole numbers.

Step 2: The decimal point in the product is placed so that the number of decimal places in the product is equal to the **sum** of the number of decimal places in the factors.

Answers

4. a. 27.978 **b.** 12.82

5. a. 57.248 **b.** 89.81

Example 6 Multiply.

a. 0.072×3.5 **b.** 0.17×0.02

Solution:

a.

```
   0.072   3 decimal places
 ×   3.5   1 decimal place
     360
    216
  0.2520   4 decimal places
```

b.

```
     0.17   2 decimal places
 ×   0.02   2 decimal places
   0.0034   4 decimal places
```

Work Practice 6

PRACTICE 6

Multiply.

a. 0.31×4.6

b. 1.26×0.03

To divide a decimal by a whole number using long division, we place the decimal point in the quotient directly above the decimal point in the dividend. For example,

```
   2.47
3)7.41
 -6
  1 4
 -1 2
    21
   -21
     0
```

To check, see that $2.47 \times 3 = 7.41$

Helpful Hint Don't forget the names of the numbers in a division problem.

$$\text{divisor}\overline{\smash{)}\text{dividend}}^{\text{quotient}}$$

In general, to **divide** decimals, use the steps below.

To Divide Decimals

Step 1: Move the decimal point in the divisor to the right until the divisor is a whole number.

Step 2: Move the decimal point in the dividend to the right the **same number of places** as the decimal point was moved in Step 1.

Step 3: Divide. The decimal point in the quotient is directly over the moved decimal point in the dividend.

Example 7 Divide.

a. $9.46 \div 0.04$ **b.** $31.5 \div 0.007$

Solution:

a.

```
         236.5
004.)946.0     A zero is inserted
    -8         to continue dividing.
     14
    -12
      26
     -24
       20
      -20
        0
```

b.

```
          4500.
0007.)31500.    Zeros are inserted
     -28        in order to move the
       35       decimal point three places
      -35       to the right.
        0
```

Work Practice 7

PRACTICE 7

Divide.

a. $21.75 \div 0.5$

b. $15.6 \div 0.006$

Answers

6. a. 1.426 **b.** 0.0378

7. a. 43.5 **b.** 2600

Objective C Rounding Decimals

We **round** the decimal part of a decimal number in nearly the same way as we round whole numbers. The only difference is that we drop digits to the right of the rounding place, instead of replacing these digits by 0s. For example,

24.954 rounded to the nearest hundredth is 24.95
↑
hundredths place

To Round Decimals to a Place Value to the Right of the Decimal Point

Step 1: Locate the digit to the right of the given place value.

Step 2:
- If this digit is 5 or greater, add 1 to the digit in the given place value and drop all digits to its right.
- If this digit is less than 5, drop all digits to the right of the given place.

PRACTICE 8

Round 12.9187 to the nearest hundredth.

Example 8 Round 7.8265 to the nearest hundredth.

Solution: 7.8265 (hundredths place: 2)

Step 1. Locate the digit to the right of the hundredths place.
Step 2. This digit is 5 or greater, so we add 1 to the hundredths place digit and drop all digits to its right.

Thus, 7.8265 rounded to the nearest hundredth is 7.83.

Work Practice 8

PRACTICE 9

Round 245.348 to the nearest tenth.

Example 9 Round 19.329 to the nearest tenth.

Solution: 19.329 (tenths place: 3)

Step 1. Locate the digit to the right of the tenths place.
Step 2. This digit is less than 5, so we drop this digit and all digits to its right.

Thus, 19.329 rounded to the nearest tenth is 19.3.

Work Practice 9

Objective D Writing Fractions as Decimals

To write fractions as decimals, interpret the fraction bar as division and find the quotient.

To Write a Fraction as a Decimal

Divide the numerator by the denominator.

PRACTICE 10

Write $\frac{2}{5}$ as a decimal.

Example 10 Write $\frac{1}{4}$ as a decimal.

Solution:

$$\begin{array}{r} 0.25 \\ 4\overline{)1.00} \\ \underline{-8} \\ 20 \\ \underline{-20} \\ 0 \end{array} \qquad \frac{1}{4} = 0.25$$

Work Practice 10

Answers
8. 12.92 **9.** 245.3 **10.** 0.4

Example 11 Write $\frac{2}{3}$ as a decimal.

Solution:

$$\begin{array}{r} 0.666 \\ 3\overline{)2.000} \\ -1\,8 \\ \hline 20 \\ -18 \\ \hline 20 \\ -18 \\ \hline 2 \end{array}$$

This division pattern will continue so that $\frac{2}{3} = 0.6666\ldots$.

A bar can be placed over the digit 6 to indicate that it repeats. We call this a **repeating decimal.**

$$\frac{2}{3} = 0.666\ldots = 0.\overline{6}$$

Work Practice 11

PRACTICE 11

Write $\frac{5}{6}$ as a decimal.

We can also write a decimal approximation for $\frac{2}{3}$. For example, $\frac{2}{3}$ rounded to the nearest hundredth is 0.67. This can be written as $\frac{2}{3} \approx 0.67$. The $\approx$ sign means "is approximately equal to."

✓**Concept Check** The notation $0.5\overline{2}$ is the same as

a. $\frac{52}{100}$ **b.** $\frac{52\ldots}{100}$ **c.** $0.52222222\ldots$

Example 12 Write $\frac{22}{7}$ as a decimal. Round to the nearest hundredth.

Solution:

$$\begin{array}{r} 3.142 \approx 3.14 \\ 7\overline{)22.000} \\ -21 \\ \hline 1\,0 \\ -7 \\ \hline 30 \\ -28 \\ \hline 20 \\ -14 \\ \hline 6 \end{array}$$

If rounding to the nearest hundredth, carry the division process out to one more decimal place, the thousandths place.

The fraction $\frac{22}{7}$ in decimal form is approximately 3.14. (The fraction $\frac{22}{7}$ is an approximation for π.)

Work Practice 12

PRACTICE 12

Write $\frac{1}{9}$ as a decimal. Round to the nearest thousandth.

Objective E Writing Percents as Decimals and Decimals as Percents

The word **percent** comes from the Latin phrase *per centum,* which means **"per 100."** The % symbol is used to denote percent. Thus, 53% means 53 per 100, or

$$53\% = \frac{53}{100}$$

Answers

11. $0.8\overline{3}$ **12.** 0.111

✓ **Concept Check Answer**

c

When solving problems containing percents, it is often necessary to write a percent as a decimal. To see how this is done, study the chart below.

Percent	Fraction	Decimal
7%	$\frac{7}{100}$	0.07
63%	$\frac{63}{100}$	0.63
109%	$\frac{109}{100}$	1.09

To convert directly from a percent to a decimal, notice that

7% = 0.07

To Write a Percent as a Decimal

Drop the percent symbol, %, and move the decimal point two places to the left.

PRACTICE 13

Write each percent as a decimal.

a. 20%
b. 1.4%
c. 465%

Example 13 Write each percent as a decimal.

a. 25% **b.** 2.6% **c.** 195%

Solution: We drop the % and move the decimal point two places to the left. Recall that the decimal point of a whole number is to the right of the ones place digit.

a. 25% = 25.% = 0.25
b. 2.6% = 02.6% = 0.026
c. 195% = 195.% = 1.95

Work Practice 13

To write a decimal as a percent, we simply reverse the preceding steps. That is, we move the decimal point two places to the right and attach the percent symbol, %.

To Write a Decimal as a Percent

Move the decimal point two places to the right and attach the percent symbol, %.

PRACTICE 14

Write each decimal as a percent.

a. 0.42
b. 0.003
c. 2.36
d. 0.7

Example 14 Write each decimal as a percent.

a. 0.85 **b.** 1.25 **c.** 0.012 **d.** 0.6

Solution: We move the decimal point two places to the right and attach the percent symbol, %.

a. 0.85 = 0.85 = 85%
b. 1.25 = 1.25 = 125%
c. 0.012 = 0.012 = 1.2%
d. 0.6 = 0.60 = 60%

Work Practice 14

Answers

13. a. 0.20 **b.** 0.014 **c.** 4.65

14. a. 42% **b.** 0.3% **c.** 236% **d.** 70%

Vocabulary and Readiness Check

Fill in each blank with one of the choices listed below. Some choices may be used more than once and some not at all.

vertically	decimal	right	100%	percent
left	0.01	sum	denominator	numerator

1. Like fractional notation, ____________ notation is used to denote a part of a whole.
2. To write fractions as decimals, divide the ____________ by the ____________.
3. To add or subtract decimals, write the decimals so that the decimal points line up ____________.
4. When multiplying decimals, the decimal point in the product is placed so that the number of decimal places in the product is equal to the ____________ of the number of decimal places in the factors.
5. ____________ means "per hundred."
6. ____________ = 1.
7. The % symbol is read as ____________.
8. To write a percent as a *decimal,* drop the % symbol and move the decimal point two places to the ____________.
9. To write a decimal as a *percent*, move the decimal point two places to the ____________ and attach the % symbol.

R.3 Exercise Set

FOR EXTRA HELP

Objective A *Write each decimal as a fraction. Do not simplify. See Examples 1 through 3.*

1. 0.6 **2.** 0.9 **3.** 1.86 **4.** 7.23

5. 0.114 **6.** 0.239 **7.** 123.1 **8.** 892.7

Objective B *Add or subtract as indicated. See Examples 4 and 5.*

9. $5.7 + 1.13$ **10.** $2.31 + 6.4$ **11.** $24.6 + 2.39 + 0.0678$ **12.** $32.4 + 1.58 + 0.0934$

13. $8.8 - 2.3$ **14.** $7.6 - 2.1$ **15.** $18 - 2.78$ **16.** $28 - 3.31$

Multiply or divide as indicated. See Examples 6 and 7.

17. $\begin{array}{r} 0.2 \\ \times\ 0.6 \\ \hline \end{array}$ **18.** $\begin{array}{r} 0.7 \\ \times\ 0.9 \\ \hline \end{array}$ **19.** $\begin{array}{r} 0.063 \\ \times\ \ \ 4.2 \\ \hline \end{array}$ **20.** $\begin{array}{r} 0.079 \\ \times\ \ \ 3.6 \\ \hline \end{array}$

21. $5\overline{)8.4}$ **22.** $2\overline{)11.7}$ **23.** $0.82\overline{)4.756}$ **24.** $0.92\overline{)3.312}$

Mixed Practice *Perform the indicated operation. See Examples 4 through 7.*

25. $\begin{array}{r} 45.02 \\ 3.006 \\ +\ 8.405 \\ \hline \end{array}$ **26.** $\begin{array}{r} 65.0028 \\ 5.0903 \\ +\ 6.9\ \ \ \ \ \\ \hline \end{array}$ **27.** $\begin{array}{r} 6.75 \\ \times\ \ \ 10 \\ \hline \end{array}$ **28.** $\begin{array}{r} 8.91 \\ \times\ 100 \\ \hline \end{array}$ **29.** $0.6\overline{)42}$

30. $0.9\overline{)36}$

31. $\begin{array}{r} 654.9 \\ -\ 56.67 \\ \hline \end{array}$

32. $\begin{array}{r} 863.2 \\ -\ 39.45 \\ \hline \end{array}$

33. $\begin{array}{r} 5.62 \\ \times\ 7.7 \\ \hline \end{array}$

34. $\begin{array}{r} 8.03 \\ \times\ 5.5 \\ \hline \end{array}$

35. $0.063\overline{)52.92}$

36. $0.054\overline{)51.84}$

37. $\begin{array}{r} 16.003 \\ \times\ 5.31 \\ \hline \end{array}$

38. $\begin{array}{r} 31.006 \\ \times\ \ 3.71 \\ \hline \end{array}$

Objective C *Round each decimal to the given place value. See Examples 8 and 9.*

39. 0.57, nearest tenth

40. 0.75, nearest tenth

41. 0.234, nearest hundredth

42. 0.452, nearest hundredth

43. 0.5945, nearest thousandth

44. 63.4529, nearest thousandth

45. 98,207.23, nearest tenth

46. 68,936.543, nearest tenth

47. 12.347, nearest hundredth

48. 42.9878, nearest thousandth

Objective D *Write each fraction as a decimal. If the decimal is a repeating decimal, write using the bar notation and then round to the nearest hundredth. See Examples 10 through 12.*

49. $\frac{3}{4}$

50. $\frac{9}{25}$

51. $\frac{1}{3}$

52. $\frac{7}{9}$

53. $\frac{7}{16}$

54. $\frac{5}{8}$

55. $\frac{6}{11}$

56. $\frac{1}{6}$

57. $\frac{29}{6}$

58. $\frac{34}{9}$

Objective E *Write each percent as a decimal. See Example 13.*

59. 28%

60. 36%

61. 3.1%

62. 2.2%

63. 135%

64. 417%

65. 200%

66. 700%

67. 96.55%

68. 81.49%

69. 0.1%

70. 0.6%

71. In the United States recently, 15.8% of households had no landlines, just cell phones. (*Source:* CTIA—The Wireless Association)

72. Japan exports 73.2% of all motorcycles manufactured there. (*Source:* Japan Automobile Manufacturers Association)

Write each decimal as a percent. See Example 14.

73. 0.68

74. 0.32

75. 0.876

76. 0.521

77. 1

78. 3

79. 0.5

80. 0.1

81. 1.92

82. 2.15

83. 0.004

84. 0.005

85. In a recent year, 0.781 of all electricity produced in France was nuclear generated.

86. The United States' share of the total world motor vehicle production is 0.142. (*Source: World Almanac*)

Concept Extensions

In Exercises 87 through 90, write the percent from the circle graph as a decimal and a fraction.

World Population by Continent

Africa	14.2%
Asia	60.6%
South America	5.8%
North America	7.9%
Europe	11.0%
Australia	0.5%

87. Australia: 0.5%

88. Europe: 11%

89. Africa: 14.2%

90. Asia: 60.6%

Solve. See the Concept Checks in this section.

91. In the number 3.659, identify the place value of the

a. 6
b. 9
c. 3

92. The notation $0.\overline{67}$ is the same as

a. 0.6777...
b. 0.67666...
c. 0.6767...

93. In your own words, describe how to multiply decimal numbers.

94. In your own words, describe how to add or subtract decimal numbers.

The chart shows the average number of pounds of various dairy products consumed by each U.S. citizen. Use this chart for Exercises 95 and 96. (Source: Dairy Information Center)

Dairy Product	Pounds
Fluid Milk	213.4
Cheese	30.8
Butter	4.4

95. How much more fluid milk products than cheese products does the average U.S. citizen consume?

96. What is the total amount of these milk products consumed by the average U.S. citizen annually?

97. Given the percent 52.8647%, round as indicated.

a. Round to the nearest tenth percent.
b. Round to the nearest hundredth percent.

98. Given the percent 0.5269%, round as indicated.

a. Round to the nearest tenth percent.
b. Round to the nearest hundredth percent.

99. Which of the following are correct?

a. 6.5% = 0.65 **b.** 7.8% = 0.078
c. 120% = 0.12 **d.** 0.35% = 0.0035

100. Which of the following are correct?

a. 0.231 = 23.1% **b.** 5.12 = 0.0512%
c. 3.2 = 320% **d.** 0.0175 = 0.175%

Recall that 1 = 100%. This means that 1 whole is 100%. Use this for Exercises 101 and 102. (Source: Some Body, by Dr. Pete Rowen)

101. The four blood types are A, B, O, and AB. (Each blood type can also be further classified as Rh-positive or Rh-negative depending upon whether your blood contains protein or not.) Given the percent blood types for people in the United States below, calculate the percent of the U.S. population with AB blood type.

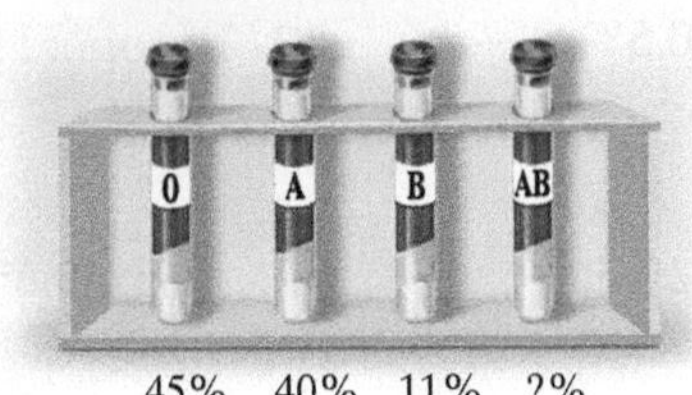

45% 40% 11% ?%

102. The top four components of bone are below. Find the missing percent.

1. Minerals—45%
2. Living tissue—30%
3. Water—20%
4. Other—?

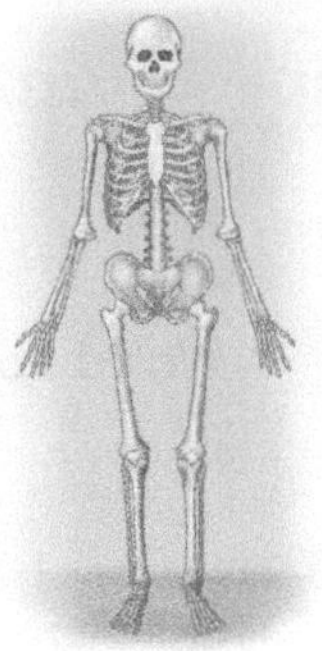

The bar graph shows the predicted fastest-growing occupations. Use this graph for Exercises 103 through 106.

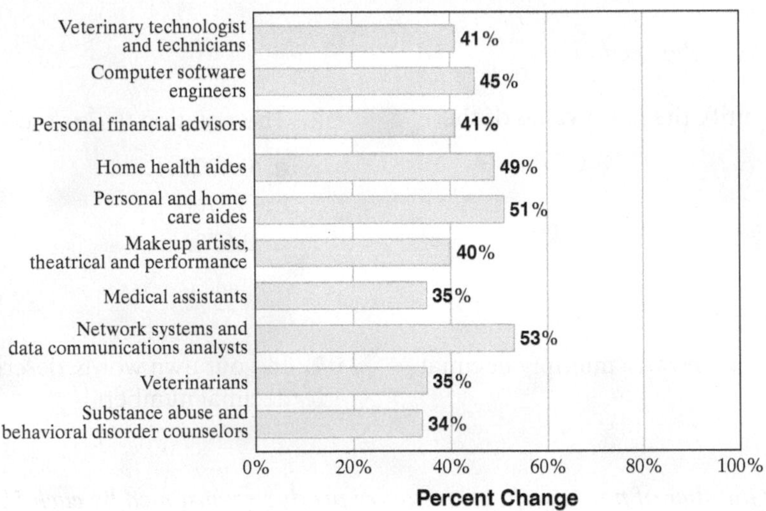

Source: Bureau of Labor Statistics

103. What occupation is predicted to be the fastest growing?

104. What occupation is predicted to be the second fastest growing?

105. Write the percent change for veterinarians as a decimal.

106. Write the percent change for makeup artists as a decimal.

107. In your own words, explain how to write a percent as a decimal.

108. In your own words, explain how to write a decimal as a percent.

Chapter R Group Activity

Interpreting Survey Results

This activity may be completed by working in groups or individually.

Conduct the following survey with 12 students in one of your classes and record the results.

a. What is your age?
Under 20 20s 30s 40s 50s 60 and older

b. What is your gender?
Female Male

c. How did you arrive on campus today?
Walked Drove Bicycled
Took public transportation Other

1. For each survey question, tally the results for each category.

Age	
Category	**Tally**
Under 20	
20s	
30s	
40s	
50s	
60+	
Total	

Gender	
Category	**Tally**
Female	
Male	
Total	

Mode of Transportation	
Category	**Tally**
Walk	
Drive	
Bicycle	
Public Transit	
Other	
Total	

2. For each survey question, find the fraction of the total number of responses that fall in each answer category. Use the tallies from Question 1 to complete the Fraction columns of the tables at the right.

3. For each survey question, convert the fraction of the total number of responses that fall in each answer category to a decimal number. Use the fractions from Question 2 to complete the Decimal columns of the tables below.

4. For each survey question, find the percent of the total number of responses that falls in each answer category. Complete the Percent columns of the tables below.

5. Study the tables. What may you conclude from them? What do they tell you about your survey respondents? Write a paragraph summarizing your findings.

Age			
Category	**Fraction**	**Decimal**	**Percent**
Under 20			
20s			
30s			
40s			
50s			
60+			

Gender			
Category	**Fraction**	**Decimal**	**Percent**
Female			
Male			

Mode of Transportation			
Category	**Fraction**	**Decimal**	**Percent**
Walk			
Drive			
Bicycle			
Public Transit			
Other			

Chapter R Vocabulary Check

Fill in each blank with one of the words or phrases listed below.

mixed number	factor	improper fraction	percent
multiple	composite number	proper fraction	simplified
prime number	equivalent		

1. To ______________ means to write as a product.
2. A(n) ______________ of a number is the product of that number and any natural number.
3. A(n) ______________ is a natural number greater than 1 that is not prime.
4. The word ______________ means per 100.
5. Fractions that represent the same portion of a whole are called ______________ fractions.
6. A(n) ______________ is a fraction whose numerator is greater than or equal to its denominator.
7. A(n) ______________ is a natural number greater than 1 whose only factors are 1 and itself.
8. A fraction is ______________ when the numerator and the denominator have no factors in common other than 1.
9. A(n) ______________ is one whose numerator is less than its denominator.
10. A(n) ______________ contains a whole number part and a fraction part.

Helpful Hint Are you preparing for your test? Don't forget to take the Chapter R Test on page R-35. Then check your answers at the back of the text and use the Chapter Test Prep Videos to see the fully worked-out solutions to any of the exercises you want to review.

R Chapter Highlights

Definitions and Concepts	Examples
Section R.1 Factors and the Least Common Multiple	
To **factor** means to write as a product. Since $2 \cdot 6 = 12$, 2 and 6 are **factors** of 12.	The factors of 12 are 1, 2, 3, 4, 6, 12
When a number is written as a product of primes, this product is called the **prime factorization** of a number.	Write the prime factorization of 60. $60 = 6 \cdot 10$ $= 2 \cdot 3 \cdot 2 \cdot 5$ The prime factorization of 60 is $2 \cdot 2 \cdot 3 \cdot 5$.
The **least common multiple (LCM)** of a list of numbers is the smallest number that is a multiple of all the numbers in the list.	
To Find the LCM of a List of Numbers **Step 1.** Write the prime factorization of each number. **Step 2.** Write the product containing each different prime factor (from Step 1) the greatest number of times that it appears in any one factorization. This product is the LCM.	Find the LCM of 12 and 40. $12 = 2 \cdot 2 \cdot 3$ $40 = 2 \cdot 2 \cdot 2 \cdot 5$ $\text{LCM} = 2 \cdot 2 \cdot 2 \cdot 3 \cdot 5 = 120$

Definitions and Concepts	Examples
Section R.2 Fractions	
Fractions that represent the same portion of a whole are called **equivalent fractions.**	$\frac{1}{5} = \frac{1 \cdot 4}{5 \cdot 4} = \frac{4}{20}$ $\frac{1}{5}$ and $\frac{4}{20}$ are equivalent fractions.
To write an equivalent fraction, $\frac{a}{b} = \frac{a}{b} \cdot \frac{c}{c} = \frac{a \cdot c}{b \cdot c}$	Write $\frac{8}{21}$ as an equivalent fraction with a denominator of 63. $\frac{8}{21} = \frac{8}{21} \cdot \frac{3}{3} = \frac{8 \cdot 3}{21 \cdot 3} = \frac{24}{63}$
A fraction is **simplified** when the numerator and the denominator have no factors in common other than 1.	$\frac{13}{17}$ is simplified.
To simplify a fraction, $\frac{a \cdot c}{b \cdot c} = \frac{a}{b} \cdot \frac{c}{c} = \frac{a}{b}$	Simplify. $\frac{6}{14} = \frac{2 \cdot 3}{2 \cdot 7} = \frac{2}{2} \cdot \frac{3}{7} = \frac{3}{7}$
Two fractions are **reciprocals** if their product is 1. The reciprocal of $\frac{a}{b}$ is $\frac{b}{a}$, as long as a and b are not 0.	The reciprocal of $\frac{6}{25}$ is $\frac{25}{6}$.
To multiply fractions, multiply numerator times numerator to find the numerator of the product and denominator times denominator to find the denominator of the product.	$\frac{2}{5} \cdot \frac{3}{7} = \frac{6}{35}$
To divide fractions, multiply the first fraction by the reciprocal of the second fraction.	$\frac{5}{9} \div \frac{2}{7} = \frac{5}{9} \cdot \frac{7}{2} = \frac{35}{18}$
To add fractions with the same denominator, add the numerators and place the sum over the common denominator.	$\frac{5}{11} + \frac{3}{11} = \frac{8}{11}$
To subtract fractions with the same denominator, subtract the numerators and place the difference over the common denominator.	$\frac{13}{15} - \frac{3}{15} = \frac{10}{15} = \frac{2}{3}$
To add or subtract fractions with different denominators, first write each fraction as an equivalent fraction with the LCD as denominator.	$\frac{2}{9} + \frac{3}{6} = \frac{2 \cdot 2}{9 \cdot 2} + \frac{3 \cdot 3}{6 \cdot 3} = \frac{4 + 9}{18} = \frac{13}{18}$
Section R.3 Decimals and Percents	
To write decimals as fractions, use place values.	$0.11 = \frac{11}{100}$
TO ADD OR SUBTRACT DECIMALS **Step 1.** Write the decimals so that the decimal points line up vertically. **Step 2.** Add or subtract as for whole numbers. **Step 3.** Place the decimal point in the sum or difference so that it lines up vertically with the decimal points in the problem.	Subtract: 2.8 − 1.04 $\begin{array}{r} \overset{7\ 10}{2.\cancel{8}\cancel{0}} \\ -1.04 \\ \hline 1.76 \end{array}$ Add: 25 + 0.02 $\begin{array}{r} 25. \\ +\ 0.02 \\ \hline 25.02 \end{array}$

(*continued*)

Definitions and Concepts	Examples
Section R.3 Decimals and Percents (*continued*)	
To Multiply Decimals **Step 1.** Multiply the decimals as though they are whole numbers. **Step 2.** The decimal point in the product is placed so that the number of decimal places in the product is equal to the **sum** of the number of decimal places in the factors.	Multiply: 1.48×5.9 1.48 ← 2 decimal places $\times\ 5.9$ ← 1 decimal place 1332 740 8.732 ← 3 decimal places
To Divide Decimals **Step 1.** Move the decimal point in the divisor to the right until the divisor is a whole number. **Step 2.** Move the decimal point in the dividend to the right the **same number of places** as the decimal point was moved in Step 1. **Step 3.** Divide. The decimal point in the quotient is directly over the moved decimal point in the dividend.	Divide: $1.118 \div 2.6$ 0.43 $26.\overline{)11.18}$ $-10\ 4$ 78 -78 0
To write fractions as decimals, divide the numerator by the denominator.	Write $\frac{3}{8}$ as a decimal. 0.375 $8\overline{)3.000}$ $-2\ 4$ 60 -56 40 -40 0
To write a percent as a decimal, drop the percent symbol, %, and move the decimal point two places to the left.	$25\% = 25.\% = 0.25$
To write a decimal as a percent, move the decimal point two places to the right and attach the percent symbol, %.	$0.7 = 0.70 = 70\%$

Chapter R Review

(R.1) *Write the prime factorization of each number.*

1. 42

2. 800

Find the least common multiple (LCM) of each list of numbers.

3. 12, 30

4. 7, 42

5. 4, 6, 10

6. 2, 5, 7

(R.2) *Write each fraction as an equivalent fraction with the given denominator.*

7. $\frac{5}{8}$ with a denominator of 24

8. $\frac{2}{3}$ with a denominator of 60

Simplify each fraction.

9. $\frac{8}{20}$

10. $\frac{15}{100}$

11. $\frac{12}{6}$

12. $\frac{8}{8}$

Perform each indicated operation and simplify.

13. $\frac{1}{7} \cdot \frac{8}{11}$

14. $\frac{5}{12} + \frac{2}{15}$

15. $\frac{3}{10} \div 6$

16. $\frac{7}{9} - \frac{1}{6}$

17. $3\frac{3}{8} \cdot 4\frac{1}{4}$

18. $2\frac{1}{3} - 1\frac{5}{6}$

19. $16\frac{9}{10} + 3\frac{2}{3}$

20. $6\frac{2}{7} \div 2\frac{1}{5}$

The area of a plane figure is a measure of the amount of surface of the figure. Find the area of each figure below. (The area of a rectangle is the product of its length and width. The area of a triangle is $\frac{1}{2}$ the product of its base and height.)

△ **21.**

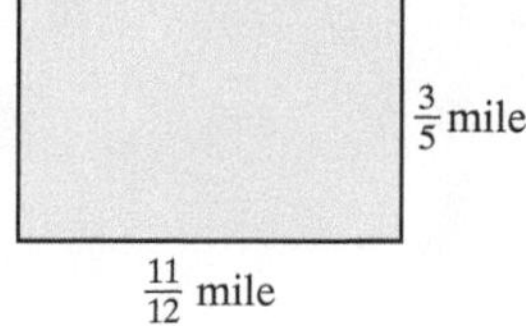

△ **22.**

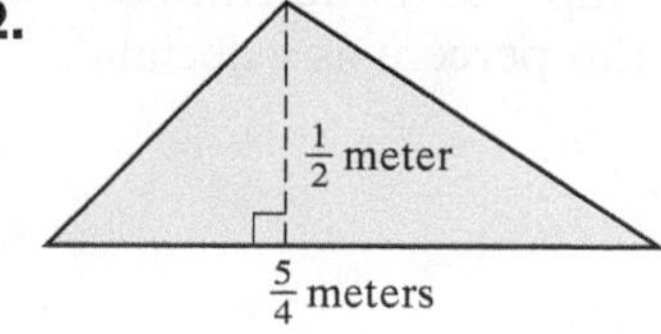

(R.3) *Write each decimal as a fraction. Do not simplify.*

23. 1.81

24. 0.035

Perform each indicated operation.

25. $\begin{array}{r} 76.358 \\ +18.76 \\ \hline \end{array}$

26. $35 + 0.02 + 1.765$

27. $18 - 4.62$

28. $\begin{array}{r} 804.062 \\ -112.489 \\ \hline \end{array}$

29. $\begin{array}{r} 7.6 \\ \times 12 \\ \hline \end{array}$

30. $\begin{array}{r} 14.63 \\ \times \quad 3.2 \\ \hline \end{array}$

31. $27\overline{)772.2}$

32. $0.06\overline{)13.8}$

Round each decimal to the given place value.

33. 0.7652, nearest hundredth

34. 25.6293, nearest tenth

Write each fraction as a decimal. If the decimal is a repeating decimal, write it using the bar notation and then round to the nearest thousandth.

35. $\frac{1}{2}$

36. $\frac{3}{8}$

37. $\frac{4}{11}$

38. $\frac{5}{6}$

Write each percent as a decimal.

39. 29%

40. 1.4%

Write each decimal as a percent.

41. 0.39

42. 1.2

43. In 2003, the home ownership rate in the United States was 68.3%. Write this percent as a decimal.

44. Choose the true statement.

a. 2.3% = 0.23

b. 5 = 500%

c. 40% = 4

Chapter R Test

Step-by-step test solutions are found on the Chapter Test Prep Videos available via the Interactive DVD Lecture Series, in MyMathLab or on YouTube (search "MartinGayIntroAlg" and click on "Channels").

Answers

1. ______
2. ______
3. ______
4. ______
5. ______
6. ______
7. ______
8. ______
9. ______
10. ______
11. ______
12. ______
13. ______
14. ______
15. ______
16. ______
17. ______
18. ______
19. ______
20. ______

1. Write the prime factorization of 72.

2. Find the LCM of 5, 18, 20.

3. Write $\frac{5}{12}$ as an equivalent fraction with a denominator of 60.

Simplify each fraction.

4. $\frac{15}{20}$

5. $\frac{48}{100}$

6. Write 1.3 as a fraction.

Perform each indicated operation and simplify.

7. $\frac{5}{8} + \frac{7}{10}$

8. $\frac{2}{3} \cdot \frac{27}{49}$

9. $\frac{9}{10} \div 18$

10. $\frac{8}{9} - \frac{1}{12}$

11. $1\frac{2}{9} + 3\frac{2}{3}$

12. $5\frac{6}{11} - 3\frac{7}{22}$

13. $6\frac{7}{8} \div \frac{1}{8}$

14. $2\frac{1}{10} \cdot 6\frac{1}{2}$

Perform each indicated operation.

15. $43 + 0.21 + 1.9$

16. $123.6 - 57.72$

17. $\begin{array}{r} 7.93 \\ \times\ 1.6 \\ \hline \end{array}$

18. $0.25\overline{)80}$

19. Round 23.7272 to the nearest hundredth.

20. Write $\frac{7}{8}$ as a decimal.

21. ______

22. ______

23. ______

24. ______

25. ______

26. ______

27. ______

28. ______

29. ______

30. ______

21. Write $\frac{1}{6}$ as a repeating decimal. Then approximate the result to the nearest thousandth.

22. Write 63.2% as a decimal.

23. Write 0.09 as a percent.

24. Write $\frac{3}{4}$ as a percent. (*Hint:* Write $\frac{3}{4}$ as a decimal, and then write the decimal as a percent.)

Most of the water on Earth is in the form of oceans. Only a small part is fresh water. The graph below is called a circle graph or pie chart. This particular circle graph shows the distribution of fresh water on Earth. Use this graph to answer Exercises 25 through 28. (Source: Philip's World Atlas)

Fresh Water Distribution

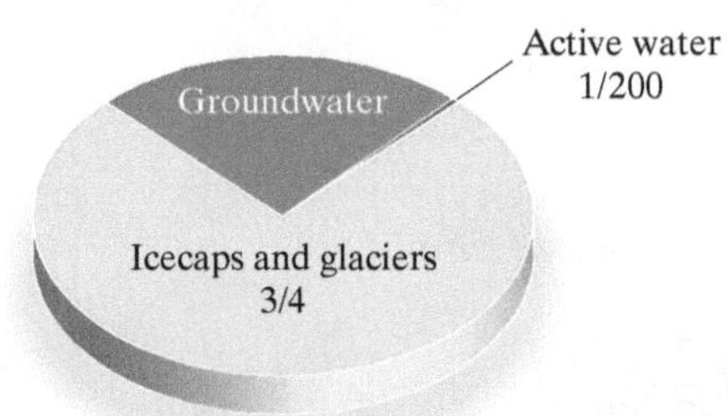

25. What fractional part of fresh water is icecaps and glaciers?

26. What fractional part of fresh water is active water?

27. What fractional part of fresh water is groundwater?

28. What fractional part of fresh water is groundwater or icecaps and glaciers?

Find the area of each figure. (The area of a rectangle is the product of its length and width. The area of a triangle is $\frac{1}{2}$ the product of its base and height.)

△ **29.**

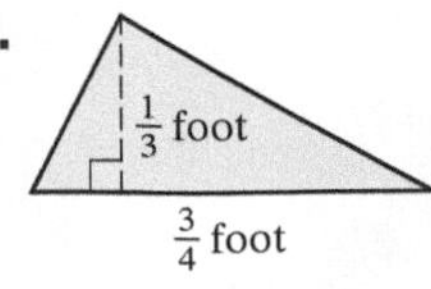

△ **30.**

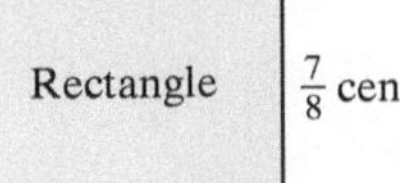

Real Numbers and Introduction to Algebra

1

Sections

Check Your Progress

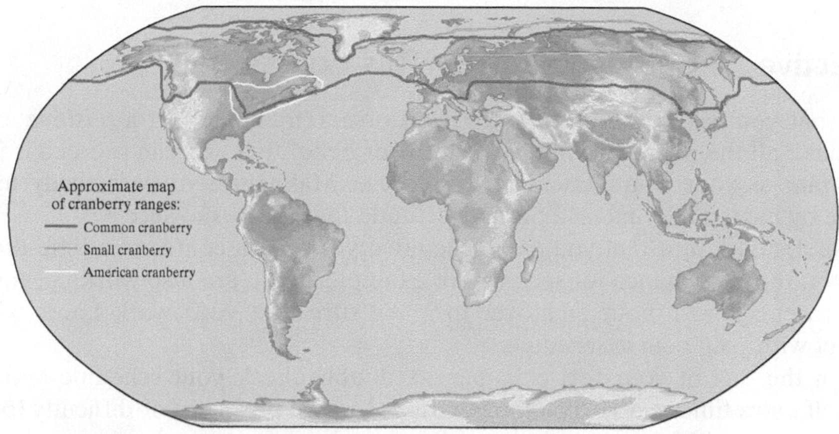

In this chapter, we begin with a review of the basic symbols–the language–of mathematics. We then introduce algebra by using a variable in place of a number. From there, we translate phrases to algebraic expressions and sentences to equations. This is the beginning of problem solving, which we formally study in Chapter 2.

The cranberry is one of only three fruits that are native to North America (the other two are the blueberry and the Concord grape). Native Americans pounded cranberries into paste, which they mixed with dried meat to create pemmican. American and Canadian sailors took cranberries on long sea voyages to combat scurvy, because of their high vitamin C content. Cranberries received their common name from "crane berry" because colonists thought the flower resembled the head, neck, and beak of the crane.

Americans consume 400 million pounds annually, 20% of them during Thanksgiving week. They are available in many forms: fresh, jellied, dried, or in juice. They are high in antioxidants and beneficial to the health of gums and teeth. In Exercises 81–84, Section 1.2, you will explore information about cranberry crops from the top five cranberry-producing states. (*Source:* Cape Cod Cranberry Growers Association)

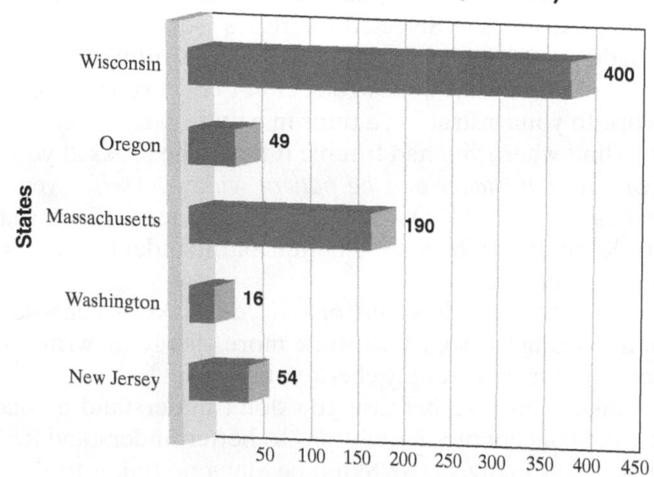

Source: National Agricultural Statistics Service

Objectives

A Get Ready for This Course.

B Understand Some General Tips for Success.

C Understand How to Use This Text.

D Get Help as Soon as You Need It.

E Learn How to Prepare for and Take an Exam.

F Develop Good Time Management.

1.1 TIPS FOR SUCCESS IN MATHEMATICS

Before reading this section, remember that your instructor is your best source of information. Please see your instructor for any additional help or information.

Objective A Getting Ready for This Course

Now that you have decided to take this course, remember that a *positive attitude* will make all the difference in the world. Your belief that you can succeed is just as important as your commitment to this course. Make sure you are ready for this course by having the time and positive attitude that it takes to succeed.

Next, make sure that you have scheduled your math course at a time that will give you the best chance for success. For example, if you are also working, you may want to check with your employer to make sure that your work hours will not conflict with your course schedule.

On the day of your first class period, double-check your schedule and allow yourself extra time to arrive on time in case of traffic problems or difficulty locating your classroom. Make sure that you bring at least your textbook, paper, and a writing instrument. Are you required to have a lab manual, graph paper, calculator, or some other supplies besides this text? If so, also bring this material with you.

Objective B General Tips for Success

Below are some general tips that will increase your chance for success in a mathematics class. Many of these tips will also help you in other courses you may be taking.

Exchange names and phone numbers or e-mail addresses with at least one other person in class. This contact person can be a great help if you miss an assignment or want to discuss math concepts or exercises that you find difficult.

Choose to attend all class periods. If possible, sit near the front of the classroom. This way, you will see and hear the presentation better. It may also be easier for you to participate in classroom activities.

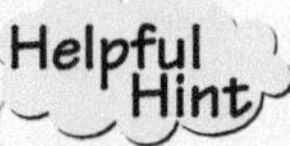

MyMathLab® and **MathXL®** If you are doing your homework online, you can work and re-work those exercises that you struggle with until you master them. Try working through all the assigned exercises twice before the due date.

Do your homework. You've probably heard the phrase "practice makes perfect" in relation to music and sports. It also applies to mathematics. You will find that the more time you spend solving mathematics exercises, the easier the process becomes. Be sure to schedule enough time to complete your assignments before the next due date assigned by your instructor.

MyMathLab® and **MathXL®** If you are completing your homework online, it's important to work each exercise on paper before submitting the answer. That way, you can check your work and follow your steps to find and correct any mistakes.

Check your work. Review the steps you made while working a problem. Learn to check your answers in the original problems. You may also compare your answers with the "Answers to Selected Exercises" section in the back of the book. If you have made a mistake, try to figure out what went wrong. Then correct your mistake. If you can't find what went wrong, don't erase your work or throw it away. Bring your work to your instructor, a tutor in a math lab, or a classmate. It is easier for someone to find where you had trouble if he or she looks at your original work.

Learn from your mistakes and be patient with yourself. Everyone, even your instructor, makes mistakes. (That definitely includes me—Elayn Martin-Gay.) Use your errors to learn and to become a better math student. The key is finding and understanding your errors.

Was your mistake a careless one, or did you make it because you can't read your own math writing? If so, try to work more slowly or write more neatly and make a conscious effort to carefully check your work.

Did you make a mistake because you don't understand a concept? Take the time to review the concept or ask questions to better understand it.

Did you skip too many steps? Skipping steps or trying to do too many steps mentally may lead to preventable mistakes.

Know how to get help if you need it. It's all right to ask for help. In fact, it's a good idea to ask for help whenever there is something that you don't understand. Make sure you know when your instructor has office hours and how to find his or her office. Find out whether math tutoring services are available on your campus. Check on the hours, location, and requirements of the tutoring service.

Organize your class materials, including homework assignments, graded quizzes and tests, and notes from your class or lab. All of these items will make valuable references throughout your course and when studying for upcoming tests and the final exam. Make sure that you can locate these materials when you need them.

MyMathLab® and **MathXL®**
When assignments are turned in online, keep a hard copy of your complete written work. You will need to refer to your written work to be able to ask questions and to study for tests later.

Read your textbook before class. Reading a mathematics textbook is unlike reading a novel or a newspaper. Your pace will be much slower. It is helpful to have paper and a pencil with you when you read. Try to work out examples on your own as you encounter them in your text. You should also write down any questions that you want to ask in class. When you read a mathematics textbook, sometimes some of the information in a section will be unclear. But after you hear a lecture or watch a lecture video on that section, you will understand it much more easily than if you had not read your text beforehand.

Don't be afraid to ask questions. You are not the only person in class with questions. Other students are normally grateful that someone has spoken up.

Turn in assignments on time. This way you can be sure that you will not lose points for being late. Show every step of a problem and be neat and organized. Also be sure that you understand which problems are assigned for homework. If allowed, you can always double-check the assignment with another student in your class.

Helpful Hint

MyMathLab® and **MathXL®**
Be aware of assignments and due dates set by your instructor. Don't wait until the last minute to submit work online. Allow 6–8 hours before the deadline in case you have technology trouble.

Objective C Using This Text

There are many helpful resources that are available to you. It is important that you become familiar with and use these resources. They should increase your chances for success in this course.

- *Practice Exercises.* Each example in every section has a parallel Practice exercise. As you read a section, try each Practice exercise after you've finished the corresponding example. This "learn-by-doing" approach will help you grasp ideas before you move on to other concepts. Answers are at the bottom of the page.
- *Chapter Test Prep Videos.* These videos provide solutions to all of the Chapter Test exercises worked out by the author. This supplement is very helpful before a test or exam.
- *Interactive DVD Lecture Series.* Exercises marked with a are fully worked out by the author on the DVDs. The lecture series provides approximately 20 minutes of instruction per section.
- *Symbols at the Beginning of an Exercise Set.* If you need help with a particular section, the symbols listed at the beginning of each exercise set will remind you of the numerous supplements available.
- *Objectives.* The main section of exercises in each exercise set is referenced by an objective, such as A or B, and also an example(s). There is also often a section of exercises entitled "Mixed Practice," which is referenced by two or more objectives or sections. These are mixed exercises written to prepare you for your next exam. Use all of this referencing if you have trouble completing an assignment from the exercise set.
- *Icons (Symbols).* Make sure that you understand the meaning of the icons that are beside many exercises. tells you that the corresponding exercise may be viewed on the video segment that corresponds to that section. tells you that this exercise is a writing exercise in which you should answer in complete sentences. △ tells you that the exercise involves geometry.
- *Integrated Reviews.* Found in the middle of each chapter, these reviews offer you a chance to practice—in one place—the many concepts that you have learned separately over several sections.

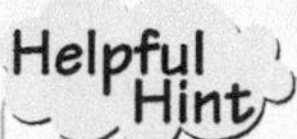

MyMathLab®
In MyMathLab, you have access to the following video resources:

- Lecture Videos for each section
- Chapter Test Prep Videos

Use these videos provided by the author to prepare for class, review, and study for tests.

- *End-of-Chapter Opportunities.* There are many opportunities at the end of each chapter to help you understand the concepts of the chapter.

  Vocabulary Checks contain key vocabulary terms introduced in the chapter.

  Chapter Highlights contain chapter summaries and examples.

  Chapter Reviews contain review problems. The first part is organized section by section and the second part contains a set of mixed exercises.

  Chapter Tests are sample tests to help you prepare for an exam. The Chapter Test Prep Videos, found in this text, contain all the Chapter Test exercises worked by the author.

  Cumulative Reviews are reviews consisting of material from the beginning of the book to the end of that particular chapter.
- *Student Resources in Your Textbook.* You will find a **Student Resources** section at the back of this textbook. It contains the following to help you study and prepare for tests:

  Study Skill Builders contain study skills advice. To increase your chance for success in the course, read these study tips, and answer the questions.

  Bigger Picture—Study Guide Outline provides you with a study guide outline of the course, with examples.

  Practice Final provides you with a Practice Final Exam to help you prepare for a final. The video solutions to each question are provided in the Interactive DVD Lecture Series and within MyMathLab®.
- *Resources to Check Your Work.* The **Answers to Selected Exercises** section provides answers to all odd-numbered section exercises and all chapter test exercises.

Helpful Hint

MyMathLab® and **MathXL®**

- Use the **Help Me Solve This** button to get step-by-step help for the exercise you are working. You will need to work an additional exercise of the same type before you can get credit for having worked it correctly.
- Use the **Video** button to view a video clip of the author working a similar exercise.

Objective D Getting Help

If you have trouble completing assignments or understanding the mathematics, get help as soon as you need it! This tip is presented as an objective on its own because it is so important. In mathematics, usually the material presented in one section builds on your understanding of the previous section. This means that if you don't understand the concepts covered during a class period, there is a good chance that you will not understand the concepts covered during the next class period. If this happens to you, get help as soon as you can.

Where can you get help? Many suggestions have been made in this section on where to get help, and now it is up to you to get it. Try your instructor, a tutoring center, or a math lab, or you may want to form a study group with fellow classmates. If you do decide to see your instructor or go to a tutoring center, make sure that you have a neat notebook and are ready with your questions.

Helpful Hint

MyMathLab® and **MathXL®**

Review your written work for previous assignments. Then, go back and re-work previous assignments. Open a previous assignment, and click **Similar Exercise** to generate new exercises. Re-work the exercises until you fully understand them and can work them without help features.

Objective E Preparing for and Taking an Exam

Make sure that you allow yourself plenty of time to prepare for a test. If you think that you are a little "math anxious," it may be that you are not preparing for a test in a way that will ensure success. The way that you prepare for a test in mathematics is important. To prepare for a test:

1. Review your previous homework assignments.
2. Review any notes from class and section-level quizzes you have taken. (If this is a final exam, also review chapter tests you have taken.)
3. Review concepts and definitions by reading the Chapter Highlights at the end of each chapter.
4. Practice working out exercises by completing the Chapter Review found at the end of each chapter. (If this is a final exam, go through a Cumulative Review. There is one found at the end of each chapter except Chapter 1. Choose the review found at the end of the latest chapter that you have covered in your course.) *Don't stop here!*

5. It is important that you place yourself in conditions similar to test conditions to find out how you will perform. In other words, as soon as you feel that you know the material, get a few blank sheets of paper and take a sample test. There is a Chapter Test available at the end of each chapter, or you can work selected problems from the Chapter Review. Your instructor may also provide you with a review sheet. During this sample test, do not use your notes or your textbook. Then check your sample test. If you are not satisfied with the results, study the areas that you are weak in and try again.
6. On the day of the test, allow yourself plenty of time to arrive at where you will be taking your exam.

When taking your test:

1. Read the directions on the test carefully.
2. Read each problem carefully as you take the test. Make sure that you answer the question asked.
3. Watch your time and pace yourself so that you can attempt each problem on your test.
4. If you have time, check your work and answers.
5. Do not turn your test in early. If you have extra time, spend it double-checking your work.

Objective F Managing Your Time

As a college student, you know the demands that classes, homework, work, and family place on your time. Some days you probably wonder how you'll ever get everything done. One key to managing your time is developing a schedule. Here are some hints for making a schedule:

1. Make a list of all of your weekly commitments for the term. Include classes, work, regular meetings, extracurricular activities, etc. You may also find it helpful to list such things as laundry, regular workouts, grocery shopping, etc.
2. Next, estimate the time needed for each item on the list. Also make a note of how often you will need to do each item. Don't forget to include time estimates for the reading, studying, and homework you do outside of your classes. You may want to ask your instructor for help estimating the time needed.
3. In the exercise set that follows, you are asked to block out a typical week on the schedule grid given. Start with items with fixed time slots like classes and work.
4. Next, include the items on your list with flexible time slots. Think carefully about how best to schedule items such as study time.
5. Don't fill up every time slot on the schedule. Remember that you need to allow time for eating, sleeping, and relaxing! You should also allow a little extra time in case some items take longer than planned.
6. If you find that your weekly schedule is too full for you to handle, you may need to make some changes in your workload, classload, or in other areas of your life. You may want to talk to your advisor, manager or supervisor at work, or someone in your college's academic counseling center for help with such decisions.

1.1 Exercise Set

FOR EXTRA HELP

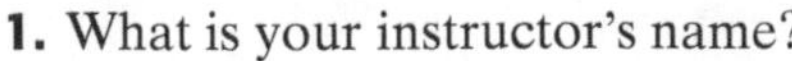

MyMathLab® | Math XP PRACTICE | WATCH | DOWNLOAD | READ | REVIEW

1. What is your instructor's name?

2. What are your instructor's office location and office hours?

3. What is the best way to contact your instructor?

4. Do you have the name and contact information of at least one other student in class?

5. Will your instructor allow you to use a calculator in this class?

6. Why is it important that you write step-by-step solutions to homework exercises and keep a hard copy of all work submitted?

7. Is there a tutoring service available on campus? If so, what are its hours? What services are available?

8. Have you attempted this course before? If so, write down ways that you might improve your chances of success during this second attempt.

9. List some steps that you can take if you begin having trouble understanding the material or completing an assignment. If you are completing your homework in MyMathLab® and MathXL®, list the resources you can use for help.

10. How many hours of studying does your instructor advise for each hour of instruction?

11. What does the ✎ icon in this text mean?

12. What does the 📱 icon in this text mean?

13. What does the △ icon in this text mean?

14. Search the minor columns in your text. What are Practice exercises?

15. When might be the best time to work a Practice exercise?

16. Where are the answers to Practice exercises?

17. What answers are contained in this text and where are they?

18. What and where are the study skills builders?

19. What and where are Integrated Reviews?

20. How many times is it suggested that you work through the homework exercises in MathXL® before the submission deadline?

21. How far in advance of the assigned due date is it suggested that homework be submitted online? Why?

22. Chapter Highlights are found at the end of each chapter. Find the Chapter 1 Highlights and explain how you might use it and how it might be helpful.

23. Chapter Reviews are found at the end of each chapter. Find the Chapter 1 Review and explain how you might use it and how it might be useful.

24. Chapter Tests are found at the end of each chapter. Find the Chapter 1 Test and explain how you might use it and how it might be helpful when preparing for an exam on Chapter 1. Include how the Chapter Test Prep Videos may help. If you are working in MyMathLab® and MathXL®, how can you use previous homework assignments to study?

25. Read or reread objective **F** and fill out the schedule grid on the next page.

	Monday	Tuesday	Wednesday	Thursday	Friday	Saturday	Sunday
4:00 a.m.							
5:00 a.m.							
6:00 a.m.							
7:00 a.m.							
8:00 a.m.							
9:00 a.m.							
10:00 a.m.							
11:00 a.m.							
12:00 p.m.							
1:00 p.m.							
2:00 p.m.							
3:00 p.m.							
4:00 p.m.							
5:00 p.m.							
6:00 p.m.							
7:00 p.m.							
8:00 p.m.							
9:00 p.m.							
10:00 p.m.							
11:00 p.m.							
Midnight							
1:00 a.m.							
2:00 a.m.							
3:00 a.m.							

Objectives

A **Define the Meaning of the Symbols =, ≠, <, >, ≤, and ≥.**

B **Translate Sentences into Mathematical Statements.**

C **Identify Integers, Rational Numbers, Irrational Numbers, and Real Numbers.**

D **Find the Absolute Value of a Real Number.**

1.2 SYMBOLS AND SETS OF NUMBERS

We begin with a review of the set of natural numbers and the set of whole numbers and how we use symbols to compare these numbers. A **set** is a collection of objects, each of which is called a **member** or **element** of the set. A pair of brace symbols { } encloses the list of elements and is translated as "the set of" or "the set containing."

Natural Numbers

$\{1, 2, 3, 4, 5, 6, \ldots\}$

Whole Numbers

$\{0, 1, 2, 3, 4, 5, 6, \ldots\}$

Helpful Hint

The three dots (an ellipsis) at the end of the list of elements of a set means that the list continues in the same manner indefinitely.

Objective A Equality and Inequality Symbols

Picturing natural numbers and whole numbers on a number line helps us to see the order of the numbers. Symbols can be used to describe in writing the order of two quantities. We will use equality symbols and inequality symbols to compare quantities.

Below is a review of these symbols. The letters *a* and *b* are used to represent quantities. Letters such as *a* and *b* that are used to represent numbers or quantities are called **variables.**

Equality and Inequality Symbols

		Meaning
Equality symbol:	$a = b$	*a* is equal to *b*.
Inequality symbols:	$a \neq b$	*a* is not equal to *b*.
	$a < b$	*a* is less than *b*.
	$a > b$	*a* is greater than *b*.
	$a \leq b$	*a* is less than or equal to *b*.
	$a \geq b$	*a* is greater than or equal to *b*.

These symbols may be used to form **mathematical statements** such as

$2 = 2$ and $2 \neq 6$

Recall that on a number line, we see that a number **to the right of** another number is **larger.** Similarly, a number **to the left of** another number is **smaller.** For example, 3 is to the left of 5 on the number line, which means that 3 is less than 5, or $3 < 5$. Similarly, 2 is to the right of 0 on the number line, which means that 2 is greater than 0, or $2 > 0$. Since 0 is to the left of 2, we can also say that 0 is less than 2, or $0 < 2$.

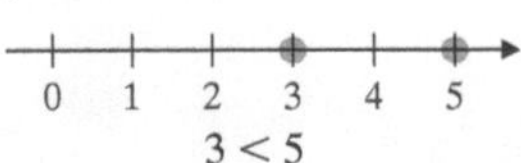

$3 < 5$

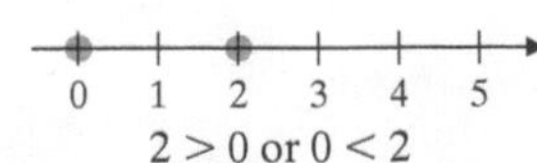

$2 > 0$ or $0 < 2$

Helpful Hint

Recall that $2 > 0$ has exactly the same meaning as $0 < 2$. Switching the order of the numbers and reversing the direction of the inequality symbol does not change the meaning of the statement.

$6 > 4$ has the same meaning as $4 < 6$.

Also notice that when the statement is true, the inequality arrow points to the smaller number.

Our discussion above can be generalized in the order property below.

Order Property for Real Numbers

For any two real numbers a and b, a is less than b if a is to the left of b on a number line.

$a < b$ or also $b > a$

Examples Determine whether each statement is true or false.

1. $2 < 3$ True. Since 2 is to the left of 3 on a number line
2. $72 < 27$ False. 72 is to the right of 27 on a number line, so $72 > 27$.
3. $8 \geq 8$ True. Since $8 = 8$ is true
4. $8 \leq 8$ True. Since $8 = 8$ is true
5. $23 \leq 0$ False. Since neither $23 < 0$ nor $23 = 0$ is true
6. $0 \leq 23$ True. Since $0 < 23$ is true

Work Practice 1–6

PRACTICE 1–6

Determine whether each statement is true or false.

1. $8 < 6$
2. $100 > 10$
3. $21 \leq 21$
4. $21 \geq 21$
5. $0 \geq 5$
6. $25 \geq 22$

Helpful Hint

If either $3 < 3$ or $3 = 3$ is true, then $3 \leq 3$ is true.

Objective B Translating Sentences into Mathematical Statements

Now, let's use the symbols discussed above to translate sentences into mathematical statements.

Example 7 Translate each sentence into a mathematical statement.

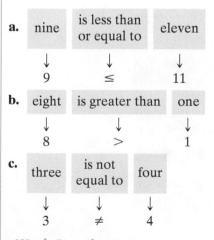

a. Nine is less than or equal to eleven.
b. Eight is greater than one.
c. Three is not equal to four.

Solution:

a. nine → 9; is less than or equal to → $\leq$; eleven → 11

b. eight → 8; is greater than → $>$; one → 1

c. three → 3; is not equal to → $\neq$; four → 4

Work Practice 7

PRACTICE 7

Translate each sentence into a mathematical statement.

a. Fourteen is greater than or equal to fourteen.
b. Zero is less than five.
c. Nine is not equal to ten.

Answers

1. false 2. true 3. true 4. true 5. false 6. true 7. a. $14 \geq 14$ b. $0 < 5$ c. $9 \neq 10$

Objective C Identifying Common Sets of Numbers

Whole numbers are not sufficient to describe many situations in the real world. For example, quantities smaller than zero must sometimes be represented, such as temperatures less than 0 degrees.

Recall that we can place numbers less than zero on a number line as follows: Numbers less than 0 are to the left of 0 and are labeled −1, −2, −3, and so on. The numbers we have labeled on the number line below are called the set of **integers.**

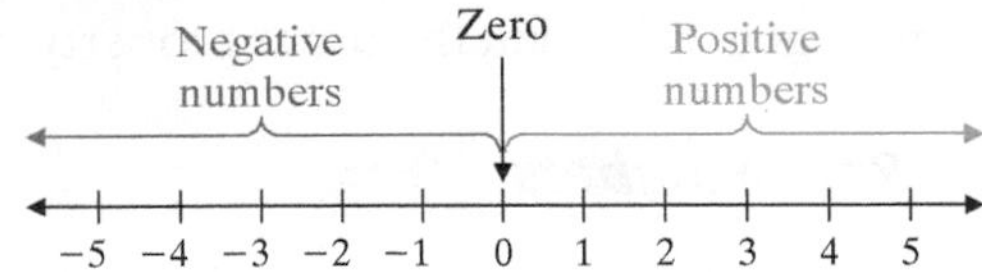

Integers to the left of 0 are called **negative integers;** integers to the right of 0 are called **positive integers.** The integer 0 is neither positive nor negative.

> ***Integers***
>
> $\{\ldots, -3, -2, -1, 0, 1, 2, 3, \ldots\}$

Helpful Hint

A − sign, such as the one in −2, tells us that the number is to the left of 0 on a number line.

−2 is read "negative two."

A + sign or no sign tells us that the number lies to the right of 0 on a number line. For example, 3 and +3 both mean positive three.

PRACTICE 8

Use an integer to express the number in the following. The elevation of New Orleans, Louisiana, is an average of 8 feet below sea level. (*Source: The World Almanac*)

Answer

8. −8

Example 8 Use an integer to express the number in the following. "The lowest temperature ever recorded at South Pole Station, Antarctica, occurred during the month of June. The record-low temperature was 117 degrees below zero." (*Source:* The National Oceanic and Atmospheric Administration)

Solution: The integer −117 represents 117 degrees below zero.

Work Practice 8

A problem with integers in real-life settings arises when quantities are smaller than some integer but greater than the next smallest integer. On a number line, these quantities may be visualized by points between integers. Some of these quantities between integers can be represented as a quotient of integers. For example,

The point on the number line halfway between 0 and 1 can be represented by $\frac{1}{2}$, a quotient of integers.

The point on the number line halfway between 0 and -1 can be represented by $-\frac{1}{2}$. Other quotients of integers and their graphs are shown below.

$-\frac{7}{4}$ $-\frac{1}{2}$ $\frac{1}{2}$ $\frac{4}{3}$ $\frac{5}{2}$

-5 -4 -3 -2 -1 0 1 2 3 4 5

These numbers, each of which can be represented as a quotient of integers, are examples of **rational numbers.** It's not possible to list the set of rational numbers using the notation that we have been using. For this reason, we will use a different notation.

Rational Numbers

$$\left\{ \frac{a}{b} \middle| \, a \text{ and } b \text{ are integers and } b \neq 0 \right\}$$

We read this set as "the set of numbers $\frac{a}{b}$ such that a and b are integers and **b is not equal to 0.**"

Helpful Hint

We commonly refer to rational numbers as fractions.

Notice that every integer is also a rational number since each integer can be written as a quotient of integers. For example, the integer 5 is also a rational number since $5 = \frac{5}{1}$. For the rational number $\frac{5}{1}$, recall that the top number, 5, is called the numerator and the bottom number, 1, is called the denominator.

Let's practice **graphing** numbers on a number line.

Example 9 Graph the numbers on a number line.

$$-\frac{4}{3}, \ \frac{1}{4}, \ \frac{3}{2}, \ -2\frac{1}{8}, \ 3.5$$

Solution: To help graph the improper fractions in the list, we first write them as mixed numbers.

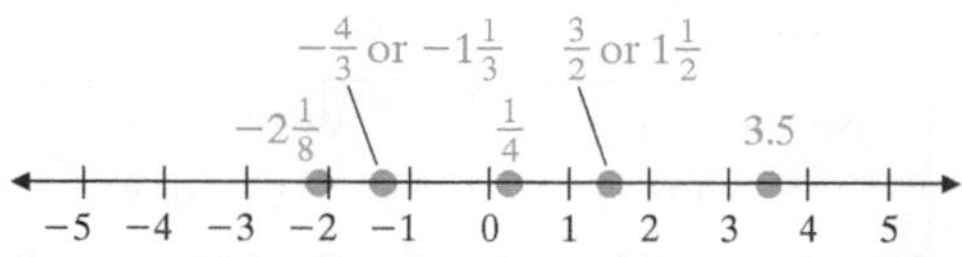

Work Practice 9

PRACTICE 9

Graph the numbers on the number line.

$$-2\frac{1}{2}, \ -\frac{2}{3}, \ \frac{1}{5}, \ \frac{5}{4}, \ 2.25$$

-5 -4 -3 -2 -1 0 1 2 3 4 5

Every rational number has a point on the number line that corresponds to it. But not every point on the number line corresponds to a rational number. Those points that do not correspond to rational numbers correspond instead to **irrational numbers.**

Answer

9.

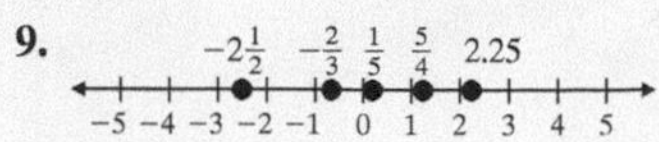

Irrational Numbers

{Nonrational numbers that correspond to points on a number line}

An irrational number that you have probably seen is π. Also, $\sqrt{2}$, the length of the diagonal of the square shown below, is an irrational number.

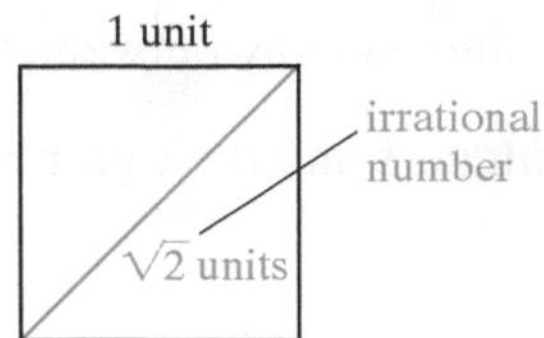

Both rational and irrational numbers can be written as decimal numbers. The decimal equivalent of a rational number will either terminate or repeat in a pattern. For example, upon dividing we find that

$$\frac{3}{4} = 0.75 \qquad \text{(Decimal number terminates or ends.)}$$

$$\frac{2}{3} = 0.66666\ldots \qquad \text{(Decimal number repeats in a pattern.)}$$

The decimal representation of an irrational number will neither terminate nor repeat. (For further review of decimals, see Section R.3.)

The set of numbers, each of which corresponds to a point on a number line, is called the set of **real numbers.** One and only one point on a number line corresponds to each real number.

Real Numbers

{All numbers that correspond to points on a number line}

Several different sets of numbers have been discussed in this section. The following diagram shows the relationships among these sets of real numbers. Notice that, together, the rational numbers and the irrational numbers make up the real numbers.

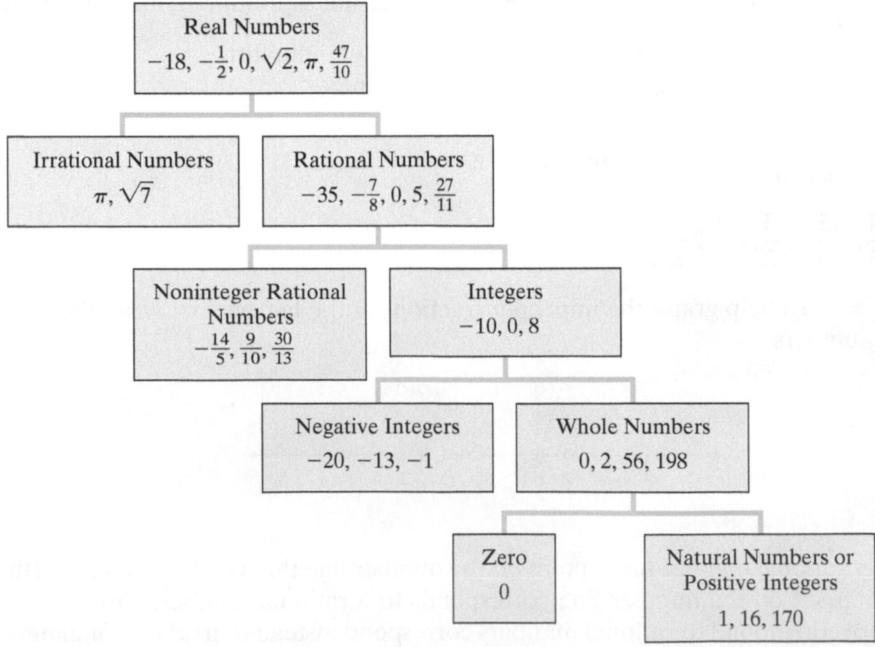

Now that other sets of numbers have been reviewed, let's continue our practice of comparing numbers.

Example 10 Insert <, >, or = between the pairs of numbers to form true statements.

a. −5   −6   **b.** 3.195   3.2   **c.** $\frac{1}{4}$ $\frac{1}{3}$

Solution:

a. $-5 > -6$ since −5 lies to the right of −6 on a number line.

b. By comparing digits in the same place values, we find that $3.195 < 3.2$, since $0.1 < 0.2$.

c. By dividing, we find that $\frac{1}{4} = 0.25$ and $\frac{1}{3} = 0.33\ldots$. Since $0.25 < 0.33\ldots$, $\frac{1}{4} < \frac{1}{3}$.

Work Practice 10

PRACTICE 10

Insert <, >, or = between the pairs of numbers to form true statements.

a. −11   −9

b. 4.511   4.151

c. $\frac{7}{8}$ $\frac{2}{3}$

Example 11 Given the set $\{-2, 0, \frac{1}{4}, 112, -3, 11, \sqrt{2}\}$, list the numbers in this set that belong to the set of:

a. Natural numbers   **b.** Whole numbers   **c.** Integers
d. Rational numbers   **e.** Irrational numbers   **f.** Real numbers

Solution:

a. The natural numbers are 11 and 112.

b. The whole numbers are 0, 11, and 112.

c. The integers are −3, −2, 0, 11, and 112.

d. Recall that integers are rational numbers also. The rational numbers are $-3, -2, 0, \frac{1}{4}$, 11, and 112.

e. The only irrational number is $\sqrt{2}$.

f. All numbers in the given set are real numbers.

Work Practice 11

PRACTICE 11

Given the set $\{-100, -\frac{2}{5}, 0, \pi, 6, 913\}$, list the numbers in this set that belong to the set of:

a. Natural numbers

b. Whole numbers

c. Integers

d. Rational numbers

e. Irrational numbers

f. Real numbers

Objective D Finding the Absolute Value of a Number

The number line not only gives us a picture of the real numbers, it also helps us visualize the distance between numbers. The distance between a real number a and 0 is given a special name called the **absolute value** of a. "The absolute value of a" is written in symbols as $|a|$.

Absolute Value

The **absolute value** of a real number a, denoted by $|a|$, is the distance between a and 0 on a number line.

Helpful Hint Since $|a|$ is a distance, $|a|$ is always either positive or 0. It is never negative. That is, **for any real number a, $|a| \geq 0$.**

For example, $|3| = 3$ and $|-3| = 3$ since both 3 and −3 are a distance of 3 units from 0 on the number line.

3 units   3 units

−5 −4 −3 −2 −1 0 1 2 3 4 5

Answers

10. a. < **b.** > **c.** >
11. a. 6, 913 **b.** 0, 6, 913 **c.** −100, 0, 6, 913 **d.** $-100, -\frac{2}{5}, 0, 6, 913$ **e.** π **f.** all numbers in the given set

PRACTICE 12

Find the absolute value of each number.

a. $|7|$ **b.** $|-8|$ **c.** $\left|\frac{2}{3}\right|$
d. $|0|$ **e.** $|-3.06|$

Example 12 Find the absolute value of each number.

a. $|4|$ **b.** $|-5|$ **c.** $|0|$
d. $\left|-\frac{2}{9}\right|$ **e.** $|4.93|$

Solution:

a. $|4| = 4$ since 4 is 4 units from 0 on the number line.
b. $|-5| = 5$ since -5 is 5 units from 0 on the number line.
c. $|0| = 0$ since 0 is 0 units from 0 on the number line.
d. $\left|-\frac{2}{9}\right| = \frac{2}{9}$
e. $|4.93| = 4.93$

Work Practice 12

PRACTICE 13

Insert <, >, or = in the appropriate space to make each statement true.

a. $|-4|$ 4
b. -3 $|0|$
c. $|-2.7|$ $|-2|$
d. $|-6|$ $|-16|$
e. $|10|$ $\left|-10\frac{1}{3}\right|$

Example 13 Insert <, >, or = in the appropriate space to make each statement true.

a. $|0|$ 2 **b.** $|-5|$ 5 **c.** $|-3|$ $|-2|$
d. $|-9|$ $|-9.7|$ **e.** $\left|-7\frac{1}{6}\right|$ $|7|$

Solution:

a. $|0| < 2$ since $|0| = 0$ and $0 < 2$.
b. $|-5| = 5$.
c. $|-3| > |-2|$ since $3 > 2$.
d. $|-9| < |-9.7|$ since $9 < 9.7$.
e. $\left|-7\frac{1}{6}\right| > |7|$ since $7\frac{1}{6} > 7$.

Work Practice 13

Answers
12. a. 7 **b.** 8 **c.** $\frac{2}{3}$ **d.** 0 **e.** 3.06
13. a. = **b.** < **c.** > **d.** < **e.** <

Vocabulary and Readiness Check

Use the choices below to fill in each blank. Not all choices will be used.

real	natural	absolute value	$\frac{1}{2}$	$\frac{1}{4}$	$\lvert a \rvert$	whole
rational	inequality	integers	0	1	$\lvert -1 \rvert$	

1. The ____________ numbers are $\{0, 1, 2, 3, 4, \ldots\}$.
2. The ____________ numbers are $\{1, 2, 3, 4, 5, \ldots\}$.
3. The symbols $\neq, \leq$, and $>$ are called ____________ symbols.
4. The ____________ are $\{\ldots, -3, -2, -1, 0, 1, 2, 3, \ldots\}$.
5. The ____________ numbers are {all numbers that correspond to points on a number line}.
6. The ____________ numbers are $\left\{\frac{a}{b} \middle| a \text{ and } b \text{ are integers}, b \neq 0\right\}$.
7. The integer ____________ is neither positive nor negative.
8. The point on the number line halfway between 0 and $\frac{1}{2}$ can be represented by____________.
9. The distance between a real number a and 0 is called the ____________ of a.
10. The absolute value of a is written in symbols as ____________.

1.2 Exercise Set

Objectives **A** **C** **Mixed Practice** *Insert $<$, $>$, or $=$ in the space between the paired numbers to make each statement true. See Examples 1 through 6 and 10.*

1. 4 10

2. 8 5

3. 7 3

4. 9 15

5. 6.26 6.26

6. 1.13 1.13

7. 0 7

8. 20 0

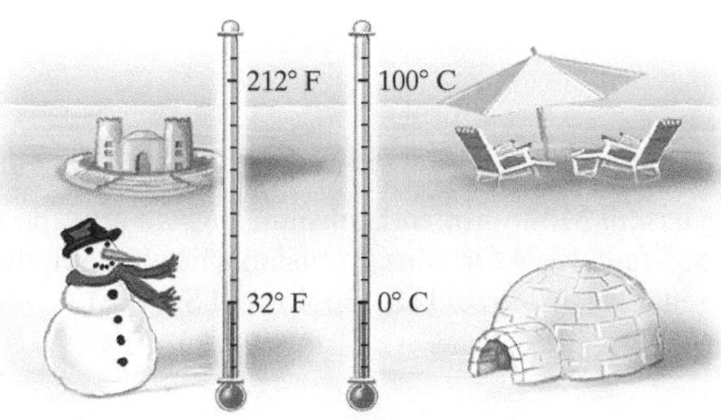

9. The freezing point of water is 32° Fahrenheit. The boiling point of water is 212° Fahrenheit. Write an inequality statement using $<$ or $>$ comparing the numbers 32 and 212.

10. The freezing point of water is 0° Celsius. The boiling point of water is 100° Celsius. Write an inequality statement using $<$ or $>$ comparing the numbers 0 and 100.

△ **11.** An angle measuring 30° and an angle measuring 45° are shown. Write an inequality statement using $\leq$ or $\geq$ comparing the numbers 30 and 45.

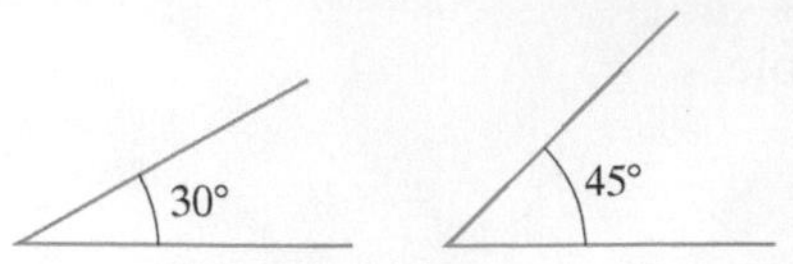

△ **12.** The sum of the measures of the angles of a parallelogram is 360°. The sum of the measures of the angles of a triangle is 180°. Write an inequality statement using $\leq$ or $\geq$ comparing the numbers 360 and 180.

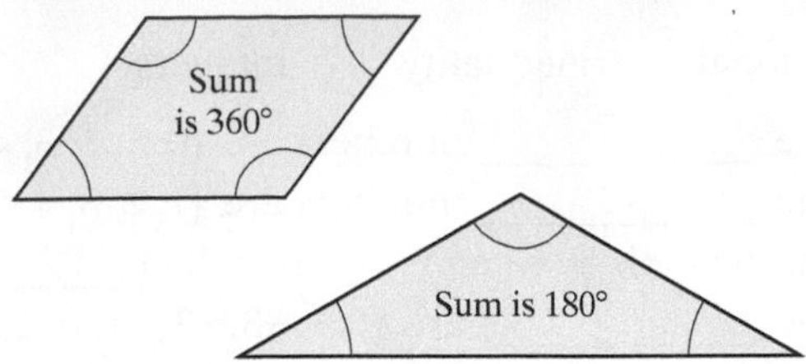

Determine whether each statement is true or false. See Examples 1 through 6 and 10.

13. $11 \leq 11$ **14.** $8 \geq 9$ **15.** $-11 > -10$ **16.** $-16 > -17$

17. $5.092 < 5.902$ **18.** $1.02 > 1.021$ **19.** $\frac{9}{10} \leq \frac{8}{9}$ **20.** $\frac{4}{5} \leq \frac{9}{11}$

Rewrite each inequality so that the inequality symbol points in the opposite direction and the resulting statement has the same meaning as the given one. See Examples 1 through 6 and 10.

21. $25 \geq 20$ **22.** $-13 \leq 13$ **23.** $0 < 6$

24. $5 > 3$ **25.** $-10 > -12$ **26.** $-4 < -2$

Objectives B C **Mixed Practice–Translating** *Write each sentence as a mathematical statement. See Examples 7 and 10.*

27. Seven is less than eleven.

28. Twenty is greater than two.

29. Five is greater than or equal to four.

30. Negative ten is less than or equal to thirty-seven.

31. Fifteen is not equal to negative two.

32. Negative seven is not equal to seven.

Use integers to represent the values in each statement. See Example 8.

33. The highest elevation in California is Mt. Whitney, with an altitude of 14,494 feet. The lowest elevation in California is Death Valley, with an altitude of 282 feet below sea level. (*Source:* U.S. Geological Survey)

34. Driskill Mountain, in Louisiana, has an altitude of 535 feet. New Orleans, Louisiana, lies 8 feet below sea level. (*Source:* U.S. Geological Survey)

35. The number of graduate students at the University of Texas at Austin is 28,000 fewer than the number of undergraduate students. (*Source:* University of Texas at Austin)

36. The number of students admitted to the class of 2011 at UCLA is 38,792 fewer students than the number that had applied. (*Source:* UCLA)

37. Gretchen Bertani deposited \$475 in her savings account. She later withdrew \$195.

38. David Lopez was deep-sea diving. During his dive, he ascended 17 feet and later descended 15 feet.

Graph each set of numbers on the number line. See Example 9.

39. $-4, 0, 2, -2$

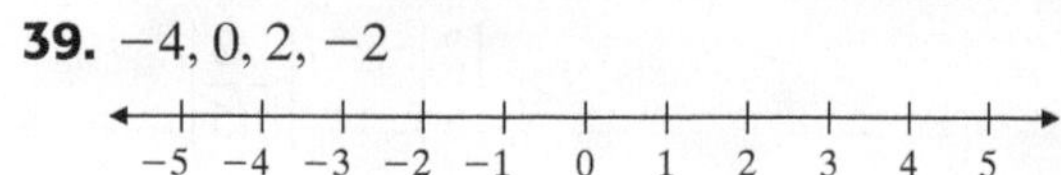

40. $-3, 0, 1, -5$

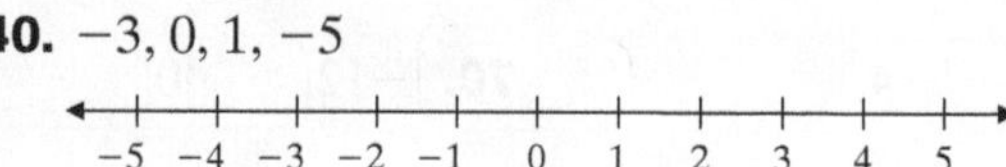

41. $-2, 4, \frac{1}{3}, -\frac{1}{4}$

42. $-5, 3, -\frac{1}{3}, \frac{7}{8}$

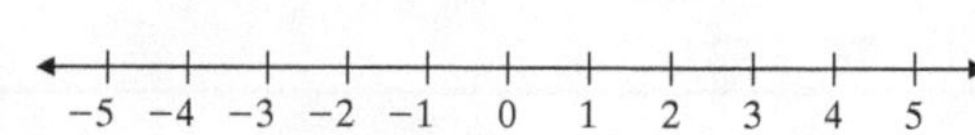

43. $-4.5, \frac{7}{4}, 3.25, -\frac{3}{2}$

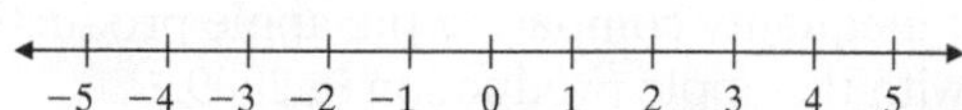

44. $4.5, -\frac{9}{4}, 1.75, -\frac{7}{2}$

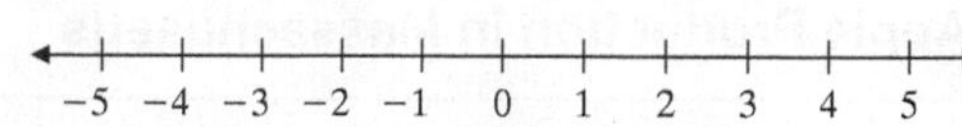

Tell which set or sets each number belongs to: natural numbers, whole numbers, integers, rational numbers, irrational numbers, or real numbers. See Example 11.

45. 0

46. $\frac{1}{4}$

47. -7

48. $-\frac{1}{7}$

49. 265

50. 7941

51. $\frac{2}{3}$

52. $\sqrt{3}$

Determine whether each statement is true or false.

53. Every rational number is also an integer.

54. Every natural number is positive.

55. 0 is a real number.

56. $\frac{1}{2}$ is an integer.

57. Every negative number is also a rational number.

58. Every rational number is also a real number.

59. Every real number is also a rational number.

60. Every whole number is an integer.

Objective **D** *Find each absolute value. See Example 12.*

61. $|8.9|$

62. $|11.2|$

63. $|-20|$

64. $|-17|$

65. $\left|\frac{9}{2}\right|$

66. $\left|\frac{10}{7}\right|$

67. $\left|-\frac{12}{13}\right|$

68. $\left|-\frac{1}{15}\right|$

Insert <, >, or = in the appropriate space to make each statement true. See Examples 12 and 13.

69. $|-5| \quad -4$

70. $|-12| \quad |0|$

71. $\left|-\frac{5}{8}\right| \quad \left|\frac{5}{8}\right|$

72. $\left|\frac{2}{5}\right| \quad \left|-\frac{2}{5}\right|$

73. $|-2| \quad |-2.7|$

74. $|-5.01| \quad |-5|$

75. $|0| \quad |-8|$

76. $|-12| \quad \frac{-24}{2}$

Concept Extensions

The graph below is called a bar graph. This graph shows apple production in Massachusetts from 2003 through 2009. Each bar represents a different year, and the height of each bar represents the apple production for that year in thousands of bushels. (The federal standard for bushel is 48 lb, although 42 lb is also commonly used.)

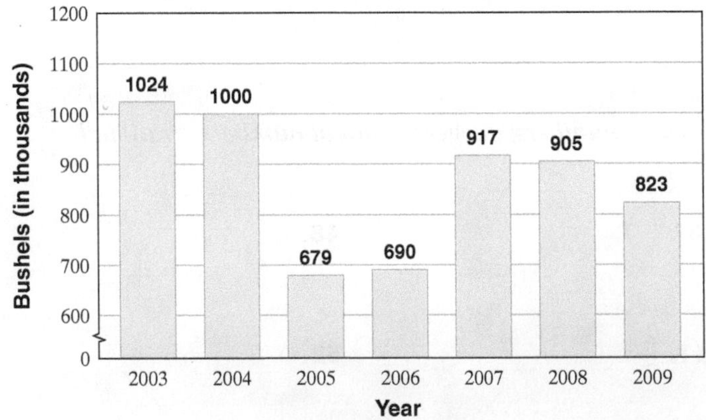

(*Note:* The ⸗ symbol means that some numbers are missing. Along the vertical data line, notice the numbers between 0 and 600 are missing or not shown.) (*Source:* New England Agriculture Statistical Service and Agricultural Statistics Board.)

77. Write an inequality comparing the apple production in 2008 with the apple production in 2009.

78. Write an inequality comparing the apple production in 2006 with the apple production in 2007.

79. Determine the change in apple production between 2003 and 2004.

80. According to the bar graph, which year shown produced the largest crop?

The bar graph shows cranberry production from the top five cranberry-producing states. (Source: National Agricultural Statistics Service)

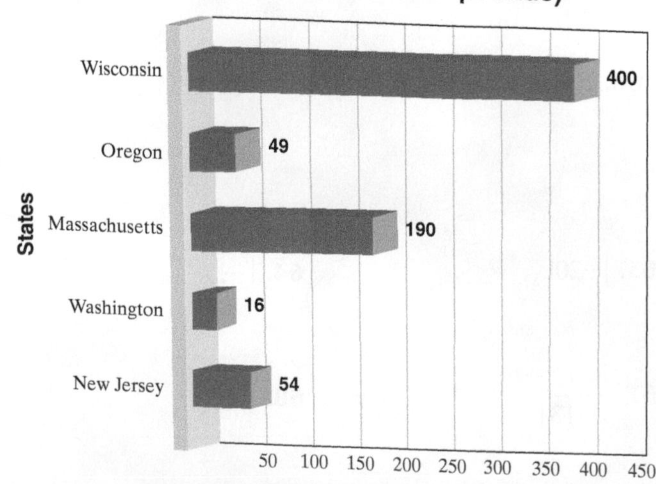

Source: National Agricultural Statistics Service

81. Write an inequality comparing the 2009 cranberry production in Oregon with the 2009 cranberry production in Washington.

82. Write an inequality comparing the 2009 cranberry production in Massachusetts with the 2009 cranberry production in Wisconsin.

83. Determine the difference between the 2009 cranberry production in Washington and the 2009 cranberry production in New Jersey.

84. According to the bar graph, which two states had almost equal 2009 cranberry crops?

The apparent magnitude of a star is the measure of its brightness as seen by someone on Earth. The smaller the apparent magnitude, the brighter the star. Below, the apparent magnitudes of some stars are listed. Use this table to answer Exercises 85 through 90.

Star	Apparent Magnitude	Star	Apparent Magnitude
Arcturus	−0.04	Spica	0.98
Sirius	−1.46	Rigel	0.12
Vega	0.03	Regulus	1.35
Antares	0.96	Canopus	−0.72
Sun	−26.7	Hadar	0.61

(*Source: Norton's 2000.0: Star Atlas and Reference Handbook,* 18th ed., Longman Group, UK, 1989)

85. The apparent magnitude of the sun is −26.7. The apparent magnitude of the star Arcturus is −0.04. Write an inequality statement comparing the numbers −0.04 and−26.7.

86. The apparent magnitude of Antares is 0.96. The apparent magnitude of Spica is 0.98. Write an inequality statement comparing the numbers 0.96 and 0.98.

87. Which is brighter, the sun or Arcturus?

88. Which is dimmer, Antares or Spica?

89. Which star listed is the brightest?

90. Which star listed is the dimmest?

91. In your own words, explain how to find the absolute value of a number.

92. Give an example of a real-life situation that can be described with integers but not with whole numbers.

Objectives

A Define and Use Exponents and the Order of Operations.

B Evaluate Algebraic Expressions, Given Replacement Values for Variables.

C Determine Whether a Number Is a Solution of a Given Equation.

D Translate Phrases into Expressions and Sentences into Equations.

1.3 EXPONENTS, ORDER OF OPERATIONS, AND VARIABLE EXPRESSIONS

Objective A Exponents and the Order of Operations

Frequently in algebra, products occur that contain repeated multiplication of the same factor. For example, the volume of a cube whose sides each measure 2 centimeters is $(2 \cdot 2 \cdot 2)$ cubic centimeters. We may use **exponential notation** to write such products in a more compact form. For example,

$2 \cdot 2 \cdot 2$ may be written as 2^3.

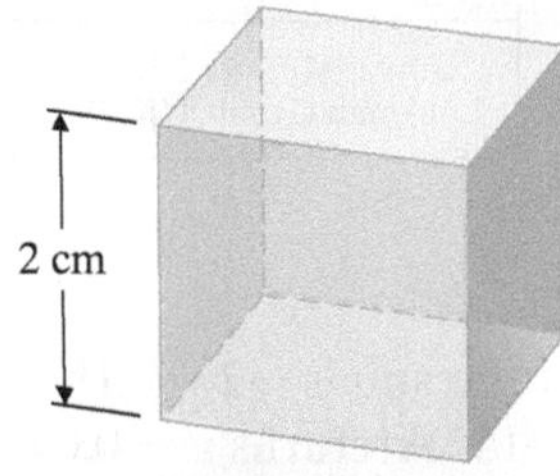

Volume is $(2 \cdot 2 \cdot 2)$ cubic centimeters.

The 2 in 2^3 is called the **base;** it is the repeated factor. The 3 in 2^3 is called the **exponent** and is the number of times the base is used as a factor. The expression 2^3 is called an **exponential expression.**

exponent

$2^3 = 2 \cdot 2 \cdot 2 = 8$

base — 2 is a factor 3 times.

PRACTICE 1

Evaluate each expression.

a. 4^2
b. 2^2
c. 3^4
d. 9^1
e. $\left(\frac{2}{5}\right)^3$
f. $(0.8)^2$

Helpful Hint

$2^3 \neq 2 \cdot 3$ since 2^3 indicates **repeated multiplication of the same factor.**

$2^3 = 2 \cdot 2 \cdot 2 = 8,$

whereas $2 \cdot 3 = 6$

Example 1 Evaluate (find the value of) each expression.

a. 3^2 [read as "3 squared" or as "3 to the second power"]
b. 5^3 [read as "5 cubed" or as "5 to the third power"]
c. 2^4 [read as "2 to the fourth power"]
d. 7^1
e. $\left(\frac{3}{7}\right)^2$
f. $(0.6)^2$

Solution:

a. $3^2 = 3 \cdot 3 = 9$
b. $5^3 = 5 \cdot 5 \cdot 5 = 125$
c. $2^4 = 2 \cdot 2 \cdot 2 \cdot 2 = 16$
d. $7^1 = 7$
e. $\left(\frac{3}{7}\right)^2 = \left(\frac{3}{7}\right)\left(\frac{3}{7}\right) = \frac{3 \cdot 3}{7 \cdot 7} = \frac{9}{49}$
f. $(0.6)^2 = (0.6)(0.6) = 0.36$

Work Practice 1

Answers

1. a. 16 **b.** 4 **c.** 81 **d.** 9 **e.** $\frac{8}{125}$ **f.** 0.64

Using symbols for mathematical operations is a great convenience. The more operation symbols presented in an expression, the more careful we must be when performing the indicated operation. For example, in the expression $2 + 3 \cdot 7$, do we add first or multiply first? To eliminate confusion, **grouping symbols** are used. Examples of grouping symbols are parentheses ( ), brackets [ ], braces { }, absolute value bars | |, and the fraction bar. If we wish $2 + 3 \cdot 7$ to be simplified by adding first, we enclose $2 + 3$ in parentheses.

$$(2 + 3) \cdot 7 = 5 \cdot 7 = 35$$

If we wish to multiply first, $3 \cdot 7$ may be enclosed in parentheses.

$$2 + (3 \cdot 7) = 2 + 21 = 23$$

To eliminate confusion when no grouping symbols are present, we use the following agreed-upon order of operations.

Order of Operations

1. Perform all operations within grouping symbols first, starting with the innermost set.
2. Evaluate exponential expressions.
3. Multiply or divide in order from left to right.
4. Add or subtract in order from left to right.

Using this order of operations, we now simplify $2 + 3 \cdot 7$. There are no grouping symbols and no exponents, so we multiply and then add.

$$2 + 3 \cdot 7 = 2 + 21 \quad \text{Multiply.}$$
$$= 23 \quad \text{Add.}$$

Examples Simplify each expression.

2. $6 \div 3 + 5^2 = 6 \div 3 + 25$ Evaluate 5^2
$= 2 + 25$ Divide.
$= 27$ Add.

3. $20 \div 5 \cdot 4 = 4 \cdot 4$
$= 16$

Helpful Hint Remember to multiply or divide in order from left to right.

4. $\frac{3}{2} \cdot \frac{1}{2} - \frac{1}{2} = \frac{3}{4} - \frac{1}{2}$ Multiply.
$= \frac{3}{4} - \frac{2}{4}$ The least common denominator is 4.
$= \frac{1}{4}$ Subtract.

5. $1 + 2[5(2 \cdot 3 + 1) - 10] = 1 + 2[5(7) - 10]$ Simplify the expression in the innermost set of parentheses. $2 \cdot 3 + 1 = 6 + 1 = 7$.
$= 1 + 2[35 - 10]$ Multiply 5 and 7.
$= 1 + 2[25]$ Subtract inside the brackets.
$= 1 + 50$ Multiply 2 and 25.
$= 51$ Add.

Work Practice 2–5

In the next example, the fraction bar serves as a grouping symbol and separates the numerator and denominator. Simplify each separately.

PRACTICE 2–5

Simplify each expression.

2. $3 \cdot 2 + 4^2$

3. $28 \div 7 \cdot 2$

4. $\frac{9}{5} \cdot \frac{1}{3} - \frac{1}{3}$

5. $5 + 3[2(3 \cdot 4 + 1) - 20]$

Answers

2. 22 **3.** 8 **4.** $\frac{4}{15}$ **5.** 23

PRACTICE 6

Simplify: $\dfrac{1 + |7 - 4| + 3^2}{8 - 5}$

Example 6 Simplify: $\dfrac{3 + |4 - 3| + 2^2}{6 - 3}$

Solution:

$$\frac{3 + |4 - 3| + 2^2}{6 - 3} = \frac{3 + |1| + 2^2}{6 - 3}$$ Simplify the expression inside the absolute value bars.

$$= \frac{3 + 1 + 2^2}{3}$$ Find the absolute value and simplify the denominator.

$$= \frac{3 + 1 + 4}{3}$$ Evaluate the exponential expression.

$$= \frac{8}{3}$$ Simplify the numerator.

Work Practice 6

Helpful Hint

Be careful when evaluating an exponential expression.

$3 \cdot 4^2 = 3 \cdot 16 = 48$ ↑ Base is 4.

$(3 \cdot 4)^2 = (12)^2 = 144$ ↑ Base is $3 \cdot 4$.

Objective B Evaluating Algebraic Expressions

Recall that letters used to represent quantities are called **variables.** An **algebraic expression** is a collection of numbers, variables, operation symbols, and grouping symbols. For example,

$$2x, \quad -3, \quad 2x - 10, \quad 5(p^2 + 1), \quad xy, \quad \text{and} \quad \frac{3y^2 - 6y + 1}{5}$$

are algebraic expressions.

Expressions	Meaning
$2x$	$2 \cdot x$
$5(p^2 + 1)$	$5 \cdot (p^2 + 1)$
$3y^2$	$3 \cdot y^2$
xy	$x \cdot y$

If we give a specific value to a variable, we can **evaluate an algebraic expression.** To evaluate an algebraic expression means to find its numerical value once we know the values of the variables.

Algebraic expressions are often used in problem solving. For example, the expression

$16t^2$

gives the distance in feet (neglecting air resistance) that an object will fall in t seconds.

Answer

6. $\dfrac{13}{3}$

Example 7 Evaluate each expression when $x = 3$ and $y = 2$.

a. $5x^2$ **b.** $2x - y$ **c.** $\frac{3x}{2y}$ **d.** $\frac{x}{y} + \frac{y}{2}$ **e.** $x^2 - y^2$

Solution:

a. Replace x with 3. Then simplify.

$5x^2 = 5 \cdot (3)^2 = 5 \cdot 9 = 45$

b. Replace x with 3 and y with 2. Then simplify.

$2x - y = 2(3) - 2$ Let $x = 3$ and $y = 2$.
$= 6 - 2$ Multiply.
$= 4$ Subtract.

c. Replace x with 3 and y with 2. Then simplify.

$\frac{3x}{2y} = \frac{3 \cdot 3}{2 \cdot 2} = \frac{9}{4}$ Let $x = 3$ and $y = 2$.

d. Replace x with 3 and y with 2. Then simplify.

$\frac{x}{y} + \frac{y}{2} = \frac{3}{2} + \frac{2}{2} = \frac{5}{2}$

e. Replace x with 3 and y with 2. Then simplify.

$x^2 - y^2 = 3^2 - 2^2 = 9 - 4 = 5$

Work Practice 7

PRACTICE 7

Evaluate each expression when $x = 1$ and $y = 4$.

a. $3y^2$

b. $2y - x$

c. $\frac{11x}{3y}$

d. $\frac{x}{y} + \frac{6}{y}$

e. $y^2 - x^2$

Objective C Solutions of Equations

Many times a problem-solving situation is modeled by an equation. An **equation** is a mathematical statement that two expressions have equal value. The equal symbol "=" is used to equate the two expressions. For example,

$3 + 2 = 5$, $7x = 35$, $\frac{2(x - 1)}{3} = 0$, and $I = PRT$ are all equations.

Helpful Hint

An equation contains the equal symbol "=". An algebraic expression does not.

✓Concept Check Which of the following are equations? Which are expressions?

a. $5x = 8$ **b.** $5x - 8$ **c.** $12y + 3x$ **d.** $12y = 3x$

When an equation contains a variable, deciding which value(s) of the variable make the equation a true statement is called **solving** the equation for the variable. A **solution** of an equation is a value for the variable that makes the equation a true statement. For example, 3 is a solution of the equation $x + 4 = 7$, because if x is replaced with 3 the statement is true.

$x + 4 = 7$
↓
$3 + 4 \stackrel{?}{=} 7$ Replace x with 3.
$7 = 7$ True

Similarly, 1 is not a solution of the equation $x + 4 = 7$, because $1 + 4 = 7$ is **not** a true statement.

Answers

7. a. 48 **b.** 7 **c.** $\frac{11}{12}$ **d.** $\frac{7}{4}$ **e.** 15

✓ Concept Check Answer

equations: **a, d**; expressions: **b, c**

PRACTICE 8

Decide whether 3 is a solution of $5x - 10 = x + 2$.

Example 8 Decide whether 2 is a solution of $3x + 10 = 8x$.

Solution: Replace x with 2 and see if a true statement results.

$3x + 10 = 8x$ Original equation

$3(2) + 10 \stackrel{?}{=} 8(2)$ Replace x with 2.

$6 + 10 \stackrel{?}{=} 16$ Simplify each side.

$16 = 16$ True

Since we arrived at a true statement after replacing x with 2 and simplifying both sides of the equation, 2 is a solution of the equation.

Work Practice 8

Objective D Translating Words to Symbols

Now that we know how to represent an unknown number by a variable, let's practice translating phrases into algebraic expressions (no "=" symbol) and sentences into equations (with "=" symbol). Oftentimes solving problems involves the ability to translate word phrases and sentences into symbols. Below is a list of key words and phrases to help us translate.

Helpful Hint

Order matters when subtracting and also dividing, so be especially careful with these translations.

Addition (+)	Subtraction (−)	Multiplication (·)	Division (÷)	Equality (=)
Sum	Difference of	Product	Quotient	Equals
Plus	Minus	Times	Divide	Gives
Added to	Subtracted from	Multiply	Into	Is/was/should be
More than	Less than	Twice	Ratio	Yields
Increased by	Decreased by	Of	Divided by	Amounts to
Total	Less			Represents
				Is the same as

PRACTICE 9

Write an algebraic expression that represents each phrase. Let the variable x represent the unknown number.

a. The product of 5 and a number
b. A number added to 7
c. A number divided by 11.2
d. A number subtracted from 8
e. Twice a number, plus 1

Example 9 Write an algebraic expression that represents each phrase. Let the variable x represent the unknown number.

a. The sum of a number and 3
b. The product of 3 and a number
c. The quotient of 7.3 and a number
d. 10 decreased by a number
e. 5 times a number, increased by 7

Solution:

a. $x + 3$ since "sum" means to add
b. $3 \cdot x$ and $3x$ are both ways to denote the product of 3 and x
c. $7.3 \div x$ or $\frac{7.3}{x}$
d. $10 - x$ because "decreased by" means to subtract
e. $\underbrace{5x}_{\text{5 times a number}} + 7$

Work Practice 9

Answers

8. It is a solution.
9. a. $5 \cdot x$ or $5x$. b. $7 + x$ c. $x \div 11.2$ or $\frac{x}{11.2}$ d. $8 - x$ e. $2x + 1$

Helpful Hint

Make sure you understand the difference when translating phrases containing "decreased by," "subtracted from," and "less than."

Phrase	Translation	
A number decreased by 10	$x - 10$	Notice the order.
A number subtracted from 10	$10 - x$	
10 less than a number	$x - 10$	
A number less 10	$x - 10$	

Now let's practice translating sentences into equations.

Example 10 Write each sentence as an equation. Let x represent the unknown number.

a. The quotient of 15 and a number is 4.
b. Three subtracted from 12 is a number.
c. 17 added to four times a number is 21.

Solution:

a. In words: the quotient of 15 and a number | is | 4

Translate: $\frac{15}{x} = 4$

b. In words: three subtracted **from** 12 | is | a number

Translate: $12 - 3 = x$

Care must be taken when the operation is subtraction. The expression $3 - 12$ would be incorrect. Notice that $3 - 12 \neq 12 - 3$.

c. In words: 17 | added to | four times a number | is | 21

Translate: $17 + 4x = 21$

Work Practice 10

PRACTICE 10

Write each sentence as an equation. Let x represent the unknown number.

a. The ratio of a number and 6 is 24.
b. The difference of 10 and a number is 18.
c. One less than twice a number is 99.

Answers

10. a. $\frac{x}{6} = 24$, **b.** $10 - x = 18$, **c.** $2x - 1 = 99$

Calculator Explorations

Exponents

To evaluate exponential expressions on a calculator, find the key marked $\boxed{y^x}$ or $\boxed{\wedge}$. To evaluate, for example, 6^5, press the following keys: $\boxed{6}\,\boxed{y^x}\,\boxed{5}\,\boxed{=}$ or

$\boxed{6}\,\boxed{\wedge}\,\boxed{5}\,\boxed{=}$.

↕ or

$\boxed{\text{ENTER}}$

The display should read $\boxed{7776}$

Order of Operations

Some calculators follow the order of operations, and others do not. To see whether or not your calculator has the order of operations built in, use your calculator to find $2 + 3 \cdot 4$. To do this, press the following sequence of keys:

$\boxed{2}\,\boxed{+}\,\boxed{3}\,\boxed{\times}\,\boxed{4}\,\boxed{=}$

↕ or

$\boxed{\text{ENTER}}$

The correct answer is 14 because the order of operations is to multiply before we add. If the calculator displays $\boxed{14}$, then it has the order of operations built in.

Even if the order of operations is built in, parentheses must sometimes be inserted. For example, to simplify $\frac{5}{12 - 7}$, press the keys

$\boxed{5}\,\boxed{\div}\,\boxed{(}\,\boxed{1}\,\boxed{2}\,\boxed{-}\,\boxed{7}\,\boxed{)}\,\boxed{=}$.

↕ or

$\boxed{\text{ENTER}}$

The display should read $\boxed{1}$.

Use a calculator to evaluate each expression.

1. 5^3

2. 7^4

3. 9^5

4. 8^6

5. $2(20 - 5)$

6. $3(14 - 7) + 21$

7. $24(862 - 455) + 89$

8. $99 + (401 + 962)$

9. $\frac{4623 + 129}{36 - 34}$

10. $\frac{956 - 452}{89 - 86}$

Vocabulary and Readiness Check

Use the choices below to fill in each blank. Some choices may be used more than once.

addition	multiplication	exponent	expression	solution	evaluating the expression
subtraction	division	base	equation	variable(s)	

1. In 2^5, the 2 is called the ______________ and the 5 is called the ______________.
2. True or false: 2^5 means 2.5. ______________.
3. To simplify $8 + 2 \cdot 6$, which operation should be performed first? ______________
4. To simplify $(8 + 2) \cdot 6$, which operation should be performed first? ______________
5. To simplify $9(3 - 2) \div 3 + 6$, which operation should be performed first? ______________
6. To simplify $8 \div 2 \cdot 6$, which operation should be performed first? ______________
7. A combination of operations on letters (variables) and numbers is a(n) ______________.
8. A letter that represents a number is a(n) ______________.
9. $3x - 2y$ is called a(n) ______________ and the letters x and y are ______________.
10. Replacing a variable in an expression by a number and then finding the value of the expression is called ______________.
11. A statement of the form "expression = expression" is called a(n) ______________.
12. A value for the variable that makes the equation a true statement is called a(n) ______________.

1.3 Exercise Set

FOR EXTRA HELP

Objective **A** *Evaluate. See Example 1.*

1. 3^5 **2.** 5^4 **3.** 3^3 **4.** 4^4 **5.** 1^5 **6.** 1^8

7. 5^1 **8.** 8^1 **9.** 7^2 **10.** 9^2 **11.** $\left(\frac{2}{3}\right)^4$ **12.** $\left(\frac{6}{11}\right)^2$

13. $\left(\frac{1}{5}\right)^3$ **14.** $\left(\frac{1}{2}\right)^5$ **15.** $(1.2)^2$ **16.** $(1.5)^2$ **17.** $(0.7)^3$ **18.** $(0.4)^3$

△ **19.** The area of a square whose sides each measure 5 meters is $(5 \cdot 5)$ square meters. Write this area using exponential notation.

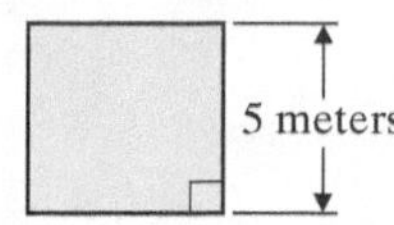

△ **20.** The area of a circle whose radius is 9 meters is $(9 \cdot 9 \cdot \pi)$ square meters. Write this area using exponential notation.

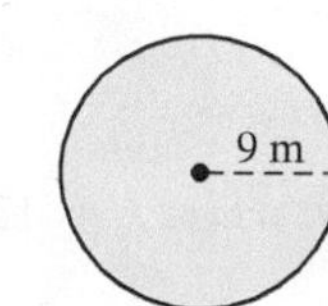

Simplify each expression. See Examples 2 through 6.

21. $5 + 6 \cdot 2$ **22.** $8 + 5 \cdot 3$ **23.** $4 \cdot 8 - 6 \cdot 2$ **24.** $12 \cdot 5 - 3 \cdot 6$

25. $18 \div 3 \cdot 2$ **26.** $48 \div 6 \cdot 2$ **27.** $2 + (5 - 2) + 4^2$ **28.** $6 - 2 \cdot 2 + 2^5$

29. $5 \cdot 3^2$ **30.** $2 \cdot 5^2$ **31.** $\frac{1}{4} \cdot \frac{2}{3} - \frac{1}{6}$ **32.** $\frac{3}{4} \cdot \frac{1}{2} + \frac{2}{3}$

33. $\frac{6 - 4}{9 - 2}$ **34.** $\frac{8 - 5}{24 - 20}$ **35.** $2[5 + 2(8 - 3)]$ **36.** $3[4 + 3(6 - 4)]$

37. $\frac{19 - 3 \cdot 5}{6 - 4}$ **38.** $\frac{14 - 2 \cdot 3}{12 - 8}$ **39.** $\frac{|6 - 2| + 3}{8 + 2 \cdot 5}$ **40.** $\frac{15 - |3 - 1|}{12 - 3 \cdot 2}$

41. $\frac{3 + 3(5 + 3)}{3^2 + 1}$ **42.** $\frac{3 + 6(8 - 5)}{4^2 + 2}$ **43.** $\frac{6 + |8 - 2| + 3^2}{18 - 3}$ **44.** $\frac{16 + |13 - 5| + 4^2}{17 - 5}$

45. $2 + 3[10(4 \cdot 5 - 16) - 30]$ **46.** $3 + 4[8(5 \cdot 5 - 20) - 41]$

47. $\left(\frac{2}{3}\right)^3 + \frac{1}{9} + \frac{1}{3} \cdot \frac{4}{3}$ **48.** $\left(\frac{3}{8}\right)^2 + \frac{1}{4} + \frac{1}{8} \cdot \frac{3}{2}$

Objective B *Evaluate each expression when $x = 1$, $y = 3$, and $z = 5$. See Example 7.*

49. $3y$ **50.** $4x$ **51.** $\frac{z}{5x}$ **52.** $\frac{y}{2z}$ **53.** $3x - 2$ **54.** $6y - 8$

55. $|2x + 3y|$ **56.** $|5z - 2y|$ **57.** $xy + z$ **58.** $yz - x$ **59.** $5y^2$ **60.** $2z^2$

Evaluate each expression when $x = 12$, $y = 8$, and $z = 4$. See Example 7.

61. $\frac{x}{z} + 3y$ **62.** $\frac{y}{z} + 8x$ **63.** $x^2 - 3y + x$ **64.** $y^2 - 3x + y$ **65.** $\frac{x^2 + z}{y^2 + 2z}$ **66.** $\frac{y^2 + x}{x^2 + 3y}$

Objective C *Decide whether the given number is a solution of the given equation. See Example 8.*

67. $3x - 6 = 9; 5$

68. $2x + 7 = 3x; 6$

69. $2x + 6 = 5x - 1; 0$

70. $4x + 2 = x + 8; 2$

71. $2x - 5 = 5; 8$

72. $3x - 10 = 8; 6$

73. $x + 6 = x + 6; 2$

74. $x + 6 = x + 6; 10$

75. $x = 5x + 15; 0$

76. $4 = 1 - x; 1$

77. $\frac{1}{3}x = 9; 27$

78. $\frac{2}{7}x = \frac{3}{14}; 6$

Objective D *Write each phrase as an algebraic expression. Let x represent the unknown number. See Example 9.*

79. Fifteen more than a number

80. A number increased by 9

81. Five subtracted from a number

82. Five decreased by a number

83. The ratio of a number and 4

84. The quotient of a number and 9

85. Three times a number, increased by 22

86. Twice a number, decreased by 72

Write each sentence as an equation or inequality. Use x to represent any unknown number. See Example 10.

87. One increased by two equals the quotient of nine and three.

88. Four subtracted from eight is equal to two squared.

89. Three is not equal to four divided by two.

90. The difference of sixteen and four is greater than ten.

91. The sum of 5 and a number is 20.

92. Seven subtracted from a number is 0.

93. The product of 7.6 and a number is 17.

94. 9.1 times a number equals 4

95. Thirteen minus three times a number is 13.

96. Eight added to twice a number is 42.

Concept Extensions

97. Are parentheses necessary in the expression $2 + (3 \cdot 5)$? Explain your answer.

98. Are parentheses necessary in the expression $(2 + 3) \cdot 5$? Explain your answer.

For Exercises 99 and 100, match each expression in the first column with its value in the second column.

99. a. $(6 + 2) \cdot (5 + 3)$ — 19
b. $(6 + 2) \cdot 5 + 3$ — 22
c. $6 + 2 \cdot 5 + 3$ — 64
d. $6 + 2 \cdot (5 + 3)$ — 43

100. a. $(1 + 4) \cdot 6 - 3$ — 15
b. $1 + 4 \cdot (6 - 3)$ — 13
c. $1 + 4 \cdot 6 - 3$ — 27
d. $(1 + 4) \cdot (6 - 3)$ — 22

△ *Recall that perimeter measures the distance around a plane figure and area measures the amount of surface of a plane figure. The expression $2l + 2w$ gives the perimeter of the rectangle below (measured in units), and the expression lw gives its area (measured in square units). Complete the chart below for the given lengths and widths. Be sure to include units.*

	Length: l	Width: w	Perimeter of Rectangle: $2l + 2w$	Area of Rectangle: lw
101.	4 in.	3 in.		
102.	6 in.	1 in.		
103.	5.3 in.	1.7 in.		
104.	4.6 in.	2.4 in.		

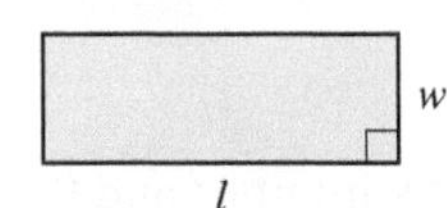

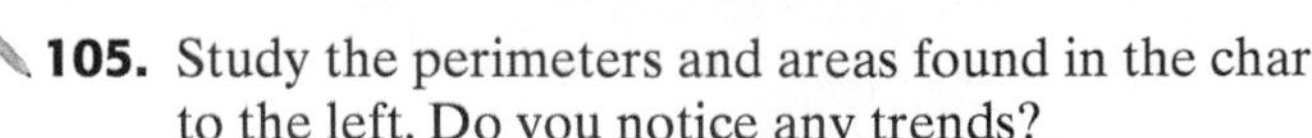

105. Study the perimeters and areas found in the chart to the left. Do you notice any trends?

106. In your own words, explain the difference between an expression and an equation.

107. Insert one set of parentheses so that the following expression simplifies to 32.

$20 - 4 \cdot 4 \div 2$

108. Insert parentheses so that the following expression simplifies to 28.

$2 \cdot 5 + 3^2$

Determine whether each is an expression or an equation. See the Concept Check in this section.

109. a. $5x + 6$
b. $2a = 7$
c. $3a + 2 = 9$
d. $4x + 3y - 8z$
e. $5^2 - 2(6 - 2)$

110. a. $3x^2 - 26$
b. $3x^2 - 26 = 1$
c. $2x - 5 = 7x - 5$
d. $9y + x - 8$
e. $3^2 - 4(5 - 3)$

111. △ Why is 4^3 usually read as "four cubed"? (*Hint:* What is the volume of the **cube** below?)

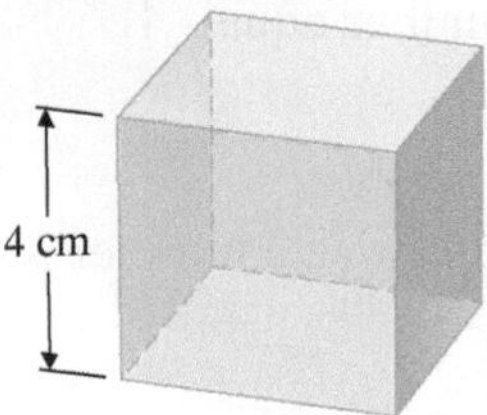

112. △ Why is 8^2 usually read as "eight squared"? (*Hint:* What is the area of the **square** below?)

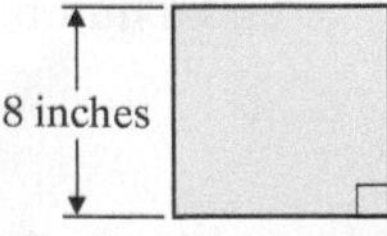

113. Write any expression, using 3 or more numbers, that simplifies to −11.

114. Write any expression, using 4 or more numbers, that simplifies to 7.

1.4 ADDING REAL NUMBERS

Objectives

A Add Real Numbers.

B Find the Opposite of a Number.

C Evaluate Algebraic Expressions Using Real Numbers.

D Solve Applications That Involve Addition of Real Numbers.

Real numbers can be added, subtracted, multiplied, divided, and raised to powers, just as whole numbers can.

Objective A Adding Real Numbers

Adding real numbers can be visualized by using a number line. A positive number can be represented on the number line by an arrow of appropriate length pointing to the right, and a negative number by an arrow of appropriate length pointing to the left.

Both arrows represent 2 or +2.

They both point to the right, and they are both 2 units long.

Both arrows represent −3.

They both point to the left, and they are both 3 units long.

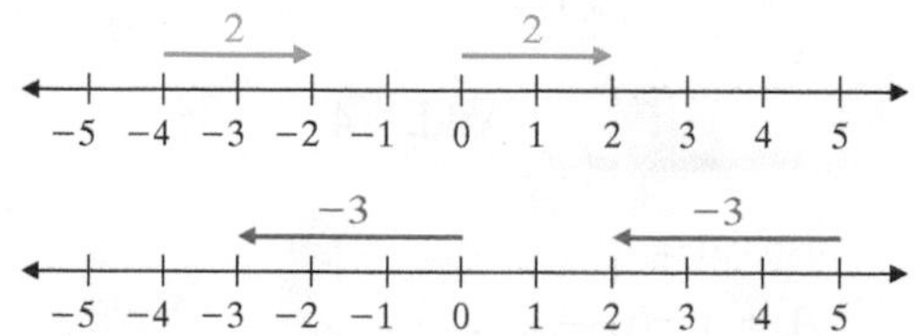

To add signed numbers such as $5 + (-2)$ on a number line, we start at 0 on the number line and draw an arrow representing 5. From the tip of this arrow, we draw another arrow representing −2. The tip of the second arrow ends at their sum, 3.

$5 + (-2) = 3$

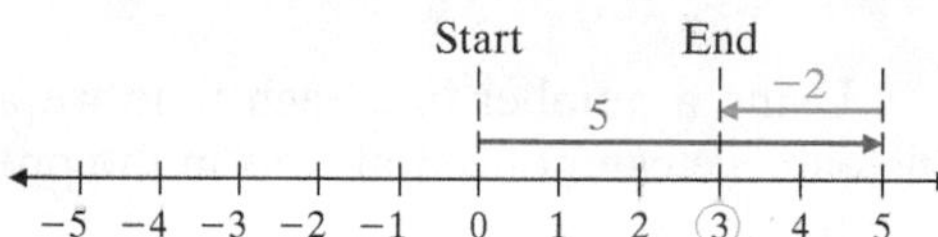

To add $-1 + (-4)$ on the number line, we start at 0 and draw an arrow representing −1. From the tip of this arrow, we draw another arrow representing −4. The tip of the second arrow ends at their sum, −5.

$-1 + (-4) = -5$

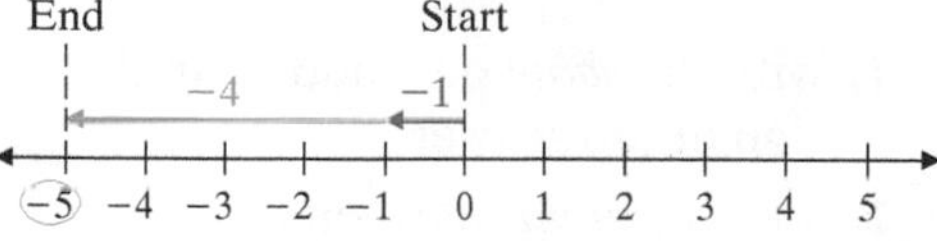

Example 1 Add: $-1 + (-2)$

Solution:

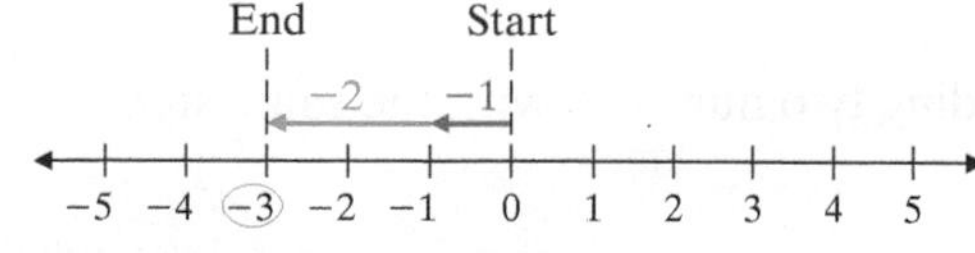

$-1 + (-2) = -3$

Work Practice 1

PRACTICE 1

Add using a number line:
$-2 + (-4)$

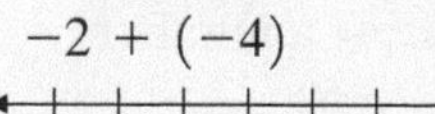

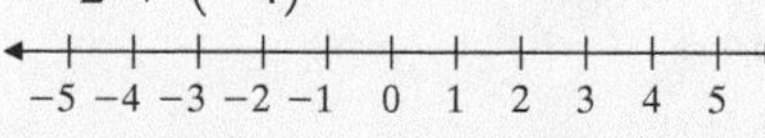

Thinking of integers as money earned or lost might help make addition more meaningful. Earnings can be thought of as positive numbers. If \$1 is earned and later another \$3 is earned, the total amount earned is \$4. In other words, $1 + 3 = 4$.

On the other hand, losses can be thought of as negative numbers. If \$1 is lost and later another \$3 is lost, a total of \$4 is lost. In other words, $(-1) + (-3) = -4$.

In Example 1, we added numbers with the same sign. Adding numbers whose signs are not the same can be pictured on a number line also.

Answer

1. −6

PRACTICE 2

Add using a number line:
$-5 + 8$

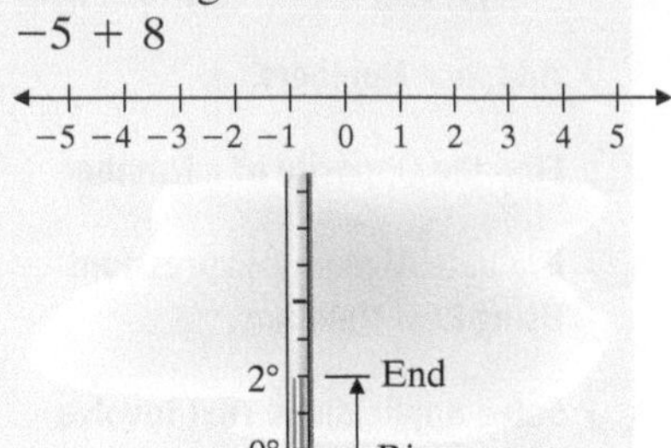

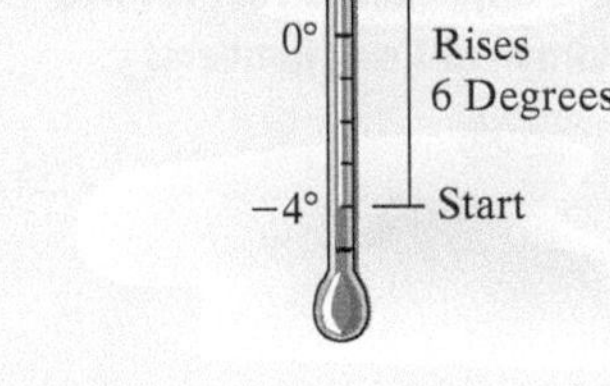

Example 2 Add: $-4 + 6$

Solution:

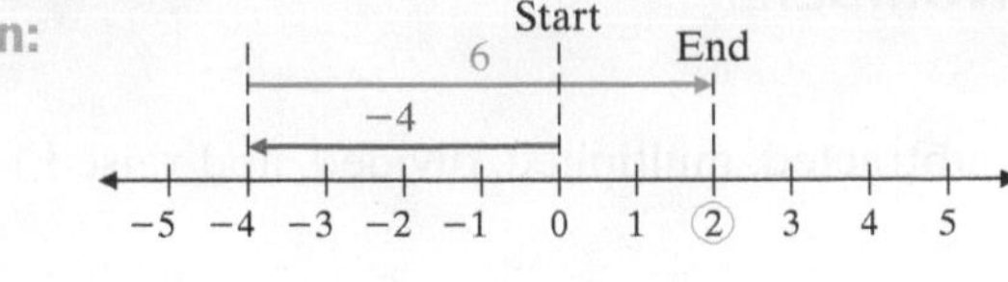

$-4 + 6 = 2$

Work Practice 2

Let's use temperature as an example. If the thermometer registers 4 degrees below 0 degrees and then rises 6 degrees, the new temperature is 2 degrees above 0 degrees. Thus, it is reasonable that $-4 + 6 = 2$. (See the diagram in the margin.)

PRACTICE 3

Add using a number line:
$5 + (-4)$

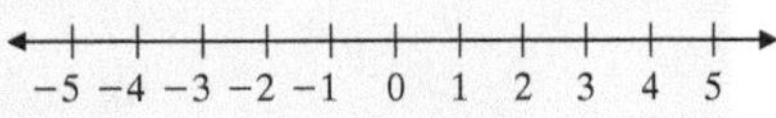

Example 3 Add: $4 + (-6)$

Solution:

$4 + (-6) = -2$

Start
End
-6
4
-5 -4 -3 -2 -1 0 1 2 3 4 5

Work Practice 3

Using a number line each time we add two numbers can be time consuming. Instead, we can notice patterns in the previous examples and write rules for adding real numbers.

Adding Real Numbers

To add two real numbers

1. with the *same sign,* add their absolute values. Use their common sign as the sign of the answer.
2. with *different signs,* subtract their absolute values. Give the answer the same sign as the number with the larger absolute value.

PRACTICE 4

Add without using a number line: $(-8) + (-5)$

Example 4 Add without using a number line: $(-7) + (-6)$

Solution: Here, we are adding two numbers with the same sign.

$(-7) + (-6) = -13$

↑ same sign ↖ sum of absolute values ($|-7| = 7, |-6| = 6, 7 + 6 = 13$)

Work Practice 4

PRACTICE 5

Add without using a number line: $(-14) + 6$

Example 5 Add without using a number line: $(-10) + 4$

Solution: Here, we are adding two numbers with different signs.

$(-10) + 4 = -6$

↑ sign of number with larger absolute value, -10 ↖ difference of absolute values ($|-10| = 10, |4| = 4, 10 - 4 = 6$)

Work Practice 5

Answers
2. 3 **3.** 1 **4.** −13 **5.** −8

Examples Add without using a number line.

6. $(-8) + (-11) = -19$
7. $(-2) + 10 = 8$
8. $0.2 + (-0.5) = -0.3$
9. $-\frac{7}{10} + \left(-\frac{1}{10}\right) = -\frac{8}{10} = -\frac{\overset{1}{\cancel{2}} \cdot 4}{\underset{1}{\cancel{2}} \cdot 5} = -\frac{4}{5}$
10. $11.4 + (-4.7) = 6.7$
11. $-\frac{3}{8} + \frac{2}{5} = -\frac{15}{40} + \frac{16}{40} = \frac{1}{40}$

Work Practice 6–11

PRACTICE 6–11

Add without using a number line.

6. $(-17) + (-10)$
7. $(-4) + 12$
8. $1.5 + (-3.2)$
9. $-\frac{5}{12} + \left(-\frac{1}{12}\right)$
10. $12.1 + (-3.6)$
11. $-\frac{4}{5} + \frac{2}{3}$

In Example 12a, we add three numbers. Remember that by the associative and commutative properties for addition, we may add numbers in any order that we wish. For Example 12a, let's add the numbers from left to right.

Example 12 Find each sum.

a. $3 + (-7) + (-8)$
b. $[7 + (-10)] + [-2 + (-4)]$

Solution:

a. Perform the additions from left to right.

$3 + (-7) + (-8) = -4 + (-8)$ Adding numbers with different signs

$= -12$ Adding numbers with like signs

b. Simplify inside the brackets first.

$[7 + (-10)] + [-2 + (-4)] = [-3] + [-6]$

$= -9$ Add.

Work Practice 12

PRACTICE 12

Find each sum.

a. $16 + (-9) + (-9)$
b. $[3 + (-13)] + [-4 + (-7)]$

Helpful Hint Don't forget that brackets are grouping symbols. We simplify within them first.

Objective B Finding Opposites

To help us subtract real numbers in the next section, we first review what we mean by opposites. The graphs of 4 and −4 are shown on the number line below.

4 units 4 units

−5 −4 −3 −2 −1 0 1 2 3 4 5

Notice that the graphs of 4 and −4 lie on opposite sides of 0, and each is 4 units away from 0. Such numbers are known as **opposites** or **additive inverses** of each other.

Opposite or Additive Inverse

Two numbers that are the same distance from 0 but lie on opposite sides of 0 are called **opposites** or **additive inverses** of each other.

Answers

6. −27 7. 8 8. −1.7 9. $-\frac{1}{2}$ 10. 8.5 11. $-\frac{2}{15}$ 12. a. −2 b. −21

PRACTICE 13–16

Find the opposite of each number.

13. -35 **14.** 12

15. $-\frac{3}{11}$ **16.** 1.9

Examples Find the opposite of each number.

13. 10 The opposite of 10 is -10.

14. -3 The opposite of -3 is 3.

15. $\frac{1}{2}$ The opposite of $\frac{1}{2}$ is $-\frac{1}{2}$.

16. -4.5 The opposite of -4.5 is 4.5.

Work Practice 13–16

We use the symbol "−" to represent the phrase "the opposite of" or "the additive inverse of." In general, if a is a number, we write the opposite or additive inverse of a as $-a$. We know that the opposite of -3 is 3. Notice that this translates as

the opposite of	-3	is	3
↓	↓	↓	↓
$-$	(-3)	$=$	**3**

This is true in general.

If a is a number, then $-(-a) = a$.

PRACTICE 17

Simplify each expression.

a. $-(-22)$

b. $-\left(-\frac{2}{7}\right)$

c. $-(-x)$

d. $-|-14|$

e. $-|2.3|$

Example 17 Simplify each expression.

a. $-(-10)$ **b.** $-\left(-\frac{1}{2}\right)$ **c.** $-(-2x)$

d. $-|-6|$ **e.** $-|4.1|$

Solution:

a. $-(-10) = 10$

b. $-\left(-\frac{1}{2}\right) = \frac{1}{2}$

c. $-(-2x) = 2x$

d. $-|-6| = -6$ Since $|-6| = 6$.

e. $-|4.1| = -4.1$ Since $|4.1| = 4.1$

Work Practice 17

Let's discover another characteristic about opposites. Notice that the sum of a number and its opposite is always 0.

$10 + (-10) = 0$ (opposites) $-3 + 3 = 0$ (opposites)

$\frac{1}{2} + \left(-\frac{1}{2}\right) = 0$ (opposites)

In general, we can write the following:

The sum of a number a and its opposite $-a$ is 0.

$a + (-a) = 0$ Also, $-a + a = 0$.

Notice that this means that the opposite of 0 is then 0 since $0 + 0 = 0$.

Answers

13. 35 **14.** -12 **15.** $\frac{3}{11}$ **16.** -1.9

17. a. 22 **b.** $\frac{2}{7}$ **c.** x **d.** -14 **e.** -2.3

Examples Add.

18. $-56 + 56 = 0$
19. $17 + (-17) = 0$

Work Practice 18–19

PRACTICE 18–19
Add.
18. $30 + (-30)$
19. $-81 + 81$

✓**Concept Check** What is wrong with the following calculation?

$5 + (-22) = 17$

Objective C Evaluating Algebraic Expressions

We can continue our work with algebraic expressions by evaluating expressions given real-number replacement values.

Example 20 Evaluate $2x + y$ for $x = 3$ and $y = -5$.

Solution: Replace x with 3 and y with -5 in $2x + y$.

$$\begin{aligned} 2x + y &= 2 \cdot 3 + (-5) \\ &= 6 + (-5) \\ &= 1 \end{aligned}$$

Work Practice 20

PRACTICE 20
Evaluate $x + 3y$ for $x = -6$ and $y = 2$.

Example 21 Evaluate $x + y$ for $x = -2$ and $y = -10$.

Solution: $x + y = (-2) + (-10)$ Replace x with -2 and y with -10.
$= -12$

Work Practice 21

PRACTICE 21
Evaluate $x + y$ for $x = -13$ and $y = -9$.

Objective D Solving Applications That Involve Addition

Positive and negative numbers are used in everyday life. Stock market returns show gains and losses as positive and negative numbers. Temperatures in cold climates often dip into the negative range, commonly referred to as "below zero" temperatures. Bank statements report deposits and withdrawals as positive and negative numbers.

Example 22 Calculating Temperature

In Philadelphia, Pennsylvania, the record extreme high temperature is 104°F. Decrease this temperature by 111 degrees, and the result is the record extreme low temperature. Find this temperature. (*Source:* National Climatic Data Center)

Solution:

In words:	extreme low temperature	=	extreme high temperature	+	decrease of 111°
	↓		↓		↓
Translate:	extreme low temperature	=	104	+	(−111)
		= −7			

The record extreme low temperature in Philadelphia, Pennsylvania, is −7°F.

Work Practice 22

PRACTICE 22
If the temperature was −7° Fahrenheit at 6 a.m., and it rose 4 degrees by 7 a.m. and then rose another 7 degrees in the hour from 7 a.m. to 8 a.m., what was the temperature at 8 a.m.?

Answers
18. 0 **19.** 0 **20.** 0
21. −22 **22.** 4°F

✓ **Concept Check Answer**
$5 + (-22) = -17$

Vocabulary and Readiness Check

Use the choices below to fill in each blank. Not all choices will be used.

$-a$ a 0 commutative associative

1. If n is a number, then $-n + n =$ ____________.
2. Since $x + n = n + x$, we say that addition is ____________.
3. If a is a number, then $-(-a) =$ ____________.
4. Since $n + (x + a) = (n + x) + a$, we say that addition is ____________.

1.4 Exercise Set

FOR EXTRA HELP

MyMathLab

PRACTICE

WATCH

DOWNLOAD

READ

REVIEW

Objectives A B Mixed Practice *Add. See Examples 1 through 12, 18 and 19.*

1. $6 + (-3)$ **2.** $9 + (-12)$ **3.** $-6 + (-8)$ **4.** $-6 + (-14)$

5. $8 + (-7)$ **6.** $16 + (-4)$ **7.** $-14 + 2$ **8.** $-10 + 5$

9. $-2 + (-3)$ **10.** $-7 + (-4)$ **11.** $-9 + (-3)$ **12.** $-11 + (-5)$

13. $-7 + 3$ **14.** $-5 + 9$ **15.** $10 + (-3)$ **16.** $8 + (-6)$

17. $5 + (-7)$ **18.** $3 + (-6)$ **19.** $-16 + 16$ **20.** $23 + (-23)$

21. $27 + (-46)$ **22.** $53 + (-37)$ **23.** $-18 + 49$ **24.** $-26 + 14$

25. $-33 + (-14)$ **26.** $-18 + (-26)$ **27.** $6.3 + (-8.4)$ **28.** $9.2 + (-11.4)$

29. $117 + (-79)$ **30.** $144 + (-88)$ **31.** $-9.6 + (-3.5)$ **32.** $-6.7 + (-7.6)$

33. $-\frac{3}{8} + \frac{5}{8}$ **34.** $-\frac{5}{12} + \frac{7}{12}$ **35.** $-\frac{7}{16} + \frac{1}{4}$ **36.** $-\frac{5}{9} + \frac{1}{3}$

37. $-\frac{7}{10} + \left(-\frac{3}{5}\right)$ **38.** $-\frac{5}{6} + \left(-\frac{2}{3}\right)$ **39.** $|-8| + (-16)$ **40.** $|-6| + (-61)$

41. $-15 + 9 + (-2)$ **42.** $-9 + 15 + (-5)$ **43.** $-21 + (-16) + (-22)$ **44.** $-18 + (-6) + (-40)$

45. $-23 + 16 + (-2)$ **46.** $-14 + (-3) + 11$ **47.** $|5 + (-10)|$ **48.** $|7 + (-17)|$

49. $6 + (-4) + 9$ **50.** $8 + (-2) + 7$ **51.** $[-17 + (-4)] + [-12 + 15]$

52. $[-2 + (-7)] + [-11 + 22]$ **53.** $|9 + (-12)| + |-16|$ **54.** $|43 + (-73)| + |-20|$

55. $-13 + [5 + (-3) + 4]$

56. $-30 + [1 + (-6) + 8]$

57. Find the sum of -38 and 12.

58. Find the sum of -44 and 16.

Objective **B** *Find each additive inverse or opposite. See Examples 13 through 17.*

59. 6

60. 4

61. -2

62. -8

63. 0

64. $-\frac{1}{4}$

65. $|-6|$

66. $|-11|$

Simplify each of the following. See Example 17.

67. $-|-2|$

68. $-|-5|$

69. $-(-7)$

70. $-(-14)$

71. $-(-7.9)$

72. $-(-8.4)$

73. $-(-5z)$

74. $-(-7m)$

75. $\left|-\frac{2}{3}\right|$

76. $-\left|-\frac{2}{3}\right|$

Objective **C** *Evaluate $x + y$ for the given replacement values. See Examples 20 and 21.*

77. $x = -20$ and $y = -50$

78. $x = -1$ and $y = -29$

Evaluate $3x + y$ for the given replacement values. See Examples 20 and 21.

79. $x = 2$ and $y = -3$

80. $x = 7$ and $y = -11$

Objective **D** **Translating** *Translate each phrase; then simplify. See Example 22.*

81. Find the sum of -6 and 25.

82. Find the sum of -30 and 15.

83. Find the sum of -31, -9, and 30.

84. Find the sum of -49, -2, and 40.

Solve. See Example 22.

85. Suppose a deep-sea diver dives from the surface to 215 feet below the surface. He then dives down 16 more feet. Use positive and negative numbers to represent this situation. Then find the diver's present depth.

86. Suppose a diver dives from the surface to 248 meters below the surface and then swims up 8 meters, down 16 meters, down another 28 meters, and then up 32 meters. Use positive and negative numbers to represent this situation. Then find the diver's depth after these movements.

87. The lowest temperature ever recorded in Massachusetts was $-35°$F. The highest recorded temperature in Massachusetts was 142° higher than the record low temperature. Find Massachusetts' highest recorded temperature. (*Source:* National Climatic Data Center)

88. On January 2, 1943, the temperature was $-4°$ at 7:30 a.m. in Spearfish, South Dakota. Incredibly, it got 49° warmer in the next 2 minutes. To what temperature did it rise by 7:32?

89. The lowest elevation on Earth is −411 meters (that is, 411 meters below sea level) at the Dead Sea. If you are standing 316 meters above the Dead Sea, what is your elevation? (*Source:* National Geographic Society)

90. The lowest elevation in Australia is −52 feet at Lake Eyre. If you are standing at a point 439 feet above Lake Eyre, what is your elevation? (*Source:* National Geographic Society)

91. During the PGA 2008 Wyndham Championship tournament, the winner, Carl Pettersson, had scores of −6, −9, −4, and −2. What was his total score for the tournament? (*Source:* Professional Golfer's Association)

92. Catriona Matthew won the HSBC LPGA Brasil Cup 2009 Tournament with the following hole scores for round 1: −2, +2, −2, −2, −2. What was her final score for round 1? (*Source:* LPGA of America)

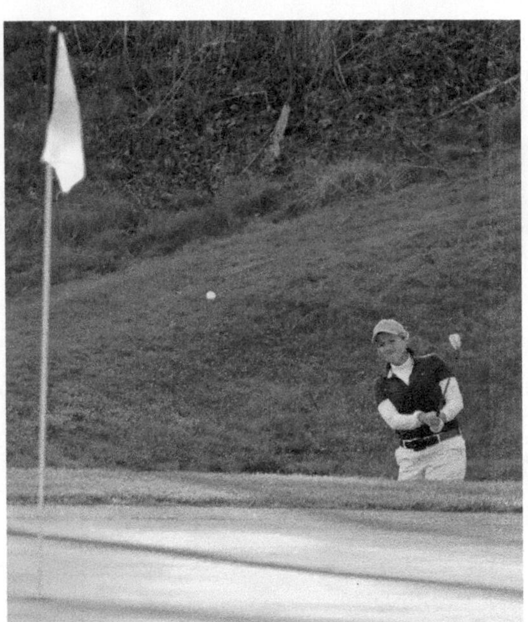

93. A negative net income results when a company spends more money than it brings in. Johnson Outdoors Inc. had the following quarterly net incomes during its 2009 fiscal year. (*Source:* Yahoo Finance)

Quarter of Fiscal 2009	Net Income (in millions)
First	2.5
Second	9
Third	−14.2
Fourth	−4.2

What was the total net income for fiscal year 2009?

94. LeapFrog Enterprises Inc. had the following quarterly net incomes during its 2009 fiscal year. (*Source:* Yahoo Finance)

Quarter of Fiscal 2009	Net Income (in millions)
First	−27.1
Second	−12.2
Third	7.2
Fourth	29.4

What was the total net income for fiscal year 2009?

Concept Extensions

The following bar graph shows each month's average daily low temperature in degrees Fahrenheit for Barrow, Alaska. Use this graph to answer Exercises 95 through 100.

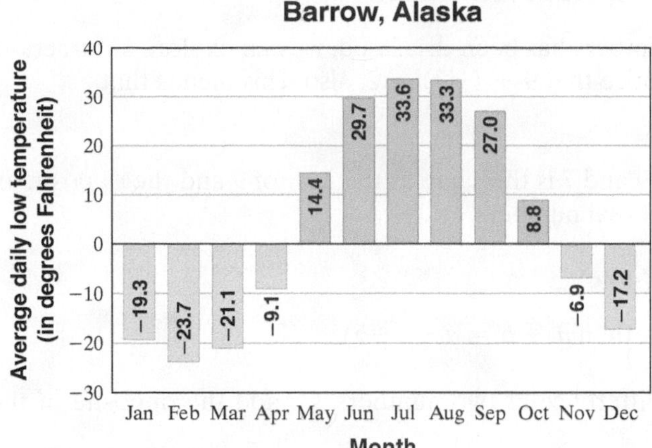

Source: National Climatic Data Center

95. For what month is the graphed temperature the highest?

96. For what month is the graphed temperature the lowest?

97. For what month is the graphed temperature positive *and* closest to 0°?

98. For what month is the graphed temperature negative *and* closest to 0°?

99. Find the average of the temperatures shown for the months of April, May, and October. (To find the average of three temperatures, find their sum and divide by 3.)

100. Find the average of the temperatures shown for the months of January, September, and October. (To find the average of three temperatures, find their sum and divide by 3.)

101. Name 2 numbers whose sum is −17.

102. Name 2 numbers whose sum is −30.

Each calculation below is incorrect. Find the error and correct it. See the Concept Check in this section.

103. $7 + (-10) \stackrel{?}{=} 17$

104. $-4 + 14 \stackrel{?}{=} -18$

105. $-10 + (-12) \stackrel{?}{=} -120$

106. $-15 + (-17) \stackrel{?}{=} 32$

For Exercises 107 through 110, determine whether each statement is true or false.

107. The sum of two negative numbers is always a negative number.

108. The sum of two positive numbers is always a positive number.

109. The sum of a positive number and a negative number is always a negative number.

110. The sum of zero and a negative number is always a negative number.

111. In your own words, explain how to add two negative numbers.

112. In your own words, explain how to add a positive number and a negative number.

Objectives

A Subtract Real Numbers.

B Evaluate Algebraic Expressions Using Real Numbers.

C Determine Whether a Number Is a Solution of a Given Equation.

D Solve Applications That Involve Subtraction of Real Numbers.

E Find Complementary and Supplementary Angles.

1.5 SUBTRACTING REAL NUMBERS

Objective A Subtracting Real Numbers

Now that addition of real numbers has been discussed, we can explore subtraction. We know that $9 - 7 = 2$. Notice that $9 + (-7) = 2$, also. This means that

$$9 - 7 = 9 + (-7)$$

Notice that the *difference* of 9 and 7 is the same as the *sum* of 9 and the opposite of 7. This is how we can subtract real numbers.

Subtracting Real Numbers

If a and b are real numbers, then $a - b = a + (-b)$.

In other words, to find the difference of two numbers, we add the opposite of the number being subtracted.

Example 1 Subtract.

a. $-13 - 4$ **b.** $5 - (-6)$ **c.** $3 - 6$ **d.** $-1 - (-7)$

Solution:

a. $-13 - 4 = -13 + (-4)$ (add; opposite) Add −13 to the opposite of 4, which is −4.

$= -17$

b. $5 - (-6) = 5 + (6)$ (add; opposite) Add 5 to the opposite of −6, which is 6.

$= 11$

c. $3 - 6 = 3 + (-6)$ Add 3 to the opposite of 6, which is −6.

$= -3$

d. $-1 - (-7) = -1 + (7) = 6$

Work Practice 1

PRACTICE 1

Subtract.

a. $-20 - 6$

b. $3 - (-5)$

c. $7 - 17$

d. $-4 - (-9)$

Helpful Hint

Study the patterns indicated.

No change → ; Change to addition. ; Change to opposite.

$5 - 11 = 5 + (-11) = -6$

$-3 - 4 = -3 + (-4) = -7$

$7 - (-1) = 7 + (1) = 8$

Examples Subtract.

2. $5.3 - (-4.6) = 5.3 + (4.6) = 9.9$

3. $-\frac{3}{10} - \frac{5}{10} = -\frac{3}{10} + \left(-\frac{5}{10}\right) = -\frac{8}{10} = -\frac{4}{5}$

4. $-\frac{2}{3} - \left(-\frac{4}{5}\right) = -\frac{2}{3} + \left(\frac{4}{5}\right) = -\frac{10}{15} + \frac{12}{15} = \frac{2}{15}$

Work Practice 2–4

PRACTICE 2–4

Subtract.

2. $9.6 - (-5.7)$

3. $-\frac{4}{9} - \frac{2}{9}$

4. $-\frac{1}{4} - \left(-\frac{2}{5}\right)$

Answers

1. a. −26 **b.** 8 **c.** −10 **d.** 5

2. 15.3 **3.** $-\frac{2}{3}$ **4.** $\frac{3}{20}$

Example 5 Write each phrase as an expression and simplify.

a. Subtract 8 from -4. **b.** Decrease 10 by -20.

Solution: Be careful when interpreting these. The order of numbers in subtraction is important.

a. 8 is to be subtracted **from** -4.

$-4 - 8 = -4 + (-8) = -12$

b. To decrease 10 by -20, we find 10 **minus** -20.

$10 - (-20) = 10 + 20 = 30$

Work Practice 5

PRACTICE 5

Write each phrase as an expression and simplify.

a. Subtract 7 from -11.

b. Decrease 35 by -25.

If an expression contains additions and subtractions, just write the subtractions as equivalent additions. Then simplify from left to right.

Example 6 Simplify each expression.

a. $-14 - 8 + 10 - (-6)$ **b.** $1.6 - (-10.3) + (-5.6)$

Solution:

a. $-14 - 8 + 10 - (-6) = -14 + (-8) + 10 + 6 = -6$

b. $1.6 - (-10.3) + (-5.6) = 1.6 + 10.3 + (-5.6) = 6.3$

Work Practice 6

PRACTICE 6

Simplify each expression.

a. $-20 - 5 + 12 - (-3)$

b. $5.2 - (-4.4) + (-8.8)$

When an expression contains parentheses and brackets, remember the order of operations. Start with the innermost set of parentheses or brackets and work your way outward.

Example 7 Simplify each expression.

a. $-3 + [(-2 - 5) - 2]$ **b.** $2^3 - 10 + [-6 - (-5)]$

Solution:

a. Start with the innermost set of parentheses. Rewrite $-2 - 5$ as an addition.

$$
\begin{aligned}
-3 + [(-2 - 5) - 2] &= -3 + [(-2 + (-5)) - 2] \\
&= -3 + [(-7) - 2] && \text{Add: } -2 + (-5). \\
&= -3 + [-7 + (-2)] && \text{Write } -7 - 2 \text{ as an addition.} \\
&= -3 + [-9] && \text{Add.} \\
&= -12 && \text{Add.}
\end{aligned}
$$

b. Start simplifying the expression inside the brackets by writing $-6 - (-5)$ as an addition.

$$
\begin{aligned}
2^3 - 10 + [-6 - (-5)] &= 2^3 - 10 + [-6 + 5] \\
&= 2^3 - 10 + [-1] && \text{Add.} \\
&= 8 - 10 + (-1) && \text{Evaluate } 2^3. \\
&= 8 + (-10) + (-1) && \text{Write } 8 - 10 \text{ as an addition.} \\
&= -2 + (-1) && \text{Add.} \\
&= -3 && \text{Add.}
\end{aligned}
$$

Work Practice 7

PRACTICE 7

Simplify each expression.

a. $-9 + [(-4 - 1) - 10]$

b. $5^2 - 20 + [-11 - (-3)]$

Answers

5. a. -18 **b.** 60 **6. a.** -10 **b.** 0.8 **7. a.** -24 **b.** -3

Objective B Evaluating Algebraic Expressions

It is important to be able to evaluate expressions for given replacement values. This helps, for example, when checking solutions of equations.

PRACTICE 8

Find the value of each expression when $x = 1$ and $y = -4$.

a. $\frac{x - y}{14 + x}$

b. $x^2 - y$

Example 8 Find the value of each expression when $x = 2$ and $y = -5$.

a. $\frac{x - y}{12 + x}$ **b.** $x^2 - y$

Solution:

a. Replace x with 2 and y with -5. Be sure to put parentheses around -5 to separate signs. Then simplify the resulting expression.

$$\frac{x - y}{12 + x} = \frac{2 - (-5)}{12 + 2} = \frac{2 + 5}{14} = \frac{7}{14} = \frac{1}{2}$$

b. Replace x with 2 and y with -5 and simplify.

$$x^2 - y = 2^2 - (-5) = 4 - (-5) = 4 + 5 = 9$$

Work Practice 8

Helpful Hint

For additional help when replacing variables with replacement values, first place parentheses about any variables.

For Example 8b above, we have

$$x^2 - y = \underbrace{(x)^2 - (y)}_{\text{Place parentheses about variables}} = \underbrace{(2)^2 - (-5)}_{\text{Replace variables with values}} = 4 - (-5) = 4 + 5 = 9$$

Objective C Solutions of Equations

Recall from Section 1.3 that a solution of an equation is a value for the variable that makes the equation true.

PRACTICE 9

Determine whether -2 is a solution of $-1 + x = 1$.

Example 9 Determine whether -4 is a solution of $x - 5 = -9$.

Solution: Replace x with -4 and see if a true statement results.

$$x - 5 = -9 \quad \text{Original equation}$$
$$-4 - 5 \stackrel{?}{=} -9 \quad \text{Replace } x \text{ with } -4.$$
$$-4 + (-5) \stackrel{?}{=} -9$$
$$-9 = -9 \quad \text{True}$$

Thus -4 is a solution of $x - 5 = -9$.

Work Practice 9

Objective D Solving Applications That Involve Subtraction

Another use of real numbers is in recording altitudes above and below sea level, as shown in the next example.

Answers

8. a. $\frac{1}{3}$ **b.** 5 **9.** -2 is not a solution.

Example 10 Finding a Change in Elevation

The highest point in the United States is the top of Mount McKinley, at a height of 20,320 feet above sea level. The lowest point is Death Valley, California, which is 282 feet below sea level. How much higher is Mount McKinley than Death Valley? (*Source:* U.S. Geological Survey)

Solution: To find "how much higher," we subtract. Don't forget that since Death Valley is 282 feet *below* sea level, we represent its height by −282. Draw a diagram to help visualize the problem.

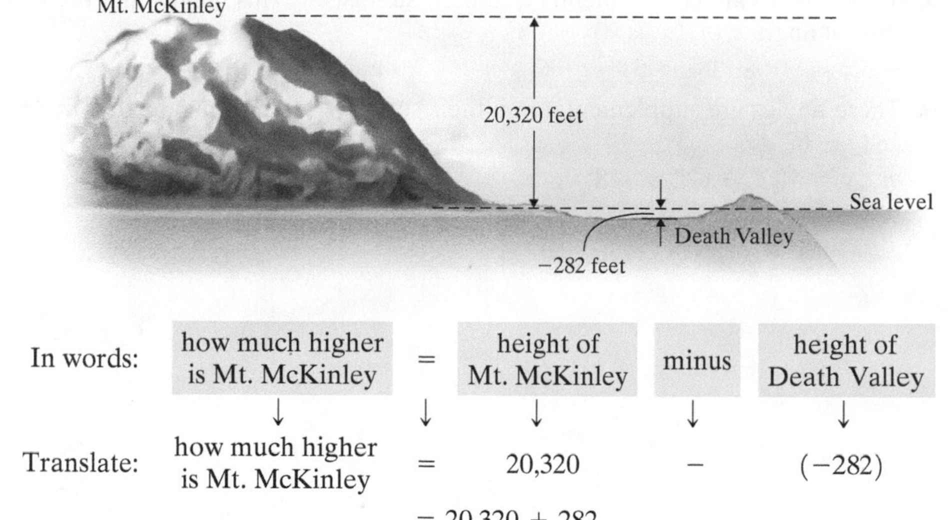

In words:	how much higher is Mt. McKinley	=	height of Mt. McKinley	minus	height of Death Valley
	↓	↓	↓	↓	↓
Translate:	how much higher is Mt. McKinley	=	20,320	−	(−282)

$$= 20{,}320 + 282$$
$$= 20{,}602$$

Thus, Mount McKinley is 20,602 feet higher than Death Valley.

Work Practice 10

PRACTICE 10

The highest point in Asia is the top of Mount Everest, at a height of 29,028 feet above sea level. The lowest point is the Dead Sea, which is 1312 feet below sea level. How much higher is Mount Everest than the Dead Sea? (*Source:* National Geographic Society)

Objective E Finding Complementary and Supplementary Angles

A knowledge of geometric concepts is needed by many professionals, such as doctors, carpenters, electronic technicians, gardeners, machinists, and pilots, just to name a few. With this in mind, we review the geometric concepts of **complementary** and **supplementary angles.**

Complementary and Supplementary Angles

Two angles are **complementary** if the sum of their measures is 90°.

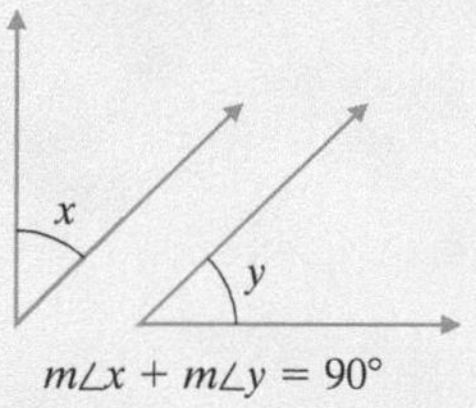

$m\angle x + m\angle y = 90°$

Two angles are **supplementary** if the sum of their measures is 180°.

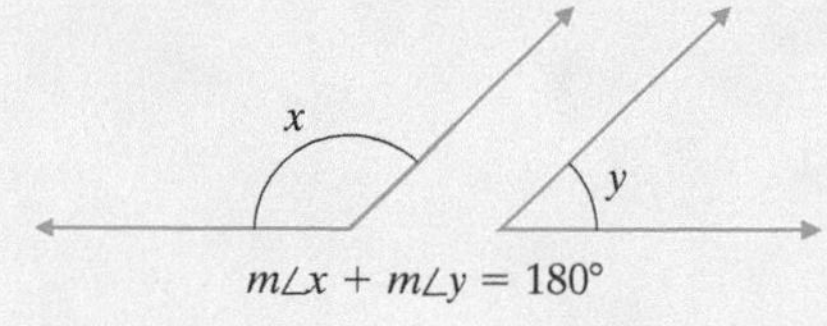

$m\angle x + m\angle y = 180°$

Answer

10. 30,340 ft

PRACTICE 11

Find the measure of each unknown complementary or supplementary angle.

a.

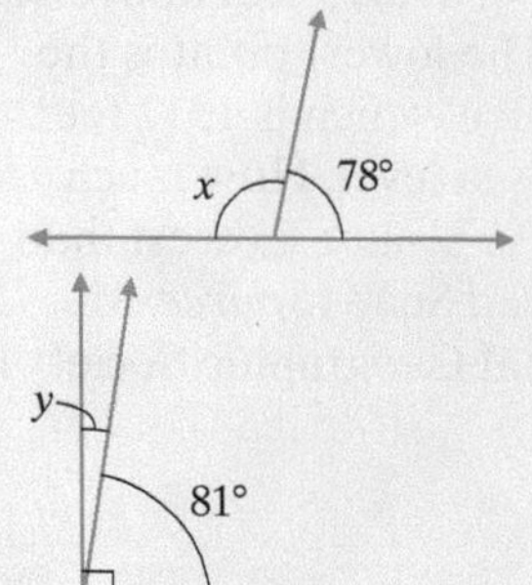

b.

Example 11 Find the measure of each unknown complementary or supplementary angle.

a.

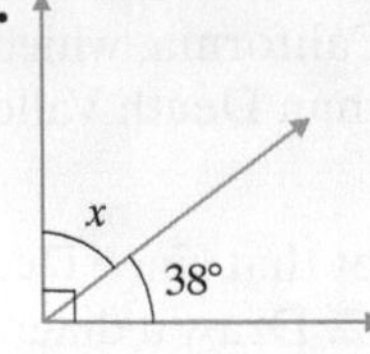

b.

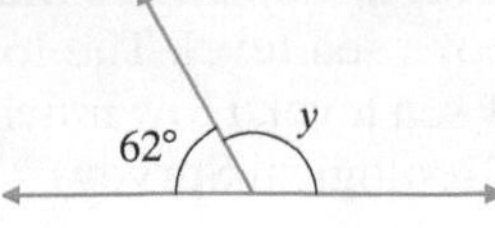

Solution:

a. These angles are complementary, so their sum is 90°. This means that the measure of angle x, $m\angle x$, is $90° - 38°$.

$m\angle x = 90° - 38° = 52°$

b. These angles are supplementary, so their sum is 180°. This means that $m\angle y$ is $180° - 62°$.

$m\angle y = 180° - 62° = 118°$

Work Practice 11

Answers

11. a. 102° **b.** 9°

Vocabulary and Readiness Check

Multiple choice: Select the correct lettered response following each exercise.

1. It is true that $a - b =$ ________.

a. $b - a$ **b.** $a + (-b)$ **c.** $a + b$

2. The opposite of n is ________.

a. $-n$ **b.** $-(-n)$ **c.** n

3. To evaluate $x - y$ for $x = -10$ and $y = -14$, we replace x with -10 and y with -14 and evaluate ________.

a. $10 - 14$ **b.** $-10 - 14$ **c.** $-14 - 10$ **d.** $-10 - (-14)$

4. The expression $-5 - 10$ equals ________.

a. $5 - 10$ **b.** $5 + 10$ **c.** $-5 + (-10)$ **d.** $10 - 5$

1.5 Exercise Set

FOR EXTRA HELP

Objective A *Subtract. See Examples 1 through 4.*

1. $-6 - 4$ **2.** $-12 - 8$ **3.** $4 - 9$ **4.** $8 - 11$ **5.** $16 - (-3)$

6. $12 - (-5)$ **7.** $7 - (-4)$ **8.** $3 - (-6)$ **9.** $-26 - (-18)$ **10.** $-60 - (-48)$

11. $-6 - 5$ **12.** $-8 - 4$ **13.** $16 - (-21)$ **14.** $15 - (-33)$ **15.** $-6 - (-11)$

16. $-4 - (-16)$ **17.** $-44 - 27$ **18.** $-36 - 51$ **19.** $-21 - (-21)$ **20.** $-17 - (-17)$

21. $-\frac{3}{11} - \left(-\frac{5}{11}\right)$ **22.** $-\frac{4}{7} - \left(-\frac{1}{7}\right)$ **23.** $9.7 - 16.1$ **24.** $8.3 - 11.2$ **25.** $-2.6 - (-6.7)$

26. $-6.1 - (-5.3)$ **27.** $\frac{1}{2} - \frac{2}{3}$ **28.** $\frac{3}{4} - \frac{7}{8}$ **29.** $-\frac{1}{6} - \frac{3}{4}$ **30.** $-\frac{1}{10} - \frac{7}{8}$

31. $8.3 - (-0.62)$ **32.** $4.3 - (-0.87)$ **33.** $0 - 8.92$ **34.** $0 - (-4.21)$

Translating *Translate each phrase to an expression and simplify. See Example 5.*

35. Subtract -5 from 8.

36. Subtract -2 from 3.

37. Find the difference between -6 and -1.

38. Find the difference between -17 and -1.

39. Subtract 8 from 7.

40. Subtract 9 from -4.

41. Decrease -8 by 15.

42. Decrease 11 by -14.

Mixed Practice (Sections 1.3, 1.4, 1.5) *Simplify each expression. (Remember the order of operations.) See Examples 6 and 7.*

43. $-10 - (-8) + (-4) - 20$

44. $-16 - (-3) + (-11) - 14$

45. $5 - 9 + (-4) - 8 - 8$

46. $7 - 12 + (-5) - 2 + (-2)$

47. $-6 - (2 - 11)$

48. $-9 - (3 - 8)$

49. $3^3 - 8 \cdot 9$

50. $2^3 - 6 \cdot 3$

51. $2 - 3(8 - 6)$

52. $4 - 6(7 - 3)$

53. $(3 - 6) + 4^2$

54. $(2 - 3) + 5^2$

55. $-2 + [(8 - 11) - (-2 - 9)]$

56. $-5 + [(4 - 15) - (-6) - 8]$

57. $|-3| + 2^2 + [-4 - (-6)]$

58. $|-2| + 6^2 + (-3 - 8)$

Objective B *Evaluate each expression when $x = -5$, $y = 4$, and $t = 10$. See Example 8.*

59. $x - y$

60. $y - x$

61. $\frac{9 - x}{y + 6}$

62. $\frac{15 - x}{y + 2}$

63. $|x| + 2t - 8y$

64. $|y| + 3x - 2t$

65. $y^2 - x$

66. $t^2 - x$

67. $\frac{|x - (-10)|}{2t}$

68. $\frac{|5y - x|}{6t}$

Objective C *Decide whether the given number is a solution of the given equation. See Example 9.*

69. $x - 9 = 5$; -4

70. $x - 10 = -7$; 3

71. $-x + 6 = -x - 1$; -2

72. $-x - 6 = -x - 1$; -10

73. $-x - 13 = -15$; 2

74. $4 = 1 - x$; 5

Objectives D E **Mixed Practice** *Solve. See Examples 10 and 11.*

75. The coldest temperature ever recorded on Earth was $-129°F$ in Antarctica. The warmest temperature ever recorded was 136°F in the Sahara Desert. How many degrees warmer is 136°F than $-129°F$? (*Source: Questions Kids Ask*, Grolier Limited, 1991, and *The World Almanac*)

76. The coldest temperature ever recorded in the United States was $-80°F$ in Alaska. The warmest temperature ever recorded was 134°F in California. How many degrees warmer is 134°F than $-80°F$? (*Source: The World Almanac*, 2005)

77. Mauna Kea in Hawaii has an elevation of 13,796 feet above sea level. The Mid-America Trench in the Pacific Ocean has an elevation of 21,857 feet below sea level. Find the difference in elevation between those two points. (*Source:* National Geographic Society and Defense Mapping Agency)

78. A woman received a statement of her charge account at Old Navy. She spent $93 on purchases last month. She returned an $18 top because she didn't like the color. She also returned a $26 nightshirt because it was damaged. What does she actually owe on her account?

79. Find x if the angles below are complementary angles.

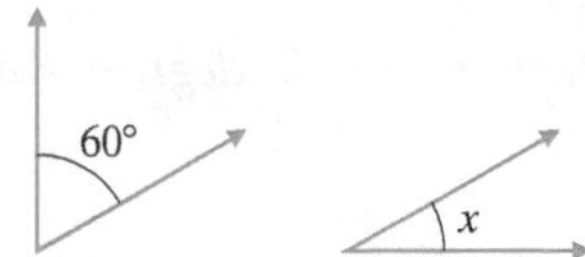

80. Find y if the angles below are supplementary angles.

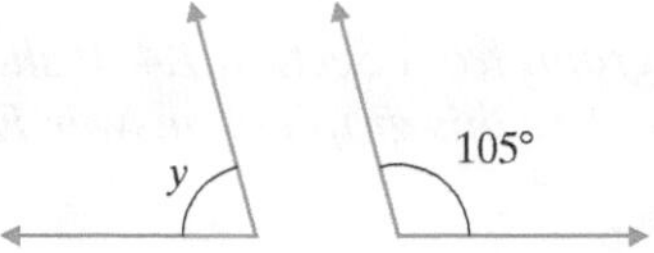

81. A commercial jetliner hits an air pocket and drops 250 feet. After climbing 120 feet, it drops another 178 feet. What is its overall vertical change?

82. In some card games, it is possible to have a negative score. Lavonne Schultz currently has a score of 15 points. She then loses 24 points. What is her new score?

83. The highest point in Africa is Mt. Kilimanjaro, Tanzania, at an elevation of 19,340 feet. The lowest point is Lake Assal, Djibouti, at 512 feet below sea level. How much higher is Mt. Kilimanjaro than Lake Assal? (*Source:* National Geographic Society)

84. The airport in Bishop, California, is at an elevation of 4101 feet above sea level. The nearby Furnace Creek Airport in Death Valley, California, is at an elevation of 226 feet below sea level. How much higher in elevation is the Bishop Airport than the Furnace Creek Airport? (*Source:* National Climatic Data Center)

Find each unknown complementary or supplementary angle.

85.

y 50°

86.

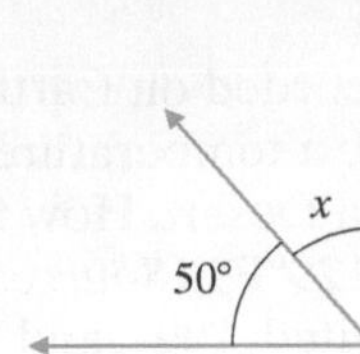

Mixed Practice–Translating (*Sections 1.4, 1.5*) *Translate each phrase to an algebraic expression. Use "x" to represent "a number."*

87. The sum of -5 and a number.

88. The difference of -3 and a number.

89. Subtract a number from -20.

90. Add a number and -36.

Concept Extensions

Recall the bar graph from Section 1.4. It shows each month's average daily low temperature in degrees Fahrenheit for Barrow, Alaska. Use this graph to answer Exercises 91 through 94.

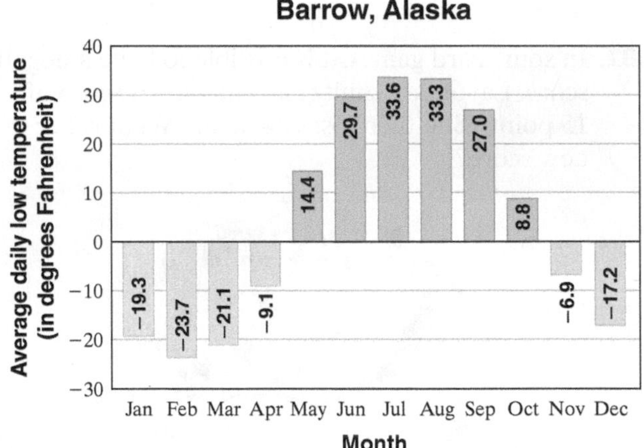

Source: National Climatic Data Center

91. Record the monthly increases and decreases in the low temperature from the previous month.

Month	Monthly Increase or Decrease (from the previous month)
February	
March	
April	
May	
June	

92. Record the monthly increases and decreases in the low temperature from the previous month.

Month	Monthly Increase or Decrease (from the previous month)
July	
August	
September	
October	
November	
December	

93. Which month had the greatest increase in temperature?

94. Which month had the greatest decrease in temperature?

95. Find two numbers whose difference is -5.

96. Find two numbers whose difference is -9.

Each calculation below is ***incorrect.*** *Find the error and correct it.*

97. $9 - (-7) \stackrel{?}{=} 2$

98. $-4 - 8 \stackrel{?}{=} 4$

99. $10 - 30 \stackrel{?}{=} 20$

100. $-3 - (-10) \stackrel{?}{=} -13$

If p is a positive number and n is a negative number, determine whether each statement is true or false. Explain your answer.

101. $p - n$ is always a positive number.

102. $n - p$ is always a negative number.

103. $|n| - |p|$ is always a positive number.

104. $|n - p|$ is always a positive number.

Without calculating, determine whether each answer is positive or negative. Then use a calculator to find the exact difference.

105. 56,875 − 87,262

106. 4.362 − 7.0086

Answers

1. ______
2. ______
3. ______
4. ______
5. ______
6. ______
7. ______
8. ______
9. ______
10. ______
11. ______
12. ______
13. ______
14. ______
15. ______
16. ______
17. ______
18. ______
19. ______
20. ______
21. ______
22. ______
23. ______
24. ______

Integrated Review Sections 1.1–1.5

Operations on Real Numbers

Answer the following with positive, negative, or 0.

1. The opposite of a positive number is a ______ number.

2. The sum of two negative numbers is a ______ number.

3. The absolute value of a negative number is a ______ number.

4. The absolute value of zero is ______.

5. The sum of two positive numbers is a ______ number.

6. The sum of a number and its opposite is ______.

7. The absolute value of a positive number is a ______ number.

8. The opposite of a negative number is a ______ number.

Fill in the chart:

	Number	Opposite	Absolute Value
9.	$\frac{1}{7}$		
10.	$-\frac{12}{5}$		
11.		-3	
12.		$\frac{9}{11}$	

Perform each indicated operation and simplify. For Exercises 39 and 40, perform the operations within the parentheses first.

13. $-19 + (-23)$ **14.** $7 - (-3)$ **15.** $-15 + 17$ **16.** $-8 - 10$

17. $18 + (-25)$ **18.** $-2 + (-37)$ **19.** $-14 - (-12)$ **20.** $5 - 14$

21. $4.5 - 7.9$ **22.** $-8.6 - 1.2$ **23.** $-\frac{3}{4} - \frac{1}{7}$ **24.** $\frac{2}{3} - \frac{7}{8}$

25. $-9 - (-7) + 4 - 6$

26. $11 - 20 + (-3) - 12$

27. $24 - 6(14 - 11)$

28. $30 - 5(10 - 8)$

29. $(7 - 17) + 4^2$

30. $9^2 + (10 - 30)$

31. $|-9| + 3^2 + (-4 - 20)$

32. $|-4 - 5| + 5^2 + (-50)$

33. $-7 + [(1 - 2) + (-2 - 9)]$

34. $-6 + [(-3 + 7) + (4 - 15)]$

35. Subtract 5 from 1.

36. Subtract -2 from -3.

37. Subtract $-\frac{2}{5}$ from $\frac{1}{4}$.

38. Subtract $\frac{1}{10}$ from $-\frac{5}{8}$.

39. $2(19 - 17)^3 - 3(-7 + 9)^2$

40. $3(10 - 9)^2 + 6(20 - 19)^3$

Evaluate each expression when $x = -2$, $y = -1$, and $z = 9$.

41. $x - y$

42. $x + y$

43. $y + z$

44. $z - y$

45. $\frac{|5z - x|}{y - x}$

46. $\frac{|-x - y + z|}{2z}$

25. ______

26. ______

27. ______

28. ______

29. ______

30. ______

31. ______

32. ______

33. ______

34. ______

35. ______

36. ______

37. ______

38. ______

39. ______

40. ______

41. ______

42. ______

43. ______

44. ______

45. ______

46. ______

Objectives

A Multiply Real Numbers.

B Find the Reciprocal of a Real Number.

C Divide Real Numbers.

D Evaluate Expressions Using Real Numbers.

E Determine Whether a Number is a Solution of a Given Equation.

F Solve Applications That Involve Multiplication or Division of Real Numbers

1.6 MULTIPLYING AND DIVIDING REAL NUMBERS

Objective A Multiplying Real Numbers

Multiplication of real numbers is similar to multiplication of whole numbers. We just need to determine when the answer is positive, when it is negative, and when it is zero. To discover sign patterns for multiplication, recall that multiplication is repeated addition. For example, 3(2) means that 2 is added to itself three times, or

$$3(2) = 2 + 2 + 2 = 6$$

Also,

$$3(-2) = (-2) + (-2) + (-2) = -6$$

Since $3(-2) = -6$, this suggests that the product of a positive number and a negative number is a negative number.

What about the product of two negative numbers? To find out, consider the following pattern.

$-3 \cdot 2 = -6$ Factor decreases by 1 each time.

$-3 \cdot 1 = -3$ Product increases by 3 each time.

$-3 \cdot 0 = 0$

$-3 \cdot -1 = 3$

$-3 \cdot -2 = 6$

This suggests that the product of two negative numbers is a positive number. Our results are given below.

Multiplying Real Numbers

1. The product of two numbers with the *same* sign is a positive number.
2. The product of two numbers with *different* signs is a negative number.

Examples Multiply.

1. $-7(6) = -42$ Different signs, so the product is negative.
2. $2(-10) = -20$
3. $-2(-14) = 28$ Same sign, so the product is positive.
4. $-\frac{2}{3} \cdot \frac{4}{7} = -\frac{2 \cdot 4}{3 \cdot 7} = -\frac{8}{21}$
5. $5(-1.7) = -8.5$
6. $-18(-3) = 54$

Work Practice 1-6

PRACTICE 1-6

Multiply.

1. $-8(3)$ 2. $5(-30)$

3. $-4(-12)$ 4. $-\frac{5}{6} \cdot \frac{1}{4}$

5. $6(-2.3)$ 6. $-15(-2)$

Answers

1. -24 2. -150 3. 48 4. $-\frac{5}{24}$ 5. -13.8 6. 30

We already know that the product of 0 and any whole number is 0. This is true of all real numbers.

Products Involving Zero

If b is a real number, then $b \cdot 0 = 0$. Also $0 \cdot b = 0$.

Example 7 Multiply.

a. $7(0)(-6)$ **b.** $(-2)(-3)(-4)$ **c.** $(-1)(-5)(-9)(-2)$

Solution:

a. By the order of operations, we multiply from left to right. Notice that because one of the factors is 0, the product is 0.

$$7(0)(-6) = 0(-6) = 0$$

b. Multiply two factors at a time, from left to right.

$$(-2)(-3)(-4) = (6)(-4) \quad \text{Multiply } (-2)(-3).$$
$$= -24$$

c. Multiply from left to right.

$$(-1)(-5)(-9)(-2) = (5)(-9)(-2) \quad \text{Multiply } (-1)(-5).$$
$$= -45(-2) \quad \text{Multiply } 5(-9).$$
$$= 90$$

Work Practice 7

PRACTICE 7

Multiply.

a. $5(0)(-3)$

b. $(-1)(-6)(-7)$

c. $(-2)(4)(-8)(-1)$

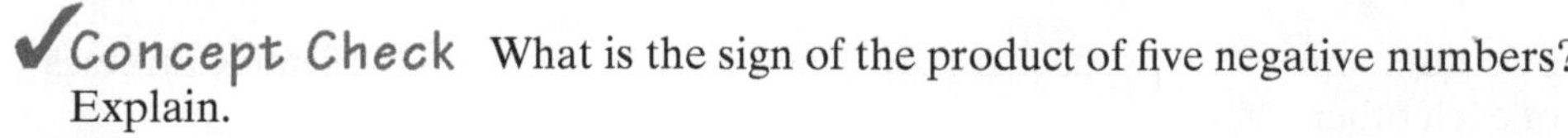

✓**Concept Check** What is the sign of the product of five negative numbers? Explain.

Helpful Hint

Have you noticed a pattern when multiplying signed numbers?

If we let $(-)$ represent a negative number and $(+)$ represent a positive number, then

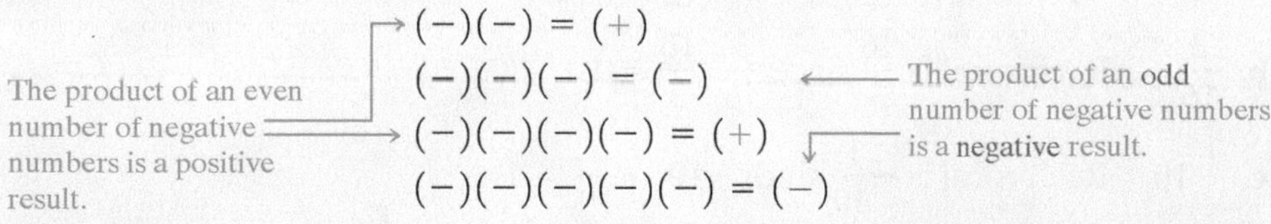

$(-)(-) = (+)$

$(-)(-)(-) = (-)$

$(-)(-)(-)(-) = (+)$

$(-)(-)(-)(-)(-) = (-)$

The product of an even number of negative numbers is a positive result.

The product of an odd number of negative numbers is a negative result.

Now that we know how to multiply positive and negative numbers, let's see how we find the values of $(-5)^2$ and -5^2, for example. Although these two expressions look similar, the difference between the two is the parentheses. In $(-5)^2$, the parentheses tell us that the base, or repeated factor, is -5. In -5^2, only 5 is the base. Thus,

$$(-5)^2 = (-5)(-5) = 25 \quad \text{The base is } -5.$$
$$-5^2 = -(5 \cdot 5) = -25 \quad \text{The base is 5.}$$

Example 8 Evaluate.

a. $(-2)^3$ **b.** -2^3 **c.** $(-3)^2$ **d.** -3^2 **e.** $\left(-\frac{2}{3}\right)^2$

Solution:

a. $(-2)^3 = (-2)(-2)(-2) = -8$ The base is -2.

b. $-2^3 = -(2 \cdot 2 \cdot 2) = -8$ The base is 2.

c. $(-3)^2 = (-3)(-3) = 9$ The base is -3.

d. $-3^2 = -(3 \cdot 3) = -9$ The base is 3.

e. $\left(-\frac{2}{3}\right)^2 = \left(-\frac{2}{3}\right)\left(-\frac{2}{3}\right) = \frac{4}{9}$ The base is $-\frac{2}{3}$.

Work Practice 8

PRACTICE 8

Evaluate.

a. $(-2)^4$ **b.** -2^4

c. $(-1)^5$ **d.** -1^5

e. $\left(-\frac{7}{9}\right)^2$

Answers

7. a. 0 **b.** -42 **c.** -64

8. a. 16 **b.** -16 **c.** -1 **d.** -1 **e.** $\frac{49}{81}$

✓ **Concept Check Answer**

negative

Helpful Hint

Be careful when identifying the base of an exponential expression.

$(-3)^2$	-3^2
Base is -3	Base is 3
$(-3)^2 = (-3)(-3) = 9$	$-3^2 = -(3 \cdot 3) = -9$

Objective B Finding Reciprocals

Addition and subtraction are related. Every difference of two numbers $a - b$ can be written as the sum $a + (-b)$. Multiplication and division are related also. For example, the quotient $6 \div 3$ can be written as the product $6 \cdot \frac{1}{3}$. Recall that the pair of numbers 3 and $\frac{1}{3}$ has a special relationship. Their product is 1 and they are called **reciprocals** or **multiplicative inverses** of each other.

Reciprocal or Multiplicative Inverse

Two numbers whose product is 1 are called **reciprocals** or **multiplicative inverses** of each other.

PRACTICE 9

Find the reciprocal of each number.

a. 13 **b.** $\frac{7}{15}$

c. -5 **d.** $-\frac{8}{11}$

e. 7.9

Example 9 Find the reciprocal of each number.

a. 22 Reciprocal is $\frac{1}{22}$ since $22 \cdot \frac{1}{22} = 1$.

b. $\frac{3}{16}$ Reciprocal is $\frac{16}{3}$ since $\frac{3}{16} \cdot \frac{16}{3} = 1$.

c. -10 Reciprocal is $-\frac{1}{10}$ since $-10 \cdot -\frac{1}{10} = 1$.

d. $-\frac{9}{13}$ Reciprocal is $-\frac{13}{9}$ since $-\frac{9}{13} \cdot -\frac{13}{9} = 1$.

e. 1.7 Reciprocal is $\frac{1}{1.7}$ since $1.7 \cdot \frac{1}{1.7} = 1$.

Work Practice 9

Helpful Hint

The fraction $\frac{1}{1.7}$ is not simplified since the denominator is a decimal number. For the purpose of finding a reciprocal, we will leave the fraction as is.

Does the number 0 have a reciprocal? If it does, it is a number n such that $0 \cdot n = 1$. Notice that this can never be true since $0 \cdot n = 0$. This means that 0 has no reciprocal.

Quotients Involving Zero

The number 0 does not have a reciprocal.

Answers

9. a. $\frac{1}{13}$ **b.** $\frac{15}{7}$ **c.** $-\frac{1}{5}$ **d.** $-\frac{11}{8}$ **e.** $\frac{1}{7.9}$

Objective C Dividing Real Numbers

We may now write a quotient as an equivalent product.

Quotient of Two Real Numbers

If a and b are real numbers and b is not 0, then

$$a \div b = \frac{a}{b} = a \cdot \frac{1}{b}$$

In other words, the quotient of two real numbers is the product of the first number and the multiplicative inverse or reciprocal of the second number.

Example 10 Use the definition of the quotient of two numbers to find each quotient. $\left(a \div b = a \cdot \frac{1}{b}\right)$

a. $-18 \div 3$ **b.** $\frac{-14}{-2}$ **c.** $\frac{20}{-4}$

Solution:

a. $-18 \div 3 = -18 \cdot \frac{1}{3} = -6$

b. $\frac{-14}{-2} = -14 \cdot -\frac{1}{2} = 7$

c. $\frac{20}{-4} = 20 \cdot -\frac{1}{4} = -5$

Work Practice 10

Since the quotient $a \div b$ can be written as the product $a \cdot \frac{1}{b}$, it follows that sign patterns for dividing two real numbers are the same as sign patterns for multiplying two real numbers.

Dividing Real Numbers

1. The quotient of two numbers with the *same* sign is a positive number.
2. The quotient of two numbers with *different* signs is a negative number.

Example 11 Divide.

a. $\frac{-30}{-10} = 3$ Same sign, so the quotient is positive.

b. $\frac{-100}{5} = -20$

c. $\frac{20}{-2} = -10$ Different signs, so the quotient is negative.

d. $\frac{42}{-0.6} = -70$ $0.6\overline{)42.0}$ = 70.

Work Practice 11

✓Concept Check What is wrong with the following calculation?

$\frac{-36}{-9} = -4$

PRACTICE 10

Use the definition of the quotient of two numbers to find each quotient.

a. $-12 \div 4$ **b.** $\frac{-20}{-10}$

c. $\frac{36}{-4}$

PRACTICE 11

Divide.

a. $\frac{-25}{5}$ **b.** $\frac{-48}{-6}$

c. $\frac{50}{-2}$ **d.** $\frac{-72}{0.2}$

Answers

10. a. -3 **b.** 2 **c.** -9

11. a. -5 **b.** 8 **c.** -25 **d.** -360

✓ Concept Check Answer

$\frac{-36}{-9} = 4$

In the examples on the previous page, we divided mentally or by long division. When we divide by a fraction, it is usually easier to multiply by its reciprocal.

PRACTICE 12–13

Divide.

12. $-\frac{5}{9} \div \frac{2}{3}$ **13.** $-\frac{2}{7} \div \left(-\frac{1}{5}\right)$

Examples Divide.

12. $\frac{2}{3} \div \left(-\frac{5}{4}\right) = \frac{2}{3} \cdot \left(-\frac{4}{5}\right) = -\frac{8}{15}$

13. $-\frac{1}{6} \div \left(-\frac{2}{3}\right) = -\frac{1}{6} \cdot \left(-\frac{3}{2}\right) = \frac{3}{12} = \frac{\overset{1}{\cancel{3}}}{\underset{1}{\cancel{3}} \cdot 4} = \frac{1}{4}$

Work Practice 12–13

Our definition of the quotient of two real numbers does not allow for division by 0 because 0 does not have a reciprocal. How then do we interpret $\frac{3}{0}$? We say that an expression such as this one is **undefined.** Can we divide 0 by a number other than 0? Yes; for example,

$$\frac{0}{3} = 0 \cdot \frac{1}{3} = 0$$

Division Involving Zero

If a is a nonzero number, then $\frac{0}{a} = 0$ and $\frac{a}{0}$ is undefined.

PRACTICE 14

Divide if possible.

a. $\frac{-7}{0}$ **b.** $\frac{0}{-2}$

Example 14 Divide, if possible.

a. $\frac{1}{0}$ is undefined. **b.** $\frac{0}{-3} = 0$

Work Practice 14

Notice that $\frac{12}{-2} = -6$, $-\frac{12}{2} = -6$, and $\frac{-12}{2} = -6$. This means that

$$\frac{12}{-2} = -\frac{12}{2} = \frac{-12}{2}$$

In other words, a single negative sign in a fraction can be written in the denominator, in the numerator, or in front of the fraction without changing the value of the fraction.

If a and b are real numbers, and $b \neq 0$, then $\frac{a}{-b} = \frac{-a}{b} = -\frac{a}{b}$.

Objective D Evaluating Expressions

Examples combining basic arithmetic operations along with the principles of the order of operations help us to review these concepts of multiplying and dividing real numbers.

Answers

12. $-\frac{5}{6}$ **13.** $\frac{10}{7}$

14. a. undefined **b.** 0

Example 15 Use order of operations to evaluate each expression.

a. $\frac{0(-8)}{2}$ **b.** $-4(-11) - 5(-2)$

c. $(-2)^2 + 3[(-3 - 2) - |4 - 6|]$ **d.** $\frac{(-12)(-3) + 4}{-7 - (-2)}$

e. $\frac{2(-3)^2 - 20}{|-5| + 4}$

Solution:

a. $\frac{0(-8)}{2} = \frac{0}{2} = 0$

b. $(-4)(-11) - 5(-2) = 44 - (-10)$ Find the products.
$= 44 + 10$ Add 44 to the opposite of -10.
$= 54$ Add.

c. $(-2)^2 + 3[(-3 - 2) - |4 - 6|] = (-2)^2 + 3[(-5) - |-2|]$ Simplify within innermost sets of grouping symbols.
$= (-2)^2 + 3[-5 - 2]$ Write $|-2|$ as 2.
$= (-2)^2 + 3(-7)$ Combine.
$= 4 + (-21)$ Evaluate $(-2)^2$ and multiply $3(-7)$.
$= -17$ Add.

For parts d and e, first simplify the numerator and denominator separately; then divide.

d. $\frac{(-12)(-3) + 4}{-7 - (-2)} = \frac{36 + 4}{-7 + 2}$
$= \frac{40}{-5}$
$= -8$ Divide.

e. $\frac{2(-3)^2 - 20}{|-5| + 4} = \frac{2 \cdot 9 - 20}{5 + 4} = \frac{18 - 20}{9} = \frac{-2}{9} = -\frac{2}{9}$

Work Practice 15

PRACTICE 15

Use order of operations to evaluate each expression.

a. $\frac{0(-5)}{3}$

b. $-3(-9) - 4(-4)$

c. $(-3)^2 + 2[(5 - 15) - |-4 - 1|]$

d. $\frac{-7(-4) + 2}{-10 - (-5)}$

e. $\frac{5(-2)^3 + 52}{-4 + 1}$

Using what we have learned about multiplying and dividing real numbers, we continue to practice evaluating algebraic expressions.

Example 16 Evaluate each expression when $x = -2$ and $y = -4$.

a. $\frac{3x}{2y}$ **b.** $x^3 - y^2$ **c.** $\frac{x - y}{-x}$

Solution: Replace x with -2 and y with -4 and simplify.

a. $\frac{3x}{2y} = \frac{3(-2)}{2(-4)} = \frac{-6}{-8} = \frac{6}{8} = \frac{\overset{1}{\cancel{2}} \cdot 3}{\underset{1}{\cancel{2}} \cdot 4} = \frac{3}{4}$

Continued on next page

PRACTICE 16

Evaluate each expression when $x = -1$ and $y = -5$.

a. $\frac{3y}{45x}$

b. $x^2 - y^3$

c. $\frac{x + y}{3x}$

Answers

15. a. 0 **b.** 43 **c.** -21 **d.** -6 **e.** -4 **16. a.** $\frac{1}{3}$ **b.** 126 **c.** 2

b. $x^3 - y^2 = (-2)^3 - (-4)^2$ Substitute the given values for the variables.
$= -8 - (16)$ Evaluate $(-2)^3$ and $(-4)^2$.
$= -8 + (-16)$ Write as a sum.
$= -24$ Add.

c. $\dfrac{x - y}{-x} = \dfrac{-2 - (-4)}{-(-2)} = \dfrac{-2 + 4}{2} = \dfrac{2}{2} = 1$

Work Practice 16

Helpful Hint

Remember: For additional help when replacing variables with replacement values, first place parentheses about any variables.

Evaluate $3x - y^2$ when $x = 5$ and $y = -4$.

$3x - y^2 = 3(x) - (y)^2$ Place parentheses about variables only.
$= 3(5) - (-4)^2$ Replace variables with values.
$= 15 - 16$ Simplify.
$= -1$

Objective E Solutions of Equations

We use our skills in multiplying and dividing real numbers to check possible solutions of an equation.

PRACTICE 17

Determine whether -8 is a solution of $\dfrac{x}{4} - 3 = x + 3$.

Example 17 Determine whether -10 is a solution of $\dfrac{-20}{x} + 15 = 2x$.

Solution: $\dfrac{-20}{x} + 15 = 2x$ Original equation

$\dfrac{-20}{-10} + 15 \stackrel{?}{=} 2(-10)$ Replace x with -10.

$2 + 15 \stackrel{?}{=} -20$ Divide and multiply.

$17 = -20$ False

Since we have a false statement, -10 is *not* a solution of the equation.

Work Practice 17

Objective F Solving Applications That Involve Multiplying or Dividing Numbers

Many real-life problems involve multiplication and division of numbers.

Answer
17. -8 is a solution

Example 18 Calculating a Total Golf Score

A professional golfer finished seven strokes under par (-7) for each of three days of a tournament. What was her total score for the tournament?

Solution:

Although the key word is "total," since this is repeated addition of the same number, we multiply.

In words:	golfer's total score	=	number of days	·	score each day
	↓	↓	↓	↓	↓
Translate:	golfer's total	=	3	·	(-7)
		= -21			

Thus, the golfer's total score was -21, or 21 strokes under par.

Work Practice 18

PRACTICE 18

A card player had a score of -13 for each of four games. Find the total score.

Answer

18. -52

Calculator Explorations

Entering Negative Numbers on a Scientific Calculator

To enter a negative number on a scientific calculator, find a key marked [+/−]. (On some calculators, this key is marked [CHS] for "change sign.") To enter -8, for example, press the keys [8] [+/−]. The display will read [−8].

Entering Negative Numbers on a Graphing Calculator

To enter a negative number on a graphing calculator, find a key marked [(−)]. Do not confuse this key with the key [−], which is used for subtraction. To enter -8, for example, press the keys [(−)] [8]. The display will read [−8].

Operations with Real Numbers

To evaluate $-2(7 - 9) - 20$ on a calculator, press the keys

[2] [+/−] [×] [(] [7] [−] [9] [)] [−] [2] [0] [=], or [(−)] [2] [(] [7] [−] [9] [)] [−] [2] [0] [ENTER].

The display will read [−16] or [−2(7 − 9) − 20 −16]

Use a calculator to simplify each expression.

1. $-38(26 - 27)$
2. $-59(-8) + 1726$
3. $134 + 25(68 - 91)$
4. $45(32) - 8(218)$
5. $\dfrac{-50(294)}{175 - 205}$
6. $\dfrac{-444 - 444.8}{-181 - (-181)}$
7. $9^5 - 4550$
8. $5^8 - 6259$
9. $(-125)^2$ (Be careful.)
10. -125^2 (Be careful.)

Vocabulary and Readiness Check

Use the choices below to fill in each blank. Each choice may be used more than once.

negative 0

positive undefined

1. The product of a negative number and a positive number is a(n) _________ number.
2. The product of two negative numbers is a(n) _________ number.
3. The quotient of two negative numbers is a(n) _________ number.
4. The quotient of a negative number and a positive number is a(n) _________ number.
5. The product of a negative number and zero is _________.
6. The reciprocal of a negative number is a _________ number.
7. The quotient of 0 and a negative number is _________.
8. The quotient of a negative number and 0 is _________.

1.6 Exercise Set

FOR EXTRA HELP

PRACTICE

WATCH

DOWNLOAD

READ

REVIEW

Objective A *Multiply. See Examples 1 through 7.*

1. $-6(4)$ **2.** $-8(5)$ **3.** $2(-1)$ **4.** $7(-4)$

5. $-5(-10)$ **6.** $-6(-11)$ **7.** $-3 \cdot 15$ **8.** $-2 \cdot 37$

9. $-\frac{1}{2}\left(-\frac{3}{5}\right)$ **10.** $-\frac{1}{8}\left(-\frac{1}{3}\right)$ **11.** $5(-1.4)$ **12.** $6(-2.5)$

13. $(-1)(-3)(-5)$ **14.** $(-2)(-3)(-4)$ **15.** $(2)(-1)(-3)(0)$ **16.** $(3)(-5)(-2)(0)$

Evaluate. See Example 8.

17. $(-4)^2$ **18.** $(-3)^3$ **19.** -4^2 **20.** -6^2

21. $\left(-\frac{3}{4}\right)^2$ **22.** $\left(-\frac{2}{7}\right)^2$ **23.** -0.7^2 **24.** -0.8^2

Objective B *Find each reciprocal. See Example 9.*

25. $\frac{2}{3}$ **26.** $\frac{1}{7}$ **27.** -14 **28.** -8

29. $-\frac{3}{11}$ **30.** $-\frac{6}{13}$ **31.** 0.2 **32.** 1.5

Objective C *Divide. See Examples 10 through 14.*

33. $\frac{18}{-2}$

34. $\frac{36}{-9}$

35. $-48 \div 12$

36. $-60 \div 5$

37. $\frac{0}{-4}$

38. $\frac{0}{-9}$

39. $\frac{5}{0}$

40. $\frac{8}{0}$

41. $\frac{6}{7} \div \left(-\frac{1}{3}\right)$

42. $\frac{4}{5} \div \left(-\frac{1}{2}\right)$

43. $-3.2 \div -0.02$

44. $-4.9 \div -0.07$

Objectives A C **Mixed Practice** *Perform the indicated operation. See Examples 1–14.*

45. $(-8)(-8)$

46. $(-7)(-7)$

47. $\frac{2}{3}\left(-\frac{4}{9}\right)$

48. $\frac{2}{7}\left(-\frac{2}{11}\right)$

49. $\frac{-12}{-4}$

50. $\frac{-45}{-9}$

51. $\frac{30}{-2}$

52. $\frac{14}{-2}$

53. $(-5)^3$

54. $(-2)^5$

55. $(-0.2)^3$

56. $(-0.3)^3$

57. $-\frac{3}{4}\left(-\frac{8}{9}\right)$

58. $-\frac{5}{6}\left(-\frac{3}{10}\right)$

59. $-\frac{5}{9} \div \left(-\frac{3}{4}\right)$

60. $-\frac{1}{10} \div \left(-\frac{8}{11}\right)$

61. $-2.1(-0.4)$

62. $-1.3(-0.6)$

63. $\frac{-48}{1.2}$

64. $\frac{-86}{2.5}$

65. $(-3)^4$

66. -3^4

67. -1^7

68. $(-1)^7$

69. Multiply -11 by 11.

70. Multiply -12 by 12.

71. Find the quotient of $-\frac{4}{9}$ and $\frac{4}{9}$.

72. Find the quotient of $-\frac{5}{12}$ and $\frac{5}{12}$.

Mixed Practice (Sections 1.4, 1.5, 1.6) *Perform the indicated operation.*

73. $-9 - 10$

74. $-8 - 11$

75. $-9(-10)$

76. $-8(-11)$

77. $7(-12)$

78. $6(-15)$

79. $7 + (-12)$

80. $6 + (-15)$

Objective **D** *Evaluate each expression. See Example 15.*

81. $\frac{-9(-3)}{-6}$

82. $\frac{-6(-3)}{-4}$

83. $-3(2-8)$

84. $-4(3-9)$

85. $-7(-2)-3(-1)$

86. $-8(-3)-4(-1)$

87. $2^2-3[(2-8)-(-6-8)]$

88. $3^2-2[(3-5)-(2-9)]$

89. $\frac{-6^2+4}{-2}$

90. $\frac{3^2+4}{5}$

91. $\frac{-3-5^2}{2(-7)}$

92. $\frac{-2-4^2}{3(-6)}$

93. $\frac{22+(3)(-2)^2}{-5-2}$

94. $\frac{-20+(-4)^2(3)}{1-5}$

95. $\frac{(-4)^2-16}{4-12}$

96. $\frac{(-2)^2-4}{4-9}$

97. $\frac{6-2(-3)}{4-3(-2)}$

98. $\frac{8-3(-2)}{2-5(-4)}$

99. $\frac{|5-9|+|10-15|}{|2(-3)|}$

100. $\frac{|-3+6|+|-2+7|}{|-2\cdot 2|}$

101. $\frac{-7(-1)+(-3)4}{(-2)(5)+(-6)(-8)}$

102. $\frac{8(-7)+(-2)(-6)}{(-9)(3)+(-10)(-11)}$

Evaluate each expression when $x=-5$ and $y=-3$. See Example 16.

103. $\frac{2x-5}{y-2}$

104. $\frac{2y-12}{x-4}$

105. $\frac{6-y}{x-4}$

106. $\frac{10-y}{x-8}$

107. $\frac{4-2x}{y+3}$

108. $\frac{2y+3}{-5-x}$

109. $\frac{x^2+y}{3y}$

110. $\frac{y^2-x}{2x}$

Objective **E** *Decide whether the given number is a solution of the given equation. See Example 17.*

111. $-3x-5=-20$; 5

112. $17-4x=x+27$; -2

113. $\frac{x}{5}+2=-1$; 15

114. $\frac{x}{6}-3=5$; 48

115. $\frac{x-3}{7}=-2$; -11

116. $\frac{x+4}{5}=-6$; -30

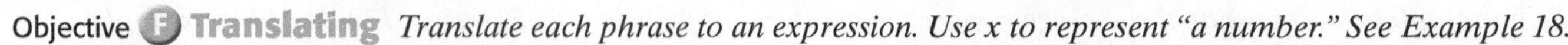

Objective **F** **Translating** *Translate each phrase to an expression. Use x to represent "a number." See Example 18.*

117. The product of −71 and a number

118. The quotient of −8 and a number

119. Subtract a number from −16.

120. The sum of a number and −12

121. −29 increased by a number

122. The difference of a number and −10

123. Divide a number by −33.

124. Multiply a number by −17.

Solve. See Example 18.

125. A football team lost four yards on each of three consecutive plays. Represent the total loss as a product of signed numbers and find the total loss.

126. Joe Norstrom lost $400 on each of seven consecutive days in the stock market. Represent his total loss as a product of signed numbers and find his total loss.

127. A deep-sea diver must move up or down in the water in short steps in order to keep from getting a physical condition called the "bends." Suppose a diver moves down from the surface in five steps of 20 feet each. Represent his total movement as a product of signed numbers and find the product.

128. A weather forecaster predicts that the temperature will drop five degrees each hour for the next six hours. Represent this drop as a product of signed numbers and find the total drop in temperature.

Concept Extensions

State whether each statement is true or false.

129. The product of three negative integers is negative.

130. The product of three positive integers is positive.

131. The product of four negative integers is negative.

132. The product of four positive integers is positive.

Study the bar graph below showing the average surface temperatures of planets. Use Exercises 133 and 134 to complete the planet temperatures on the graph. (Pluto is now classified as a dwarf planet.)

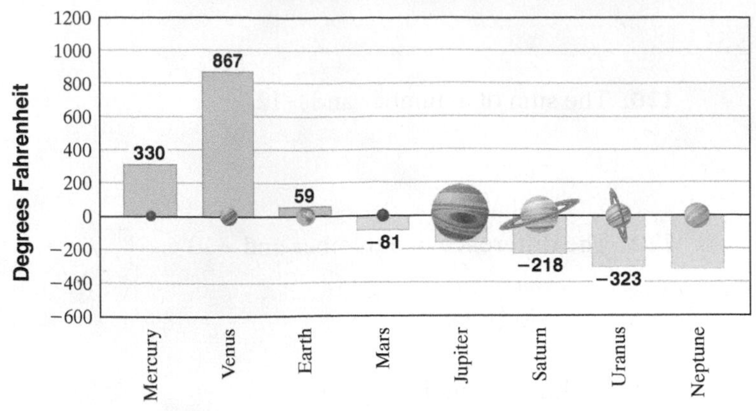

*(For some planets, the temperature given is the temperature where the atmosphere pressure equals 1 Earth atmosphere; Source: *The World Almanac*)

133. The surface temperature of Jupiter is twice the temperature of Mars. Find this temperature.

134. The surface temperature of Neptune is equal to the temperature of Mercury divided by -1. Find this temperature.

135. Explain why the product of an even number of negative numbers is a positive number.

136. If a and b are any real numbers, is the statement $a \cdot b = b \cdot a$ always true? Why or why not?

137. Find two real numbers that are their own reciprocal. Explain why there are only two.

138. Explain why 0 has no reciprocal.

Mixed Practice (1.4, 1.5, 1.6) *Write each as an algebraic expression. Then simplify the expression.*

139. 7 subtracted from the quotient of 0 and 5

140. Twice the sum of -3 and -4

141. -1 added to the product of -8 and -5

142. The difference of -9 and the product of -4 and -6

1.7 PROPERTIES OF REAL NUMBERS

Objectives

A Use the Commutative and Associative Properties.

B Use the Distributive Property.

C Use the Identity and Inverse Properties.

Objective A Using the Commutative and Associative Properties

In this section we review properties of real numbers with which we are already familiar. Throughout this section, the variables *a, b*, and *c* represent real numbers.

We know that order does not matter when adding numbers. For example, we know that $7 + 5$ is the same as $5 + 7$. This property is given a special name—the **commutative property of addition.** We also know that order does not matter when multiplying numbers. For example, we know that $-5(6) = 6(-5)$. This property means that multiplication is commutative also and is called the **commutative property of multiplication.**

Commutative Properties

Addition:	$a + b = b + a$
Multiplication:	$a \cdot b = b \cdot a$

These properties state that the *order* in which any two real numbers are added or multiplied does not change their sum or product. For example, if we let $a = 3$ and $b = 5$, then the commutative properties guarantee that

$$3 + 5 = 5 + 3 \quad \text{and} \quad 3 \cdot 5 = 5 \cdot 3$$

Helpful Hint

Is subtraction also commutative? Try an example. Is $3 - 2 = 2 - 3$? **No!** The left side of this statement equals 1; the right side equals -1. There is no commutative property of subtraction. Similarly, there is no commutative property of division. For example, $10 \div 2$ does not equal $2 \div 10$.

Example 1 Use a commutative property to complete each statement.

a. $x + 5 =$ _____ **b.** $3 \cdot x =$ _____

Solution:

a. $x + 5 = 5 + x$ By the commutative property of addition

b. $3 \cdot x = x \cdot 3$ By the commutative property of multiplication

Work Practice 1

PRACTICE 1

Use a commutative property to complete each statement.

a. $7 \cdot y =$ _____

b. $4 + x =$ _____

✓**Concept Check** Which of the following pairs of actions are commutative?

a. "raking the leaves" and "bagging the leaves"

b. "putting on your left glove" and "putting on your right glove"

c. "putting on your coat" and "putting on your shirt"

d. "reading a novel" and "reading a newspaper"

Answers

1. a. $y \cdot 7$ **b.** $x + 4$

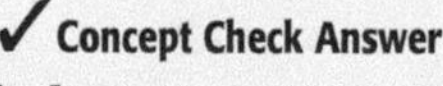

✓ **Concept Check Answer**

b, d

Let's now discuss grouping numbers. When we add three numbers, the way in which they are grouped or associated does not change their sum. For example, we know that $2 + (3 + 4) = 2 + 7 = 9$. This result is the same if we group the numbers differently. In other words, $(2 + 3) + 4 = 5 + 4 = 9$, also. Thus, $2 + (3 + 4) = (2 + 3) + 4$. This property is called the **associative property of addition.**

In the same way, changing the grouping of numbers when multiplying does not change their product. For example, $2 \cdot (3 \cdot 4) = (2 \cdot 3) \cdot 4$ (check it). This is the **associative property of multiplication.**

Associative Properties

Addition: $(a + b) + c = a + (b + c)$

Multiplication: $(a \cdot b) \cdot c = a \cdot (b \cdot c)$

These properties state that the way in which three numbers are *grouped* does not change their sum or their product.

PRACTICE 2

Use an associative property to complete each statement.

a. $5 \cdot (-3 \cdot 6) =$ _____
b. $(-2 + 7) + 3 =$ _____
c. $(q + r) + 17 =$ _____
d. $(ab) \cdot 21 =$ _____

Example 2 Use an associative property to complete each statement.

a. $5 + (4 + 6) =$ _____ **b.** $(-1 \cdot 2) \cdot 5 =$ _____
c. $(m + n) + 9 =$ _____ **d.** $(xy) \cdot 12 =$ _____

Solution:

a. $5 + (4 + 6) = (5 + 4) + 6$ By the associative property of addition
b. $(-1 \cdot 2) \cdot 5 = -1 \cdot (2 \cdot 5)$ By the associative property of multiplication
c. $(m + n) + 9 = m + (n + 9)$ By the associative property of addition
d. $(xy) \cdot 12 = x \cdot (y \cdot 12)$ Recall that xy means $x \cdot y$.

Work Practice 2

Helpful Hint

Remember the difference between the commutative properties and the associative properties. The commutative properties have to do with the *order* of numbers and the associative properties have to do with the *grouping* of numbers.

PRACTICE 3–4

Determine whether each statement is true by an associative property or a commutative property.

3. $5 \cdot (4 \cdot 7) = 5 \cdot (7 \cdot 4)$
4. $-2 + (4 + 9) = (-2 + 4) + 9$

Examples Determine whether each statement is true by an associative property or a commutative property.

3. $(7 + 10) + 4 = (10 + 7) + 4$ Since the order of two numbers was changed and their grouping was not, this is true by the commutative property of addition.

4. $2 \cdot (3 \cdot 1) = (2 \cdot 3) \cdot 1$ Since the grouping of the numbers was changed and their order was not, this is true by the associative property of multiplication.

Work Practice 3–4

Let's now illustrate how these properties can help us simplify expressions.

Answers
2. a. $(5 \cdot -3) \cdot 6$ **b.** $-2 + (7 + 3)$ **c.** $q + (r + 17)$ **d.** $a \cdot (b \cdot 21)$ **3.** commutative **4.** associative

Examples Simplify each expression.

5. $10 + (x + 12) = 10 + (12 + x)$ By the commutative property of addition
$= (10 + 12) + x$ By the associative property of addition
$= 22 + x$ Add.

6. $-3(7x) = (-3 \cdot 7)x$ By the associative property of multiplication
$= -21x$ Multiply.

Work Practice 5–6

PRACTICE 5–6

Simplify each expression.

5. $(-3 + x) + 17$
6. $4(5x)$

Objective B Using the Distributive Property

The **distributive property of multiplication over addition** is used repeatedly throughout algebra. It is useful because it allows us to write a product as a sum or a sum as a product.

We know that $7(2 + 4) = 7(6) = 42$. Compare that with

$$7(2) + 7(4) = 14 + 28 = 42$$

Since both original expressions equal 42, they must equal each other, or

$$7(2 + 4) = 7(2) + 7(4)$$

This is an example of the distributive property. The product on the left side of the equal sign is equal to the sum on the right side. We can think of the 7 as being distributed to each number inside the parentheses.

Distributive Property of Multiplication Over Addition

$$a(b + c) = ab + ac$$

Since multiplication is commutative, this property can also be written as

$$(b + c)a = ba + ca$$

The distributive property can also be extended to more than two numbers inside the parentheses. For example,

$$3(x + y + z) = 3(x) + 3(y) + 3(z)$$
$$= 3x + 3y + 3z$$

Since we define subtraction in terms of addition, the distributive property is also true for subtraction. For example,

$$2(x - y) = 2(x) - 2(y)$$
$$= 2x - 2y$$

Examples Use the distributive property to write each expression without parentheses. Then simplify the result.

7. $2(x + y) = 2(x) + 2(y)$
$= 2x + 2y$

8. $-5(-3 + 2z) = -5(-3) + (-5)(2z)$
$= 15 - 10z$

9. $5(x + 3y - z) = 5(x) + 5(3y) - 5(z)$
$= 5x + 15y - 5z$

Continued on next page

PRACTICE 7–12

Use the distributive property to write each expression without parentheses. Then simplify the result.

7. $5(x + y)$
8. $-3(2 + 7x)$
9. $4(x + 6y - 2z)$
10. $-1(3 - a)$
11. $-(8 + a - b)$
12. $\frac{1}{2}(2x + 4) + 9$

Answers

5. $14 + x$ 6. $20x$ 7. $5x + 5y$
8. $-6 - 21x$ 9. $4x + 24y - 8z$
10. $-3 + a$ 11. $-8 - a + b$
12. $x + 11$

10. $-1(2 - y) = (-1)(2) - (-1)(y)$
$= -2 + y$

11. $-(3 + x - w) = -1(3 + x - w)$
$= (-1)(3) + (-1)(x) - (-1)(w)$
$= -3 - x + w$

Helpful Hint

Notice in Example 11 that $-(3 + x - w)$ can be rewritten as $-1(3 + x - w)$.

12. $\frac{1}{2}(6x + 14) + 10 = \frac{1}{2}(6x) + \frac{1}{2}(14) + 10$ Apply the distributive property.
$= 3x + 7 + 10$ Multiply.
$= 3x + 17$ Add.

Work Practice 7–12

The distributive property can also be used to write a sum as a product.

PRACTICE 13–14

Use the distributive property to write each sum as a product.

13. $9 \cdot 3 + 9 \cdot y$

14. $4x + 4y$

Examples Use the distributive property to write each sum as a product.

13. $8 \cdot 2 + 8 \cdot x = 8(2 + x)$

14. $7s + 7t = 7(s + t)$

Work Practice 13–14

Objective C Using the Identity and Inverse Properties

Next, we look at the **identity properties.**

The number 0 is called the identity for addition because when 0 is added to any real number, the result is the same real number. In other words, the *identity* of the real number is not changed.

The number 1 is called the identity for multiplication because when a real number is multiplied by 1, the result is the same real number. In other words, the *identity* of the real number is not changed.

Identities for Addition and Multiplication

0 is the identity element for addition.

$a + 0 = a$ and $0 + a = a$

1 is the identity element for multiplication.

$a \cdot 1 = a$ and $1 \cdot a = a$

Notice that 0 is the *only* number that can be added to any real number with the result that the sum is the same real number. Also, 1 is the *only* number that can be multiplied by any real number with the result that the product is the same real number.

Additive inverses or **opposites** were introduced in Section 1.4. Two numbers are called additive inverses or opposites if their sum is 0. The additive inverse or opposite of 6 is -6 because $6 + (-6) = 0$. The additive inverse or opposite of -5 is 5 because $-5 + 5 = 0$.

Reciprocals or **multiplicative inverses** were introduced in Section 1.6. Two nonzero numbers are called reciprocals or multiplicative inverses if their product is 1. The reciprocal or multiplicative inverse of $\frac{2}{3}$ is $\frac{3}{2}$ because $\frac{2}{3} \cdot \frac{3}{2} = 1$. Likewise, the reciprocal of -5 is $-\frac{1}{5}$ because $-5\left(-\frac{1}{5}\right) = 1$.

Answers

13. $9(3 + y)$ **14.** $4(x + y)$

Additive or Multiplicative Inverses

The numbers a and $-a$ are additive inverses or opposites of each other because their sum is 0; that is,

$$a + (-a) = 0$$

The numbers b and $\frac{1}{b}$ (for $b \neq 0$) are reciprocals or multiplicative inverses of each other because their product is 1; that is,

$$b \cdot \frac{1}{b} = 1$$

✓**Concept Check** Which of the following is

a. the opposite of $-\frac{3}{10}$, and

b. the reciprocal of $-\frac{3}{10}$?

$1, -\frac{10}{3}, \frac{3}{10}, 0, \frac{10}{3}, -\frac{3}{10}$

Examples Name the property illustrated by each true statement.

15. $3(x + y) = 3 \cdot x + 3 \cdot y$ — Distributive property

16. $(x + 7) + 9 = x + (7 + 9)$ — Associative property of addition (grouping changed)

17. $(b + 0) + 3 = b + 3$ — Identity element for addition

18. $2 \cdot (z \cdot 5) = 2 \cdot (5 \cdot z)$ — Commutative property of multiplication (order changed)

19. $-2 \cdot \left(-\frac{1}{2}\right) = 1$ — Multiplicative inverse property

20. $-2 + 2 = 0$ — Additive inverse property

21. $-6 \cdot (y \cdot 2) = (-6 \cdot 2) \cdot y$ — Commutative and associative properties of multiplication (order and grouping changed)

Work Practice 15–21

PRACTICE 15–21

Name the property illustrated by each true statement.

15. $7(a + b) = 7 \cdot a + 7 \cdot b$

16. $12 + y = y + 12$

17. $-4 \cdot (6 \cdot x) = (-4 \cdot 6) \cdot x$

18. $6 + (z + 2) = 6 + (2 + z)$

19. $3\left(\frac{1}{3}\right) = 1$

20. $(x + 0) + 23 = x + 23$

21. $(7 \cdot y) \cdot 10 = y \cdot (7 \cdot 10)$

Answers

15. distributive property
16. commutative property of addition
17. associative property of multiplication
18. commutative property of addition
19. multiplicative inverse property
20. identity element for addition
21. commutative and associative properties of multiplication

✓ **Concept Check Answers**

a. $\frac{3}{10}$ **b.** $-\frac{10}{3}$

Vocabulary and Readiness Check

Use the choices below to fill in each blank.

distributive property	associative property of multiplication	commutative property of addition
opposites or additive inverses	associative property of addition	
reciprocals or multiplicative inverses	commutative property of multiplication	

1. $x + 5 = 5 + x$ is a true statement by the ________________.
2. $x \cdot 5 = 5 \cdot x$ is a true statement by the ________________.
3. $3(y + 6) = 3 \cdot y + 3 \cdot 6$ is true by the ________________.
4. $2 \cdot (x \cdot y) = (2 \cdot x) \cdot y$ is a true statement by the ________________.
5. $x + (7 + y) = (x + 7) + y$ is a true statement by the ________________.
6. The numbers $-\frac{2}{3}$ and $-\frac{3}{2}$ are called ________________.
7. The numbers $-\frac{2}{3}$ and $\frac{2}{3}$ are called ________________.

1.7 Exercise Set

FOR EXTRA HELP

PRACTICE

WATCH

DOWNLOAD

READ

REVIEW

Objective A *Use a commutative property to complete each statement. See Examples 1 and 3.*

1. $x + 16 =$ ____ **2.** $8 + y =$ ____ **3.** $-4 \cdot y =$ ____ **4.** $-2 \cdot x =$ ____

5. $xy =$ ____ **6.** $ab =$ ____ **7.** $2x + 13 =$ ____ **8.** $19 + 3y =$ ____

Use an associative property to complete each statement. See Examples 2 and 4.

9. $(xy) \cdot z =$ ____ **10.** $3 \cdot (x \cdot y) =$ ____ **11.** $2 + (a + b) =$ ____

12. $(y + 4) + z =$ ____ **13.** $4 \cdot (ab) =$ ____ **14.** $(-3y) \cdot z =$ ____

15. $(a + b) + c =$ ____ **16.** $6 + (r + s) =$ ____

Use the commutative and associative properties to simplify each expression. See Examples 5 and 6.

17. $8 + (9 + b)$ **18.** $(r + 3) + 11$ **19.** $4(6y)$ **20.** $2(42x)$ **21.** $\frac{1}{5}(5y)$

22. $\frac{1}{8}(8z)$ **23.** $(13 + a) + 13$ **24.** $7 + (x + 4)$ **25.** $-9(8x)$ **26.** $-3(12y)$

27. $\frac{3}{4}\left(\frac{4}{3}s\right)$ **28.** $\frac{2}{7}\left(\frac{7}{2}r\right)$ **29.** $-\frac{1}{2}(5x)$ **30.** $-\frac{1}{3}(7x)$

Objective B *Use the distributive property to write each expression without parentheses. Then simplify the result, if possible. See Examples 7 through 12.*

31. $4(x + y)$

32. $7(a + b)$

33. $9(x - 6)$

34. $11(y - 4)$

35. $2(3x + 5)$

36. $5(7 + 8y)$

37. $7(4x - 3)$

38. $3(8x - 1)$

39. $3(6 + x)$

40. $2(x + 5)$

41. $-2(y - z)$

42. $-3(z - y)$

43. $-\frac{1}{3}(3y + 5)$

44. $-\frac{1}{2}(2r + 11)$

45. $5(x + 4m + 2)$

46. $8(3y + z - 6)$

47. $-4(1 - 2m + n) + 4$

48. $-4(4 + 2p + 5) + 16$

49. $-(5x + 2)$

50. $-(9r + 5)$

51. $-(r - 3 - 7p)$

52. $-(q - 2 + 6r)$

53. $\frac{1}{2}(6x + 7) + \frac{1}{2}$

54. $\frac{1}{4}(4x - 2) - \frac{7}{2}$

55. $-\frac{1}{3}(3x - 9y)$

56. $-\frac{1}{5}(10a - 25b)$

57. $3(2r + 5) - 7$

58. $10(4s + 6) - 40$

59. $-9(4x + 8) + 2$

60. $-11(5x + 3) + 10$

61. $-0.4(4x + 5) - 0.5$

62. $-0.6(2x + 1) - 0.1$

Use the distributive property to write each sum as a product. See Examples 13 and 14.

63. $4 \cdot 1 + 4 \cdot y$

64. $14 \cdot z + 14 \cdot 5$

65. $11x + 11y$

66. $9a + 9b$

67. $(-1) \cdot 5 + (-1) \cdot x$

68. $(-3)a + (-3)y$

69. $30a + 30b$

70. $25x + 25y$

Objectives A C **Mixed Practice** *Name the property illustrated by each true statement. See Examples 15 through 21.*

71. $3 \cdot 5 = 5 \cdot 3$

72. $4(3 + 8) = 4 \cdot 3 + 4 \cdot 8$

73. $2 + (x + 5) = (2 + x) + 5$

74. $9 \cdot (x \cdot 7) = (9 \cdot x) \cdot 7$

75. $(x + 9) + 3 = (9 + x) + 3$

76. $1 \cdot 9 = 9$

77. $(4 \cdot y) \cdot 9 = 4 \cdot (y \cdot 9)$

78. $-4 \cdot (8 \cdot 3) = (8 \cdot 3) \cdot (-4)$

79. $0 + 6 = 6$

80. $(a + 9) + 6 = a + (9 + 6)$

81. $-4(y + 7) = -4 \cdot y + (-4) \cdot 7$

82. $(11 + r) + 8 = (r + 11) + 8$

83. $6 \cdot \frac{1}{6} = 1$

84. $r + 0 = r$

85. $-6 \cdot 1 = -6$

86. $-\frac{3}{4}\left(-\frac{4}{3}\right) = 1$

Concept Extensions

Fill in the table with the opposite (additive inverse), the reciprocal (multiplicative inverse), or the expression. Assume that the value of each expression is not 0.

	87.	**88.**	**89.**	**90.**	**91.**	**92.**
Expression	8	$-\frac{2}{3}$	x	$4y$		
Opposite						$7x$
Reciprocal					$\frac{1}{2x}$	

Decide whether each statement is true or false. See the second Concept Check in this section.

93. The opposite of $-\frac{a}{2}$ is $-\frac{2}{a}$.

94. The reciprocal of $-\frac{a}{2}$ is $\frac{a}{2}$.

Determine which pairs of actions are commutative. See the first Concept Check in this section.

95. "taking a test" and "studying for the test"

96. "putting on your shoes" and "putting on your socks"

97. "putting on your left shoe" and "putting on your right shoe"

98. "reading the sports section" and "reading the comics section"

99. "mowing the lawn" and "trimming the hedges"

100. "baking a cake" and "eating the cake"

101. "feeding the dog" and "feeding the cat"

102. "dialing a number" and "turning on the cell phone"

Name the property illustrated by each step.

103. a. $\triangle + (\square + \bigcirc) = (\square + \bigcirc) + \triangle$

b. $= (\bigcirc + \square) + \triangle$

c. $= \bigcirc + (\square + \triangle)$

104. a. $(x + y) + z = x + (y + z)$

b. $= (y + z) + x$

c. $= (z + y) + x$

105. Explain why 0 is called the identity element for addition.

106. Explain why 1 is called the identity element for multiplication.

107. Write an example that shows that division is not commutative.

108. Write an example that shows that subtraction is not commutative.

Objectives

A **Identify Terms, Like Terms, and Unlike Terms.**

B **Combine Like Terms.**

C **Simplify Expressions Containing Parentheses.**

D **Write Word Phrases as Algebraic Expressions.**

1.8 SIMPLIFYING EXPRESSIONS

As we explore in this section, we will see that an expression such as $3x + 2x$ is not written as simply as possible. This is because—even without replacing x by a value—we can perform the indicated addition.

Objective A Identifying Terms, Like Terms, and Unlike Terms

Before we practice simplifying expressions, we must learn some new language. A **term** is a number or the product of a number and variables raised to powers.

Terms

$-y,\quad 2x^3,\quad -5,\quad 3xz^2,\quad \frac{2}{y},\quad 0.8z$

The **numerical coefficient** of a term is the numerical factor. The numerical coefficient of $3x$ is 3. Recall that $3x$ means $3 \cdot x$.

Term	Numerical Coefficient
$3x$	3
$\frac{y^3}{5}$	$\frac{1}{5}$ since $\frac{y^3}{5}$ means $\frac{1}{5} \cdot y^3$
$-0.7ab^3c^5$	-0.7
z	1
$-y$	-1
-5	-5

Helpful Hint

The term z means $1z$ and thus has a numerical coefficient of 1.
The term $-y$ means $-1y$ and thus has a numerical coefficient of -1.

PRACTICE 1

Identify the numerical coefficient of each term.

a. $-4x$ **b.** $15y^3$ **c.** x

d. $-y$ **e.** $\frac{z}{4}$

Example 1 Identify the numerical coefficient of each term.

a. $-3y$ **b.** $22z^4$ **c.** y **d.** $-x$ **e.** $\frac{x}{7}$

Solution:

a. The numerical coefficient of $-3y$ is -3.
b. The numerical coefficient of $22z^4$ is 22.
c. The numerical coefficient of y is 1, since y is $1y$.
d. The numerical coefficient of $-x$ is -1, since $-x$ is $-1x$.
e. The numerical coefficient of $\frac{x}{7}$ is $\frac{1}{7}$, since $\frac{x}{7}$ is $\frac{1}{7} \cdot x$.

Work Practice 1

Answers

1. a. -4 **b.** 15 **c.** 1 **d.** -1 **e.** $\frac{1}{4}$

Terms with the same variables raised to exactly the same powers are called **like terms.** Terms that aren't like terms are called **unlike terms.**

Like Terms	Unlike Terms	Reason Why
$3x, 2x$	$5x, 5x^2$	Why? Same variable x, but different powers of x and x^2
$-6x^2y, 2x^2y, 4x^2y$	$7y, 3z, 8x^2$	Why? Different variables
$2ab^2c^3, ac^3b^2$	$6abc^3, 6ab^2$	Why? Different variables and different powers

Helpful Hint

In like terms, each variable and its exponent must match exactly, but these factors don't need to be in the same order.

$2x^2y$ and $3yx^2$ are like terms.

Example 2 Determine whether the terms are like or unlike.

a. $2x, 3x^2$ b. $4x^2y, x^2y, -2x^2y$ c. $-2yz, -3zy$
d. $-x^4, x^4$ e. $-8a^5, 8a^5$

Solution:

a. Unlike terms, since the exponents on x are not the same.
b. Like terms, since each variable and its exponent match.
c. Like terms, since $zy = yz$ by the commutative property.
d. Like terms. The variable and its exponent match.
e. Like terms. The variable and its exponent match.

Work Practice 2

PRACTICE 2

Determine whether the terms are like or unlike.

a. $7x^2, -6x^3$
b. $3x^2y^2, -x^2y^2, 4x^2y^2$
c. $-5ab, 3ba$
d. $2x^3, 4y^3$
e. $-7m^4, 7m^4$

Objective B Combining Like Terms

An algebraic expression containing the sum or difference of like terms can be simplified by applying the distributive property. For example, by the distributive property, we rewrite the sum of the like terms $6x + 2x$ as

$$6x + 2x = (6 + 2)x = 8x$$

Also,

$$-y^2 + 5y^2 = (-1 + 5)y^2 = 4y^2$$

Simplifying the sum or difference of like terms is called **combining like terms.**

Example 3 Simplify each expression by combining like terms.

a. $7x - 3x$ b. $10y^2 + y^2$
c. $8x^2 + 2x - 3x$ d. $9n^2 - 5n^2 + n^2$

Solution:

a. $7x - 3x = (7 - 3)x = 4x$
b. $10y^2 + y^2 = (10 + 1)y^2 = 11y^2$
c. $8x^2 + 2x - 3x = 8x^2 + (2 - 3)x = 8x^2 - 1x$ or $8x^2 - x$
d. $9n^2 - 5n^2 + n^2 = (9 - 5 + 1)n^2 = 5n^2$

Work Practice 3

PRACTICE 3

Simplify each expression by combining like terms.

a. $9y - 4y$
b. $11x^2 + x^2$
c. $5y - 3x + 4x$
d. $14m^2 - m^2 + 3m^2$

Answers

2. a. unlike b. like c. like d. unlike e. like 3. a. $5y$ b. $12x^2$ c. $5y + x$ d. $16m^2$

The preceding examples suggest the following.

Combining Like Terms

To **combine like terms**, combine the numerical coefficients and multiply the result by the common variable factors.

PRACTICE 4–7

Simplify each expression by combining like terms.

4. $7y + 2y + 6 + 10$
5. $-2x + 4 + x - 11$
6. $3z - 3z^2$
7. $8.9y + 4.2y - 3$

Examples Simplify each expression by combining like terms.

4. $2x + 3x + 5 + 2 = (2 + 3)x + (5 + 2)$
$= 5x + 7$

5. $-5a - 3 + a + 2 = -5a + 1a + (-3 + 2)$
$= (-5 + 1)a + (-3 + 2)$
$= -4a - 1$

6. $4y - 3y^2$
These two terms cannot be combined because they are unlike terms.

7. $2.3x + 5x - 6 = (2.3 + 5)x - 6$
$= 7.3x - 6$

Work Practice 4–7

Objective C Simplifying Expressions Containing Parentheses

In simplifying expressions we make frequent use of the distributive property to remove parentheses.

It may be helpful to study the examples below.

$$+(3a + 2) = +1(3a + 2) = +1(3a) + (+1)(2) = 3a + 2$$

(+ means +1)

$$-(3a + 2) = -1(3a + 2) = -1(3a) + (-1)(2) = -3a - 2$$

(− means −1)

PRACTICE 8–10

Find each product by using the distributive property to remove parentheses.

8. $3(11y + 6)$
9. $-4(x + 0.2y - 3)$
10. $-(3x + 2y + z - 1)$

Examples Find each product by using the distributive property to remove parentheses.

8. $5(3x + 2) = 5(3x) + 5(2)$ Apply the distributive property.
$= 15x + 10$ Multiply.

9. $-2(y + 0.3z - 1) = -2(y) + (-2)(0.3z) - (-2)(1)$ Apply the distributive property.
$= -2y - 0.6z + 2$ Multiply.

10. $-(9x + y - 2z + 6) = -1(9x + y - 2z + 6)$ Distribute −1 over each term.
$= -1(9x) + (-1)(y) - (-1)(2z) + (-1)(6)$
$= -9x - y + 2z - 6$

Work Practice 8–10

Answers

4. $9y + 16$ 5. $-x - 7$
6. $3z - 3z^2$ 7. $13.1y - 3$
8. $33y + 18$ 9. $-4x - 0.8y + 12$
10. $-3x - 2y - z + 1$

Helpful Hint

If a "−" sign precedes parentheses, the sign of each term inside the parentheses is changed when the distributive property is applied to remove the parentheses.

Examples:

$$-(2x + 1) = -2x - 1$$
$$-(x - 2y) = -x + 2y$$
$$-(-5x + y - z) = 5x - y + z$$
$$-(-3x - 4y - 1) = 3x + 4y + 1$$

When simplifying an expression containing parentheses, we often use the distributive property first to remove parentheses and then again to combine any like terms.

Examples Simplify each expression.

11. $3(2x - 5) + 1 = 6x - 15 + 1$ Apply the distributive property.
$= 6x - 14$ Combine like terms.

12. $8 - (7x + 2) + 3x = 8 - 7x - 2 + 3x$ Apply the distributive property.
$= -7x + 3x + 8 - 2$
$= -4x + 6$ Combine like terms.

13. $-2(4x + 7) - (3x - 1) = -8x - 14 - 3x + 1$ Apply the distributive property.
$= -11x - 13$ Combine like terms.

14. $9 + 3(4x - 10) = 9 + 12x - 30$ Apply the distributive property.
$= -21 + 12x$ Combine like terms.
or $12x - 21$

Don't forget to use the distributive property and multiply before adding or subtracting like terms.

Work Practice 11–14

PRACTICE 11–14

Simplify each expression.

11. $4(4x - 6) + 20$
12. $5 - (3x + 9) + 6x$
13. $-3(7x + 1) - (4x - 2)$
14. $8 + 11(2y - 9)$

Example 15 Subtract $4x - 2$ from $2x - 3$.

Solution: We first note that "subtract $4x - 2$ **from** $2x - 3$" translates to $(2x - 3) - (4x - 2)$. Notice that parentheses were placed around each given expression. This is to ensure that the entire expression after the subtraction sign is subtracted. Next, we simplify the algebraic expression.

$(2x - 3) - (4x - 2) = 2x - 3 - 4x + 2$ Apply the distributive property.
$= -2x - 1$ Combine like terms.

Work Practice 15

PRACTICE 15

Subtract $9x - 10$ from $4x - 3$.

Objective D Writing Algebraic Expressions

To prepare for problem solving, we next practice writing word phrases as algebraic expressions.

Answers
11. $16x - 4$ **12.** $3x - 4$
13. $-25x - 1$ **14.** $-91 + 22y$
15. $-5x + 7$

PRACTICE 16–19

Write each phrase as an algebraic expression and simplify if possible. Let x represent the unknown number.

16. Three times a number, subtracted from 10

17. The sum of a number and 2, divided by 5

18. Three times a number, added to the sum of a number and 6

19. Seven times the difference of a number and 4.

Examples Write each phrase as an algebraic expression and simplify if possible. Let x represent the unknown number.

16. Twice a number, plus 6

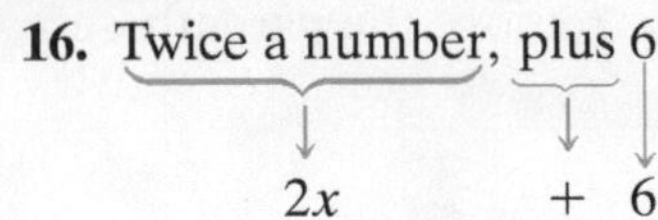

$2x \quad + \quad 6$

This expression cannot be simplified.

17. The difference of a number and 4, divided by 7

$(x - 4) \quad \div \quad 7$ or $\frac{x-4}{7}$

This expression cannot be simplified.

18. Five plus the sum of a number and 1

$5 \quad + \quad (x + 1)$

We can simplify this expression.

$$5 + (x + 1) = 5 + x + 1$$
$$= 6 + x$$

19. Four times the sum of a number and 3

$4 \quad \cdot \quad (x + 3)$

Use the distributive property to simplify the expression.

$$4 \cdot (x + 3) = 4(x + 3)$$
$$= 4 \cdot x + 4 \cdot 3$$
$$= 4x + 12$$

Work Practice 16–19

Answers

16. $10 - 3x$ **17.** $(x + 2) \div 5$ or $\frac{x+2}{5}$ **18.** $4x + 6$ **19.** $7x - 28$

Vocabulary and Readiness Check

Use the choices below to fill in each blank. Some choices may be used more than once.

numerical coefficient	expression	unlike	distributive
combine like terms	like	term	

1. $14y^2 + 2x - 23$ is called a(n) ________________ while $14y^2$, $2x$, and -23 are each called a(n) ________________.
2. To multiply $3(-7x + 1)$, we use the ________________ property.
3. To simplify an expression like $y + 7y$, we ________________.
4. The term z has an understood ________________ of 1.
5. The terms $-x$ and $5x$ are ________________ terms and the terms $5x$ and $5y$ are ________________ terms.
6. For the term $-3x^2y$, -3 is called the ________________.

Objective A *Identify the numerical coefficient of each term. See Example 1.*

7. $-7y$
8. $3x$
9. x
10. $-y$
11. $17x^2y$
12. $1.2xyz$

Indicate whether the terms in each list are like or unlike. See Example 2.

13. $5y, -y$
14. $-2x^2y, 6xy$
15. $2z, 3z^2$
16. $ab^2, -7ab^2$
17. $8wz, \frac{1}{7}zw$
18. $7.4p^3q^2, 6.2p^3q^2r$

1.8 Exercise Set

FOR EXTRA HELP

MyMathLab

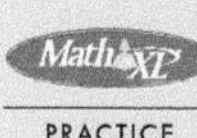

PRACTICE

WATCH

DOWNLOAD

READ

REVIEW

Objective B *Simplify each expression by combining any like terms. See Examples 3 through 7.*

1. $7y + 8y$
2. $3x + 2x$
3. $8w - w + 6w$
4. $c - 7c + 2c$
5. $3b - 5 - 10b - 4$
6. $6g + 5 - 3g - 7$
7. $m - 4m + 2m - 6$
8. $a + 3a - 2 - 7a$
9. $5g - 3 - 5 - 5g$
10. $8p + 4 - 8p - 15$
11. $6.2x - 4 + x - 1.2$
12. $7.9y - 0.7 - y + 0.2$
13. $2k - k - 6$
14. $7c - 8 - c$
15. $-9x + 4x + 18 - 10x$
16. $5y - 14 + 7y - 20y$
17. $6x - 5x + x - 3 + 2x$
18. $8h + 13h - 6 + 7h - h$

19. $7x^2 + 8x^2 - 10x^2$

20. $8x^3 + x^3 - 11x^3$

21. $3.4m - 4 - 3.4m - 7$

22. $2.8w - 0.9 - 0.5 - 2.8w$

23. $6x + 0.5 - 4.3x - 0.4x + 3$

24. $0.4y - 6.7 + y - 0.3 - 2.6y$

Objective **C** *Simplify each expression. Use the distributive property to remove any parentheses. See Examples 8 through 10.*

25. $5(y + 4)$

26. $7(r + 3)$

27. $-2(x + 2)$

28. $-4(y + 6)$

29. $-5(2x - 3y + 6)$

30. $-2(4x - 3z - 1)$

31. $-(3x - 2y + 1)$

32. $-(y + 5z - 7)$

Objectives **B** **C** **Mixed Practice** *Remove parentheses and simplify each expression. See Examples 8 through 14.*

33. $7(d - 3) + 10$

34. $9(z + 7) - 15$

35. $-4(3y - 4) + 12y$

36. $-3(2x + 5) - 6x$

37. $3(2x - 5) - 5(x - 4)$

38. $2(6x - 1) - (x - 7)$

39. $-2(3x - 4) + 7x - 6$

40. $8y - 2 - 3(y + 4)$

41. $5k - (3k - 10)$

42. $-11c - (4 - 2c)$

43. $(3x + 4) - (6x - 1)$

44. $(8 - 5y) - (4 + 3y)$

45. $5(x + 2) - (3x - 4)$

46. $4(2x - 3) - (x + 1)$

47. $\frac{1}{3}(7y - 1) + \frac{1}{6}(4y + 7)$

48. $\frac{1}{5}(9y + 2) + \frac{1}{10}(2y - 1)$

49. $2 + 4(6x - 6)$

50. $8 + 4(3x - 4)$

51. $0.5(m + 2) + 0.4m$

52. $0.2(k + 8) - 0.1k$

53. $10 - 3(2x + 3y)$

54. $14 - 11(5m + 3n)$

55. $6(3x - 6) - 2(x + 1) - 17x$

56. $7(2x + 5) - 4(x + 2) - 20x$

57. $\frac{1}{2}(12x - 4) - (x + 5)$

58. $\frac{1}{3}(9x - 6) - (x - 2)$

Perform each indicated operation. Don't forget to simplify if possible. See Example 15.

59. Add $6x + 7$ to $4x - 10$.

60. Add $3y - 5$ to $y + 16$.

61. Subtract $7x + 1$ from $3x - 8$.

62. Subtract $4x - 7$ from $12 + x$.

63. Subtract $5m - 6$ from $m - 9$.

64. Subtract $m - 3$ from $2m - 6$.

Objective **D** *Write each phrase as an algebraic expression and simplify if possible. Let x represent the unknown number. See Examples 16 through 19.*

65. Twice a number, decreased by four

66. The difference of a number and two, divided by five

67. Three-fourths of a number, increased by twelve

68. Eight more than triple a number

69. The sum of 5 times a number and -2, added to 7 times the number

70. The sum of 3 times a number and 10, **subtracted from** 9 times the number

71. Eight times the sum of a number and six

72. Six times the difference of a number and five

73. Double a number minus the sum of the number and ten

74. Half a number minus the product of the number and eight

Concept Extensions

Given the following information, determine whether each scale is balanced or not.

1 cone balances 1 cube

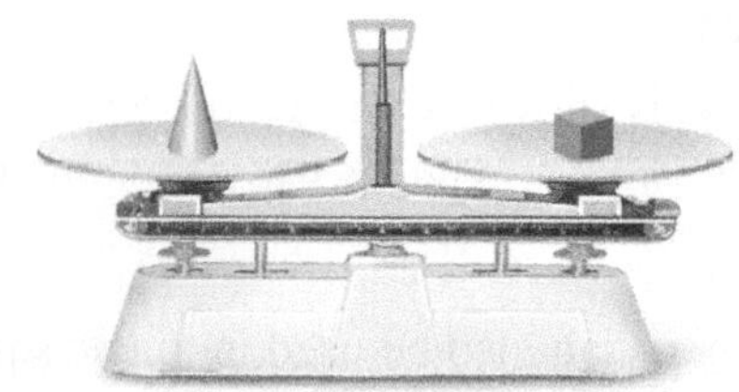

1 cylinder balances 2 cubes

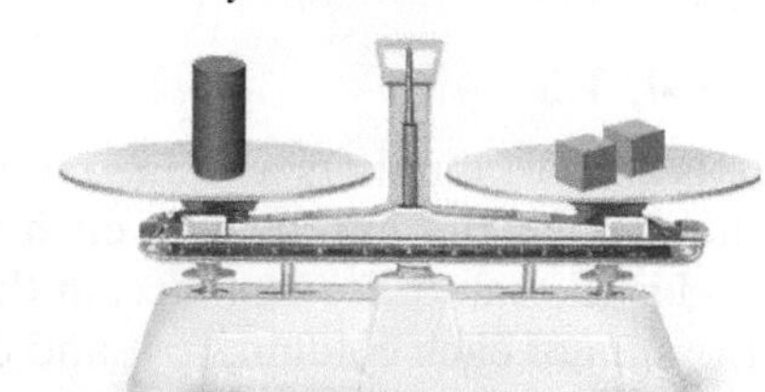

75.

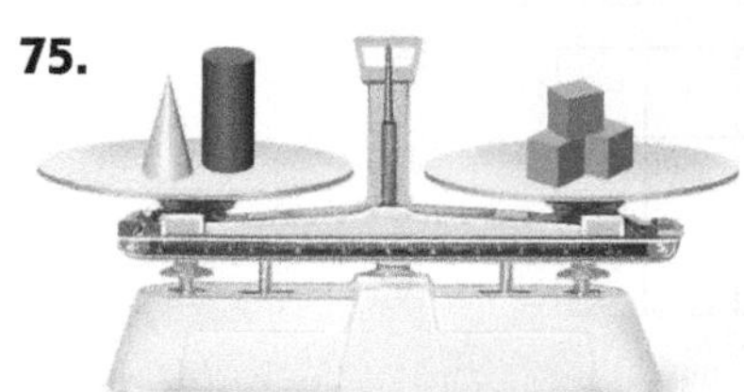

76.

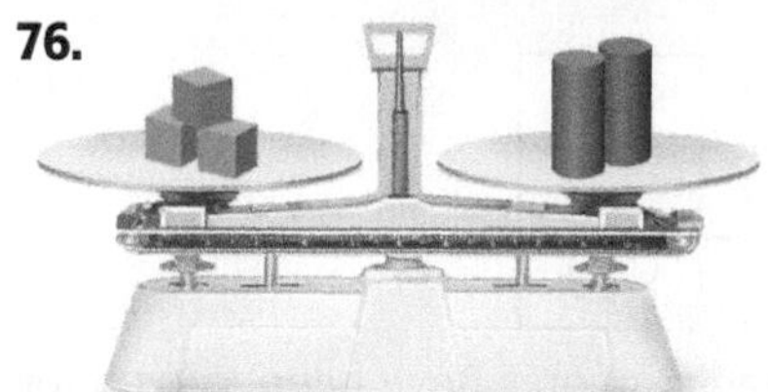

77.

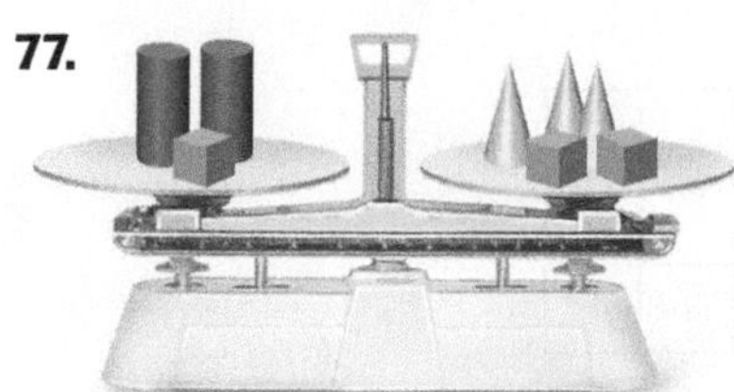

78.

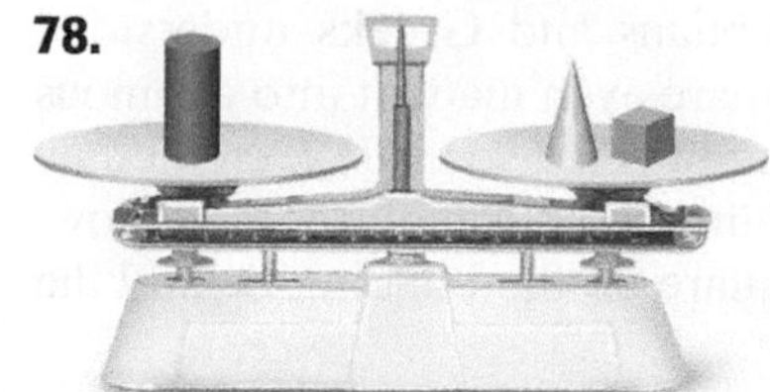

Write each algebraic expression described.

79. Write an expression with 4 terms that simplifies to $3x - 4$.

80. Write an expression of the form _____(_____+_____) whose product is $6x + 24$.

81. Recall that the perimeter of a figure is the total distance around the figure. Given the following rectangle, express the perimeter as an algebraic expression containing the variable x.

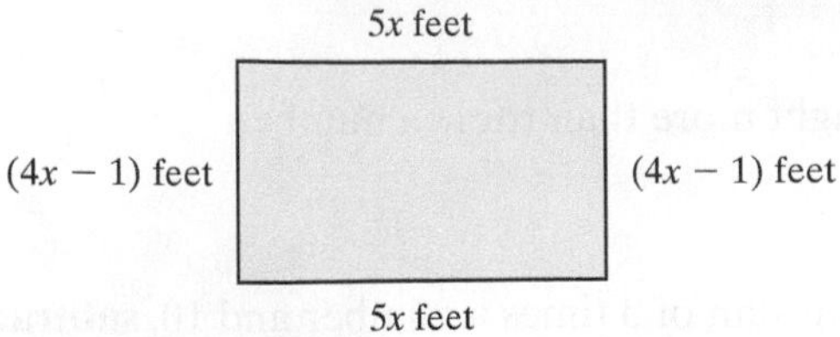

82. Recall that the perimeter of a figure is the total distance around the figure. Given the following triangle, express its perimeter as an algebraic expression containing the variable x.

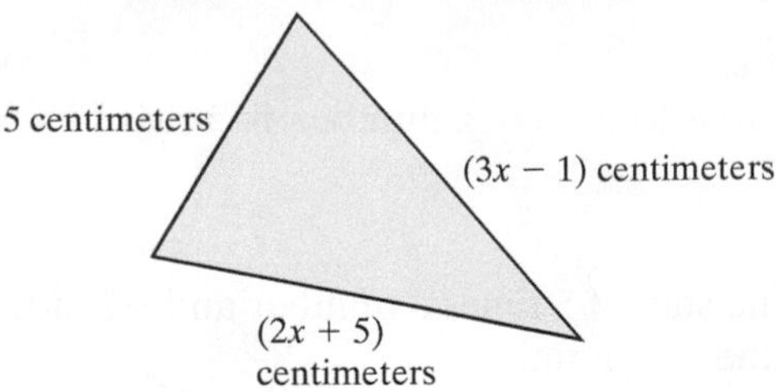

83. To convert from feet to inches, we multiply by 12. For example, the number of inches in 2 feet is $12 \cdot 2$ inches. If one board has a length of $(x + 2)$ *feet* and a second board has a length of $(3x - 1)$ *inches,* express their total length in inches as an algebraic expression.

84. The value of 7 nickels is $5 \cdot 7$ cents. Likewise, the value of x nickels is $5x$ cents. If the money box in a drink machine contains x *nickels,* $3x$ *dimes,* and $(30x - 1)$ *quarters,* express their total value in cents as an algebraic expression.

85. In your own words, explain how to combine like terms.

86. Do like terms always contain the same numerical coefficients? Explain your answer.

Chapter 1 Group Activity

Magic Squares

Sections 1.3, 1.4, 1.5

A magic square is a set of numbers arranged in a square table so that the sum of the numbers in each column, row, and diagonal is the same. For instance, in the magic square below, the sum of each column, row, and diagonal is 15. Notice that no number is used more than once in the magic square.

2	9	4
7	5	3
6	1	8

The properties of magic squares have been known for a very long time and once were thought to be good luck charms. The ancient Egyptians and Greeks understood their patterns. A magic square even made it into a famous work of art. The engraving titled *Melencolia I,* created by German artist Albrecht Dürer in 1514, features the following four-by-four magic square on the building behind the central figure.

16	3	2	13
5	10	11	8
9	6	7	12
4	15	14	1

Group Exercises

1. Verify that what is shown in the Dürer engraving is, in fact, a magic square. What is the common sum of the columns, rows, and diagonals?

2. Negative numbers can also be used in magic squares. Complete the following magic square:

		−2
	−1	
0		−4

3. Use the numbers −12, −9, −6, −3, 0, 3, 6, 9, and 12 to form a magic square.

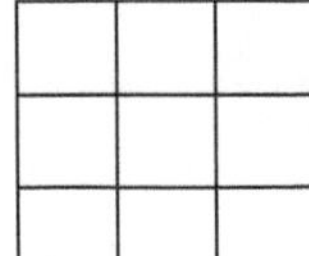

Chapter 1 Vocabulary Check

Fill in each blank with one of the words or phrases listed below.

inequality symbols	exponent	term	numerical coefficient
grouping symbols	solution	like terms	unlike terms
equation	absolute value	numerator	denominator
opposites	base	reciprocals	variable

1. The symbols $\neq$, $<$, and $>$ are called ________________.
2. A mathematical statement that two expressions are equal is called a(n) ________________.
3. The ________________ of a number is the distance between that number and 0 on a number line.
4. A symbol used to represent a number is called a(n) ________________.
5. Two numbers that are the same distance from 0 but lie on opposite sides of 0 are called ________________.
6. The number in a fraction above the fraction bar is called the ________________.
7. A(n) ________________ of an equation is a value for the variable that makes the equation a true statement.
8. Two numbers whose product is 1 are called ________________.
9. In 2^3, the 2 is called the ________________ and the 3 is called the ________________.
10. The ________________ of a term is its numerical factor.
11. The number in a fraction below the fraction bar is called the ________________.
12. Parentheses and brackets are examples of ________________.
13. A(n) ________________ is a number or the product of a number and variables raised to powers.
14. Terms with the same variables raised to the same powers are called ________________.
15. If terms are not like terms, then they are ________________.

Helpful Hint Are you preparing for your test? Don't forget to take the Chapter 1 Test on page 92. Then check your answers at the back of the text and use the Chapter Test Prep Videos to see the fully worked-out solutions to any of the exercises you want to review.

1 Chapter Highlights

Definitions and Concepts	Examples
Section 1.2 Symbols and Sets of Numbers	
A **set** is a collection of objects, called **elements,** enclosed in braces.	$\{a, c, e\}$
Natural numbers: $\{1, 2, 3, 4, \dots\}$ **Whole numbers:** $\{0, 1, 2, 3, 4, \dots\}$ **Integers:** $\{\dots, -3, -2, -1, 0, 1, 2, 3, \dots\}$	Given the set $\left\{-3.4, \sqrt{3}, 0, \frac{2}{3}, 5, -4\right\}$ list the numbers that belong to the set of Natural numbers: 5 Whole numbers: 0, 5 Integers: -4, 0, 5
Rational numbers: { real numbers that can be expressed as a quotient of integers }	Rational numbers: $-3.4, 0, \frac{2}{3}, 5, -4$
Irrational numbers: { real numbers that cannot be expressed as a quotient of integers }	Irrational numbers: $\sqrt{3}$
A line used to picture numbers is called a **number line.**	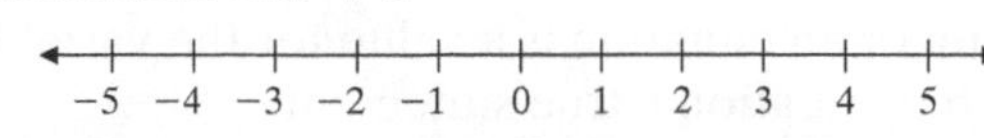
Real numbers: { all numbers that correspond to points on the number line }	Real numbers: $-3.4, \sqrt{3}, 0, \frac{2}{3}, 5, -4$

(continued)

Definitions and Concepts	Examples
Section 1.2 Symbols and Sets of Numbers (*continued*)	
The **absolute value** of a real number a denoted by $\lvert a \rvert$ is the distance between a and 0 on a number line.	$\lvert 5 \rvert = 5 \quad \lvert 0 \rvert = 0 \quad \lvert -2 \rvert = 2$
SYMBOLS: $=$ is equal to $\neq$ is not equal to $>$ is greater than $<$ is less than $\leq$ is less than or equal to $\geq$ is greater than or equal to	$-7 = -7$ $3 \neq -3$ $4 > 1$ $1 < 4$ $6 \leq 6$ $18 \geq -\frac{1}{3}$
ORDER PROPERTY FOR REAL NUMBERS For any two real numbers a and b, a is less than b if a is to the left of b on the number line.	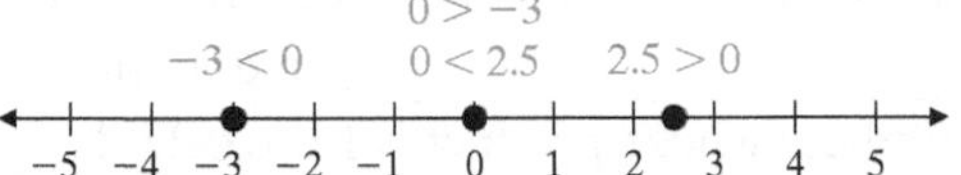
Section 1.3 Exponents, Order of Operations, and Variable Expressions	
The expression a^n is an **exponential expression.** The number a is called the **base;** it is the repeated factor. The number n is called the **exponent;** it is the number of times that the base is a factor.	$4^3 = 4 \cdot 4 \cdot 4 = 64$ $7^2 = 7 \cdot 7 = 49$
ORDER OF OPERATIONS **1.** Perform all operations within grouping symbols first, starting with the innermost set. **2.** Evaluate exponential expressions. **3.** Multiply or divide in order from left to right. **4.** Add or subtract in order from left to right.	$\frac{8^2 + 5(7-3)}{3 \cdot 7} = \frac{8^2 + 5(4)}{21}$ $= \frac{64 + 5(4)}{21}$ $= \frac{64 + 20}{21}$ $= \frac{84}{21}$ $= 4$
A symbol used to represent a number is called a **variable.**	Examples of variables are q, x, z
An **algebraic expression** is a collection of numbers, variables, operation symbols, and grouping symbols.	Examples of algebraic expressions are $5x, \quad 2(y-6), \quad \frac{q^2 - 3q + 1}{6}$
To **evaluate an algebraic expression** containing a variable, substitute a given number for the variable and simplify.	Evaluate $x^2 - y^2$ when $x = 5$ and $y = 3$. $x^2 - y^2 = (5)^2 - 3^2$ $= 25 - 9$ $= 16$
A mathematical statement that two expressions are equal is called an **equation.**	Equations: $3x - 9 = 20$ $A = \pi r^2$
A **solution** of an equation is a value for the variable that makes the equation a true statement.	Determine whether 4 is a solution of $5x + 7 = 27$. $5x + 7 = 27$ $5(4) + 7 \stackrel{?}{=} 27$ $20 + 7 \stackrel{?}{=} 27$ $27 = 27$ True 4 is a solution.

Definitions and Concepts	Examples
Section 1.4 Adding Real Numbers	
To Add Two Numbers with the Same Sign **1.** Add their absolute values. **2.** Use their common sign as the sign of the sum.	Add. $10 + 7 = 17$ $-3 + (-8) = -11$
To Add Two Numbers with Different Signs **1.** Subtract their absolute values. **2.** Use the sign of the number whose absolute value is larger as the sign of the sum.	$-25 + 5 = -20$ $14 + (-9) = 5$
Two numbers that are the same distance from 0 but lie on opposite sides of 0 are called **opposites** or **additive inverses.** The opposite of a number a is denoted by $-a$.	The opposite of -7 is 7. The opposite of 123 is -123.
Section 1.5 Subtracting Real Numbers	
To subtract two numbers a and b, add the first number a to the opposite of the second number, b. $a - b = a + (-b)$	Subtract. $3 - (-44) = 3 + 44 = 47$ $-5 - 22 = -5 + (-22) = -27$ $-30 - (-30) = -30 + 30 = 0$
Section 1.6 Multiplying and Dividing Real Numbers	
Multiplying Real Numbers The product of two numbers with the same sign is a positive number. The product of two numbers with different signs is a negative number.	Multiply. $7 \cdot 8 = 56$ $-7 \cdot (-8) = 56$ $-2 \cdot 4 = -8$ $2 \cdot (-4) = -8$
Products Involving Zero The product of 0 and any number is 0. $b \cdot 0 = 0$ and $0 \cdot b = 0$	$-4 \cdot 0 = 0$ $0 \cdot \left(-\frac{3}{4}\right) = 0$
Quotient of Two Real Numbers $\frac{a}{b} = a \cdot \frac{1}{b}$	Divide. $\frac{42}{2} = 42 \cdot \frac{1}{2} = 21$
Dividing Real Numbers The quotient of two numbers with the same sign is a positive number. The quotient of two numbers with different signs is a negative number.	$\frac{90}{10} = 9$ $\frac{-90}{-10} = 9$ $\frac{42}{-6} = -7$ $\frac{-42}{6} = -7$
Quotients Involving Zero Let a be a nonzero number. $\frac{0}{a} = 0$ and $\frac{a}{0}$ is undefined.	$\frac{0}{18} = 0$ $\frac{0}{-47} = 0$ $\frac{-85}{0}$ is undefined.

Definitions and Concepts	Examples
Section 1.7 Properties of Real Numbers	
COMMUTATIVE PROPERTIES	
Addition: $a + b = b + a$	$3 + (-7) = -7 + 3$
Multiplication: $a \cdot b = b \cdot a$	$-8 \cdot 5 = 5 \cdot (-8)$
ASSOCIATIVE PROPERTIES	
Addition: $(a + b) + c = a + (b + c)$	$(5 + 10) + 20 = 5 + (10 + 20)$
Multiplication: $(a \cdot b) \cdot c = a \cdot (b \cdot c)$	$(-3 \cdot 2) \cdot 11 = -3 \cdot (2 \cdot 11)$
Two numbers whose product is 1 are called **multiplicative inverses** or **reciprocals.** The reciprocal of a nonzero number a is $\frac{1}{a}$ because $a \cdot \frac{1}{a} = 1$.	The reciprocal of 3 is $\frac{1}{3}$. The reciprocal of $-\frac{2}{5}$ is $-\frac{5}{2}$.
DISTRIBUTIVE PROPERTY	
$a(b + c) = a \cdot b + a \cdot c$	$5(6 + 10) = 5 \cdot 6 + 5 \cdot 10$ $-2(3 + x) = -2 \cdot 3 + (-2)(x)$
IDENTITIES	
$a + 0 = a$ $0 + a = a$	$5 + 0 = 5$ $0 + (-2) = -2$
$a \cdot 1 = a$ $1 \cdot a = a$	$-14 \cdot 1 = -14$ $1 \cdot 27 = 27$
INVERSES	
Additive or opposite: $a + (-a) = 0$	$7 + (-7) = 0$
Multiplicative or reciprocal: $b \cdot \frac{1}{b} = 1, \quad b \neq 0$	$3 \cdot \frac{1}{3} = 1$
Section 1.8 Simplifying Expressions	
The **numerical coefficient** of a **term** is its numerical factor.	**Term** / **Numerical Coefficient** $-7y$ / -7 x / 1 $\frac{1}{5}a^2b$ / $\frac{1}{5}$
Terms with the same variables raised to exactly the same powers are **like terms.**	**Like Terms** / **Unlike Terms** $12x, -x$ / $3y, 3y^2$ $-2xy, 5yx$ / $7a^2b, -2ab^2$
To combine like terms, add the numerical coefficients and multiply the result by the common variable factor.	$9y + 3y = 12y$ $-4z^2 + 5z^2 - 6z^2 = -5z^2$
To remove parentheses, apply the distributive property.	$-4(x + 7) + 10(3x - 1)$ $= -4x - 28 + 30x - 10$ $= 26x - 38$

Chapter 1 Review

(1.2) *Insert $<$, $>$, or $=$ in the appropriate space to make each statement true.*

1. $8 \quad 10$

2. $7 \quad 2$

3. $-4 \quad -5$

4. $\frac{12}{2} \quad -8$

5. $|-7| \quad |-8|$

6. $|-9| \quad -9$

7. $-|-1| \quad -1$

8. $|-14| \quad -(-14)$

9. $1.2 \quad 1.02$

10. $-\frac{3}{2} \quad -\frac{3}{4}$

Translate each statement into symbols.

11. Four is greater than or equal to negative three.

12. Six is not equal to five.

13. 0.03 is less than 0.3.

14. New York City has 155 museums and 400 art galleries. Write an inequality comparing the numbers 155 and 400. (*Source:* Absolute Trivia.com)

Given the sets of numbers below, list the numbers in each set that also belong to the set of:

a. Natural numbers
b. Whole numbers
c. Integers
d. Rational numbers
e. Irrational numbers
f. Real numbers

15. $\left\{-6, 0, 1, 1\frac{1}{2}, 3, \pi, 9.62\right\}$

16. $\left\{-3, -1.6, 2, 5, \frac{11}{2}, 15.1, \sqrt{5}, 2\pi\right\}$

The following chart shows the gains and losses in dollars of Density Oil and Gas stock for a particular week. Use this chart to answer Exercises 17 and 18.

Day	Gain or Loss (in dollars)
Monday	+1
Tuesday	−2
Wednesday	+5
Thursday	+1
Friday	−4

17. Which day showed the greatest loss?

18. Which day showed the greatest gain?

(1.3) *Choose the correct answer for each statement.*

19. The expression $6 \cdot 3^2 + 2 \cdot 8$ simplifies to
a. -52 **b.** 448 **c.** 70 **d.** 64

20. The expression $68 - 5 \cdot 2^3$ simplifies to
a. -232 **b.** 28 **c.** 38 **d.** 504

Simplify each expression.

21. $3(1 + 2\cdot 5) + 4$

22. $8 + 3(2\cdot 6 - 1)$

23. $\frac{4 + |6 - 2| + 8^2}{4 + 6\cdot 4}$

24. $5[3(2 + 5) - 5]$

Translate each word statement to symbols.

25. The difference of twenty and twelve is equal to the product of two and four.

26. The quotient of nine and two is greater than negative five.

Evaluate each expression when $x = 6$, $y = 2$, and $z = 8$.

27. $2x + 3y$

28. $x(y + 2z)$

29. $\frac{x}{y} + \frac{z}{2y}$

30. $x^2 - 3y^2$

△ **31.** The expression $180 - a - b$ represents the measure of the unknown angle of the given triangle. Replace a with 37 and b with 80 to find the measure of the unknown angle.

△ **32.** The expression $360 - a - b - c$ represents the measure of the unknown angle of the given quadrilateral. Replace a with 93, b with 80, and c with 82 to find the measure of the unknown angle.

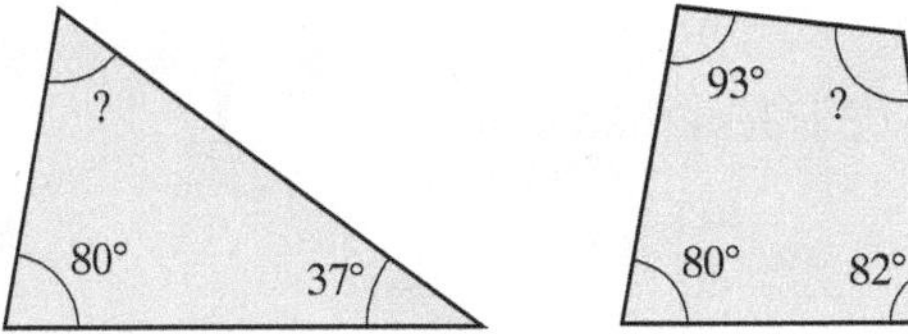

Decide whether the given number is a solution to the given equation.

33. $7x - 3 = 18$; 3

34. $3x^2 + 4 = x - 1$; 1

(1.4) *Find the additive inverse or opposite of each number.*

35. -9

36. $\frac{2}{3}$

37. $|-2|$

38. $-|-7|$

Add.

39. $-15 + 4$

40. $-6 + (-11)$

41. $\frac{1}{16} + \left(-\frac{1}{4}\right)$

42. $-8 + |-3|$

43. $-4.6 + (-9.3)$

44. $-2.8 + 6.7$

(1.5) *Perform each indicated operation.*

45. $6 - 20$

46. $-3.1 - 8.4$

47. $-6 - (-11)$

48. $4 - 15$

49. $-21 - 16 + 3(8 - 2)$

50. $\frac{11 - (-9) + 6(8 - 2)}{2 + 3 \cdot 4}$

Evaluate each expression for $x = 3$, $y = -6$, and $z = -9$. Then choose the correct evaluation.

51. $2x^2 - y + z$

a. 15 **b.** 3 **c.** 27 **d.** −3

52. $\frac{|y - 4x|}{2x}$

a. 3 **b.** 1 **c.** −1 **d.** −3

53. At the beginning of the week the price of Density Oil and Gas stock from Exercises 17 and 18 is $50 per share. Find the price of a share of stock at the end of the week.

54. Find the price of a share of stock by the end of the day on Wednesday.

Find each multiplicative inverse or reciprocal.

55. -6

56. $\frac{3}{5}$

(1.6) *Simplify each expression.*

57. $6(-8)$

58. $(-2)(-14)$

59. $\frac{-18}{-6}$

60. $\frac{42}{-3}$

61. $-3(-6)(-2)$

62. $(-4)(-3)(0)(-6)$

63. $\frac{4(-3) + (-8)}{2 + (-2)}$

64. $\frac{3(-2)^2 - 5}{-14}$

(1.7) *Name the property illustrated in each equation.*

65. $-6 + 5 = 5 + (-6)$

66. $6 \cdot 1 = 6$

67. $3(8 - 5) = 3 \cdot 8 - 3 \cdot 5$

68. $4 + (-4) = 0$

69. $2 + (3 + 9) = (2 + 3) + 9$

70. $2 \cdot 8 = 8 \cdot 2$

71. $6(8 + 5) = 6 \cdot 8 + 6 \cdot 5$

72. $(3 \cdot 8) \cdot 4 = 3 \cdot (8 \cdot 4)$

73. $4 \cdot \frac{1}{4} = 1$

74. $8 + 0 = 8$

75. $4(8 + 3) = 4(3 + 8)$

76. $5(2 + 1) = 5 \cdot 2 + 5 \cdot 1$

(1.8) *Simplify each expression.*

77. $5x - x + 2x$

78. $0.2z - 4.6z - 7.4z$

79. $\frac{1}{2}x + 3 + \frac{7}{2}x - 5$

80. $\frac{4}{5}y + 1 + \frac{6}{5}y + 2$

81. $2(n - 4) + n - 10$

82. $3(w + 2) - (12 - w)$

83. Subtract $7x - 2$ from $x + 5$.

84. Subtract $1.4y - 3$ from $y - 0.7$.

Write each phrase as an algebraic expression. Simplify if possible.

85. Three times a number decreased by 7

86. Twice the sum of a number and 2.8, added to 3 times the number

Mixed Review

Insert $<$, $>$, or $=$ in the space between each pair of numbers.

87. $-|-11| \quad |11.4|$

88. $-1\frac{1}{2} \quad -2\frac{1}{2}$

Perform the indicated operations.

89. $-7.2 + (-8.1)$

90. $14 - 20$

91. $4(-20)$

92. $\frac{-20}{4}$

93. $-\frac{4}{5}\left(\frac{5}{16}\right)$

94. $-0.5(-0.3)$

95. $8 \div 2 \cdot 4$

96. $(-2)^4$

97. $\dfrac{-3 - 2(-9)}{-15 - 3(-4)}$

98. $5 + 2[(7 - 5)^2 + (1 - 3)]$

99. $-\dfrac{5}{8} \div \dfrac{3}{4}$

100. $\dfrac{-15 + (-4)^2 + |-9|}{10 - 2 \cdot 5}$

Remove parentheses and simplify each expression.

101. $7(3x - 3) - 5(x + 4)$

102. $8 + 2(9x - 10)$

Chapter 1 Test

Step-by-step test solutions are found on the Chapter Test Prep Videos available via the Interactive DVD Lecture Series, in MyMathLab or on YouTube (search "MartinGayIntroAlg" and click on "Channels").

Answers

1. ______
2. ______
3. ______
4. ______
5. ______
6. ______
7. ______
8. ______
9. ______
10. ______
11. ______
12. ______
13. ______
14. ______
15. ______
16. ______
17. ______
18. ______
19. ______
20. ______
21. ______

Translate each statement into symbols.

1. The absolute value of negative seven is greater than five.

2. The sum of nine and five is greater than or equal to four.

Simplify each expression.

3. $-13 + 8$

4. $-13 - (-2)$

5. $6 \cdot 3 - 8 \cdot 4$

6. $13(-3)$

7. $(-6)(-2)$

8. $\frac{|-16|}{-8}$

9. $\frac{-8}{0}$

10. $\frac{|-6| + 2}{5 - 6}$

11. $\frac{1}{2} - \frac{5}{6}$

12. $-1\frac{1}{8} + 5\frac{3}{4}$

13. $-\frac{3}{5} + \frac{15}{8}$

14. $3(-4)^2 - 80$

15. $6[5 + 2(3 - 8) - 3]$

16. $\frac{-12 + 3 \cdot 8}{4}$

17. $\frac{(-2)(0)(-3)}{-6}$

Insert $<$, $>$, or $=$ in the appropriate space to make each statement true.

18. $-3 \quad -7$

19. $4 \quad -8$

20. $|-3| \quad 2$

21. $|-2| \quad -1 - (-3)$

22. Given $\left\{-5, -1, \frac{1}{4}, 0, 1, 7, 11.6, \sqrt{7}, 3\pi\right\}$, list the numbers in this set that also belong to the set of:

a. Natural numbers
b. Whole numbers
c. Integers
d. Rational numbers
e. Irrational numbers
f. Real numbers

Evaluate each expression when $x = 6$, $y = -2$, and $z = -3$.

23. $x^2 + y^2$
24. $x + yz$
25. $2 + 3x - y$
26. $\dfrac{y + z - 1}{x}$

Identify the property illustrated by each expression.

27. $8 + (9 + 3) = (8 + 9) + 3$
28. $6 \cdot 8 = 8 \cdot 6$

29. $-6(2 + 4) = -6 \cdot 2 + (-6) \cdot 4$
30. $\frac{1}{6}(6) = 1$

31. Find the opposite of -9.
32. Find the reciprocal of $-\frac{1}{3}$.

The New Orleans Saints were 22 yards from the goal when the series of gains and losses shown in the chart occurred. Use this chart to answer Exercises 33 and 34.

	Gains and Losses (in yards)
First down	5
Second down	−10
Third down	−2
Fourth down	29

33. During which down did the greatest loss of yardage occur?

34. Was a touchdown scored?

35. The temperature at the Winter Olympics was a frigid 14° below zero in the morning, but by noon it had risen 31°. What was the temperature at noon?

36. A stockbroker decided to sell 280 shares of stock, which decreased in value by \$1.50 per share yesterday. How much money did she lose?

Simplify each expression.

37. $2y - 6 - y - 4$
38. $2.7x + 6.1 + 3.2x - 4.9$
39. $4(x - 2) - 3(2x - 6)$
40. $-5(y + 1) + 2(3 - 5y)$

22. a. ______
b. ______
c. ______
d. ______
e. ______
f. ______
23. ______
24. ______
25. ______
26. ______
27. ______
28. ______
29. ______
30. ______
31. ______
32. ______
33. ______
34. ______
35. ______
36. ______
37. ______
38. ______
39. ______
40. ______

2 Equations, Inequalities, and Problem Solving

In this chapter, we solve equations and inequalities. Once we know how to solve equations and inequalities, we may solve word problems. Of course, problem solving is an integral topic in algebra and its discussion is continued throughout this text.

Sections

Check Your Progress

A glacier is formed when snow accumulates over time, turns to ice, and begins to flow outwards and downwards under the pressure of its own weight and gravity. Presently 10% of land area is covered with glaciers and about 75% of the fresh water in the world is stored in glacial fields. Glaciers are excellent indicators of past and present climate change. The GLIMS project (Global Land Ice Measurements from Space) is currently creating a glacier database on measurements of the world's estimated 160,000 glaciers. In Section 2.5, Example 1 and Exercise 86 we will examine the distance a glacier covers and the speed at which it travels.

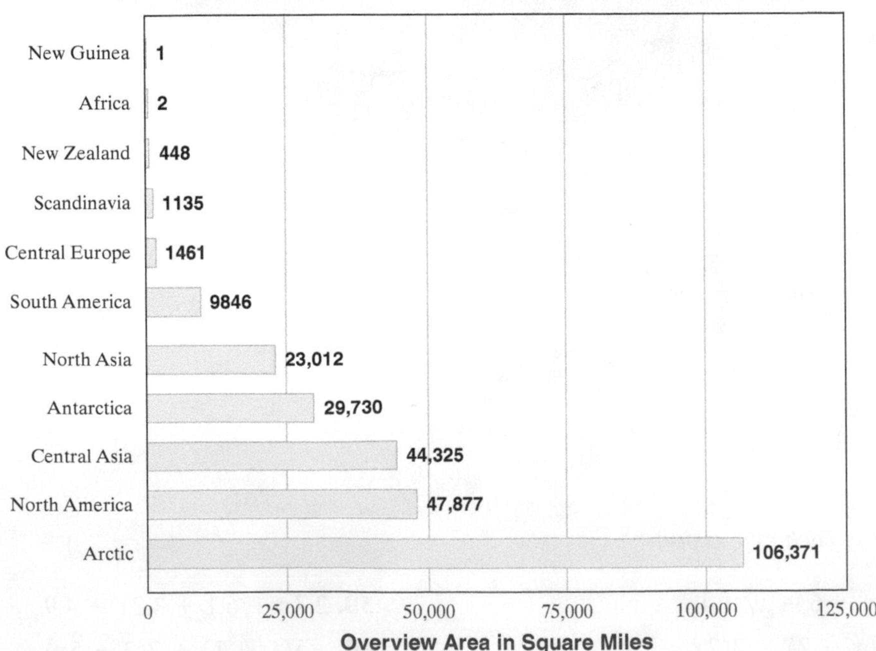

2.1 THE ADDITION PROPERTY OF EQUALITY

Objectives

A Use the Addition Property of Equality to Solve Linear Equations.

B Simplify an Equation and Then Use the Addition Property of Equality.

C Write Word Phrases as Algebraic Expressions.

Let's recall from Section 1.3 the difference between an equation and an expression. A combination of operations on variables and numbers is an expression, and an equation is of the form "expression = expression."

Equations	Expressions
$3x - 1 = -17$	$3x - 1$
area = length · width	$5(20 - 3) + 10$
$8 + 16 = 16 + 8$	y^3
$-9a + 11b = 14b + 3$	$-x^2 + y - 2$

Now, let's concentrate on equations.

Helpful Hint Simply stated, an equation contains "=" while an expression does not. Also, we *simplify* expressions and *solve* equations.

Objective A Using the Addition Property

A value of the variable that makes an equation a true statement is called a solution or root of the equation. The process of finding the solution of an equation is called **solving** the equation for the variable. In this section, we concentrate on solving *linear equations* in one variable.

Linear Equation in One Variable

A **linear equation in one variable** can be written in the form

$$Ax + B = C$$

where A, B, and C are real numbers and $A \neq 0$.

Evaluating each side of a linear equation for a given value of the variable, as we did in Section 1.3, can tell us whether that value is a solution. But we can't rely on this as our method of solving it—with what value would we start?

Instead, to solve a linear equation in x, we write a series of simpler equations, all *equivalent* to the original equation, so that the final equation has the form

x = number or number = x

Equivalent equations are equations that have the same solution. This means that the "number" above is the solution to the original equation.

The first property of equality that helps us write simpler equivalent equations is the **addition property of equality.**

Addition Property of Equality

Let a, b, and c represent numbers. Then

$a = b$	Also, $a = b$
and $a + c = b + c$	and $a - c = b - c$
are equivalent equations.	are equivalent equations.

In other words, **the same number may be added to or subtracted from both sides** of an equation without changing the solution of the equation. (We may subtract the same number from both sides since subtraction is defined in terms of addition.)

Let's visualize how we use the addition property of equality to solve an equation. Picture the equation $x - 2 = 1$ as a balanced scale. The left side of the equation has the same value (weight) as the right side.

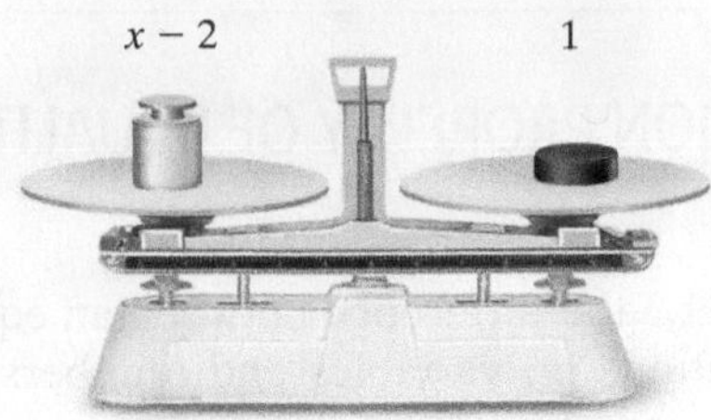

If the same weight is added to each side of a scale, the scale remains balanced. Likewise, if the same number is added to each side of an equation, the left side continues to have the same value as the right side.

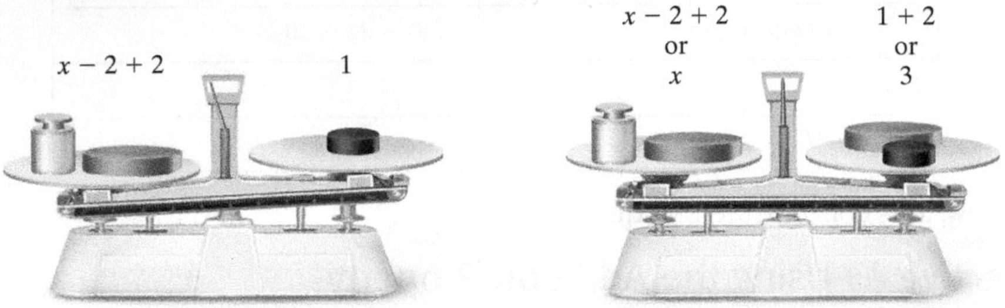

We use the addition property of equality to write equivalent equations until the variable is alone (by itself on one side of the equation) and the equation looks like "$x =$ number" or "number $= x$."

✓Concept Check Use the addition property to fill in the blanks so that the middle equation simplifies to the last equation.

$$x - 5 = 3$$
$$x - 5 + \_\_ = 3 + \_\_$$
$$x = 8$$

PRACTICE 1

Solve: $x - 5 = 8$ for x.

Example 1 Solve $x - 7 = 10$ for x.

Solution: To solve for x, we first get x alone on one side of the equation. To do this, we add 7 to both sides of the equation.

$x - 7 = 10$

$x - 7 + 7 = 10 + 7$ Add 7 to both sides.

$x = 17$ Simplify.

The solution of the equation $x = 17$ is obviously 17.
Since we are writing equivalent equations, the solution of the equation $x - 7 = 10$ is also 17.

Check: To check, replace x with 17 in the original equation.

$x - 7 = 10$ Original equation.

$17 - 7 \stackrel{?}{=} 10$ Replace x with 17.

$10 = 10$ True

Since the statement is true, 17 is the solution.

Work Practice 1

PRACTICE 2

Solve: $y + 1.7 = 0.3$

Example 2 Solve: $y + 0.6 = -1.0$

Solution: To solve for y (get y alone on one side of the equation), we subtract 0.6 from both sides of the equation.

Answers

1. $x = 13$ **2.** $y = -1.4$

✓ Concept Check Answer

5

$$y + 0.6 = -1.0$$
$$y + 0.6 - 0.6 = -1.0 - 0.6 \quad \text{Subtract 0.6 from both sides.}$$
$$y = -1.6 \quad \text{Combine like terms.}$$

Check: $y + 0.6 = -1.0$ Original equation.
$-1.6 + 0.6 \stackrel{?}{=} -1.0$ Replace y with -1.6.
$-1.0 = -1.0$ True

The solution is -1.6.

Work Practice 2

Example 3 Solve: $\frac{1}{2} = x - \frac{3}{4}$

Solution: To get x alone, we add $\frac{3}{4}$ to both sides.

$$\frac{1}{2} = x - \frac{3}{4}$$
$$\frac{1}{2} + \frac{3}{4} = x - \frac{3}{4} + \frac{3}{4} \quad \text{Add } \frac{3}{4} \text{ to both sides.}$$
$$\frac{1}{2} \cdot \frac{2}{2} + \frac{3}{4} = x \quad \text{The LCD is 4.}$$
$$\frac{2}{4} + \frac{3}{4} = x \quad \text{Add the fractions.}$$
$$\frac{5}{4} = x$$

Check: $\frac{1}{2} = x - \frac{3}{4}$ Original equation.
$\frac{1}{2} \stackrel{?}{=} \frac{5}{4} - \frac{3}{4}$ Replace x with $\frac{5}{4}$.
$\frac{1}{2} \stackrel{?}{=} \frac{2}{4}$ Subtract.
$\frac{1}{2} = \frac{1}{2}$ True

The solution is $\frac{5}{4}$.

Work Practice 3

PRACTICE 3

Solve: $\frac{7}{8} = y - \frac{1}{3}$

Helpful Hint We may solve an equation so that the variable is alone on *either* side of the equation. For example, $\frac{5}{4} = x$ is equivalent to $x = \frac{5}{4}$.

Example 4 Solve: $5t - 5 = 6t$

Solution: To solve for t, we first want all terms containing t on one side of the equation and numbers on the other side. Notice that if we subtract $5t$ from both sides of the equation, then variable terms will be on one side of the equation and the number -5 will be alone on the other side.

$$5t - 5 = 6t$$
$$5t - 5 - 5t = 6t - 5t \quad \text{Subtract } 5t \text{ from both sides.}$$
$$-5 = t \quad \text{Combine like terms.}$$

Check: $5t - 5 = 6t$ Original equation.
$5(-5) - 5 \stackrel{?}{=} 6(-5)$ Replace t with -5.
$-25 - 5 \stackrel{?}{=} -30$
$-30 = -30$ True

The solution is -5.

Work Practice 4

PRACTICE 4

Solve: $3x + 10 = 4x$

Helpful Hint For Example 4, why not subtract $6t$ from both sides? The addition property allows us to do this, and we would have $-t - 5 = 0$. We are just no closer to our goal of having variable terms on one side of the equation and numbers on the other.

Answers

3. $y = \frac{29}{24}$ 4. $x = 10$

Objective B Simplifying Equations

Many times, it is best to simplify one or both sides of an equation before applying the addition property of equality.

PRACTICE 5

Solve:
$10w + 3 - 4w + 4 = -2w + 3 + 7w$

Example 5 Solve: $2x + 3x - 5 + 7 = 10x + 3 - 6x - 4$

Solution: First we simplify both sides of the equation.

$$2x + 3x - 5 + 7 = 10x + 3 - 6x - 4$$
$$5x + 2 = 4x - 1 \quad \text{Combine like terms on each side of the equation.}$$

Next, we want all terms with a variable on one side of the equation and all numbers on the other side.

$$5x + 2 - 4x = 4x - 1 - 4x \quad \text{Subtract } 4x \text{ from both sides.}$$
$$x + 2 = -1 \quad \text{Combine like terms.}$$
$$x + 2 - 2 = -1 - 2 \quad \text{Subtract 2 from both sides to get } x \text{ alone.}$$
$$x = -3 \quad \text{Combine like terms.}$$

Check:

$$2x + 3x - 5 + 7 = 10x + 3 - 6x - 4 \quad \text{Original equation.}$$
$$2(-3) + 3(-3) - 5 + 7 \stackrel{?}{=} 10(-3) + 3 - 6(-3) - 4 \quad \text{Replace } x \text{ with } -3.$$
$$-6 - 9 - 5 + 7 \stackrel{?}{=} -30 + 3 + 18 - 4 \quad \text{Multiply.}$$
$$-13 = -13 \quad \text{True}$$

The solution is -3.

Work Practice 5

If an equation contains parentheses, we use the distributive property to remove them, as before. Then we combine any like terms.

PRACTICE 6

Solve:
$3(2w - 5) - (5w + 1) = -3$

Example 6 Solve: $6(2a - 1) - (11a + 6) = 7$

Solution:

$$6(2a - 1) - 1(11a + 6) = 7$$
$$6(2a) + 6(-1) - 1(11a) - 1(6) = 7 \quad \text{Apply the distributive property.}$$
$$12a - 6 - 11a - 6 = 7 \quad \text{Multiply.}$$
$$a - 12 = 7 \quad \text{Combine like terms.}$$
$$a - 12 + 12 = 7 + 12 \quad \text{Add 12 to both sides.}$$
$$a = 19 \quad \text{Simplify.}$$

Check: Check by replacing a with 19 in the original equation.

Work Practice 6

PRACTICE 7

Solve: $12 - y = 9$

Example 7 Solve: $3 - x = 7$

Solution: First we subtract 3 from both sides.

$$3 - x = 7$$
$$3 - x - 3 = 7 - 3 \quad \text{Subtract 3 from both sides.}$$
$$-x = 4 \quad \text{Simplify.}$$

We have not yet solved for x since x is not alone. However, this equation does say that the opposite of x is 4. If the opposite of x is 4, then x is the opposite of 4, or $x = -4$.

If $-x = 4$,
then $x = -4$.

Answers

5. $w = -4$ 6. $w = 13$ 7. $y = 3$

Check:

$$3 - x = 7 \quad \text{Original equation.}$$
$$3 - (-4) \stackrel{?}{=} 7 \quad \text{Replace } x \text{ with } -4.$$
$$3 + 4 \stackrel{?}{=} 7 \quad \text{Add.}$$
$$7 = 7 \quad \text{True}$$

The solution is -4.

Work Practice 7

Objective C Writing Algebraic Expressions

In this section, we continue to practice writing algebraic expressions.

Example 8

a. The sum of two numbers is 8. If one number is 3, find the other number.
b. The sum of two numbers is 8. If one number is x, write an expression representing the other number.

Solution:

a. If the sum of two numbers is 8 and one number is 3, we find the other number by subtracting 3 from 8. The other number is $8 - 3$, or 5.

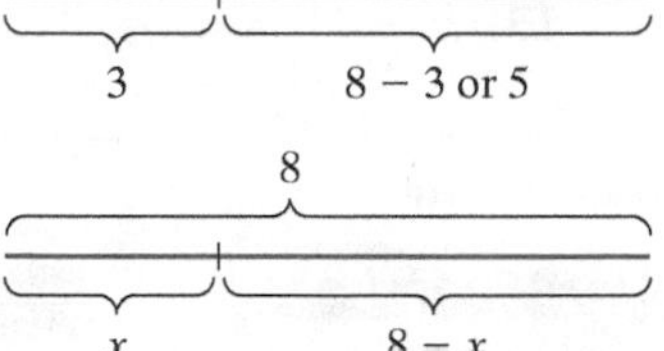

b. If the sum of two numbers is 8 and one number is x, we find the other number by subtracting x from 8. The other number is represented by $8 - x$.

8

x $8 - x$

Work Practice 8

PRACTICE 8

a. The sum of two numbers is 11. If one number is 4, find the other number.
b. The sum of two numbers is 11. If one number is x, write an expression representing the other number.
c. The sum of two numbers is 56. If one number is a, write an expression representing the other number.

Example 9 The Verrazano-Narrows Bridge in New York City is the longest suspension bridge in North America. The Golden Gate Bridge in San Francisco is 60 feet shorter than the Verrazano-Narrows Bridge. If the length of the Verrazano-Narrows Bridge is m feet, express the length of the Golden Gate Bridge as an algebraic expression in m. (*Source:* Survey of State Highway Engineers)

Solution: Since the Golden Gate Bridge is 60 feet shorter than the Verrazano-Narrows Bridge, we have that its length is

In words:	Length of Verrazano-Narrows Bridge	minus	60
Translate:	m	$-$	60

The Golden Gate Bridge is $(m - 60)$ feet long.

Work Practice 9

PRACTICE 9

In a recent House of Representatives race in California, Mike Thompson received 100,445 more votes than Zane Starkewolf. If Zane received n votes, how many did Mike receive? (*Source:* Voter News Service)

Answers

8. a. $11 - 4$ or 7 **b.** $11 - x$ **c.** $56 - a$ **9.** $(n + 100{,}445)$ votes

Vocabulary and Readiness Check

Use the choices below to fill in each blank. Some choices may be used more than once or not at all.

equation	multiplication	addition
expression	solution	equivalent

1. A combination of operations on variables and numbers is called a(n) ____________.
2. A statement of the form "expression = expression" is called a(n) ____________.
3. A(n) ____________ contains an equal sign (=).
4. A(n) ____________ does not contain an equal sign (=).
5. A(n) ____________ may be simplified and evaluated while a(n) ____________ may be solved.
6. A(n) ____________ of an equation is a number that when substituted for a variable makes the equation a true statement.
7. ____________ equations have the same solution.
8. By the ____________ property of equality, the same number may be added to or subtracted from both sides of an equation without changing the solution of the equation.

Solve each equation mentally. See Examples 1 and 2.

9. $x + 4 = 6$ **10.** $x + 7 = 17$ **11.** $n + 18 = 30$

12. $z + 22 = 40$ **13.** $b - 11 = 6$ **14.** $d - 16 = 5$

2.1 Exercise Set

FOR EXTRA HELP

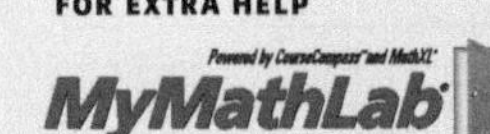

Objective A *Solve each equation. Check each solution. See Examples 1 through 4.*

1. $x + 7 = 10$ **2.** $x + 14 = 25$ **3.** $x - 2 = -4$ **4.** $y - 9 = 1$

5. $-11 = 3 + x$ **6.** $-8 = 8 + z$ **7.** $r - 8.6 = -8.1$ **8.** $t - 9.2 = -6.8$

9. $x - \frac{2}{5} = -\frac{3}{20}$ **10.** $y - \frac{4}{7} = -\frac{3}{14}$ **11.** $\frac{1}{3} + f = \frac{3}{4}$ **12.** $c + \frac{1}{6} = \frac{3}{8}$

Objective B *Solve each equation. Don't forget to first simplify each side of the equation, if possible. Check each solution. See Examples 5 through 7.*

13. $7x + 2x = 8x - 3$ **14.** $3n + 2n = 7 + 4n$ **15.** $\frac{5}{6}x + \frac{1}{6}x = -9$

16. $\frac{13}{11}y - \frac{2}{11}y = -3$ **17.** $2y + 10 = 5y - 4y$ **18.** $4x - 4 = 10x - 7x$

19. $-5(n - 2) = 8 - 4n$ **20.** $-4(z - 3) = 2 - 3z$ **21.** $\frac{3}{7}x + 2 = -\frac{4}{7}x - 5$

22. $\frac{1}{5}x - 1 = -\frac{4}{5}x - 13$ **23.** $5x - 6 = 6x - 5$ **24.** $2x + 7 = x - 10$

25. $8y + 2 - 6y = 3 + y - 10$ **26.** $4p - 11 - p = 2 + 2p - 20$ **27.** $-3(x - 4) = -4x$

28. $-2(x - 1) = -3x$ **29.** $\frac{3}{8}x - \frac{1}{6} = -\frac{5}{8}x - \frac{2}{3}$ **30.** $\frac{2}{5}x - \frac{1}{12} = -\frac{3}{5}x - \frac{3}{4}$

31. $2(x - 4) = x + 3$ **32.** $3(y + 7) = 2y - 5$

33. $3(n - 5) - (6 - 2n) = 4n$

34. $5(3 + z) - (8z + 9) = -4z$

35. $-2(x + 6) + 3(2x - 5) = 3(x - 4) + 10$

36. $-5(x + 1) + 4(2x - 3) = 2(x + 2) - 8$

Objectives A B Mixed Practice *Solve. See Examples 1 through 7.*

37. $13x - 3 = 14x$

38. $18x - 9 = 19x$

39. $5b - 0.7 = 6b$

40. $9x + 5.5 = 10x$

41. $3x - 6 = 2x + 5$

42. $7y + 2 = 6y + 2$

43. $13x - 9 + 2x - 5 = 12x - 1 + 2x$

44. $15x + 20 - 10x - 9 = 25x + 8 - 21x - 7$

45. $7(6 + w) = 6(2 + w)$

46. $6(5 + c) = 5(c - 4)$

47. $n + 4 = 3.6$

48. $m + 2 = 7.1$

49. $10 - (2x - 4) = 7 - 3x$

50. $15 - (6 - 7k) = 2 + 6k$

51. $\frac{1}{3} = x + \frac{2}{3}$

52. $\frac{1}{11} = y + \frac{10}{11}$

53. $-6.5 - 4x - 1.6 - 3x = -6x + 9.8$

54. $-1.4 - 7x - 3.6 - 2x = -8x + 4.4$

Objective C *Write each algebraic expression described. See Examples 8 and 9.*

55. A 10-foot board is cut into two pieces. If one piece is x feet long, express the other length in terms of x.

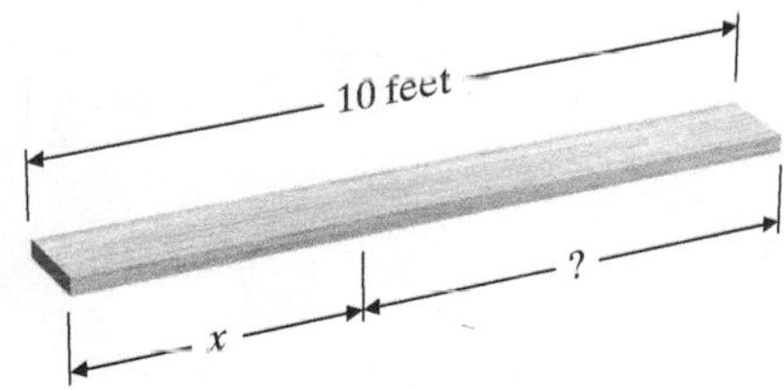

56. A 5-foot piece of string is cut into two pieces. If one piece is x feet long, express the other length in terms of x.

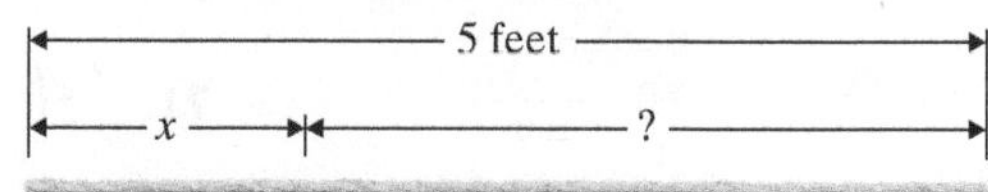

57. Recall that two angles are *supplementary* if their sum is 180°. If one angle measures $x°$, express the measure of its supplement in terms of x.

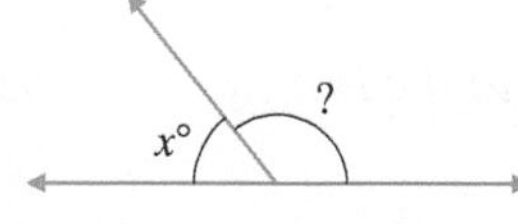

58. Recall that two angles are *complementary* if their sum is 90°. If one angle measures $x°$, express the measure of its complement in terms of x.

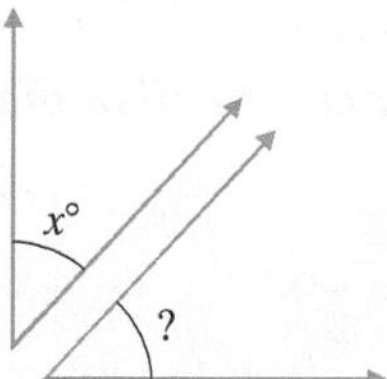

59. In 2009, the number of graduate students at the University of Texas at Austin was approximately 28,000 fewer than the number of undergraduate students. If the number of undergraduate students was n, how many graduate students attend UT Austin? (*Source:* University of Texas at Austin)

60. The longest interstate highway in the U.S. is I-90, which connects Seattle, Washington, and Boston, Massachusetts. The second longest interstate highway, I-80 (connecting San Francisco, California, and Teaneck, New Jersey), is 178.5 miles shorter than I-90. If the length of I-80 is m miles, express the length of I-90 as an algebraic expression in m. (*Source:* U.S. Department of Transportation—Federal Highway Administration)

61. The area of the Sahara Desert in Africa is 7 times the area of the Gobi Desert in Asia. If the area of the Gobi Desert is x square miles, express the area of the Sahara Desert as an algebraic expression in x.

62. The largest meteorite in the world is the Hoba West located in Namibia. Its weight is 3 times the weight of the Armanty meteorite located in Outer Mongolia. If the weight of the Armanty meteorite is y kilograms, express the weight of the Hoba West meteorite as an algebraic expression in y.

Review

Find each multiplicative inverse or reciprocal. See Section 1.7.

63. $\frac{5}{8}$ **64.** $\frac{7}{6}$ **65.** 2 **66.** 5 **67.** $-\frac{1}{9}$ **68.** $-\frac{3}{5}$

Perform each indicated operation and simplify. See Sections 1.6 and 1.8.

69. $\frac{3x}{3}$ **70.** $\frac{-2y}{-2}$ **71.** $-5\left(-\frac{1}{5}y\right)$ **72.** $7\left(\frac{1}{7}r\right)$ **73.** $\frac{3}{5}\left(\frac{5}{3}x\right)$ **74.** $\frac{9}{2}\left(\frac{2}{9}x\right)$

Concept Extensions

75. Write two terms whose sum is $-3x$.

76. Write four terms whose sum is $2y - 6$.

Use the addition property to fill in the blank so that the middle equation simplifies to the last equation. See the Concept Check in this section.

77.
$$x - 4 = -9$$
$$x - 4 + (\quad) = -9 + (\quad)$$
$$x = -5$$

78.
$$a + 9 = 15$$
$$a + 9 + (\quad) = 15 + (\quad)$$
$$a = 6$$

Fill in the blanks with numbers of your choice so that each equation has the given solution. Note: Each blank will be replaced with a different number.

79. ____ $+ x =$ ____; Solution: -3

80. $x -$ ____ $=$ ____; Solution: -10

Solve.

81. The sum of the angles of a triangle is 180°. If one angle of a triangle measures $x°$ and a second angle measures $(2x + 7)°$, express the measure of the third angle in terms of x. Simplify the expression.

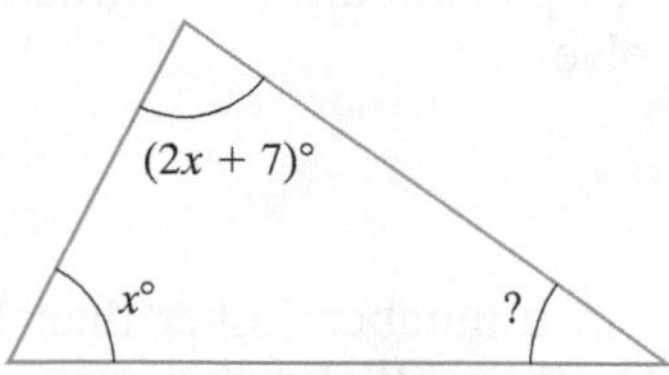

82. A quadrilateral is a four-sided figure (like the one shown in the figure) whose angle sum is 360°. If one angle measures $x°$, a second angle measures $3x°$, and a third angle measures $5x°$, express the measure of the fourth angle in terms of x. Simplify the expression.

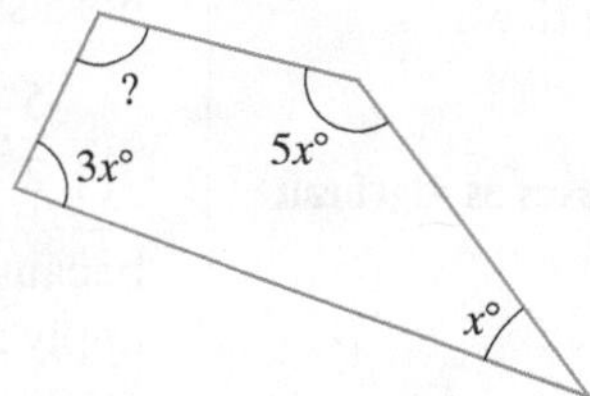

83. In your own words, explain what is meant by the solution of an equation.

84. In your own words, explain how to check a solution of an equation.

Use a calculator to determine the solution of each equation.

85. $36.766 + x = -108.712$

86. $-85.325 = x - 97.985$

Objectives

A Use the Multiplication Property of Equality to Solve Linear Equations.

B Use Both the Addition and Multiplication Properties of Equality to Solve Linear Equations.

C Write Word Phrases as Algebraic Expressions.

2.2 THE MULTIPLICATION PROPERTY OF EQUALITY

Objective A Using the Multiplication Property

As useful as the addition property of equality is, it cannot help us solve every type of linear equation in one variable. For example, adding or subtracting a value on both sides of the equation does not help solve

$$\frac{5}{2}x = 15$$

because the variable x is being multiplied by a number (other than 1). Instead, we apply another important property of equality, the **multiplication property of equality.**

Multiplication Property of Equality

Let a, b, and c represent numbers and let $c \neq 0$. Then

$a = b$	Also, $a = b$
and $a \cdot c = b \cdot c$	and $\frac{a}{c} = \frac{b}{c}$
are equivalent equations.	are equivalent equations.

In other words, **both sides** of an equation **may be multiplied or divided by the same nonzero number** without changing the solution of the equation. (We may divide both sides by the same nonzero number since division is defined in terms of multiplication.)

Picturing again our balanced scale, if we multiply or divide the weight on each side by the same nonzero number, the scale (or equation) remains balanced.

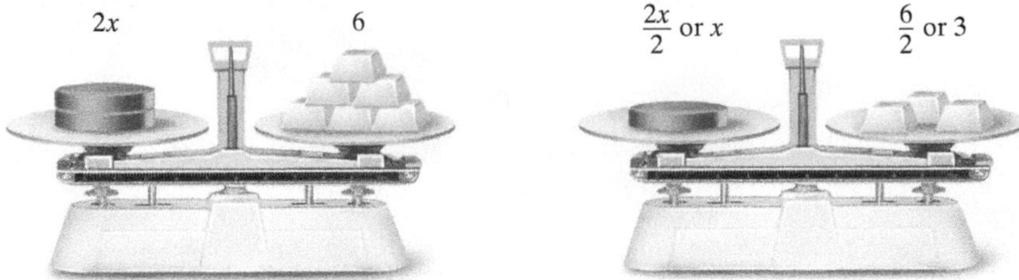

PRACTICE 1

Solve: $\frac{3}{7}x = 9$

Example 1 Solve: $\frac{5}{2}x = 15$

Solution: To get x alone, we multiply both sides of the equation by the reciprocal (or multiplicative inverse) of $\frac{5}{2}$, which is $\frac{2}{5}$.

$$\frac{5}{2}x = 15$$

$$\frac{2}{5}\cdot\left(\frac{5}{2}x\right) = \frac{2}{5}\cdot 15 \quad \text{Multiply both sides by } \frac{2}{5}.$$

$$\left(\frac{2}{5}\cdot\frac{5}{2}\right)x = \frac{2}{5}\cdot 15 \quad \text{Apply the associative property.}$$

$$1x = 6 \quad \text{Simplify.}$$

or

$$x = 6$$

Answer

1. $x = 21$

Check: Replace x with 6 in the original equation.

$$\frac{5}{2}x = 15 \quad \text{Original equation.}$$

$$\frac{5}{2}(6) \stackrel{?}{=} 15 \quad \text{Replace } x \text{ with 6.}$$

$$15 = 15 \quad \text{True}$$

The solution is 6.

Work Practice 1

In the equation $\frac{5}{2}x = 15$, $\frac{5}{2}$ is the coefficient of x. When the coefficient of x is a *fraction,* we will get x alone by multiplying by the reciprocal. When the coefficient of x is an integer or a decimal, it is usually more convenient to divide both sides by the coefficient. (Dividing by a number is, of course, the same as multiplying by the reciprocal of the number.)

Example 2 Solve: $5x = 30$

PRACTICE 2

Solve: $7x = 42$

Solution: To get x alone, we divide both sides of the equation by 5, the coefficient of x.

$$5x = 30$$

$$\frac{5x}{5} = \frac{30}{5} \quad \text{Divide both sides by 5.}$$

$$1 \cdot x = 6 \quad \text{Simplify.}$$

$$x = 6$$

Check: $5x = 30$ Original equation.

$5 \cdot 6 \stackrel{?}{=} 30$ Replace x with 6.

$30 = 30$ True

The solution is 6.

Work Practice 2

Example 3 Solve: $-3x = 33$

PRACTICE 3

Solve: $-4x = 52$

Solution: Recall that $-3x$ means $-3 \cdot x$. To get x alone, we divide both sides by the coefficient of x, that is, -3.

$$-3x = 33$$

$$\frac{-3x}{-3} = \frac{33}{-3} \quad \text{Divide both sides by } -3.$$

$$1x = -11 \quad \text{Simplify.}$$

$$x = -11$$

Check: $-3x = 33$ Original equation.

$-3(-11) \stackrel{?}{=} 33$ Replace x with -11.

$33 = 33$ True

The solution is -11.

Work Practice 3

Answers

2. $x = 6$ **3.** $x = -13$

PRACTICE 4

Solve: $\frac{y}{5} = 13$

Example 4 Solve: $\frac{y}{7} = 20$

Solution: Recall that $\frac{y}{7} = \frac{1}{7}y$. To get y alone, we multiply both sides of the equation by 7, the reciprocal of $\frac{1}{7}$.

$$\frac{y}{7} = 20$$
$$\frac{1}{7}y = 20$$
$$7 \cdot \frac{1}{7}y = 7 \cdot 20 \quad \text{Multiply both sides by 7.}$$
$$1y = 140 \quad \text{Simplify.}$$
$$y = 140$$

Check: $\frac{y}{7} = 20$ Original equation.

$$\frac{140}{7} \stackrel{?}{=} 20 \quad \text{Replace } y \text{ with 140.}$$
$$20 = 20 \quad \text{True}$$

The solution is 140.

Work Practice 4

PRACTICE 5

Solve: $2.6x = 13.52$

Example 5 Solve: $3.1x = 4.96$

Solution:

$$3.1x = 4.96$$
$$\frac{3.1x}{3.1} = \frac{4.96}{3.1} \quad \text{Divide both sides by 3.1.}$$
$$1x = 1.6 \quad \text{Simplify.}$$
$$x = 1.6$$

Check: Check by replacing x with 1.6 in the original equation. The solution is 1.6.

Work Practice 5

PRACTICE 6

Solve: $-\frac{5}{6}y = -\frac{3}{5}$

Example 6 Solve: $-\frac{2}{3}x = -\frac{5}{2}$

Solution: To get x alone, we multiply both sides of the equation by $-\frac{3}{2}$, the reciprocal of the coefficient of x.

$$-\frac{2}{3}x = -\frac{5}{2}$$
$$-\frac{3}{2} \cdot -\frac{2}{3}x = -\frac{3}{2} \cdot -\frac{5}{2} \quad \text{Multiply both sides by } -\frac{3}{2}\text{, the reciprocal of } -\frac{2}{3}.$$
$$x = \frac{15}{4} \quad \text{Simplify.}$$

Check: Check by replacing x with $\frac{15}{4}$ in the original equation. The solution is $\frac{15}{4}$.

Work Practice 6

Answers

4. $y = 65$ 5. $x = 5.2$ 6. $y = \frac{18}{25}$

Objective B Using Both the Addition and Multiplication Properties

We are now ready to combine the skills learned in the last section with the skills learned in this section to solve equations by applying more than one property.

Example 7 Solve: $-z - 4 = 6$

Solution: First, let's get $-z$, the term containing the variable, alone. To do so, we add 4 to both sides of the equation.

$$-z - 4 + 4 = 6 + 4 \quad \text{Add 4 to both sides.}$$
$$-z = 10 \quad \text{Simplify.}$$

Next, recall that $-z$ means $-1 \cdot z$. Thus to get z alone, we either multiply or divide both sides of the equation by -1. In this example, we divide.

$$-z = 10$$
$$\frac{-z}{-1} = \frac{10}{-1} \quad \text{Divide both sides by the coefficient } -1.$$
$$1z = -10 \quad \text{Simplify.}$$
$$z = -10$$

Check: $-z - 4 = 6$ Original equation.

$$-(-10) - 4 \stackrel{?}{=} 6 \quad \text{Replace } z \text{ with } -10.$$
$$10 - 4 \stackrel{?}{=} 6$$
$$6 = 6 \quad \text{True}$$

The solution is -10.

Work Practice 7

PRACTICE 7

Solve: $-x + 7 = -12$

Don't forget to first simplify one or both sides of an equation, if possible.

Example 8 Solve: $a + a - 10 + 7 = -13$

Solution: First, we simplify the left side of the equation by combining like terms.

$$a + a - 10 + 7 = -13$$
$$2a - 3 = -13 \quad \text{Combine like terms.}$$
$$2a - 3 + 3 = -13 + 3 \quad \text{Add 3 to both sides.}$$
$$2a = -10 \quad \text{Simplify.}$$
$$\frac{2a}{2} = \frac{-10}{2} \quad \text{Divide both sides by 2.}$$
$$a = -5 \quad \text{Simplify.}$$

Check: To check, replace a with -5 in the original equation. The solution is -5.

Work Practice 8

PRACTICE 8

Solve:
$-7x + 2x + 3 - 20 = -2$

Example 9 Solve: $7x - 3 = 5x + 9$

Solution: To get x alone, let's first use the addition property to get variable terms on one side of the equation and numbers on the other side. One way to get variable terms on one side is to subtract $5x$ from both sides.

$$7x - 3 = 5x + 9$$
$$7x - 3 - 5x = 5x + 9 - 5x \quad \text{Subtract } 5x \text{ from both sides.}$$
$$2x - 3 = 9 \quad \text{Simplify.}$$

Continued on next page

PRACTICE 9

Solve: $10x - 4 = 7x + 14$

Answers
7. $x = 19$ **8.** $x = -3$ **9.** $x = 6$

Now, to get numbers on the other side, let's add 3 to both sides.

$$2x - 3 + 3 = 9 + 3 \quad \text{Add 3 to both sides.}$$
$$2x = 12 \quad \text{Simplify.}$$

Use the multiplication property to get x alone.

$$\frac{2x}{2} = \frac{12}{2} \quad \text{Divide both sides by 2.}$$
$$x = 6 \quad \text{Simplify.}$$

Check: To check, replace x with 6 in the original equation to see that a true statement results. The solution is 6.

Work Practice 9

If an equation has parentheses, don't forget to use the distributive property to remove them. Then combine any like terms.

PRACTICE 10

Solve: $4(3x - 2) = -1 + 4$

Example 10 Solve: $5(2x + 3) = -1 + 7$

Solution:

$$5(2x + 3) = -1 + 7$$
$$5(2x) + 5(3) = -1 + 7 \quad \text{Apply the distributive property.}$$
$$10x + 15 = 6 \quad \text{Multiply and write } -1 + 7 \text{ as 6.}$$
$$10x + 15 - 15 = 6 - 15 \quad \text{Subtract 15 from both sides.}$$
$$10x = -9 \quad \text{Simplify.}$$
$$\frac{10x}{10} = -\frac{9}{10} \quad \text{Divide both sides by 10.}$$
$$x = -\frac{9}{10} \quad \text{Simplify.}$$

Check: To check, replace x with $-\frac{9}{10}$ in the original equation to see that a true statement results. The solution is $-\frac{9}{10}$.

Work Practice 10

PRACTICE 11

a. If x is the first of two consecutive integers, express the sum of the two integers in terms of x. Simplify if possible.

b. If x is the first of two consecutive odd integers (see next page), express the sum of the two integers in terms of x. Simplify if possible.

Objective C Writing Algebraic Expressions

We continue to sharpen our problem-solving skills by writing algebraic expressions.

Example 11 Writing an Expression for Consecutive Integers

If x is the first of three consecutive integers, express the sum of the three integers in terms of x. Simplify if possible.

Solution: An example of three consecutive integers is 7, 8, and 9.

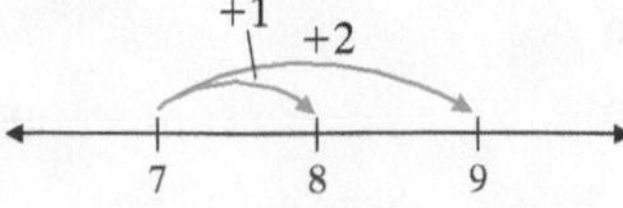

Answers

10. $x = \frac{11}{12}$ **11. a.** $2x + 1$ **b.** $2x + 2$

The second consecutive integer is always 1 more than the first, and the third consecutive integer is 2 more than the first. If x is the first of three consecutive integers, the three consecutive integers are x, $x + 1$, and $x + 2$.

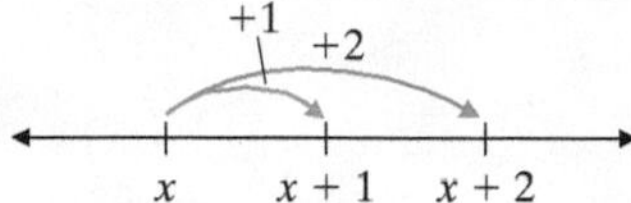

Their sum is shown below.

In words:	first integer	+	second integer	+	third integer
Translate:	x	+	$(x + 1)$	+	$(x + 2)$

This simplifies to $3x + 3$.

Work Practice 11

Study these examples of consecutive even and consecutive odd integers.

Consecutive even integers:

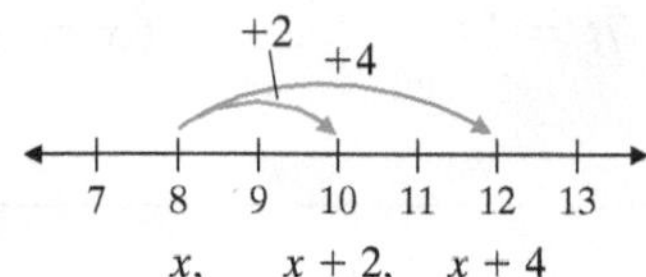

Consecutive odd integers:

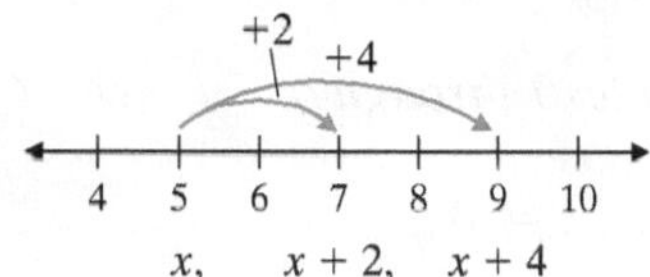

Helpful Hint

If x is an odd integer, then $x + 2$ is the next odd integer. This 2 simply means that odd integers are always 2 units from each other.

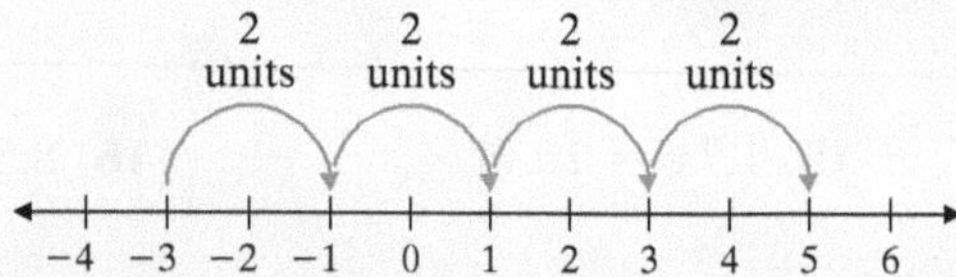

Vocabulary and Readiness Check

Use the choices below to fill in each blank. Some choices may be used more than once. Many of these exercises contain an important review of Section 2.1 also.

equation	multiplication	addition
expression	solution	equivalent

1. By the ____________ property of equality, both sides of an equation may be multiplied or divided by the same nonzero number without changing the solution of the equation.
2. By the ____________ property of equality, the same number may be added to or subtracted from both sides of an equation without changing the solution of the equation.
3. A(n) ____________ may be solved while a(n) ____________ may be simplified and evaluated.
4. A(n) ____________ contains an equal sign (=) while a(n) ____________ does not.
5. ____________ equations have the same solution.
6. A(n) ____________ of an equation is a number that when substituted for a variable makes the equation a true statement.

Solve each equation mentally. See Examples 2 and 3.

7. $3a = 27$ **8.** $9c = 54$ **9.** $5b = 10$ **10.** $7t = 14$ **11.** $6x = -30$ **12.** $8r = -64$

2.2 Exercise Set

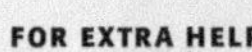
FOR EXTRA HELP

PRACTICE

WATCH

DOWNLOAD

READ

REVIEW

Objective A *Solve each equation. Check each solution. See Examples 1 through 6.*

1. $-5x = -20$ **2.** $-7x = -49$ **3.** $3x = 0$ **4.** $2x = 0$

5. $-x = -12$ **6.** $-y = 8$ **7.** $\frac{2}{3}x = -8$ **8.** $\frac{3}{4}n = -15$

9. $\frac{1}{6}d = \frac{1}{2}$ **10.** $\frac{1}{8}v = \frac{1}{4}$ **11.** $\frac{a}{2} = 1$ **12.** $\frac{d}{15} = 2$

13. $\frac{k}{-7} = 0$ **14.** $\frac{f}{-5} = 0$ **15.** $1.7x = 10.71$ **16.** $8.5y = 19.55$

Objective B *Solve each equation. Check each solution. See Examples 7 and 8.*

17. $2x - 4 = 16$ **18.** $3x - 1 = 26$ **19.** $-x + 2 = 22$ **20.** $-x + 4 = -24$

21. $6a + 3 = 3$ **22.** $8t + 5 = 5$ **23.** $\frac{x}{3} - 2 = -5$ **24.** $\frac{b}{4} - 1 = -7$

25. $6z - 8 - z + 3 = 0$ **26.** $4a + 1 + a - 11 = 0$ **27.** $1 = 0.4x - 0.6x - 5$ **28.** $19 = 0.4x - 0.9x - 6$

29. $\frac{2}{3}y - 11 = -9$ **30.** $\frac{3}{5}x - 14 = -8$ **31.** $\frac{3}{4}t - \frac{1}{2} = \frac{1}{3}$ **32.** $\frac{2}{7}z - \frac{1}{5} = \frac{1}{2}$

Solve each equation. See Examples 9 and 10.

33. $8x + 20 = 6x + 18$

34. $11x + 13 = 9x + 9$

35. $3(2x + 5) = -18 + 9$

36. $2(4x + 1) = -12 + 6$

37. $2x - 5 = 20x + 4$

38. $6x - 4 = -2x - 10$

39. $2 + 14 = -4(3x - 4)$

40. $8 + 4 = -6(5x - 2)$

41. $-6y - 3 = -5y - 7$

42. $-17z - 4 = -16z - 20$

43. $\frac{1}{2}(2x - 1) = -\frac{1}{7} - \frac{3}{7}$

44. $\frac{1}{3}(3x - 1) = -\frac{1}{10} - \frac{2}{10}$

45. $-10z - 0.5 = -20z + 1.6$

46. $-14y - 1.8 = -24y + 3.9$

47. $-4x + 20 = 4x - 20$

48. $-3x + 15 = 3x - 15$

Objectives **A** **B** **Mixed Practice** *See Examples 1 through 10.*

49. $42 = 7x$

50. $81 = 3x$

51. $4.4 = -0.8x$

52. $6.3 = -0.6x$

53. $6x + 10 = -20$

54. $10y + 15 = -5$

55. $5 - 0.3k = 5$

56. $2 - 0.4p = 2$

57. $13x - 5 = 11x - 11$

58. $20x - 20 = 16x - 40$

59. $9(3x + 1) = 4x - 5x$

60. $7(2x + 1) = 18x - 19x$

61. $-\frac{3}{7}p = -2$

62. $-\frac{4}{5}r = -5$

63. $-\frac{4}{3}x = 12$

64. $-\frac{10}{3}x = 30$

65. $-2x - \frac{1}{2} = \frac{7}{2}$

66. $-3n - \frac{1}{3} = \frac{8}{3}$

67. $10 = 2x - 1$

68. $12 = 3j - 4$

69. $10 - 3x - 6 - 9x = 7$

70. $12x + 30 + 8x - 6 = 10$

71. $z - 5z = 7z - 9 - z$

72. $t - 6t = -13 + t - 3t$

73. $-x - \frac{4}{5} = x + \frac{1}{2} + \frac{2}{5}$

74. $x + \frac{3}{7} = -x + \frac{1}{3} + \frac{4}{7}$

75. $-15 + 37 = -2(x + 5)$

76. $-19 + 74 = -5(x + 3)$

Objective C *Write each algebraic expression described. Simplify if possible. See Example 11.*

77. If x represents the first of two consecutive odd integers, express the sum of the two integers in terms of x.

78. If x is the first of three consecutive even integers, write their sum as an algebraic expression in x.

79. If x is the first of four consecutive integers, express the sum of the first integer and the third integer as an algebraic expression containing the variable x.

80. If x is the first of two consecutive integers, express the sum of 20 and the second consecutive integer as an algebraic expression containing the variable x.

81. Classrooms on one side of the science building are all numbered with consecutive even integers. If the first room on this side of the building is numbered x, write an expression in x for the sum of five classroom numbers in a row. Then simplify this expression.

82. Two sides of a quadrilateral have the same length, x, while the other two sides have the same length, both being the next consecutive odd integer. Write the sum of these lengths. Then simplify this expression.

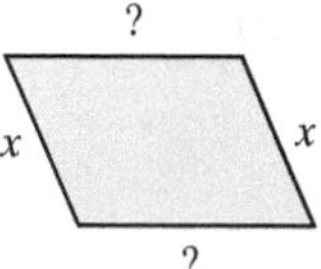

Review

Simplify each expression. See Section 1.8.

83. $5x + 2(x - 6)$

84. $-7y + 2y - 3(y + 1)$

85. $6(2z + 4) + 20$

86. $-(3a - 3) + 2a - 6$

87. $-(x - 1) + x$

88. $8(z - 6) + 7z - 1$

Concept Extensions

Fill in the blank with a number of your choice so that each equation has the given solution.

89. $6x =$ ____; solution: -8

90. ____ $x = 10$; solution: $\frac{1}{2}$

91. The equation $3x + 6 = 2x + 10 + x - 4$ is true for all real numbers. Substitute a few real numbers for x to see that this is so and then try solving the equation. Describe what happens.

92. The equation $6x + 2 - 2x = 4x + 1$ has no solution. Try solving this equation for x and describe what happens.

93. From the results of Exercises 91 and 92, when do you think an equation has all real numbers as its solutions?

94. From the results of Exercises 91 and 92, when do you think an equation has no solution?

Solve.

95. $0.07x - 5.06 = -4.92$

96. $0.06y + 2.63 = 2.5562$

2.3 FURTHER SOLVING LINEAR EQUATIONS

Objective A Solving Linear Equations

Let's begin by restating the formal definition of a linear equation in one variable.

A **linear equation in one variable** can be written in the form

$Ax + B = C$

where A, B, and C are real numbers and $A \neq 0$.

We now combine our knowledge from the previous sections into a general strategy for solving linear equations.

To Solve Linear Equations in One Variable

Step 1: If an equation contains fractions, multiply both sides by the LCD to clear the equation of fractions.

Step 2: Use the distributive property to remove parentheses if they are present.

Step 3: Simplify each side of the equation by combining like terms.

Step 4: Get all variable terms on one side and all numbers on the other side by using the addition property of equality.

Step 5: Get the variable alone by using the multiplication property of equality.

Step 6: Check the solution by substituting it into the original equation.

We will use these steps as we solve the equations in Examples 1–5.

Example 1 Solve: $4(2x - 3) + 7 = 3x + 5$

Solution: There are no fractions, so we begin with Step 2.

$$4(2x - 3) + 7 = 3x + 5$$

Step 2: $8x - 12 + 7 = 3x + 5$ Use the distributive property.

Step 3: $8x - 5 = 3x + 5$ Combine like terms.

Step 4: Get all variable terms on one side of the equation and all numbers on the other side. One way to do this is by subtracting $3x$ from both sides and then adding 5 to both sides.

$8x - 5 - 3x = 3x + 5 - 3x$ Subtract $3x$ from both sides.

$5x - 5 = 5$ Simplify.

$5x - 5 + 5 = 5 + 5$ Add 5 to both sides.

$5x = 10$ Simplify.

Step 5: Use the multiplication property of equality to get x alone.

$\frac{5x}{5} = \frac{10}{5}$ Divide both sides by 5.

$x = 2$ Simplify.

Step 6: Check.

$4(2x - 3) + 7 = 3x + 5$ Original equation

$4[2(2) - 3] + 7 \stackrel{?}{=} 3(2) + 5$ Replace x with 2.

$4(4 - 3) + 7 \stackrel{?}{=} 6 + 5$

$4(1) + 7 \stackrel{?}{=} 11$

$4 + 7 \stackrel{?}{=} 11$

$11 = 11$ True

The solution is 2.

Work Practice 1

Objectives

A Apply the General Strategy for Solving a Linear Equation.

B Solve Equations Containing Fractions or Decimals.

C Recognize Identities and Equations with No Solution.

PRACTICE 1

Solve:
$5(3x - 1) + 2 = 12x + 6$

Answer

1. $x = 3$

PRACTICE 2

Solve: $9(5 - x) = -3x$

Helpful Hint When checking solutions, use the original equation.

Example 2 Solve: $8(2 - t) = -5t$

Solution: First, we apply the distributive property.

$$8(2 - t) = -5t$$

Step 2: $16 - 8t = -5t$ Use the distributive property.

Step 4: $16 - 8t + 8t = -5t + 8t$ Add $8t$ to both sides.

$16 = 3t$ Combine like terms.

Step 5: $\frac{16}{3} = \frac{3t}{3}$ Divide both sides by 3.

$\frac{16}{3} = t$ Simplify.

Step 6: Check.

$8(2 - t) = -5t$ Original equation

$8\left(2 - \frac{16}{3}\right) \stackrel{?}{=} -5\left(\frac{16}{3}\right)$ Replace t with $\frac{16}{3}$.

$8\left(\frac{6}{3} - \frac{16}{3}\right) \stackrel{?}{=} -\frac{80}{3}$ The LCD is 3.

$8\left(-\frac{10}{3}\right) \stackrel{?}{=} -\frac{80}{3}$ Subtract fractions.

$-\frac{80}{3} = -\frac{80}{3}$ True

The solution is $\frac{16}{3}$.

Work Practice 2

Objective B Solving Equations Containing Fractions or Decimals

If an equation contains fractions, we can clear the equation of fractions by multiplying both sides by the LCD of all denominators. By doing this, we avoid working with time-consuming fractions.

PRACTICE 3

Solve: $\frac{5}{2}x - 1 = \frac{3}{2}x - 4$

Example 3 Solve: $\frac{x}{2} - 1 = \frac{2}{3}x - 3$

Solution: We begin by clearing fractions. To do this, we multiply both sides of the equation by the LCD, which is 6.

$$\frac{x}{2} - 1 = \frac{2}{3}x - 3$$

Step 1: $6\left(\frac{x}{2} - 1\right) = 6\left(\frac{2}{3}x - 3\right)$ Multiply both sides by the LCD, 6.

Step 2: $6\left(\frac{x}{2}\right) - 6(1) = 6\left(\frac{2}{3}x\right) - 6(3)$ Use the distributive property.

$3x - 6 = 4x - 18$ Simplify.

Helpful Hint Don't forget to multiply *each* term by the LCD.

There are no longer grouping symbols and no like terms on either side of the equation, so we continue with Step 4.

Answers

2. $x = \frac{15}{2}$ 3. $x = -3$

$3x - 6 = 4x - 18$

Step 4: $3x - 6 - 3x = 4x - 18 - 3x$ Subtract $3x$ from both sides.
$-6 = x - 18$ Simplify.
$-6 + 18 = x - 18 + 18$ Add 18 to both sides.
$12 = x$ Simplify.

Step 5: The variable is now alone, so there is no need to apply the multiplication property of equality.

Step 6: Check.

$\frac{x}{2} - 1 = \frac{2}{3}x - 3$ Original equation
$\frac{12}{2} - 1 \stackrel{?}{=} \frac{2}{3} \cdot 12 - 3$ Replace x with 12.
$6 - 1 \stackrel{?}{=} 8 - 3$ Simplify.
$5 = 5$ True

The solution is 12.

Work Practice 3

Example 4 Solve: $\frac{2(a + 3)}{3} = 6a + 2$

Solution: We clear the equation of fractions first.

$$\frac{2(a + 3)}{3} = 6a + 2$$

Step 1: $3 \cdot \frac{2(a + 3)}{3} = 3(6a + 2)$ Clear the fraction by multiplying both sides by the LCD, 3.

$2(a + 3) = 3(6a + 2)$ Simplify.

Step 2: Next, we use the distributive property to remove parentheses.

$2a + 6 = 18a + 6$ Use the distributive property.

Step 4: $2a + 6 - 18a = 18a + 6 - 18a$ Subtract $18a$ from both sides.
$-16a + 6 = 6$ Simplify.
$-16a + 6 - 6 = 6 - 6$ Subtract 6 from both sides.
$-16a = 0$

Step 5: $\frac{-16a}{-16} = \frac{0}{-16}$ Divide both sides by -16.
$a = 0$ Simplify.

Step 6: To check, replace a with 0 in the original equation. The solution is 0.

Work Practice 4

PRACTICE 4

Solve: $\frac{3(x - 2)}{5} = 3x + 6$

Helpful Hint

Remember: When solving an equation, it makes no difference on which side of the equation variable terms lie. Just make sure that constant terms lie on the other side.

When solving a problem about money, you may need to solve an equation containing decimals. If you choose, you may multiply to clear the equation of decimals.

Answer

4. $x = -3$

PRACTICE 5

Solve:
$0.06x - 0.10(x - 2) = -0.16$

Example 5 Solve: $0.25x + 0.10(x - 3) = 1.1$

Solution: First we clear this equation of decimals by multiplying both sides of the equation by 100. Recall that multiplying a decimal number by 100 has the effect of moving the decimal point 2 places to the right.

$$0.25x + 0.10(x - 3) = 1.1$$

Step 1: $0.25x + 0.10(x - 3) = 1.10$ Multiply both sides by 100

$$25x + 10(x - 3) = 110$$

Step 2: $25x + 10x - 30 = 110$ Apply the distributive property.

Step 3: $35x - 30 = 110$ Combine like terms.

Step 4: $35x - 30 + 30 = 110 + 30$ Add 30 to both sides.

$35x = 140$ Combine like terms.

Step 5: $\frac{35x}{35} = \frac{140}{35}$ Divide both sides by 35.

$$x = 4$$

Step 6: To check, replace x with 4 in the original equation. The solution is 4.

Work Practice 5

Helpful Hint

If you have trouble with this step, try removing parentheses first.

$0.25x + 0.10(x - 3) = 1.1$

$0.25x + 0.10x - 0.3 = 1.1$

$0.25x + 0.10x - 0.30 = 1.10$

$25x + 10x - 30 = 110$

Then continue.

Objective C Recognizing Identities and Equations with No Solution

So far, each equation that we have solved has had a single solution. However, not every equation in one variable has a single solution. Some equations have no solution, while others have an infinite number of solutions. For example,

$$x + 5 = x + 7$$

has **no solution** since no matter which real number we replace x with, the equation is false.

real number + 5 = same real number + 7 FALSE

On the other hand,

$$x + 6 = x + 6$$

has infinitely many solutions since x can be replaced by any real number and the equation will always be true.

real number + 6 = same real number + 6 TRUE

The equation $x + 6 = x + 6$ is called an **identity.** The next two examples illustrate special equations like these.

PRACTICE 6

Solve:
$5(2 - x) + 8x = 3(x - 6)$

Example 6 Solve: $-2(x - 5) + 10 = -3(x + 2) + x$

Solution:

$-2(x - 5) + 10 = -3(x + 2) + x$

$-2x + 10 + 10 = -3x - 6 + x$ Apply the distributive property on both sides.

$-2x + 20 = -2x - 6$ Combine like terms.

$-2x + 20 + 2x = -2x - 6 + 2x$ Add $2x$ to both sides.

$20 = -6$ Combine like terms.

The final equation contains no variable terms, and the result is the false statement $20 = -6$. This means that there is no value for x that makes $20 = -6$ a true equation. Thus, we conclude that there is **no solution** to this equation.

Work Practice 6

Answers

5. $x = 9$ **6.** no solution

Example 7 Solve: $3(x - 4) = 3x - 12$

Solution:

$$3(x - 4) = 3x - 12$$
$$3x - 12 = 3x - 12 \quad \text{Apply the distributive property.}$$

The left side of the equation is now identical to the right side. Every real number may be substituted for x and a true statement will result. We arrive at the same conclusion if we continue.

$$3x - 12 = 3x - 12$$
$$3x - 12 - 3x = 3x - 12 - 3x \quad \text{Subtract } 3x \text{ from both sides.}$$
$$-12 = -12 \quad \text{Combine like terms.}$$

Again, the final equation contains no variables, but this time the result is the true statement $-12 = -12$. This means that one side of the equation is identical to the other side. Thus, $3(x - 4) = 3x - 12$ is an **identity** and **every real number** is a solution.

Work Practice 7

PRACTICE 7

Solve:
$-6(2x + 1) - 14$
$= -10(x + 2) - 2x$

Answer

7. Every real number is a solution.

✓Concept Check Suppose you have simplified several equations and obtained the following results. What can you conclude about the solutions to the original equation?

a. $7 = 7$ **b.** $x = 0$ **c.** $7 = -4$

✓ Concept Check Answer

a. Every real number is a solution.
b. The solution is 0.
c. There is no solution.

Calculator Explorations Checking Equations

We can use a calculator to check possible solutions of equations. To do this, replace the variable by the possible solution and evaluate each side of the equation separately.

Equation: $3x - 4 = 2(x + 6)$ Solution: $x = 16$

$$3x - 4 = 2(x + 6)$$
$$3(16) - 4 \stackrel{?}{=} 2(16 + 6)$$

Now evaluate each side with your calculator.

Evaluate left side: [3] [×] [16]  [–] [4] [=] or [ENTER]

Display: [44]

Evaluate right side: [2] [(] [16] [+] [6] [)] [=] or [ENTER]

Display: [44]

Since the left side equals the right side, the equation checks.

Use a calculator to check the possible solutions to each equation.

1. $2x = 48 + 6x;\quad x = -12$

2. $-3x - 7 = 3x - 1;\quad x = -1$

3. $5x - 2.6 = 2(x + 0.8);\quad x = 4.4$

4. $-1.6x - 3.9 = -6.9x - 25.6;\quad x = 5$

5. $\frac{564x}{4} = 200x - 11(649);\quad x = 121$

6. $20(x - 39) = 5x - 432;\quad x = 23.2$

Vocabulary and Readiness Check

Throughout algebra, it is important to be able to identify equations and expressions.

Remember,

- an equation contains an equal sign and
- an expression does not.

Among other things,

- we solve equations and
- we simplify or perform operations on expressions.

Identify each as an equation or an expression.

1. $x = -7$ ______ **2.** $x - 7$ ______ **3.** $4y - 6 + 9y + 1$ ______

4. $4y - 6 = 9y + 1$ ______ **5.** $\frac{1}{x} - \frac{x-1}{8}$ ______ **6.** $\frac{1}{x} - \frac{x-1}{8} = 6$ ______

7. $0.1x + 9 = 0.2x$ ______ **8.** $0.1x^2 + 9y - 0.2x^2$ ______

2.3 Exercise Set

FOR EXTRA HELP

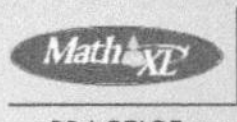

PRACTICE

WATCH

DOWNLOAD

READ

REVIEW

Objective A *Solve each equation. See Examples 1 and 2.*

1. $-4y + 10 = -2(3y + 1)$

2. $-3x + 1 = -2(4x + 2)$

3. $15x - 8 = 10 + 9x$

4. $15x - 5 = 7 + 12x$

5. $-2(3x - 4) = 2x$

6. $-(5x - 10) = 5x$

7. $5(2x - 1) - 2(3x) = 1$

8. $3(2 - 5x) + 4(6x) = 12$

9. $-6(x - 3) - 26 = -8$

10. $-4(n - 4) - 23 = -7$

11. $8 - 2(a + 1) = 9 + a$

12. $5 - 6(2 + b) = b - 14$

13. $4x + 3 = -3 + 2x + 14$

14. $6y - 8 = -6 + 3y + 13$

15. $-2y - 10 = 5y + 18$

16. $-7n + 5 = 8n - 10$

Objective B *Solve each equation. See Examples 3 through 5.*

17. $\frac{2}{3}x + \frac{4}{3} = -\frac{2}{3}$

18. $\frac{4}{5}x - \frac{8}{5} = -\frac{16}{5}$

19. $\frac{3}{4}x - \frac{1}{2} = 1$

20. $\frac{2}{9}x - \frac{1}{3} = 1$

21. $0.50x + 0.15(70) = 35.5$

22. $0.40x + 0.06(30) = 9.8$

23. $\frac{2(x+1)}{4} = 3x - 2$

24. $\frac{3(y+3)}{5} = 2y + 6$

25. $x + \frac{7}{6} = 2x - \frac{7}{6}$

26. $\frac{5}{2}x - 1 = x + \frac{1}{4}$

27. $0.12(y - 6) + 0.06y = 0.08y - 0.7$

28. $0.60(z - 300) + 0.05z = 0.70z - 205$

Objective C *Solve each equation. See Examples 6 and 7.*

29. $4(3x + 2) = 12x + 8$

30. $14x + 7 = 7(2x + 1)$

31. $\frac{x}{4} + 1 = \frac{x}{4}$

32. $\frac{x}{3} - 2 = \frac{x}{3}$

33. $3x - 7 = 3(x + 1)$

34. $2(x - 5) = 2x + 10$

35. $-2(6x - 5) + 4 = -12x + 14$

36. $-5(4y - 3) + 2 = -20y + 17$

Objectives A B C **Mixed Practice** *Solve. See Examples 1 through 7.*

37. $\frac{6(3-z)}{5} = -z$

38. $\frac{4(5-w)}{3} = -w$

39. $-3(2t - 5) + 2t = 5t - 4$

40. $-(4a - 7) - 5a = 10 + a$

41. $5y + 2(y - 6) = 4(y + 1) - 2$

42. $9x + 3(x - 4) = 10(x - 5) + 7$

43. $\frac{3(x-5)}{2} = \frac{2(x+5)}{3}$

44. $\frac{5(x-1)}{4} = \frac{3(x+1)}{2}$

45. $0.7x - 2.3 = 0.5$

46. $0.9x - 4.1 = 0.4$

47. $5x - 5 = 2(x + 1) + 3x - 7$

48. $3(2x - 1) + 5 = 6x + 2$

49. $4(2n + 1) = 3(6n + 3) + 1$

50. $4(4y + 2) = 2(1 + 6y) + 8$

51. $x + \frac{5}{4} = \frac{3}{4}x$

52. $\frac{7}{8}x + \frac{1}{4} = \frac{3}{4}x$

53. $\frac{x}{2} - 1 = \frac{x}{5} + 2$

54. $\frac{x}{5} - 7 = \frac{x}{3} - 5$

55. $2(x + 3) - 5 = 5x - 3(1 + x)$

56. $4(2 + x) + 1 = 7x - 3(x - 2)$

57. $0.06 - 0.01(x + 1) = -0.02(2 - x)$

58. $-0.01(5x + 4) = 0.04 - 0.01(x + 4)$

59. $\frac{9}{2} + \frac{5}{2}y = 2y - 4$

60. $3 - \frac{1}{2}x = 5x - 8$

61. $\frac{3}{4}x - 1 + \frac{1}{2}x = \frac{5}{12}x + \frac{1}{6}$

62. $\frac{5}{9}x + 2 - \frac{1}{6}x = \frac{11}{18}x + \frac{1}{3}$

63. $3x + \frac{5}{16} = \frac{3}{4} - \frac{1}{8}x - \frac{1}{2}$

64. $2x - \frac{1}{10} = \frac{2}{5} - \frac{1}{4}x - \frac{17}{20}$

Review

Translating *Write each algebraic expression described. See Section 1.8. Recall that the perimeter of a figure is the total distance around the figure.*

65. A plot of land is in the shape of a triangle. If one side is x meters, a second side is $(2x - 3)$ meters, and a third side is $(3x - 5)$ meters, express the perimeter of the lot as a simplified expression in x.

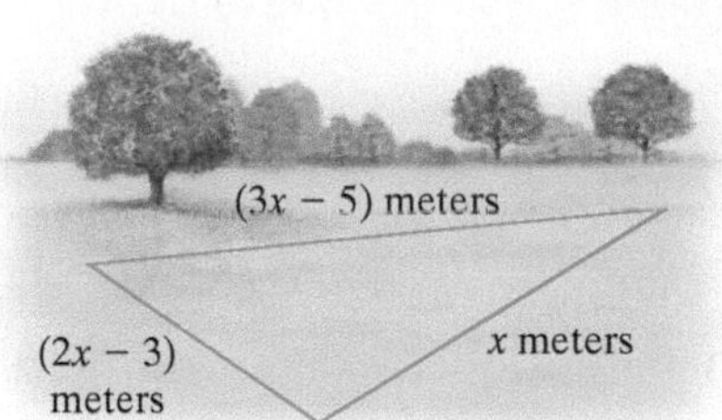

66. A portion of a board has length x feet. The other part has length $(7x - 9)$ feet. Express the total length of the board as a simplified expression in x.

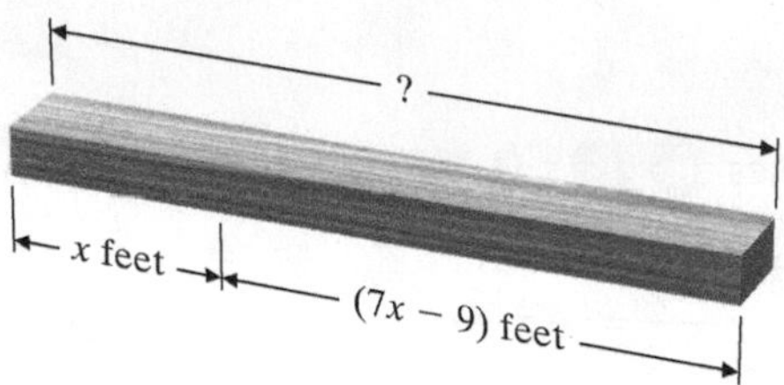

Translating *Write each phrase as an algebraic expression. Use x for the unknown number. See Section 1.8.*

67. A number subtracted from -8

68. Three times a number

69. The sum of -3 and twice a number

70. The difference of 8 and twice a number

71. The product of 9 and the sum of a number and 20

72. The quotient of -12 and the difference of a number and 3

Concept Extensions

See the Concept Check in this section.

73. **a.** Solve: $x + 3 = x + 3$

b. If you simplify an equation (such as the one in part a) and get a true statement such as $3 = 3$ or $0 = 0$, what can you conclude about the solution(s) of the original equation?

c. On your own, construct an equation for which every real number is a solution.

74. **a.** Solve: $x + 3 = x + 5$

b. If you simplify an equation (such as the one in part a) and get a false statement such as $3 = 5$ or $10 = 17$, what can you conclude about the solution(s) of the original equation?

c. On your own, construct an equation that has no solution.

Match each equation in the first column with its solution in the second column. Items in the second column may be used more than once.

75. $5x + 1 = 5x + 1$

76. $3x + 1 = 3x + 2$

77. $2x - 6x - 10 = -4x + 3 - 10$

78. $x - 11x - 3 = -10x - 1 - 2$

79. $9x - 20 = 8x - 20$

80. $-x + 15 = x + 15$

a. all real numbers
b. no solution
c. 0

81. Explain the difference between simplifying an expression and solving an equation.

82. On your own, write an expression and then an equation. Label each.

For Exercises 83 and 84, ***a.*** *Write an equation for perimeter. (Recall that the perimeter of a geometric figure is the sum of the lengths of its sides.)* ***b.*** *Solve the equation in part (a).* ***c.*** *Find the length of each side.*

83. The perimeter of the following pentagon (five-sided figure) is 28 centimeters.

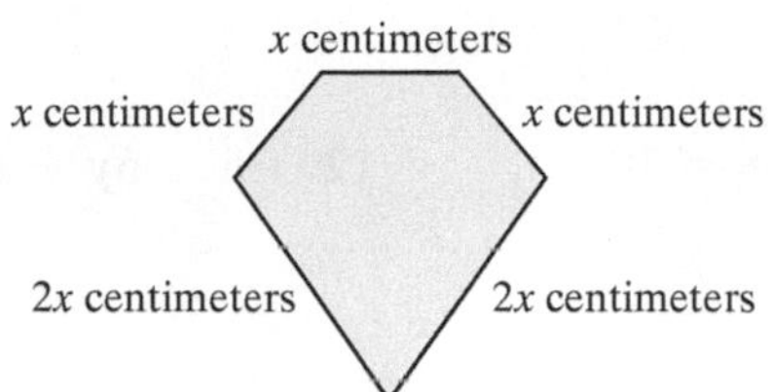

84. The perimeter of the following triangle is 35 meters.

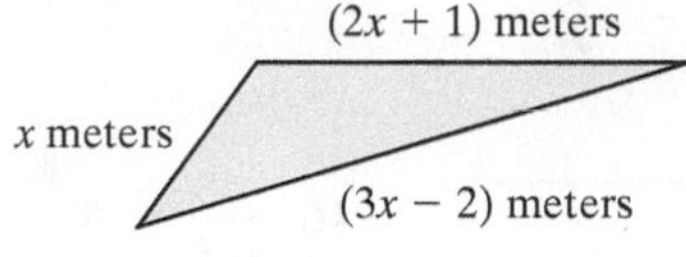

Fill in the blanks with numbers of your choice so that each equation has the given solution. Note: Each blank will be replaced by a different number.

85. $x +$ ____ $= 2x -$ ____; solution: 9

86. $-5x -$ ____ $=$ ____; solution: 2

Solve.

87. $1000(7x - 10) = 50(412 + 100x)$

88. $1000(x + 40) = 100(16 + 7x)$

89. $0.035x + 5.112 = 0.010x + 5.107$

90. $0.127x - 2.685 = 0.027x - 2.38$

Answers

1. ______

2. ______

3. ______

4. ______

5. ______

6. ______

7. ______

8. ______

9. ______

10. ______

11. ______

12. ______

13. ______

14. ______

15. ______

16. ______

17. ______

18. ______

19. ______

20. ______

21. ______

22. ______

Integrated Review Sections 2.1–2.3

Solving Linear Equations

Solve. Feel free to use the steps given in Section 2.3.

1. $x - 10 = -4$

2. $y + 14 = -3$

3. $9y = 108$

4. $-3x = 78$

5. $-6x + 7 = 25$

6. $5y - 42 = -47$

7. $\frac{2}{3}x = 9$

8. $\frac{4}{5}z = 10$

9. $\frac{r}{-4} = -2$

10. $\frac{y}{-8} = 8$

11. $6 - 2x + 8 = 10$

12. $-5 - 6y + 6 = 19$

13. $2x - 7 = 6x - 27$

14. $3 + 8y = 3y - 2$

15. $9(3x - 1) = -4 + 49$

16. $12(2x + 1) = -6 + 66$

17. $-3a + 6 + 5a = 7a - 8a$

18. $4b - 8 - b = 10b - 3b$

19. $-\frac{2}{3}x = \frac{5}{9}$

20. $-\frac{3}{8}y = -\frac{1}{16}$

21. $10 = -6n + 16$

22. $-5 = -2m + 7$

23. $3(5c - 1) - 2 = 13c + 3$

24. $4(3t + 4) - 20 = 3 + 5t$

25. $\frac{2(z + 3)}{3} = 5 - z$

26. $\frac{3(w + 2)}{4} = 2w + 3$

27. $-2(2x - 5) = -3x + 7 - x + 3$

28. $-4(5x - 2) = -12x + 4 - 8x + 4$

29. $0.02(6t - 3) = 0.04(t - 2) + 0.02$

30. $0.03(m + 7) = 0.02(5 - m) + 0.03$

31. $-3y = \frac{4(y - 1)}{5}$

32. $-4x = \frac{5(1 - x)}{6}$

33. $\frac{5}{3}x - \frac{7}{3} = x$

34. $\frac{7}{5}n + \frac{3}{5} = -n$

35. $\frac{1}{10}(3x - 7) = \frac{3}{10}x + 5$

36. $\frac{1}{7}(2x - 5) = \frac{2}{7}x + 1$

37. $5 + 2(3x - 6) = -4(6x - 7)$

38. $3 + 5(2x - 4) = -7(5x + 2)$

23. ____________
24. ____________
25. ____________
26. ____________
27. ____________
28. ____________
29. ____________
30. ____________
31. ____________
32. ____________
33. ____________
34. ____________
35. ____________
36. ____________
37. ____________
38. ____________

2.4 AN INTRODUCTION TO PROBLEM SOLVING

Objectives

A **Solve Problems Involving Direct Translations.**

B **Solve Problems Involving Relationships Among Unknown Quantities.**

C **Solve Problems Involving Consecutive Integers.**

First, let's review a list of key words and phrases from Section 1.3 to help us translate.

Helpful Hint

Order matters when subtracting and also dividing, so be especially careful with these translations.

Addition (+)	Subtraction (−)	Multiplication (·)	Division (÷)	Equality (=)
Sum	Difference of	Product	Quotient	Equals
Plus	Minus	Times	Divide	Gives
Added to	Subtracted from	Multiply	Into	Is/was/should be
More than	Less than	Twice	Ratio	Yields
Increased by	Decreased by	Of	Divided by	Amounts to
Total	Less			Represents
				Is the same as

We are now ready to put all our translating skills to practical use. To begin, we present a general strategy for problem solving.

General Strategy for Problem Solving

1. UNDERSTAND the problem. During this step, become comfortable with the problem. Some ways of doing this are:

   Read and reread the problem.

   Choose a variable to represent the unknown.

   Construct a drawing.

   Propose a solution and check. Pay careful attention to how you check your proposed solution. This will help when writing an equation to model the problem.
2. TRANSLATE the problem into an equation.
3. SOLVE the equation.
4. INTERPRET the results: *Check* the proposed solution in the stated problem and *state* your conclusion.

Objective A Solving Direct Translation Problems

Much of problem solving involves a direct translation from a sentence to an equation.

PRACTICE 1

Three times a number, minus 6, is the same as two times the number, plus 3. Find the number.

Example 1 Finding an Unknown Number

Twice a number, added to seven, is the same as three subtracted from the number. Find the number.

Solution: Translate the sentence into an equation and solve.

In words:	twice a number	added to	seven	is the same as	three subtracted from the number
	↓	↓	↓	↓	↓
Translate:	$2x$	$+$	7	$=$	$x - 3$

Answer

1. The number is 9.

To solve, begin by subtracting x from both sides to isolate the variable term.

$$2x + 7 = x - 3$$
$$2x + 7 - x = x - 3 - x \quad \text{Subtract } x \text{ from both sides.}$$
$$x + 7 = -3 \quad \text{Combine like terms.}$$
$$x + 7 - 7 = -3 - 7 \quad \text{Subtract 7 from both sides.}$$
$$x = -10 \quad \text{Combine like terms.}$$

Check the solution in the problem as it was originally stated. To do so, replace "number" in the sentence with -10. Twice "-10" added to 7 is the same as 3 subtracted from "-10."

$$2(-10) + 7 = -10 - 3$$
$$-13 = -13$$

The unknown number is -10.

Work Practice 1

Helpful Hint

When checking solutions, go back to the original stated problem rather than to your equation in case errors have been made in translating to an equation.

Example 2 Finding an Unknown Number

Twice the sum of a number and 4 is the same as four times the number decreased by 12. Find the number.

Solution:

1. UNDERSTAND. Read and reread the problem. If we let $x =$ the unknown number, then
"the sum of a number and 4" translates to "$x + 4$" and
"four times the number" translates to "$4x$"
2. TRANSLATE.

twice	sum of a number and 4	is the same as	four times the number	decreased by	12
↓	↓	↓	↓	↓	↓
2	$(x + 4)$	=	$4x$	−	12

3. SOLVE

$$2(x + 4) = 4x - 12$$
$$2x + 8 = 4x - 12 \quad \text{Apply the distributive property.}$$
$$2x + 8 - 4x = 4x - 12 - 4x \quad \text{Subtract } 4x \text{ from both sides.}$$
$$-2x + 8 = -12$$
$$-2x + 8 - 8 = -12 - 8 \quad \text{Subtract 8 from both sides.}$$
$$-2x = -20$$
$$\frac{-2x}{-2} = \frac{-20}{-2} \quad \text{Divide both sides by } -2.$$
$$x = 10$$

4. INTERPRET.

Check: Check this solution in the problem as it was originally stated. To do so, replace "number" with 10. Twice the sum of "10" and 4 is 28, which is the same as 4 times "10" decreased by 12.

State: The number is 10.

Work Practice 2

PRACTICE 2

Three times the difference of a number and 5 is the same as twice the number decreased by 3. Find the number.

Answer

2. The number is 12.

Objective B Solving Problems Involving Relationships Among Unknown Quantities

PRACTICE 3

An 18-foot wire is to be cut so that the length of the longer piece is 5 times the length of the shorter piece. Find the length of each piece.

Example 3 Finding the Length of a Board

A 10-foot board is to be cut into two pieces so that the length of the longer piece is 4 times the length of the shorter. Find the length of each piece.

Solution:

1. UNDERSTAND the problem. To do so, read and reread the problem. You may also want to propose a solution. For example, if 3 feet represents the length of the shorter piece, then $4(3) = 12$ feet is the length of the longer piece, since it is 4 times the length of the shorter piece. This guess gives a total board length of 3 feet + 12 feet = 15 feet, which is too long. However, the purpose of proposing a solution is not to guess correctly, but to help better understand the problem and how to model it.

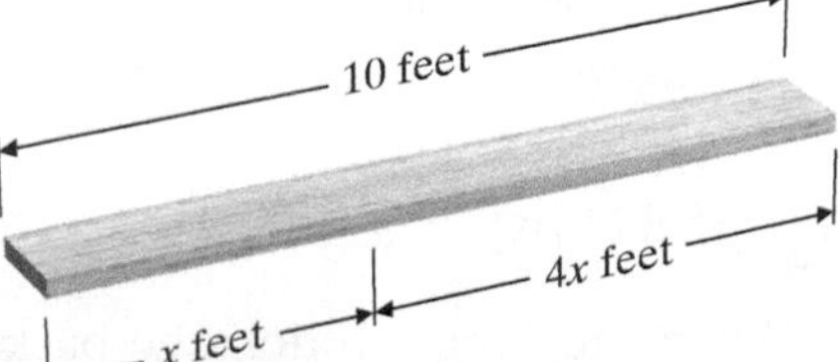

In general, if we let

x = length of shorter piece, then
$4x$ = length of longer piece

2. TRANSLATE the problem. First, we write the equation in words.

length of shorter piece	added to	length of longer piece	equals	total length of board
↓	↓	↓	↓	↓
x	$+$	$4x$	$=$	10

3. SOLVE.

$$x + 4x = 10$$
$$5x = 10 \quad \text{Combine like terms.}$$
$$\frac{5x}{5} = \frac{10}{5} \quad \text{Divide both sides by 5.}$$
$$x = 2$$

4. INTERPRET.

Check: Check the solution in the stated problem. If the length of the shorter piece of board is 2 feet, the length of the longer piece is $4 \cdot (2 \text{ feet}) = 8$ feet and the sum of the lengths of the two pieces is 2 feet + 8 feet = 10 feet.

State: The shorter piece of board is 2 feet and the longer piece of board is 8 feet.

Work Practice 3

Helpful Hint

Make sure that units are included in your answer, if appropriate.

PRACTICE 4

Through the year 2010, the state of California will have 21 more electoral votes for president than the state of Texas. If the total electoral votes for these two states is 89, find the number of electoral votes for each state.

Example 4 Finding the Number of Republican and Democratic Senators

The 111th Congress, which began at noon on January 3, 2009, had a total of 434 Democrats and Republicans. There were 78 more Democratic representatives than Republican. Find the number of representatives from each party. (*Source: New York Times*)

Answers

3. shorter piece: 3 feet; longer piece: 15 feet
4. Texas: 34 electoral votes; California: 55 electoral votes

Solution:

1. UNDERSTAND the problem. Read and reread the problem. Let's suppose that there are 200 Republican representatives. Since there are 78 more Democrats than Republicans, there must be 200 + 78 = 278 Democrats. The total number of Republicans and Democrats is then 200 + 278 = 478. This is incorrect since the total should be 434, but we now have a better understanding of the problem.

   In general, if we let

$$x = \text{number of Republicans, then}$$
$$x + 78 = \text{number of Democrats}$$

2. TRANSLATE the problem. First, we write the equation in words.

number of Republicans	added to	number of Democrats	equals	434
↓	↓	↓	↓	↓
x	$+$	$(x + 78)$	$=$	434

3. SOLVE.

$$x + (x + 78) = 434$$
$$2x + 78 = 434 \quad \text{Combine like terms.}$$
$$2x + 78 - 78 = 434 - 78 \quad \text{Subtract 78 from both sides.}$$
$$2x = 356$$
$$\frac{2x}{2} = \frac{356}{2} \quad \text{Divide both sides by 2.}$$
$$x = 178$$

4. INTERPRET.

Check: If there were 178 Republican representatives, then there were 178 + 78 = 256 Democratic representatives. The total number of representatives is then 178 + 256 = 434. The results check.

State: There were 178 Republican and 256 Democratic representatives at the beginning of the 111th Congress.

Work Practice 4

Example 5 Calculating Hours on the Job

A computer science major at a local university has a part-time job working on computers for his clients. He charges $20 to come to your home or office and then $25 per hour. During one month he visited 10 homes or offices and his total income was $575. How many hours did he spend working on computers?

Solution:

1. UNDERSTAND. Read and reread the problem. Let's propose that the student spent 20 hours working on computers. Pay careful attention as to how his income is calculated. For 20 hours and 10 visits, his income is 20($25) + 10($20) = $700, which is more than $575. We now have a better understanding of the problem and know that the time working on computers is less than 20 hours.

   Let's let

$$x = \text{hours working on computers. Then}$$
$$25x = \text{amount of money made while working on computers}$$

Continued on next page

PRACTICE 5

A car rental agency charges $28 a day and $0.15 a mile. If you rent a car for a day and your bill (before taxes) is $52, how many miles did you drive?

Answer

5. 160 miles

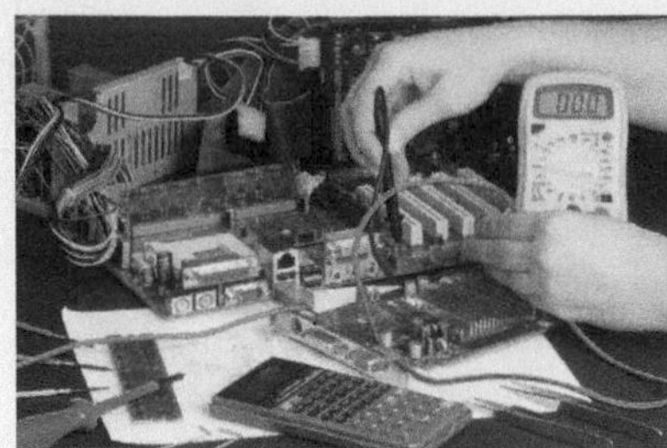

2. TRANSLATE.

money made while working on computers	plus	money made for visits	is equal to	575
↓	↓	↓	↓	↓
$25x$	$+$	$10(20)$	$=$	575

3. SOLVE.

$$25x + 200 = 575$$

$$25x + 200 - 200 = 575 - 200 \quad \text{Subtract 200 from both sides.}$$

$$25x = 375 \quad \text{Simplify.}$$

$$\frac{25x}{25} = \frac{375}{25} \quad \text{Divide both sides by 25.}$$

$$x = 15 \quad \text{Simplify.}$$

4. INTERPRET.

Check: If the student works 15 hours and makes 10 visits, his income is 15($25) + 10($20) = $575.

State: The student spent 15 hours working on computers.

Work Practice 5

PRACTICE 6

The measure of the second angle of a triangle is twice the measure of the smallest angle. The measure of the third angle of the triangle is three times the measure of the smallest angle. Find the measures of the angles.

Example 6 Finding Angle Measures

If the two walls of the Vietnam Veterans Memorial in Washington, D.C., were connected, an isosceles triangle would be formed. The measure of the third angle is 97.5° more than the measure of either of the two equal angles. Find the measure of the third angle. (*Source:* National Park Service)

Solution:

1. UNDERSTAND. Read and reread the problem. We then draw a diagram (recall that an isosceles triangle has two angles with the same measure) and let

x = degree measure of one angle
x = degree measure of the second equal angle
$x + 97.5$ = degree measure of the third angle

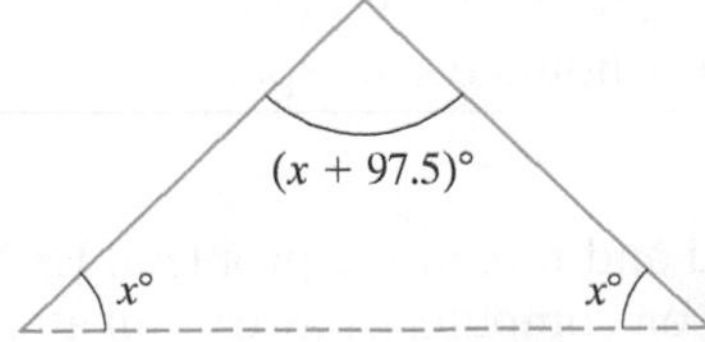

Answer

6. smallest: 30°; second: 60°; third: 90°

2. TRANSLATE. Recall that the sum of the measures of the angles of a triangle equals 180.

measure of first angle	+	measure of second angle	+	measure of third angle	equal	180
↓		↓		↓	↓	↓
x	+	x	+	$(x + 97.5)$	=	180

3. SOLVE.

$$x + x + (x + 97.5) = 180$$

$$3x + 97.5 = 180 \quad \text{Combine like terms.}$$

$$3x + 97.5 - 97.5 = 180 - 97.5 \quad \text{Subtract 97.5 from both sides.}$$

$$3x = 82.5$$

$$\frac{3x}{3} = \frac{82.5}{3} \quad \text{Divide both sides by 3.}$$

$$x = 27.5$$

4. INTERPRET.

Check: If $x = 27.5$, then the measure of the third angle is $x + 97.5 = 125$. The sum of the angles is then $27.5 + 27.5 + 125 = 180$, the correct sum.

State: The third angle measures 125°.*

Work Practice 6

Objective C Solving Consecutive Integer Problems

The next example has to do with consecutive integers. Recall what we have learned thus far about these integers.

	Example	General Representation	
Consecutive Integers	11, 12, 13 (+1, +1)	Let x be an integer.	x, $x + 1$, $x + 2$ (+1, +1)
Consecutive Even Integers	38, 40, 42 (+2, +2)	Let x be an even integer.	x, $x + 2$, $x + 4$ (+2, +2)
Consecutive Odd Integers	57, 59, 61 (+2, +2)	Let x be an odd integer.	x, $x + 2$, $x + 4$ (+2, +2)

The next example has to do with consecutive integers.

*The two walls actually meet at an angle of 125 degrees 12 minutes. The measurement of 97.5° given in the problem is an approximation.

PRACTICE 7

The sum of three consecutive even integers is 144. Find the integers.

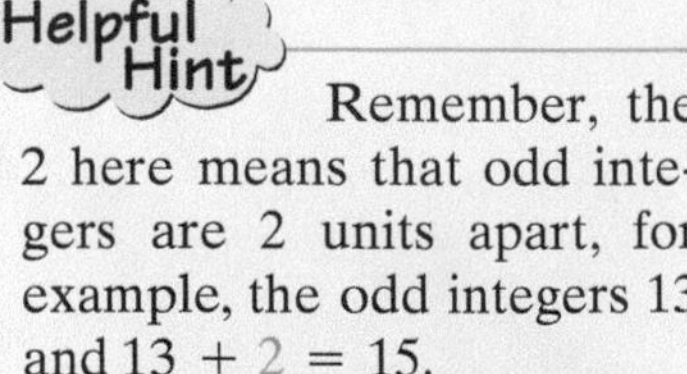

Remember, the 2 here means that odd integers are 2 units apart, for example, the odd integers 13 and $13 + 2 = 15$.

Example 7 Some states have a single area code for the entire state. Two such states have area codes that are consecutive odd integers. If the sum of these integers is 1208, find the two area codes. (*Source: World Almanac*)

Solution:

1. UNDERSTAND. Read and reread the problem. If we let

$$x = \text{the first odd integer, then}$$
$$x + 2 = \text{the next odd integer}$$

2. TRANSLATE.

first odd integer	added to	next odd integer	is	1208
↓	↓	↓		
x	$+$	$(x + 2)$	$=$	1208

3. SOLVE.

$$\begin{aligned} x + x + 2 &= 1208 \\ 2x + 2 &= 1208 \\ 2x + 2 - 2 &= 1208 - 2 \\ 2x &= 1206 \\ \frac{2x}{2} &= \frac{1206}{2} \\ x &= 603 \end{aligned}$$

4. INTERPRET.

Check: If $x = 603$, then the next odd integer $x + 2 = 603 + 2 = 605$. Notice their sum, $603 + 605 = 1208$, as needed.

State: The area codes are 603 and 605.

Note: New Hampshire's area code is 603 and South Dakota's area code is 605.

Work Practice 7

Answer

7. 46, 48, 50

Vocabulary and Readiness Check

Fill in the table.

	A number:		
1.	A number: → x	Double the number:	→ Double the number, decreased by 31:
2.	A number: → x	Three times the number:	→ Three times the number, increased by 17:
3.	A number: → x	The sum of the number and 5:	→ Twice the sum of the number and 5:
4.	A number: → x	The difference of the number and 11: →	Seven times the difference of the number and 11:
5.	A number: → y	The difference of 20 and the number: →	The difference of 20 and the number, divided by 3:
6.	A number: → y	The sum of -10 and the number:	→ The sum of -10 and the number, divided by 9:

2.4 Exercise Set

FOR EXTRA HELP

MyMathLab

PRACTICE

WATCH

DOWNLOAD

READ

REVIEW

Objective A *Solve. For Exercises 1 through 4, write each of the following as equations. Then solve. See Examples 1 and 2.*

1. The sum of twice a number and 7 is equal to the sum of the number and 6. Find the number.

2. The difference of three times a number and 1 is the same as twice the number. Find the number.

3. Three times a number, minus 6, is equal to two times the number, plus 8. Find the number.

4. The sum of 4 times a number and -2 is equal to the sum of 5 times the number and -2. Find the number.

5. Twice the difference of a number and 8 is equal to three times the sum of the number and 3. Find the number.

6. Five times the sum of a number and -1 is the same as 6 times the number. Find the number.

7. The product of twice a number and three is the same as the difference of five times the number and $\frac{3}{4}$. Find the number.

8. If the difference of a number and four is doubled, the result is $\frac{1}{4}$ less than the number. Find the number.

Objective **B** *Solve. For Exercises 9 and 10, the solutions have been started for you. See Examples 3 and 4.*

9. A 25-inch piece of steel is cut into three pieces so that the second piece is twice as long as the first piece, and the third piece is one inch more than five times the length of the first piece. Find the lengths of the pieces.

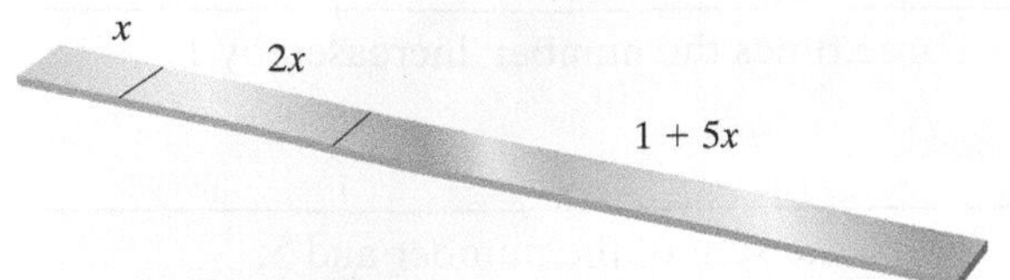

Start the solution:

1. UNDERSTAND the problem. Reread it as many times as needed.

2. TRANSLATE into an equation. (Fill in the blanks below.)

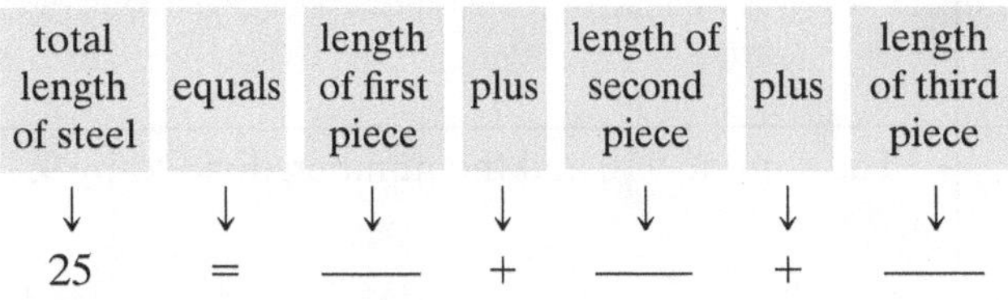

total length of steel	equals	length of first piece	plus	length of second piece	plus	length of third piece
↓	↓	↓	↓	↓	↓	↓
25	=	___	+	___	+	___

Finish with:

3. SOLVE and **4.** INTERPRET

10. A 46-foot piece of rope is cut into three pieces so that the second piece is three times as long as the first piece, and the third piece is two feet more than seven times the length of the first piece. Find the lengths of the pieces.

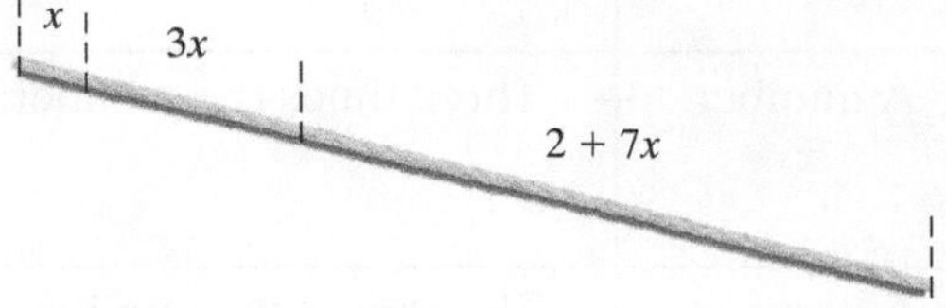

Start the solution:

1. UNDERSTAND the problem. Reread it as many times as needed.

2. TRANSLATE into an equation. (Fill in the blanks below.)

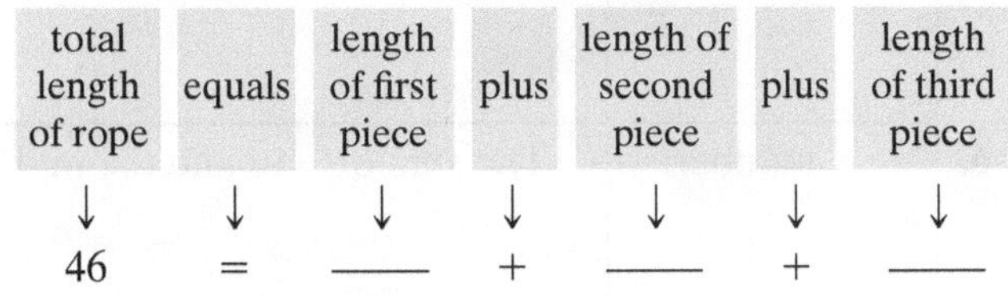

total length of rope	equals	length of first piece	plus	length of second piece	plus	length of third piece
↓	↓	↓	↓	↓	↓	↓
46	=	___	+	___	+	___

Finish with:

3. SOLVE and **4.** INTERPRET

11. A 40-inch board is to be cut into three pieces so that the second piece is twice as long as the first piece and the third piece is 5 times as long as the first piece. If x represents the length of the first piece, find the lengths of all three pieces.

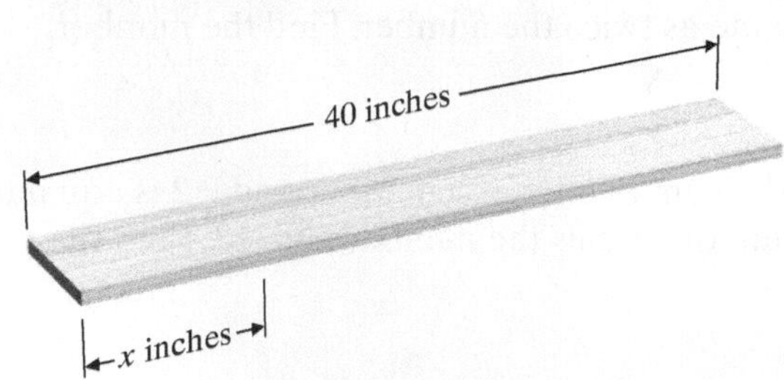

12. A 21-foot beam is to be divided so that the longer piece is 1 foot more than 3 times the length of the shorter piece. If x represents the length of the shorter piece, find the lengths of both pieces.

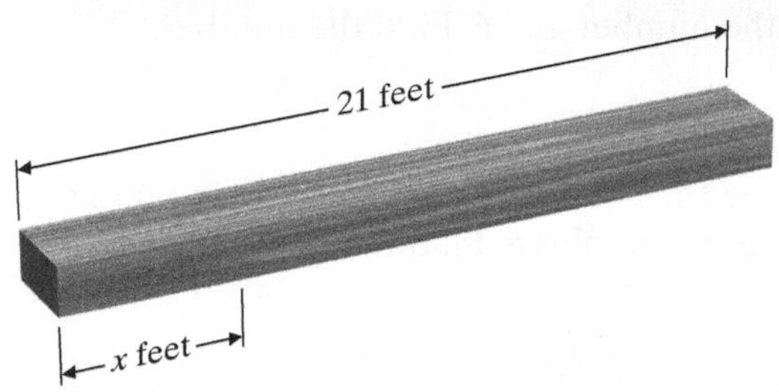

13. In 2008, New Mexico produced 15 million pounds more pecans than Texas. Together, the two states produced 75 million pounds of pecans. Find the amount of pecans grown in New Mexico and Texas in 2008. (*Source:* National Agriculture Statistics Service)

14. In the 2008 Summer Olympics, the U.S. team won 13 more gold medals than the Russian team. If the total number of gold medals won by both teams was 59, find the number of gold medals won by each team. (*Source:* Beijing 2008 Olympic Games)

Solve. See Example 5.

15. A car rental agency advertised renting a Buick Century for \$24.95 per day and \$0.29 per mile. If you rent this car for 2 days, how many whole miles can you drive on a \$100 budget?

16. A plumber gave an estimate for the renovation of a kitchen. Her hourly pay is \$27 per hour and the plumbing parts will cost \$80. If her total estimate is \$404, how many hours does she expect this job to take?

17. In one U.S. city, the taxi cost is \$3 plus \$0.80 per mile. If you are traveling from the airport, there is an additional charge of \$4.50 for tolls. How far can you travel from the airport by taxi for \$27.50?

18. A professional carpet cleaning service charges \$30 plus \$25.50 per hour to come to your home. If your total bill from this company is \$119.25 before taxes, for how many hours were you charged?

Solve. See Example 6.

△ **19.** The flag of Equatorial Guinea contains an isosceles triangle. (Recall that an isosceles triangle contains two angles with the same measure.) If the measure of the third angle of the triangle is 30° more than twice the measure of either of the other two angles, find the measure of each angle of the triangle. (*Hint:* Recall that the sum of the measures of the angles of a triangle is 180°.)

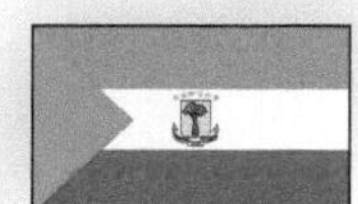

△ **20.** The flag of Brazil contains a parallelogram. One angle of the parallelogram is 15° less than twice the measure of the angle next to it. Find the measure of each angle of the parallelogram. (*Hint:* Recall that opposite angles of a parallelogram have the same measure and that the sum of the measures of the angles is 360°.)

21. The sum of the measures of the angles of a parallelogram is 360°. In the parallelogram below, angles A and D have the same measure as well as angles C and B. If the measure of angle C is twice the measure of angle A, find the measure of each angle.

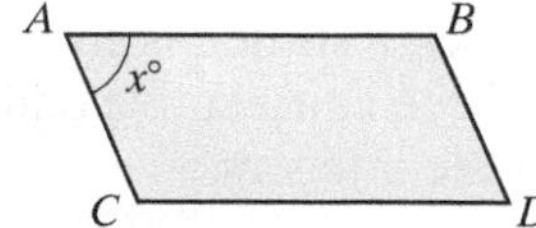

22. Recall that the sum of the measures of the angles of a triangle is 180°. In the triangle below, angle C has the same measure as angle B, and angle A measures 42° less than angle B. Find the measure of each angle.

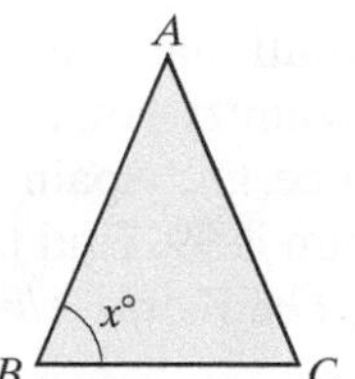

Objective **C** *Solve. See Example 7. Fill in the table. Most of the first row has been completed for you.*

	First Integer →	Next Integers →			Indicated Sum
23. Three consecutive integers:	Integer: x	$x + 1$	$x + 2$		Sum of the three consecutive integers, simplified:
24. Three consecutive integers:	Integer: x				Sum of the second and third consecutive integers, simplified:
25. Three consecutive even integers:	Even integer: x				Sum of the first and third even consecutive integers, simplified:
26. Three consecutive odd integers:	Odd integer: x				Sum of the three consecutive odd integers, simplified:
27. Four consecutive integers:	Integer: x				Sum of the four consecutive integers, simplified:
28. Four consecutive integers:	Integer: x				Sum of the first and fourth consecutive integers, simplified:
29. Three consecutive odd integers:	Odd integer: x				Sum of the second and third consecutive odd integers, simplified:
30. Three consecutive even integers:	Even integer: x				Sum of the three consecutive even integers, simplified:

Solve. See Example 7

31. The left and right page numbers of an open book are two consecutive integers whose sum is 469. Find these page numbers.

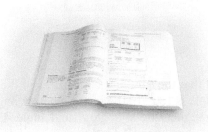

32. The room numbers of two adjacent classrooms are two consecutive even numbers. If their sum is 654, find the classroom numbers.

33. To make an international telephone call, you need the code for the country you are calling. The codes for Belgium, France, and Spain are three consecutive integers whose sum is 99. Find the code for each country. (*Source: The World Almanac and Book of Facts*)

34. The code to unlock a student's combination lock happens to be three consecutive odd integers whose sum is 51. Find the integers.

Objectives **A** **B** **C** **Mixed Practice** *Solve. See Examples 1 through 7.*

35. A 17-foot piece of string is cut into two pieces so that the longer piece is 2 feet longer than twice the length of the shorter piece. Find the lengths of both pieces.

36. A 25-foot wire is to be cut so that the longer piece is one foot longer than 5 times the length of the shorter piece. Find the length of each piece.

37. Currently, the two fastest trains are the Japanese Maglev and the French TGV. The sum of their fastest speeds is 718.2 miles per hour. If the speed of the Maglev is 3.8 mph faster than the speed of the TGV, find the speeds of each.

38. The Pentagon is the world's largest office building in terms of floor space. It has three times the amount of floor space as the Empire State Building. If the total floor space for these two buildings is approximately 8700 thousand square feet, find the floor space of each building.

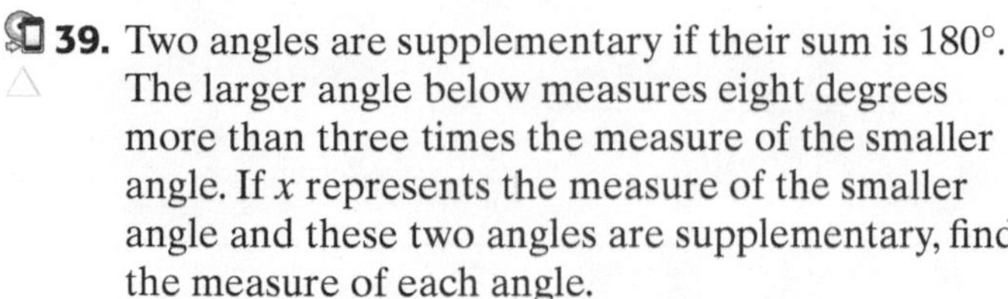

39. Two angles are supplementary if their sum is 180°. The larger angle below measures eight degrees more than three times the measure of the smaller angle. If x represents the measure of the smaller angle and these two angles are supplementary, find the measure of each angle.

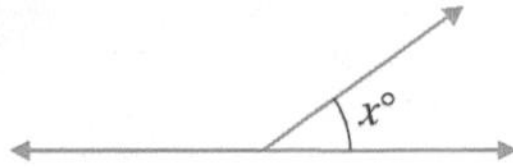

40. Two angles are complementary if their sum is 90°. Given the measures of the complementary angles shown, find the measure of each angle.

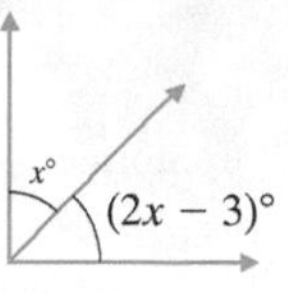

41. The measures of the angles of a triangle are 3 consecutive even integers. Find the measure of each angle.

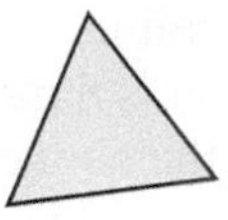

42. A quadrilateral is a polygon with 4 sides. The sum of the measures of the 4 angles in a quadrilateral is 360°. If the measures of the angles of a quadrilateral are consecutive odd integers, find the measures.

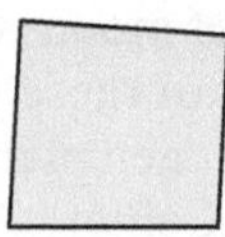

43. The sum of $\frac{1}{5}$ and twice a number is equal to $\frac{4}{5}$ subtracted from three times the number. Find the number.

44. The sum of $\frac{2}{3}$ and four times a number is equal to $\frac{5}{6}$ subtracted from five times the number. Find the number.

45. Hertz Car Rental charges a daily rate of \$39 plus \$0.20 per mile for a certain car. Suppose that you rent that car for a day and your bill (before taxes) is \$95. How many miles did you drive?

46. A woman's \$15,000 estate is to be divided so that her husband receives twice as much as her son. Find the amount of money that her husband receives and the amount of money that her son receives.

47. During the 2009 Rose Bowl, University of Southern California beat Pennsylvania State University by 14 points. If their combined scores totaled 62, find the individual team scores.

48. After a recent election, there were 8 more Democratic governors than Republican governors in the United States. How many Democrats and how many Republicans held governors' offices after this election? (*Source:* National Governors Association)

49. The number of counties in California and the number of counties in Montana are consecutive even integers whose sum is 114. If California has more counties than Montana, how many counties does each state have? (*Source: The World Almanac and Book of Facts*)

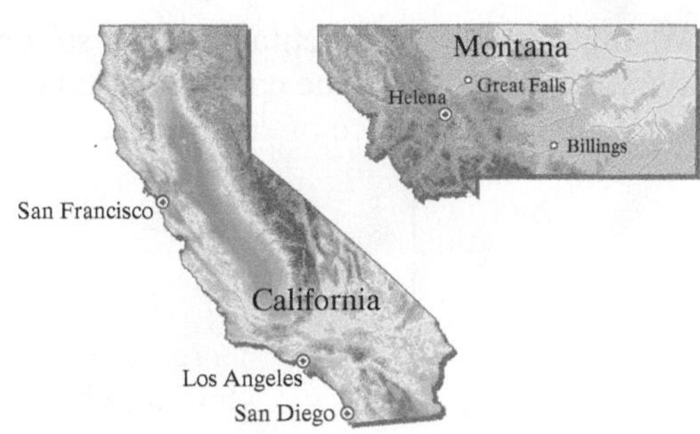

50. A student is building a bookcase with stepped shelves for her dorm room. She buys a 48-inch board and wants to cut the board into three pieces with lengths equal to three consecutive even integers. Find the three board lengths.

51. Over the past few years the satellite Voyager II has passed by the planets Saturn, Uranus, and Neptune, continually updating information about these planets, including the number of moons for each. Uranus is now believed to have 13 more moons than Neptune. Also, Saturn is now believed to have 2 more than twice the number of moons of Neptune. If the total number of moons for these planets is 47, find the number of moons for each planet. (*Source:* National Space Science Data Center)

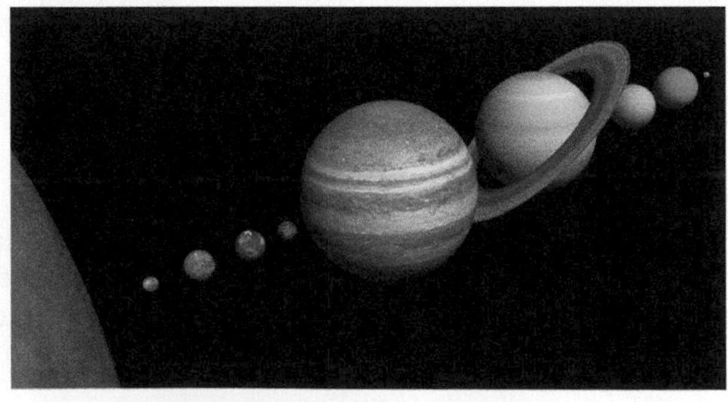

52. The Mars Odyssey spacecraft was launched in 2001, beginning a multiyear mission to observe and map the planet Mars. Mars Odyssey was launched on Boeing's Delta II 7925 launch vehicle using nine strap-on solid rocket motors. Each solid rocket motor has a height that is 8 meters more than 5 times its diameter. If the sum of the height and the diameter for a single solid rocket motor is 14 meters, find each dimension. (Recently, NASA approved a continuation of the Odyssey mission through September 2010.) (*Source:* NASA)

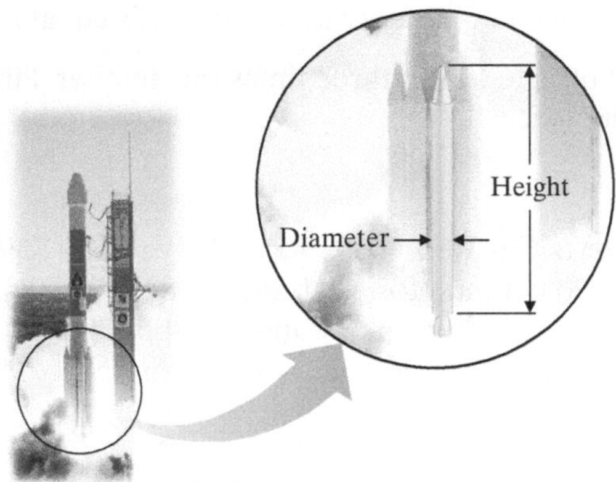

53. If the sum of a number and five is tripled, the result is one less than twice the number. Find the number.

54. Twice the sum of a number and six equals three times the sum of the number and four. Find the number.

55. The area of the Sahara Desert is 7 times the area of the Gobi Desert. If the sum of their areas is 4,000,000 square miles, find the area of each desert.

56. The largest meteorite in the world is the Hoba West, located in Namibia. Its weight is 3 times the weight of the Armanty meteorite, located in Outer Mongolia. If the sum of their weights is 88 tons, find the weight of each.

57. In the 2008 Summer Olympics, Korea won more gold medals than Germany, which won more gold medals than Australia. If the numbers of gold medals won by these three countries are three consecutive integers whose sum is 21, find the number of gold medals won by each. (*Source:* Beijing 2008 Olympics)

58. To make an international telephone call, you need the code for the country you are calling. The codes for Mali Republic, Côte d'Ivoire, and Niger are three consecutive odd integers whose sum is 675. Find the code for each country.

59. In a runoff election in Georgia for a seat in the U.S. Senate, incumbent Senator Saxby Chambliss received 315,217 more votes than challenger Jim Martin. If the total number of votes cast was 2,126,491, find the number of votes for each candidate. (*Source: New York Times*)

60. In Season 7 of *American Idol*, David Cook received 11.7 million more votes than runner-up David Archuleta. If 97.5 million votes were cast in the season finale, find the number of votes for each contestant. (*Source: Los Angeles Times*)

61. A geodesic dome, based on the design by Buckminster Fuller, is composed of two different types of triangular panels. One of these is an isosceles triangle. In one geodesic dome, the measure of the third angle is 76.5° more than the measure of either of the two equal angles. Find the measure of the three angles. (*Source:* Buckminster Fuller Institute)

62. The measures of the angles of a particular triangle are such that the second and third angles are each four times the measure of the smallest angle. Find the measures of the angles of this triangle.

The graph below shows the best-selling albums of all time. Use this graph for Exercises 63 through 66.

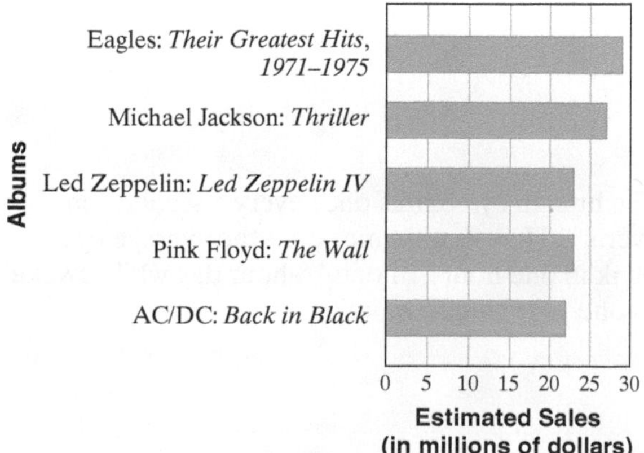

Source: Recording Industry Association of America

63. Which album is the best-selling album of all time?

64. Which albums had total sales between \$20 million and \$25 million?

65. *Thriller* and *The Wall* had sales worth a total of \$50 million. *Thriller* brought in \$4 million more than *The Wall*. Find the amount of sales that each album brought in.

66. Eagles: *Their Greatest Hits, 1971–1975*, and AC/DC: *Back in Black* had sales worth \$51 million. Eagles: *Their Greatest Hits, 1971–1975*, sold \$7 million more than AC/DC: *Back in Black*. Find the amount of sales for each album.

Compare the lengths of the bars in the graph with your results for the exercises below. Are your answers reasonable?

67. Exercise 65

68. Exercise 66

Review

Evaluate each expression for the given values. See Section 1.8.

69. $2W + 2L$; $W = 7$ and $L = 10$

70. $\frac{1}{2}Bh$; $B = 14$ and $h = 22$

71. πr^2; $r = 15$

72. $r \cdot t$; $r = 15$ and $t = 2$

Concept Extensions

△ **73.** A golden rectangle is a rectangle whose length is approximately 1.6 times its width. The early Greeks thought that a rectangle with these dimensions was the most pleasing to the eye and examples of the golden rectangle are found in many early works of art. For example, the Parthenon in Athens contains many examples of golden rectangles.

Mike Hallahan would like to plant a rectangular garden in the shape of a golden rectangle. If he has 78 feet of fencing available, find the dimensions of the garden.

△ **74.** Dr. Dorothy Smith gave the students in her geometry class at the University of New Orleans the following question. Is it possible to construct a triangle such that the second angle of the triangle has a measure that is twice the measure of the first angle and the measure of the third angle is 5 times the measure of the first? If so, find the measure of each angle. (*Hint:* Recall that the sum of the measures of the angles of a triangle is 180°.)

75. Only male crickets chirp. They chirp at different rates depending on their species and the temperature of their environment. Suppose a certain species is currently chirping at a rate of 90 chirps per minute. At this rate, how many chirps occur in one hour? In one 24-hour day? In one year?

76. The human eye blinks once every 5 seconds on average. How many times does the average eye blink in one hour? In one 16-hour day while awake? In one year while awake?

77. In your own words, explain why a solution of a word problem should be checked using the original wording of the problem and not the equation written from the wording.

78. Give an example of how you recently solved a problem using mathematics.

Recall from Exercise 73 that a golden rectangle is a rectangle whose length is approximately 1.6 times its width.

△ **79.** It is thought that for about 75% of adults, a rectangle in the shape of the golden rectangle is the most pleasing to the eye. Draw three rectangles, one in the shape of the golden rectangle, and poll your class. Do the results agree with the percentage given above?

△ **80.** Examples of golden rectangles can be found today in architecture and manufacturing packaging. Find an example of a golden rectangle in your home. A few suggestions: the front face of a book, the floor of a room, the front of a box of food.

For Exercises 81 and 82, measure the dimensions of each rectangle and decide which one best approximates the shape of a golden rectangle.

△ **81.** △ **82.**

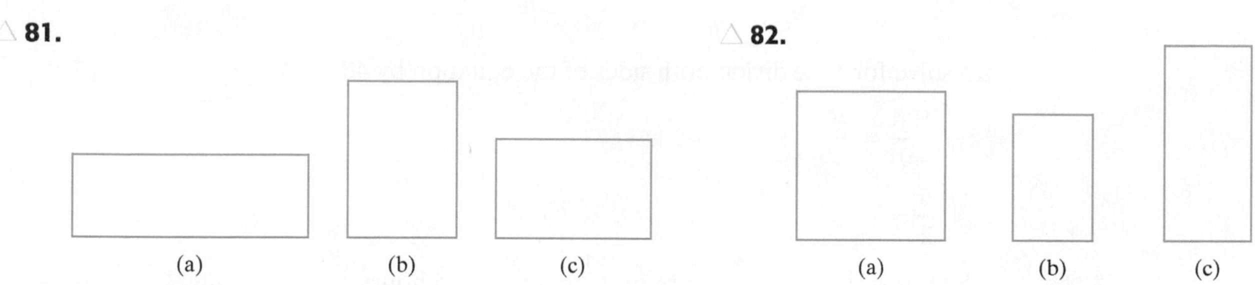

Objectives

A Use Formulas to Solve Problems.

B Solve a Formula or Equation for One of Its Variables.

2.5 FORMULAS AND PROBLEM SOLVING

Objective A Using Formulas to Solve Problems

A **formula** describes a known relationship among quantities. Many formulas are given as equations. For example, the formula

$$d = r \cdot t$$

stands for the relationship

distance = rate · time

Let's look at one way that we can use this formula.

If we know we traveled a distance of 100 miles at a rate of 40 miles per hour, we can replace the variables d and r in the formula $d = rt$ and find our travel time, t.

$d = rt$ Formula

$100 = 40t$ Replace d with 100 and r with 40.

To solve for t, we divide both sides of the equation by 40.

$\frac{100}{40} = \frac{40t}{40}$ Divide both sides by 40.

$\frac{5}{2} = t$ Simplify.

The travel times was $\frac{5}{2}$ hours, or $2\frac{1}{2}$ hours, or 2.5 hours.

In this section, we solve problems that can be modeled by known formulas. We use the same problem-solving strategy that was introduced in the previous section.

PRACTICE 1

A family is planning their vacation to visit relatives. They will drive from Cincinnati, Ohio, to Rapid City, South Dakota, a distance of 1180 miles. They plan to average a rate of 50 miles per hour. How much time will they spend driving?

Example 1 Finding Time Given Rate and Distance

A glacier is a giant mass of rocks and ice that flows downhill like a river. Portage Glacier in Alaska is about 6 miles, or 31,680 *feet,* long and moves 400 *feet* per year. Icebergs are created when the front end of the glacier flows into Portage Lake. How long does it take for ice at the head (beginning) of the glacier to reach the lake?

Solution:

1. UNDERSTAND. Read and reread the problem. The appropriate formula needed to solve this problem is the distance formula, $d = rt$. To become familiar with this formula, let's find the distance that ice traveling at a rate of 400 feet per year travels in 100 years. To do so, we let time t be 100 years and rate r be the given 400 feet per year, and substitute these values into the formula $d = rt$. We then have that distance $d = 400(100) = 40{,}000$ feet. Since we are interested in finding how long it takes ice to travel 31,680 feet, we now know that it is less than 100 years.

Answer

1. 23.6 hours

Since we are using the formula $d = rt$, we let

$t =$ the time in years for ice to reach the lake
$r =$ rate or speed of ice
$d =$ distance from beginning of glacier to lake

2. TRANSLATE. To translate to an equation, we use the formula $d = rt$ and let distance $d = 31{,}680$ feet and rate $r = 400$ feet per year.

$$d = r \cdot t$$
$$31{,}680 = 400 \cdot t \quad \text{Let } d = 31{,}680 \text{ and } r = 400.$$

3. SOLVE. Solve the equation for t. To solve for t, we divide both sides by 400.

$$\frac{31{,}680}{400} = \frac{400 \cdot t}{400} \quad \text{Divide both sides by 400.}$$
$$79.2 = t \quad \text{Simplify.}$$

4. INTERPRET.

Check: To check, substitute 79.2 for t and 400 for r in the distance formula and check to see that the distance is 31,680 feet.

State: It takes 79.2 years for the ice at the head of Portage Glacier to reach the lake.

Helpful Hint
Don't forget to include units, if appropriate.

Work Practice 1

Example 2 Calculating the Length of a Garden

Charles Pecot can afford enough fencing to enclose a rectangular garden with a perimeter of 140 feet. If the width of his garden is to be 30 feet, find the length.

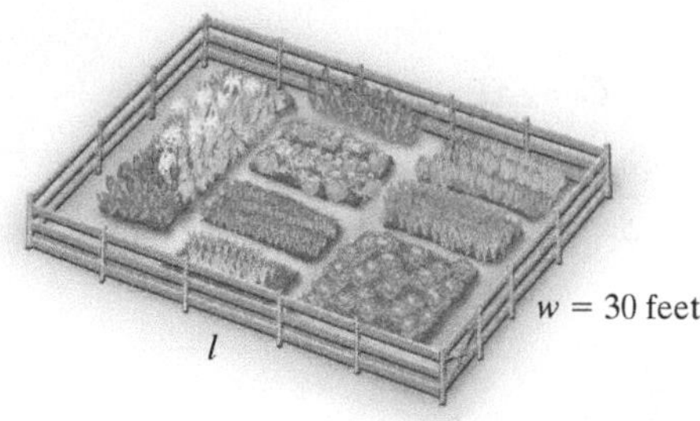

Solution:

1. UNDERSTAND. Read and reread the problem. The formula needed to solve this problem is the formula for the perimeter of a rectangle, $P = 2l + 2w$. Before continuing, let's become familar with this formula.

$l =$ the length of the rectangular garden
$w =$ the width of the rectangular garden
$P =$ perimeter of the garden

2. TRANSLATE. To translate to an equation, we use the formula $P = 2l + 2w$ and let perimeter $P = 140$ feet and width $w = 30$ feet.

$$P = 2l + 2w \quad \text{Let } P = 140 \text{ and } w = 30.$$
$$140 = 2l + 2(30)$$

Continued on next page

PRACTICE 2

A wood deck is being built behind a house. The width of the deck must be 18 feet because of the shape of the house. If there is 450 square feet of decking material, find the length of the deck.

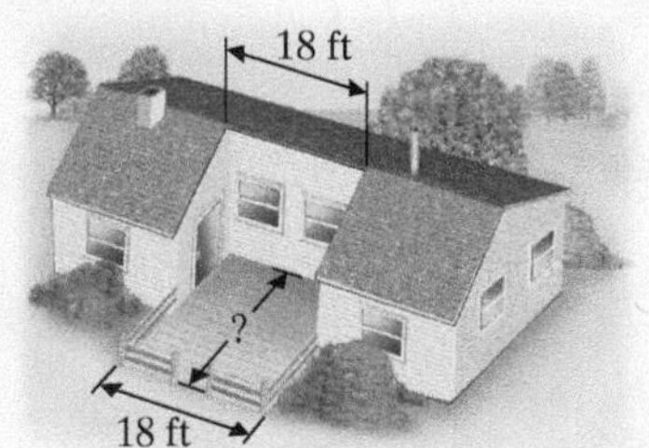

Answer
2. 25 feet

3. SOLVE.

$$\begin{aligned} 140 &= 2l + 2(30) \\ 140 &= 2l + 60 && \text{Multiply } 2(30). \\ 140 - 60 &= 2l + 60 - 60 && \text{Subtract 60 from both sides.} \\ 80 &= 2l && \text{Combine like terms.} \\ 40 &= l && \text{Divide both sides by 2.} \end{aligned}$$

4. INTERPRET.

Check: Substitute 40 for l and 30 for w in the perimeter formula and check to see that the perimeter is 140 feet.

State: The length of the rectangular garden is 40 feet.

Work Practice 2

PRACTICE 3

Convert the temperature 5°C to Fahrenheit.

Example 3 Finding an Equivalent Temperature

The average maximum temperature for January in Algiers, Algeria, is 59° Fahrenheit. Find the equivalent temperature in degrees Celsius.

Solution:

1. UNDERSTAND. Read and reread the problem. A formula that can be used to solve this problem is the formula for converting degrees Celsius to degrees Fahrenheit, $F = \frac{9}{5}C + 32$. Before continuing, become familiar with this formula. Using this formula, we let

$C =$ temperature in degrees Celsius, and
$F =$ temperature in degrees Fahrenheit.

2. TRANSLATE. To translate to an equation, we use the formula $F = \frac{9}{5}C + 32$ and let degrees Fahrenheit $F = 59$.

Formula: $F = \frac{9}{5}C + 32$

Substitute: $59 = \frac{9}{5}C + 32$ Let $F = 59$.

3. SOLVE.

$$\begin{aligned} 59 &= \frac{9}{5}C + 32 \\ 59 - 32 &= \frac{9}{5}C + 32 - 32 && \text{Subtract 32 from both sides.} \\ 27 &= \frac{9}{5}C && \text{Combine like terms.} \\ \frac{5}{9}\cdot 27 &= \frac{5}{9}\cdot\frac{9}{5}C && \text{Multiply both sides by } \frac{5}{9}. \\ 15 &= C && \text{Simplify.} \end{aligned}$$

4. INTERPRET.

Check: To check, replace C with 15 and F with 59 in the formula and see that a true statement results.

State: Thus, 59° Fahrenheit is equivalent to 15° Celsius.

Work Practice 3

Answer

3. 41°F

In the next example, we again use the formula for perimeter of a rectangle as in Example 2. In Example 2, we knew the width of the rectangle. In this example, both the length and width are unknown.

Example 4 Finding Road Sign Dimensions

The length of a rectangular road sign is 2 feet less than three times its width. Find the dimensions if the perimeter is 28 feet.

Solution:

1. UNDERSTAND. Read and reread the problem. Recall that the formula for the perimeter of a rectangle is $P = 2l + 2w$. Draw a rectangle and guess the solution. If the width of the rectangular sign is 5 feet, its length is 2 feet less than 3 times the width, or 3(5 feet) − 2 feet = 13 feet. The perimeter P of the rectangle is then 2(13 feet) + 2(5 feet) = 36 feet, too much. We now know that the width is less than 5 feet.

   Proposed rectangle:

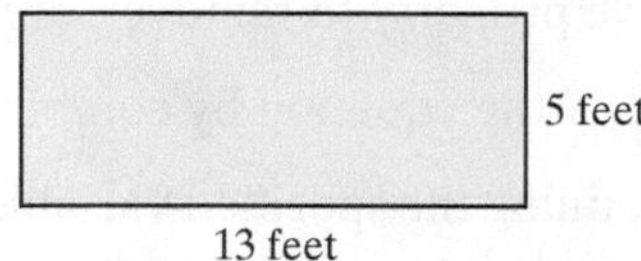

Let

w = the width of the rectangular sign; then

$3w - 2$ = the length of the sign.

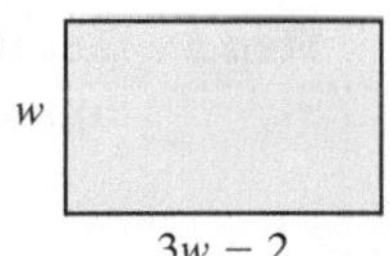

Draw a rectangle and label it with the assigned variables.

2. TRANSLATE.

   Formula: $P = 2l + 2w$

   Substitute: $28 = 2(3w - 2) + 2w$

3. SOLVE.

$$28 = 2(3w - 2) + 2w$$

$$28 = 6w - 4 + 2w \quad \text{Apply the distributive property.}$$

$$28 = 8w - 4$$

$$28 + 4 = 8w - 4 + 4 \quad \text{Add 4 to both sides.}$$

$$32 = 8w$$

$$\frac{32}{8} = \frac{8w}{8} \quad \text{Divide both sides by 8.}$$

$$4 = w$$

4. INTERPRET.

Check: If the width of the sign is 4 feet, the length of the sign is 3(4 feet) − 2 feet = 10 feet. This gives the rectangular sign a perimeter of P = 2(4 feet) + 2(10 feet) = 28 feet, the correct perimeter.

State: The width of the sign is 4 feet and the length of the sign is 10 feet.

Work Practice 4

PRACTICE 4

The length of a rectangle is one meter more than 4 times its width. Find the dimensions if the perimeter is 52 meters.

Answer

4. length: 21 m; width: 5 m

Objective B Solving a Formula for a Variable

We say that the formula

$$d = rt$$

is solved for d because d is alone on one side of the equation and the other side contains no d's. Suppose that we have a large number of problems to solve where we are given distance d and rate r and asked to find time t. In this case, it may be easier to first solve the formula $d = rt$ for t. To solve for t, we divide both sides of the equation by r.

$$d = rt$$

$$\frac{d}{r} = \frac{rt}{r} \quad \text{Divide both sides by } r.$$

$$\frac{d}{r} = t \quad \text{Simplify.}$$

To solve a formula or an equation for a specified variable, we use the same steps as for solving a linear equation except that we treat the specified variable as the only variable in the equation. These steps are listed next.

Solving Equations for a Specified Variable

Step 1: Multiply on both sides to clear the equation of fractions if they appear.

Step 2: Use the distributive property to remove parentheses if they appear.

Step 3: Simplify each side of the equation by combining like terms.

Step 4: Get all terms containing the specified variable on one side and all other terms on the other side by using the addition property of equality.

Step 5: Get the specified variable alone by using the multiplication property of equality.

PRACTICE 5

Solve $C = 2\pi r$ for r. (This formula is used to find the circumference, C, of a circle given its radius, r.)

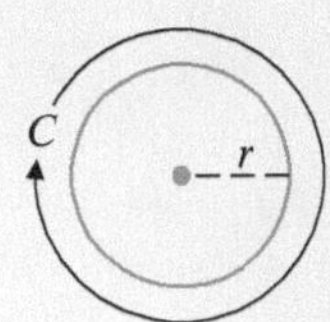

Example 5 Solve $V = lwh$ for l.

Solution: This formula is used to find the volume of a box. To solve for l, we divide both sides by wh.

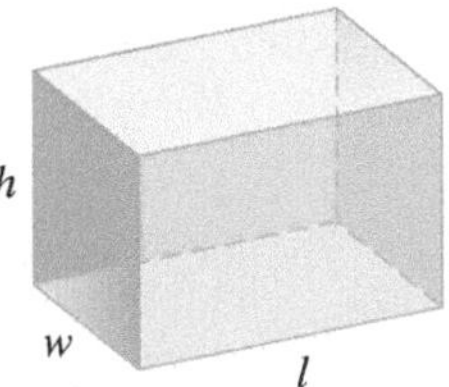

$$V = lwh$$

$$\frac{V}{wh} = \frac{lwh}{wh} \quad \text{Divide both sides by } wh.$$

$$\frac{V}{wh} = l \quad \text{Simplify.}$$

Since we have l alone on one side of the equation, we have solved for l in terms of V, w, and h. Remember that it does not matter on which side of the equation we get the variable alone.

Work Practice 5

Answer

5. $r = \frac{C}{2\pi}$

Example 6 Solve $y = mx + b$ for x.

Solution: First we get mx alone by subtracting b from both sides.

$$y = mx + b$$

$$y - b = mx + b - b \quad \text{Subtract } b \text{ from both sides.}$$

$$y - b = mx \quad \text{Combine like terms.}$$

Next we solve for x by dividing both sides by m.

$$\frac{y - b}{m} = \frac{mx}{m}$$

$$\frac{y - b}{m} = x \quad \text{Simplify.}$$

Work Practice 6

PRACTICE 6

Solve $P = 2l + 2w$ for l.

✓Concept Check Solve:

a. ● = ■ − ■ for ■

b. ● = ■ · ▲ − ■ for ■

Example 7 Solve $P = 2l + 2w$ for w.

Solution: This formula relates the perimeter of a rectangle to its length and width. Find the term containing the variable w. To get this term, $2w$, alone, subtract $2l$ from both sides.

$$P = 2l + 2w$$

$$P - 2l = 2l + 2w - 2l \quad \text{Subtract } 2l \text{ from both sides.}$$

$$P - 2l = 2w \quad \text{Combine like terms.}$$

$$\frac{P - 2l}{2} = \frac{2w}{2} \quad \text{Divide both sides by 2.}$$

$$\frac{P - 2l}{2} = w \quad \text{Simplify.}$$

w

l

Work Practice 7

PRACTICE 7

Solve $P = 2a + b - c$ for a.

Helpful Hint

The 2s may *not* be divided out here. Although 2 is a factor of the denominator, 2 is *not* a factor of the numerator since it is not a factor of both terms in the numerator.

The next example has an equation containing a fraction. We will first clear the equation of fractions and then solve for the specified variable.

Example 8 Solve $F = \frac{9}{5}C + 32$ for C.

Solution:

$$F = \frac{9}{5}C + 32$$

$$5(F) = 5\left(\frac{9}{5}C + 32\right) \quad \text{Clear the fraction by multiplying both sides by the LCD.}$$

$$5F = 9C + 160 \quad \text{Distribute the 5.}$$

$$5F - 160 = 9C + 160 - 160 \quad \text{To get the term containing the variable } C \text{ alone, subtract 160 from both sides.}$$

$$5F - 160 = 9C \quad \text{Combine like terms.}$$

$$\frac{5F - 160}{9} = \frac{9C}{9} \quad \text{Divide both sides by 9.}$$

$$\frac{5F - 160}{9} = C \quad \text{Simplify.}$$

Work Practice 8

PRACTICE 8

Solve $A = \frac{a + b}{2}$ for b.

Answers

6. $l = \frac{P - 2w}{2}$ 7. $a = \frac{P - b + c}{2}$ 8. $b = 2A - a$

✓ Concept Check Answer

a. ● + ■ b. $\frac{● + ■}{▲}$

2.5 Exercise Set

FOR EXTRA HELP

MyMathLab

PRACTICE

WATCH

DOWNLOAD

READ

REVIEW

Objective A *Substitute the given values into each given formula and solve for the unknown variable. See Examples 1 through 4.*

△ **1.** $A = bh$; $A = 45, b = 15$ (Area of a parallelogram)

2. $d = rt$; $d = 195, t = 3$ (Distance formula)

△ **3.** $S = 4lw + 2wh$; $S = 102, l = 7, w = 3$ (Surface area of a special rectangular box)

△ **4.** $V = lwh$; $l = 14, w = 8, h = 3$ (Volume of a rectangular box)

△ **5.** $A = \frac{1}{2}h(B + b)$; $A = 180, B = 11, b = 7$ (Area of a trapezoid)

△ **6.** $A = \frac{1}{2}h(B + b)$; $A = 60, B = 7, b = 3$ (Area of a trapezoid)

△ **7.** $P = a + b + c$; $P = 30, a = 8, b = 10$ (Perimeter of a triangle)

△ **8.** $V = \frac{1}{3}Ah$; $V = 45, h = 5$ (Volume of a pyramid)

△ **9.** $C = 2\pi r$; $C = 15.7$ (Circumference of a circle) (Use the approximation 3.14 for π.)

△ **10.** $A = \pi r^2$; $r = 4$ (Area of a circle) (Use the approximation 3.14 for π.)

Objective B *Solve each formula for the specified variable. See Examples 5 through 8.*

11. $f = 5gh$ for h

△ **12.** $x = 4\pi y$ for y

△ **13.** $V = lwh$ for w

14. $T = mnr$ for n

15. $3x + y = 7$ for y

16. $-x + y = 13$ for y

17. $A = P + PRT$ for R

18. $A = P + PRT$ for T

△ **19.** $V = \frac{1}{3}Ah$ for A

20. $D = \frac{1}{4}fk$ for k

△ **21.** $P = a + b + c$ for a

22. $PR = x + y + z + w$ for z

△ **23.** $S = 2\pi rh + 2\pi r^2$ for h

△ **24.** $S = 4lw + 2wh$ for h

Objective A *Solve. For Exercises 25 and 26, the solutions have been started for you. See Examples 1 through 4.*

△ **25.** The iconic NASDAQ sign in New York's Times Square has a width of 84 feet and an area of 10,080 square feet. Find the height (or length) of the sign. (*Source:* livedesignonline.com)

Start the solution:

1. UNDERSTAND the problem. Reread it as many times as needed.

2. TRANSLATE into an equation. (Fill in the blanks below.)

Area	=	length	times	width
↓	↓	↓	↓	↓
____	=	x	·	____

Finish with:

3. SOLVE and **4.** INTERPRET

△ **26.** The world's largest sign for Coca-Cola is located in Arica, Chile. The rectangular sign has a length of 400 feet and an area of 52,400 square feet. Find the width of the sign. (*Source:* Fabulous Facts about Coca-Cola, Atlanta, GA)

Start the solution:

1. UNDERSTAND the problem. Reread it as many times as needed.

2. TRANSLATE into an equation. (Fill in the blanks below.)

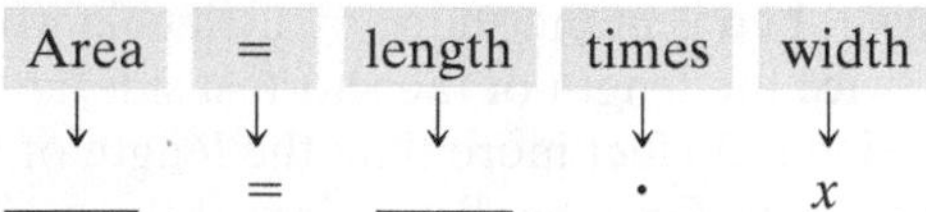

Finish with:

3. SOLVE and **4.** INTERPRET

△ **27.** A frame shop charges according to both the amount of framing needed to surround the picture and the amount of glass needed to cover the picture.

a. Find the area and perimeter of the picture below.

b. Identify whether the frame has to do with perimeter or area and the same with the glass.

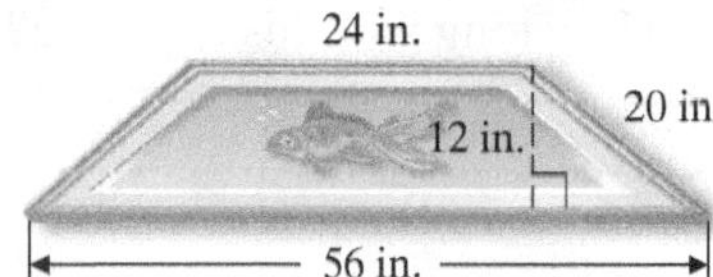

△ **28.** A decorator is painting and placing a border completely around the parallelogram-shaped wall.

a. Find the area and perimeter of the wall below. ($A = bh$)

b. Identify whether the border has to do with perimeter or area and the same with paint.

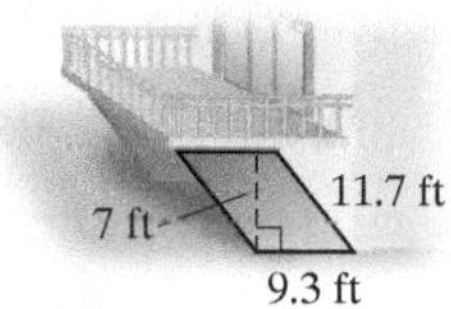

△ **29.** For the purpose of purchasing new baseboard and carpet,

a. Find the area and perimeter of the room below (neglecting doors).

b. Identify whether baseboard has to do with area or perimeter and the same with carpet.

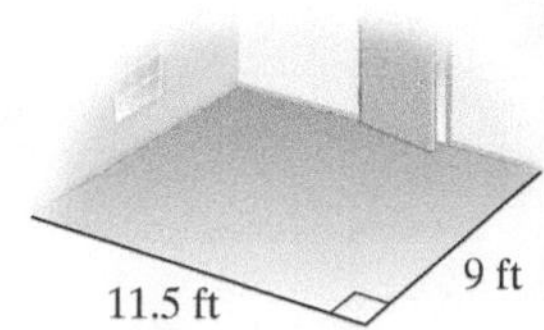

△ **30.** For the purpose of purchasing lumber for a new fence and seed to plant grass,

a. Find the area and perimeter of the yard below.

b. Identify whether a fence has to do with area or perimeter and the same with grass seed. $\left(A = \frac{1}{2}bh\right)$

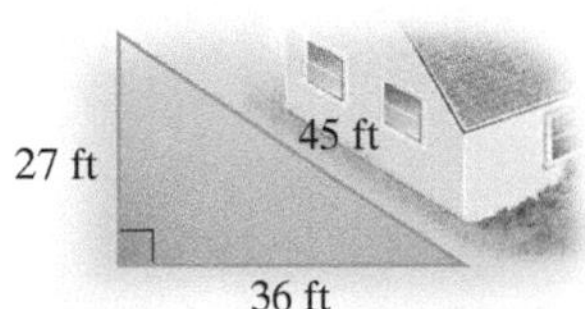

31. Convert Nome, Alaska's 14°F high temperature to Celsius.

32. Convert Paris, France's low temperature of −5°C to Fahrenheit.

33. The X-30 is a "space plane" that skims the edge of space at 4000 miles per hour. Neglecting altitude, if the circumference of Earth is approximately 25,000 miles, how long will it take for the X-30 to travel around Earth?

34. In the United States, a notable hang glider flight was a 303-mile, $8\frac{1}{2}$-hour flight from New Mexico to Kansas. What was the average rate during this flight?

35. An architect designs a rectangular flower garden such that the width is exactly two-thirds of the length. If 260 feet of antique picket fencing are to be used to enclose the garden, find the dimensions of the garden.

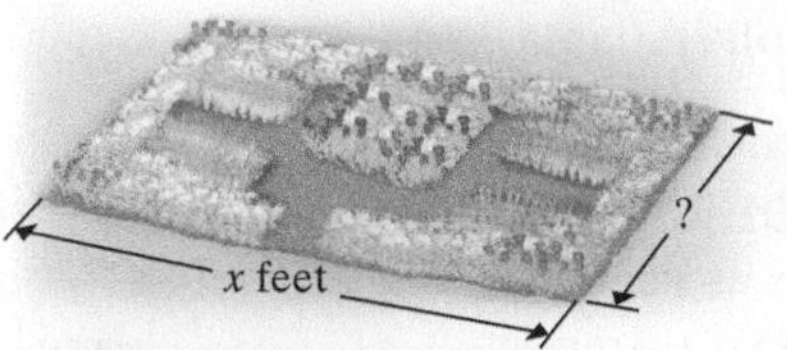

36. If the length of a rectangular parking lot is 10 meters less than twice its width, and the perimeter is 400 meters, find the length of the parking lot.

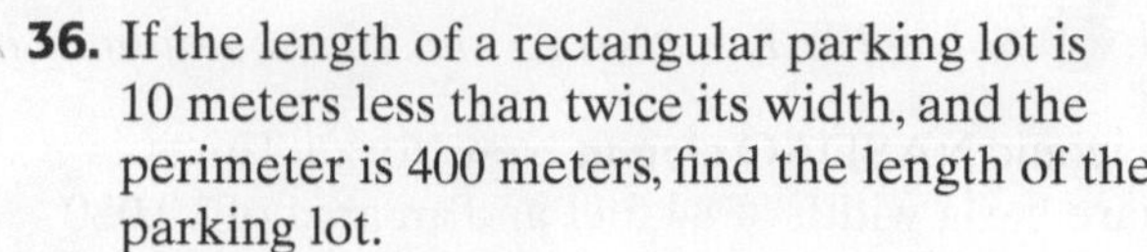

37. A flower bed is in the shape of a triangle with one side twice the length of the shortest side, and the third side is 30 feet more than the length of the shortest side. Find the dimensions if the perimeter is 102 feet.

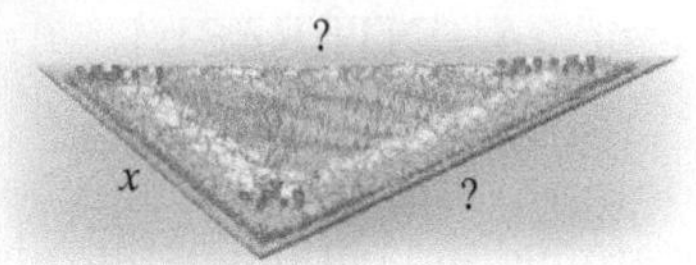

38. The perimeter of a yield sign in the shape of an isosceles triangle is 22 feet. If the shortest side is 2 feet less than the other two sides, find the length of the shortest side. (*Hint:* An isosceles triangle has two sides the same length.)

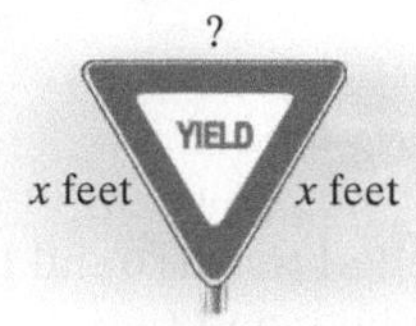

39. The Cat is a high-speed catamaran auto ferry that operates between Bar Harbor, Maine, and Yarmouth, Nova Scotia. The Cat can make the trip in about $2\frac{1}{2}$ hours at a speed of 55 mph. About how far apart are Bar Harbor and Yarmouth? (*Source:* Bay Ferries)

40. A family is planning their vacation to Disney World. They will drive from a small town outside New Orleans, Louisiana, to Orlando, Florida, a distance of 700 miles. They plan to average a rate of 55 mph. How long will this trip take?

Dolbear's Law states the relationship between the rate at which Snowy Tree Crickets chirp and the air temperature of their environment. The formula is

$$T = 50 + \frac{N - 40}{4}, \textit{ where } \begin{aligned} T &= \text{temperature in degrees Fahrenheit and} \\ N &= \text{number of chirps per minute} \end{aligned}$$

41. If $N = 86$, find the temperature in degrees Fahrenheit, T.

42. If $N = 94$, find the temperature in degrees Fahrenheit, T.

43. If $T = 55°\text{F}$, find the number of chirps per minute.

44. If $T = 65°\text{F}$, find the number of chirps per minute.

Use the results of Exercises 41–44 to complete each sentence with "increases" or "decreases."

45. As the number of cricket chirps per minute increases, the air temperature of their environment __________.

46. As the air temperature of their environment decreases, the number of cricket chirps per minute __________.

Solve. See Examples 1 through 4.

△ **47.** Piranha fish require 1.5 cubic feet of water per fish to maintain a healthy environment. Find the maximum number of piranhas you could put in a tank measuring 8 feet by 3 feet by 6 feet.

△ **48.** Find the maximum number of goldfish you can put in a cylindrical tank whose diameter is 8 meters and whose height is 3 meters, if each goldfish needs 2 cubic meters of water. ($V = \pi r^2 h$)

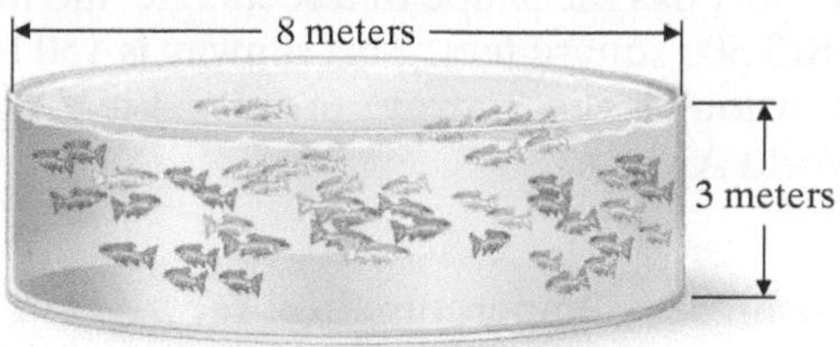

△ **49.** A lawn is in the shape of a trapezoid with a height of 60 feet and bases of 70 feet and 130 feet. How many bags of fertilizer must be purchased to cover the lawn if each bag covers 4000 square feet? $\left(A = \frac{1}{2}h(B + b)\right)$

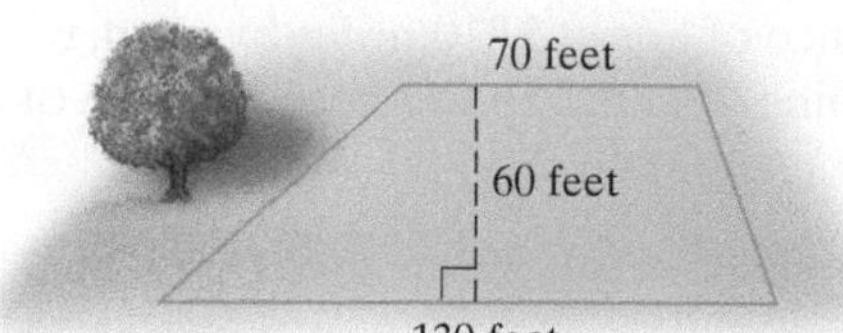

△ **50.** If the area of a right-triangularly shaped sail is 20 square feet and its base is 5 feet, find the height of the sail. $\left(A = \frac{1}{2}bh\right)$

△ **51.** Maria's Pizza sells one 16-inch cheese pizza or two 10-inch cheese pizzas for $9.99. Determine which size gives more pizza. ($A = \pi r^2$)

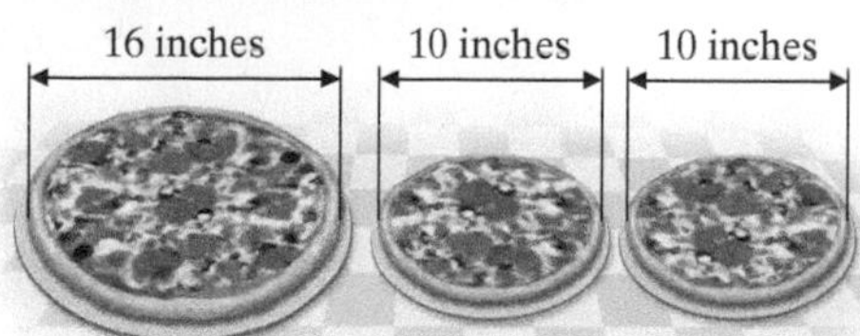

△ **52.** Find how much rope is needed to wrap around Earth at the equator, if the radius of Earth is 4000 miles. (*Hint:* Use 3.14 for π and the formula for circumference.)

53. A Japanese "bullet" train set a new world record for train speed at 552 kilometers per hour during a manned test run on the Yamanashi Maglev Test Line in April 1999. The Yamanashi Maglev Test Line is 42.8 kilometers long. How many *minutes* would a test run on the Yamanashi Line last at this record-setting speed? Round to the nearest hundredth of a minute. (*Source:* Japan Railways Central Co.)

54. In 1983, the Hawaiian volcano Kilauea began erupting in a series of episodes still occurring at the time of this writing. At times, the lava flows advanced at speeds of up to 0.5 kilometer per hour. In 1983 and 1984 lava flows destroyed 16 homes in the Royal Gardens subdivision, about 6 km away from the eruption site. Roughly how long did it take the lava to reach Royal Gardens? (*Source:* U.S. Geological Survey Hawaiian Volcano Observatory)

△ **55.** The perimeter of an equilateral triangle is 7 inches more than the perimeter of a square, and the side of the triangle is 5 inches longer than the side of the square. Find the side of the triangle. (*Hint:* An equilateral triangle has three sides the same length.)

△ **56.** A square animal pen and a pen shaped like an equilateral triangle have equal perimeters. Find the length of the sides of each pen if the sides of the triangular pen are fifteen less than twice a side of the square pen. (*Hint:* An equilateral triangle has three sides the same length.)

57. Find how long it takes Tran Nguyen to drive 135 miles on I-10 if he merges onto I-10 at 10 a.m. and drives nonstop with his cruise control set on 60 mph.

58. Beaumont, Texas, is about 150 miles from Toledo Bend. If Leo Miller leaves Beaumont at 4 a.m. and averages 45 mph, when should he arrive at Toledo Bend?

△ **59.** The longest runway at Los Angeles International Airport has the shape of a rectangle and an area of 1,813,500 square feet. This runway is 150 feet wide. How long is the runway? (*Source:* Los Angeles World Airports)

60. The return stroke of a bolt of lightning can travel at a speed of 87,000 miles per second (almost half the speed of light). At this speed, how many times can an object travel around the world in one second? (See Exercise 52.) Round to the nearest tenth. (*Source: The Handy Science Answer Book*)

61. The highest temperature ever recorded in Europe was 122°F in Seville, Spain, in August of 1881. Convert this record high temperature to Celsius. (*Source:* National Climatic Data Center)

62. The lowest temperature ever recorded in Oceania was −10°C at the Haleakala Summit in Maui, Hawaii, in January 1961. Convert this record low temperature to Fahrenheit. (*Source:* National Climatic Data Center)

△ **63.** The CART FedEx Championship Series is an open-wheeled race car competition based in the United States. A CART car has a maximum length of 199 inches, a maximum width of 78.5 inches, and a maximum height of 33 inches. When the CART series travels to another country for a grand prix, teams must ship their cars. Find the volume of the smallest shipping crate needed to ship a CART car of maximum dimensions. (*Source:* Championship Auto Racing Teams, Inc.)

CART Racing Car

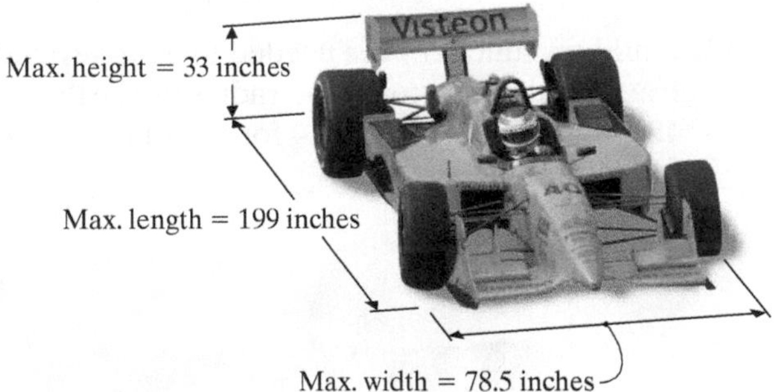

64. On a road course, a CART car's speed can average up to around 105 mph. Based on this speed, how long would it take a CART driver to travel from Los Angeles to New York City, a distance of about 2810 miles by road, without stopping? Round to the nearest tenth of an hour.

△ **65.** The Hoberman Sphere is a toy ball that expands and contracts. When it is completely closed, it has a diameter of 9.5 inches. Find the volume of the Hoberman Sphere when it is completely closed. Use 3.14 for π. Round to the nearest whole cubic inch. (*Hint:* volume of a sphere $= \frac{4}{3}\pi r^3$. *Source:* Hoberman Designs, Inc.)

△ **66.** When the Hoberman Sphere (see Exercise 65) is completely expanded, its diameter is 30 inches. Find the volume of the Hoberman Sphere when it is completely expanded. Use 3.14 for π. (*Source:* Hoberman Designs, Inc.)

67. The average temperature on the planet Mercury is 167°C. Convert this temperature to degrees Fahrenheit. Round to the nearest degree. (*Source:* National Space Science Data Center)

68. The average temperature on the planet Jupiter is −227°F. Convert this temperature to degrees Celsius. Round to the nearest degree. (*Source:* National Space Science Data Center)

Review

Write each percent as a decimal. See Section R.3.

69. 32%

70. 8%

71. 200%

72. 0.5%

Write each decimal as a percent. See Section R.3.

73. 0.17

74. 0.03

75. 7.2

76. 5

Concept Extensions

Solve.

77. $N = R + \dfrac{V}{G}$ for V (Urban forestry: tree plantings per year)

78. $B = \dfrac{F}{P - V}$ for V (Business: break-even point)

79. The formula $V = lwh$ is used to find the volume of a box. If the length of a box is doubled, the width is doubled, and the height is doubled, how does this affect the volume? Explain your answer.

80. The formula $A = bh$ is used to find the area of a parallelogram. If the base of a parallelogram is doubled and its height is doubled, how does this affect the area? Explain your answer.

81. Use the Dolbear's Law formula for Exercises 41–46 and calculate when the number of cricket chirps per minute is the same as the temperature in degrees Fahrenheit. (*Hint:* Replace T with N and solve for N or replace N with T and solve for T.)

82. Find the temperature at which the Celsius measurement and the Fahrenheit measurement are the same number.

Solve. See the Concept Check in this section.

83. ▲ − ● · ▮ = ■ for ●

84. ⬟ · ■ + ▲ = ● for ■

85. Flying fish do not *actually* fly, but glide. They have been known to travel a distance of 1300 feet at a rate of 20 miles per hour. How many seconds would it take to travel this distance? (*Hint:* First convert miles per hour to feet per second. Recall that 1 mile = 5280 feet.) Round to the nearest tenth of a second.

86. A glacier is a giant mass of rocks and ice that flows downhill like a river. Exit Glacier, near Seward, Alaska, moves at a rate of 20 inches a day. Find the distance in feet the glacier moves in a year. (Assume 365 days a year.) Round to two decimal places.

Substitute the given values into each given formula and solve for the unknown variable. If necessary, round to one decimal place.

87. $I = PRT$; $I = 1{,}056{,}000$, $R = 0.055$, $T = 6$ (Simple interest formula)

88. $I = PRT$; $I = 3750$, $P = 25{,}000$, $R = 0.05$ (Simple interest formula)

89. $V = \dfrac{4}{3}\pi r^3$; $r = 3$ (Volume of a sphere) (Use a calculator approximation for π.)

90. $V = \dfrac{1}{3}\pi r^2 h$; $V = 565.2$, $r = 6$ (Volume of a cone) (Use a calculator approximation for π.)

Objectives

A Solve Percent Equations.

B Solve Discount and Mark-Up Problems.

C Solve Percent Increase and Percent Decrease Problems.

D Solve Mixture Problems.

2.6 PERCENT AND MIXTURE PROBLEM SOLVING

This section is devoted to solving problems in the categories listed. The same problem-solving steps used in previous sections are also followed in this section. They are listed below for review.

General Strategy for Problem Solving

1. UNDERSTAND the problem. During this step, become comfortable with the problem. Some ways of doing this are as follows:
   Read and reread the problem.
   Choose a variable to represent the unknown.
   Construct a drawing, whenever possible.
   Propose a solution and check. Pay careful attention to how you check your proposed solution. This will help writing an equation to model the problem.
2. TRANSLATE the problem into an equation.
3. SOLVE the equation.
4. INTERPRET the results: *Check* the proposed solution in the stated problem and *state* your conclusion.

Objective A Solving Percent Equations

Many of today's statistics are given in terms of percent: a basketball player's free throw percent, current interest rates, stock market trends, and nutrition labeling, just to name a few. In this section, we first explore percent, percent equations, and applications involving percents. See Section R.3 if a further review of percents is needed.

PRACTICE 1

The number 22 is what percent of 40?

Example 1 The number 63 is what percent of 72?

Solution:

1. UNDERSTAND. Read and reread the problem. Next, let's suppose that the percent is 80%. To check, we find 80% of 72.

   $80\% \text{ of } 72 = 0.80(72) = 57.6$

   This is close, but not 63. At this point, though, we have a better understanding of the problem; we know the correct answer is close to and greater than 80%, and we know how to check our proposed solution later.

   Let $x =$ the unknown percent.

2. TRANSLATE. Recall that "is" means "equals" and "of" signifies multiplying. Let's translate the sentence directly.

the number 63	is	what percent	of	72
↓	↓	↓	↓	↓
63	=	x	·	72

3. SOLVE.

$$63 = 72x$$
$$0.875 = x \quad \text{Divide both sides by 72.}$$
$$87.5\% = x \quad \text{Write as a percent.}$$

Answer
1. 55%

4. INTERPRET.

Check: Verify that 87.5% of 72 is 63.

State: The number 63 is 87.5% of 72.

Work Practice 1

Example 2 The number 120 is 15% of what number?

Solution:

1. UNDERSTAND. Read and reread the problem.

   Let $x =$ the unknown number.

2. TRANSLATE.

the number 120	is	15%	of	what number
↓	↓	↓	↓	↓
120	=	15%	·	x

3. SOLVE.

   $120 = 0.15x$ Write 15% as 0.15.

   $800 = x$ Divide both sides by 0.15.

4. INTERPRET.

Check: Check the proposed solution by finding 15% of 800 and verifying that the result is 120.

State: Thus, 120 is 15% of 800.

Work Practice 2

PRACTICE 2

The number 150 is 40% of what number?

Example 3 The circle graph below shows the purpose of trips made by American travelers. Use this graph to answer the questions below.

Purpose of Trip

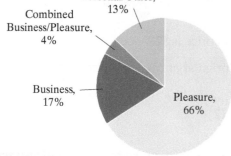

Source: Travel Industry Association of America

a. What percent of trips made by American travelers are solely for the purpose of business?

b. What percent of trips made by American travelers are for the purpose of business or combined business/pleasure?

c. On an airplane flight of 253 Americans, how many of these people might we expect to be traveling solely for business?

Solution:

a. From the circle graph, we see that 17% of trips made by American travelers are solely for the purpose of business.

Continued on next page

PRACTICE 3

Use the circle graph to answer each question.

a. What percent of trips made by American travelers are solely for pleasure?

b. What percent of trips made by American travelers are for the purpose of pleasure or combined business/pleasure?

c. On an airplane flight of 250 Americans, how many of these people might we expect to be traveling solely for pleasure?

Answers

2. 375 **3. a.** 66% **b.** 70% **c.** 165 people

b. From the circle graph, we know that 17% of trips are solely for business and 4% of trips are for combined business/pleasure. The sum 17% + 4% or 21% of trips made by American travelers are for the purpose of business or combined business/pleasure.

c. Since 17% of trips made by American travelers are for business, we find 17% of 253. Remember that "of" translates to "multiplication."

$$17\% \text{ of } 253 = 0.17(253) \quad \text{Replace "of" with the operation of multiplication.}$$
$$= 43.01$$

We might then expect that about 43 American travelers on the flight are traveling solely for business.

Work Practice 3

Objective B Solving Discount and Mark-Up Problems

The next example has to do with discounting the price of a cell phone.

PRACTICE 4

A surfboard, originally purchased for $400, was sold on eBay at a discount of 40% of the original price. What is the discount and the new price?

Example 4 Cell Phones Unlimited recently reduced the price of a $140 phone by 20%. What is the discount and the new price?

Solution:

1. UNDERSTAND. Read and reread the problem. Make sure you understand the meaning of the word "discount." Discount is the amount of money by which an item has been decreased. To find the discount, we simply find 20% of $140. In other words, we have the formulas,

discount = percent · original price   Then

new price = original price − discount

2, 3. TRANSLATE and SOLVE.

discount	=	percent	·	original price
	=	20%	·	$140
	=	0.20	·	$140
	= $28			

Thus, the discount in price is $28.

new price	=	original price	−	discount
	=	$140	−	$28
	= $112			

3. INTERPRET.

Check: Check your calculations in the formulas, and also see if our results are reasonable. They are.

State: The discount in price is $28 and the new price is $112.

Work Practice 4

A concept similar to discount is mark-up. What is the difference between the two? A discount is subtracted from the original price while a mark-up is added to the original price. For mark-ups,

mark-up = percent · original price

new price = original price + mark-up

Mark-up exercises can be found in Exercise Set 2.6.

Answer

4. discount: $160; new price: $240

Objective C Solving Percent Increase and Percent Decrease Problems

Percent increase or percent decrease is a common way to describe how some measurement has increased or decreased. For example, crime increased by 8%, teachers received a 5.5% increase in salary, or a company decreased its employees by 10%. The next example is a review of percent increase.

Example 5 Calculating the Percent Increase of Attending College

The tuition and fees cost of attending a public college rose from \$2928 in 2003 to \$5246 in 2009. Find the percent increase. (*Source*: The College Board) *Note*: These costs are an average of two-year and four-year colleges.

Solution:

1. UNDERSTAND. Read and reread the problem. Notice that the new tuition, \$5246, is almost double the old tuition of \$2928. Because of that, we know that the percent increase is close to 100%. To see this, let's guess that the percent increase is 100%. To check, we find 100% of \$2928 to find the *increase* in cost. Then we add this increase to \$2928 to find the *new cost*. In other words, $100\%(\$2928) = 1.00(\$2928) = \$2928$, the *increase* in cost. The *new cost* would be old cost + increase = $\$2928 + \$2928 = \$5856$, close to the actual new cost of \$5246. We now know that the increase is close to, but less than 100% and we know how to check our proposed solution.

Let $x =$ the percent increase.

2. TRANSLATE. First, find the **increase,** and then the **percent increase.** The increase in cost is found by:

In words:	increase	=	new cost	−	old cost	or
Translate:	increase	=	\$5246	−	\$2928	
		=	\$2318			

Next, find the percent increase. The percent increase or percent decrease is always a percent of the original number or, in this case, the old cost.

In words:	increase	is	what percent	of	old cost
Translate:	\$2318	=	x	·	\$2928

3. SOLVE.

$2318 = 2928x$

$0.792 \approx x$ Divide both sides by 2928 and round to 3 decimal places.

$79.2\% \approx x$ Write as a percent.

4. INTERPRET.

Check: Check the proposed solution

State: The percent increase in cost is approximately 79.2%.

Work Practice 5

PRACTICE 5

If a number increases from 120 to 200, find the percent increase. Round to the nearest tenth of a percent.

Percent decrease is found using a similar method. First find the decrease, then determine what percent of the original or first amount is that decrease.

Read the next example carefully. For Example 5, we were asked to find percent increase. In Example 6, we are given the percent increase and asked to find the number before the increase.

Answer

5. 66.7%

PRACTICE 6

Find the original price of a suit if the sale price is \$46 after a 20% discount.

Example 6 The fastest-growing sector of digital theater screens is 3D. Find the number of digital 3D screens in the United States and Canada last year if after a 134% increase, the number this year is 3548. Round to the nearest whole. (*Source:* MPAA)

Solution:

1. UNDERSTAND. Read and reread the problem. Let's guess a solution and see how we would check our guess. If the number of digital 3D screens last year was 1000, we would see if 1000 plus the increase is 3548; that is,

$$1000 + 134\%(1000) = 1000 + 1.34(1000) = 1000 + 1340 = 2340$$

Since 2340 is too small, we know that our guess of 1000 is too small. We also have a better understanding of the problem. Let

x = number of digital 3D screens last year

2. TRANSLATE. To translate to an equation, we remember that

In words:	number of digital 3D screens last year	plus	increase	equals	number of digital 3D screens this year
Translate:	x	$+$	$1.34x$	$=$	3548

3. SOLVE.

$$2.34x = 3548$$
$$x = \frac{3548}{2.34}$$
$$x \approx 1516$$

4. INTERPRET.

Check: Recall that x represents the number of digital 3D screens last year. If this number is approximately 1516, let's see if 1516 plus the increase is close to 3548. (We use the word "close" since 1516 is rounded.)

$$1516 + 134\%(1516) = 1516 + 1.34(1516) = 1516 + 2031.44 = 3547.44$$

which is close to 3548.

State: There were approximately 1516 digital 3D screens last year.

Work Practice 6

Objective D Solving Mixture Problems

Mixture problems involve two or more different quantities being combined to form a new mixture. These applications range from Dow Chemical's need to form a chemical mixture of a required strength to Planter's Peanut Company's need to find the correct mixture of peanuts and cashews, given taste and price constraints.

PRACTICE 7

How much 20% dye solution and 50% dye solution should be mixed to obtain 6 liters of a 40% solution?

Example 7 Calculating Percent for a Lab Experiment

A chemist working on his doctoral degree at Massachusetts Institute of Technology needs 12 liters of a 50% acid solution for a lab experiment. The stockroom has only 40% and 70% solutions. How much of each solution should be mixed together to form 12 liters of a 50% solution?

Solution:

1. UNDERSTAND. First, read and reread the problem a few times. Next, guess a solution. Suppose that we need 7 liters of the 40% solution. Then we need $12 - 7 = 5$ liters of the 70% solution. To see if this is indeed the solution, find

Answers

6. \$57.50 7. 2 liters of the 20% solution; 4 liters of the 50% solution

the amount of pure acid in 7 liters of the 40% solution, in 5 liters of the 70% solution, and in 12 liters of a 50% solution, the required amount and strength.

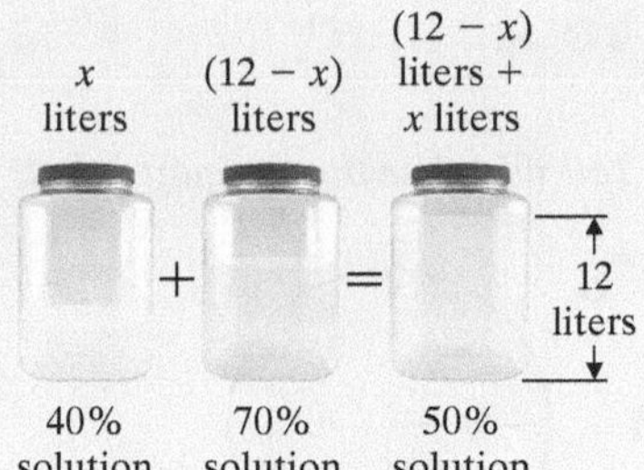

number of liters	×	acid strength	=	amount of pure acid
7 liters	×	40%	=	7(0.40) or 2.8 liters
5 liters	×	70%	=	5(0.70) or 3.5 liters
12 liters	×	50%	=	12(0.50) or 6 liters

Since 2.8 liters + 3.5 liters = 6.3 liters and not 6, our guess is incorrect, but we have gained some valuable insight into how to model and check this problem.

Let

x = number of liters of 40% solution; then
$12 - x$ = number of liters of 70% solution.

2. TRANSLATE. To help us translate to an equation, the following table summarizes the information given. Recall that the amount of acid in each solution is found by multiplying the acid strength of each solution by the number of liters.

	No. of Liters	· Acid Strength	= Amount of Acid
40% Solution	x	40%	$0.40x$
70% Solution	$12 - x$	70%	$0.70(12 - x)$
50% Solution Needed	12	50%	0.50(12)

The amount of acid in the final solution is the sum of the amounts of acid in the two beginning solutions.

In words: acid in 40% solution + acid in 70% solution = acid in 50% mixture

Translate: $0.40x + 0.70(12 - x) = 0.50(12)$

3. SOLVE.

$$0.40x + 0.70(12 - x) = 0.50(12)$$
$$0.4x + 8.4 - 0.7x = 6 \quad \text{Apply the distributive property.}$$
$$-0.3x + 8.4 = 6 \quad \text{Combine like terms.}$$
$$-0.3x = -2.4 \quad \text{Subtract 8.4 from both sides.}$$
$$x = 8 \quad \text{Divide both sides by } -0.3.$$

4. INTERPRET.

Check: To check, recall how we checked our guess.

State: If 8 liters of the 40% solution are mixed with 12 − 8 or 4 liters of the 70% solution, the result is 12 liters of a 50% solution.

Work Practice 7

Vocabulary and Readiness Check

Tell whether the percent labels in the circle graphs are correct.

1.

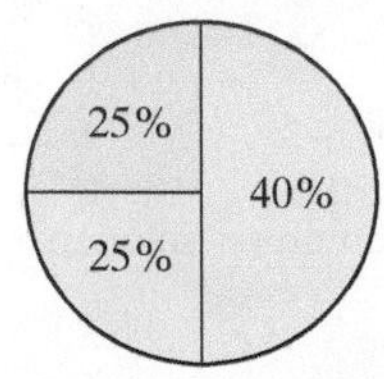

2.

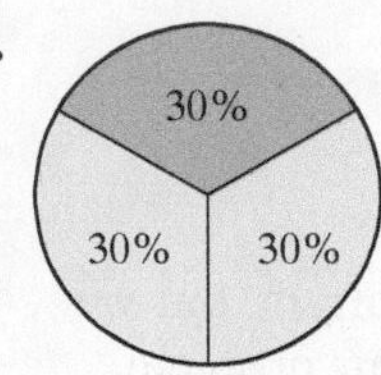

3.

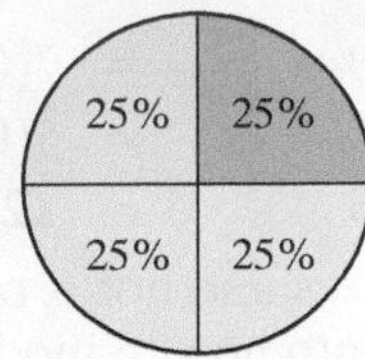

4.

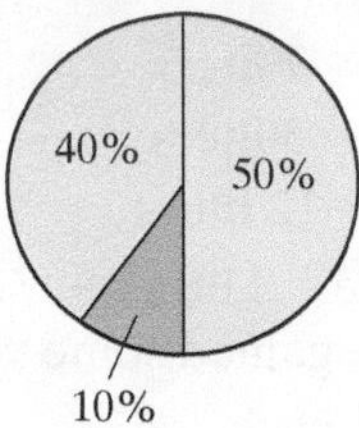

2.6 Exercise Set

FOR EXTRA HELP

MyMathLab

PRACTICE

WATCH

DOWNLOAD

READ

REVIEW

Objective A *Find each number described. For Exercises 1 and 2, the solutions have been started for you. See Examples 1 and 2.*

1. What number is 16% of 70?

Start the solution:

1. UNDERSTAND the problem. Reread it as many times as needed.

2. TRANSLATE into an equation. (Fill in the blanks below.)

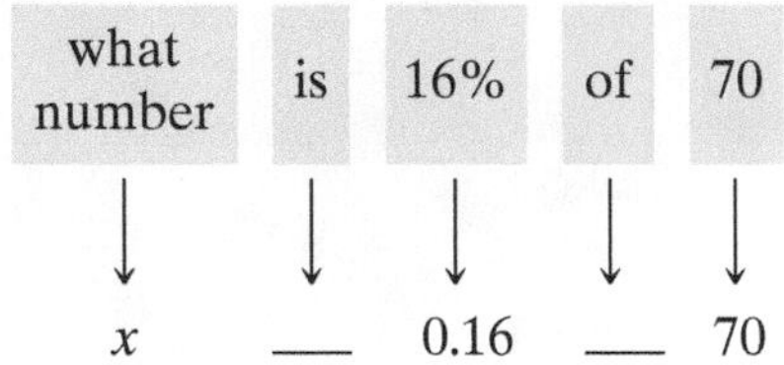

x ___ 0.16 ___ 70

Finish with:

3. SOLVE and **4.** INTERPRET

2. What number is 88% of 1000?

Start the solution:

1. UNDERSTAND the problem. Reread it as many times as needed.

2. TRANSLATE into an equation. (Fill in the blanks below.)

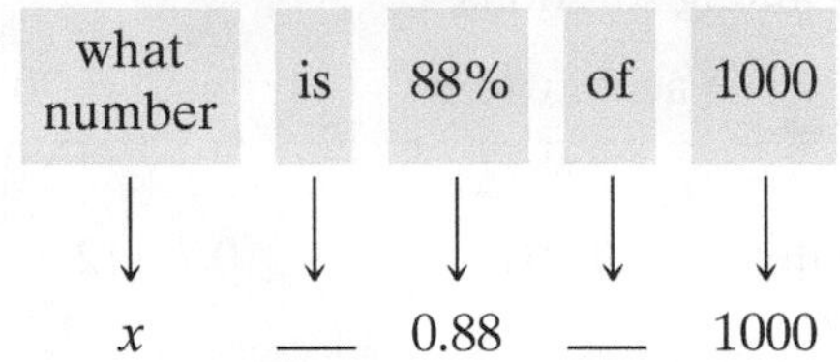

x ___ 0.88 ___ 1000

Finish with:

3. SOLVE and **4.** INTERPRET

3. The number 28.6 is what percent of 52?

4. The number 87.2 is what percent of 436?

5. The number 45 is 25% of what number?

6. The number 126 is 35% of what number?

The circle graph below shows the number of minutes that adults spend on their home phone each day. Use this graph for Exercises 7 through 10. See Example 3.

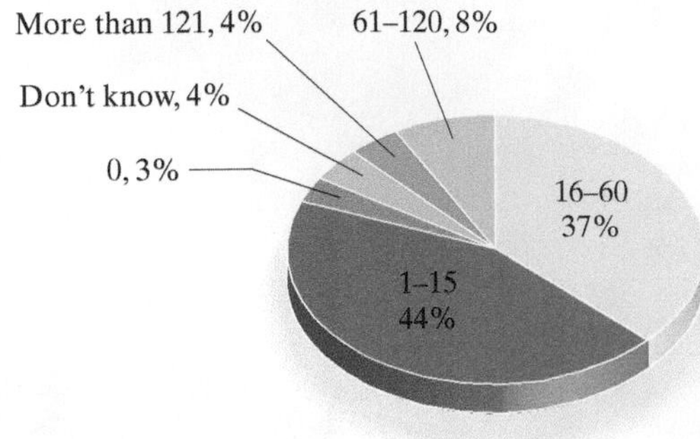

Source: Bruskin/Goldring Research for Sony Electronics

7. What percent of adults spend more than 121 minutes on the phone each day?

8. What percent of adults spend no time on the phone each day?

9. Florence is a town in Alabama whose adult population is approximately 27,000. How many of these adults might you expect to talk 16–60 minutes on the phone each day?

10. Columbus is a town in Indiana whose adult population is approximately 29,250. How many of these adults might you expect to talk 61–120 minutes on the phone each day?

Objective B *Solve. If needed, round answers to the nearest cent. See Example 4.*

11. A used automobile dealership recently reduced the price of a used sports car by 8%. If the price of the car before discount was $18,500, find the discount and the new price.

12. A music store is advertising a 25%-off sale on all new releases. Find the discount and the sale price of a newly released CD that regularly sells for $12.50.

13. A birthday celebration meal is $40.50 including tax. Find the total cost if a 15% tip is added to the cost.

14. A retirement dinner for two is $65.40 including tax. Find the total cost if a 20% tip is added to the cost.

Objective C *Solve. See Example 5.*

15. The number of fraud complaints for Internet auction sites decreased from 148,600 in 2005 to 73,900 in 2007. Find the percent decrease. Round to the nearest whole percent. (*Source:* FBI)

16. The number of text messages rose from 996 million in June to 1100 million in December. Find the percent increase. Round to the nearest whole percent.

17. By decreasing each dimension by 1 unit, the area of a rectangle decreased from 40 square feet (on the left) to 28 square feet (on the right). Find the percent decrease in area.

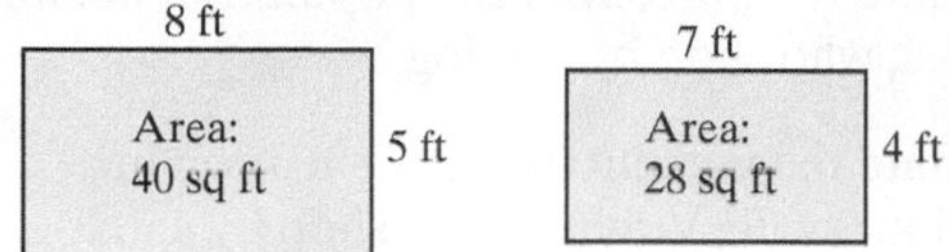

18. By decreasing the length of the side by one unit, the area of a square decreased from 100 square meters to 81 square meters. Find the percent decrease in area.

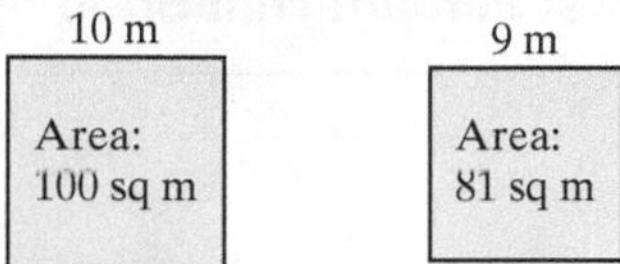

Solve. See Example 6.

19. Find the original price of a pair of shoes if the sale price is $78 after a 25% discount.

20. Find the original price of a popular pair of shoes if the increased price is $80 after a 25% increase.

21. Find last year's salary if after a 4% pay raise, this year's salary is $44,200.

22. Find last year's salary if after a 3% pay raise, this year's salary is $55,620.

Objective D *Solve. For each exercise, a table is given for you to complete and use to write an equation that models the situation. See Example 7.*

23. How much pure acid should be mixed with 2 gallons of a 40% acid solution in order to get a 70% acid solution?

	Number of Gallons ·	Acid Strength =	Amount of Acid
Pure Acid		100%	
40% Acid Solution			
70% Acid Solution Needed			

24. How many cubic centimeters (cc) of a 25% antibiotic solution should be added to 10 cubic centimeters of a 60% antibiotic solution in order to get a 30% antibiotic solution?

	Number of Cubic cm ·	Antibiotic Strength =	Amount of Antibiotic
25% Antibiotic Solution			
60% Antibiotic Solution			
30% Antibiotic Solution Needed			

25. Community Coffee Company wants a new flavor of Cajun coffee. How many pounds of coffee worth \$7 a pound should be added to 14 pounds of coffee worth \$4 a pound to get a mixture worth \$5 a pound?

	Number of Pounds ·	Cost per Pound =	Value
\$7 per lb Coffee			
\$4 per lb Coffee			
\$5 per lb Coffee Wanted			

26. Planter's Peanut Company wants to mix 20 pounds of peanuts worth \$3 a pound with cashews worth \$5 a pound in order to make an experimental mix worth \$3.50 a pound. How many pounds of cashews should be added to the peanuts?

	Number of Pounds ·	Cost per Pound =	Value
\$3 per lb Peanuts			
\$5 per lb Cashews			
\$3.50 per lb Mixture Wanted			

Objectives A B C Mixed Practice *Solve. If needed, round money amounts to two decimal places and all other amounts to one decimal place. See Examples 1 through 6.*

27. Find 23% of 20.

28. Find 140% of 86.

29. The number 40 is 80% of what number?

30. The number 56.25 is 45% of what number?

31. The number 144 is what percent of 480?

32. The number 42 is what percent of 35?

The graph shows the communities in the United States that have the highest percentages of citizens that shop by catalog. Use the graph to answer Exercises 33 through 36.

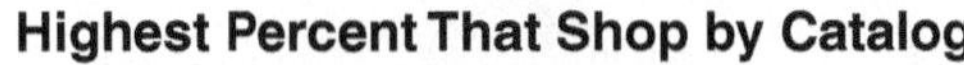

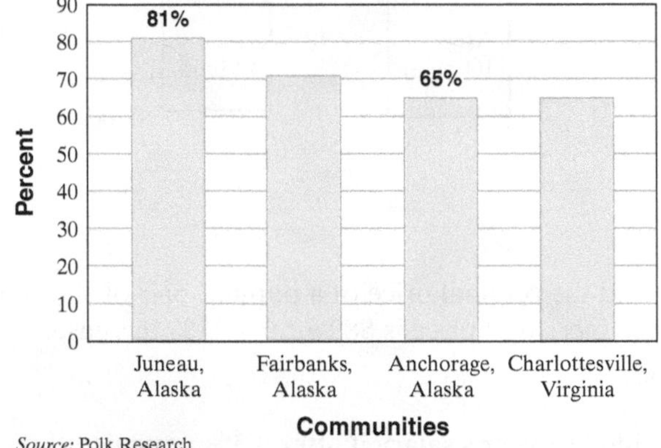

Source: Polk Research

33. Estimate the percent of the population in Fairbanks, Alaska, who shop by catalog.

34. Estimate the percent of the population in Charlottesville, Virginia, who shop by catalog.

35. According to CNN, in 2008, Anchorage had a population of 278,700. How many catalog shoppers might we predict lived in Anchorage? Round to the nearest whole number.

36. According to CNN, in 2008, Juneau had a population of 30,700. How many catalog shoppers might we predict lived in Juneau? Round to the nearest whole number.

For Exercises 37 and 38, fill in the percent column in each table. Each table contains a worked-out example.

37.

Top Cranberry-Producing States in 2008 (in millions of pounds)

	Millions of Pounds	Percent of Total (rounded to nearest percent)
Wisconsin	385	
Oregon	50	
Massachusetts	190	
Washington	15	
New Jersey	49	Example: $\frac{49}{689} \approx 7\%$
Total	689	

Source: National Agricultural Statistics Service

38.

The Gap, Inc. Brands North American Stores in 2008

Store Brand/Location	Number of Stores	Percent of Total (rounded to nearest percent)
The Gap U.S.	1136	
The Gap Canada	91	
Banana Republic U.S.	540	Example: $\frac{540}{2876} \approx 19\%$
Banana Republic Canada	33	
Old Navy–U.S.	1012	
Old Navy–Canada	64	
Total	2876	

39. Iceberg lettuce is grown and shipped to stores for about 40 cents a head, and consumers purchase it for about 70 cents a head. Find the percent increase.

40. The lettuce consumption per capita in 1990 was 31.5 pounds, and in 2007 the consumption dropped to 29.5 pounds. Find the percent decrease.

41. A student at the University of New Orleans makes money by buying and selling used cars. Charles bought a used car and later sold it for a 20% profit. If he sold it for $4680, how much did Charles pay for the car?

42. The number of registered vehicles on the road in the United States is constantly increasing. In 2007, there were approximately 246 million registered vehicles. This represents a 3% increase over 2002. How many registered vehicles were there in the United States in 2002? Round to the nearest million. (*Source:* Federal Highway Administration)

43. By doubling each dimension, the area of a parallelogram increased from 36 square centimeters to 144 square centimeters. Find the percent increase in area.

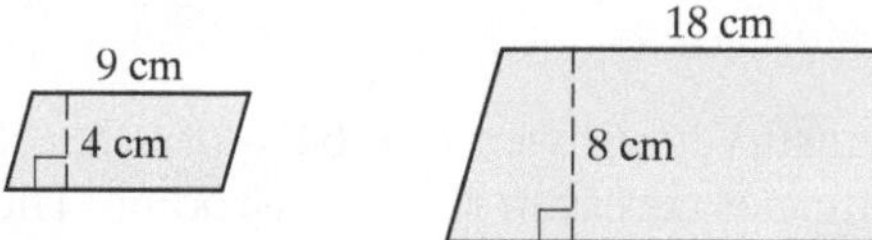

44. By doubling each dimension, the area of a triangle increased from 6 square miles to 24 square miles. Find the percent increase in area.

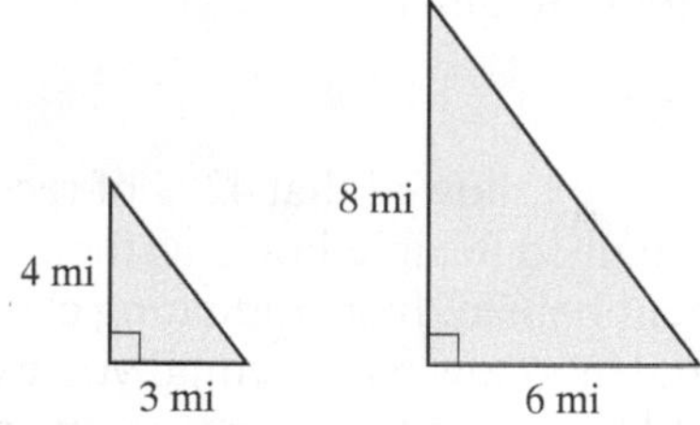

45. A gasoline station recently increased the price of one grade of gasoline by 5%. If this gasoline originally cost $2.20 per gallon, find the mark-up and the new price.

46. The price of a biology book recently increased by 10%. If this book originally cost $89.90, find the mark-up and the new price.

47. How much of an alloy that is 20% copper should be mixed with 200 ounces of an alloy that is 50% copper in order to get an alloy that is 30% copper?

48. How much water should be added to 30 gallons of a solution that is 70% antifreeze in order to get a mixture that is 60% antifreeze?

49. During the 1982–1983 term, the Supreme Court made 151 decisions while during the 2007–2008 term, they only made 72. Find the percent decrease in number of decisions. Round to the nearest tenth of a percent.

50. The number of farms in the United States is decreasing. In 1940, there were approximately 6.3 million farms, while in 2007 there were only 2.1 million farms. Find the percent decrease in the number of farms. Round to the nearest tenth of a percent.

51. A company recently downsized its number of employees by 35%. If there are still 78 employees, how many employees were there prior to the layoffs?

52. The average number of children born to each U.S. woman has decreased by 44% since 1920. If this average is now 1.9, find the average in 1920. Round to the nearest tenth.

53. Nordstrom advertised a 25%-off sale. If a London Fog coat originally sold for $256, find the decrease in price and the sale price.

54. A gasoline station decreased the price of a $0.95 cola by 15%. Find the decrease in price and the new price.

55. Scoville units are used to measure the hotness of a pepper. Measuring 577 thousand Scoville units, the "Red Savina" habañero pepper was known as the hottest chili pepper. That has recently changed with the discovery of Naga Jolokia pepper from India. It measures 48% hotter than the habañero. Find the measure of the Naga Jolokia pepper. Round to the nearest thousand units.

56. As of this writing, the women's record for throwing a disc (like a heavy Frisbee) was set by Valarie Jenkins of the United States in 2008. Her throw was 148.00 meters. The men's world record was set by Christian Sandstrom of Sweden in 2002. His throw was 68.9% farther than Valarie's. Find the distance of his throw. Round to the nearest meter. (*Source:* World Flying Disc Federation)

57. A recent survey showed that 42% of recent college graduates named flexible hours as their most desired employment benefit. In a graduating class of 860 college students, how many would you expect to rank flexible hours as their top priority in job benefits? (Round to the nearest whole.) (*Source:* JobTrak.com)

58. A recent survey showed that 64% of U.S. colleges have Internet access in their classrooms. There are approximately 9800 post-secondary institutions in the United States. How many of these would you expect to have Internet access in their classrooms? (*Source:* Market Data Retrieval, National Center for Education Statistics)

59. A new self-tanning lotion for everyday use is to be sold. First, an experimental lotion mixture is made by mixing 800 ounces of everyday moisturizing lotion worth $0.30 an ounce with self-tanning lotion worth $3 per ounce. If the experimental lotion is to cost $1.20 per ounce, how many ounces of the self-tanning lotion should be in the mixture?

60. The owner of a local chocolate shop wants to develop a new trail mix. How many pounds of chocolate-covered peanuts worth $5 a pound should be mixed with 10 pounds of granola bites worth $2 a pound to get a mixture worth $3 per pound?

Review

Place $<$, $>$, or $=$ in the appropriate space to make each a true statement. See Sections 1.2, 1.3, and 1.6.

61. $-5 \quad -7$

62. $\frac{12}{3} \quad 2^2$

63. $|-5| \quad -(-5)$

64. $-3^3 \quad (-3)^3$

65. $(-3)^2 \quad -3^2$

66. $|-2| \quad -|-2|$

Concept Extensions

67. Is it possible to mix a 10% acid solution and a 40% acid solution to obtain a 60% acid solution? Why or why not?

68. Must the percents in a circle graph have a sum of 100%? Why or why not?

Standardized nutrition labels like the one below have been displayed on food items since 1994. The percent column on the right shows the percent of daily values (based on a 2000-calorie diet) shown at the bottom of the label. For example, a serving of this food contains 4 grams of total fat, where the recommended daily fat based on a 2000-calorie diet is less than 65 grams of fat. This means that $\frac{4}{65}$ *or approximately 6% (as shown) of your daily recommended fat is taken in by eating a serving of this food. Use this nutrition label to answer Exercises 69 through 71.*

Nutrition Facts

Serving Size	**18 Crackers (31g)**
Servings Per Container	**About 9**
Amount Per Serving	
Calories 130	Calories from Fat 35
	% Daily Value*
Total Fat 4g	**6%**
Saturated Fat 0.5g	**3%**
Polyunsaturated Fat 0g	
Monounsaturated Fat 1.5g	
Cholesterol 0mg	**0%**
Sodium 230mg	*x*
Total Carbohydrate 23g	*y*
Dietary Fiber 2g	**8%**
Sugars 3g	
Protein 2g	
Vitamin A 0% •	Vitamin C 0%
Calcium 2% •	Iron 6%

* Percent Daily Values are based on a 2,000 calorie diet. Your daily values may be higher or lower depending on your calorie needs.

	Calories	2,000	2,500
Total Fat	Less than	65g	80g
Sat. Fat	Less than	20g	25g
Cholesterol	Less than	300mg	300mg
Sodium	Less than	2400mg	2400mg
Total Carbohydrate		300g	375g
Dietary Fiber		25g	30g

69. Based on a 2000-calorie diet, what percent of daily value of sodium is contained in a serving of this food? In other words, find x in the label. (Round to the nearest tenth of a percent.)

70. Based on a 2000-calorie diet, what percent of daily value of total carbohydrate is contained in a serving of this food? In other words, find y in the label. (Round to the nearest tenth of a percent.)

71. Notice on the nutrition label that one serving of this food contains 130 calories and 35 of these calories are from fat. Find the percent of calories from fat. (Round to the nearest tenth of a percent.) It is recommended that no more than 30% of calorie intake come from fat. Does this food satisfy this recommendation?

Use the nutrition label below to answer Exercises 72 through 74.

NUTRITIONAL INFORMATION PER SERVING

Serving Size: 9.8 oz.		**Servings Per Container: 1**	
Calories	280	Polyunsaturated Fat	1g
Protein	12g	Saturated Fat	3g
Carbohydrate	45g	Cholesterol	20mg
Fat	6g	Sodium	520mg
Percent of Calories from Fat	?	Potassium	220mg

72. If fat contains approximately 9 calories per gram, find the percent of calories from fat in one serving of this food. (Round to the nearest tenth of a percent.)

73. If protein contains approximately 4 calories per gram, find the percent of calories from protein from one serving of this food. (Round to the nearest tenth of a percent.)

74. Find a food that contains more than 30% of its calories per serving from fat. Analyze the nutrition label and verify that the percents shown are correct.

Objectives

A Graph Inequalities on a Number Line.

B Use the Addition Property of Inequality to Solve Inequalities.

C Use the Multiplication Property of Inequality to Solve Inequalities.

D Use Both Properties to Solve Inequalities.

E Solve Problems Modeled by Inequalities.

2.7 LINEAR INEQUALITIES AND PROBLEM SOLVING

In Chapter 1, we reviewed these inequality symbols and their meanings:

$<$ means "is less than"	$\leq$ means "is less than or equal to"
$>$ means "is greater than"	$\geq$ means "is greater than or equal to"

An **inequality** is a statement that contains one of the symbols above.

Equations	Inequalities
$x = 3$	$x \leq 3$
$5n - 6 = 14$	$5n - 6 > 14$
$12 = 7 - 3y$	$12 \leq 7 - 3y$
$\frac{x}{4} - 6 = 1$	$\frac{x}{4} - 6 > 1$

Objective A Graphing Inequalities on a Number Line

Recall that the single solution to the equation $x = 3$ is 3. The solutions of the inequality $x \leq 3$ include 3 and *all real numbers less than 3* (for example, $-10, \frac{1}{2}, 2,$ and 2.9). Because we can't list all numbers less than 3, we show instead a picture of the solutions by graphing them on a number line.

To graph the solutions of $x \leq 3$, we shade the numbers to the left of 3 since they are less than 3. Then we place a closed circle on the point representing 3. The closed circle indicates that 3 *is* a solution: 3 *is* less than or equal to 3.

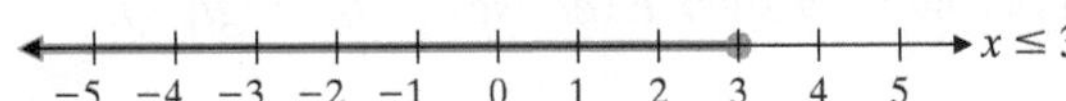

To graph the solutions of $x < 3$, we shade the numbers to the left of 3. Then we place an open circle on the point representing 3. The open circle indicates that 3 *is not* a solution: 3 *is not* less than 3.

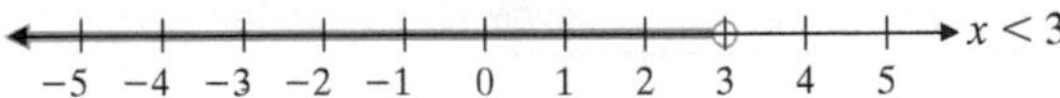

Example 1 Graph: $x \geq -1$

Solution: To graph the solutions of $x \geq -1$, we place a closed circle at -1 since the inequality symbol is $\geq$ and -1 is greater than or equal to -1. Then we shade to the right of -1.

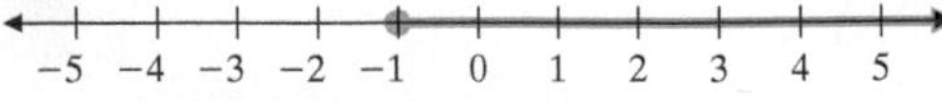

Work Practice 1

PRACTICE 1

Graph: $x \geq -2$

−5 −4 −3 −2 −1 0 1 2 3 4 5

Example 2 Graph: $-1 > x$

Solution: Recall from Section 1.2 that $-1 > x$ means the same as $x < -1$. The graph of the solutions of $x < -1$ is shown below.

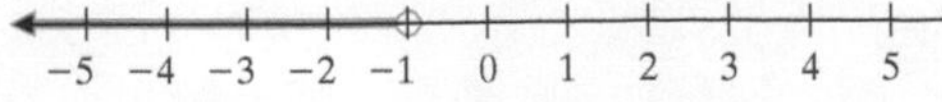

Work Practice 2

PRACTICE 2

Graph: $5 > x$

−5 −4 −3 −2 −1 0 1 2 3 4 5

Answers

1. 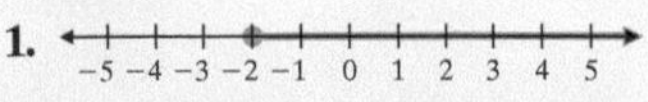

2. −5 −4 −3 −2 −1 0 1 2 3 4 5

Example 3 Graph: $-4 < x \le 2$

Solution: We read $-4 < x \le 2$ as "-4 is less than x and x is less than or equal to 2," or as "x is greater than -4 and x is less than or equal to 2." To graph the solutions of this inequality, we place an open circle at -4 (-4 is not part of the graph), a closed circle at 2 (2 is part of the graph), and we shade all numbers between -4 and 2. Why? All numbers between -4 and 2 are greater than -4 *and* also less than 2.

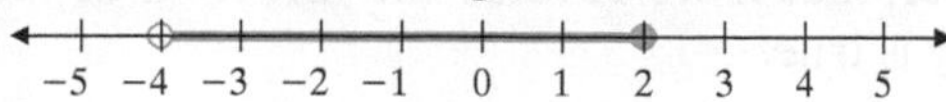

Work Practice 3

PRACTICE 3

Graph: $-3 \le x < 1$

Objective B Using the Addition Property

When solutions of a linear inequality are not immediately obvious, they are found through a process similar to the one used to solve a linear equation. Our goal is to get the variable alone on one side of the inequality. We use properties of inequality similar to properties of equality.

Addition Property of Inequality

If a, b, and c are real numbers, then

$$a < b \quad \text{and} \quad a + c < b + c$$

are equivalent inequalities.

This property also holds true for subtracting values, since subtraction is defined in terms of addition. In other words, adding or subtracting the same quantity from both sides of an inequality does not change the solutions of the inequality.

Example 4 Solve $x + 4 \le -6$. Graph the solutions.

Solution: To solve for x, subtract 4 from both sides of the inequality.

$x + 4 \le -6$ Original inequality

$x + 4 - 4 \le -6 - 4$ Subtract 4 from both sides.

$x \le -10$ Simplify.

The graph of the solutions is shown below.

Work Practice 4

PRACTICE 4

Solve $x - 6 \ge -11$. Graph the solutions.

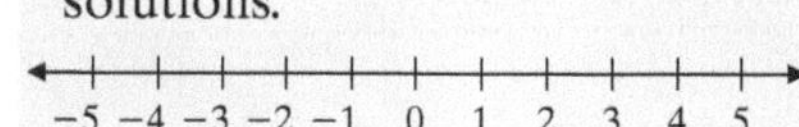

Helpful Hint

Notice that any number less than or equal to -10 is a solution to $x \le -10$. For example, solutions include

$$-10, \quad -200, \quad -11\frac{1}{2}, \quad -\sqrt{130}, \quad \text{and} \quad -50.3$$

Objective C Using the Multiplication Property

An important difference between solving linear equations and solving linear inequalities is shown when we multiply or divide both sides of an inequality by a nonzero real number. For example, start with the true statement $6 < 8$ and multiply both sides by 2. As we see below, the resulting inequality is also true.

$6 < 8$ True

$2(6) < 2(8)$ Multiply both sides by 2.

$12 < 16$ True

Answers

3.

4. $x \ge -5$

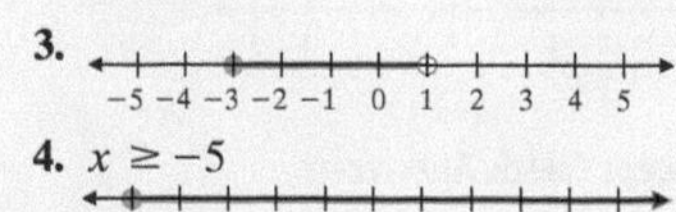

But if we start with the same true statement $6 < 8$ and multiply both sides by -2, the resulting inequality is not a true statement.

$6 < 8$ True
$-2(6) < -2(8)$ Multiply both sides by -2.
$-12 < -16$ False

Notice, however, that if we reverse the direction of the inequality symbol, the resulting inequality is true.

$-12 < -16$ False
$-12 > -16$ True

This demonstrates the multiplication property of inequality.

Multiplication Property of Inequality

1. If a, b, and c are real numbers, and c is **positive**, then

   $a < b$ and $ac < bc$

   are equivalent inequalities.
2. If a, b, and c are real numbers, and c is **negative,** then

   $a < b$ and $ac > bc$

   are equivalent inequalities.

Because division is defined in terms of multiplication, this property also holds true when dividing both sides of an inequality by a nonzero number: If we multiply or divide both sides of an inequality by a negative number, **the direction of the inequality sign must be reversed for the inequalities to remain equivalent.**

✓**Concept Check** Fill in the box with $<, >, \leq,$ or $\geq$.

a. Since $-8 < -4$, then $3(-8) \square 3(-4)$.

b. Since $5 \geq -2$, then $\frac{5}{-7} \square \frac{-2}{-7}$.

c. If $a < b$, then $2a \square 2b$.

d. If $a \geq b$, then $\frac{a}{-3} \square \frac{b}{-3}$.

PRACTICE 5

Solve $-3x \leq 12$. Graph the solutions.

$-5\ -4\ -3\ -2\ -1\ 0\ 1\ 2\ 3\ 4\ 5$

Example 5 Solve $-2x \leq -4$. Graph the solutions.

Solution: Remember to reverse the direction of the inequality symbol when dividing by a negative number.

$$-2x \leq -4$$

$$\frac{-2x}{-2} \geq \frac{-4}{-2} \quad \text{Divide both sides by } -2 \text{ and reverse the inequality sign.}$$

$$x \geq 2 \quad \text{Simplify.}$$

The graph of the solutions is shown.

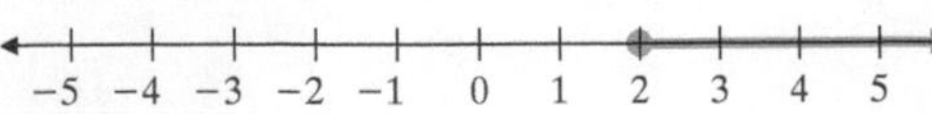

Work Practice 5

Answer

5. $x \geq -4$

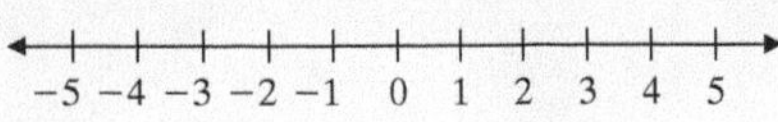

✓ **Concept Check Answer**

a. $<$ b. $\leq$ c. $<$ d. $\leq$

Example 6 Solve $2x < -4$. Graph the solutions.

Solution: $2x < -4$

$\frac{2x}{2} < \frac{-4}{2}$ Divide both sides by 2. Do not reverse the inequality sign.

$x < -2$ Simplify.

The graph of the solutions is shown.

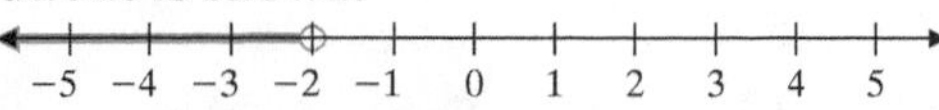

Work Practice 6

PRACTICE 6

Solve $5x > -20$. Graph the solutions.

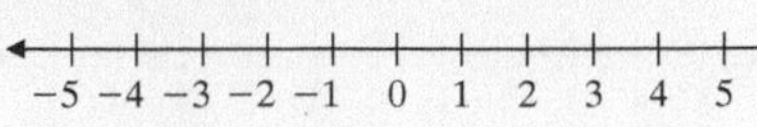

Since we cannot list all solutions to an inequality such as $x < -2$, we will use the set notation $\{x | x < -2\}$. Recall from Section 1.2 that this is read "the set of all x such that x is less than -2." We will use this notation when solving inequalities.

Objective D Using Both Properties of Inequality

The following steps may be helpful when solving inequalities in one variable. Notice that these steps are similar to the ones given in Section 2.3 for solving equations.

To Solve Linear Inequalities in One Variable

Step 1: If an inequality contains fractions, multiply both sides by the LCD to clear the inequality of fractions.

Step 2: Use the distributive property to remove parentheses if they appear.

Step 3: Simplify each side of the inequality by combining like terms.

Step 4: Get all variable terms on one side and all numbers on the other side by using the addition property of inequality.

Step 5: Get the variable alone by using the multiplication property of inequality.

Helpful Hint

Don't forget that if both sides of an inequality are multiplied or divided by a negative number, the direction of the inequality sign must be reversed.

Example 7 Solve $-4x + 7 \geq -9$. Graph the solution set.

Solution: $-4x + 7 \geq -9$

$-4x + 7 - 7 \geq -9 - 7$ Subtract 7 from both sides.

$-4x \geq -16$ Simplify.

$\frac{-4x}{-4} \leq \frac{-16}{-4}$ Divide both sides by -4 and reverse the direction of the inequality sign.

$x \leq 4$ Simplify.

The graph of the solution set $\{x | x \leq 4\}$ is shown.

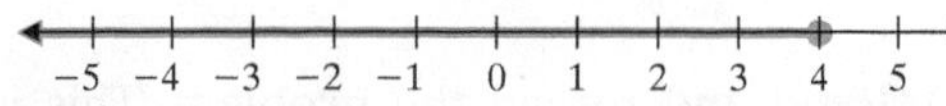

Work Practice 7

PRACTICE 7

Solve $-3x + 11 \leq -13$. Graph the solution set.

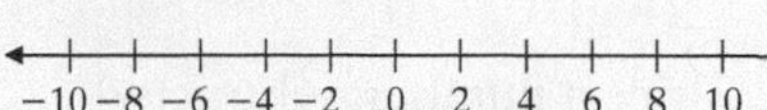

Answers

6. $x > -4$

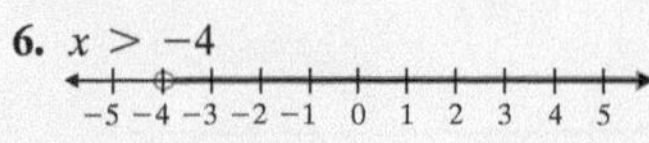

7. $\{x | x \geq 8\}$

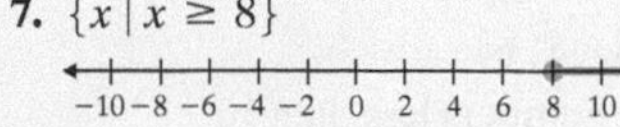

PRACTICE 8

Solve $2x - 3 > 4(x - 1)$. Graph the solution set.

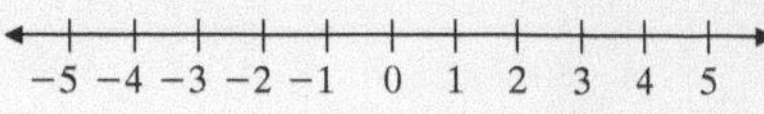

Example 8 Solve $-5x + 7 < 2(x - 3)$. Graph the solution set.

Solution: $-5x + 7 < 2(x - 3)$

$-5x + 7 < 2x - 6$	Apply the distributive property.
$-5x + 7 - 2x < 2x - 6 - 2x$	Subtract $2x$ from both sides.
$-7x + 7 < -6$	Combine like terms.
$-7x + 7 - 7 < -6 - 7$	Subtract 7 from both sides.
$-7x < -13$	Combine like terms.
$\frac{-7x}{-7} > \frac{-13}{-7}$	Divide both sides by -7 and reverse the direction of the inequality sign.
$x > \frac{13}{7}$	Simplify.

The graph of the solution set $\left\{x \middle| x > \frac{13}{7}\right\}$ is shown.

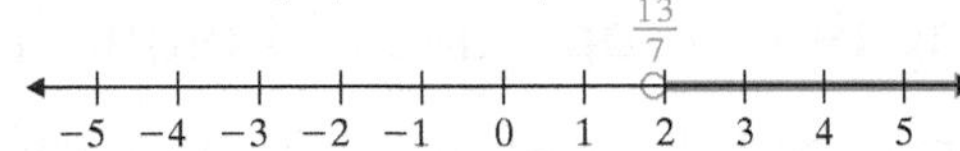

Work Practice 8

PRACTICE 9

Solve: $3(x + 5) - 1 \geq 5(x - 1) + 7$

Example 9 Solve: $2(x - 3) - 5 \leq 3(x + 2) - 18$

Solution: $2(x - 3) - 5 \leq 3(x + 2) - 18$

$2x - 6 - 5 \leq 3x + 6 - 18$	Apply the distributive property.
$2x - 11 \leq 3x - 12$	Combine like terms.
$-x - 11 \leq -12$	Subtract $3x$ from both sides.
$-x \leq -1$	Add 11 to both sides.
$\frac{-x}{-1} \geq \frac{-1}{-1}$	Divide both sides by -1 and reverse the direction of the inequality sign.
$x \geq 1$	Simplify.

The solution set is $\{x | x \geq 1\}$.

Work Practice 9

Objective E Solving Problems Modeled by Inequalities

Problems containing words such as "at least," "at most," "between," "no more than," and "no less than" usually indicate that an inequality should be solved instead of an equation. In solving applications involving linear inequalities, we use the same procedure we used to solve applications involving linear equations.

Some Inequality Translations

≥	≤	<	>
at least	at most	is less than	is greater than
no less than	no more than		

PRACTICE 10

Twice a number, subtracted from 35, is greater than 15. Find all numbers that make this true.

Example 10 12 subtracted from 3 times a number is less than 21. Find all numbers that make this statement true.

Solution:

1. UNDERSTAND. Read and reread the problem. This is a direct translation problem, and let's let

$x =$ the unknown number

Answers

8. $\left\{x \middle| x < \frac{1}{2}\right\}$

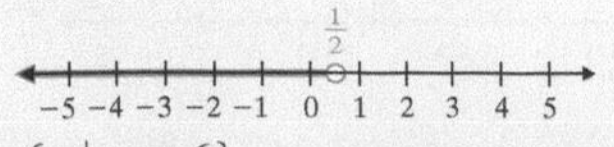

9. $\{x | x \leq 6\}$
10. all numbers less than 10

2. TRANSLATE.

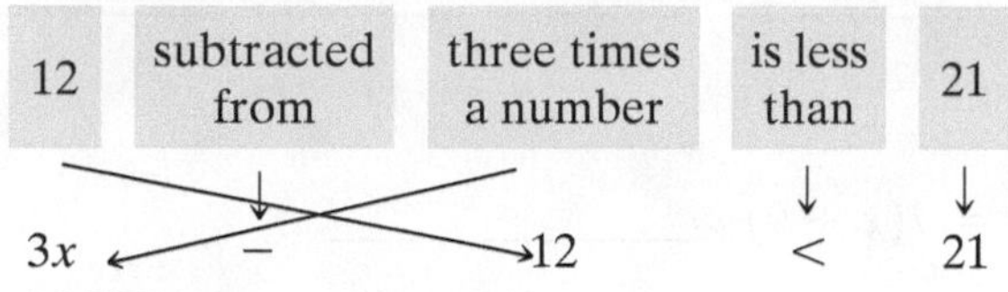

$3x - 12 < 21$

3. SOLVE. $3x - 12 < 21$

$3x < 33$ Add 12 to both sides.

$\frac{3x}{3} < \frac{33}{3}$ Divide both sides by 3 and do not reverse the direction of the inequality sign.

$x < 11$ Simplify.

4. INTERPRET.

Check: Check the translation; then let's choose a number less than 11 to see if it checks. For example, let's check 10. 12 subtracted from 3 times 10 is 12 subtracted from 30, or 18. Since 18 is less than 21, the number 10 checks.

State: All numbers less than 11 make the original statement true.

Work Practice 10

Example 11 Budgeting for a Wedding

Marie Chase and Jonathan Edwards are having their wedding reception at the Gallery reception hall. They may spend at most $1000 for the reception. If the reception hall charges a $100 cleanup fee plus $14 per person, find the greatest number of people that they can invite and still stay within their budget.

Solution:

1. UNDERSTAND. Read and reread the problem. Suppose that 50 people attend the reception. The cost is then $\$100 + \$14(50) = \$100 + \$700 = \$800$.

   Let $x =$ the number of people who attend the reception.

2. TRANSLATE.

cleanup fee	+	cost per person	times	number of people	must be less than or equal to	$1000
↓		↓	↓	↓	↓	↓
100	+	14	·	x	≤	1000

3. SOLVE.

$100 + 14x \le 1000$

$14x \le 900$ Subtract 100 from both sides.

$x \le 64\frac{2}{7}$ Divide both sides by 14.

4. INTERPRET.

Check: Since x represents the number of people, we round down to the nearest whole, or 64. Notice that if 64 people attend, the cost is $\$100 + \$14(64) = \$996$. If 65 people attend, the cost is $\$100 + \$14(65) = \$1010$, which is more than the given $1000.

State: Marie Chase and Jonathan Edwards can invite at most 64 people to the reception.

Work Practice 11

PRACTICE 11

Alex earns $600 per month plus 4% of all his sales. Find the minimum sales that will allow Alex to earn at least $3000 per month.

Answer

11. $60,000

Vocabulary and Readiness Check

Identify each as an equation, expression, or inequality.

1. $6x - 7(x + 9)$ ____________

2. $6x = 7(x + 9)$ ____________

3. $6x < 7(x + 9)$ ____________

4. $5y - 2 \geq -38$ ____________

5. $\frac{9}{7} = \frac{x + 2}{14}$ ____________

6. $\frac{9}{7} - \frac{x + 2}{14}$ ____________

Decide which number listed is not a solution to each given inequality.

7. $x \geq -3$; $-3, 0, -5, \pi$ ____________

8. $x < 6$; $-6, |-6|, 0, -3.2$ ____________

9. $x < 4.01$; $4, -4.01, 4.1, -4.1$ ____________

10. $x \geq -3$; $-4, -3, -2, -(-2)$ ____________

2.7 Exercise Set

FOR EXTRA HELP

MyMathLab

PRACTICE

WATCH

DOWNLOAD

READ

REVIEW

Objective A *Graph each inequality on the number line. See Examples 1 and 2.*

1. $x \leq -1$

−5 −4 −3 −2 −1 0 1 2 3 4 5

2. $y < 0$

−5 −4 −3 −2 −1 0 1 2 3 4 5

3. $x > \frac{1}{2}$

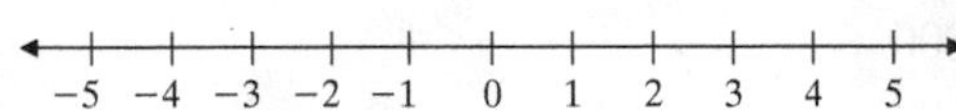

4. $z \geq -\frac{2}{3}$

−5 −4 −3 −2 −1 0 1 2 3 4 5

5. $y < 4$

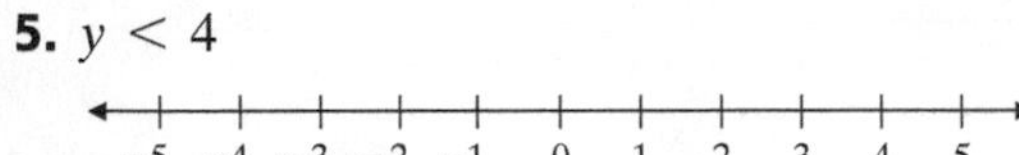

6. $x > 3$

−5 −4 −3 −2 −1 0 1 2 3 4 5

7. $-2 \leq m$

−5 −4 −3 −2 −1 0 1 2 3 4 5

8. $-5 \geq x$

−5 −4 −3 −2 −1 0 1 2 3 4 5

Graph each inequality on the number line. See Example 3.

9. $-1 < x < 3$

−5 −4 −3 −2 −1 0 1 2 3 4 5

10. $-2 \leq x \leq 3$

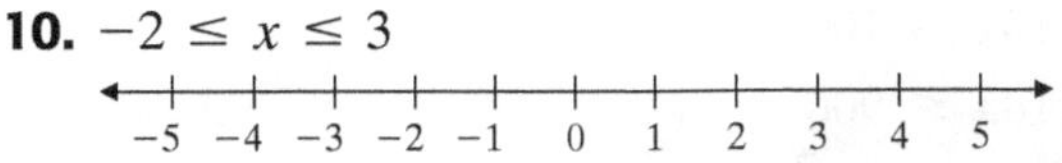

11. $0 \leq y < 2$

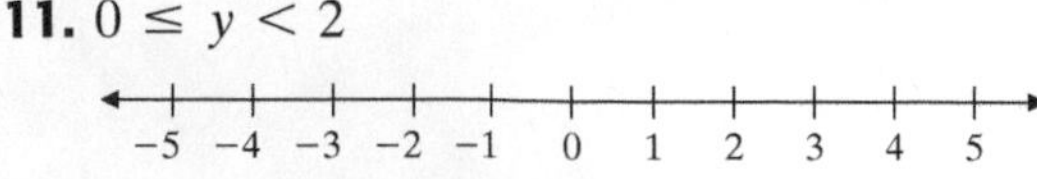

12. $-4 < x \leq 0$

−5 −4 −3 −2 −1 0 1 2 3 4 5

Objective B *Solve each inequality. Graph the solution set. Write each answer using solution set notation. See Example 4.*

13. $x - 2 \geq -7$

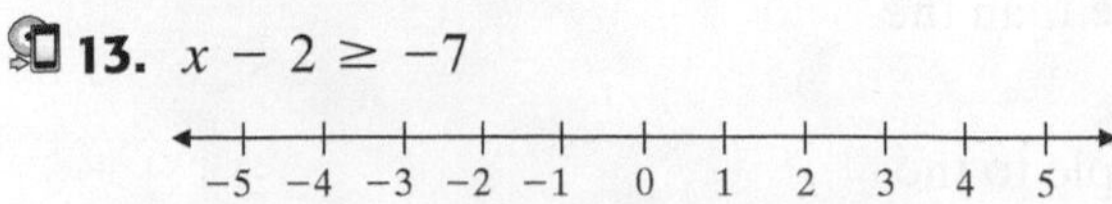

14. $x + 4 \leq 1$

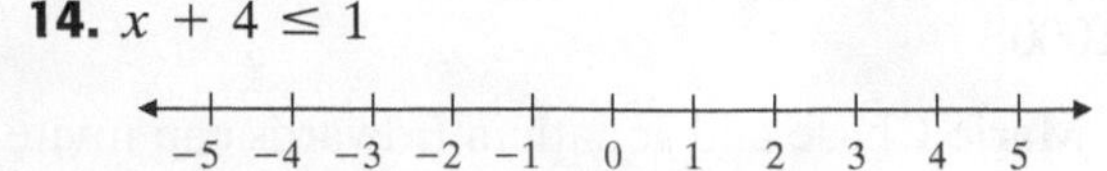

15. $-9 + y < 0$

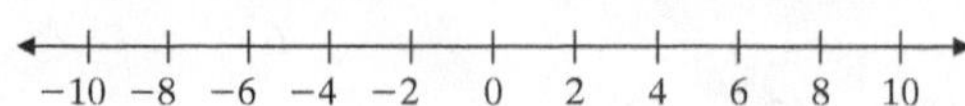

16. $-3 + m > 5$

17. $3x - 5 > 2x - 8$

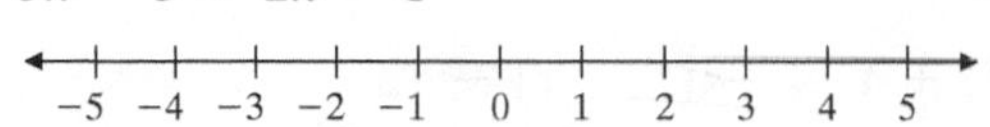

18. $3 - 7x \geq 10 - 8x$

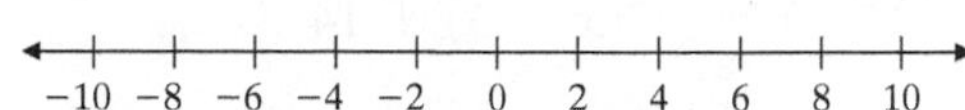

19. $4x - 1 \leq 5x - 2x$

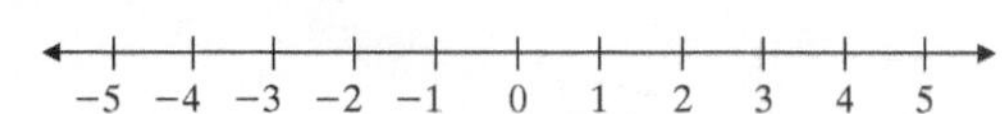

20. $7x + 3 < 9x - 3x$

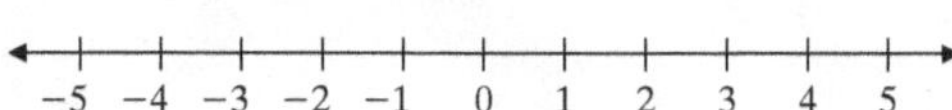

Objective **C** *Solve each inequality. Graph the solution set. See Examples 5 and 6.*

21. $2x < -6$

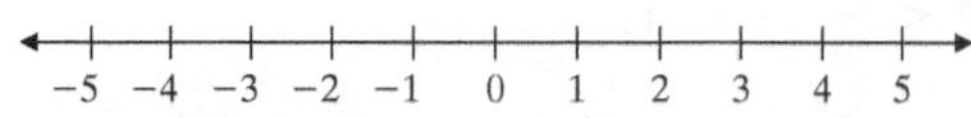

22. $3x > -9$

23. $-8x \leq 16$

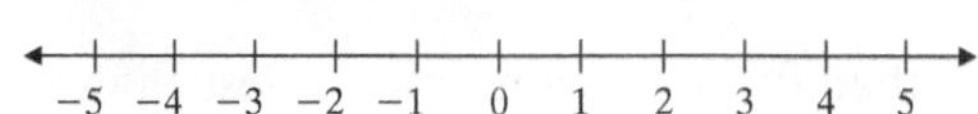

24. $-5x < 20$

25. $-x > 0$

26. $-y \geq 0$

27. $\frac{3}{4}y \geq -2$

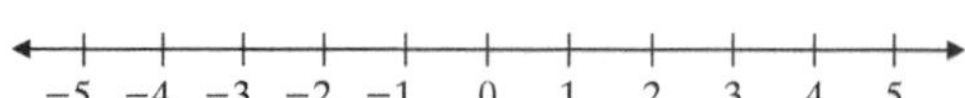

28. $\frac{5}{6}x \leq -8$

29. $-0.6y < -1.8$

30. $-0.3x > -2.4$

Objectives **B** **C** **D** **Mixed Practice** *Solve each inequality. Write each answer using solution set notation. See Examples 4 through 9.*

31. $-8 < x + 7$

32. $-11 > x + 4$

33. $7(x + 1) - 6x \geq -4$

34. $10(x + 2) - 9x \leq -1$

35. $4x > 1$

36. $6x < 5$

37. $-\frac{2}{3}y \leq 8$

38. $-\frac{3}{4}y \geq 9$

39. $4(2z + 1) < 4$

40. $6(2 - z) \geq 12$

41. $3x - 7 < 6x + 2$

42. $2x - 1 \geq 4x - 5$

43. $5x - 7x \leq x + 2$

44. $4 - x < 8x + 2x$

45. $-6x + 2 \geq 2(5 - x)$

46. $-7x + 4 > 3(4 - x)$

47. $3(x - 5) < 2(2x - 1)$

48. $5(x - 2) \leq 3(2x - 1)$

49. $4(3x - 1) \leq 5(2x - 4)$

50. $3(5x - 4) \leq 4(3x - 2)$

51. $3(x + 2) - 6 > -2(x - 3) + 14$

52. $7(x - 2) + x \leq -4(5 - x) - 12$

53. $-5(1 - x) + x \leq -(6 - 2x) + 6$

54. $-2(x - 4) - 3x < -(4x + 1) + 2x$

55. $\frac{1}{4}(x + 4) < \frac{1}{5}(2x + 3)$

56. $\frac{1}{2}(x - 5) < \frac{1}{3}(2x - 1)$

57. $-5x + 4 \leq -4(x - 1)$

58. $-6x + 2 < -3(x + 4)$

Objective **E** *Solve the following. For Exercises 61 and 62, the solutions have been started for you. See Examples 10 and 11.*

59. Six more than twice a number is greater than negative fourteen. Find all numbers that make this statement true.

60. One more than five times a number is less than or equal to ten. Find all such numbers.

61. The perimeter of a rectangle is to be no greater than 100 centimeters and the width must be 15 centimeters. Find the maximum length of the rectangle.

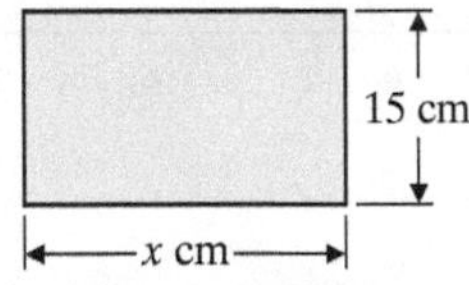

Start the solution:

1. UNDERSTAND the problem. Reread it as many times as needed.
2. TRANSLATE into an equation. (Fill in the blanks below.)

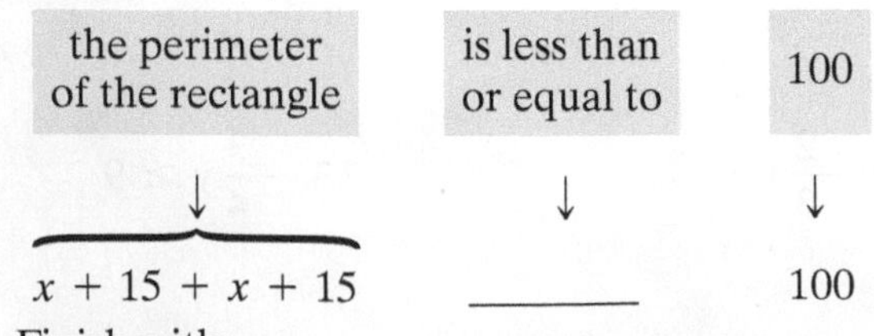

Finish with:

3. SOLVE and 4. INTERPRET

62. One side of a triangle is three times as long as another side, and the third side is 12 inches long. If the perimeter can be no longer than 32 inches, find the maximum lengths of the other two sides.

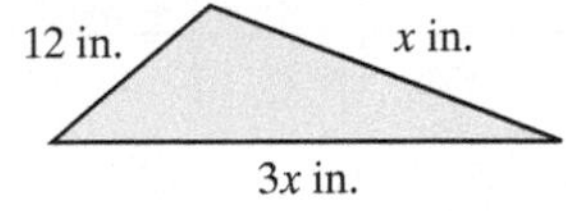

Start the solution:

1. UNDERSTAND the problem. Reread it as many times as needed.
2. TRANSLATE into an equation. (Fill in the blanks below.)

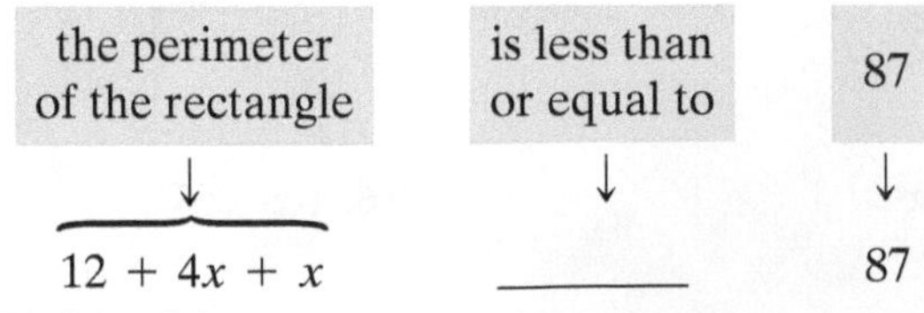

Finish with:

3. SOLVE and 4. INTERPRET

63. Ben Holladay bowled 146 and 201 in his first two games. What must he bowl in his third game to have an average of at least 180? (*Hint:* The average of a list of numbers is their sum divided by the number of numbers in the list.)

64. On an NBA team the two forwards measure 6′8″ and 6′6″ tall and the two guards measure 6′0″ and 5′9″ tall. How tall should the center be if they wish to have a starting team average height of at least 6′5″?

65. Dennis and Nancy Wood are celebrating their 30th wedding anniversary by having a reception at Tiffany Oaks reception hall. They have budgeted \$3000 for their reception. If the reception hall charges a \$50.00 cleanup fee plus \$34 per person, find the greatest number of people that they may invite and still stay within their budget.

66. A surprise retirement party is being planned for Pratap Puri. A total of \$860 has been collected for the event, which is to be held at a local reception hall. This reception hall charges a cleanup fee of \$40 and \$15 per person for drinks and light snacks. Find the greatest number of people that may be invited and still stay within the \$860 budget.

67. A 150-pound person uses 5.8 calories per minute when walking at a speed of 4 mph. How long must a person walk at this speed to use at least 200 calories? Round up to the nearest minute. (*Source:* Home & Garden Bulletin No. 72)

68. A 170-pound person uses 5.3 calories per minute when bicycling at a speed of 5.5 mph. How long must a person ride a bike at this speed in order to use at least 200 calories? Round up to the nearest minute. (*Source:* Same as Exercise 67)

Review

Evaluate each expression. See Section 1.3.

69. 3^4 **70.** 4^3 **71.** 1^8 **72.** 0^7 **73.** $\left(\frac{7}{8}\right)^2$ **74.** $\left(\frac{2}{3}\right)^3$

The graph shows the number of U.S. Starbucks locations from 2002 to 2008. The height of the graph for each year shown corresponds to the number of Starbucks locations in the United States. Use this graph to answer Exercises 75 through 80. (We study graphs such as this further in Section 6.1.)

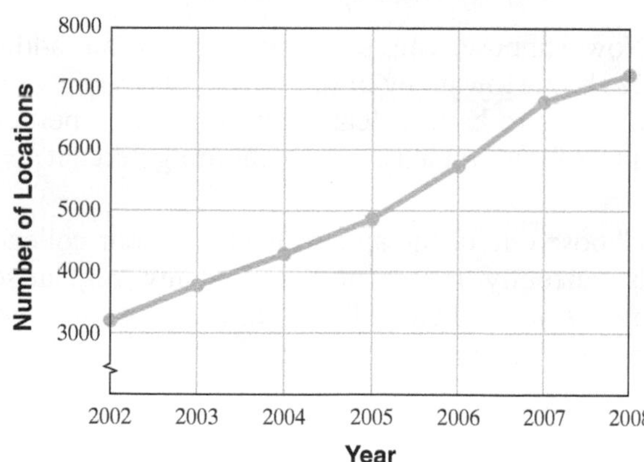

75. How many Starbucks locations were there in 2002?

76. How many Starbucks locations were there in 2007?

77. Between which two years did the greatest increase in the number of Starbucks locations occur?

78. In what year were there approximately 4900 Starbucks locations?

79. During which year did the number of Starbucks locations rise above 5000?

80. During which year did the number of Starbucks locations rise above 6000?

Concept Extensions

Fill in the box with $<$, $>$, $\leq$, or $\geq$. See the Concept Check in this section.

81. Since $3 < 5$, then $3(-4) \square 5(-4)$.

82. If $m \leq n$, then $2m \square 2n$.

83. If $m \leq n$, then $-2m \square -2n$.

84. If $-x < y$, then $x \square -y$.

85. When solving an inequality, when must you reverse the direction of the inequality symbol?

86. If both sides of the inequality $-3x < -30$ are divided by 3, do you reverse the direction of the inequality symbol? Why or why not?

Solve.

87. Eric Daly has scores of 75, 83, and 85 on his history tests. Use an inequality to find the scores he can make on his final exam to receive a B in the class. The final exam counts as **two** tests, and a B is received if the final course average is greater than or equal to 80.

88. Maria Lipco has scores of 85, 95, and 92 on her algebra tests. Use an inequality to find the scores she can make on her final exam to receive an A in the course. The final exam counts as **three** tests, and an A is received if the final course average is greater than or equal to 90. Round to one decimal place.

Chapter 2 Group Activity

Investigating Averages

Sections 2.1–2.6

Materials:

- small rubber ball or crumpled paper ball
- bucket or waste can

This activity may be completed by working in groups or individually.

1. Try shooting the ball into the bucket or waste can 5 times. Record your results below.

Shots Made	Shots Missed

2. Find your shooting percent for the 5 shots (that is, the percent of the shots you actually made out of the number you tried).

3. Suppose you are going to try an additional 5 shots. How many of the next 5 shots will you have to make to have a 50% shooting percent for all 10 shots? An 80% shooting percent?

4. Did you solve an equation in Question 3? If so, explain what you did. If not, explain how you could use an equation to find the answers.

5. Now suppose you are going to try an additional 22 shots. How many of the next 22 shots will you have to make to have at least a 50% shooting percent for all 27 shots? At least a 70% shooting percent?

6. Choose one of the sports played at your college that is currently in season. How many regular-season games are scheduled? What is the team's current percent of games won?

7. Suppose the team has a goal of finishing the season with a winning percent better than 110% of their current wins. At least how many of the remaining games must they win to achieve their goal?

Chapter 2 Vocabulary Check

Fill in each blank with one of the words or phrases listed below.

no solution	all real numbers	linear equation in one variable
equivalent equations	formula	reversed
linear inequality in one variable	the same	

1. A(n) ______________ can be written in the form $ax + b = c$.
2. Equations that have the same solution are called ______________.
3. An equation that describes a known relationship among quantities is called a(n) ______________.
4. A(n) ______________ can be written in the form $ax + b < c$, (or $>, \leq, \geq$).
5. The solution(s) to the equation $x + 5 = x + 5$ is/are ______________.
6. The solution(s) to the equation $x + 5 = x + 4$ is/are ______________.
7. If both sides of an inequality are multiplied or divided by the same positive number, the direction of the inequality symbol is ______________.
8. If both sides of an inequality are multiplied by the same negative number, the direction of the inequality symbol is ______________.

Helpful Hint Are you preparing for your test? Don't forget to take the Chapter 2 Test on page 183. Then check your answers at the back of the text and use the Chapter Test Prep Videos to see the fully worked-out solutions to any of the exercises you want to review.

2 Chapter Highlights

Definitions and Concepts	Examples
Section 2.1 The Addition Property of Equality	
A **linear equation in one variable** can be written in the form $Ax + B = C$ where A, B, and C are real numbers and $A \neq 0$.	$-3x + 7 = 2$ $3(x - 1) = -8(x + 5) + 4$
Equivalent equations are equations that have the same solution.	$x - 7 = 10$ and $x = 17$ are equivalent equations.
ADDITION PROPERTY OF EQUALITY Adding the same number to or subtracting the same number from both sides of an equation does not change its solution.	$y + 9 = 3$ $y + 9 - 9 = 3 - 9$ $y = -6$
Section 2.2 The Multiplication Property of Equality	
MULTIPLICATION PROPERTY OF EQUALITY Multiplying both sides or dividing both sides of an equation by the same nonzero number does not change its solution.	$\frac{2}{3}a = 18$ $\frac{3}{2}\left(\frac{2}{3}a\right) = \frac{3}{2}(18)$ $a = 27$

Definitions and Concepts	Examples
Section 2.3 Further Solving Linear Equations	
To Solve Linear Equations	Solve: $\frac{5(-2x+9)}{6} + 3 = \frac{1}{2}$
1. Clear the equation of fractions.	**1.** $6 \cdot \frac{5(-2x+9)}{6} + 6 \cdot 3 = 6 \cdot \frac{1}{2}$
2. Remove any grouping symbols such as parentheses.	**2.** $5(-2x+9) + 18 = 3$ Apply the distributive property. $-10x + 45 + 18 = 3$
3. Simplify each side by combining like terms.	**3.** $-10x + 63 = 3$ Combine like terms.
4. Get all variable terms on one side and all numbers on the other side by using the addition property of equality.	**4.** $-10x + 63 - 63 = 3 - 63$ Subtract 63. $-10x = -60$
5. Get the variable alone by using the multiplication property of equality.	**5.** $\frac{-10x}{-10} = \frac{-60}{-10}$ Divide by -10. $x = 6$
6. Check the solution by substituting it into the original equation.	
Section 2.4 An Introduction to Problem Solving	
Problem-Solving Steps	The height of the Hudson volcano in Chile is twice the height of the Kiska volcano in the Aleutian Islands. If the sum of their heights is 12,870 feet, find the height of each.
1. UNDERSTAND the problem.	**1.** Read and reread the problem. Guess a solution and check your guess. Let x be the height of the Kiska volcano. Then $2x$ is the height of the Hudson volcano. 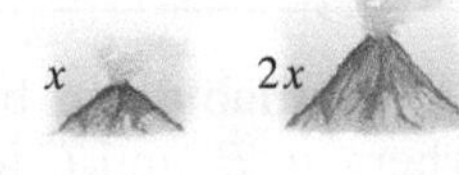
2. TRANSLATE the problem.	**2.** height of Kiska ↓ x · added to ↓ $+$ · height of Hudson ↓ $2x$ · is ↓ $=$ · 12,870 ↓ 12,870
3. SOLVE the equation.	**3.** $x + 2x = 12{,}870$ $3x = 12{,}870$ $x = 4290$
4. INTERPRET the results.	**4.** *Check:* If x is 4290, then $2x$ is 2(4290) or 8580. Their sum is 4290 + 8580 or 12,870, the required amount. *State:* The Kiska volcano is 4290 feet tall, and the Hudson volcano is 8580 feet tall.

Definitions and Concepts	Examples

Section 2.5 Formulas and Problem Solving

An equation that describes a known relationship among quantities is called a **formula.**

$A = lw$ (area of a rectangle)
$I = PRT$ (simple interest)

To solve a formula for a specified variable, use the same steps as for solving a linear equation. Treat the specified variable as the only variable of the equation.

Solve: $P = 2l + 2w$ for l.

$$P = 2l + 2w$$
$$P - 2w = 2l + 2w - 2w \quad \text{Subtract } 2w.$$
$$P - 2w = 2l$$
$$\frac{P - 2w}{2} = \frac{2l}{2} \quad \text{Divide by 2.}$$
$$\frac{P - 2w}{2} = l$$

Section 2.6 Percent and Mixture Problem Solving

Use the same problem-solving steps to solve a problem containing percents.

32% of what number is 36.8?

1. UNDERSTAND.

1. Read and reread. Propose a solution and check. Let $x =$ the unknown number.

2. TRANSLATE.

2.

32%	of	what number	is	36.8
↓	↓	↓	↓	↓
32%	·	x	=	36.8

3. SOLVE.

3. *Solve:*
$$32\% \cdot x = 36.8$$
$$0.32x = 36.8$$
$$\frac{0.32x}{0.32} = \frac{36.8}{0.32} \quad \text{Divide by 0.32.}$$
$$x = 115 \quad \text{Simplify.}$$

4. INTERPRET.

4. *Check, then state:* 32% of 115 is 36.8.

How many liters of a 20% acid solution must be mixed with a 50% acid solution in order to obtain 12 liters of a 30% solution?

1. UNDERSTAND.

1. Read and reread. Guess a solution and check. Let $x =$ number of liters of 20% solution. Then $12 - x =$ number of liters of 50% solution.

2. TRANSLATE.

2.

	No. of Liters ·	Acid Strength =	Amount of Acid
20% Solution	x	20%	$0.20x$
50% Solution	$12 - x$	50%	$0.50(12 - x)$
30% Solution Needed	12	30%	$0.30(12)$

In words:	acid in 20% solution	+	acid in 50% solution	=	acid in 30% solution
Translate:	$0.20x$	+	$0.50(12 - x)$	=	$0.30(12)$

(continued)

Definitions and Concepts	Examples
Section 2.6 Percent and Mixture Problem Solving (*continued*)	
3. SOLVE.	**3.** *Solve:* $0.20x + 0.50(12 - x) = 0.30(12)$ $0.20x + 6 - 0.50x = 3.6$ Apply the distributive property. $-0.30x + 6 = 3.6$ Combine like terms. $-0.30x = -2.4$ Subtract 6. $x = 8$ Divide by -0.30.
4. INTERPRET.	**4.** *Check, then state:* If 8 liters of a 20% acid solution are mixed with $12 - 8$ or 4 liters of a 50% acid solution, the result is 12 liters of a 30% solution.
Section 2.7 Linear Inequalities and Problem Solving	
Properties of inequalities are similar to properties of equations. However, if you multiply or divide both sides of an inequality by the same *negative* number, you must reverse the direction of the inequality symbol.	$-2x \le 4$ $\frac{-2x}{-2} \ge \frac{4}{-2}$ Divide by -2; reverse the inequality symbol. $x \ge -2$ 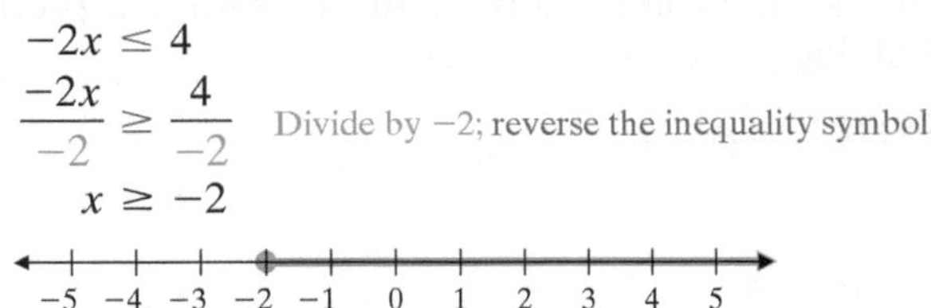
To Solve Linear Inequalities **1.** Clear the inequality of fractions. **2.** Remove grouping symbols. **3.** Simplify each side by combining like terms. **4.** Write all variable terms on one side and all numbers on the other side using the addition property of inequality. **5.** Get the variable alone by using the multiplication property of inequality.	*Solve:* $3(x + 2) \le -2 + 8$ **1.** $3(x + 2) \le -2 + 8$ No fractions to clear. **2.** $3x + 6 \le -2 + 8$ Apply the distributive property. **3.** $3x + 6 \le 6$ Combine like terms. **4.** $3x + 6 - 6 \le 6 - 6$ Subtract 6. $3x \le 0$ **5.** $\frac{3x}{3} \le \frac{0}{3}$ Divide by 3. $x \le 0$ The solution set is $\{x \mid x \le 0\}$. 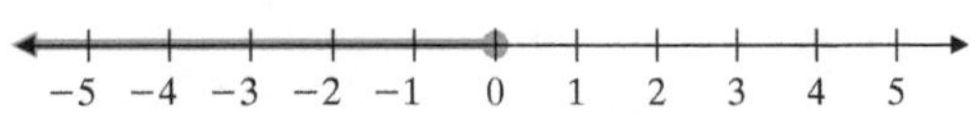

Chapter 2 Review

(2.1) *Solve each equation.*

1. $8x + 4 = 9x$

2. $5y - 3 = 6y$

3. $\frac{2}{7}x + \frac{5}{7}x = 6$

4. $3x - 5 = 4x + 1$

5. $2x - 6 = x - 6$

6. $4(x + 3) = 3(1 + x)$

7. $6(3 + n) = 5(n - 1)$

8. $5(2 + x) - 3(3x + 2) = -5(x - 6) + 2$

Choose the correct algebraic expression.

9. The sum of two numbers is 10. If one number is x, express the other number in terms of x.

a. $x - 10$
b. $10 - x$
c. $10 + x$
d. $10x$

10. Mandy is 5 inches taller than Melissa. If x inches represents the height of Mandy, express Melissa's height in terms of x.

a. $x - 5$
b. $5 - x$
c. $5 + x$
d. $5x$

△ **11.** If one angle measures $x°$, express the measure of its complement in terms of x.

a. $(180 - x)°$
b. $(90 - x)°$
c. $(x - 180)°$
d. $(x - 90)°$

△ **12.** If one angle measures $(x + 5)°$, express the measure of its supplement in terms of x.

a. $(185 + x)°$
b. $(95 + x)°$
c. $(175 - x)°$
d. $(x - 170)°$

$(x + 5)°$?

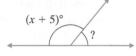

(2.2) *Solve each equation.*

13. $\frac{3}{4}x = -9$

14. $\frac{x}{6} = \frac{2}{3}$

15. $-5x = 0$

16. $-y = 7$

17. $0.2x = 0.15$

18. $\frac{-x}{3} = 1$

19. $-3x + 1 = 19$

20. $5x + 25 = 20$

21. $7(x - 1) + 9 = 5x$

22. $7x - 6 = 5x - 3$

23. $-5x + \frac{3}{7} = \frac{10}{7}$

24. $5x + x = 9 + 4x - 1 + 6$

25. Write the sum of three consecutive integers as an expression in x. Let x be the first integer.

26. Write the sum of the first and fourth of four consecutive even integers. Let x be the first even integer.

(2.3) *Solve each equation.*

27. $\frac{5}{3}x + 4 = \frac{2}{3}x$

28. $\frac{7}{8}x + 1 = \frac{5}{8}x$

29. $-(5x + 1) = -7x + 3$

30. $-4(2x + 1) = -5x + 5$

31. $-6(2x - 5) = -3(9 + 4x)$

32. $3(8y - 1) = 6(5 + 4y)$

33. $\frac{3(2 - z)}{5} = z$

34. $\frac{4(n + 2)}{5} = -n$

35. $0.5(2n - 3) - 0.1 = 0.4(6 + 2n)$

36. $-9 - 5a = 3(6a - 1)$

37. $\frac{5(c + 1)}{6} = 2c - 3$

38. $\frac{2(8 - a)}{3} = 4 - 4a$

39. $200(70x - 3560) = -179(150x - 19{,}300)$

40. $1.72y - 0.04y = 0.42$

(2.4) *Solve each of the following.*

41. The height of the Washington Monument is 50.5 inches more than 10 times the length of a side of its square base. If the sum of these two dimensions is 7327 inches, find the height of the Washington Monument. (*Source:* National Park Service)

42. A 12-foot board is to be divided into two pieces so that one piece is twice as long as the other. If x represents the length of the shorter piece, find the length of each piece.

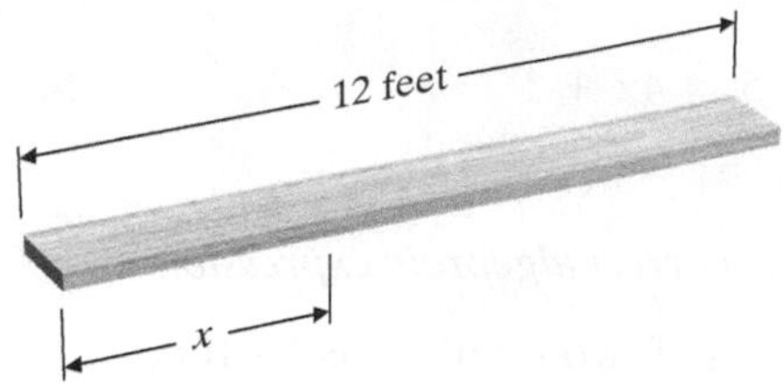

43. The Harvard University library system and the Cornell University library system consist of a total of 119 different library sites. The number of Harvard libraries is two more than twice the number of Cornell libraries. How many libraries does each university support? (*Source*: Harvard University, Cornell University)

44. Find three consecutive integers whose sum is -114.

45. The quotient of a number and 3 is the same as the difference of the number and two. Find the number.

46. Double the sum of a number and 6 is the opposite of the number. Find the number.

(2.5) *Substitute the given values into the given formulas and solve for the unknown variable.*

47. $P = 2l + 2w$; $P = 46, l = 14$

48. $V = lwh$; $V = 192, l = 8, w = 6$

Solve each equation for the indicated variable or constant.

49. $y = mx + b$ for m

50. $r = vst - 5$ for s

51. $2y - 5x = 7$ for x

52. $3x - 6y = -2$ for y

△ **53.** $C = \pi D$ for π

△ **54.** $C = 2\pi r$ for π

△ **55.** A swimming pool holds 900 cubic meters of water. If its length is 20 meters and its height is 3 meters, find its width.

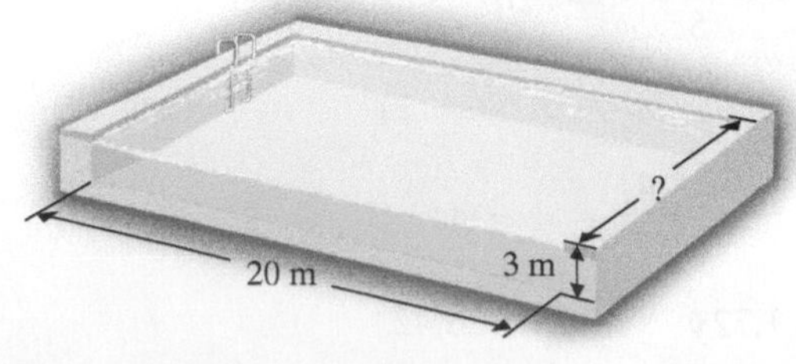

56. The perimeter of a rectangular billboard is 60 feet and the billboard has a length 6 feet longer than its width. Find the dimensions of the billboard.

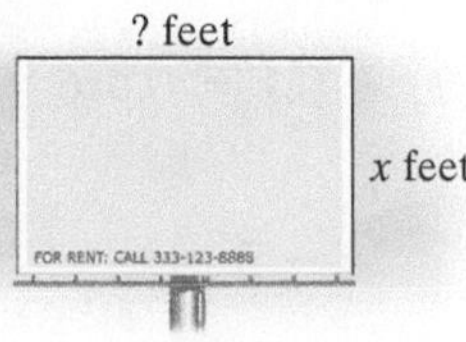

57. A charity 10K race is given annually to benefit a local hospice organization. How long will it take to run/walk a 10K race (10 kilometers or 10,000 meters) if your average pace is 125 **meters** per minute? Give your time in hours and minutes.

58. On April 28, 2001, the highest temperature recorded in the United States was 104°F, which occurred in Death Valley, California. Convert this temperature to degrees Celsius. (*Source:* National Weather Service)

(2.6) *Find each of the following.*

59. The number 9 is what percent of 45?

60. The number 59.5 is what percent of 85?

61. The number 137.5 is 125% of what number?

62. The number 768 is 60% of what number?

63. The price of a small diamond ring was recently increased by 11%. If the ring originally cost $1900, find the mark-up and the new price of the ring.

64. A recent survey found that 66.9% of Americans use the Internet. If a city has a population of 76,000 how many people in that city would you expect to use the Internet? (*Source:* UCLA Center for Communication Policy)

65. Thirty gallons of a 20% acid solution are needed for an experiment. Only 40% and 10% acid solutions are available. How much of each should be mixed to form the needed solution?

66. The ACT Assessment is a college entrance exam taken by about 60% of college-bound students. The national average was 20.7 in 1993 and rose to 21.1 in 2008. Find the percent increase. (Round to the nearest tenth of a percent.)

The graph below shows the percent(s) of cell phone users who have engaged in various behaviors while driving and talking on their cell phones. Use this graph to answer Exercises 67 through 70.

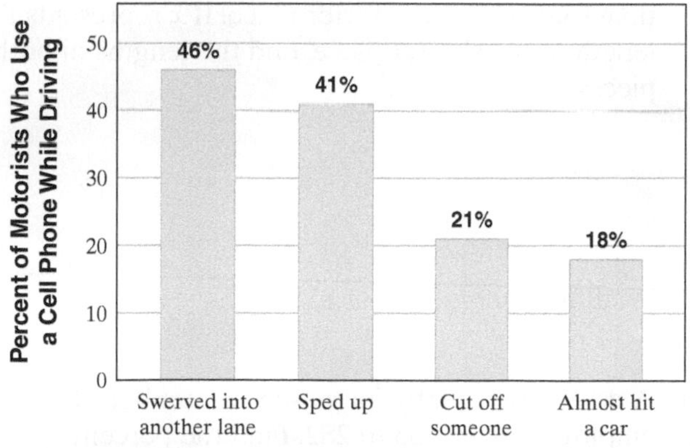

Source: Progressive Insurance

67. What percent of motorists who use a cell phone while driving have almost hit another car?

68. What is the most common effect of cell phone use on driving?

69. If a cell phone service has an estimated 4600 customers who use their cell phones while driving, how many of these customers would you expect to have cut someone off while driving and talking on their cell phones?

70. Do the percents in the graph to the left have a sum of 100%? Why or why not?

(2.7) *Graph on a number line.*

71. $x \leq -2$

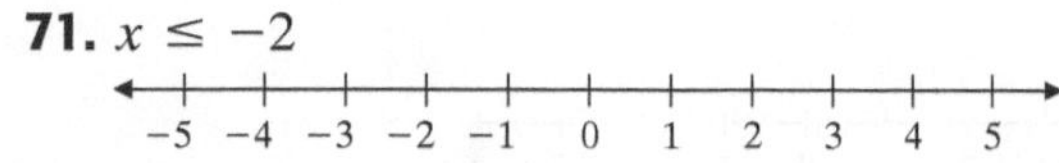

72. $0 < x \leq 5$

−5 −4 −3 −2 −1 0 1 2 3 4 5

Solve each inequality.

73. $x - 5 \leq -4$

74. $x + 7 > 2$

75. $-2x \geq -20$

76. $-3x > 12$

77. $5x - 7 > 8x + 5$

78. $x + 4 \geq 6x - 16$

79. $\frac{2}{3}y > 6$

80. $-0.5y \leq 7.5$

81. $-2(x - 5) > 2(3x - 2)$

82. $4(2x - 5) \leq 5x - 1$

83. Carol Abolafia earns \$175 per week plus a 5% commission on all her sales. Find the minimum amount of sales she must make to ensure that she earns at least \$300 per week.

84. Joseph Barrow shot rounds of 76, 82, and 79 golfing. What must he shoot on his next round so that his average will be below 80?

Mixed Review

Solve each equation.

85. $6x + 2x - 1 = 5x + 11$

86. $2(3y - 4) = 6 + 7y$

87. $4(3 - a) - (6a + 9) = -12a$

88. $\frac{x}{3} - 2 = 5$

89. $2(y + 5) = 2y + 10$

90. $7x - 3x + 2 = 2(2x - 1)$

Solve.

91. The sum of six and twice a number is equal to seven less than the number. Find the number.

92. A 23-inch piece of string is to be cut into two pieces so that the length of the longer piece is three more than four times the shorter piece. If x represents the length of the shorter piece, find the lengths of both pieces.

Solve for the specified variable.

93. $V = \frac{1}{3}Ah$ for h

94. What number is 26% of 85?

95. The number 72 is 45% of what number?

96. A company recently increased its number of employees from 235 to 282. Find the percent increase.

Solve each inequality. Graph the solution set.

97. $4x - 7 > 3x + 2$

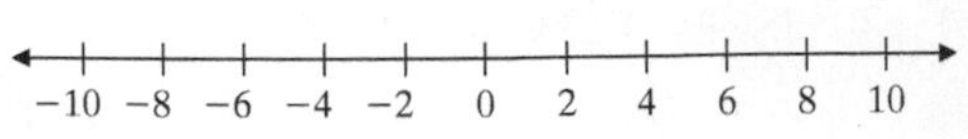

98. $-5x < 20$

−5 −4 −3 −2 −1 0 1 2 3 4 5

99. $-3(1 + 2x) + x \geq -(3 - x)$

−5 −4 −3 −2 −1 0 1 2 3 4 5

Chapter 2 Test

Step-by-step test solutions are found on the Chapter Test Prep Videos available via the Interactive DVD Lecture Series, in MyMathLab or on YouTube (search "MartinGayIntroAlg" and click on "Channels").

Solve each equation.

1. $-\frac{4}{5}x = 4$

2. $4(n - 5) = -(4 - 2n)$

3. $5y - 7 + y = -(y + 3y)$

4. $4z + 1 - z = 1 + z$

5. $\frac{2(x + 6)}{3} = x - 5$

6. $\frac{4(y - 1)}{5} = 2y + 3$

7. $\frac{1}{2} - x + \frac{3}{2} = x - 4$

8. $\frac{1}{3}(y + 3) = 4y$

9. $-0.3(x - 4) + x = 0.5(3 - x)$

10. $-4(a + 1) - 3a = -7(2a - 3)$

11. $-2(x - 3) = x + 5 - 3x$

Solve each application.

12. A number increased by two-thirds of the number is 35. Find the number.

△ **13.** A gallon of water seal covers 200 square feet. How many gallons are needed to paint two coats of water seal on a deck that measures 20 feet by 35 feet?

14. Find the value of x if $y = -14$, $m = -2$, and $b = -2$ in the formula $y = mx + b$.

Solve each equation for the indicated variable.

15. $V = \pi r^2 h$ for h

16. $3x - 4y = 10$ for y

Answers

1. ______
2. ______
3. ______
4. ______
5. ______
6. ______
7. ______
8. ______
9. ______
10. ______
11. ______
12. ______
13. ______
14. ______
15. ______
16. ______

17. ______

18. ______

19. ______

20. ______

21. ______

22. ______

23. ______

24. ______

25. ______

Solve each inequality. Graph the solution set.

17. $3x - 5 \geq 7x + 3$

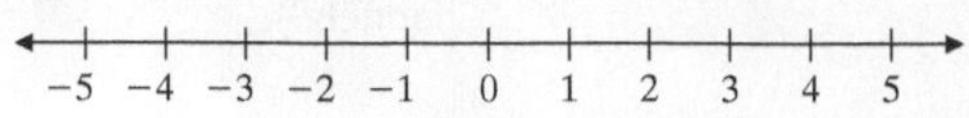

18. $x + 6 > 4x - 6$

−5 −4 −3 −2 −1 0 1 2 3 4 5

Solve each inequality.

19. $-0.3x \geq 2.4$

20. $-5(x - 1) + 6 \leq -3(x + 4) + 1$

21. $\frac{2(5x + 1)}{3} > 2$

The following graph shows the breakdown of tornadoes occurring in the United States by strength. The corresponding Fujita Tornado Scale categories are shown in parentheses. Use this graph to answer Exercise 22.

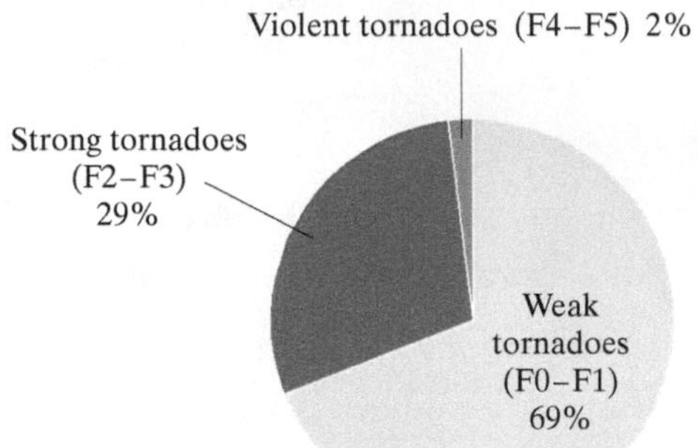

Source: National Climatic Data Center

22. According to the National Climatic Data Center, in an average year, about 800 tornadoes are reported in the United States. How many of these would you expect to be classified as "weak" tornadoes?

23. The number 72 is what percent of 180?

24. Some states have a single area code for the entire state. Two such states have area codes where one is double the other. If the sum of these integers is 1203, find the two area codes.

25. New York State has more public libraries than any other state. It has 696 more public libraries than Georgia does. If the total number of public libraries for these states is 812, find the number of public libraries in New York and the number in Georgia. (*Source: The World Almanac and Book of Facts*)

Cumulative Review Chapters 1–2

Determine whether each statement is true or false.

1. $8 \geq 8$

2. $-4 < -6$

3. $8 \leq 8$

4. $3 > -3$

5. $23 \leq 0$

6. $-8 \geq -8$

7. $0 \leq 23$

8. $-8 \leq -8$

9. Insert <, >, or = in the appropriate space to make each statement true.

a. $|0| \quad 2$

b. $|-5| \quad 5$

c. $|-3| \quad |-2|$

d. $|-9| \quad |-9.7|$

e. $\left|-7\frac{1}{6}\right| \quad |7|$

10. Find the absolute value of each number.

a. $|5|$

b. $|-8|$

c. $\left|-\frac{2}{3}\right|$

Simplify.

11. $\dfrac{3 + |4 - 3| + 2^2}{6 - 3}$

12. $1 + 2(9 - 7)^3 + 4^2$

Add without using number lines.

13. $(-8) + (-11)$

14. $-2 + (-8)$

15. $(-2) + 10$

16. $-10 + 20$

17. $0.2 + (-0.5)$

18. $1.2 + (-1.2)$

Answers

1. ______
2. ______
3. ______
4. ______
5. ______
6. ______
7. ______
8. ______
9. a. ______
b. ______
c. ______
d. ______
e. ______
10. a. ______
b. ______
c. ______
11. ______
12. ______
13. ______
14. ______
15. ______
16. ______
17. ______
18. ______

19. a. ______
b. ______
20. a. ______
b. ______
c. ______
d. ______
21. a. ______
b. ______
c. ______
22. a. ______
b. ______
c. ______
23. a. ______
b. ______
c. ______
24. a. ______
b. ______
25. ______
26. ______
27. ______
28. ______
29. a. ______
b. ______
c. ______
d. ______
e. ______

19. Simplify each expression.

a. $-3 + [(-2 - 5) - 2]$

b. $2^3 - 10 + [-6 - (-5)]$

20. Simplify each expression.

a. $-(-5)$

b. $-\left(-\frac{2}{3}\right)$

c. $-(-a)$

d. $-|-3|$

21. Multiply.

a. $7(0)(-6)$

b. $(-2)(-3)(-4)$

c. $(-1)(-5)(-9)(-2)$

22. Subtract.

a. $-2.7 - 8.4$

b. $-\frac{4}{5} - \left(-\frac{3}{5}\right)$

c. $\frac{1}{4} - \left(-\frac{1}{2}\right)$

23. Use the definition of the quotient of two numbers to find each quotient.

a. $-18 \div 3$

b. $\frac{-14}{-2}$

c. $\frac{20}{-4}$

24. Find each product.

a. $(4.5)(-0.08)$

b. $-\frac{3}{4} \cdot -\frac{8}{17}$

Use the distributive property to write each expression without parentheses. Then simplify the result.

25. $-5(-3 + 2z)$

26. $2(x^2 - 3x + 4)$

27. $\frac{1}{2}(6x + 14) + 10$

28. $-(x + 4) + 3(x + 4)$

29. Determine whether the terms are like or unlike.

a. $2x, 3x^2$

b. $4x^2y, x^2y, -2x^2y$

c. $-2yz, -3zy$

d. $-x^4, x^4$

e. $-8a^5, 8a^5$

30. Find each quotient.

a. $\frac{-32}{8}$ **b.** $\frac{-108}{-12}$

c. $-\frac{5}{7} \div \left(-\frac{9}{2}\right)$

31. Subtract $4x - 2$ from $2x - 3$.

32. Subtract $10x + 3$ from $-5x + 1$.

33. Solve: $x - 7 = 10$

Solve.

34. $\frac{5}{6} + x = \frac{2}{3}$

35. $-z - 4 = 6$

36. $-3x + 1 - (-4x - 6) = 10$

37. $\frac{2(a + 3)}{3} = 6a + 2$

38. $\frac{x}{4} = 18$

39. The 111th Congress, which began at noon on January 3, 2009, had a total of 434 Democrats and Republicans. There were 78 more Democratic representatives than Republican. Find the number of representatives from each party. (*Source: New York Times*)

40. $6x + 5 = 4(x + 4) - 1$

41. A glacier is a giant mass of rocks and ice that flows downhill like a river. Portage Glacier in Alaska is about 6 miles, or 31,680 feet, long and moves 400 feet per year. Icebergs are created when the front end of the glacier flows into Portage Lake. How long does it take for ice at the head (beginning) of the glacier to reach the lake?

42. A number increased by 4 is the same as 3 times the number decreased by 8. Find the number.

43. The number 63 is what percent of 72?

44. Solve: $C = 2\pi r$ for r.

45. Solve: $5(2x + 3) = -1 + 7$

46. Solve: $x - 3 > 2$

47. Graph $-1 > x$.

−5 −4 −3 −2 −1 0 1 2 3 4 5

48. Solve: $3x - 4 \leq 2x - 14$

49. Solve: $2(x - 3) - 5 \leq 3(x + 2) - 18$

50. Solve: $-3x \geq 9$

30. a. ______

b. ______

c. ______

31. ______

32. ______

33. ______

34. ______

35. ______

36. ______

37. ______

38. ______

39. ______

40. ______

41. ______

42. ______

43. ______

44. ______

45. ______

46. ______

47. ______

48. ______

49. ______

50. ______

3 Exponents and Polynomials

Sections

Check Your Progress

Recall from Chapter 1 that an exponent is a shorthand notation for repeated factors. This chapter explores additional concepts about exponents and exponential expressions. An especially useful type of exponential expression is a polynomial. Polynomials model many real-world phenomena. Our goal in this chapter is to become proficient with operations on polynomials.

According to a recent survey, the average American adult owns 2.4 cell phones, and over 56% of those surveyed still have their old cell phones. In fact, it is estimated that 130 million cell phones will be retired this year. With new cell phone models having new features and increased technologies, this number of retired cell phones will probably only increase. The good news is that the number of cell phones being recycled is increasing. Below is a graph showing the growth of cell phones recycled by the largest recycler. (*Source:* Recycling for Charities) In Exercises 25 and 26 of Section 3.3, you will explore some information about the growth of wireless technology.

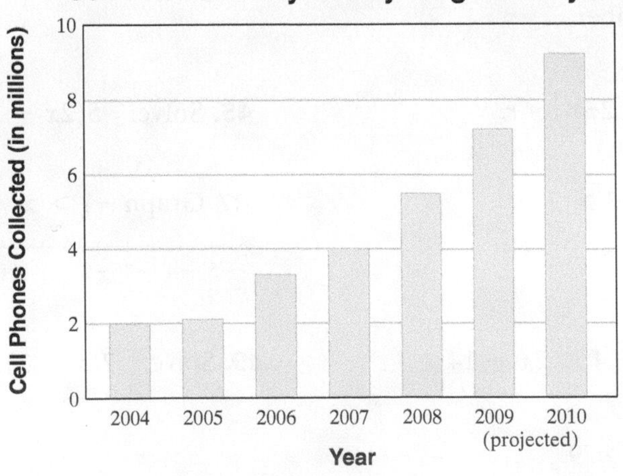

Source: ReCellular.com (independent projections)

3.1 EXPONENTS

Objective A Evaluating Exponential Expressions

In this section, we continue our work with integer exponents. Recall from Section 1.3 that repeated multiplication of the same factor can be written using exponents. For example,

$$2 \cdot 2 \cdot 2 \cdot 2 \cdot 2 = 2^5$$

The exponent 5 tells us how many times 2 is a factor. The expression 2^5 is called an **exponential expression.** It is also called the fifth **power** of 2, or we can say that 2 is **raised** to the fifth power.

$$5^6 = \underbrace{5 \cdot 5 \cdot 5 \cdot 5 \cdot 5 \cdot 5}_{\text{6 factors; each factor is 5}} \quad \text{and} \quad (-3)^4 = \underbrace{(-3) \cdot (-3) \cdot (-3) \cdot (-3)}_{\text{4 factors; each factor is } -3}$$

The base of an exponential expression is the repeated factor. The exponent is the number of times that the base is used as a factor.

$$\overset{\text{exponent or power}}{\underset{\text{base}}{a^n}} = \underbrace{a \cdot a \cdot a \cdots a}_{n \text{ factors; each factor is } a}$$

Examples Evaluate each expression.

1. $2^3 = 2 \cdot 2 \cdot 2 = 8$
2. $3^1 = 3$. To raise 3 to the first power means to use 3 as a factor only once. When no exponent is shown, the exponent is assumed to be 1.
3. $(-4)^2 = (-4)(-4) = 16$
4. $-4^2 = -(4 \cdot 4) = -16$
5. $\left(\frac{1}{2}\right)^4 = \frac{1}{2} \cdot \frac{1}{2} \cdot \frac{1}{2} \cdot \frac{1}{2} = \frac{1}{16}$
6. $4 \cdot 3^2 = 4 \cdot 9 = 36$

Work Practice 1–6

Notice how similar -4^2 is to $(-4)^2$ in the examples above. The difference between the two is the parentheses. In $(-4)^2$, the parentheses tell us that the base, or the repeated factor, is -4. In -4^2, only 4 is the base.

Helpful Hint

Be careful when identifying the base of an exponential expression. Pay close attention to the use of parentheses.

$(-3)^2$	-3^2	$2 \cdot 3^2$
The base is -3.	The base is 3.	The base is 3.
$(-3)^2 = (-3)(-3) = 9$	$-3^2 = -(3 \cdot 3) = -9$	$2 \cdot 3^2 = 2 \cdot 3 \cdot 3 = 18$

An exponent has the same meaning whether the base is a number or a variable. If x is a real number and n is a positive integer, then x^n is the product of n factors, each of which is x.

$$x^n = \underbrace{x \cdot x \cdot x \cdot x \cdot x \cdots x}_{n \text{ factors; each factor is } x}$$

Objectives

A Evaluate Exponential Expressions.

B Use the Product Rule for Exponents.

C Use the Power Rule for Exponents.

D Use the Power Rules for Products and Quotients.

E Use the Quotient Rule for Exponents, and Define a Number Raised to the 0 Power.

F Decide Which Rule(s) to Use to Simplify an Expression.

PRACTICE 1–6

Evaluate each expression.

1. 3^4
2. 7^1
3. $(-2)^3$
4. -2^3
5. $\left(\frac{2}{3}\right)^2$
6. $5 \cdot 6^2$

Answers

1. 81 2. 7 3. −8 4. −8 5. $\frac{4}{9}$ 6. 180

PRACTICE 7

Evaluate each expression for the given value of x.

a. $3x^2$ when x is 4

b. $\frac{x^4}{-8}$ when x is -2

Example 7 Evaluate each expression for the given value of x.

a. $2x^3$ when x is 5 **b.** $\frac{9}{x^2}$ when x is -3

Solution:

a. When x is 5, $2x^3 = 2 \cdot 5^3$

$$= 2 \cdot (5 \cdot 5 \cdot 5)$$
$$= 2 \cdot 125$$
$$= 250$$

b. When x is -3, $\frac{9}{x^2} = \frac{9}{(-3)^2}$

$$= \frac{9}{(-3)(-3)}$$
$$= \frac{9}{9} = 1$$

Work Practice 7

Objective B Using the Product Rule

Exponential expressions can be multiplied, divided, added, subtracted, and themselves raised to powers. Let's see if we can discover a shortcut method for multiplying exponential expressions with the same base. By our definition of an exponent,

$$5^4 \cdot 5^3 = \underbrace{(5 \cdot 5 \cdot 5 \cdot 5)}_{\text{4 factors of 5}} \cdot \underbrace{(5 \cdot 5 \cdot 5)}_{\text{3 factors of 5}}$$
$$= \underbrace{5 \cdot 5 \cdot 5 \cdot 5 \cdot 5 \cdot 5 \cdot 5}_{\text{7 factors of 5}}$$
$$= 5^7$$

Also,

$$x^2 \cdot x^3 = \underbrace{(x \cdot x)}_{\text{2 factors of } x} \cdot \underbrace{(x \cdot x \cdot x)}_{\text{3 factors of } x}$$
$$= x \cdot x \cdot x \cdot x \cdot x$$
$$= x^5$$

In both cases, notice that the result is exactly the same if the exponents are added.

$$5^4 \cdot 5^3 = 5^{4+3} = 5^7 \quad \text{and} \quad x^2 \cdot x^3 = x^{2+3} = x^5$$

This suggests the following rule.

Product Rule for Exponents

If m and n are positive integers and a is a real number, then

$$a^m \cdot a^n = a^{m+n}$$ ← Add exponents.
↑ Keep common base.

For example,

$$3^5 \cdot 3^7 = 3^{5+7} = 3^{12}$$ ← Add exponents.
↑ Keep common base.

Answers

7. a. 48 **b.** -2

Helpful Hint

Don't forget that

$3^5 \cdot 3^7 \neq 9^{12}$ ← Add exponents. ↑ Common base *not* kept.

$3^5 \cdot 3^7 = \underbrace{3 \cdot 3 \cdot 3 \cdot 3 \cdot 3}_{\text{5 factors of 3}} \cdot \underbrace{3 \cdot 3 \cdot 3 \cdot 3 \cdot 3 \cdot 3 \cdot 3}_{\text{7 factors of 3}}$

$= 3^{12}$ 12 factors of 3, *not* 9

In other words, to multiply two exponential expressions with the **same base**, we keep the base and add the exponents. We call this **simplifying** the exponential expression.

Examples Use the product rule to simplify each expression.

8. $4^2 \cdot 4^5 = 4^{2+5} = 4^7$ ← Add exponents. ↑ Keep common base.

9. $x^2 \cdot x^5 = x^{2+5} = x^7$

10. $y^3 \cdot y = y^3 \cdot y^1$
$= y^{3+1}$
$= y^4$

Helpful Hint Don't forget that if no exponent is written, it is assumed to be 1.

11. $y^3 \cdot y^2 \cdot y^7 = y^{3+2+7} = y^{12}$

12. $(-5)^7 \cdot (-5)^8 = (-5)^{7+8} = (-5)^{15}$

Work Practice 8–12

PRACTICE 8–12

Use the product rule to simplify each expression.

8. $7^3 \cdot 7^2$ **9.** $x^4 \cdot x^9$
10. $r^5 \cdot r$ **11.** $s^6 \cdot s^2 \cdot s^3$
12. $(-3)^9 \cdot (-3)$

✓Concept Check Where possible, use the product rule to simplify the expression.

a. $z^2 \cdot z^{14}$ **b.** $x^2 \cdot z^{14}$ **c.** $9^8 \cdot 9^3$ **d.** $9^8 \cdot 2^7$

Example 13 Use the product rule to simplify $(2x^2)(-3x^5)$.

Solution: Recall that $2x^2$ means $2 \cdot x^2$ and $-3x^5$ means $-3 \cdot x^5$.

$(2x^2)(-3x^5) = (2 \cdot x^2) \cdot (-3 \cdot x^5)$

$= (2 \cdot -3) \cdot (x^2 \cdot x^5)$ Group factors with common bases (using commutative and associative properties).

$= -6x^7$ Simplify.

Work Practice 13

PRACTICE 13

Use the product rule to simplify $(6x^3)(-2x^9)$.

Examples Simplify.

14. $(x^2y)(x^3y^2) = (x^2 \cdot x^3) \cdot (y^1 \cdot y^2)$ Group like bases and write y as y^1.

$= x^5 \cdot y^3$ or x^5y^3 Multiply.

15. $(-a^7b^4)(3ab^9) = (-1 \cdot 3) \cdot (a^7 \cdot a^1) \cdot (b^4 \cdot b^9)$

$= -3a^8b^{13}$

Work Practice 14–15

PRACTICE 14–15

Simplify.

14. $(m^5n^{10})(mn^8)$

15. $(-x^9y)(4x^2y^{11})$

Answers

8. 7^5 **9.** x^{13} **10.** r^6 **11.** s^{11} **12.** $(-3)^{10}$ **13.** $-12x^{12}$ **14.** m^6n^{18} **15.** $-4x^{11}y^{12}$

✓ Concept Check Answers

a. z^{16} **b.** cannot be simplified
c. 9^{11} **d.** cannot be simplified

Helpful Hint

These examples will remind you of the difference between adding and multiplying terms.

Addition

$5x^3 + 3x^3 = (5 + 3)x^3 = 8x^3$ — By the distributive property

$7x + 4x^2 = 7x + 4x^2$ — Cannot be combined

Multiplication

$(5x^3)(3x^3) = 5 \cdot 3 \cdot x^3 \cdot x^3 = 15x^{3+3} = 15x^6$ — By the product rule

$(7x)(4x^2) = 7 \cdot 4 \cdot x \cdot x^2 = 28x^{1+2} = 28x^3$ — By the product rule

Objective C Using the Power Rule

Exponential expressions can themselves be raised to powers. Let's try to discover a rule that simplifies an expression like $(x^2)^3$. By the definition of a^n,

$(x^2)^3 = (x^2)(x^2)(x^2)$ — $(x^2)^3$ means 3 factors of (x^2).

which can be simplified by the product rule for exponents.

$(x^2)^3 = (x^2)(x^2)(x^2) = x^{2+2+2} = x^6$

Notice that the result is exactly the same if we multiply the exponents.

$(x^2)^3 = x^{2 \cdot 3} = x^6$

The following rule states this result.

Power Rule for Exponents

If m and n are positive integers and a is a real number, then

$(a^m)^n = a^{mn}$ ← Multiply exponents. (Keep the base.)

For example,

$(7^2)^5 = 7^{2 \cdot 5} = 7^{10}$ ← Multiply exponents. (Keep the base.)

$[(-5)^3]^7 = (-5)^{3 \cdot 7} = (-5)^{21}$ ← Multiply exponents. (Keep the base.)

In other words, to raise an exponential expression to a power, we keep the base and multiply the exponents.

PRACTICE 16–17

Use the power rule to simplify each expression.

16. $(9^4)^{10}$ **17.** $(z^6)^3$

Examples Use the power rule to simplify each expression.

16. $(5^3)^6 = 5^{3 \cdot 6} = 5^{18}$

17. $(y^8)^2 = y^{8 \cdot 2} = y^{16}$

Work Practice 16–17

Helpful Hint

Take a moment to make sure that you understand when to apply the product rule and when to apply the power rule.

Product Rule → Add Exponents	Power Rule → Multiply Exponents
$x^5 \cdot x^7 = x^{5+7} = x^{12}$	$(x^5)^7 = x^{5 \cdot 7} = x^{35}$
$y^6 \cdot y^2 = y^{6+2} = y^8$	$(y^6)^2 = y^{6 \cdot 2} = y^{12}$

Answers

16. 9^{40} **17.** z^{18}

Objective D Using the Power Rules for Products and Quotients

When the base of an exponential expression is a product, the definition of a^n still applies. For example, simplify $(xy)^3$ as follows.

$$\begin{aligned}(xy)^3 &= (xy)(xy)(xy) && (xy)^3 \text{ means 3 factors of } (xy). \\ &= x \cdot x \cdot x \cdot y \cdot y \cdot y && \text{Group factors with common bases.} \\ &= x^3y^3 && \text{Simplify.}\end{aligned}$$

Notice that to simplify the expression $(xy)^3$, we raise each factor within the parentheses to a power of 3.

$$(xy)^3 = x^3y^3$$

In general, we have the following rule.

Power of a Product Rule

If n is a positive integer and a and b are real numbers, then

$$(ab)^n = a^nb^n$$

For example,

$$(3x)^5 = 3^5x^5$$

In other words, to raise a product to a power, we raise each factor to the power.

Examples Simplify each expression.

18. $(st)^4 = s^4 \cdot t^4 = s^4t^4$ Use the power of a product rule.
19. $(2a)^3 = 2^3 \cdot a^3 = 8a^3$ Use the power of a product rule.
20. $(-5x^2y^3z)^2 = (-5)^2 \cdot (x^2)^2 \cdot (y^3)^2 \cdot (z^1)^2$ Use the power of a product rule.
$= 25x^4y^6z^2$
21. $(-xy^3)^5 = (-1xy^3)^5 = (-1)^5 \cdot x^5 \cdot (y^3)^5$ Use the power of a product rule.
$= -1x^5y^{15}$ or $-x^5y^{15}$

Work Practice 18–21

PRACTICE 18–21

Simplify each expression.

18. $(xy)^7$ 19. $(3y)^4$
20. $(-2p^4q^2r)^3$ 21. $(-a^4b)^7$

Let's see what happens when we raise a quotient to a power. For example, we simplify $\left(\frac{x}{y}\right)^3$ as follows.

$$\begin{aligned}\left(\frac{x}{y}\right)^3 &= \left(\frac{x}{y}\right)\left(\frac{x}{y}\right)\left(\frac{x}{y}\right) && \left(\frac{x}{y}\right)^3 \text{ means 3 factors of } \left(\frac{x}{y}\right). \\ &= \frac{x \cdot x \cdot x}{y \cdot y \cdot y} && \text{Multiply fractions.} \\ &= \frac{x^3}{y^3} && \text{Simplify.}\end{aligned}$$

Notice that to simplify the expression $\left(\frac{x}{y}\right)^3$, we raise both the numerator and the denominator to a power of 3.

$$\left(\frac{x}{y}\right)^3 = \frac{x^3}{y^3}$$

In general, we have the following rule.

Answers
18. x^7y^7 19. $81y^4$ 20. $-8p^{12}q^6r^3$
21. $-a^{28}b^7$

Power of a Quotient Rule

If n is a positive integer and a and c are real numbers, then

$$\left(\frac{a}{c}\right)^n = \frac{a^n}{c^n}, \quad c \neq 0$$

For example,

$$\left(\frac{y}{7}\right)^3 = \frac{y^3}{7^3}$$

In other words, to raise a quotient to a power, we raise both the numerator and the denominator to the power.

PRACTICE 22–23

Simplify each expression.

22. $\left(\frac{r}{s}\right)^6$ **23.** $\left(\frac{5x^6}{9y^3}\right)^2$

Examples Simplify each expression.

22. $\left(\frac{m}{n}\right)^7 = \frac{m^7}{n^7}, \quad n \neq 0$ Use the power of a quotient rule.

23. $\left(\frac{2x^4}{3y^5}\right)^4 = \frac{2^4 \cdot (x^4)^4}{3^4 \cdot (y^5)^4}$ Use the power of a quotient rule and the power of a product rule.

$= \frac{16x^{16}}{81y^{20}}, \quad y \neq 0$ Use the power rule for exponents.

Work Practice 22–23

Objective E Using the Quotient Rule and Defining the Zero Exponent

Another pattern for simplifying exponential expressions involves quotients.

$$\frac{x^5}{x^3} = \frac{x \cdot x \cdot x \cdot x \cdot x}{x \cdot x \cdot x}$$
$$= \frac{x \cdot x \cdot x \cdot x \cdot x}{x \cdot x \cdot x}$$
$$= 1 \cdot 1 \cdot 1 \cdot x \cdot x$$
$$= x \cdot x$$
$$= x^2$$

Notice that the result is exactly the same if we subtract exponents of the common bases.

$$\frac{x^5}{x^3} = x^{5-3} = x^2$$

The following rule states this result in a general way.

Quotient Rule for Exponents

If m and n are positive integers and a is a real number, then

$$\frac{a^m}{a^n} = a^{m-n}, \quad a \neq 0$$

For example,

$$\frac{x^6}{x^2} = x^{6-2} = x^4, \quad x \neq 0$$

Answers

22. $\frac{r^6}{s^6}, \; s \neq 0$ **23.** $\frac{25x^{12}}{81y^6}, \; y \neq 0$

In other words, to divide one exponential expression by another with a common base, we keep the base and subtract the exponents.

Examples Simplify each quotient.

24. $\frac{x^5}{x^2} = x^{5-2} = x^3$ Use the quotient rule.

25. $\frac{4^7}{4^3} = 4^{7-3} = 4^4 = 256$ Use the quotient rule.

26. $\frac{(-3)^5}{(-3)^2} = (-3)^3 = -27$ Use the quotient rule.

27. $\frac{2x^5y^2}{xy} = 2 \cdot \frac{x^5}{x^1} \cdot \frac{y^2}{y^1}$

$= 2 \cdot (x^{5-1}) \cdot (y^{2-1})$ Use the quotient rule.

$= 2x^4y^1$ or $2x^4y$

Work Practice 24–27

PRACTICE 24–27

Simplify each quotient.

24. $\frac{y^7}{y^3}$ **25.** $\frac{5^9}{5^6}$

26. $\frac{(-2)^{14}}{(-2)^{10}}$ **27.** $\frac{7a^4b^{11}}{ab}$

Let's now give meaning to an expression such as x^0. To do so, we will simplify $\frac{x^3}{x^3}$ in two ways and compare the results.

$\frac{x^3}{x^3} = x^{3-3} = x^0$ Apply the quotient rule.

$\frac{x^3}{x^3} = \frac{x \cdot x \cdot x}{x \cdot x \cdot x} = 1$ Divide the numerator and denominator by all common factors.

Since $\frac{x^3}{x^3} = x^0$ and $\frac{x^3}{x^3} = 1$, we define that $x^0 = 1$ as long as x is not 0.

Zero Exponent

$a^0 = 1$, as long as a is not 0.

For example, $5^0 = 1$.

In other words, a base raised to the 0 power is 1, as long as the base is not 0.

Examples Simplify each expression.

28. $3^0 = 1$

29. $(5x^3y^2)^0 = 1$

30. $(-4)^0 = 1$

31. $-4^0 = -1 \cdot 4^0 = -1 \cdot 1 = -1$

32. $5x^0 = 5 \cdot x^0 = 5 \cdot 1 = 5$

Work Practice 28–32

PRACTICE 28–32

Simplify each expression.

28. 8^0 **29.** $(2r^2s)^0$

30. $(-7)^0$ **31.** -7^0

32. $7y^0$

Answers

24. y^4 **25.** 125 **26.** 16 **27.** $7a^3b^{10}$
28. 1 **29.** 1 **30.** 1 **31.** -1
32. 7

✓**Concept Check** Suppose you are simplifying each expression. Tell whether you would *add* the exponents, *subtract* the exponents, *multiply* the exponents, *divide* the exponents, or *none of these.*

a. $(x^{63})^{21}$ **b.** $\frac{y^{15}}{y^3}$ **c.** $z^{16} + z^8$ **d.** $w^{45} \cdot w^9$

Objective F Deciding Which Rule to Use

Let's practice deciding which rule to use to simplify an expression. We will continue this discussion with more examples in the next section.

PRACTICE 33

Simplify each expression.

a. $\frac{x^7}{x^4}$ **b.** $(3y^4)^4$ **c.** $\left(\frac{x}{4}\right)^3$

Example 33 Simplify each expression.

a. $x^7 \cdot x^4$ **b.** $\left(\frac{t}{2}\right)^4$ **c.** $(9y^5)^2$

Solution:

a. Here, we have a product, so we use the product rule to simplify.

$x^7 \cdot x^4 = x^{7+4} = x^{11}$

b. This is a quotient raised to a power, so we use the power of a quotient rule.

$\left(\frac{t}{2}\right)^4 = \frac{t^4}{2^4} = \frac{t^4}{16}$

c. This is a product raised to a power, so we use the power of a product rule.

$(9y^5)^2 = 9^2(y^5)^2 = 81y^{10}$

Work Practice 33

PRACTICE 34

Simplify each expression.

a. $2^3 - 2^0$ **b.** $(y^0)^7 + (5^0)^3$

c. $\left(\frac{7x^9}{14y^6}\right)^2$ **d.** $\frac{(3a^2b^5)^3}{-27a^6b^4}$

Example 34 Simplify each expression.

a. $4^2 - 4^0$ **b.** $(x^0)^3 + (2^0)^5$ **c.** $\left(\frac{3y^7}{6x^5}\right)^2$ **d.** $\frac{(2a^3b^4)^3}{-8a^9b^2}$

Solution:

a. $4^2 - 4^0 = 16 - 1 = 15$ Remember that $4^0 = 1$.

b. $(x^0)^3 + (2^0)^5 = 1^3 + 1^5 = 1 + 1 = 2$

c. $\left(\frac{3y^7}{6x^5}\right)^2 = \frac{3^2(y^7)^2}{6^2(x^5)^2} = \frac{9 \cdot y^{14}}{36 \cdot x^{10}} = \frac{y^{14}}{4x^{10}}$

d. $\frac{(2a^3b^4)^3}{-8a^9b^2} = \frac{2^3(a^3)^3(b^4)^3}{-8a^9b^2} = \frac{8a^9b^{12}}{-8a^9b^2} = -1 \cdot (a^{9-9}) \cdot (b^{12-2})$

$= -1 \cdot a^0 \cdot b^{10} = -1 \cdot 1 \cdot b^{10} = -b^{10}$

Work Practice 34

Answers

33. a. x^3 **b.** $81y^{16}$ **c.** $\frac{x^3}{64}$

34. a. 7 **b.** 2 **c.** $\frac{x^{18}}{4y^{12}}$ **d.** $-b^{11}$

✓ **Concept Check Answers**

a. multiply **b.** subtract

c. none of these **d.** add

Vocabulary and Readiness Check

Use the choices below to fill in each blank. Some choices may be used more than once.

0	base	add
1	exponent	multiply

1. Repeated multiplication of the same factor can be written using a(n) __________.
2. In 5^2, the 2 is called the __________ and the 5 is called the __________.
3. To simplify $x^2 \cdot x^7$, keep the base and __________ the exponents.
4. To simplify $(x^3)^6$, keep the base and __________ the exponents.
5. The understood exponent on the term y is __________.
6. If $x^{\square} = 1$, the exponent is __________.

For each of the following expressions, state the exponent shown and its corresponding base.

7. 3^2
8. $(-3)^6$
9. -4^2
10. $5 \cdot 3^4$
11. $5x^2$
12. $(5x)^2$

3.1 Exercise Set

FOR EXTRA HELP

MyMathLab

PRACTICE WATCH DOWNLOAD READ REVIEW

Objective A *Evaluate each expression. See Examples 1 through 6.*

1. 7^2
2. -3^2
3. $(-5)^1$
4. $(-3)^2$
5. -2^4
6. -4^3
7. $(-2)^4$
8. $(-4)^3$
9. $\left(\frac{1}{3}\right)^3$
10. $\left(-\frac{1}{9}\right)^2$
11. $7 \cdot 2^4$
12. $9 \cdot 2^2$

Evaluate each expression with the given replacement values. See Example 7.

13. x^2 when $x = -2$
14. x^3 when $x = -2$
15. $5x^3$ when $x = 3$
16. $4x^2$ when $x = 5$
17. $2xy^2$ when $x = 3$ and $y = -5$
18. $-4x^2y^3$ when $x = 2$ and $y = -1$
19. $\frac{2z^4}{5}$ when $z = -2$
20. $\frac{10}{3y^3}$ when $y = -3$

Objective B *Use the product rule to simplify each expression. See Examples 8 through 15.*

21. $x^2 \cdot x^5$
22. $y^2 \cdot y$
23. $(-3)^3 \cdot (-3)^9$
24. $(-5)^7 \cdot (-5)^6$
25. $(5y^4)(3y)$
26. $(-2z^3)(-2z^2)$
27. $(x^9y)(x^{10}y^5)$
28. $(a^2b)(a^{13}b^{17})$
29. $(-8mn^6)(9m^2n^2)$
30. $(-7a^3b^3)(7a^{19}b)$
31. $(4z^{10})(-6z^7)(z^3)$
32. $(12x^5)(-x^6)(x^4)$

△ **33.** The rectangle below has width $4x^2$ feet and length $5x^3$ feet. Find its area as an expression in x.

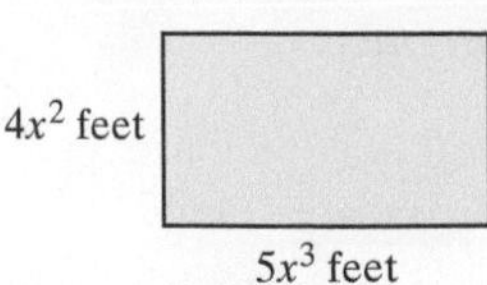

△ **34.** The parallelogram below has base length $9y^7$ meters and height $2y^{10}$ meters. Find its area as an expression in y.

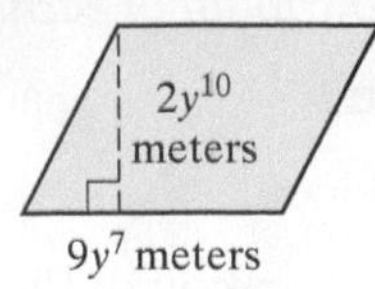

Objectives C D Mixed Practice *Use the power rule and the power of a product or quotient rule to simplify each expression. See Examples 16 through 23.*

35. $(x^9)^4$

36. $(y^7)^5$

37. $(pq)^8$

38. $(ab)^6$

39. $(2a^5)^3$

40. $(4x^6)^2$

41. $(x^2y^3)^5$

42. $(a^4b)^7$

43. $(-7a^2b^5c)^2$

44. $(-3x^7yz^2)^3$

45. $\left(\frac{r}{s}\right)^9$

46. $\left(\frac{q}{t}\right)^{11}$

47. $\left(\frac{mp}{n}\right)^9$

48. $\left(\frac{xy}{7}\right)^2$

49. $\left(\frac{-2xz}{y^5}\right)^2$

50. $\left(\frac{xy^4}{-3z^3}\right)^3$

△ **51.** The square shown has sides of length $8z^5$ decimeters. Find its area.

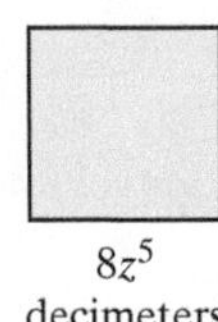

△ **52.** Given the circle below with radius $5y$ centimeters, find its area. Do not approximate π.

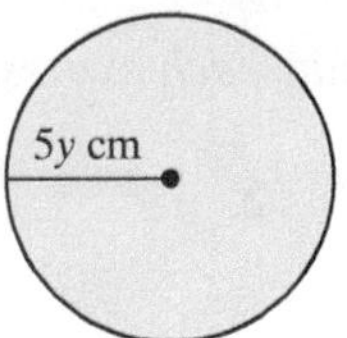

△ **53.** The vault below is in the shape of a cube. If each side is $3y^4$ feet, find its volume.

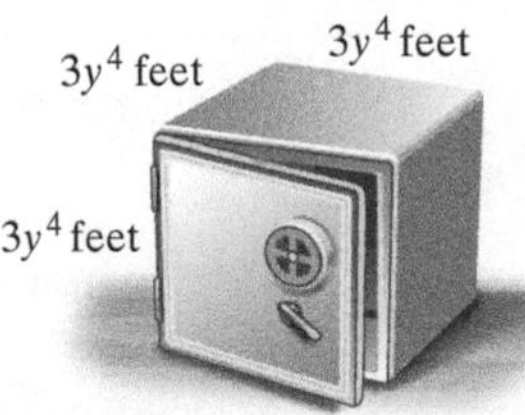

△ **54.** The silo shown is in the shape of a cylinder. If its radius is $4x$ meters and its height is $5x^3$ meters, find its volume. Do not approximate π.

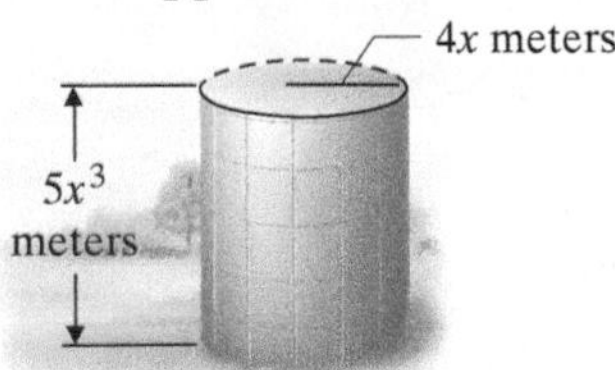

Objective E *Use the quotient rule and simplify each expression. See Examples 24 through 27.*

55. $\frac{x^3}{x}$

56. $\frac{y^{10}}{y^9}$

57. $\frac{(-4)^6}{(-4)^3}$

58. $\frac{(-6)^{13}}{(-6)^{11}}$

59. $\frac{p^7q^{20}}{pq^{15}}$

60. $\frac{x^8y^6}{xy^5}$

61. $\frac{7x^2y^6}{14x^2y^3}$

62. $\frac{9a^4b^7}{27ab^2}$

Simplify each expression. See Examples 28 through 32.

63. 7^0

64. 23^0

65. $(2x)^0$

66. $(4y)^0$

67. $-7x^0$

68. $-2x^0$

69. $5^0 + y^0$

70. $-3^0 + 4^0$

Objectives A B C D E F Mixed Practice *Simplify each expression. See Examples 1 through 6, and 8 through 34.*

71. -9^2

72. $(-9)^2$

73. $\left(\frac{1}{4}\right)^3$

74. $\left(\frac{2}{3}\right)^3$

75. b^4b^2

76. y^4y

77. $a^2a^3a^4$

78. $x^2x^{15}x^9$

79. $(2x^3)(-8x^4)$

80. $(3y^4)(-5y)$

81. $(a^7b^{12})(a^4b^8)$

82. $(y^2z^2)(y^{15}z^{13})$

83. $(-2mn^6)(-13m^8n)$

84. $(-3s^5t)(-7st^{10})$

85. $(z^4)^{10}$

86. $(t^5)^{11}$

87. $(4ab)^3$

88. $(2ab)^4$

89. $(-6xyz^3)^2$

90. $(-3xy^2a^3)^3$

91. $\frac{3x^5}{x^4}$

92. $\frac{5x^9}{x^3}$

93. $(9xy)^2$

94. $(2ab)^5$

95. $2^3 + 2^0$

96. $7^2 - 7^0$

97. $\left(\frac{3y^5}{6x^4}\right)^3$

98. $\left(\frac{2ab}{6yz}\right)^4$

99. $\frac{2x^3y^2z}{xyz}$

100. $\frac{x^{12}y^{13}}{x^5y^7}$

101. $(5^0)^3 + (y^0)^7$

102. $(9^0)^4 + (z^0)^5$

103. $\left(\frac{5x^9}{10y^{11}}\right)^2$

104. $\left(\frac{3a^4}{9b^5}\right)^2$

105. $\frac{(2a^5b^3)^4}{-16a^{20}b^7}$

106. $\frac{(2x^6y^2)^5}{-32x^{20}y^{10}}$

Review

Subtract. See Section 1.5.

107. $5 - 7$

108. $9 - 12$

109. $3 - (-2)$

110. $5 - (-10)$

111. $-11 - (-4)$

112. $-15 - (-21)$

Concept Extensions

Solve. See the Concept Checks in this section. For Exercises 113 through 116, match the expression with the operation needed to simplify each. A letter may be used more than once and a letter may not be used at all.

113. $(x^{14})^{23}$

114. $x^{14} \cdot x^{23}$

115. $x^{14} + x^{23}$

116. $\frac{x^{35}}{x^{17}}$

a. Add the exponents.
b. Subtract the exponents.
c. Multiply the exponents.
d. Divide the exponents.
e. None of these

Fill in the boxes so that each statement is true. (More than one answer is possible for each exercise.)

117. $x^{\square} \cdot x^{\square} = x^{12}$

118. $(x^{\square})^{\square} = x^{20}$

119. $\dfrac{y^{\square}}{y^{\square}} = y^7$

120. $(y^{\square})^{\square} \cdot (y^{\square})^{\square} = y^{30}$

△ **121.** The formula $V = x^3$ can be used to find the volume V of a cube with side length x. Find the volume of a cube with side length 7 meters. (Volume is measured in cubic units.)

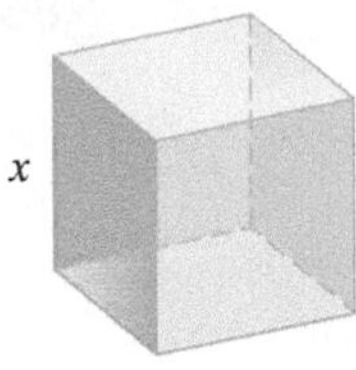

△ **122.** The formula $S = 6x^2$ can be used to find the surface area S of a cube with side length x. Find the surface area of a cube with side length 5 meters. (Surface area is measured in square units.)

△ **123.** To find the amount of water that a swimming pool in the shape of a cube can hold, do we use the formula for volume of the cube or surface area of the cube? (See Exercises 121 and 122.)

△ **124.** To find the amount of material needed to cover an ottoman in the shape of a cube, do we use the formula for volume of the cube or surface area of the cube? (See Exercises 121 and 122.)

125. Explain why $(-5)^4 = 625$, while $-5^4 = -625$.

126. Explain why $5 \cdot 4^2 = 80$, while $(5 \cdot 4)^2 = 400$.

127. In your own words, explain why $5^0 = 1$.

128. In your own words, explain when $(-3)^n$ is positive and when it is negative.

Simplify each expression. Assume that variables represent positive integers.

129. $x^{5a}x^{4a}$

130. $b^{9a}b^{4a}$

131. $(a^b)^5$

132. $(2a^{4b})^4$

133. $\dfrac{x^{9a}}{x^{4a}}$

134. $\dfrac{y^{15b}}{y^{6b}}$

3.2 NEGATIVE EXPONENTS AND SCIENTIFIC NOTATION

Objectives

A Simplify Expressions Containing Negative Exponents.

B Use the Rules and Definitions for Exponents to Simplify Exponential Expressions.

C Write Numbers in Scientific Notation.

D Convert Numbers in Scientific Notation to Standard Form.

Objective A Simplifying Expressions Containing Negative Exponents

Our work with exponential expressions so far has been limited to exponents that are positive integers or 0. Here we will also give meaning to an expression like x^{-3}.

Suppose that we wish to simplify the expression $\frac{x^2}{x^5}$. If we use the quotient rule for exponents, we subtract exponents:

$$\frac{x^2}{x^5} = x^{2-5} = x^{-3}, \quad x \neq 0$$

But what does x^{-3} mean? Let's simplify $\frac{x^2}{x^5}$ using the definition of a^n.

$$\frac{x^2}{x^5} = \frac{x \cdot x}{x \cdot x \cdot x \cdot x \cdot x}$$

$$= \frac{x \cdot x}{x \cdot x \cdot x \cdot x \cdot x}$$ Divide numerator and denominator by common factors.

$$= \frac{1}{x^3}$$

If the quotient rule is to hold true for negative exponents, then x^{-3} must equal $\frac{1}{x^3}$.

From this example, we state the definition for negative exponents.

Negative Exponents

If a is a real number other than 0 and n is an integer, then

$$a^{-n} = \frac{1}{a^n}$$

For example,

$$x^{-3} = \frac{1}{x^3}$$

In other words, another way to write a^{-n} is to take its reciprocal and change the sign of its exponent.

Examples Simplify by writing each expression with positive exponents only.

1. $3^{-2} = \frac{1}{3^2} = \frac{1}{9}$ Use the definition of negative exponents.
2. $2x^{-3} = 2^1 \cdot \frac{1}{x^3} = \frac{2^1}{x^3}$ or $\frac{2}{x^3}$ Use the definition of negative exponents.
3. $2^{-1} + 4^{-1} = \frac{1}{2} + \frac{1}{4} = \frac{2}{4} + \frac{1}{4} = \frac{3}{4}$
4. $(-2)^{-4} = \frac{1}{(-2)^4} = \frac{1}{(-2)(-2)(-2)(-2)} = \frac{1}{16}$

Helpful Hint Don't forget that since there are no parentheses, only x is the base for the exponent -3.

Work Practice 1–4

PRACTICE 1–4

Simplify by writing each expression with positive exponents only.

1. 5^{-3}
2. $7x^{-4}$
3. $5^{-1} + 3^{-1}$
4. $(-3)^{-4}$

Answers

1. $\frac{1}{125}$ 2. $\frac{7}{x^4}$ 3. $\frac{8}{15}$ 4. $\frac{1}{81}$

Helpful Hint

A negative exponent *does not affect* the sign of its base.
Remember: Another way to write a^{-n} is to take its reciprocal and change the sign of its exponent: $a^{-n} = \frac{1}{a^n}$. For example,

$$x^{-2} = \frac{1}{x^2}, \qquad 2^{-3} = \frac{1}{2^3} \text{ or } \frac{1}{8}$$

$$\frac{1}{y^{-4}} = \frac{1}{\frac{1}{y^4}} = y^4, \qquad \frac{1}{5^{-2}} = 5^2 \text{ or } 25$$

From the preceding Helpful Hint, we know that $x^{-2} = \frac{1}{x^2}$ and $\frac{1}{y^{-4}} = y^4$. We can use this to include another statement in our definition of negative exponents.

Negative Exponents

If a is a real number other than 0 and n is an integer, then

$$a^{-n} = \frac{1}{a^n} \quad \text{and} \quad \frac{1}{a^{-n}} = a^n$$

PRACTICE 5–8

Simplify each expression. Write each result using positive exponents only.

5. $\left(\frac{6}{7}\right)^{-2}$
6. $\frac{x}{x^{-4}}$
7. $\frac{y^{-9}}{z^{-5}}$
8. $\frac{y^{-4}}{y^6}$

Examples Simplify each expression. Write each result using positive exponents only.

5. $\left(\frac{2}{x}\right)^{-3} = \frac{2^{-3}}{x^{-3}} = \frac{2^{-3}}{1} \cdot \frac{1}{x^{-3}} = \frac{1}{2^3} \cdot \frac{x^3}{1} = \frac{x^3}{2^3} = \frac{x^3}{8}$ Use the negative exponents rule.

6. $\frac{y}{y^{-2}} = \frac{y^1}{y^{-2}} = y^{1-(-2)} = y^3$ Use the quotient rule.

7. $\frac{p^{-4}}{q^{-9}} = p^{-4} \cdot \frac{1}{q^{-9}} = \frac{1}{p^4} \cdot q^9 = \frac{q^9}{p^4}$ Use the negative exponents rule.

8. $\frac{x^{-5}}{x^7} = x^{-5-7} = x^{-12} = \frac{1}{x^{12}}$

Work Practice 5–8

Objective B Simplifying Exponential Expressions

All the previously stated rules for exponents apply for negative exponents also. Here is a summary of the rules and definitions for exponents.

Summary of Exponent Rules

If m and n are integers and a, b, and c are real numbers, then

Product rule for exponents: $a^m \cdot a^n = a^{m+n}$

Power rule for exponents: $(a^m)^n = a^{m \cdot n}$

Power of a product: $(ab)^n = a^n b^n$

Power of a quotient: $\left(\frac{a}{c}\right)^n = \frac{a^n}{c^n}, \quad c \neq 0$

Quotient rule for exponents: $\frac{a^m}{a^n} = a^{m-n}, \quad a \neq 0$

Zero exponent: $a^0 = 1, \quad a \neq 0$

Negative exponent: $a^{-n} = \frac{1}{a^n}, \quad a \neq 0$

Answers

5. $\frac{49}{36}$ 6. x^5 7. $\frac{z^5}{y^9}$ 8. $\frac{1}{y^{10}}$

Examples Simplify each expression. Write each result using positive exponents only.

9. $\dfrac{(2x^3)^4x}{x^7} = \dfrac{2^4 \cdot x^{12} \cdot x}{x^7} = \dfrac{16 \cdot x^{12+1}}{x^7}$ Use the power rule.

$= \dfrac{16 \cdot x^{13}}{x^7} = 16 \cdot x^{13-7} = 16x^6$

10. $\left(\dfrac{3a^2}{b}\right)^{-3} = \dfrac{3^{-3}(a^2)^{-3}}{b^{-3}}$ Raise each factor in the numerator and the denominator to the −3 power.

$= \dfrac{3^{-3}a^{-6}}{b^{-3}}$ Use the power rule.

$= \dfrac{b^3}{3^3a^6}$ Use the negative exponent rule.

$= \dfrac{b^3}{27a^6}$ Write 3^3 as 27.

11. $(y^{-3}z^6)^{-6} = (y^{-3})^{-6}(z^6)^{-6}$ Raise each factor to the −6 power.

$= y^{18}z^{-36} = \dfrac{y^{18}}{z^{36}}$

12. $\dfrac{x^{-7}}{(x^4)^3} = \dfrac{x^{-7}}{x^{12}} = x^{-7-12} = x^{-19} = \dfrac{1}{x^{19}}$

13. $(5y^3)^{-2} = 5^{-2}(y^3)^{-2} = 5^{-2}y^{-6} = \dfrac{1}{5^2y^6} = \dfrac{1}{25y^6}$

14. $\dfrac{3a^4b^0c^6}{6ab^2c^8} = \dfrac{3}{6} \cdot a^{4-1} \cdot b^{0-2} \cdot c^{6-8} = \dfrac{1}{2} \cdot a^3b^{-2}c^{-2} = \dfrac{a^3}{2b^2c^2}$

Note: Since $b^0 = 1$, another way to proceed above is to first replace b^0 with 1, then continue.

15. $-\dfrac{22a^7b^{-5}}{11a^{-2}b^3} = -\dfrac{22}{11} \cdot a^{7-(-2)}b^{-5-3} = -2a^9b^{-8} = -\dfrac{2a^9}{b^8}$

16. $\dfrac{(2xy)^{-3}}{(x^2y^3)^2} = \dfrac{2^{-3}x^{-3}y^{-3}}{(x^2)^2(y^3)^2} = \dfrac{2^{-3}x^{-3}y^{-3}}{x^4y^6} = 2^{-3}x^{-3-4}y^{-3-6}$

$= 2^{-3}x^{-7}y^{-9} = \dfrac{1}{2^3x^7y^9}$ or $\dfrac{1}{8x^7y^9}$

Work Practice 9–16

PRACTICE 9–16

Simplify each expression. Write each result using positive exponents only.

9. $\dfrac{(3x^5)^3x}{x^4}$

10. $\left(\dfrac{9x^3}{y}\right)^{-2}$

11. $(a^{-4}b^7)^{-5}$

12. $\dfrac{y^{-10}}{(y^5)^4}$

13. $(4a^2)^{-3}$

14. $\dfrac{5x^7y^3z^0}{15xy^8z^3}$

15. $-\dfrac{32x^{-3}y^{-6}}{8x^{-5}y^{-2}}$

16. $\dfrac{(3x^{-2}y)^{-2}}{(2x^7y)^3}$

Objective C Writing Numbers in Scientific Notation

Both very large and very small numbers frequently occur in many fields of science. For example, the distance between the sun and the dwarf planet Pluto is approximately 5,906,000,000 kilometers, and the mass of a proton is approximately 0.00000000000000000000000165 gram. It can be tedious to write these numbers in this standard decimal notation, so **scientific notation** is used as a convenient shorthand for expressing very large and very small numbers.

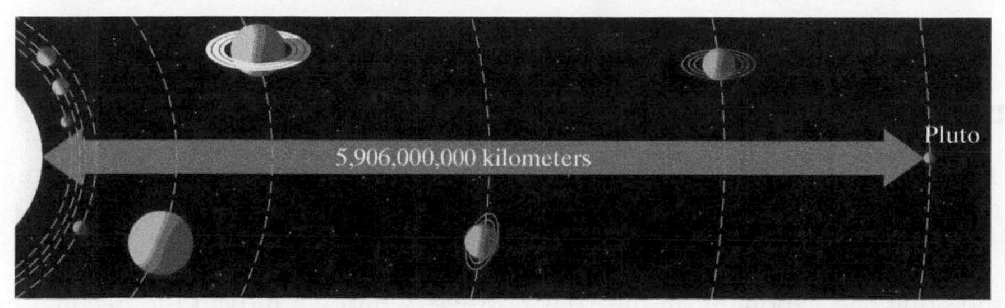

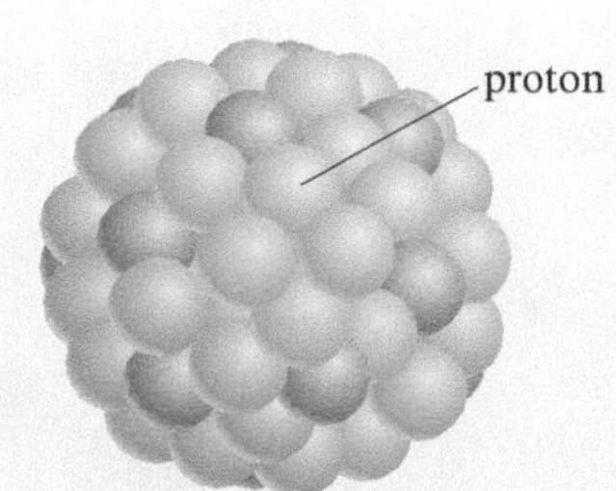

Mass of proton is approximately 0.000 000 000 000 000 000 000 001 65 gram

Answers

9. $27x^{12}$ **10.** $\dfrac{y^2}{81x^6}$ **11.** $\dfrac{a^{20}}{b^{35}}$ **12.** $\dfrac{1}{y^{30}}$ **13.** $\dfrac{1}{64a^6}$ **14.** $\dfrac{x^6}{3y^5z^3}$ **15.** $-\dfrac{4x^2}{y^4}$ **16.** $\dfrac{1}{72x^{17}y^5}$

Scientific Notation

A positive number is written in scientific notation if it is written as the product of a number a, where $1 \le a < 10$, and an integer power r of 10: $a \times 10^r$.

The following numbers are written in scientific notation. The $\times$ sign for multiplication is used as part of the notation.

2.03×10^2 $\quad 7.362 \times 10^7$ $\quad 5.906 \times 10^9$ (Distance between the sun and Pluto)

1×10^{-3} $\quad 8.1 \times 10^{-5}$ $\quad 1.65 \times 10^{-24}$ (Mass of a proton)

The following steps are useful when writing numbers in scientific notation.

To Write a Number in Scientific Notation

Step 1: Move the decimal point in the original number so that the new number has a value between 1 and 10.

Step 2: Count the number of decimal places the decimal point is moved in Step 1. If the original number is 10 or greater, the count is positive. If the original number is less than 1, the count is negative.

Step 3: Multiply the new number in Step 1 by 10 raised to an exponent equal to the count found in Step 2.

PRACTICE 17

Write each number in scientific notation.

a. 420,000 **b.** 0.00017
c. 9,060,000,000 **d.** 0.000007

Example 17 Write each number in scientific notation.

a. 367,000,000 **b.** 0.000003
c. 20,520,000,000 **d.** 0.00085

Solution:

a. Step 1: Move the decimal point until the number is between 1 and 10.

367,000,000.

8 places

Step 2: The decimal point is moved 8 places and the original number is 10 or greater, so the count is positive 8.

Step 3: $367{,}000{,}000 = 3.67 \times 10^8$

b. Step 1: Move the decimal point until the number is between 1 and 10.

0.000003

6 places

Step 2: The decimal point is moved 6 places and the original number is less than 1, so the count is -6.

Step 3: $0.000003 = 3.0 \times 10^{-6}$

c. $20{,}520{,}000{,}000 = 2.052 \times 10^{10}$

d. $0.00085 = 8.5 \times 10^{-4}$

Work Practice 17

Objective D Converting Numbers to Standard Form

A number written in scientific notation can be rewritten in standard form. For example, to write 8.63×10^3 in standard form, recall that $10^3 = 1000$.

$$8.63 \times 10^3 = 8.63(1000) = 8630$$

Notice that the exponent on the 10 is positive 3, and we moved the decimal point 3 places to the right.

Answers

17. a. 4.2×10^5 **b.** 1.7×10^{-4} **c.** 9.06×10^9 **d.** 7×10^{-6}

To write 7.29×10^{-3} in standard form, recall that $10^{-3} = \frac{1}{10^3} = \frac{1}{1000}$.

$$7.29 \times 10^{-3} = 7.29\left(\frac{1}{1000}\right) = \frac{7.29}{1000} = 0.00729$$

The exponent on the 10 is negative 3, and we moved the decimal to the left 3 places.

In general, **to write a scientific notation number in standard form,** move the decimal point the same number of places as the exponent on 10. If the exponent is positive, move the decimal point to the right; if the exponent is negative, move the decimal point to the left.

✓**Concept Check** Which number in each pair is larger?

a. 7.8×10^3 or 2.1×10^5
b. 9.2×10^{-2} or 2.7×10^4
c. 5.6×10^{-4} or 6.3×10^{-5}

Example 18 Write each number in standard form, without exponents.

a. 1.02×10^5 **b.** 7.358×10^{-3}
c. 8.4×10^7 **d.** 3.007×10^{-5}

Solution:

a. Move the decimal point 5 places to the right.

$1.02 \times 10^5 = 102{,}000.$

b. Move the decimal point 3 places to the left.

$7.358 \times 10^{-3} = 0.007358$

c. $8.4 \times 10^7 = 84{,}000{,}000.$ 7 places to the right

d. $3.007 \times 10^{-5} = 0.00003007$ 5 places to the left

Work Practice 18

PRACTICE 18

Write the numbers in standard form, without exponents.

a. 3.062×10^{-4}
b. 5.21×10^4
c. 9.6×10^{-5}
d. 6.002×10^6

Performing operations on numbers written in scientific notation makes use of the rules and definitions for exponents.

Example 19 Perform each indicated operation. Write each result in standard decimal notation.

a. $(8 \times 10^{-6})(7 \times 10^3)$
b. $\frac{12 \times 10^2}{6 \times 10^{-3}}$

Solution:

a. $(8 \times 10^{-6})(7 \times 10^3) = 8 \cdot 7 \cdot 10^{-6} \cdot 10^3$
$= 56 \times 10^{-3}$
$= 0.056$

b. $\frac{12 \times 10^2}{6 \times 10^{-3}} = \frac{12}{6} \times 10^{2-(-3)} = 2 \times 10^5 = 200{,}000$

Work Practice 19

PRACTICE 19

Perform each indicated operation. Write each result in standard decimal notation.

a. $(9 \times 10^7)(4 \times 10^{-9})$
b. $\frac{8 \times 10^4}{2 \times 10^{-3}}$

Answers

18. a. 0.0003062 **b.** 52,100 **c.** 0.000096 **d.** 6,002,000
19. a. 0.36 **b.** 40,000,000

✓ **Concept Check Answers**

a. 2.1×10^5 **b.** 2.7×10^4 **c.** 5.6×10^{-4}

Calculator Explorations Scientific Notation

To enter a number written in scientific notation on a scientific calculator, locate the scientific notation key, which may be marked EE or EXP. To enter 3.1×10^7, press 3.1 EE 7. The display should read 3.1 07.

Enter each number written in scientific notation on your calculator.

1. 5.31×10^3
2. -4.8×10^{14}
3. 6.6×10^{-9}
4. -9.9811×10^{-2}

Multiply each of the following on your calculator. Notice the form of the result.

5. $3{,}000{,}000 \times 5{,}000{,}000$
6. $230{,}000 \times 1000$

Multiply each of the following on your calculator. Write the product in scientific notation.

7. $(3.26 \times 10^6)(2.5 \times 10^{13})$
8. $(8.76 \times 10^{-4})(1.237 \times 10^9)$

Vocabulary and Readiness Check

Fill in each blank with the correct choice.

1. The expression x^{-3} equals ______________.

a. $-x^3$ **b.** $\frac{1}{x^3}$ **c.** $\frac{-1}{x^3}$ **d.** $\frac{1}{x^{-3}}$

2. The expression 5^{-4} equals ______________.

a. -20 **b.** -625 **c.** $\frac{1}{20}$ **d.** $\frac{1}{625}$

3. The number 3.021×10^{-3} is written in ______________.

a. standard form **b.** expanded form
c. scientific notation

4. The number 0.0261 is written in ______________.

a. standard form **b.** expanded form
c. scientific notation

Write each expression using positive exponents only.

5. $5x^{-2}$ **6.** $3x^{-3}$ **7.** $\frac{1}{y^{-6}}$ **8.** $\frac{1}{x^{-3}}$ **9.** $\frac{4}{y^{-3}}$ **10.** $\frac{16}{y^{-7}}$

3.2 Exercise Set

FOR EXTRA HELP

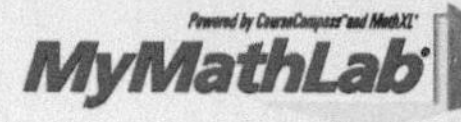

Objective A *Simplify each expression. Write each result using positive exponents only. See Examples 1 through 8.*

1. 4^{-3} **2.** 6^{-2} **3.** $7x^{-3}$ **4.** $(7x)^{-3}$ **5.** $\left(-\frac{1}{4}\right)^{-3}$ **6.** $\left(-\frac{1}{8}\right)^{-2}$

7. $3^{-1} + 2^{-1}$ **8.** $4^{-1} + 4^{-2}$ **9.** $\frac{1}{p^{-3}}$ **10.** $\frac{1}{q^{-5}}$ **11.** $\frac{p^{-5}}{q^{-4}}$ **12.** $\frac{r^{-5}}{s^{-2}}$

13. $\frac{x^{-2}}{x}$ **14.** $\frac{y}{y^{-3}}$ **15.** $\frac{z^{-4}}{z^{-7}}$ **16.** $\frac{x^{-4}}{x^{-1}}$ **17.** $3^{-2} + 3^{-1}$ **18.** $4^{-2} - 4^{-3}$

19. $(-3)^{-2}$ **20.** $(-2)^{-6}$ **21.** $\frac{-1}{p^{-4}}$ **22.** $\frac{-1}{y^{-6}}$ **23.** $-2^0 - 3^0$ **24.** $5^0 + (-5)^0$

Objective B *Simplify each expression. Write each result using positive exponents only. See Examples 9 through 16.*

25. $\frac{x^2x^5}{x^3}$ **26.** $\frac{y^4y^5}{y^6}$ **27.** $\frac{p^2p}{p^{-1}}$ **28.** $\frac{y^3y}{y^{-2}}$ **29.** $\frac{(m^5)^4m}{m^{10}}$ **30.** $\frac{(x^2)^8x}{x^9}$

31. $\frac{r}{r^{-3}r^{-2}}$ **32.** $\frac{p}{p^{-3}p^{-5}}$ **33.** $(x^5y^3)^{-3}$ **34.** $(z^5x^5)^{-3}$ **35.** $\frac{(x^2)^3}{x^{10}}$ **36.** $\frac{(y^4)^2}{y^{12}}$

37. $\frac{(a^5)^2}{(a^3)^4}$ **38.** $\frac{(x^2)^5}{(x^4)^3}$ **39.** $\frac{8k^4}{2k}$ **40.** $\frac{27r^6}{3r^4}$ **41.** $\frac{-6m^4}{-2m^3}$ **42.** $\frac{15a^4}{-15a^5}$

43. $\frac{-24a^6b}{6ab^2}$ **44.** $\frac{-5x^4y^5}{15x^4y^2}$ **45.** $\frac{6x^2y^3z^0}{-7x^2y^5z^5}$ **46.** $\frac{-8xa^2b^0}{-5xa^5b}$ **47.** $(3a^2b^{-4})^3$ **48.** $(5x^3y^{-2})^2$

49. $(a^{-5}b^2)^{-6}$

50. $(4^{-1}x^5)^{-2}$

51. $\left(\frac{x^{-2}y^4z^0}{x^3y^7}\right)^2$

52. $\left(\frac{a^5bc^0}{a^7b^{-2}}\right)^{-3}$

53. $\frac{4^2z^{-3}}{4^3z^{-5}}$

54. $\frac{5^{-1}z^7}{5^{-2}z^9}$

55. $\frac{3^{-1}x^4}{3^3x^{-7}}$

56. $\frac{2^{-3}x^{-4}}{2^2x}$

57. $\frac{7ab^{-4}}{7^{-1}a^{-3}b^2}$

58. $\frac{6^{-5}x^{-1}y^2}{6^{-2}x^{-4}y^4}$

59. $\frac{-12m^5n^{-7}}{4m^{-2}n^{-3}}$

60. $\frac{-15r^{-6}s}{5r^{-4}s^{-3}}$

61. $\left(\frac{a^{-5}b}{ab^3}\right)^{-4}$

62. $\left(\frac{r^{-2}s^{-3}}{r^{-4}s^{-3}}\right)^{-3}$

63. $(5^2)(8)(2^0)$

64. $(3^4)(7^0)(2)$

65. $\frac{(xy^3)^5}{(xy)^{-4}}$

66. $\frac{(rs)^{-3}}{(r^2s^3)^2}$

67. $\frac{(-2xy^{-3})^{-3}}{(xy^{-1})^{-1}}$

68. $\frac{(-3x^2y^2)^{-2}}{(xyz)^{-2}}$

69. $\frac{(a^4b^{-7})^{-5}}{(5a^2b^{-1})^{-2}}$

70. $\frac{(a^6b^{-2})^4}{(4a^{-3}b^{-3})^3}$

△ **71.** Find the volume of the cube.

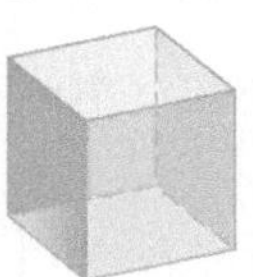
$\frac{3x^{-2}}{z}$ inches

△ **72.** Find the area of the triangle.

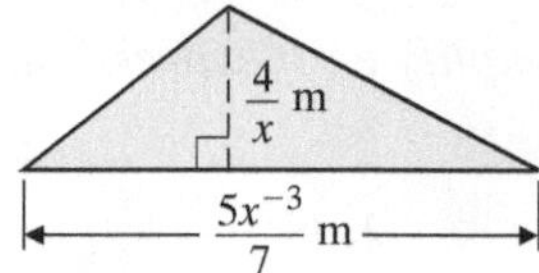
$\frac{4}{x}$ m

$\frac{5x^{-3}}{7}$ m

Objective **C** *Write each number in scientific notation. See Example 17.*

73. 78,000

74. 9,300,000,000

75. 0.00000167

76. 0.00000017

77. 0.00635

78. 0.00194

79. 1,160,000

80. 700,000

81. As of this writing, the world's largest optical telescope is the Gran Telescopio Canaris, located in La Palma, Canary Islands, Spain. The elevation of this telescope is 2400 meters above sea level. Write 2400 in scientific notation.

82. In January 2009, the twin Mars rovers, Spirit and Opportunity, celebrated their fifth anniversary of landing on Mars. These rovers, which were expected to last about 90 days, have defied all expectations, and have been transmitting signals back to Earth from as far away as 250,000,000 miles. Write 250,000,000 in scientific notation. (*Source:* NASA)

Objective **D** *Write each number in standard form. See Example 18.*

83. 8.673×10^{-10}

84. 9.056×10^{-4}

85. 3.3×10^{-2}

86. 4.8×10^{-6}

87. 2.032×10^{4}

88. 9.07×10^{10}

89. Each second, the sun converts 7.0×10^{8} tons of hydrogen into helium and energy in the form of gamma rays. Write this number in standard form. (*Source:* Students for the Exploration and Development of Space)

90. In chemistry, Avogadro's number is the number of atoms in one mole of an element. Avogadro's number is $6.02214199 \times 10^{23}$. Write this number in standard form. (*Source:* National Institute of Standards and Technology)

Objectives **C** **D** **Mixed Practice** *See Examples 17 and 18. Below are some interesting facts about selected countries' national debts during a certain time period. If a number is written in standard form, write it in scientific notation. If a number is written in scientific notation, write it in standard form. (Source:* CIA World Factbook*)*

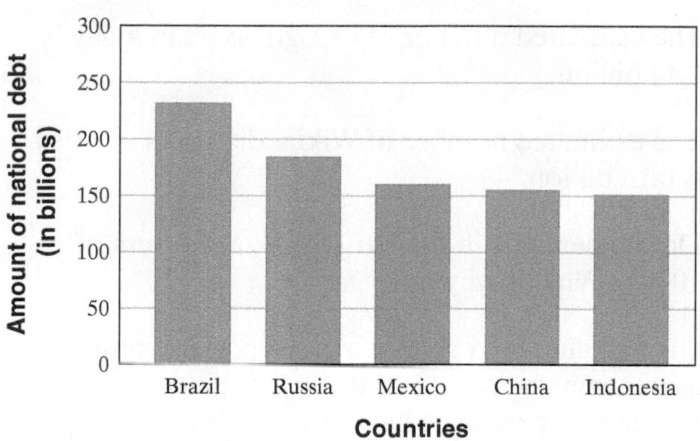

91. The national debt of Russia during a certain time period was $184,000,000,000.

92. The amount by which Russia's debt is greater than Mexico's debt is $24,000,000,000.

93. At a certain time period, China's national debt was $\$1.55 \times 10^{11}$.

94. At a certain time period, the national debt of the United States was $\$1.1 \times 10^{13}$.

95. At a certain time period, the estimated per person share of the United States' national debt was $\$3.5 \times 10^{4}$.

96. The bar graph shows thc national debt of five different countries. Estimate the height of the tallest bar and the shortest bar in standard notation. Then write each number in scientific notation.

Objective **D** *Evaluate each expression using exponential rules. Write each result in standard form. See Example 19.*

97. $(1.2 \times 10^{-3})(3 \times 10^{-2})$

98. $(2.5 \times 10^{6})(2 \times 10^{-6})$

99. $(4 \times 10^{-10})(7 \times 10^{-9})$

100. $(5 \times 10^{6})(4 \times 10^{-8})$

101. $\dfrac{8 \times 10^{-1}}{16 \times 10^{5}}$

102. $\dfrac{25 \times 10^{-4}}{5 \times 10^{-9}}$

103. $\dfrac{1.4 \times 10^{-2}}{7 \times 10^{-8}}$

104. $\dfrac{0.4 \times 10^{5}}{0.2 \times 10^{11}}$

105. Although the actual amount varies by season and time of day, the average volume of water that flows over Niagara Falls (the American and Canadian falls combined) each second is 7.5×10^{5} gallons. How much water flows over Niagara Falls in an hour? Write the result in scientific notation. (*Hint:* 1 hour equals 3600 seconds.) (*Source:* niagarafallslive.com)

106. A beam of light travels 9.460×10^{12} kilometers per year. How far does light travel in 10,000 years? Write the result in scientific notation.

Review

Simplify each expression by combining any like terms. See Section 1.8.

107. $3x - 5x + 7$

108. $7w + w - 2w$

109. $y - 10 + y$

110. $-6z + 20 - 3z$

111. $7x + 2 - 8x - 6$

112. $10y - 14 - y - 14$

Concept Extensions

For Exercises 113–118, write each number in standard form. Then write the number in scientific notation.

113. The Facebook Web site has more than 90 million active users.

114. Facebook has more than 24 million photos uploaded daily.

115. There are over 1 billion Internet users worldwide.

116. The English version of Wikipedia has more than 2.3 million articles.

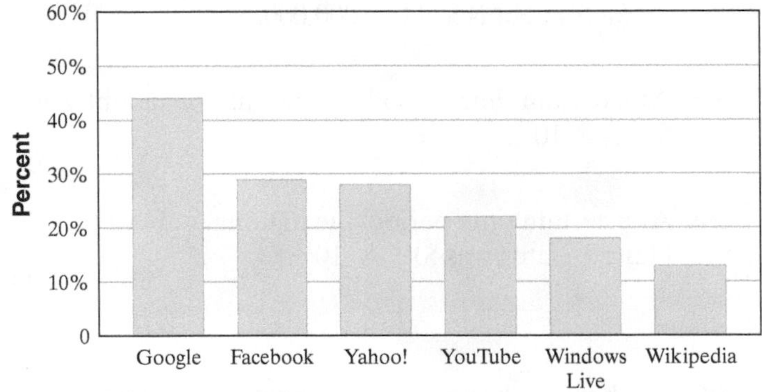

117. The estimated number of Google users in a day is 0.44 billion.

118. The estimated number of Wikipedia users in a day is 0.13 billion.

119. Do the percents in the bar graph have a sum of 100%? Why or why not?

120. Give a value for x so that x^{-1} is a positive number, and then a value for x so that x^{-1} is a negative number. In general, what does this mean?

Simplify.

121. $(2a^3)^3a^4 + a^5a^8$

122. $(2a^3)^3a^{-3} + a^{11}a^{-5}$

Fill in the boxes so that each statement is true. (More than one answer may be possible for these exercises.)

123. $x^{\square} = \frac{1}{x^5}$

124. $7^{\square} = \frac{1}{49}$

125. $z^{\square} \cdot z^{\square} = z^{-10}$

126. $(x^{\square})^{\square} = x^{-15}$

127. Which is larger? See the Concept Check in this section.

a. 9.7×10^{-2} or 1.3×10^1

b. 8.6×10^5 or 4.4×10^7

c. 6.1×10^{-2} or 5.6×10^{-4}

128. Determine whether each statement is true or false.

a. $5^{-1} < 5^{-2}$

b. $\left(\frac{1}{5}\right)^{-1} < \left(\frac{1}{5}\right)^{-2}$

c. $a^{-1} < a^{-2}$ for all nonzero numbers.

129. It was stated earlier that for an integer n,

$$x^{-n} = \frac{1}{x^n}, \quad x \neq 0$$

Explain why x may not equal 0.

130. The quotient rule states that

$$\frac{a^m}{a^n} = a^{m-n}, a \neq 0.$$

Explain why a may not equal 0.

Simplify each expression. Assume that variables represent positive integers.

131. $(x^{-3s})^3$

132. $a^{-4m} \cdot a^{5m}$

133. $a^{4m+1} \cdot a^4$

134. $(3y^{2z})^3$

3.3 INTRODUCTION TO POLYNOMIALS

Objective A Defining Term and Coefficient

In this section, we introduce a special algebraic expression called a polynomial. Let's first review some definitions presented in Section 1.8.

Recall that a term is a number or the product of a number and variables raised to powers. The terms of an expression are separated by plus signs. The terms of the expression $4x^2 + 3x$ are $4x^2$ and $3x$. The terms of the expression $9x^4 - 7x - 1$, or $9x^4 + (-7x) + (-1)$, are $9x^4$, $-7x$, and -1.

Expression	Terms
$4x^2 + 3x$	$4x^2, 3x$
$9x^4 - 7x - 1$	$9x^4, -7x, -1$
$7y^3$	$7y^3$

The **numerical coefficient** of a term, or simply the **coefficient,** is the numerical factor of each term. If no numerical factor appears in the term, then the coefficient is understood to be 1. If the term is a number only, it is called a **constant term** or simply a **constant.**

Term	Coefficient
x^5	1
$3x^2$	3
$-4x$	-4
$-x^7y$	-1
3 (constant)	3

Example 1 Complete the table for the expression $7x^5 - 8x^4 + x^2 - 3x + 5$.

Term	Coefficient
x^2	
	-8
$-3x$	
	7
5	

Solution: The completed table is shown below.

Term	Coefficient
x^2	1
$-8x^4$	-8
$-3x$	-3
$7x^5$	7
5	5

Work Practice 1

Objectives

A Define Term and Coefficient of a Term.

B Define Polynomial, Monomial, Binomial, Trinomial, and Degree.

C Evaluate Polynomials for Given Replacement Values.

D Simplify a Polynomial by Combining Like Terms.

E Simplify a Polynomial in Several Variables.

F Write a Polynomial in Descending Powers of the Variable and with No Missing Powers of the Variable.

PRACTICE 1

Complete the table for the expression $-6x^6 + 4x^5 + 7x^3 - 9x^2 - 1$.

Term	Coefficient
$7x^3$	
	-9
$-6x^6$	
	4
-1	

Answer

1. term: $-9x^2$, $4x^5$; coefficient: 7, -6, -1

Objective B Defining Polynomial, Monomial, Binomial, Trinomial, and Degree

Now we are ready to define what we mean by a polynomial.

Polynomial

A **polynomial in x** is a finite sum of terms of the form ax^n, where a is a real number and n is a whole number.

For example,

$$x^5 - 3x^3 + 2x^2 - 5x + 1$$

is a polynomial in x. Notice that this polynomial is written in **descending powers** of x, because the powers of x decrease from left to right. (Recall that the term 1 can be thought of as $1x^0$.)

On the other hand,

$$x^{-5} + 2x - 3$$

is **not** a polynomial because one of its terms contains a variable with an exponent, -5, that is not a whole number.

Types of Polynomials

A **monomial** is a polynomial with exactly one term.

A **binomial** is a polynomial with exactly two terms.

A **trinomial** is a polynomial with exactly three terms.

The following are examples of monomials, binomials, and trinomials. Each of these examples is also a polynomial.

Polynomials			
Monomials	**Binomials**	**Trinomials**	**More than Three Terms**
ax^2	$x + y$	$x^2 + 4xy + y^2$	$5x^3 - 6x^2 + 3x - 6$
$-3z$	$3p + 2$	$x^5 + 7x^2 - x$	$-y^5 + y^4 - 3y^3 - y^2 + y$
4	$4x^2 - 7$	$-q^4 + q^3 - 2q$	$x^6 + x^4 - x^3 + 1$

Each term of a polynomial has a degree. The **degree of a term in one variable** is the exponent on the variable.

PRACTICE 2

Identify the degree of each term of the trinomial $-15x^3 + 2x^2 - 5$.

Example 2 Identify the degree of each term of the trinomial $12x^4 - 7x + 3$.

Solution: The term $12x^4$ has degree 4.

The term $-7x$ has degree 1 since $-7x$ is $-7x^1$.

The term 3 has degree 0 since 3 is $3x^0$.

Work Practice 2

Each polynomial also has a degree.

Degree of a Polynomial

The **degree of a polynomial** is the greatest degree of any term of the polynomial.

Answer

2. 3; 2; 0

Example 3 Find the degree of each polynomial and tell whether the polynomial is a monomial, binomial, trinomial, or none of these.

a. $-2t^2 + 3t + 6$ **b.** $15x - 10$ **c.** $7x + 3x^3 + 2x^2 - 1$

Solution:

a. The degree of the trinomial $-2t^2 + 3t + 6$ is 2, the greatest degree of any of its terms.

b. The degree of the binomial $15x - 10$ or $15x^1 - 10$ is 1.

c. The degree of the polynomial $7x + 3x^3 + 2x^2 - 1$ is 3. The polynomial is neither a monomial, binomial, nor trinomial.

Work Practice 3

PRACTICE 3

Find the degree of each polynomial and tell whether the polynomial is a monomial, binomial, trinomial, or none of these.

a. $-6x + 14$

b. $9x - 3x^6 + 5x^4 + 2$

c. $10x^2 - 6x - 6$

Objective C Evaluating Polynomials

Polynomials have different values depending on the replacement values for the variables. When we find the value of a polynomial for a given replacement value, we are evaluating the polynomial for that value.

Example 4 Evaluate each polynomial when $x = -2$.

a. $-5x + 6$ **b.** $3x^2 - 2x + 1$

Solution:

a. $-5x + 6 = -5(-2) + 6$ Replace x with -2.

$= 10 + 6$

$= 16$

b. $3x^2 - 2x + 1 = 3(-2)^2 - 2(-2) + 1$ Replace x with -2.

$= 3(4) + 4 + 1$

$= 12 + 4 + 1$

$= 17$

Work Practice 4

PRACTICE 4

Evaluate each polynomial when $x = -1$.

a. $-2x + 10$

b. $6x^2 + 11x - 20$

Many physical phenomena can be modeled by polynomials.

Example 5 Finding Free-Fall Time

The Swiss Re Building, completed in London in 2003, is a unique building. Londoners often refer to it as the "pickle building." The building is 592.1 feet tall. An object is dropped from the highest point of this building. Neglecting air resistance, the height in feet of the object above ground at time t seconds is given by the polynomial $-16t^2 + 592.1$. Find the height of the object when $t = 1$ second and when $t = 6$ seconds.

Solution: To find each height, we evaluate the polynomial when $t = 1$ and when $t = 6$.

$-16t^2 + 592.1 = -16(1)^2 + 592.1$ Replace t with 1.

$= -16(1) + 592.1$

$= -16 + 592.1$

$= 576.1$

Continued on next page

PRACTICE 5

Find the height of the object in Example 5 when $t = 2$ seconds and $t = 4$ seconds.

Answers

3. a. binomial, 1 **b.** none of these, 6 **c.** trinomial, 2 **4. a.** 12 **b.** -25 **5.** 528.1 feet, 336.1 feet

The height of the object at 1 second is 576.1 feet.

$$-16t^2 + 592.1 = -16(6)^2 + 592.1 \quad \text{Replace } t \text{ with 6.}$$
$$= -16(36) + 592.1$$
$$= -576 + 592.1 = 16.1$$

The height of the object at 6 seconds is 16.1 feet.

Work Practice 5

Objective D Simplifying Polynomials by Combining Like Terms

We can simplify polynomials with like terms by combining the like terms. Recall from Section 1.8 that like terms are terms that contain exactly the same variables raised to exactly the same powers.

Like Terms	Unlike Terms
$5x^2, -7x^2$	$3x, 3y$
$y, 2y$	$-2x^2, -5x$
$\frac{1}{2}a^2b, -a^2b$	$6st^2, 4s^2t$

Only like terms can be combined. We combine like terms by applying the distributive property.

Examples Simplify each polynomial by combining any like terms.

6. $-3x + 7x = (-3 + 7)x = 4x$

7. $11x^2 + 5 + 2x^2 - 7 = 11x^2 + 2x^2 + 5 - 7$
$= 13x^2 - 2$

8. $9x^3 + x^3 = 9x^3 + 1x^3$ Write x^3 as $1x^3$.
$= 10x^3$

9. $5x^2 + 6x - 9x - 3 = 5x^2 - 3x - 3$ Combine like terms $6x$ and $-9x$.

10. $\frac{2}{5}x^4 + \frac{2}{3}x^3 - x^2 + \frac{1}{10}x^4 - \frac{1}{6}x^3$

$$= \left(\frac{2}{5} + \frac{1}{10}\right)x^4 + \left(\frac{2}{3} - \frac{1}{6}\right)x^3 - x^2$$
$$= \left(\frac{4}{10} + \frac{1}{10}\right)x^4 + \left(\frac{4}{6} - \frac{1}{6}\right)x^3 - x^2$$

PRACTICE 6–10

Simplify each polynomial by combining any like terms.

6. $-6y + 8y$
7. $14y^2 + 3 - 10y^2 - 9$
8. $7x^3 + x^3$
9. $23x^2 - 6x - x - 15$
10. $\frac{2}{7}x^3 - \frac{1}{4}x + 2 - \frac{1}{2}x^3 + \frac{3}{8}x$

Answers

6. $2y$ 7. $4y^2 - 6$ 8. $8x^3$
9. $23x^2 - 7x - 15$
10. $-\frac{3}{14}x^3 + \frac{1}{8}x + 2$

$$= \frac{5}{10}x^4 + \frac{3}{6}x^3 - x^2$$

$$= \frac{1}{2}x^4 + \frac{1}{2}x^3 - x^2$$

Work Practice 6–10

Example 11 Write a polynomial that describes the total area of the squares and rectangles shown below. Then simplify the polynomial.

Solution: Recall that the area of a rectangle is length times width.

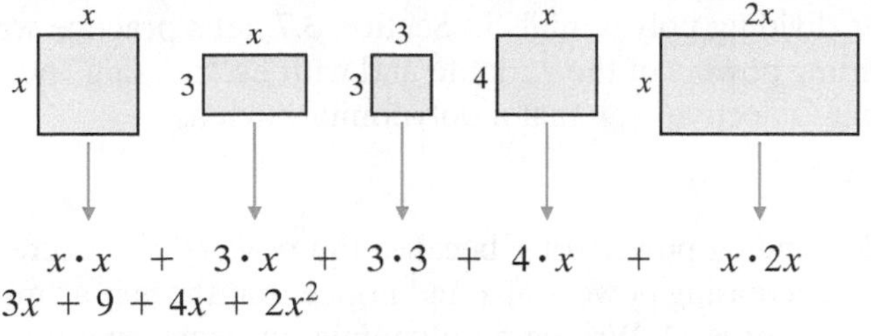

Area: $x \cdot x + 3 \cdot x + 3 \cdot 3 + 4 \cdot x + x \cdot 2x$

$= x^2 + 3x + 9 + 4x + 2x^2$

$= 3x^2 + 7x + 9$ Combine like terms.

Work Practice 11

PRACTICE 11

Write a polynomial that describes the total area of the squares and rectangles shown below. Then simplify the polynomial.

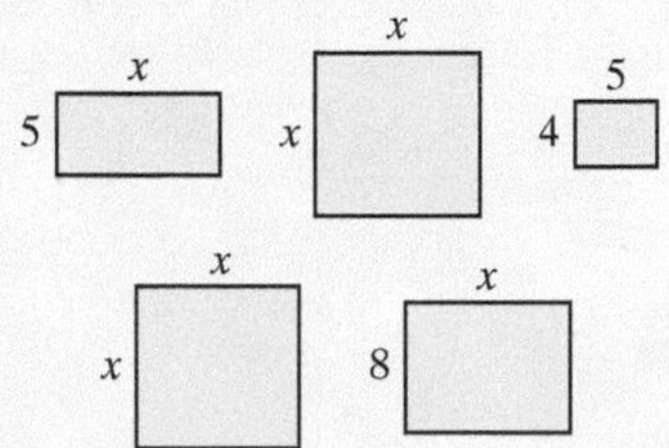

Objective E Simplifying Polynomials Containing Several Variables

A polynomial may contain more than one variable. One example is

$$5x + 3xy^2 - 6x^2y^2 + x^2y - 2y + 1$$

We call this expression a polynomial in several variables.

The **degree of a term** with more than one variable is the sum of the exponents on the variables. The **degree of a polynomial** in several variables is still the greatest degree of the terms of the polynomial.

Example 12 Identify the degrees of the terms and the degree of the polynomial $5x + 3xy^2 - 6x^2y^2 + x^2y - 2y + 1$.

Solution: To organize our work, we use a table.

Terms of Polynomial	Degree of Term	Degree of Polynomial
$5x$	1	
$3xy^2$	1 + 2, or 3	
$-6x^2y^2$	2 + 2, or 4	4 (greatest degree)
x^2y	2 + 1, or 3	
$-2y$	1	
1	0	

Work Practice 12

PRACTICE 12

Identify the degrees of the terms and the degree of the polynomial $-2x^3y^2 + 4 - 8xy + 3x^3y + 5xy^2$.

To simplify a polynomial containing several variables, we combine any like terms.

Answers

11. $5x + x^2 + 20 + x^2 + 8x$; $2x^2 + 13x + 20$

12. 5, 0, 2, 4, 3; 5

PRACTICE 13–14

Simplify each polynomial by combining any like terms.

13. $11ab - 6a^2 - ba + 8b^2$

14. $7x^2y^2 + 2y^2 - 4y^2x^2 + x^2 - y^2 + 5x^2$

Examples Simplify each polynomial by combining any like terms.

13. $3xy - 5y^2 + 7yx - 9x^2 = (3 + 7)xy - 5y^2 - 9x^2$
$= 10xy - 5y^2 - 9x^2$

14. $9a^2b - 6a^2 + 5b^2 + a^2b - 11a^2 + 2b^2$
$= 10a^2b - 17a^2 + 7b^2$

Work Practice 13–14

Helpful Hint This term can be written as $7yx$ or $7xy$.

Objective F Inserting "Missing" Terms

To prepare for dividing polynomials in Section 3.7, let's practice writing a polynomial in descending powers of the variable and with no "missing" powers.

Recall from Objective B that a polynomial such as

$$x^5 - 3x^3 + 2x^2 - 5x + 1$$

is written in descending powers of x because the powers of x decrease from left to right. Study the decreasing powers of x and notice that there is a "missing" power of x. This missing power is x^4. Writing a polynomial in decreasing powers of the variable helps you immediately determine important features of the polynomial, such as its degree. It is also sometimes helpful to write a polynomial so that there are no "missing" powers of x. For our polynomial above, if we simply insert a term of $0x^4$, which equals 0, we have an equivalent polynomial with no missing powers of x.

$$x^5 - 3x^3 + 2x^2 - 5x + 1 = x^5 + 0x^4 - 3x^3 + 2x^2 - 5x + 1$$

PRACTICE 15

Write each polynomial in descending powers of the variable with no missing powers.

a. $x^2 + 9$

b. $9m^3 + m^2 - 5$

c. $-3a^3 + a^4$

Example 15 Write each polynomial in descending powers of the variable with no missing powers.

a. $x^2 - 4$

b. $3m^3 - m + 1$

c. $2x + x^4$

Solution:

a. $x^2 - 4 = x^2 + 0x^1 - 4$ or $x^2 + 0x - 4$ Insert a missing term of $0x^1$ or $0x$.

b. $3m^3 - m + 1 = 3m^3 + 0m^2 - m + 1$ Insert a missing term of $0m^2$.

c. $2x + x^4 = x^4 + 2x$ Write in descending powers of variable.
$= x^4 + 0x^3 + 0x^2 + 2x + 0x^0$ Insert missing terms of $0x^3$, $0x^2$, and $0x^0$ (or 0).

Work Practice 15

Helpful Hint

Since there is no constant as a last term, we insert a $0x^0$. This $0x^0$ (or 0) is the final power of x in our polynomial.

Answers

13. $10ab - 6a^2 + 8b^2$

14. $3x^2y^2 + y^2 + 6x^2$

15. a. $x^2 + 0x + 9$
b. $9m^3 + m^2 + 0m - 5$
c. $a^4 - 3a^3 + 0a^2 + 0a + 0a^0$

Vocabulary and Readiness Check

Use the choices below to fill in each blank. Not all choices will be used.

least   monomial   trinomial   coefficient

greatest   binomial   constant

1. A ________ is a polynomial with exactly two terms.
2. A ________ is a polynomial with exactly one term.
3. A ________ is a polynomial with exactly three terms.
4. The numerical factor of a term is called the ________.
5. A number term is also called a ________.
6. The degree of a polynomial is the ________ degree of any term of the polynomial.

3.3 Exercise Set

FOR EXTRA HELP

Objective A *Complete each table for each polynomial. See Example 1.*

1. $x^2 - 3x + 5$

Term	Coefficient
x^2	
	-3
5	

2. $2x^3 - x + 4$

Term	Coefficient
	2
$-x$	
4	

3. $-5x^4 + 3.2x^2 + x - 5$

Term	Coefficient
$-5x^4$	
$3.2x^2$	
x	
-5	

4. $9.7x^7 - 3x^5 + x^3 - \frac{1}{4}x^2$

Term	Coefficient
$9.7x^7$	
$-3x^5$	
x^3	
$-\frac{1}{4}x^2$	

Objective B *Find the degree of each polynomial and determine whether it is a monomial, binomial, trinomial, or none of these. See Examples 2 and 3.*

5. $x + 2$

6. $-6y + 4$

7. $9m^3 - 5m^2 + 4m - 8$

8. $a + 5a^2 + 3a^3 - 4a^4$

9. $12x^4 - x^6 - 12x^2$

10. $7r^2 + 2r - 3r^5$

11. $3z - 5z^4$

12. $5y^6 + 2$

Objective C *Evaluate each polynomial when **(a)** $x = 0$ and **(b)** $x = -1$. See Examples 4 and 5.*

13. $5x - 6$

14. $2x - 10$

15. $x^2 - 5x - 2$

16. $x^2 + 3x - 4$

17. $-x^3 + 4x^2 - 15$

18. $-2x^3 + 3x^2 - 6$

A rocket is fired upward from the ground with an initial velocity of 200 feet per second. Neglecting air resistance, the height of the rocket at any time t can be described in feet by the polynomial $-16t^2 + 200t$. Find the height of the rocket at the time given in Exercises 19 through 22. See Example 5.

	Time, t (in seconds)	Height $-16t^2 + 200t$
19.	1	
20.	5	
21.	7.6	
22.	10.3	

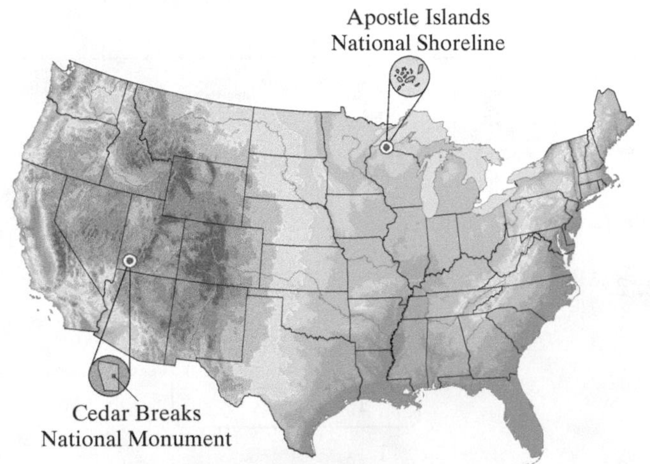

23. The polynomial $-7.5x^2 + 93x - 100$ models the yearly number of visitors (in thousands) x years after 2000 at Apostle Islands National Park. Use this polynomial to estimate the number of visitors to the park in 2008 ($x = 8$).

24. The polynomial $8x^2 - 90.6x + 752$ models the yearly number of visitors (in thousands) x years after 2000 at Cedar Breaks National Park. Use this polynomial to estimate the number of visitors to the park in 2007 ($x = 7$).

25. The number of wireless telephone subscribers (in millions) x years after 1995 is given by the polynomial $0.52x^2 + 11.4x + 27.87$ for 1995 through 2008. Use this model to predict the number of wireless telephone subscribers in 2012 ($x = 17$). (*Source:* Based on data from Cellular Telecommunications & Internet Association)

26. The penetration rate of American wireless telephone subscribers—that is, the percent of the population who have cell phones—x years after 1995 is given by $0.1x^2 + 4.4x + 10.7$ for 1995 through 2008. Assuming the same rate of growth, use this model to predict the penetration rate of wireless subscribers in the United States in 2010 ($x = 15$). (*Source:* Based on data from Cellular Telecommunications & Internet Association)

Objective D *Simplify each expression by combining like terms. See Examples 6 through 10.*

27. $9x - 20x$

28. $14y - 30y$

29. $14x^3 + 9x^3$

30. $18x^3 + 4x^3$

31. $7x^2 + 3 + 9x^2 - 10$

32. $8x^2 + 4 + 11x^2 - 20$

33. $15x^2 - 3x^2 - 13$

34. $12k^3 - 9k^3 + 11$

35. $8s - 5s + 4s$

36. $5y + 7y - 6y$

37. $0.1y^2 - 1.2y^2 + 6.7 - 1.9$

38. $7.6y + 3.2y^2 - 8y - 2.5y^2$

39. $\frac{2}{3}x^4 + 12x^3 + \frac{1}{6}x^4 - 19x^3 - 19$

40. $\frac{2}{5}x^4 - 23x^2 + \frac{1}{15}x^4 + 5x^2 - 5$

41. $\frac{3}{20}x^3 + \frac{1}{10} - \frac{3}{10}x - \frac{1}{5} - \frac{7}{20}x + 6x^2$

42. $\frac{5}{16}x^3 - \frac{1}{8} + \frac{3}{8}x + \frac{1}{4} - \frac{9}{16}x - 14x^2$

Write a polynomial that describes the total area of each set of rectangles and squares shown in Exercises 43 and 44. Then simplify the polynomial. See Example 11.

△ **43.**

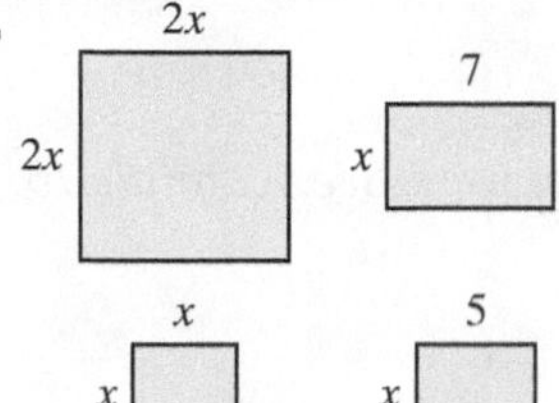

△ **44.**

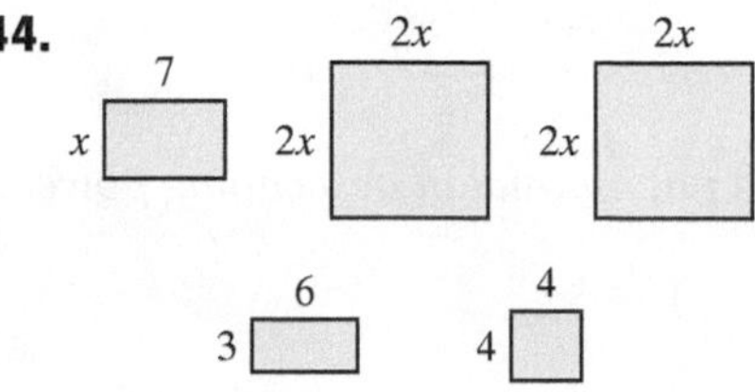

Recall that the perimeter of a figure such as the ones shown in Exercises 45 and 46 is the sum of the lengths of its sides. Write each perimeter as a polynomial. Then simplify the polynomial.

△ **45.**

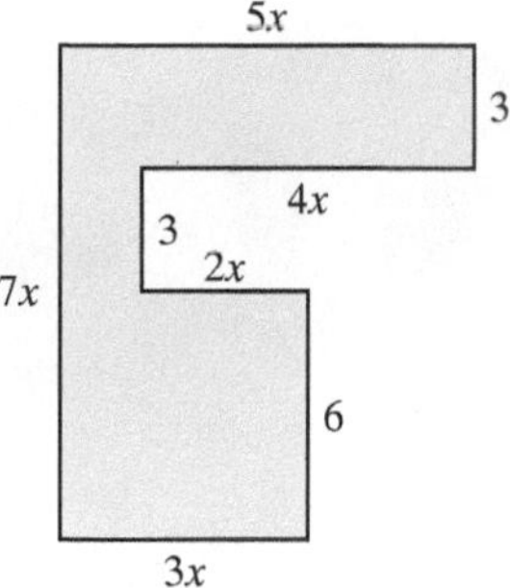

△ **46.**

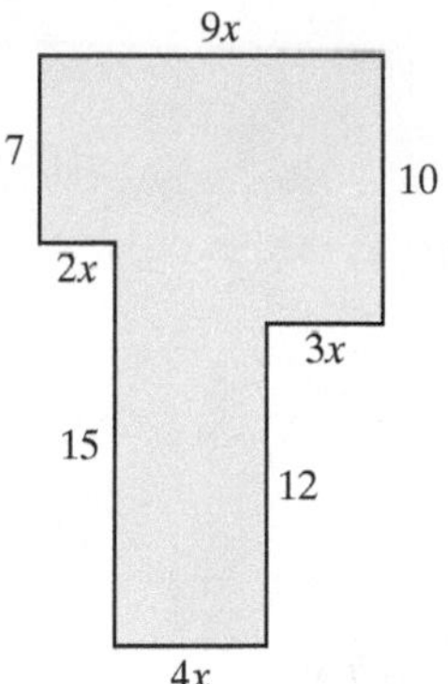

Objective **E** *Identify the degrees of the terms and the degree of the polynomial. See Example 12.*

47. $9ab - 6a + 5b - 3$

48. $y^4 - 6y^3x + 2x^2y^2 - 5y^2 + 3$

49. $x^3y - 6 + 2x^2y^2 + 5y^3$

50. $2a^2b + 10a^4b - 9ab + 6$

Simplify each polynomial by combining any like terms. See Examples 13 and 14.

51. $3ab - 4a + 6ab - 7a$

52. $-9xy + 7y - xy - 6y$

53. $4x^2 - 6xy + 3y^2 - xy$

54. $3a^2 - 9ab + 4b^2 - 7ab$

55. $5x^2y + 6xy^2 - 5yx^2 + 4 - 9y^2x$

56. $17a^2b - 16ab^2 + 3a^3 + 4ba^3 - b^2a$

57. $14y^3 - 9 + 3a^2b^2 - 10 - 19b^2a^2$

58. $18x^4 + 2x^3y^3 - 1 - 2y^3x^3 - 17x^4$

Objective **F** *Write each polynomial in descending powers of the variable and with no missing powers. See Example 15.*

59. $7x^2 + 3$

60. $5x^2 - 2$

61. $x^3 - 64$

62. $x^3 - 8$

63. $5y^3 + 2y - 10$

64. $6m^3 - 3m + 4$

65. $8y + 2y^4$

66. $11z + 4z^4$

67. $6x^5 + x^3 - 3x + 15$

68. $9y^5 - y^2 + 2y - 11$

Review

Simplify each expression. See Section 1.8.

69. $4 + 5(2x + 3)$

70. $9 - 6(5x + 1)$

71. $2(x - 5) + 3(5 - x)$

72. $-3(w + 7) + 5(w + 1)$

Concept Extensions

73. Describe how to find the degree of a term.

74. Describe how to find the degree of a polynomial.

75. Explain why xyz is a monomial while $x + y + z$ is a trinomial.

76. Explain why the degree of the term $5y^3$ is 3 and the degree of the polynomial $2y + y + 2y$ is 1.

Simplify, if possible.

77. $x^4 \cdot x^9$

78. $x^4 + x^9$

79. $a \cdot b^3 \cdot a^2 \cdot b^7$

80. $a + b^3 + a^2 + b^7$

81. $(y^5)^4 + (y^2)^{10}$

82. $x^5y^2 + y^2x^5$

Fill in the boxes so that the terms in each expression can be combined. Then simplify. Each exercise has more than one solution.

83. $7x^{\square} + 2x^{\square}$

84. $(3y^2)^{\square} + (4y^3)^{\square}$

85. Explain why the height of the rocket in Exercises 19 through 22 increases and then decreases as time passes.

86. Approximate (to the nearest tenth of a second) how long before the rocket in Exercises 19 through 22 hits the ground.

Simplify each polynomial by combining like terms.

87. $1.85x^2 - 3.76x + 9.25x^2 + 10.76 - 4.21x$

88. $7.75x + 9.16x^2 - 1.27 - 14.58x^2 - 18.34$

Objectives

A Add Polynomials.

B Subtract Polynomials.

C Add or Subtract Polynomials in One Variable.

D Add or Subtract Polynomials in Several Variables.

3.4 ADDING AND SUBTRACTING POLYNOMIALS

Objective A Adding Polynomials

To add polynomials, we use commutative and associative properties and then combine like terms. To see if you are ready to add polynomials, try the Concept Check.

✓**Concept Check** When combining like terms in the expression $5x - 8x^2 - 8x$, which of the following is the proper result?

a. $-11x^2$ **b.** $-3x - 8x^2$ **c.** $-11x$ **d.** $-11x^4$

To Add Polynomials

To add polynomials, combine all like terms.

PRACTICE 1–2

Add.

1. $(3x^5 - 7x^3 + 2x - 1) + (3x^3 - 2x)$

2. $(5x^2 - 2x + 1) + (-6x^2 + x - 1)$

Examples Add.

1. $(4x^3 - 6x^2 + 2x + 7) + (5x^2 - 2x)$

$= 4x^3 - 6x^2 + 2x + 7 + 5x^2 - 2x$ Remove parentheses.

$= 4x^3 + (-6x^2 + 5x^2) + (2x - 2x) + 7$ Combine like terms.

$= 4x^3 - x^2 + 7$ Simplify.

2. $(-2x^2 + 5x - 1) + (-2x^2 + x + 3)$

$= -2x^2 + 5x - 1 - 2x^2 + x + 3$ Remove parentheses.

$= (-2x^2 - 2x^2) + (5x + 1x) + (-1 + 3)$ Combine like terms.

$= -4x^2 + 6x + 2$ Simplify.

Work Practice 1–2

Just as we can add numbers vertically, polynomials can be added vertically if we line up like terms underneath one another.

PRACTICE 3

Add $(9y^2 - 6y + 5)$ and $(4y + 3)$ using a vertical format.

Example 3 Add $(7y^3 - 2y^2 + 7)$ and $(6y^2 + 1)$ using a vertical format.

Solution: Vertically line up like terms and add.

$$\begin{array}{r} 7y^3 - 2y^2 + 7 \\ 6y^2 + 1 \\ \hline 7y^3 + 4y^2 + 8 \end{array}$$

Work Practice 3

Objective B Subtracting Polynomials

To subtract one polynomial from another, recall the definition of subtraction. To subtract a number, we add its opposite: $a - b = a + (-b)$. To subtract a polynomial, we also add its opposite. Just as $-b$ is the opposite of b, $-(x^2 + 5)$ is the opposite of $(x^2 + 5)$.

To Subtract Polynomials

To subtract two polynomials, change the signs of the terms of the polynomial being subtracted and then add.

Answers

1. $3x^5 - 4x^3 - 1$ **2.** $-x^2 - x$
3. $9y^2 - 2y + 8$

✓ **Concept Check Answer**

b

Example 4 Subtract: $(5x - 3) - (2x - 11)$

Solution: From the definition of subtraction, we have

$$\begin{aligned}(5x - 3) - (2x - 11) &= (5x - 3) + [-(2x - 11)] && \text{Add the opposite.}\\ &= (5x - 3) + (-2x + 11) && \text{Apply the distributive property.}\\ &= 5x - 3 - 2x + 11 && \text{Remove parentheses.}\\ &= 3x + 8 && \text{Combine like terms.}\end{aligned}$$

Work Practice 4

PRACTICE 4

Subtract:
$(9x + 5) - (4x - 3)$

Example 5 Subtract: $(2x^3 + 8x^2 - 6x) - (2x^3 - x^2 + 1)$

Solution: First, we change the sign of each term of the second polynomial; then we add.

$$\begin{aligned}&(2x^3 + 8x^2 - 6x) - (2x^3 - x^2 + 1)\\ &= (2x^3 + 8x^2 - 6x) + (-2x^3 + x^2 - 1)\\ &= 2x^3 + 8x^2 - 6x - 2x^3 + x^2 - 1\\ &= 2x^3 - 2x^3 + 8x^2 + x^2 - 6x - 1\\ &= 9x^2 - 6x - 1 \qquad \text{Combine like terms.}\end{aligned}$$

Work Practice 5

PRACTICE 5

Subtract:
$(4x^3 - 10x^2 + 1)$
$-(-4x^3 + x^2 - 11)$

Just as polynomials can be added vertically, so can they be subtracted vertically.

Example 6 Subtract $(5y^2 + 2y - 6)$ from $(-3y^2 - 2y + 11)$ using a vertical format.

Solution: Arrange the polynomials in a vertical format, lining up like terms.

$$\begin{array}{r} -3y^2 - 2y + 11 \\ \underline{-(5y^2 + 2y - 6)} \end{array} \qquad \begin{array}{r} -3y^2 - 2y + 11 \\ \underline{-5y^2 - 2y + 6} \\ -8y^2 - 4y + 17 \end{array}$$

Work Practice 6

PRACTICE 6

Subtract $(6y^2 - 3y + 2)$ from $(2y^2 - 2y + 7)$ using a vertical format.

Helpful Hint

Don't forget to change the sign of each term in the polynomial being subtracted.

Objective C Adding and Subtracting Polynomials in One Variable

Let's practice adding and subtracting polynomials in one variable.

Example 7 Subtract $(5z - 7)$ from the sum of $(8z + 11)$ and $(9z - 2)$.

Solution: Notice that $(5z - 7)$ is to be subtracted **from** a sum. The translation is

$$\begin{aligned}&[(8z + 11) + (9z - 2)] - (5z - 7)\\ &= 8z + 11 + 9z - 2 - 5z + 7 && \text{Remove grouping symbols.}\\ &= 8z + 9z - 5z + 11 - 2 + 7 && \text{Group like terms.}\\ &= 12z + 16 && \text{Combine like terms.}\end{aligned}$$

Work Practice 7

PRACTICE 7

Subtract $(3x + 1)$ from the sum of $(4x - 3)$ and $(12x - 5)$.

Answers

4. $5x + 8$ **5.** $8x^3 - 11x^2 + 12$
6. $-4y^2 + y + 5$ **7.** $13x - 9$

Objective D Adding and Subtracting Polynomials in Several Variables

Now that we know how to add or subtract polynomials in one variable, we can also add and subtract polynomials in several variables.

PRACTICE 8–9

Add or subtract as indicated.

8. $(2a^2 - ab + 6b^2) + (-3a^2 + ab - 7b^2)$

9. $(5x^2y^2 + 3 - 9x^2y + y^2) - (-x^2y^2 + 7 - 8xy^2 + 2y^2)$

Examples Add or subtract as indicated.

8. $(3x^2 - 6xy + 5y^2) + (-2x^2 + 8xy - y^2)$
$= 3x^2 - 6xy + 5y^2 - 2x^2 + 8xy - y^2$
$= x^2 + 2xy + 4y^2$ Combine like terms.

9. $(9a^2b^2 + 6ab - 3ab^2) - (5b^2a + 2ab - 3 - 9b^2)$
$= 9a^2b^2 + 6ab - 3ab^2 - 5b^2a - 2ab + 3 + 9b^2$
$= 9a^2b^2 + 4ab - 8ab^2 + 9b^2 + 3$ Combine like terms.

Work Practice 8–9

✓**Concept Check** If possible, simplify each expression by performing the indicated operation.

a. $2y + y$
b. $2y \cdot y$
c. $-2y - y$
d. $(-2y)(-y)$
e. $2x + y$

Answers

8. $-a^2 - b^2$
9. $6x^2y^2 - 4 - 9x^2y + 8xy^2 - y^2$

✓ **Concept Check Answers**

a. $3y$ b. $2y^2$ c. $-3y$ d. $2y^2$
e. cannot be simplified

Vocabulary and Readiness Check

Simplify by combining like terms if possible.

1. $-9y - 5y$ **2.** $6m^5 + 7m^5$ **3.** $x + 6x$

4. $7z - z$ **5.** $5m^2 + 2m$ **6.** $8p^3 + 3p^2$

3.4 Exercise Set

FOR EXTRA HELP

PRACTICE

WATCH

DOWNLOAD

READ

REVIEW

Objective A *Add. See Examples 1 and 2.*

1. $(3x + 7) + (9x + 5)$

2. $(-y - 2) + (3y + 5)$

3. $(-7x + 5) + (-3x^2 + 7x + 5)$

4. $(3x - 8) + (4x^2 - 3x + 3)$

5. $(-5x^2 + 3) + (2x^2 + 1)$

6. $(3x^2 + 7) + (3x^2 + 9)$

7. $(-3y^2 - 4y) + (2y^2 + y - 1)$

8. $(7x^2 + 2x - 9) + (-3x^2 + 5)$

9. $(1.2x^3 - 3.4x + 7.9) + (6.7x^3 + 4.4x^2 - 10.9)$

10. $(9.6y^3 + 2.7y^2 - 8.6) + (1.1y^3 - 8.8y + 11.6)$

11. $\left(\frac{3}{4}m^2 - \frac{2}{5}m + \frac{1}{8}\right) + \left(-\frac{1}{4}m^2 - \frac{3}{10}m + \frac{11}{16}\right)$

12. $\left(-\frac{4}{7}n^2 + \frac{5}{6}m - \frac{1}{20}\right) + \left(\frac{3}{7}n^2 - \frac{5}{12}m - \frac{3}{10}\right)$

Add using a vertical format. See Example 3.

13. $\begin{array}{r} 3t^2 + 4 \\ \underline{5t^2 - 8} \end{array}$

14. $\begin{array}{r} 7x^3 + 3 \\ \underline{2x^3 - 7} \end{array}$

15. $\begin{array}{r} 10a^3 - 8a^2 + 4a + 9 \\ \underline{5a^3 + 9a^2 - 7a + 7} \end{array}$

16. $\begin{array}{r} 2x^3 - 3x^2 + x - 4 \\ \underline{5x^3 + 2x^2 - 3x + 2} \end{array}$

Objective B *Subtract. See Examples 4 and 5.*

17. $(2x + 5) - (3x - 9)$

18. $(4 + 5a) - (-a - 5)$

19. $(5x^2 + 4) - (-2y^2 + 4)$

20. $(-7y^2 + 5) - (-8y^2 + 12)$

21. $3x - (5x - 9)$

22. $4 - (-y - 4)$

23. $(2x^2 + 3x - 9) - (-4x + 7)$

24. $(-7x^2 + 4x + 7) - (-8x + 2)$

25. $(5x + 8) - (-2x^2 - 6x + 8)$

26. $(-6y^2 + 3y - 4) - (9y^2 - 3y)$

27. $(0.7x^2 + 0.2x - 0.8) - (0.9x^2 + 1.4)$

28. $(-0.3y^2 + 0.6y - 0.3) - (0.5y^2 + 0.3)$

29. $\left(\frac{1}{4}z^2 - \frac{1}{5}z\right) - \left(-\frac{3}{20}z^2 + \frac{1}{10}z - \frac{7}{20}\right)$

30. $\left(\frac{1}{3}x^2 - \frac{2}{7}x\right) - \left(\frac{4}{21}x^2 + \frac{1}{21}x - \frac{2}{3}\right)$

Subtract using a vertical format. See Example 6.

31. $\begin{array}{r} 4z^2 - 8z + 3 \\ \underline{-(6z^2 + 8z - 3)} \end{array}$

32. $\begin{array}{r} 7a^2 - 9a + 6 \\ \underline{-(11a^2 - 4a + 2)} \end{array}$

33. $\begin{array}{r} 5u^5 - 4u^2 + 3u - 7 \\ \underline{-(3u^5 + 6u^2 - 8u + 2)} \end{array}$

34. $\begin{array}{r} 5x^3 - 4x^2 + 6x - 2 \\ \underline{-(3x^3 - 2x^2 - x - 4)} \end{array}$

Objectives A B C **Mixed Practice** *Add or subtract as indicated. See Examples 1 through 7.*

35. $(3x + 5) + (2x - 14)$

36. $(2y + 20) + (5y - 30)$

37. $(9x - 1) - (5x + 2)$

38. $(7y + 7) - (y - 6)$

39. $(14y + 12) + (-3y - 5)$

40. $(26y + 17) + (-20y - 10)$

41. $(x^2 + 2x + 1) - (3x^2 - 6x + 2)$

42. $(5y^2 - 3y - 1) - (2y^2 + y + 1)$

43. $(3x^2 + 5x - 8) + (5x^2 + 9x + 12) - (8x^2 - 14)$

44. $(2x^2 + 7x - 9) + (x^2 - x + 10) - (3x^2 - 30)$

45. $(-a^2 + 1) - (a^2 - 3) + (5a^2 - 6a + 7)$

46. $(-m^2 + 3) - (m^2 - 13) + (6m^2 - m + 1)$

Translating *Perform each indicated operation. See Examples 3, 6, and 7.*

47. Subtract $4x$ from $(7x - 3)$.

48. Subtract y from $(y^2 - 4y + 1)$.

49. Add $(4x^2 - 6x + 1)$ and $(3x^2 + 2x + 1)$.

50. Add $(-3x^2 - 5x + 2)$ and $(x^2 - 6x + 9)$.

51. Subtract $(5x + 7)$ from $(7x^2 + 3x + 9)$.

52. Subtract $(5y^2 + 8y + 2)$ from $(7y^2 + 9y - 8)$.

53. Subtract $(4y^2 - 6y - 3)$ from the sum of $(8y^2 + 7)$ and $(6y + 9)$.

54. Subtract $(4x^2 - 2x + 2)$ from the sum of $(x^2 + 7x + 1)$ and $(7x + 5)$.

55. Subtract $(3x^2 - 4)$ from the sum of $(x^2 - 9x + 2)$ and $(2x^2 - 6x + 1)$.

56. Subtract $(y^2 - 9)$ from the sum of $(3y^2 + y + 4)$ and $(2y^2 - 6y - 10)$.

Objective D *Add or subtract as indicated. See Examples 8 and 9.*

57. $(9a + 6b - 5) + (-11a - 7b + 6)$

58. $(3x - 2 + 6y) + (7x - 2 - y)$

59. $(4x^2 + y^2 + 3) - (x^2 + y^2 - 2)$

60. $(7a^2 - 3b^2 + 10) - (-2a^2 + b^2 - 12)$

61. $(x^2 + 2xy - y^2) + (5x^2 - 4xy + 20y^2)$

62. $(a^2 - ab + 4b^2) + (6a^2 + 8ab - b^2)$

63. $(11r^2s + 16rs - 3 - 2r^2s^2) - (3sr^2 + 5 - 9r^2s^2)$

64. $(3x^2y - 6xy + x^2y^2 - 5) - (11x^2y^2 - 1 + 5yx^2)$

For Exercises 65 through 68, find the perimeter of each figure.

65.

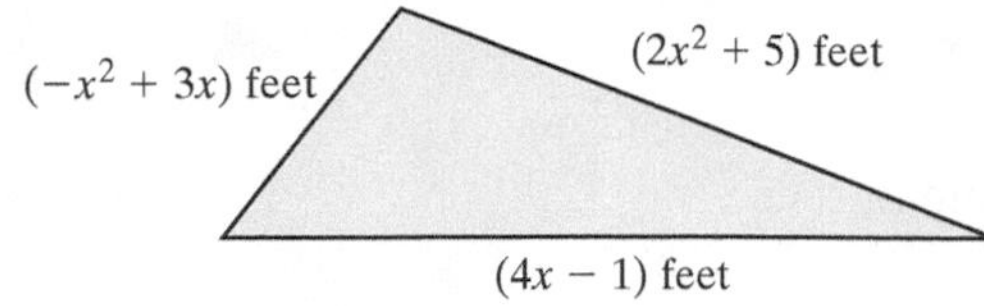

66.

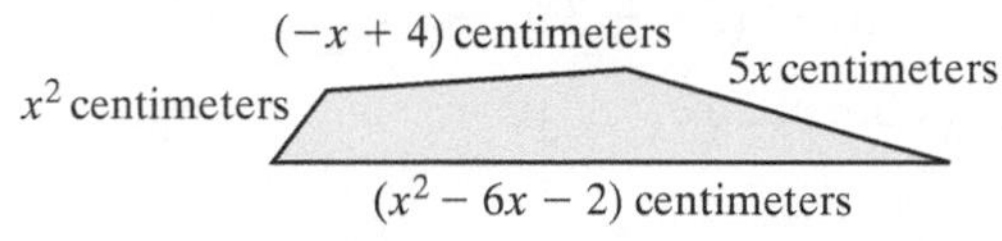

67.

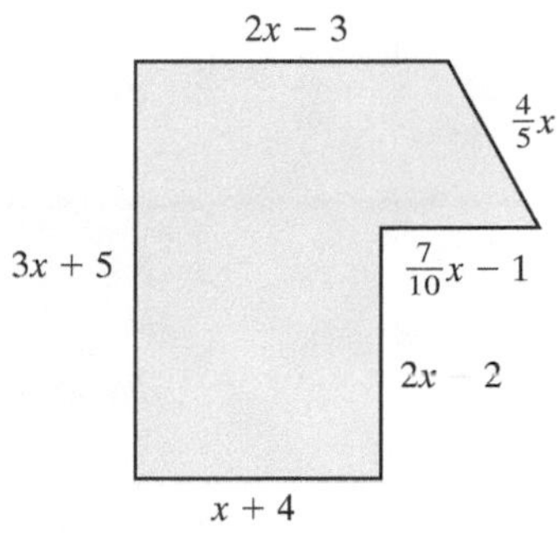

68.

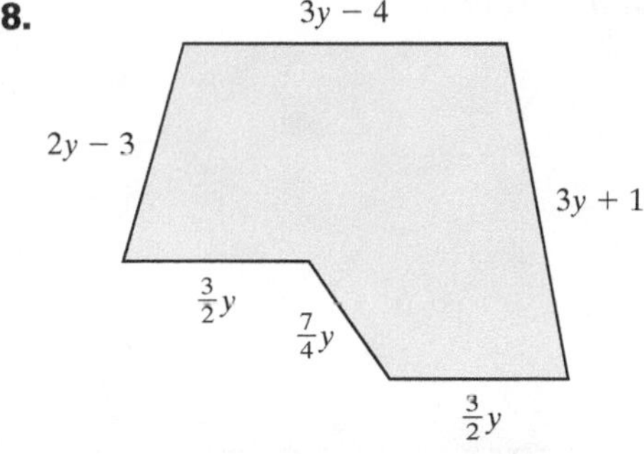

69. A wooden beam is $(4y^2 + 4y + 1)$ meters long. If a piece $(y^2 - 10)$ meters is cut off, express the length of the remaining piece of beam as a polynomial in y.

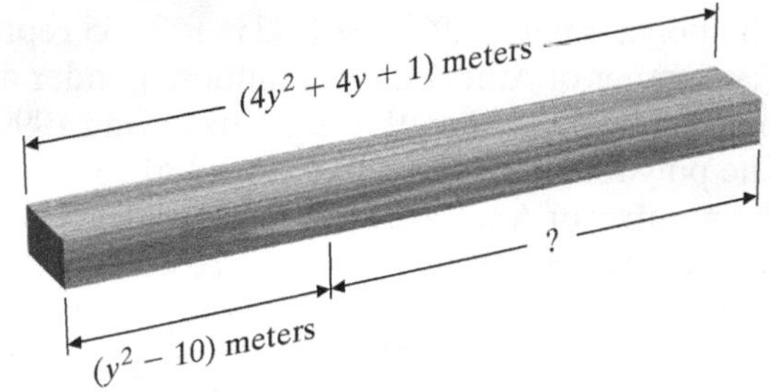

70. A piece of quarter-round molding is $(13x - 7)$ inches long. If a piece $(2x + 2)$ inches long is removed, express the length of the remaining piece of molding as a polynomial in x.

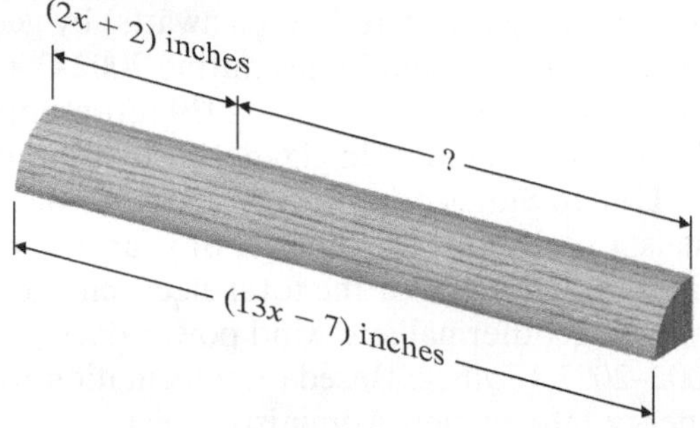

Perform each indicated operation.

71. $[(1.2x^2 - 3x + 9.1) - (7.8x^2 - 3.1 + 8)] + (1.2x - 6)$

72. $[(7.9y^4 - 6.8y^3 + 3.3y) + (6.1y^3 - 5)] - (4.2y^4 + 1.1y - 1)$

Review

Multiply. See Section 3.1.

73. $3x(2x)$

74. $-7x(x)$

75. $(12x^3)(-x^5)$

76. $6r^3(7r^{10})$

77. $10x^2(20xy^2)$

78. $-z^2y(11zy)$

Concept Extensions

Fill in the squares so that each is a true statement.

79. $3x^{\square} + 4x^2 = 7x^{\square}$

80. $9y^7 + 3y^{\square} = 12y^7$

81. $2x^{\square} + 3x^{\square} - 5x^{\square} + 4x^{\square} = 6x^4 - 2x^3$

82. $3y^{\square} + 7y^{\square} - 2y^{\square} - y^{\square} = 10y^5 - 3y^2$

Match each expression on the left with its simplification on the right. Not all letters on the right must be used and a letter may be used more than once.

83. $10y - 6y^2 - y$

84. $5x + 5x$

85. $(5x - 3) + (5x - 3)$

86. $(15x - 3) - (5x - 3)$

a. $3y$
b. $9y - 6y^2$
c. $10x$
d. $25x^2$
e. $10x - 6$
f. none of these

Simplify each expression by performing the indicated operation. Explain how you arrived at each answer. See the last Concept Check in this section.

87. a. $z + 3z$
b. $z \cdot 3z$
c. $-z - 3z$
d. $(-z)(-3z)$

88. a. $2y + y$
b. $2y \cdot y$
c. $-2y - y$
d. $(-2y)(-y)$

89. a. $m \cdot m \cdot m$
b. $m + m + m$
c. $(-m)(-m)(-m)$
d. $-m - m - m$

90. a. $x + x$
b. $x \cdot x$
c. $-x - x$
d. $(-x)(-x)$

91. The polynomial $-20x^2 + 156x + 14{,}437$ represents the electricity generated (in gigawatts) by geothermal sources in the United States during 2002–2007. The polynomial $894x^2 - 90x + 10{,}939$ represents the electricity generated (in gigawatts) by wind power in the United States during 2002–2007. In both polynomials, x represents the number of years after 2002. Find a polynomial for the total electricity generated by both geothermal and wind power during 2002–2007. (*Source:* Based on information from the Energy Information Administration)

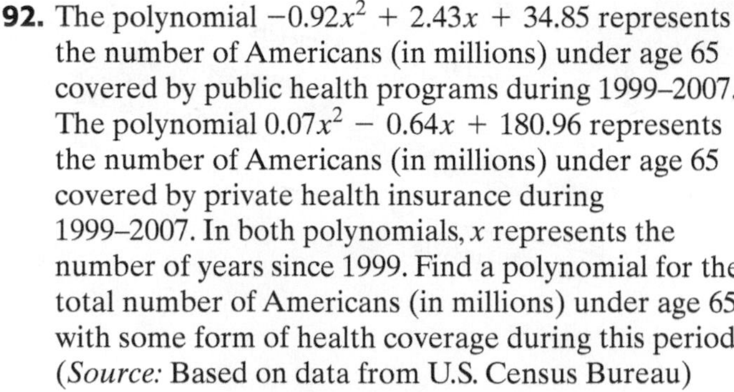

92. The polynomial $-0.92x^2 + 2.43x + 34.85$ represents the number of Americans (in millions) under age 65 covered by public health programs during 1999–2007. The polynomial $0.07x^2 - 0.64x + 180.96$ represents the number of Americans (in millions) under age 65 covered by private health insurance during 1999–2007. In both polynomials, x represents the number of years since 1999. Find a polynomial for the total number of Americans (in millions) under age 65 with some form of health coverage during this period. (*Source:* Based on data from U.S. Census Bureau)

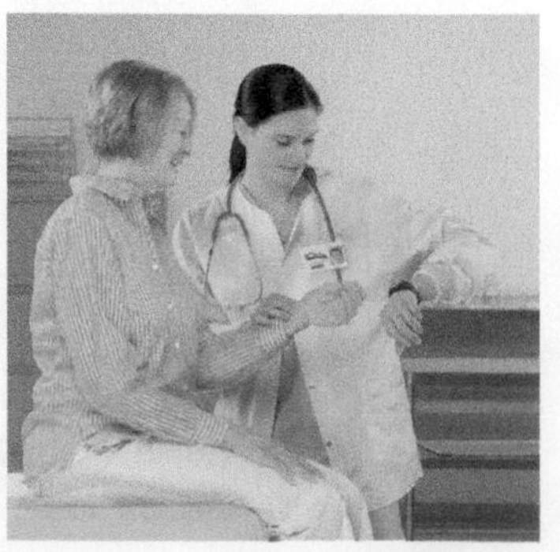

3.5 MULTIPLYING POLYNOMIALS

Objectives

A **Multiply Monomials.**

B **Multiply a Monomial by a Polynomial.**

C **Multiply Two Polynomials.**

D **Multiply Polynomials Vertically.**

Objective A Multiplying Monomials

Recall from Section 3.1 that to multiply two monomials such as $(-5x^3)$ and $(-2x^4)$, we use the associative and commutative properties and regroup. Remember also that to multiply exponential expressions with a common base, we use the product rule for exponents and add exponents.

$(-5x^3)(-2x^4) = (-5)(-2)(x^3 \cdot x^4)$ Use the commutative and associative properties.

$= 10x^7$ Multiply.

Examples Multiply.

1. $6x \cdot 4x = (6 \cdot 4)(x \cdot x)$ Use the commutative and associative properties.
   $= 24x^2$ Multiply.
2. $-7x^2 \cdot 2x^5 = (-7 \cdot 2)(x^2 \cdot x^5)$
   $= -14x^7$
3. $(-12x^5)(-x) = (-12x^5)(-1x)$
   $= (-12)(-1)(x^5 \cdot x)$
   $= 12x^6$

Work Practice 1–3

PRACTICE 1–3

Multiply.

1. $10x \cdot 9x$
2. $8x^3(-11x^7)$
3. $(-5x^4)(-x)$

✓Concept Check Simplify.

a. $3x \cdot 2x$ **b.** $3x + 2x$

Objective B Multiplying Monomials by Polynomials

To multiply a monomial such as $7x$ by a trinomial such as $x^2 + 2x + 5$, we use the distributive property.

Examples Multiply.

4. $7x(x^2 + 2x + 5) = 7x(x^2) + 7x(2x) + 7x(5)$ Apply the distributive property.
   $= 7x^3 + 14x^2 + 35x$ Multiply.
5. $5x(2x^3 + 6) = 5x(2x^3) + 5x(6)$ Apply the distributive property.
   $= 10x^4 + 30x$ Multiply.
6. $-3x^2(5x^2 + 6x - 1)$
   $= (-3x^2)(5x^2) + (-3x^2)(6x) + (-3x^2)(-1)$ Apply the distributive property.
   $= -15x^4 - 18x^3 + 3x^2$ Multiply.

Work Practice 4–6

PRACTICE 4–6

Multiply.

4. $4x(x^2 + 4x + 3)$
5. $8x(7x^4 + 1)$
6. $-2x^3(3x^2 - x + 2)$

Answers

1. $90x^2$ **2.** $-88x^{10}$ **3.** $5x^5$ **4.** $4x^3 + 16x^2 + 12x$ **5.** $56x^5 + 8x$ **6.** $-6x^5 + 2x^4 - 4x^3$

✓ Concept Check Answers

a. $6x^2$ **b.** $5x$

Objective C Multiplying Two Polynomials

We also use the distributive property to multiply two binomials.

PRACTICE 7

Multiply:

a. $(x + 5)(x + 10)$

b. $(4x + 5)(3x - 4)$

Example 7 Multiply.

a. $(m + 4)(m + 6)$ **b.** $(3x + 2)(2x - 5)$

Solution:

a. $(m + 4)(m + 6) = m(m + 6) + 4(m + 6)$ Use the distributive property.

$= m \cdot m + m \cdot 6 + 4 \cdot m + 4 \cdot 6$ Use the distributive property.

$= m^2 + 6m + 4m + 24$ Multiply.

$= m^2 + 10m + 24$ Combine like terms.

b. $(3x + 2)(2x - 5) = 3x(2x - 5) + 2(2x - 5)$ Use the distributive property.

$= 3x(2x) + 3x(-5) + 2(2x) + 2(-5)$

$= 6x^2 - 15x + 4x - 10$ Multiply.

$= 6x^2 - 11x - 10$ Combine like terms.

Work Practice 7

This idea can be expanded so that we can multiply any two polynomials.

To Multiply Two Polynomials

Multiply each term of the first polynomial by each term of the second polynomial, and then combine like terms.

PRACTICE 8–9

Multiply.

8. $(3x - 2y)^2$

9. $(x + 3)(2x^2 - 5x + 4)$

Examples Multiply.

8. $(2x - y)^2$

$= (2x - y)(2x - y)$ Using the meaning of an exponent, we have 2 factors of $(2x - y)$.

$= 2x(2x) + 2x(-y) + (-y)(2x) + (-y)(-y)$

$= 4x^2 - 2xy - 2xy + y^2$ Multiply.

$= 4x^2 - 4xy + y^2$ Combine like terms.

9. $(t + 2)(3t^2 - 4t + 2)$

$= t(3t^2) + t(-4t) + t(2) + 2(3t^2) + 2(-4t) + 2(2)$

$= 3t^3 - 4t^2 + 2t + 6t^2 - 8t + 4$

$= 3t^3 + 2t^2 - 6t + 4$ Combine like terms.

Work Practice 8–9

✓**Concept Check** Square where indicated. Simplify if possible.

a. $(4a)^2 + (3b)^2$ **b.** $(4a + 3b)^2$

Objective D Multiplying Polynomials Vertically

Another convenient method for multiplying polynomials is to multiply vertically, similar to the way we multiply real numbers. This method is shown in the next examples.

Answers

7. a. $x^2 + 15x + 50$

b. $12x^2 - x - 20$

8. $9x^2 - 12xy + 4y^2$

9. $2x^3 + x^2 - 11x + 12$

✓ **Concept Check Answers**

a. $16a^2 + 9b^2$ **b.** $16a^2 + 24ab + 9b^2$

Example 10 Multiply vertically: $(2y^2 + 5)(y^2 - 3y + 4)$

Solution:

$$\begin{array}{rl}
y^2 - 3y + 4 & \\
2y^2 + 5 & \\
\hline
5y^2 - 15y + 20 & \text{Multiply } y^2 - 3y + 4 \text{ by } 5. \\
2y^4 - 6y^3 + 8y^2 & \text{Multiply } y^2 - 3y + 4 \text{ by } 2y^2. \\
\hline
2y^4 - 6y^3 + 13y^2 - 15y + 20 & \text{Combine like terms.}
\end{array}$$

Work Practice 10

PRACTICE 10

Multiply vertically: $(3y^2 + 1)(y^2 - 4y + 5)$

Example 11 Find the product of $(2x^2 - 3x + 4)$ and $(x^2 + 5x - 2)$ using a vertical format.

Solution: First, we arrange the polynomials in a vertical format. Then we multiply each term of the second polynomial by each term of the first polynomial.

$$\begin{array}{rl}
2x^2 - 3x + 4 & \\
x^2 + 5x - 2 & \\
\hline
-4x^2 + 6x - 8 & \text{Multiply } 2x^2 - 3x + 4 \text{ by } -2. \\
10x^3 - 15x^2 + 20x & \text{Multiply } 2x^2 - 3x + 4 \text{ by } 5x. \\
2x^4 - 3x^3 + 4x^2 & \text{Multiply } 2x^2 - 3x + 4 \text{ by } x^2. \\
\hline
2x^4 + 7x^3 - 15x^2 + 26x - 8 & \text{Combine like terms.}
\end{array}$$

Work Practice 11

PRACTICE 11

Find the product of $(4x^2 - x - 1)$ and $(3x^2 + 6x - 2)$ using a vertical format.

Answers

10. $3y^4 - 12y^3 + 16y^2 - 4y + 5$
11. $12x^4 + 21x^3 - 17x^2 - 4x + 2$

Vocabulary and Readiness Check

Fill in each blank with the correct choice.

1. The expression $5x(3x + 2)$ equals $5x \cdot 3x + 5x \cdot 2$ by the ______________ property.
   a. commutative **b.** associative **c.** distributive
2. The expression $(x + 4)(7x - 1)$ equals $x(7x - 1) + 4(7x - 1)$ by the ______________ property.
   a. commutative **b.** associative **c.** distributive
3. The expression $(5y - 1)^2$ equals ______________.
   a. $2(5y - 1)$ **b.** $(5y - 1)(5y + 1)$ **c.** $(5y - 1)(5y - 1)$
4. The expression $9x \cdot 3x$ equals ______________.
   a. $27x$ **b.** $27x^2$ **c.** $12x$ **d.** $12x^2$

Perform the indicated operation, if possible.

5. $x^3 \cdot x^5$ **6.** $x^2 \cdot x^6$ **7.** $x^3 + x^5$ **8.** $x^2 + x^6$

9. $x^7 \cdot x^7$ **10.** $x^{11} \cdot x^{11}$ **11.** $x^7 + x^7$ **12.** $x^{11} + x^{11}$

13. $9y^2 \cdot 11y^2$ **14.** $6z^3 \cdot 7z^3$ **15.** $9y^2 + 11y^2$ **16.** $6z^3 + 7z^3$

3.5 Exercise Set

FOR EXTRA HELP

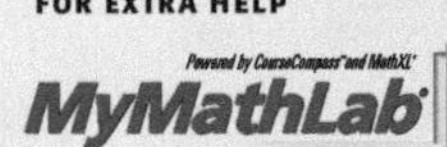

PRACTICE

WATCH

DOWNLOAD

READ

REVIEW

Objective A *Multiply. See Examples 1 through 3.*

1. $8x^2 \cdot 3x$ **2.** $6x \cdot 3x^2$ **3.** $(-x^3)(-x)$ **4.** $(-x^6)(-x)$

5. $-4n^3 \cdot 7n^7$ **6.** $9t^6(-3t^5)$ **7.** $(-3.1x^3)(4x^9)$ **8.** $(-5.2x^4)(3x^4)$

9. $\left(-\frac{1}{3}y^2\right)\left(\frac{2}{5}y\right)$ **10.** $\left(-\frac{3}{4}y^7\right)\left(\frac{1}{7}y^4\right)$ **11.** $(2x)(-3x^2)(4x^5)$ **12.** $(x)(5x^4)(-6x^7)$

Objective B *Multiply. See Examples 4 through 6.*

13. $3x(2x + 5)$ **14.** $2x(6x + 3)$ **15.** $7x(x^2 + 2x - 1)$ **16.** $5y(y^2 + y - 10)$

17. $-2a(a + 4)$ **18.** $-3a(2a + 7)$ **19.** $3x(2x^2 - 3x + 4)$ **20.** $4x(5x^2 - 6x - 10)$

21. $3a^2(4a^3 + 15)$ **22.** $9x^3(5x^2 + 12)$ **23.** $-2a^2(3a^2 - 2a + 3)$ **24.** $-4b^2(3b^3 - 12b^2 - 6)$

25. $3x^2y(2x^3 - x^2y^2 + 8y^3)$

26. $4xy^2(7x^3 + 3x^2y^2 - 9y^3)$

27. $-y(4x^3 - 7x^2y + xy^2 + 3y^3)$

28. $-x(6y^3 - 5xy^2 + x^2y - 5x^3)$

29. $\frac{1}{2}x^2(8x^2 - 6x + 1)$

30. $\frac{1}{3}y^2(9y^2 - 6y + 1)$

Objective C *Multiply. See Examples 7 through 9.*

31. $(x + 4)(x + 3)$

32. $(x + 2)(x + 9)$

33. $(a + 7)(a - 2)$

34. $(y - 10)(y + 11)$

35. $\left(x + \frac{2}{3}\right)\left(x - \frac{1}{3}\right)$

36. $\left(x + \frac{3}{5}\right)\left(x - \frac{2}{5}\right)$

37. $(3x^2 + 1)(4x^2 + 7)$

38. $(5x^2 + 2)(6x^2 + 2)$

39. $(4x - 3)(3x - 5)$

40. $(8x - 3)(2x - 4)$

41. $(1 - 3a)(1 - 4a)$

42. $(3 - 2a)(2 - a)$

43. $(2y - 4)^2$

44. $(6x - 7)^2$

45. $(x - 2)(x^2 - 3x + 7)$

46. $(x + 3)(x^2 + 5x - 8)$

47. $(x + 5)(x^3 - 3x + 4)$

48. $(a + 2)(a^3 - 3a^2 + 7)$

49. $(2a - 3)(5a^2 - 6a + 4)$

50. $(3 + b)(2 - 5b - 3b^2)$

51. $(7xy - y)^2$

52. $(x^2 - 4)^2$

Objective D *Multiply vertically. See Examples 10 and 11.*

53. $(2x - 11)(6x + 1)$

54. $(4x - 7)(5x + 1)$

55. $(x + 3)(2x^2 + 4x - 1)$

56. $(4x - 5)(8x^2 + 2x - 4)$

57. $(x^2 + 5x - 7)(2x^2 - 7x - 9)$

58. $(3x^2 - x + 2)(x^2 + 2x + 1)$

Objectives A B C D **Mixed Practice** *Multiply. See Examples 1 through 11.*

59. $-1.2y(-7y^6)$

60. $-4.2x(-2x^5)$

61. $-3x(x^2 + 2x - 8)$

62. $-5x(x^2 - 3x + 10)$

63. $(x + 19)(2x + 1)$

64. $(3y + 4)(y + 11)$

65. $\left(x + \frac{1}{7}\right)\left(x - \frac{3}{7}\right)$

66. $\left(m + \frac{2}{9}\right)\left(m - \frac{1}{9}\right)$

67. $(3y + 5)^2$

68. $(7y + 2)^2$

69. $(a + 4)(a^2 - 6a + 6)$

70. $(t + 3)(t^2 - 5t + 5)$

Express as the product of polynomials. Then multiply.

△ **71.** Find the area of the rectangle.

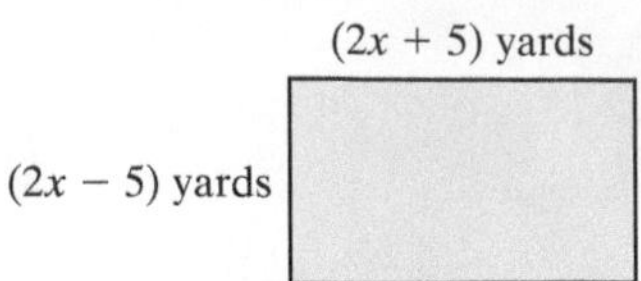

△ **72.** Find the area of the square field.

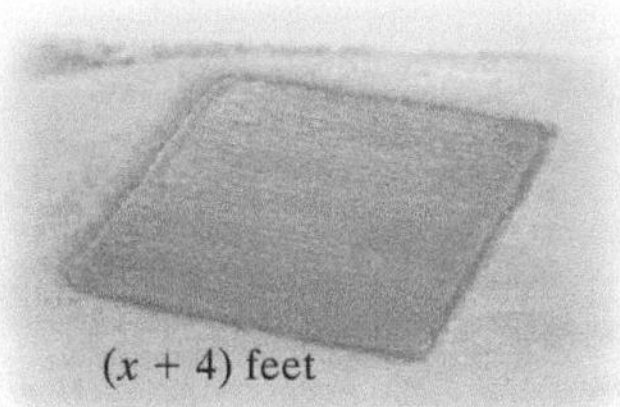

△ **73.** Find the area of the triangle.

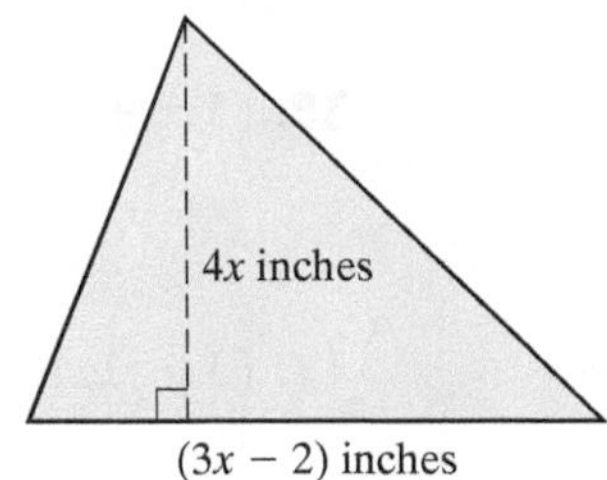

△ **74.** Find the volume of the cube-shaped glass block.

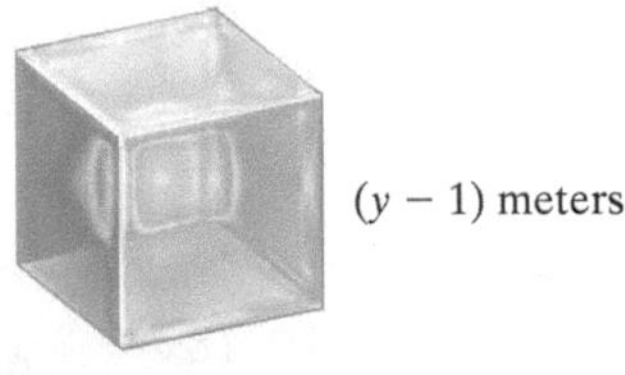

Review

In this section, we review operations on monomials. Study the box below, then proceed. See Sections 1.8, 3.1, and 3.2.

Operations on Monomials	
Multiply	Review the product rule for exponents.
Divide	Review the quotient rule for exponents.
Add or Subtract	Remember, we may only combine like terms.

Perform the operations on the monomials, if possible. The first two rows have been completed for you.

	Monomials	Add	Subtract	Multiply	Divide
	$6x, 3x$	$6x + 3x = 9x$	$6x - 3x = 3x$	$6x \cdot 3x = 18x^2$	$\frac{6x}{3x} = 2$
	$-12x^2, 2x$	$-12x^2 + 2x$; can't be simplified	$-12x^2 - 2x$; can't be simplified	$-12x^2 \cdot 2x = -24x^3$	$\frac{-12x^2}{2x} = -6x$
75.	$5a, 15a$				
76.	$4y^3, 4y^7$				
77.	$-3y^5, 9y^4$				
78.	$-14x^2, 2x^2$				

Concept Extensions

79. Perform each indicated operation. Explain the difference between the two expressions.

a. $(3x + 5) + (3x + 7)$
b. $(3x + 5)(3x + 7)$

80. Perform each indicated operation. Explain the difference between the two expressions.

a. $(8x - 3) - (5x - 2)$
b. $(8x - 3)(5x - 2)$

Mixed Practice *Perform the indicated operations. See Sections 3.4 and 3.5.*

81. $(3x - 1) + (10x - 6)$

82. $(2x - 1) + (10x - 7)$

83. $(3x - 1)(10x - 6)$

84. $(2x - 1)(10x - 7)$

85. $(3x - 1) - (10x - 6)$

86. $(2x - 1) - (10x - 7)$

87. The area of the largest rectangle below is $x(x + 3)$. Find another expression for this area by finding the sum of the areas of the smaller rectangles.

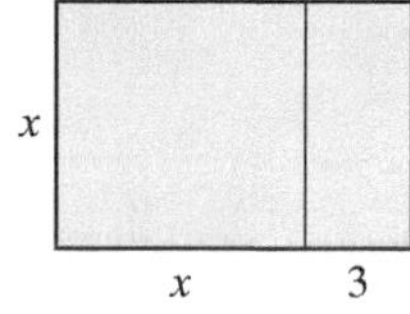

88. The area of the figure below is $(x + 2)(x + 3)$. Find another expression for this area by finding the sum of the areas of the smaller rectangles.

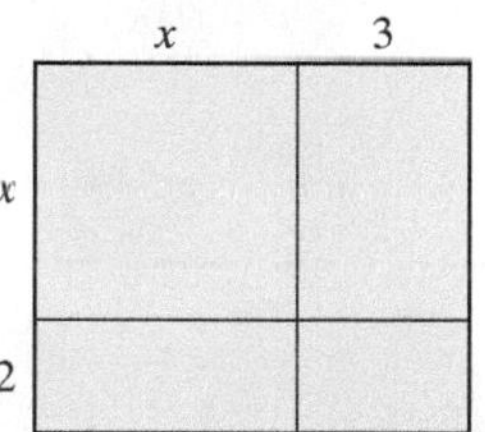

89. Write an expression for the area of the largest rectangle below in two different ways.

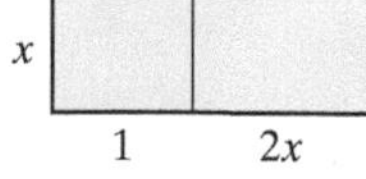

90. Write an expression for the area of the figure below in two different ways.

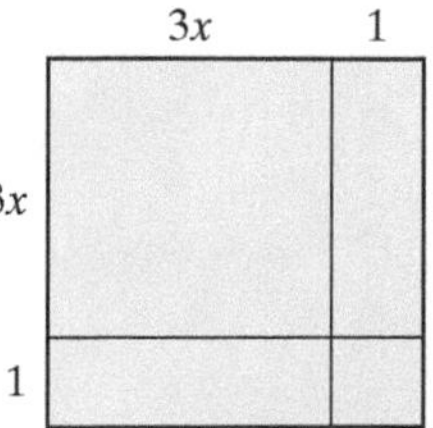

Simplify. See the Concept Checks in this section.

91. $5a + 6a$

92. $5a \cdot 6a$

Square where indicated. Simplify if possible.

93. $(5x)^2 + (2y)^2$

94. $(5x + 2y)^2$

95. Multiply each of the following polynomials.

a. $(a + b)(a - b)$
b. $(2x + 3y)(2x - 3y)$
c. $(4x + 7)(4x - 7)$
d. Can you make a general statement about all products of the form $(x + y)(x - y)$?

96. Evaluate each of the following.

a. $(2 + 3)^2$; $2^2 + 3^2$
b. $(8 + 10)^2$; $8^2 + 10^2$
c. Does $(a + b)^2 = a^2 + b^2$ no matter what the values of a and b are? Why or why not?

3.6 SPECIAL PRODUCTS

Objectives

A Multiply Two Binomials Using the FOIL Method.

B Square a Binomial.

C Multiply the Sum and Difference of Two Terms.

D Use Special Products to Multiply Binomials.

Objective A Using the FOIL Method

In this section, we multiply binomials using special products. First, we introduce a special order for multiplying binomials called the FOIL order or method. This order, or pattern, is a result of the distributive property. We demonstrate by multiplying $(3x + 1)$ by $(2x + 5)$.

The FOIL Method

F stands for the product of the **First** terms. $(3x + 1)(2x + 5)$

$(3x)(2x) = 6x^2$ F

O stands for the product of the **Outer** terms. $(3x + 1)(2x + 5)$

$(3x)(5) = 15x$ O

I stands for the product of the **Inner** terms. $(3x + 1)(2x + 5)$

$(1)(2x) = 2x$ I

L stands for the product of the **Last** terms. $(3x + 1)(2x + 5)$

$(1)(5) = 5$ L

$$\begin{aligned}(3x + 1)(2x + 5) &= \overset{F}{6x^2} + \overset{O}{15x} + \overset{I}{2x} + \overset{L}{5} \\ &= 6x^2 + 17x + 5 \quad \text{Combine like terms.}\end{aligned}$$

Let's practice multiplying binomials using the FOIL method.

Example 1 Multiply: $(x - 3)(x + 4)$

Solution:

$$\begin{aligned}(x - 3)(x + 4) &= \overset{F}{(x)(x)} + \overset{O}{(x)(4)} + \overset{I}{(-3)(x)} + \overset{L}{(-3)(4)} \\ &= x^2 + 4x - 3x - 12 \\ &= x^2 + x - 12 \quad \text{Combine like terms.}\end{aligned}$$

Work Practice 1

PRACTICE 1

Multiply: $(x + 7)(x - 5)$

Helpful Hint Remember that the FOIL order for multiplying can be used only for the product of 2 binomials.

Example 2 Multiply: $(5x - 7)(x - 2)$

Solution:

$$\begin{aligned}(5x - 7)(x - 2) &= \overset{F}{5x(x)} + \overset{O}{5x(-2)} + \overset{I}{(-7)(x)} + \overset{L}{(-7)(-2)} \\ &= 5x^2 - 10x - 7x + 14 \\ &= 5x^2 - 17x + 14 \quad \text{Combine like terms.}\end{aligned}$$

Work Practice 2

PRACTICE 2

Multiply: $(6x - 1)(x - 4)$

Answers

1. $x^2 + 2x - 35$ **2.** $6x^2 - 25x + 4$

PRACTICE 3

Multiply: $(2y^2 + 3)(y - 4)$

Example 3 Multiply: $(y^2 + 6)(2y - 1)$

Solution: F O I L

$$(y^2 + 6)(2y - 1) = 2y^3 - 1y^2 + 12y - 6$$

Notice in this example that there are no like terms that can be combined, so the product is $2y^3 - y^2 + 12y - 6$.

Work Practice 3

Objective B Squaring Binomials

An expression such as $(3y + 1)^2$ is called the square of a binomial. Since $(3y + 1)^2 = (3y + 1)(3y + 1)$, we can use the FOIL method to find this product.

PRACTICE 4

Multiply: $(2x + 9)^2$

Example 4 Multiply: $(3y + 1)^2$

Solution:

$$\begin{aligned}(3y + 1)^2 &= (3y + 1)(3y + 1) \\ &\quad\ \text{F} \qquad \text{O} \qquad \text{I} \qquad \text{L} \\ &= (3y)(3y) + (3y)(1) + 1(3y) + 1(1) \\ &= 9y^2 + 3y + 3y + 1 \\ &= 9y^2 + 6y + 1\end{aligned}$$

Work Practice 4

Notice the pattern that appears in Example 4.

$$(3y + 1)^2 = 9y^2 + 6y + 1$$

- $9y^2$ is the first term of the binomial squared: $(3y)^2 = 9y^2$.
- $6y$ is 2 times the product of both terms of the binomial: $(2)(3y)(1) = 6y$.
- 1 is the second term of the binomial squared: $(1)^2 = 1$.

This pattern leads to the formulas below, which can be used when squaring a binomial. We call these **special products.**

Squaring a Binomial

A binomial squared is equal to the square of the first term plus or minus twice the product of both terms plus the square of the second term.

$$(a + b)^2 = a^2 + 2ab + b^2$$
$$(a - b)^2 = a^2 - 2ab + b^2$$

This product can be visualized geometrically.

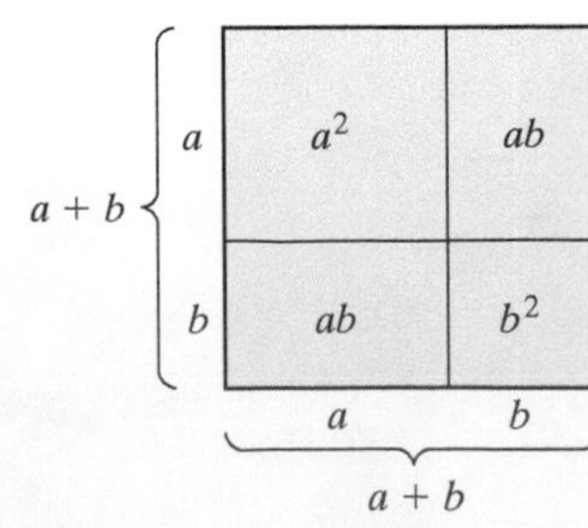

The area of the large square is side · side.
Area $= (a + b)(a + b) = (a + b)^2$
The area of the large square is also the sum of the areas of the smaller rectangles.
Area $= a^2 + ab + ab + b^2 = a^2 + 2ab + b^2$
Thus, $(a + b)^2 = a^2 + 2ab + b^2$.

Answers
3. $2y^3 - 8y^2 + 3y - 12$
4. $4x^2 + 36x + 81$

Examples Use a special product to square each binomial.

		first term squared	plus or minus	twice the product of the terms	plus	second term squared
5.	$(t + 2)^2 =$	t^2	$+$	$2(t)(2)$	$+$	$2^2 = t^2 + 4t + 4$
6.	$(p - q)^2 =$	p^2	$-$	$2(p)(q)$	$+$	$q^2 = p^2 - 2pq + q^2$
7.	$(2x + 5)^2 =$	$(2x)^2$	$+$	$2(2x)(5)$	$+$	$5^2 = 4x^2 + 20x + 25$
8.	$(x^2 - 7y)^2 =$	$(x^2)^2$	$-$	$2(x^2)(7y)$	$+$	$(7y)^2 = x^4 - 14x^2y + 49y^2$

Work Practice 5–8

PRACTICE 5–8

Use a special product to square each binomial.

5. $(y + 3)^2$
6. $(r - s)^2$
7. $(6x + 5)^2$
8. $(x^2 - 3y)^2$

Helpful Hint

Notice that

$(a + b)^2 \neq a^2 + b^2$ The middle term, $2ab$, is missing.

$(a + b)^2 = (a + b)(a + b) = a^2 + 2ab + b^2$

Likewise,

$(a - b)^2 \neq a^2 - b^2$

$(a - b)^2 = (a - b)(a - b) = a^2 - 2ab + b^2$

Objective C Multiplying the Sum and Difference of Two Terms

Another special product is the product of the sum and difference of the same two terms, such as $(x + y)(x - y)$. Finding this product by the FOIL method, we see a pattern emerge.

$$\begin{aligned}(x + y)(x - y) &= \overset{F}{x^2} - \overset{O}{xy} + \overset{I}{xy} - \overset{L}{y^2} \\ &= x^2 - y^2\end{aligned}$$

Notice that the two middle terms subtract out. This is because the **O**uter product is the opposite of the **I**nner product. Only the **difference of squares** remains.

Multiplying the Sum and Difference of Two Terms

The product of the sum and difference of two terms is the square of the first term minus the square of the second term.

$$(a + b)(a - b) = a^2 - b^2$$

Answers

5. $y^2 + 6y + 9$ **6.** $r^2 - 2rs + s^2$
7. $36x^2 + 60x + 25$
8. $x^4 - 6x^2y + 9y^2$

PRACTICE 9–13

Use a special product to multiply.

9. $(x + 9)(x - 9)$
10. $(5 + 4y)(5 - 4y)$
11. $\left(x - \frac{1}{3}\right)\left(x + \frac{1}{3}\right)$
12. $(3a - b)(3a + b)$
13. $(2x^2 - 6y)(2x^2 + 6y)$

Examples Use a special product to multiply.

	first term squared	minus	second term squared
9. $(x + 4)(x - 4) =$	x^2	$-$	$4^2 = x^2 - 16$
10. $(6t + 7)(6t - 7) =$	$(6t)^2$	$-$	$7^2 = 36t^2 - 49$
11. $\left(x - \frac{1}{4}\right)\left(x + \frac{1}{4}\right) =$	x^2	$-$	$\left(\frac{1}{4}\right)^2 = x^2 - \frac{1}{16}$

12. $(2p - q)(2p + q) = (2p)^2 - q^2 = 4p^2 - q^2$
13. $(3x^2 - 5y)(3x^2 + 5y) = (3x^2)^2 - (5y)^2 = 9x^4 - 25y^2$

Work Practice 9–13

✓**Concept Check** Match each expression on the left to the equivalent expression or expressions in the list on the right.

$(a + b)^2$ — **a.** $(a + b)(a + b)$
$(a + b)(a - b)$ — **b.** $a^2 - b^2$
c. $a^2 + b^2$
d. $a^2 - 2ab + b^2$
e. $a^2 + 2ab + b^2$

Objective D Using Special Products

Let's now practice using our special products on a variety of multiplication problems. This practice will help us recognize when to apply what special product formula.

PRACTICE 14–17

Use a special product to multiply, if possible.

14. $(7x - 1)^2$
15. $(5y + 3)(2y - 5)$
16. $(2a - 1)(2a + 1)$
17. $\left(5y - \frac{1}{9}\right)^2$

Examples Use a special product to multiply, if possible.

14. $(4x - 9)(4x + 9)$ — This is the sum and difference of the same two terms.
$= (4x)^2 - 9^2 = 16x^2 - 81$

15. $(3y + 2)^2$ — This is a binomial squared.
$= (3y)^2 + 2(3y)(2) + 2^2$
$= 9y^2 + 12y + 4$

16. $(6a + 1)(a - 7)$ — No special product applies.
F O I L — Use the FOIL method.
$= 6a \cdot a + 6a(-7) + 1 \cdot a + 1(-7)$
$= 6a^2 - 42a + a - 7$
$= 6a^2 - 41a - 7$

17. $\left(4x - \frac{1}{11}\right)^2$ — This is a binomial squared.
$= (4x)^2 - 2(4x)\left(\frac{1}{11}\right) + \left(\frac{1}{11}\right)^2$
$= 16x^2 - \frac{8}{11}x + \frac{1}{121}$

Work Practice 14–17

Helpful Hint

- When multiplying two binomials, you may always use the FOIL order or method.
- When multiplying any two polynomials, you may always use the distributive property to find the product.

Answers
9. $x^2 - 81$ **10.** $25 - 16y^2$ **11.** $x^2 - \frac{1}{9}$ **12.** $9a^2 - b^2$ **13.** $4x^4 - 36y^2$ **14.** $49x^2 - 14x + 1$ **15.** $10y^2 - 19y - 15$ **16.** $4a^2 - 1$ **17.** $25y^2 - \frac{10}{9}y + \frac{1}{81}$

✓ **Concept Check Answer**
a and e, b

Vocabulary and Readiness Check

Answer each exercise true or false.

1. $(x + 4)^2 = x^2 + 16$

2. For $(x + 6)(2x - 1)$, the product of the first terms is $2x^2$.

3. $(x + 4)(x - 4) = x^2 + 16$

4. The product $(x - 1)(x^3 + 3x - 1)$ is a polynomial of degree 5.

3.6 Exercise Set

FOR EXTRA HELP

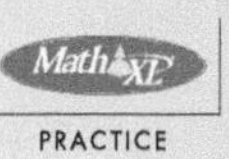
PRACTICE

WATCH

DOWNLOAD

READ

REVIEW

Objective A *Multiply using the FOIL method. See Examples 1 through 3.*

1. $(x + 3)(x + 4)$

2. $(x + 5)(x + 1)$

3. $(x - 5)(x + 10)$

4. $(y - 12)(y + 4)$

5. $(5x - 6)(x + 2)$

6. $(3y - 5)(2y + 7)$

7. $(y - 6)(4y - 1)$

8. $(2x - 9)(x - 11)$

9. $(2x + 5)(3x - 1)$

10. $(6x + 2)(x - 2)$

11. $(y^2 + 7)(6y + 4)$

12. $(y^2 + 3)(5y + 6)$

13. $\left(x - \frac{1}{3}\right)\left(x + \frac{2}{3}\right)$

14. $\left(x - \frac{2}{5}\right)\left(x + \frac{1}{5}\right)$

15. $(0.4 - 3a)(0.2 - 5a)$

16. $(0.3 - 2a)(0.6 - 5a)$

17. $(x + 5y)(2x - y)$

18. $(x + 4y)(3x - y)$

Objective B *Multiply. See Examples 4 through 8.*

19. $(x + 2)^2$

20. $(x + 7)^2$

21. $(2a - 3)^2$

22. $(7x - 3)^2$

23. $(3a - 5)^2$

24. $(5a - 2)^2$

25. $(x^2 + 0.5)^2$

26. $(x^2 + 0.3)^2$

27. $\left(y - \frac{2}{7}\right)^2$

28. $\left(y - \frac{3}{4}\right)^2$

29. $(2x - 1)^2$

30. $(5b - 4)^2$

31. $(5x + 9)^2$

32. $(6s + 2)^2$

33. $(3x - 7y)^2$

34. $(4s - 2y)^2$

35. $(4m + 5n)^2$

36. $(3n + 5m)^2$

37. $(5x^4 - 3)^2$

38. $(7x^3 - 6)^2$

Objective C *Multiply. See Examples 9 through 13.*

39. $(a - 7)(a + 7)$
40. $(b + 3)(b - 3)$
41. $(x + 6)(x - 6)$
42. $(x - 8)(x + 8)$

43. $(3x - 1)(3x + 1)$
44. $(7x - 5)(7x + 5)$
45. $(x^2 + 5)(x^2 - 5)$
46. $(a^2 + 6)(a^2 - 6)$

47. $(2y^2 - 1)(2y^2 + 1)$
48. $(3x^2 + 1)(3x^2 - 1)$
49. $(4 - 7x)(4 + 7x)$
50. $(8 - 7x)(8 + 7x)$

51. $\left(3x - \frac{1}{2}\right)\left(3x + \frac{1}{2}\right)$
52. $\left(10x + \frac{2}{7}\right)\left(10x - \frac{2}{7}\right)$
53. $(9x + y)(9x - y)$
54. $(2x - y)(2x + y)$

55. $(2m + 5n)(2m - 5n)$
56. $(5m + 4n)(5m - 4n)$

Objectives D **Mixed Practice** *Multiply. See Examples 14 through 17.*

57. $(a + 5)(a + 4)$
58. $(a + 5)(a + 7)$
59. $(a - 7)^2$
60. $(b - 2)^2$

61. $(4a + 1)(3a - 1)$
62. $(6a + 7)(6a + 5)$
63. $(x + 2)(x - 2)$
64. $(x - 10)(x + 10)$

65. $(3a + 1)^2$
66. $(4a + 2)^2$
67. $(x + y)(4x - y)$
68. $(3x + 2)(4x - 2)$

69. $\left(\frac{1}{3}a^2 - 7\right)\left(\frac{1}{3}a^2 + 7\right)$
70. $\left(\frac{a}{2} + 4y\right)\left(\frac{a}{2} - 4y\right)$
71. $(3b + 7)(2b - 5)$
72. $(3y - 13)(y - 3)$

73. $(x^2 + 10)(x^2 - 10)$
74. $(x^2 + 8)(x^2 - 8)$
75. $(4x + 5)(4x - 5)$
76. $(3x + 5)(3x - 5)$

77. $(5x - 6y)^2$
78. $(4x - 9y)^2$
79. $(2r - 3s)(2r + 3s)$
80. $(6r - 2x)(6r + 2x)$

Express each as a product of polynomials in x. Then multiply and simplify.

81. Find the area of the square rug if its side is $(2x + 1)$ feet.

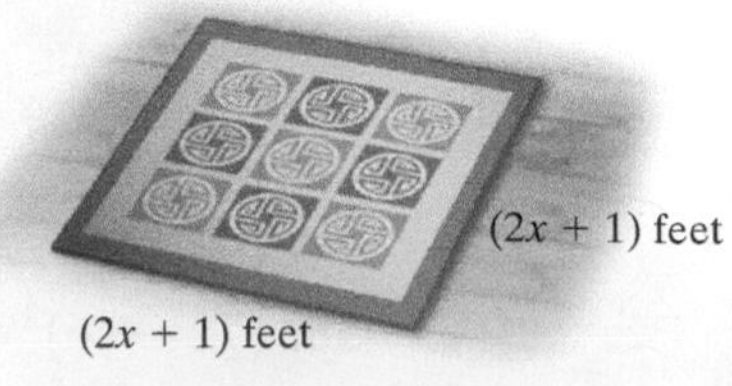

82. Find the area of the rectangular canvas if its length is $(3x - 2)$ inches and its width is $(x - 4)$ inches.

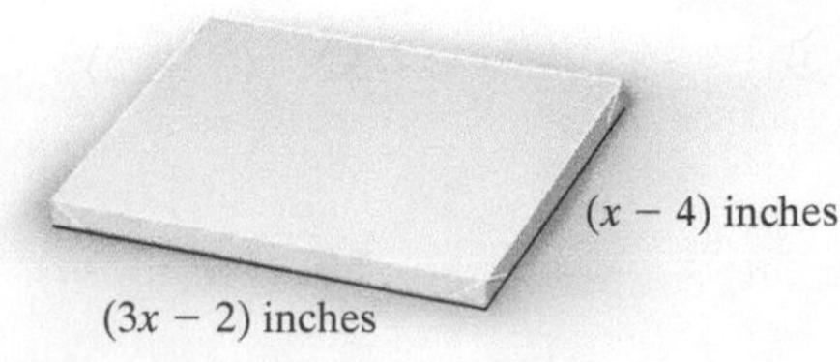

Review

Simplify each expression. See Sections 3.1 and 3.2.

83. $\dfrac{50b^{10}}{70b^5}$ **84.** $\dfrac{60y^6}{80y^2}$ **85.** $\dfrac{8a^{17}b^5}{-4a^7b^{10}}$ **86.** $\dfrac{-6a^8y}{3a^4y}$ **87.** $\dfrac{2x^4y^{12}}{3x^4y^4}$ **88.** $\dfrac{-48ab^6}{32ab^3}$

Concept Extensions

Match each expression on the left to the equivalent expression on the right. See the Concept Check in this section. (Not all choices will be used.)

89. $(a - b)^2$

90. $(a - b)(a + b)$

91. $(a + b)^2$

92. $(a + b)^2(a - b)^2$

a. $a^2 - b^2$

b. $a^2 + b^2$

c. $a^2 - 2ab + b^2$

d. $a^2 + 2ab + b^2$

e. none of these

Fill in the squares so that a true statement forms.

93. $(x^{\square} + 7)(x^{\square} + 3) = x^4 + 10x^2 + 21$

94. $(5x^{\square} - 2)^2 = 25x^6 - 20x^3 + 4$

Find the area of the shaded figure. To do so, subtract the area of the smaller square(s) from the area of the larger geometric figure.

95.

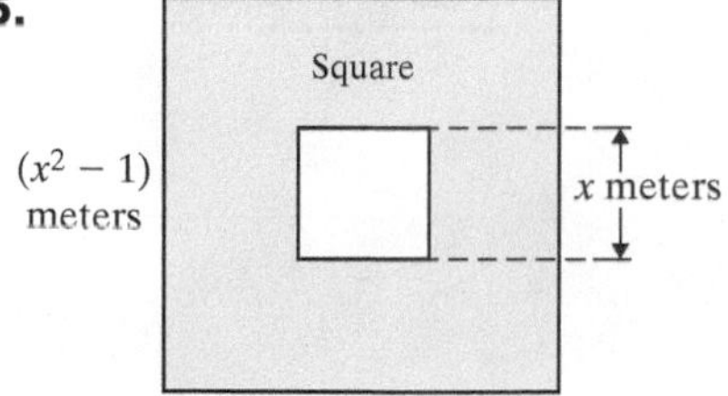

96.

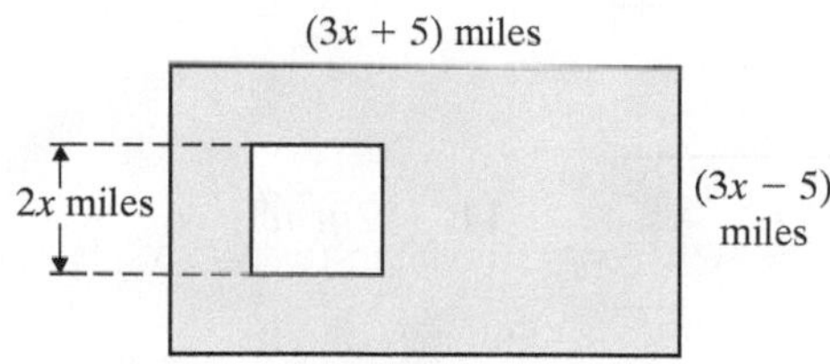

97.

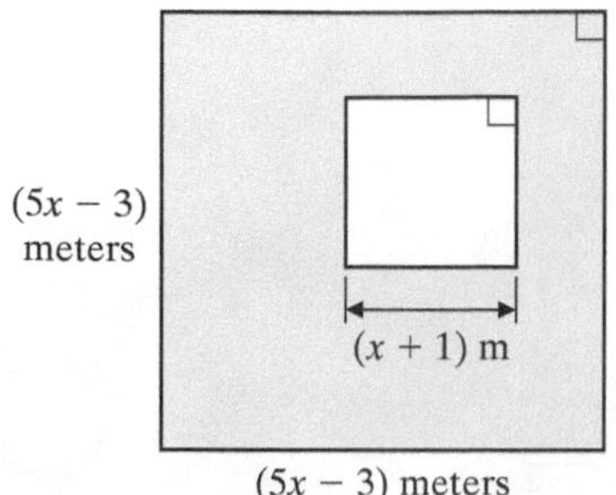

98.

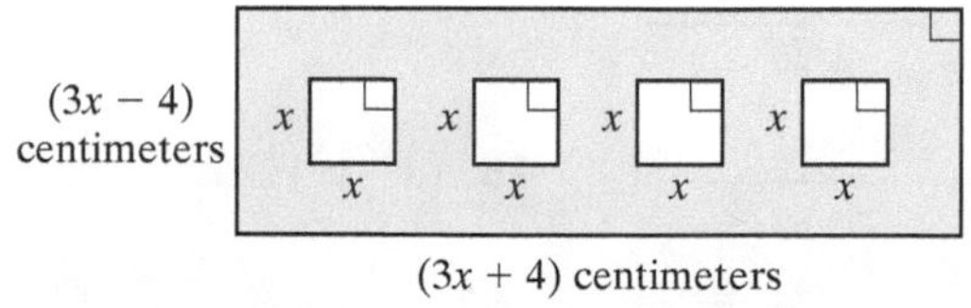

99. In your own words, describe the different methods that can be used to find the product: $(2x - 5)(3x + 1)$.

100. In your own words, describe the different methods that can be used to find the product: $(5x + 1)^2$.

101. Suppose that a classmate asked you why $(2x + 1)^2$ is **not** $(4x^2 + 1)$. Write down your response to this classmate.

102. Suppose that a classmate asked you why $(2x + 1)^2$ **is** $(4x^2 + 4x + 1)$. Write down your response to this classmate.

Integrated Review Sections 3.1–3.6

Exponents and Operations on Polynomials

Perform operations and simplify.

1. $(5x^2)(7x^3)$

2. $(4y^2)(-8y^7)$

3. -4^2

4. $(-4)^2$

5. $(x - 5)(2x + 1)$

6. $(3x - 2)(x + 5)$

7. $(x - 5) + (2x + 1)$

8. $(3x - 2) + (x + 5)$

9. $\dfrac{7x^9y^{12}}{x^3y^{10}}$

10. $\dfrac{20a^2b^8}{14a^2b^2}$

11. $(12m^7n^6)^2$

12. $(4y^9z^{10})^3$

13. $(4y - 3)(4y + 3)$

14. $(7x - 1)(7x + 1)$

15. $(x^{-7}y^5)^9$

16. 8^{-2}

17. $(3^{-1}x^9)^3$

18. $\dfrac{(r^7s^{-5})^6}{(2r^{-4}s^{-4})^4}$

19. $(7x^2 - 2x + 3) - (5x^2 + 9)$

20. $(10x^2 + 7x - 9) - (4x^2 - 6x + 2)$

Answers

1. ______
2. ______
3. ______
4. ______
5. ______
6. ______
7. ______
8. ______
9. ______
10. ______
11. ______
12. ______
13. ______
14. ______
15. ______
16. ______
17. ______
18. ______
19. ______
20. ______

21. $0.7y^2 - 1.2 + 1.8y^2 - 6y + 1$

22. $7.8x^2 - 6.8x - 3.3 + 0.6x^2 - 0.9$

23. Subtract $y^2 + 2$ from $3y^2 - 6y + 1$.

24. $(z^2 + 5) - (3z^2 - 1) + \left(8z^2 + 2z - \frac{1}{2}\right)$

25. $(x + 4)^2$

26. $(y - 9)^2$

27. $(x + 4) + (x + 4)$

28. $(y - 9) + (y - 9)$

29. $7x^2 - 6xy + 4(y^2 - xy)$

30. $5a^2 - 3ab + 6(b^2 - a^2)$

31. $(x - 3)(x^2 + 5x - 1)$

32. $(x + 1)(x^2 - 3x - 2)$

33. $(2x - 7)(3x + 10)$

34. $(5x - 1)(4x + 5)$

35. $(2x - 7)(x^2 - 6x + 1)$

36. $(5x - 1)(x^2 + 2x - 3)$

37. $\left(2x + \frac{5}{9}\right)\left(2x - \frac{5}{9}\right)$

38. $\left(12y + \frac{3}{7}\right)\left(12y - \frac{3}{7}\right)$

21. ________
22. ________
23. ________
24. ________
25. ________
26. ________
27. ________
28. ________
29. ________
30. ________
31. ________
32. ________
33. ________
34. ________
35. ________
36. ________
37. ________
38. ________

3.7 DIVIDING POLYNOMIALS

Objectives

A Divide a Polynomial by a Monomial.

B Use Long Division to Divide a Polynomial by a Polynomial Other than a Monomial.

Objective A Dividing by a Monomial

To divide a polynomial by a monomial, recall addition of fractions. Fractions that have a common denominator are added by adding the numerators:

$$\frac{a}{c} + \frac{b}{c} = \frac{a + b}{c}$$

If we read this equation from right to left and let a, b, and c be monomials, $c \neq 0$, we have the following.

To Divide a Polynomial by a Monomial

Divide each term of the polynomial by the monomial.

$$\frac{a + b}{c} = \frac{a}{c} + \frac{b}{c}, \quad c \neq 0$$

Throughout this section, we assume that denominators are not 0.

PRACTICE 1

Divide: $(25x^3 + 5x^2) \div 5x^2$

Example 1 Divide: $(6m^2 + 2m) \div 2m$

Solution: We begin by writing the quotient in fraction form. Then we divide each term of the polynomial $6m^2 + 2m$ by the monomial $2m$ and use the quotient rule for exponents to simplify.

$$\frac{6m^2 + 2m}{2m} = \frac{6m^2}{2m} + \frac{2m}{2m}$$

$$= 3m + 1 \quad \text{Simplify.}$$

Check: To check, we multiply.

$$2m(3m + 1) = 2m(3m) + 2m(1) = 6m^2 + 2m$$

The quotient $3m + 1$ checks.

Work Practice 1

✓Concept Check In which of the following is $\frac{x + 5}{5}$ simplified correctly?

a. $\frac{x}{5} + 1$ **b.** x **c.** $x + 1$

PRACTICE 2

Divide: $\frac{24x^7 + 12x^2 - 4x}{4x^2}$

Example 2 Divide: $\frac{9x^5 - 12x^2 + 3x}{3x^2}$

Solution:

$$\frac{9x^5 - 12x^2 + 3x}{3x^2} = \frac{9x^5}{3x^2} - \frac{12x^2}{3x^2} + \frac{3x}{3x^2} \quad \text{Divide each term by } 3x^2.$$

$$= 3x^3 - 4 + \frac{1}{x} \quad \text{Simplify.}$$

Notice that the quotient is not a polynomial because of the term $\frac{1}{x}$. This expression is called a rational expression—we will study rational expressions in Chapter 5. Although the quotient of two polynomials is not always a polynomial, we may still check by multiplying.

Answers

1. $5x + 1$ 2. $6x^5 + 3 - \frac{1}{x}$

✓ Concept Check Answer

a

Check: $3x^2\left(3x^3 - 4 + \frac{1}{x}\right) = 3x^2(3x^3) - 3x^2(4) + 3x^2\left(\frac{1}{x}\right)$
$= 9x^5 - 12x^2 + 3x$

Work Practice 2

Example 3 Divide: $\dfrac{8x^2y^2 - 16xy + 2x}{4xy}$

Solution: $\dfrac{8x^2y^2 - 16xy + 2x}{4xy} = \dfrac{8x^2y^2}{4xy} - \dfrac{16xy}{4xy} + \dfrac{2x}{4xy}$ Divide each term by $4xy$.

$= 2xy - 4 + \dfrac{1}{2y}$ Simplify.

Check: $4xy\left(2xy - 4 + \frac{1}{2y}\right) = 4xy(2xy) - 4xy(4) + 4xy\left(\frac{1}{2y}\right)$
$= 8x^2y^2 - 16xy + 2x$

Work Practice 3

PRACTICE 3

Divide: $\dfrac{12x^3y^3 - 18xy + 6y}{3xy}$

Objective B Dividing by a Polynomial Other than a Monomial

To divide a polynomial by a polynomial other than a monomial, we use a process known as long division. Polynomial long division is similar to number long division, so we review long division by dividing 13 into 3660.

```
    281
13)3660
   26↓        2·13 = 26
   106        Subtract and bring down the next digit in the dividend.
   104↓       8·13 = 104
     20       Subtract and bring down the next digit in the dividend.
     13       1·13 = 13
      7       Subtract. There are no more digits to bring down, so the remainder is 7.
```

Helpful Hint Recall that 3660 is called the dividend.

The quotient is 281 R 7, which can be written as $281\frac{7}{13}$. ← remainder ← divisor

Recall that division can be checked by multiplication. To check this division problem, we see that

$13 \cdot 281 + 7 = 3660$, the dividend.

Now we demonstrate long division of polynomials.

Example 4 Divide $x^2 + 7x + 12$ by $x + 3$ using long division.

Solution:

To subtract, change the signs of these terms and add.

```
            x
x + 3)x² + 7x + 12      How many times does x divide x²? x²/x = x.
  →  x² + 3x      ↓     Multiply: x(x + 3)
          4x + 12       Subtract and bring down the next term.
```

Continued on next page

PRACTICE 4

Divide $x^2 + 12x + 35$ by $x + 5$ using long division.

Answers

3. $4x^2y^2 - 6 + \dfrac{2}{x}$ **4.** $x + 7$

Now we repeat this process.

$$\begin{array}{r} x + 4 \\ x + 3\overline{)x^2 + 7x + 12} \\ \underline{x^2 + 3x} \\ 4x + 12 \\ \underline{4x + 12} \\ 0 \end{array}$$

How many times does x divide $4x$? $\frac{4x}{x} = 4$.

To subtract, change the signs of these terms and add.

Multiply: $4(x + 3)$

Subtract. The remainder is 0.

The quotient is $x + 4$.

Check: We check by multiplying.

divisor	·	quotient	+	remainder	=	dividend
or ↓		↓		↓		↓
$(x + 3)$	·	$(x + 4)$	+	0	=	$x^2 + 7x + 12$

The quotient checks.

Work Practice 4

PRACTICE 5

Divide: $8x^2 + 2x - 7$ by $2x - 1$

Example 5 Divide $6x^2 + 10x - 5$ by $3x - 1$ using long division.

Solution:

$$\begin{array}{r} 2x + 4 \\ 3x - 1\overline{)6x^2 + 10x - 5} \\ \underline{6x^2 - 2x} \\ 12x - 5 \\ \underline{12x - 4} \\ -1 \end{array}$$

$\frac{6x^2}{3x} = 2x$, so $2x$ is a term of the quotient.

Multiply: $2x(3x - 1)$

Subtract and bring down the next term.

$\frac{12x}{3x} = 4$. Multiply: $4(3x - 1)$

Subtract. The remainder is -1.

Thus $(6x^2 + 10x - 5)$ divided by $(3x - 1)$ is $(2x + 4)$ with a remainder of -1. This can be written as follows.

$$\frac{6x^2 + 10x - 5}{3x - 1} = 2x + 4 + \frac{-1}{3x - 1} \quad \begin{array}{l} \leftarrow \text{remainder} \\ \leftarrow \text{divisor} \end{array}$$

$$\text{or } 2x + 4 - \frac{1}{3x - 1}$$

Check: To check, we multiply $(3x - 1)(2x + 4)$. Then we add the remainder, -1, to this product.

$$(3x - 1)(2x + 4) + (-1) = (6x^2 + 12x - 2x - 4) - 1$$
$$= 6x^2 + 10x - 5$$

The quotient checks.

Work Practice 5

Notice that the division process is continued until the degree of the remainder polynomial is less than the degree of the divisor polynomial.

Recall that in Section 3.3 we practiced writing polynomials in descending order of powers and with no missing terms. For example, $2 - 4x^2$ written in this form is $-4x^2 + 0x + 2$. Writing the dividend and divisor in this form is helpful when dividing polynomials.

Answer

5. $4x + 3 + \frac{-4}{2x - 1}$ or $4x + 3 - \frac{4}{2x - 1}$

Example 6 Divide: $(2 - 4x^2) \div (x + 1)$

Solution: We use the rewritten form of $2 - 4x^2$ from the previous page.

$$\begin{array}{r} -4x + 4 \\ x + 1 \overline{) -4x^2 + 0x + 2} \\ \underline{-4x^2 - 4x} \\ 4x + 2 \\ \underline{4x + 4} \\ -2 \end{array}$$

$\frac{-4x^2}{x} = -4x$, so $-4x$ is a term of the quotient.

Multiply: $-4x(x + 1)$

Subtract and bring down the next term.

$\frac{4x}{x} = 4$. Multiply: $4(x + 1)$

Remainder

Thus, $\frac{-4x^2 + 0x + 2}{x + 1}$ or $\frac{2 - 4x^2}{x + 1} = -4x + 4 + \frac{-2}{x + 1}$ or $-4x + 4 - \frac{2}{x + 1}$.

Check: To check, see that $(x + 1)(-4x + 4) + (-2) = 2 - 4x^2$.

Work Practice 6

PRACTICE 6

Divide: $(15 - 2x^2) \div (x - 3)$

Example 7 Divide: $\frac{4x^2 + 7 + 8x^3}{2x + 3}$

Solution: Before we begin the division process, we rewrite $4x^2 + 7 + 8x^3$ as $8x^3 + 4x^2 + 0x + 7$. Notice that we have written the polynomial in descending order and have represented the missing x-term by $0x$.

$$\begin{array}{r} 4x^2 - 4x + 6 \\ 2x + 3 \overline{) 8x^3 + 4x^2 + 0x + 7} \\ \underline{8x^3 + 12x^2} \\ -8x^2 + 0x \\ \underline{-8x^2 - 12x} \\ 12x + 7 \\ \underline{12x + 18} \\ -11 \end{array}$$

Remainder

Thus, $\frac{4x^2 + 7 + 8x^3}{2x + 3} = 4x^2 - 4x + 6 + \frac{-11}{2x + 3}$ or $4x^2 - 4x + 6 - \frac{11}{2x + 3}$.

Work Practice 7

PRACTICE 7

Divide: $\frac{5 - x + 9x^3}{3x + 2}$

Example 8 Divide $x^3 - 8$ by $x - 2$.

Solution: Notice that the polynomial $x^3 - 8$ is missing an x^2-term and an x-term. We'll represent these terms by inserting $0x^2$ and $0x$.

$$\begin{array}{r} x^2 + 2x + 4 \\ x - 2 \overline{) x^3 + 0x^2 + 0x - 8} \\ \underline{x^3 - 2x^2} \\ 2x^2 + 0x \\ \underline{2x^2 - 4x} \\ 4x - 8 \\ \underline{4x - 8} \\ 0 \end{array}$$

Thus, $\frac{x^3 - 8}{x - 2} = x^2 + 2x + 4$.

Check: To check, see that $(x^2 + 2x + 4)(x - 2) = x^3 - 8$.

Work Practice 8

PRACTICE 8

Divide: $x^3 - 1$ by $x - 1$

Answers

6. $-2x - 6 + \frac{-3}{x - 3}$ or $-2x - 6 - \frac{3}{x - 3}$

7. $3x^2 - 2x + 1 + \frac{3}{3x + 2}$

8. $x^2 + x + 1$

Vocabulary and Readiness Check

Use the choices below to fill in each blank. Choices may be used more than once

dividend divisor quotient

1. In $6\overline{)18}$ with quotient 3, the 18 is the ________, the 3 is the ________ and the 6 is the ________.

2. In $x+1\overline{)x^2+3x+2}$ with quotient $x+2$, the $x + 1$ is the ________, the $x^2 + 3x + 2$ is the ________, and the $x + 2$ is the ________.

Simplify each expression mentally.

3. $\dfrac{a^6}{a^4}$ **4.** $\dfrac{p^8}{p^3}$ **5.** $\dfrac{y^2}{y}$ **6.** $\dfrac{a^3}{a}$

3.7 Exercise Set

FOR EXTRA HELP

Objective A *Perform each division. See Examples 1 through 3.*

1. $\dfrac{12x^4 + 3x^2}{x}$

2. $\dfrac{15x^2 - 9x^5}{x}$

3. $\dfrac{20x^3 - 30x^2 + 5x + 5}{5}$

4. $\dfrac{8x^3 - 4x^2 + 6x + 2}{2}$

5. $\dfrac{15p^3 + 18p^2}{3p}$

6. $\dfrac{6x^5 + 3x^4}{3x^4}$

7. $\dfrac{-9x^4 + 18x^5}{6x^5}$

8. $\dfrac{14m^2 - 27m^3}{7m}$

9. $\dfrac{-9x^5 + 3x^4 - 12}{3x^3}$

10. $\dfrac{6a^2 - 4a + 12}{-2a^2}$

11. $\dfrac{4x^4 - 6x^3 + 7}{-4x^4}$

12. $\dfrac{-12a^3 + 36a - 15}{3a}$

Objective B *Find each quotient using long division. See Examples 4 and 5.*

13. $\dfrac{x^2 + 4x + 3}{x + 3}$

14. $\dfrac{x^2 + 7x + 10}{x + 5}$

15. $\dfrac{2x^2 + 13x + 15}{x + 5}$

16. $\dfrac{3x^2 + 8x + 4}{x + 2}$

17. $\dfrac{2x^2 - 7x + 3}{x - 4}$

18. $\dfrac{3x^2 - x - 4}{x - 1}$

19. $\dfrac{9a^3 - 3a^2 - 3a + 4}{3a + 2}$

20. $\dfrac{4x^3 + 12x^2 + x - 14}{2x + 3}$

21. $\dfrac{8x^2 + 10x + 1}{2x + 1}$

22. $\dfrac{3x^2 + 17x + 7}{3x + 2}$

23. $\dfrac{2x^3 + 2x^2 - 17x + 8}{x - 2}$

24. $\dfrac{4x^3 + 11x^2 - 8x - 10}{x + 3}$

Find each quotient using long division. Don't forget to write the polynomials in descending order and fill in any missing terms. See Examples 6 through 8.

25. $\frac{x^2 - 36}{x - 6}$

26. $\frac{a^2 - 49}{a - 7}$

27. $\frac{x^3 - 27}{x - 3}$

28. $\frac{x^3 + 64}{x + 4}$

29. $\frac{1 - 3x^2}{x + 2}$

30. $\frac{7 - 5x^2}{x + 3}$

31. $\frac{-4b + 4b^2 - 5}{2b - 1}$

32. $\frac{-3y + 2y^2 - 15}{2y + 5}$

Objectives **A** **B** **Mixed Practice** *Divide. If the divisor contains 2 or more terms, use long division. See Examples 1 through 8.*

33. $\frac{a^2b^2 - ab^3}{ab}$

34. $\frac{m^3n^2 - mn^4}{mn}$

35. $\frac{8x^2 + 6x - 27}{2x - 3}$

36. $\frac{18w^2 + 18w - 8}{3w + 4}$

37. $\frac{2x^2y + 8x^2y^2 - xy^2}{2xy}$

38. $\frac{11x^3y^3 - 33xy + x^2y^2}{11xy}$

39. $\frac{2b^3 + 9b^2 + 6b - 4}{b + 4}$

40. $\frac{2x^3 + 3x^2 - 3x + 4}{x + 2}$

41. $\frac{y^3 + 3y^2 + 4}{y - 2}$

42. $\frac{3x^3 + 11x + 12}{x + 4}$

43. $\frac{5 - 6x^2}{x - 2}$

44. $\frac{3 - 7x^2}{x - 3}$

45. $\frac{x^5 + x^2}{x^2 + x}$

46. $\frac{x^6 - x^3}{x^3 - x^2}$

Review

Fill in each blank. See Section 3.1

47. $12 = 4 \cdot$ ___

48. $12 = 2 \cdot$ ___

49. $20 = -5 \cdot$ ___

50. $20 = -4 \cdot$ ___

51. $9x^2 = 3x \cdot$ ___

52. $9x^2 = 9x \cdot$ ___

53. $36x^2 = 4x \cdot$ ___

54. $36x^2 = 2x \cdot$ ___

Concept Extensions

Solve.

55. The perimeter of a square is $(12x^3 + 4x - 16)$ feet. Find the length of its side.

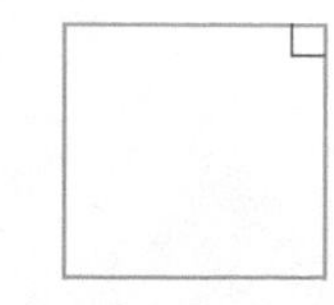

Perimeter is $(12x^3 + 4x - 16)$ feet

56. The volume of the swimming pool shown is $(36x^5 - 12x^3 + 6x^2)$ cubic feet. If its height is $2x$ feet and its width is $3x$ feet, find its length.

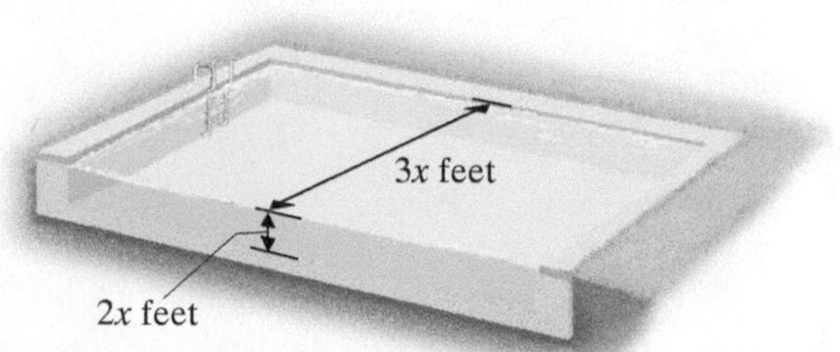

△ **57.** The area of the parallelogram shown is $(10x^2 + 31x + 15)$ square meters. If its base is $(5x + 3)$ meters, find its height.

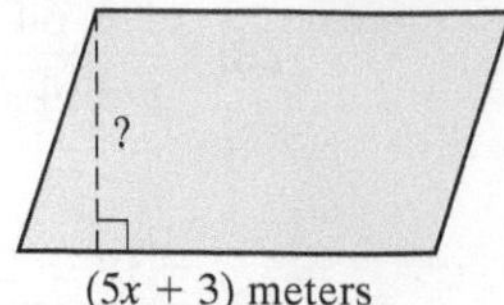

△ **58.** The area of the top of the Ping-Pong table shown is $(49x^2 + 70x - 200)$ square inches. If its length is $(7x + 20)$ inches, find its width.

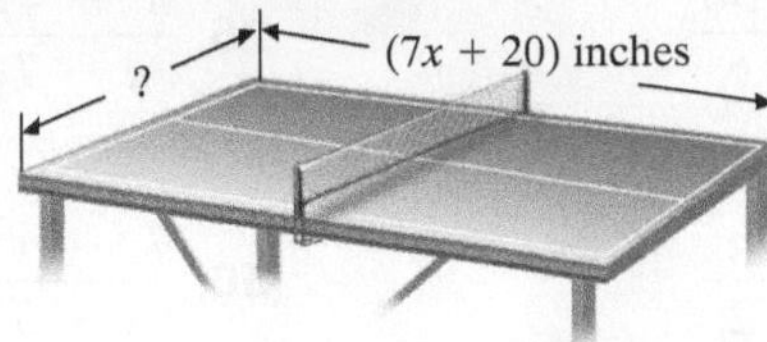

59. Explain how to check a polynomial long division result when the remainder is 0.

60. Explain how to check a polynomial long division result when the remainder is not 0.

61. In which of the following is $\frac{a + 7}{7}$ simplified correctly? See the Concept Check in this section.

a. $a + 1$
b. a
c. $\frac{a}{7} + 1$

62. In which of the following is $\frac{5x + 15}{5}$ simplified correctly? See the Concept Check in this section.

a. $x + 15$
b. $x + 3$
c. $x + 1$

Chapter 3 Group Activity

Modeling with Polynomials

Materials

Calculator

This activity may be completed by working in groups or individually.

The polynomial model $-16x^2 + 150x + 8945$ gives the average daily total supply of motor gasoline (in thousand barrels per day) in the United States for the period 2003–2007. The polynomial model $8x^2 + 80x + 8443$ gives the average daily supply of domestically produced motor gasoline (in thousand barrels per day) in the United States for the same period. In both models, x is the number of years after 2003. The other source of motor gasoline in the United States, contributing to the total supply, is imported motor gasoline. (*Source:* Based on data from the Energy Information Administration)

1. Use the given polynomials to complete the following table showing the average daily supply (both total and domestic) over the period 2003–2007 by evaluating each polynomial at the given values of x. Then subtract each value in the fourth column from the corresponding value in the third column. Record the result in the last column, labeled "Difference." What do you think these values represent?

Year	x	Average Daily Total Supply (thousand barrels per day)	Average Daily Domestic Supply (thousand barrels per day)	Difference
2003	0			
2004	1			
2005	2			
2006	3			
2007	4			

2. Use the polynomial models to find a new polynomial model representing the average daily supply of imported motor gasoline. Then evaluate your new polynomial model to complete the accompanying table.

Year	x	Average Daily Imported Supply (thousand barrels per day)
2003	0	
2004	1	
2005	2	
2006	3	
2007	4	

3. Compare the values in the last column of the table in Question 1 to the values in the last column of the table in Question 2. What do you notice? What can you conclude?

4. Make a bar graph of the data in the table in Question 2. Describe what you see.

Chapter 3 Vocabulary Check

Fill in each blank with one of the words or phrases listed below.

term	coefficient	monomial	binomial	trinomial
polynomials	degree of a term	degree of a polynomial	distributive	FOIL

1. A ________________ is a number or the product of a number and variables raised to powers.
2. The ________________ method may be used when multiplying two binomials.
3. A polynomial with exactly 3 terms is called a ________________.
4. The ________________ is the greatest degree of any term of the polynomial.
5. A polynomial with exactly 2 terms is called a ________________.
6. The ________________ of a term is its numerical factor.
7. The ________________ is the sum of the exponents on the variables in the term.
8. A polynomial with exactly 1 term is called a ________________.
9. Monomials, binomials, and trinomials are all examples of ________________.
10. The ________________ property is used to multiply $2x(x - 4)$.

Helpful Hint Are you preparing for your test? Don't forget to take the Chapter 3 Test on page 262. Then check your answers at the back of the text and use the Chapter Test Prep Videos to see the fully worked-out solutions to any of the exercises you want to review.

3 Chapter Highlights

Definitions and Concepts	Examples
Section 3.1 Exponents	
a^n means the product of n factors, each of which is a.	$3^2 = 3 \cdot 3 = 9$ $(-5)^3 = (-5)(-5)(-5) = -125$ $\left(\frac{1}{2}\right)^4 = \frac{1}{2}\cdot\frac{1}{2}\cdot\frac{1}{2}\cdot\frac{1}{2} = \frac{1}{16}$
Let m and n be integers and no denominators be 0.	
Product Rule: $a^m \cdot a^n = a^{m+n}$	$x^2 \cdot x^7 = x^{2+7} = x^9$
Power Rule: $(a^m)^n = a^{mn}$	$(5^3)^8 = 5^{3\cdot 8} = 5^{24}$
Power of a Product Rule: $(ab)^n = a^n b^n$	$(7y)^4 = 7^4 y^4$
Power of a Quotient Rule: $\left(\frac{a}{b}\right)^n = \frac{a^n}{b^n}$	$\left(\frac{x}{8}\right)^3 = \frac{x^3}{8^3}$
Quotient Rule: $\frac{a^m}{a^n} = a^{m-n}$	$\frac{x^9}{x^4} = x^{9-4} = x^5$
Zero Exponent: $a^0 = 1, a \neq 0$	$5^0 = 1; x^0 = 1, x \neq 0$

Definitions and Concepts	Examples
Section 3.2 Negative Exponents and Scientific Notation	
If $a \neq 0$ and n is an integer, $a^{-n} = \frac{1}{a^n}$	$3^{-2} = \frac{1}{3^2} = \frac{1}{9}$; $5x^{-2} = \frac{5}{x^2}$ Simplify: $\left(\frac{x^{-2}y}{x^5}\right)^{-2} = \frac{x^4y^{-2}}{x^{-10}}$ $= x^{4-(-10)}y^{-2}$ $= \frac{x^{14}}{y^2}$
A positive number is written in scientific notation if it is written as the product of a number a, where $1 \leq a < 10$, and an integer power r of 10. $a \times 10^r$	$1200 = 1.2 \times 10^3$ $0.000000568 = 5.68 \times 10^{-7}$
Section 3.3 Introduction to Polynomials	
A **term** is a number or the product of a number and variables raised to powers.	$-5x, 7a^2b, \frac{1}{4}y^4, 0.2$
The **numerical coefficient,** or **coefficient,** of a term is its numerical factor.	**Term** / **Coefficient** $7x^2$ — 7 y — 1 $-a^2b$ — -1
A **polynomial** is a finite sum of terms of the form ax^n where a is a real number and n is a whole number.	$5x^3 - 6x^2 + 3x - 6$ (Polynomial)
A **monomial** is a polynomial with exactly 1 term.	$\frac{5}{6}y^3$ (Monomial)
A **binomial** is a polynomial with exactly 2 terms.	$-0.2a^2b - 5b^2$ (Binomial)
A **trinomial** is a polynomial with exactly 3 terms.	$3x^2 - 2x + 1$ (Trinomial)
The **degree of a polynomial** is the greatest degree of any term of the polynomial.	**Polynomial** / **Degree** $5x^2 - 3x + 2$ — 2 $7y + 8y^2z^3 - 12$ — $2 + 3 = 5$
Section 3.4 Adding and Subtracting Polynomials	
To add polynomials, combine like terms.	Add. $(7x^2 - 3x + 2) + (-5x - 6)$ $= 7x^2 - 3x + 2 - 5x - 6$ $= 7x^2 - 8x - 4$
To subtract two polynomials, change the signs of the terms of the second polynomial, and then add.	Subtract. $(17y^2 - 2y + 1) - (-3y^3 + 5y - 6)$ $= (17y^2 - 2y + 1) + (3y^3 - 5y + 6)$ $= 17y^2 - 2y + 1 + 3y^3 - 5y + 6$ $= 3y^3 + 17y^2 - 7y + 7$

Definitions and Concepts	Examples
Section 3.5 Multiplying Polynomials	
To multiply two polynomials, multiply each term of one polynomial by each term of the other polynomial, and then combine like terms.	Multiply. $(2x + 1)(5x^2 - 6x + 2)$ $= 2x(5x^2 - 6x + 2) + 1(5x^2 - 6x + 2)$ $= 10x^3 - 12x^2 + 4x + 5x^2 - 6x + 2$ $= 10x^3 - 7x^2 - 2x + 2$
Section 3.6 Special Products	
The **FOIL method** may be used when multiplying two binomials.	Multiply: $(5x - 3)(2x + 3)$ First, Last, Inner, Outer $(5x - 3)(2x + 3)$ F O I L $= (5x)(2x) + (5x)(3) + (-3)(2x) + (-3)(3)$ $= 10x^2 + 15x - 6x - 9$ $= 10x^2 + 9x - 9$
Squaring a Binomial $(a + b)^2 = a^2 + 2ab + b^2$ $(a - b)^2 = a^2 - 2ab + b^2$	Square each binomial. $(x + 5)^2 = x^2 + 2(x)(5) + 5^2$ $= x^2 + 10x + 25$ $(3x - 2y)^2 = (3x)^2 - 2(3x)(2y) + (2y)^2$ $= 9x^2 - 12xy + 4y^2$
Multiplying the Sum and Difference of Two Terms $(a + b)(a - b) = a^2 - b^2$	Multiply. $(6y + 5)(6y - 5) = (6y)^2 - 5^2$ $= 36y^2 - 25$
Section 3.7 Dividing Polynomials	
To divide a polynomial by a monomial, $\frac{a + b}{c} = \frac{a}{c} + \frac{b}{c}, c \neq 0$	Divide. $\frac{15x^5 - 10x^3 + 5x^2 - 2x}{5x^2}$ $= \frac{15x^5}{5x^2} - \frac{10x^3}{5x^2} + \frac{5x^2}{5x^2} - \frac{2x}{5x^2}$ $= 3x^3 - 2x + 1 - \frac{2}{5x}$
To divide a polynomial by a polynomial other than a monomial, use long division.	$$\begin{array}{r} 5x - 1 + \frac{-4}{2x+3} \\ 2x + 3 \overline{)10x^2 + 13x - 7} \\ \underline{10x^2 \not+ 15x} \\ -2x - 7 \\ \underline{\not+2x \not+ 3} \\ -4 \end{array}$$ or $5x - 1 - \frac{4}{2x + 3}$

Chapter 3 Review

(3.1) *State the base and the exponent for each expression.*

1. 3^2 **2.** $(-5)^4$ **3.** -5^4 **4.** x^6

Evaluate each expression.

5. 8^3 **6.** $(-6)^2$ **7.** -6^2 **8.** $-4^3 - 4^0$ **9.** $(3b)^0$ **10.** $\frac{8b}{8b}$

Simplify each expression.

11. $y^2 \cdot y^7$ **12.** $x^9 \cdot x^5$ **13.** $(2x^5)(-3x^6)$ **14.** $(-5y^3)(4y^4)$ **15.** $(x^4)^2$

16. $(y^3)^5$ **17.** $(3y^6)^4$ **18.** $(2x^3)^3$ **19.** $\frac{x^9}{x^4}$ **20.** $\frac{z^{12}}{z^5}$

21. $\frac{3x^4y^{10}}{12xy^6}$ **22.** $\frac{2x^7y^8}{8xy^2}$ **23.** $5a^7(2a^4)^3$ **24.** $(2x)^2(9x)$ **25.** $\frac{(4a^5b)^2}{-16ab^2}$

26. $\frac{(2x^3y)^4}{-16x^5y^4}$ **27.** $(-5a)^0 + 7^0 + 8^0$ **28.** $8x^0 + 9^0$

Simplify the given expression and choose the correct result.

29. $\left(\frac{3x^4}{4y}\right)^3$

a. $\frac{27x^{64}}{64y^3}$ **b.** $\frac{27x^{12}}{64y^3}$

c. $\frac{9x^{12}}{12y^3}$ **d.** $\frac{3x^{12}}{4y^3}$

30. $\left(\frac{5a^6}{b^3}\right)^2$

a. $\frac{10a^{12}}{b^6}$ **b.** $\frac{25a^{36}}{b^9}$

c. $\frac{25a^{12}}{b^6}$ **d.** $25a^{12}b^6$

(3.2) *Simplify each expression.*

31. 7^{-2} **32.** -7^{-2} **33.** $2x^{-4}$ **34.** $(2x)^{-4}$

35. $\left(\frac{1}{5}\right)^{-3}$ **36.** $\left(\frac{-2}{3}\right)^{-2}$ **37.** $2^0 + 2^{-4}$ **38.** $6^{-1} - 7^{-1}$

Simplify each expression. Write each answer using positive exponents only.

39. $\frac{r^{-3}}{r^{-4}}$

40. $\frac{y^{-2}}{y^{-5}}$

41. $\left(\frac{bc^{-2}}{bc^{-3}}\right)^4$

42. $\left(\frac{x^{-3}y^{-4}}{x^{-2}y^{-5}}\right)^{-3}$

43. $\frac{10a^3b^4c^0}{50ab^{11}c^3}$

44. $\frac{8a^0b^4c^5}{40a^6bc^{12}}$

45. $\frac{9x^{-4}y^{-6}}{x^2y^7}$

46. $\frac{3a^5b^{-5}}{a^{-5}b^5}$

Write each number in scientific notation.

47. 0.00027

48. 0.8868

49. 80,800,000

50. 868,000

51. In November 2008, approximately 127,000,000 Americans voted in the U.S. presidential election. Write this number in scientific notation. (*Source:* CNN)

52. The approximate diameter of the Milky Way galaxy is 150,000 light years. Write this number in scientific notation. (*Source:* NASA IMAGE/POETRY Education and Public Outreach Program)

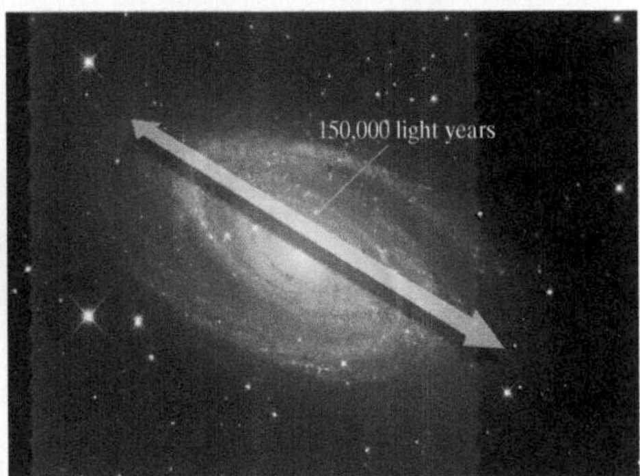

Write each number in standard form.

53. 8.67×10^5

54. 3.86×10^{-3}

55. 8.6×10^{-4}

56. 8.936×10^5

57. The volume of the planet Jupiter is 1.43128×10^{15} cubic kilometers. Write this number in standard form. (*Source:* National Space Science Data Center)

58. An angstrom is a unit of measure, equal to 1×10^{-10} meter, used for measuring wavelengths or the diameters of atoms. Write this number in standard form. (*Source:* National Institute of Standards and Technology)

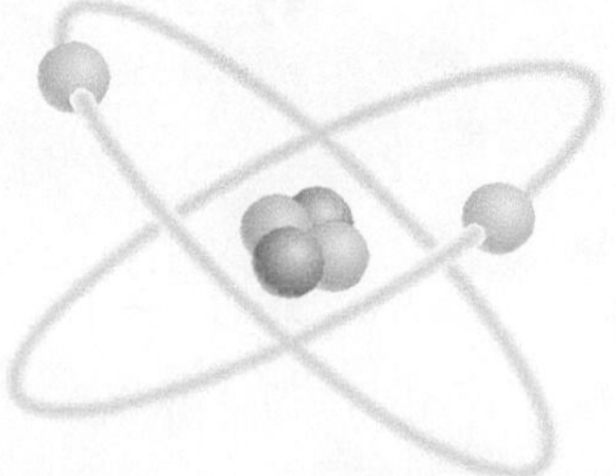

Simplify. Express each result in standard form.

59. $(8 \times 10^4)(2 \times 10^{-7})$

60. $\dfrac{8 \times 10^4}{2 \times 10^{-7}}$

(3.3) *Find the degree of each polynomial.*

61. $y^5 + 7x - 8x^4$

62. $9y^2 + 30y + 25$

63. $-14x^2y - 28x^2y^3 - 42x^2y^2$

64. $6x^2y^2z^2 + 5x^2y^3 - 12xyz$

65. The Glass Bridge Skywalk is suspended 4000 feet over the Colorado River at the very edge of the Grand Canyon. Neglecting air resistance, the height of an object dropped from the Skywalk at time t seconds is given by the polynomial $-16t^2 + 4000$. Find the height of the object at the given times below.

t	0 seconds	1 second	3 seconds	5 seconds
$-16t^2 + 4000$				

△ **66.** The surface area of a box with a square base and a height of 5 units is given by the polynomial $2x^2 + 20x$. Fill in the table below by evaluating $2x^2 + 20x$ for the given values of x.

x	1	3	5.1	10
$2x^2 + 20x$				

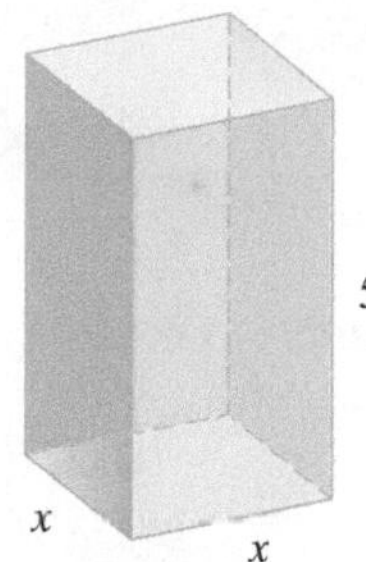

Combine like terms in each expression.

67. $7a^2 - 4a^2 - a^2$

68. $9y + y - 14y$

69. $6a^2 + 4a + 9a^2$

70. $21x^2 + 3x + x^2 + 6$

71. $4a^2b - 3b^2 - 8q^2 - 10a^2b + 7q^2$

72. $2s^{14} + 3s^{13} + 12s^{12} - s^{10}$

(3.4) *Add or subtract as indicated.*

73. $(3x^2 + 2x + 6) + (5x^2 + x)$

74. $(2x^5 + 3x^4 + 4x^3 + 5x^2) + (4x^2 + 7x + 6)$

75. $(-5y^2 + 3) - (2y^2 + 4)$

76. $(2m^7 + 3x^4 + 7m^6) - (8m^7 + 4m^2 + 6x^4)$

77. $(3x^2 - 7xy + 7y^2) - (4x^2 - xy + 9y^2)$

78. $(8x^6 - 5xy - 10y^2) - (7x^6 - 9xy - 12y^2)$

Translating *Perform the indicated operations.*

79. Add $(-9x^2 + 6x + 2)$ and $(4x^2 - x - 1)$.

80. Subtract $(4x^2 + 8x - 7)$ from the sum of $(x^2 + 7x + 9)$ and $(x^2 + 4)$.

(3.5) *Multiply each expression.*

81. $6(x + 5)$

82. $9(x - 7)$

83. $4(2a + 7)$

84. $9(6a - 3)$

85. $-7x(x^2 + 5)$

86. $-8y(4y^2 - 6)$

87. $-2(x^3 - 9x^2 + x)$

88. $-3a(a^2b + ab + b^2)$

89. $(-2a)(3a^3 - 4a + 1)$

90. $(7b)(6b^3 - 4b + 2)$

91. $(2x + 2)(x - 7)$

92. $(2x - 5)(3x + 2)$

93. $(4a - 1)(a + 7)$

94. $(6a - 1)(7a + 3)$

95. $(x + 7)(x^3 + 4x - 5)$

96. $(x + 2)(x^5 + x + 1)$

97. $(x^2 + 2x + 4)(x^2 + 2x - 4)$

98. $(x^3 + 4x + 4)(x^3 + 4x - 4)$

99. $(x + 7)^3$

100. $(2x - 5)^3$

(3.6) *Use special products to multiply each of the following.*

101. $(x + 7)^2$

102. $(x - 5)^2$

103. $(3x - 7)^2$

104. $(4x + 2)^2$

105. $(5x - 9)^2$

106. $(5x + 1)(5x - 1)$

107. $(7x + 4)(7x - 4)$

108. $(a + 2b)(a - 2b)$

109. $(2x - 6)(2x + 6)$

110. $(4a^2 - 2b)(4a^2 + 2b)$

Express each as a product of polynomials in x. Then multiply and simplify.

111. Find the area of the square if its side is $(3x - 1)$ meters.

112. Find the area of the rectangle.

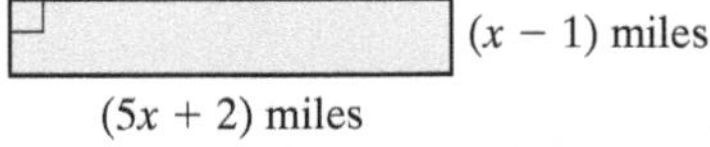

(3.7) *Divide.*

113. $\dfrac{x^2 + 21x + 49}{7x^2}$

114. $\dfrac{5a^3b - 15ab^2 + 20ab}{-5ab}$

115. $(a^2 - a + 4) \div (a - 2)$

116. $(4x^2 + 20x + 7) \div (x + 5)$

117. $\dfrac{a^3 + a^2 + 2a + 6}{a - 2}$

118. $\dfrac{9b^3 - 18b^2 + 8b - 1}{3b - 2}$

119. $\dfrac{4x^4 - 4x^3 + x^2 + 4x - 3}{2x - 1}$

120. $\dfrac{-10x^2 - x^3 - 21x + 18}{x - 6}$

△ **121.** The area of the rectangle below is $(15x^3 - 3x^2 + 60)$ square feet. If its length is $3x^2$ feet, find its width.

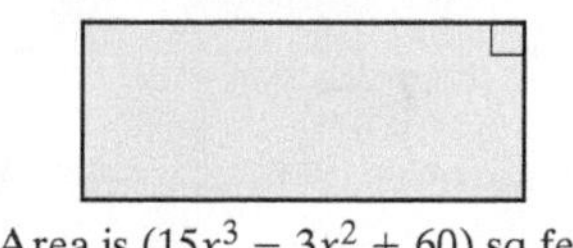

Area is $(15x^3 - 3x^2 + 60)$ sq feet

122. The perimeter of the equilateral triangle below is $(21a^3b^6 + 3a - 3)$ units. Find the length of a side.

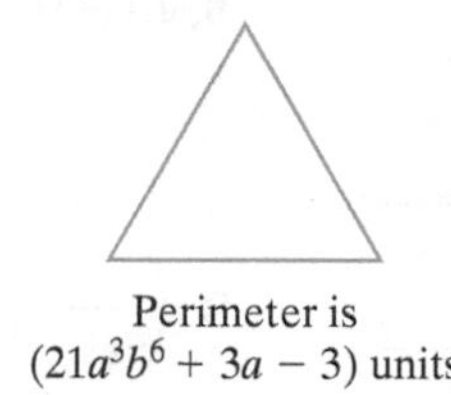

Perimeter is $(21a^3b^6 + 3a - 3)$ units

Mixed Review

Evaluate.

123. 3^3

124. $\left(-\frac{1}{2}\right)^3$

Simplify each expression. Write each answer using positive exponents only.

125. $(4xy^2)(x^3y^5)$

126. $\dfrac{18x^9}{27x^3}$

127. $\left(\dfrac{3a^4}{b^2}\right)^3$

128. $(2x^{-4}y^3)^{-4}$

129. $\dfrac{a^{-3}b^6}{9^{-1}a^{-5}b^{-2}}$

Perform the indicated operations and simplify.

130. $(-y^2 - 4) + (3y^2 - 6)$

131. $(6x + 2) + (5x - 7)$

132. $(5x^2 + 2x - 6) - (-x - 4)$

133. $(8y^2 - 3y + 1) - (3y^2 + 2)$

134. $(2x + 5)(3x - 2)$

135. $4x(7x^2 + 3)$

136. $(7x - 2)(4x - 9)$

137. $(x - 3)(x^2 + 4x - 6)$

Use special products to multiply.

138. $(5x + 4)^2$

139. $(6x + 3)(6x - 3)$

Divide.

140. $\dfrac{8a^4 - 2a^3 + 4a - 5}{2a^3}$

141. $\dfrac{x^2 + 2x + 10}{x + 5}$

142. $\dfrac{4x^3 + 8x^2 - 11x + 4}{2x - 3}$

Chapter 3 Test

Answers

Step-by-step test solutions are found on the Chapter Test Prep Videos available via the Interactive DVD Lecture Series, in *MyMathLab* or on YouTube (search "MartinGayIntroAlg" and click on "Channels").

Evaluate each expression.

1. 2^5 **2.** $(-3)^4$ **3.** -3^4 **4.** 4^{-3}

Simplify each expression. Write the result using only positive exponents.

5. $(3x^2)(-5x^9)$ **6.** $\dfrac{y^7}{y^2}$ **7.** $\dfrac{r^{-8}}{r^{-3}}$

8. $\left(\dfrac{4x^2y^3}{x^3y^{-4}}\right)^2$ **9.** $\dfrac{6^2x^{-4}y^{-1}}{6^3x^{-3}y^7}$

Express each number in scientific notation.

10. 563,000 **11.** 0.0000863

Write each number in standard form.

12. 1.5×10^{-3} **13.** 6.23×10^4

14. Simplify. Write the answer in standard form.
$(1.2 \times 10^5)(3 \times 10^{-7})$

15. a. Complete the table for the polynomial $4xy^2 + 7xyz + x^3y - 2$.

Term	Numerical Coefficient	Degree of Term
$4xy^2$		
$7xyz$		
x^3y		
-2		

b. What is the degree of the polynomial?

16. Simplify by combining like terms.
$5x^2 + 4x - 7x^2 + 11 + 8x$

Perform each indicated operation.

17. $(8x^3 + 7x^2 + 4x - 7) + (8x^3 - 7x - 6)$

18.
$$\begin{array}{r} 5x^3 + x^2 + 5x - 2 \\ -(8x^3 - 4x^2 + x - 7) \\ \hline \end{array}$$

19. Subtract $(4x + 2)$ from the sum of $(8x^2 + 7x + 5)$ and $(x^3 - 8)$.

1. ______
2. ______
3. ______
4. ______
5. ______
6. ______
7. ______
8. ______
9. ______
10. ______
11. ______
12. ______
13. ______
14. ______
15. a. ______
b. ______
16. ______
17. ______
18. ______
19. ______

Multiply in Exercises 20 through 26.

20. $(3x + 7)(x^2 + 5x + 2)$

21. $3x^2(2x^2 - 3x + 7)$

22. $(x + 7)(3x - 5)$

23. $\left(3x - \frac{1}{5}\right)\left(3x + \frac{1}{5}\right)$

24. $(4x - 2)^2$

25. $(8x + 3)^2$

26. $(x^2 - 9b)(x^2 + 9b)$

27. The height of the Bank of China in Hong Kong is 1001 feet. Neglecting air resistance, the height of an object dropped from this building at time t seconds is given by the polynomial $-16t^2 + 1001$. Find the height of the object at the given times below.

t	0 seconds	1 second	3 seconds	5 seconds
$-16t^2 + 1001$				

△ **28.** Find the area of the top of the table. Express the area as a product, then multiply and simplify.

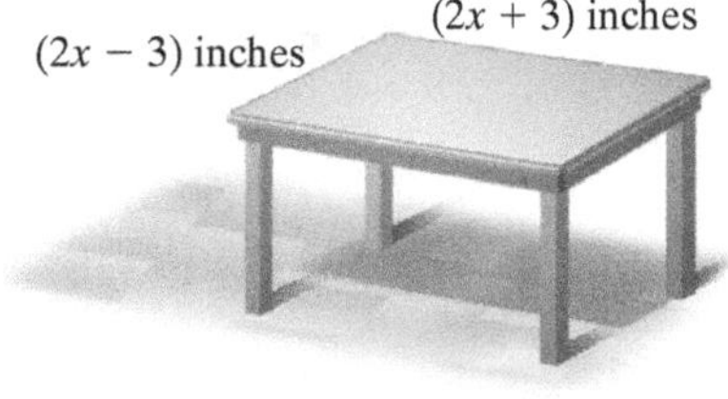

Divide.

29. $\dfrac{4x^2 + 2xy - 7x}{8xy}$

30. $(x^2 + 7x + 10) \div (x + 5)$

31. $\dfrac{27x^3 - 8}{3x + 2}$

20. __________

21. __________

22. __________

23. __________

24. __________

25. __________

26. __________

27. __________

28. __________

29. __________

30. __________

31. __________

Answers

1. a. ______
b. ______
c. ______
d. ______
e. ______
f. ______

2. a. ______
b. ______
c. ______

3. a. ______
b. ______
c. ______
d. ______
e. ______
f. ______

4. a. ______
b. ______

5. ______

6. ______

7. a. ______
b. ______
c. ______
d. ______
e. ______

Cumulative Review Chapters 1–3

1. Given the set $\left\{-2, 0, \frac{1}{4}, 112, -3, 11, \sqrt{2}\right\}$, list the numbers in this set that belong to the set of:

a. Natural numbers
b. Whole numbers
c. Integers
d. Rational numbers
e. Irrational numbers
f. Real numbers

2. Find the absolute value of each number.

a. $|-7.2|$
b. $|0|$
c. $\left|-\frac{1}{2}\right|$

3. Evaluate (find the value of) the following:

a. 3^2
b. 5^3
c. 2^4
d. 7^1
e. $\left(\frac{3}{7}\right)^2$
f. $(0.6)^2$

4. Multiply. Write products in lowest terms.

a. $\frac{3}{4} \cdot \frac{7}{21}$
b. $\frac{1}{2} \cdot 4\frac{5}{6}$

5. Simplify: $\frac{3}{2} \cdot \frac{1}{2} - \frac{1}{2}$

6. Evaluate $\frac{2x - 7y}{x^2}$ for $x = 5$ and $y = 1$.

7. Write an algebraic expression that represents each phrase. Let the variable x represent the unknown number.

a. The sum of a number and 3
b. The product of 3 and a number
c. The quotient of 7.3 and a number
d. 10 decreased by a number
e. 5 times a number, increased by 7

8. Simplify: $8 + 3(2 \cdot 6 - 1)$

9. Add: $11.4 + (-4.7)$

10. Is $x = 1$ a solution of $5x^2 + 2 = x - 8$?

11. Find the value of each expression when $x = 2$ and $y = -5$.

a. $\frac{x - y}{12 + x}$ **b.** $x^2 - y$

12. Subtract:

a. $7 - 40$

b. $-5 - (-10)$

Divide.

13. $\frac{-30}{-10}$ **14.** $\frac{-48}{6}$ **15.** $\frac{42}{-0.6}$ **16.** $\frac{-30}{-0.2}$

Find each product by using the distributive property to remove parentheses.

17. $5(3x + 2)$ **18.** $-3(2x - 3)$ **19.** $-2(y + 0.3z - 1)$

20. $4x(-x^2 + 6x - 1)$ **21.** $-(9x + y - 2z + 6)$ **22.** $-(-4xy + 6y - 2)$

23. Solve: $6(2a - 1) - (11a + 6) = 7$

24. Solve: $2x + \frac{1}{8} = x - \frac{3}{8}$

25. Solve: $\frac{y}{7} = 20$

26. Solve: $10 = 5j - 2$

27. Solve: $0.25x + 0.10(x - 3) = 1.1$

28. Solve: $\frac{7x + 5}{3} = x + 3$

29. Twice the sum of a number and 4 is the same as four times the number decreased by 12. Find the number.

30. Write the phrase as an algebraic expression and simplify if possible. Double a number, subtracted from the sum of a number and seven.

8. ______
9. ______
10. ______
11. a. ______
b. ______
12. a. ______
b. ______
13. ______
14. ______
15. ______
16. ______
17. ______
18. ______
19. ______
20. ______
21. ______
22. ______
23. ______
24. ______
25. ______
26. ______
27. ______
28. ______
29. ______
30. ______

31. ______
32. ______
33. ______
34. ______
35. ______
36. a. ______
b. ______
c. ______
37. a. ______
b. ______
c. ______
38. ______
39. ______
40. ______
41. ______
42. ______
43. ______
44. ______
45. ______
46. ______
47. ______
48. ______
49. ______

△ **31.** Charles Pecot can afford enough fencing to enclose a rectangular garden with a perimeter of 140 feet. If the width of his garden is to be 30 feet, find the length.

32. Simplify: $\dfrac{4(-3) + (-8)}{5 + (-5)}$

33. The number 120 is 15% of what number?

34. Graph $x < 5$.

−5 −4 −3 −2 −1 0 1 2 3 4 5

35. Solve: $-4x + 7 \geq -9$. Graph the solution set.

−5 −4 −3 −2 −1 0 1 2 3 4 5

36. Evaluate.

a. $(-5)^2$ **b.** -5^2 **c.** $2 \cdot 5^2$

37. Simplify each expression.

a. $x^7 \cdot x^4$

b. $\left(\dfrac{t}{2}\right)^4$

c. $(9y^5)^2$

38. Simplify: $\dfrac{(z^2)^3 \cdot z^7}{z^9}$

Simplify the following expressions. Write each result using positive exponents only.

39. $\left(\dfrac{3a^2}{b}\right)^{-3}$ **40.** $(5x^7)(-3x^9)$ **41.** $(5y^3)^{-2}$ **42.** $(-3)^{-2}$

Simplify each polynomial by combining any like terms.

43. $9x^3 + x^3$ **44.** $(5y^2 - 6) - (y^2 + 2)$ **45.** $5x^2 + 6x - 9x - 3$

46. Multiply: $(10x^2 - 3)(10x^2 + 3)$.

47. Multiply: $7x(x^2 + 2x + 5)$

48. Multiply: $(10x^2 + 3)^2$.

49. Divide: $\dfrac{9x^5 - 12x^2 + 3x}{3x^2}$

Factoring Polynomials

4

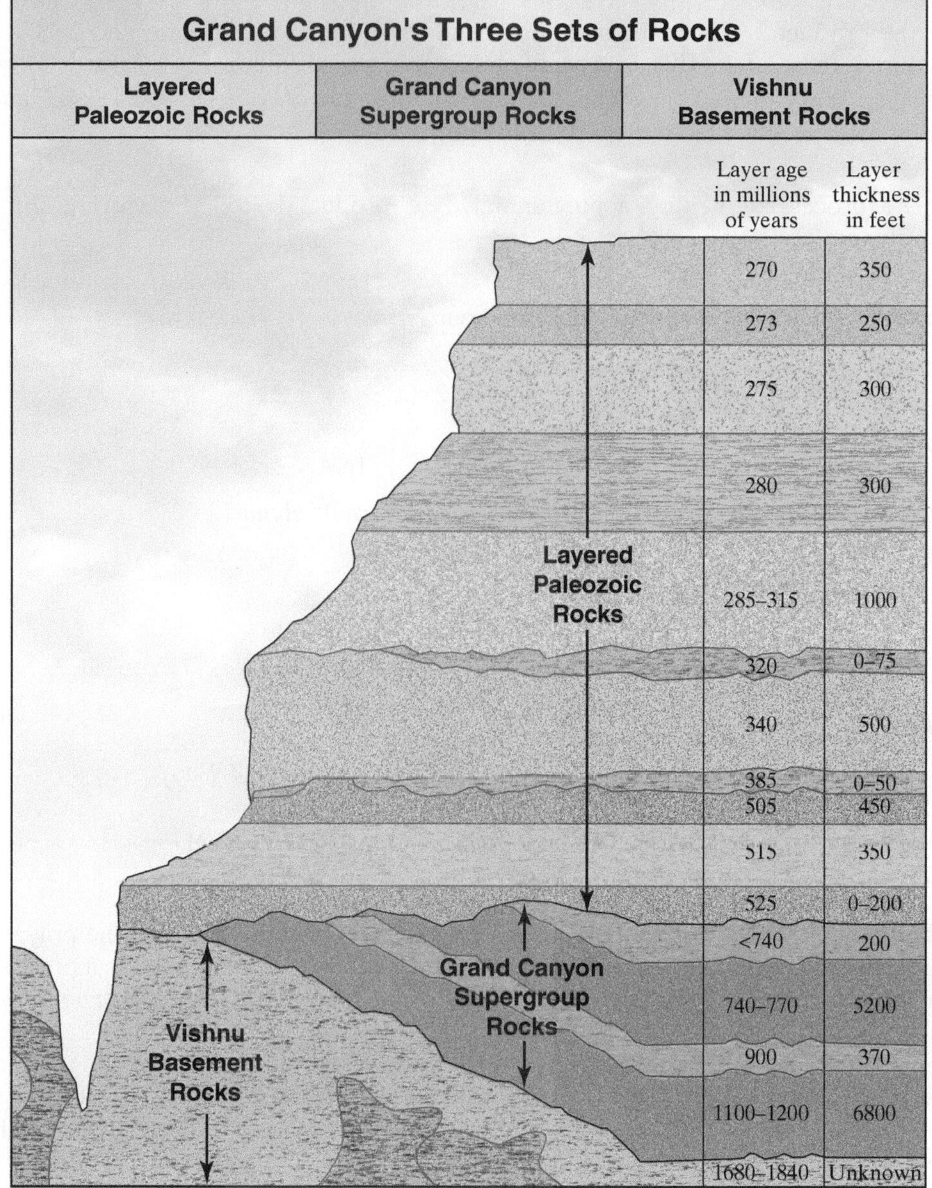

Sections

Check Your Progress

In Chapter 3, we learned how to multiply polynomials. Now we will deal with an operation that is the reverse process of multiplying–factoring. Factoring is an important algebraic skill because it allows us to write a sum as a product. As we will see in Sections 4.6 and 4.7, factoring can be used to solve equations other than linear equations. In Chapter 5, we will also use factoring to simplify and perform arithmetic operations on rational expressions.

The Grand Canyon is a part of the Colorado River basin. It is truly one of this nation's most stirring natural wonders. Grand Canyon National Park comprises more than a million acres of land, has 277 miles of rivers, and is up to 18 miles wide and a mile deep. Recent studies (somewhat controversial) have increased the estimation of the origin of the canyon from 5 to 6 million years ago to somewhere around 17 million years ago.

The diagram above depicts the Grand Canyon's layers of rock along with—most interestingly—each layer's age and thickness.

In Exercise 105, Section 4.5, you will explore information about the height of the Toroweap Overlook, on the North Rim of the canyon.

Objectives

A **Find the Greatest Common Factor of a List of Numbers.**

B **Find the Greatest Common Factor of a List of Terms.**

C **Factor Out the Greatest Common Factor from the Terms of a Polynomial.**

D **Factor by Grouping.**

4.1 THE GREATEST COMMON FACTOR

In the product $2 \cdot 3 = 6$, the numbers 2 and 3 are called **factors** of 6 and $2 \cdot 3$ is a **factored form** of 6. This is true of polynomials also. Since $(x + 2)(x + 3) = x^2 + 5x + 6$, then $(x + 2)$ and $(x + 3)$ are factors of $x^2 + 5x + 6$, and $(x + 2)(x + 3)$ is a factored form of the polynomial.

The process of writing a polynomial as a product is called **factoring** the polynomial.

Study the examples below and look for a pattern.

Multiplying: $5(x^2 + 3) = 5x^2 + 15$ $\quad 2x(x - 7) = 2x^2 - 14x$

Factoring: $5x^2 + 15 = 5(x^2 + 3)$ $\quad 2x^2 - 14x = 2x(x - 7)$

Do you see that factoring is the reverse process of multiplying?

factoring

$$x^2 + 5x + 6 = (x + 2)(x + 3)$$

multiplying

✓**Concept Check** Multiply: $2(x - 4)$
What do you think the result of factoring $2x - 8$ would be? Why?

Objective A Finding the Greatest Common Factor of a List of Numbers

The first step in factoring a polynomial is to see whether the terms of the polynomial have a common factor. If there is one, we can write the polynomial as a product by **factoring out** the common factor. We will usually factor out the *greatest* common factor (GCF).

The GCF of a list of integers is the largest integer that is a factor of all the integers in the list. For example, the GCF of 12 and 20 is 4 because 4 is the largest integer that is a factor of both 12 and 20. With large integers, the GCF may not be easily found by inspection. When this happens, we will write each integer as a product of prime numbers. Recall that a prime number is a whole number other than 1, whose only factors are 1 and itself.

PRACTICE 1

Find the GCF of each list of numbers.

a. 45 and 75 **b.** 32 and 33
c. 14, 24, and 60

Answers

1. a. 15 **b.** 1 **c.** 2

✓ **Concept Check Answer**

$2x - 8$; the result would be $2(x - 4)$ because factoring is the reverse process of multiplying.

Example 1 Find the GCF of each list of numbers.

a. 28 and 40 **b.** 55 and 21 **c.** 15, 18, and 66

Solution:

a. Write each number as a product of primes.

$28 = 2 \cdot 2 \cdot 7 = 2^2 \cdot 7$

$40 = 2 \cdot 2 \cdot 2 \cdot 5 = 2^3 \cdot 5$

There are two common factors, each of which is 2, so the GCF is

$\text{GCF} = 2 \cdot 2 = 4$

b. $55 = 5 \cdot 11$

$21 = 3 \cdot 7$

There are no common prime factors; thus, the GCF is 1.

c. $15 = 3 \cdot 5$

$18 = 2 \cdot 3 \cdot 3 = 2 \cdot 3^2$

$66 = 2 \cdot 3 \cdot 11$

The only prime factor common to all three numbers is 3, so the GCF is

$\text{GCF} = 3$

Work Practice 1

Objective B Finding the Greatest Common Factor of a List of Terms

The greatest common factor of a list of variables raised to powers is found in a similar way. For example, the GCF of x^2, x^3, and x^5 is x^2 because each term contains a factor of x^2 and no higher power of x is a factor of each term.

$$x^2 = x \cdot x$$
$$x^3 = x \cdot x \cdot x$$
$$x^5 = x \cdot x \cdot x \cdot x \cdot x$$

There are two common factors, each of which is x, so the GCF $= x \cdot x$ or x^2. From this example, we see that **the GCF of a list of common variables raised to powers is the variable raised to the smallest exponent in the list.**

Example 2 Find the GCF of each list of terms.

a. x^3, x^7, and x^5

b. y, y^4, and y^7

Solution:

a. The GCF is x^3, since 3 is the smallest exponent to which x is raised.

b. The GCF is y^1 or y, since 1 is the smallest exponent on y.

Work Practice 2

PRACTICE 2

Find the GCF of each list of terms.

a. y^4, y^5, and y^8

b. x and x^{10}

The **greatest common factor (GCF) of a list of terms** is the product of the GCF of the numerical coefficients and the GCF of the variable factors.

$$20x^2y^2 = 2 \cdot 2 \cdot 5 \cdot x \cdot x \cdot y \cdot y$$
$$6xy^3 = 2 \cdot 3 \cdot x \cdot y \cdot y \cdot y$$
$$\text{GCF} = 2 \cdot x \cdot y \cdot y = 2xy^2$$

Helpful Hint

Remember that the GCF of a list of terms contains the smallest exponent on each common variable.

The GCF of x^5y^6, x^2y^7, and x^3y^4 is x^2y^4. (Smallest exponent on x; Smallest exponent on y)

Answers

2. a. y^4 **b.** x

PRACTICE 3

Find the greatest common factor of each list of terms.

a. $6x^2$, $9x^4$, and $-12x^5$

b. $-16y$, $-20y^6$, and $40y^4$

c. a^5b^4, ab^3, and a^3b^2

Example 3 Find the greatest common factor of each list of terms.

a. $6x^2$, $10x^3$, and $-8x$

b. $-18y^2$, $-63y^3$, and $27y^4$

c. a^3b^2, a^5b, and a^6b^2

Solution:

a.

$$6x^2 = 2 \cdot 3 \cdot x^2$$
$$10x^3 = 2 \cdot 5 \cdot x^3$$
$$-8x = -1 \cdot 2 \cdot 2 \cdot 2 \cdot x^1$$

→ The GCF of x^2, x^3, and x^1 is x^1 or x.

$$\text{GCF} = 2 \cdot x^1 \quad \text{or} \quad 2x$$

b.

$$-18y^2 = -1 \cdot 2 \cdot 3 \cdot 3 \cdot y^2$$
$$-63y^3 = -1 \cdot 3 \cdot 3 \cdot 7 \cdot y^3$$
$$27y^4 = 3 \cdot 3 \cdot 3 \cdot y^4$$

→ The GCF of y^2, y^3, and y^4 is y^2.

$$\text{GCF} = 3 \cdot 3 \cdot y^2 \quad \text{or} \quad 9y^2$$

c. The GCF of a^3, a^5, and a^6 is a^3.

The GCF of b^2, b, and b^2 is b.

Thus, the GCF of a^3b^2, a^5b, and a^6b^2 is a^3b.

Work Practice 3

Objective C Factoring Out the Greatest Common Factor

To factor a polynomial such as $8x + 14$, we first see whether the terms have a greatest common factor other than 1. In this case, they do: The GCF of $8x$ and 14 is 2.

We factor out 2 from each term by writing each term as the product of 2 and the term's remaining factors.

$$8x + 14 = 2 \cdot 4x + 2 \cdot 7$$

Using the distributive property, we can write

$$8x + 14 = 2 \cdot 4x + 2 \cdot 7$$
$$= 2(4x + 7)$$

Thus, a factored form of $8x + 14$ is $2(4x + 7)$. We can check by multiplying:

$$2(4x + 7) = 2 \cdot 4x + 2 \cdot 7 = 8x + 14.$$

Helpful Hint

A factored form of $8x + 14$ is *not*

$$2 \cdot 4x + 2 \cdot 7$$

Although the *terms* have been factored (written as products), the *polynomial* $8x + 14$ has not been factored. A factored form of $8x + 14$ is the *product* $2(4x + 7)$.

✓**Concept Check** Which of the following is/are factored form(s) of $6t + 18$?

a. 6

b. $6 \cdot t + 6 \cdot 3$

c. $6(t + 3)$

d. $3(t + 6)$

Answers

3. a. $3x^2$ b. $4y$ c. ab^2

✓ **Concept Check Answer**

c

Example 4 Factor each polynomial by factoring out the greatest common factor (GCF).

a. $5ab + 10a$ **b.** $y^5 - y^{12}$

Solution:

a. The GCF of terms $5ab$ and $10a$ is $5a$. Thus,

$$5ab + 10a = 5a \cdot b + 5a \cdot 2$$
$$= 5a(b + 2) \quad \text{Apply the distributive property.}$$

We can check our work by multiplying $5a$ and $(b + 2)$.
$5a(b + 2) = 5a \cdot b + 5a \cdot 2 = 5ab + 10a$, the original polynomial.

b. The GCF of y^5 and y^{12} is y^5. Thus,

$$y^5 - y^{12} = y^5(1) - y^5(y^7)$$
$$= y^5(1 - y^7)$$

Helpful Hint: Don't forget the 1.

Work Practice 4

PRACTICE 4

Factor each polynomial by factoring out the greatest common factor (GCF).

a. $10y + 25$

b. $x^4 - x^9$

Example 5 Factor: $-9a^5 + 18a^2 - 3a$

Solution:

$$-9a^5 + 18a^2 - 3a = 3a(-3a^4) + 3a(6a) + 3a(-1)$$
$$= 3a(-3a^4 + 6a - 1)$$

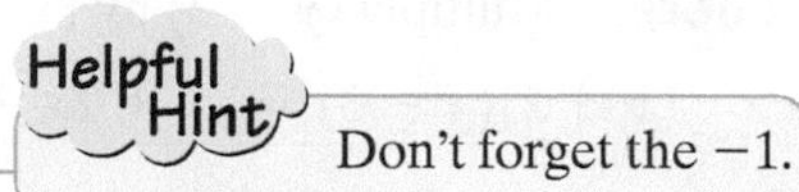

Helpful Hint: Don't forget the -1.

Work Practice 5

PRACTICE 5

Factor: $-10x^3 + 8x^2 - 2x$

In Example 5, we could have chosen to factor out $-3a$ instead of $3a$. If we factor out $-3a$, we have

$$-9a^5 + 18a^2 - 3a = (-3a)(3a^4) + (-3a)(-6a) + (-3a)(1)$$
$$= -3a(3a^4 - 6a + 1)$$

Helpful Hint

Notice the changes in signs when factoring out $-3a$.

Examples Factor.

6. $6a^4 - 12a = 6a(a^3 - 2)$

7. $\frac{3}{7}x^4 + \frac{1}{7}x^3 - \frac{5}{7}x^2 = \frac{1}{7}x^2(3x^2 + x - 5)$

8. $15p^2q^4 + 20p^3q^5 + 5p^3q^3 = 5p^2q^3(3q + 4pq^2 + p)$

Work Practice 6–8

PRACTICE 6–8

Factor.

6. $4x^3 + 12x$

7. $\frac{2}{5}a^5 - \frac{4}{5}a^3 + \frac{1}{5}a^2$

8. $6a^3b + 3a^3b^2 + 9a^2b^4$

Example 9 Factor: $5(x + 3) + y(x + 3)$

Solution: The binomial $(x + 3)$ is present in both terms and is the greatest common factor. We use the distributive property to factor out $(x + 3)$.

$$5(x + 3) + y(x + 3) = (x + 3)(5 + y)$$

Work Practice 9

PRACTICE 9

Factor: $7(p + 2) + q(p + 2)$

Answers

4. a. $5(2y + 5)$ **b.** $x^4(1 - x^5)$

5. $2x(-5x^2 + 4x - 1)$

6. $4x(x^2 + 3)$ **7.** $\frac{1}{5}a^2(2a^3 - 4a + 1)$

8. $3a^2b(2a + ab + 3b^3)$

9. $(p + 2)(7 + q)$

Objective D Factoring by Grouping

Once the GCF is factored out, we can often continue to factor the polynomial, using a variety of techniques. We discuss here a technique called **factoring by grouping.** This technique can be used to factor some polynomials with four terms.

PRACTICE 10

Factor $ab + 7a + 2b + 14$ by grouping.

Helpful Hint Notice that this form, $x(y + 2) + 3(y + 2)$, is *not* a factored form of the original polynomial. It is a sum, not a product.

Example 10 Factor $xy + 2x + 3y + 6$ by grouping.

Solution: Notice that the first two terms of this polynomial have a common factor of x and the second two terms have a common factor of 3. Because of this, group the first two terms, then the last two terms, and then factor out these common factors.

$$xy + 2x + 3y + 6 = (xy + 2x) + (3y + 6) \quad \text{Group terms.}$$
$$= x(y + 2) + 3(y + 2) \quad \text{Factor out GCF from each grouping.}$$

Next we factor out the common binomial factor, $(y + 2)$.

$$x(y + 2) + 3(y + 2) = (y + 2)(x + 3)$$

Now the result is a factored form because it is a product. We were able to write the polynomial as a product because of the common binomial factor, $(y + 2)$, that appeared. If this does not happen, try rearranging the terms of the original polynomial.

Check: Multiply $(y + 2)$ by $(x + 3)$.

$$(y + 2)(x + 3) = xy + 2x + 3y + 6,$$

the original polynomial.
Thus, the factored form of $xy + 2x + 3y + 6$ is the product $(y + 2)(x + 3)$.

Work Practice 10

You may want to try these steps when factoring by grouping.

To Factor by Grouping

Step 1: Group the terms in two groups so that each group has a common factor.

Step 2: Factor out the GCF from each group.

Step 3: If there is a common binomial factor, factor it out.

Step 4: If not, rearrange the terms and try these steps again.

PRACTICE 11–13

Factor by grouping.

11. $28x^3 - 7x^2 + 12x - 3$

12. $2xy + 5y^2 - 4x - 10y$

13. $3x^2 + 4xy + 3x + 4y$

Examples Factor by grouping.

11. $15x^3 - 10x^2 + 6x - 4$

$= (15x^3 - 10x^2) + (6x - 4)$ — Group the terms.

$= 5x^2(3x - 2) + 2(3x - 2)$ — Factor each group.

$= (3x - 2)(5x^2 + 2)$ — Factor out the common factor, $(3x - 2)$.

12. $3x^2 + 4xy - 3x - 4y$

$= (3x^2 + 4xy) + (-3x - 4y)$

$= x(3x + 4y) - 1(3x + 4y)$ — Factor each group. A -1 is factored from the second pair of terms so that there is a common factor, $(3x + 4y)$.

$= (3x + 4y)(x - 1)$ — Factor out the common factor, $(3x + 4y)$.

Answers

10. $(b + 7)(a + 2)$

11. $(4x - 1)(7x^2 + 3)$

12. $(2x + 5y)(y - 2)$

13. $(3x + 4y)(x + 1)$

13. $2a^2 + 5ab + 2a + 5b$
$= (2a^2 + 5ab) + (2a + 5b)$ Factor each group.
$= a(2a + 5b) + 1(2a + 5b)$ An understood 1 is written before $(2a + 5b)$ to help remember that $(2a + 5b)$ is $1(2a + 5b)$.
$= (2a + 5b)(a + 1)$ Factor out the common factor, $(2a + 5b)$.

Helpful Hint Notice that the factor of 1 is written when $(2a + 5b)$ is factored out.

Work Practice 11–13

Examples Factor by grouping.

14. $3x^3 - 2x - 9x^2 + 6$
$= x(3x^2 - 2) - 3(3x^2 - 2)$ Factor each group. A -3 is factored from the second pair of terms so that there is a common factor, $(3x^2 - 2)$.
$= (3x^2 - 2)(x - 3)$ Factor out the common factor, $(3x^2 - 2)$.

15. $3xy + 2 - 3x - 2y$

Notice that the first two terms have no common factor other than 1. However, if we rearrange these terms, a grouping emerges that does lead to a common factor.

$3xy + 2 - 3x - 2y$
$= (3xy - 3x) + (-2y + 2)$
$= 3x(y - 1) - 2(y - 1)$ Factor -2 from the second group.
$= (y - 1)(3x - 2)$ Factor out the common factor, $(y - 1)$.

16. $5x - 10 + x^3 - x^2 = 5(x - 2) + x^2(x - 1)$

There is no common binomial factor that can now be factored out. No matter how we rearrange the terms, no grouping will lead to a common factor. Thus, this polynomial is not factorable by grouping.

Work Practice 14–16

PRACTICE 14–16

Factor by grouping.

14. $4x^3 + x - 20x^2 - 5$

15. $3xy - 4 + x - 12y$

16. $2x - 2 + x^3 - 3x^2$

Helpful Hint

Throughout this chapter, we will be factoring polynomials. Even when the instructions do not so state, it is always a good idea to check your answers by multiplying.

Answers

14. $(4x^2 + 1)(x - 5)$
15. $(3y + 1)(x - 4)$
16. cannot be factored by grouping

Vocabulary and Readiness Check

Use the choices below to fill in each blank. Some choices may be used more than once and some may not be used at all.

greatest common factor　factors　factoring　true　false　least　greatest

1. Since $5 \cdot 4 = 20$, the numbers 5 and 4 are called ______________ of 20.
2. The ______________ of a list of integers is the largest integer that is a factor of all the integers in the list.
3. The greatest common factor of a list of common variables raised to powers is the variable raised to the ______________ exponent in the list.
4. The process of writing a polynomial as a product is called ______________.
5. True or false: A factored form of $7x + 21 + xy + 3y$ is $7(x + 3) + y(x + 3)$. ______________
6. True or false: A factored form of $3x^3 + 6x + x^2 + 2$ is $3x(x^2 + 2)$. ______________

Write the prime factorization of the following integers.

7. 14
8. 15

Write the GCF of the following pairs of integers.

9. 18, 3
10. 7, 35
11. 20, 15
12. 6, 15

4.1 Exercise Set

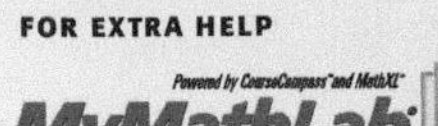

Objectives A B Mixed Practice *Find the GCF for each list. See Examples 1 through 3.*

1. 32, 36
2. 36, 90
3. 18, 42, 84
4. 30, 75, 135
5. 24, 14, 21
6. 15, 25, 27
7. y^2, y^4, y^7
8. x^3, x^2, x^5
9. z^7, z^9, z^{11}
10. y^8, y^{10}, y^{12}
11. $x^{10}y^2, xy^2, x^3y^3$
12. p^7q, p^8q^2, p^9q^3
13. $14x, 21$
14. $20y, 15$
15. $12y^4, 20y^3$
16. $32x^5, 18x^2$
17. $-10x^2, 15x^3$
18. $-21x^3, 14x$
19. $12x^3, -6x^4, 3x^5$
20. $15y^2, 5y^7, -20y^3$
21. $-18x^2y, 9x^3y^3, 36x^3y$
22. $7x^3y^3, -21x^2y^2, 14xy^4$
23. $20a^6b^2c^8, 50a^7b$
24. $40x^7y^2z, 64x^9y$

Objective C *Factor out the GCF from each polynomial. See Examples 4 through 9.*

25. $3a + 6$
26. $18a + 12$
27. $30x - 15$
28. $42x - 7$
29. $x^3 + 5x^2$

30. $y^5 + 6y^4$ **31.** $6y^4 + 2y^3$ **32.** $5x^2 + 10x^6$ **33.** $32xy - 18x^2$ **34.** $10xy - 15x^2$

35. $4x - 8y + 4$ **36.** $7x + 21y - 7$ **37.** $6x^3 - 9x^2 + 12x$ **38.** $12x^3 + 16x^2 - 8x$

39. $a^7b^6 - a^3b^2 + a^2b^5 - a^2b^2$ **40.** $x^9y^6 + x^3y^5 - x^4y^3 + x^3y^3$ **41.** $5x^3y - 15x^2y + 10xy$

42. $14x^3y + 7x^2y - 7xy$ **43.** $8x^5 + 16x^4 - 20x^3 + 12$ **44.** $9y^6 - 27y^4 + 18y^2 + 6$

45. $\frac{1}{3}x^4 + \frac{2}{3}x^3 - \frac{4}{3}x^5 + \frac{1}{3}x$ **46.** $\frac{2}{5}y^7 - \frac{4}{5}y^5 + \frac{3}{5}y^2 - \frac{2}{5}y$ **47.** $y(x^2 + 2) + 3(x^2 + 2)$

48. $x(y^2 + 1) - 3(y^2 + 1)$ **49.** $z(y + 4) + 3(y + 4)$ **50.** $8(x + 2) - y(x + 2)$

51. $r(z^2 - 6) + (z^2 - 6)$ **52.** $q(b^3 - 5) + (b^3 - 5)$

Factor a "−1" from each polynomial. See Example 5.

53. $-x - 7$ **54.** $-y - 3$ **55.** $-2 + z$

56. $-5 + y$ **57.** $3a - b + 2$ **58.** $2y - z - 11$

Objective D *Factor each four-term polynomial by grouping. If this is not possible, write "not factorable by grouping." See Examples 10 through 16.*

59. $x^3 + 2x^2 + 5x + 10$ **60.** $x^3 + 4x^2 + 3x + 12$ **61.** $5x + 15 + xy + 3y$

62. $xy + y + 2x + 2$ **63.** $6x^3 - 4x^2 + 15x - 10$ **64.** $16x^3 - 28x^2 + 12x - 21$

65. $5m^3 + 6mn + 5m^2 + 6n$ **66.** $8w^2 + 7wv + 8w + 7v$ **67.** $2y - 8 + xy - 4x$

68. $6x - 42 + xy - 7y$ **69.** $2x^3 + x^2 + 8x + 4$ **70.** $2x^3 - x^2 - 10x + 5$

71. $3x - 3 + x^3 - 4x^2$ **72.** $7x - 21 + x^3 - 2x^2$ **73.** $4x^2 - 8xy - 3x + 6y$

74. $5xy - 15x - 6y + 18$ **75.** $5q^2 - 4pq - 5q + 4p$ **76.** $6m^2 - 5mn - 6m + 5n$

Objectives C D Mixed Practice *Factor out the GCF from each polynomial. Then factor by grouping.*

77. $12x^2y - 42x^2 - 4y + 14$

78. $90 + 15y^2 - 18x - 3xy^2$

79. $6a^2 + 9ab^2 + 6ab + 9b^3$

80. $16x^2 + 4xy^2 + 8xy + 2y^3$

Review

Multiply. See section 3.5.

81. $(x + 2)(x + 5)$

82. $(y + 3)(y + 6)$

83. $(b + 1)(b - 4)$

84. $(x - 5)(x + 10)$

Fill in the chart by finding two numbers that have the given product and sum. The first column is filled in for you.

		85.	86.	87.	88.	89.	90.	91.	92.
Two Numbers	4, 7								
Their Product	28	12	20	8	16	−10	−9	−24	−36
Their Sum	11	8	9	−9	−10	3	0	−5	−5

Concept Extensions

See the Concept Checks in this section.

93. Which of the following is/are factored form(s) of $-2x + 14$?

a. $-2(x + 7)$ **b.** $-2 \cdot x + 14$
c. $-2(x - 14)$ **d.** $-2(x - 7)$

94. Which of the following is/are factored form(s) of $8a - 24$?

a. $8 \cdot a - 24$ **b.** $8(a - 3)$
c. $4(2a - 12)$ **d.** $8 \cdot a - 2 \cdot 12$

Which of the following expressions are factored?

95. $(a + 6)(a + 2)$

96. $(x + 5)(x + y)$

97. $5(2y + z) - b(2y + z)$

98. $3x(a + 2b) + 2(a + 2b)$

99. The annual cotton crop yield (in 1000 bales) in the United States for the period 2003–2007 can be approximated by the polynomial $-1264x^2 + 5056x + 18{,}960$, where x is the number of years after 2003. (*Source:* Based on data from the National Agricultural Statistics Service)

a. Find the approximate amount of the cotton harvest in 2004. To do so, let $x = 1$ and evaluate $-1264x^2 + 5056x + 18{,}960$.

b. Find the approximate amount of cotton harvested in 2007.

c. Factor the polynomial $-1264x^2 + 5056x + 18{,}960$.

100. The polynomial $-30x^2 + 180x + 210$ represents the approximate number of visitors (in thousands) per year to the White House during 2003–2007. In this polynomial, x represents the years since 2003. (*Source:* Based on data from the National Park Service)

a. Find the approximate number of visitors to the White House in 2005. To do so, let $x = 2$ and evaluate $-30x^2 + 180x + 210$.

b. Find the approximate number of visitors to the White House in 2006.

c. Factor out the GCF from the polynomial $-30x^2 + 180x + 210$.

Write an expression for the area of each shaded region. Then write the expression as a factored polynomial.

101.

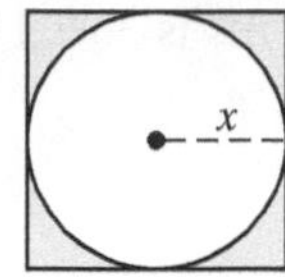

102.

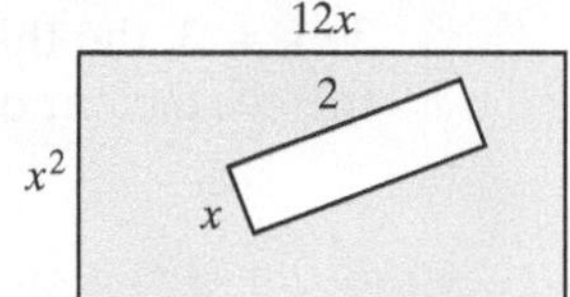

Write an expression for the length of each rectangle. (Hint: Factor the area binomial and recall that $Area = width \cdot length$.)

103.

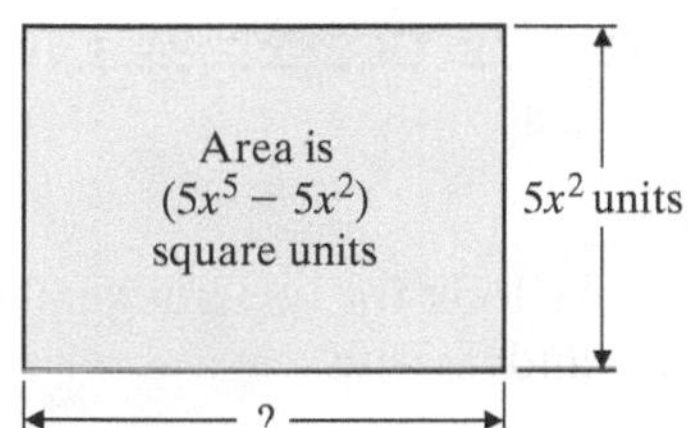

104.

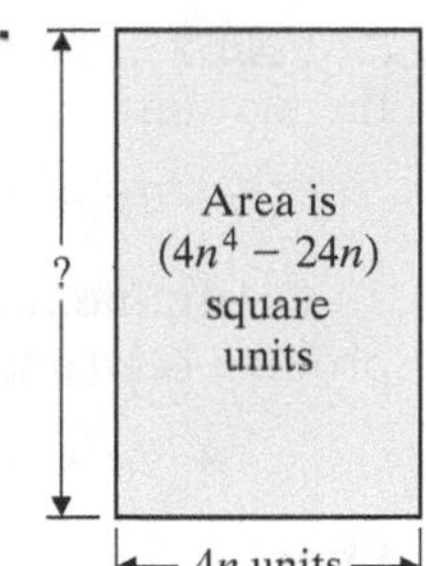

105. Construct a binomial whose greatest common factor is $5a^3$. (*Hint:* Multiply $5a^3$ by a binomial whose terms contain no common factor other than 1: $5a^3(\square + \square)$.)

106. Construct a trinomial whose greatest common factor is $2x^2$. See the hint for Exercise 105.

107. Explain how you can tell whether a polynomial is written in factored form.

108. Construct a four-term polynomial that can be factored by grouping. Explain how you constructed the polynomial.

Objectives

A **Factor Trinomials of the Form $x^2 + bx + c$.**

B **Factor Out the Greatest Common Factor and Then Factor a Trinomial of the Form $x^2 + bx + c$.**

4.2 FACTORING TRINOMIALS OF THE FORM $x^2 + bx + c$

Objective A Factoring Trinomials of the Form $x^2 + bx + c$

In this section, we factor trinomials of the form $x^2 + bx + c$, such as

$$x^2 + 7x + 12, \quad x^2 - 12x + 35, \quad x^2 + 4x - 12, \quad \text{and} \quad r^2 - r - 42$$

Notice that for these trinomials, the coefficient of the squared variable is 1.

Recall that factoring means to write as a product and that factoring and multiplying are reverse processes. Using the FOIL method of multiplying binomials, we have the following.

$$\begin{aligned}(x + 3)(x + 1) &= \overset{F}{x^2} + \overset{O}{1x} + \overset{I}{3x} + \overset{L}{3} \\ &= x^2 + 4x + 3\end{aligned}$$

Thus, a factored form of $x^2 + 4x + 3$ is $(x + 3)(x + 1)$.

Notice that the product of the first terms of the binomials is $x \cdot x = x^2$, the first term of the trinomial. Also, the product of the last two terms of the binomials is $3 \cdot 1 = 3$, the third term of the trinomial. The sum of these same terms is $3 + 1 = 4$, the coefficient of the middle, x, term of the trinomial.

The product of these numbers is 3.

$$x^2 + 4x + 3 = (x + 3)(x + 1)$$

The sum of these numbers is 4.

Many trinomials, such as the one above, factor into two binomials. To factor $x^2 + 7x + 10$, let's assume that it factors into two binomials and begin by writing two pairs of parentheses. The first term of the trinomial is x^2, so we use x and x as the first terms of the binomial factors.

$$x^2 + 7x + 10 = (x + \square)(x + \square)$$

To determine the last term of each binomial factor, we look for two integers whose product is 10 and whose sum is 7. The integers are 2 and 5. Thus,

$$x^2 + 7x + 10 = (x + 2)(x + 5)$$

Check: To see if we have factored correctly, we multiply.

$$\begin{aligned}(x + 2)(x + 5) &= x^2 + 5x + 2x + 10 \\ &= x^2 + 7x + 10 \qquad \text{Combine like terms.}\end{aligned}$$

Helpful Hint

Since multiplication is commutative, the factored form of $x^2 + 7x + 10$ can be written as either $(x + 2)(x + 5)$ or $(x + 5)(x + 2)$.

To Factor a Trinomial of the Form $x^2 + bx + c$

The product of these numbers is c.

$$x^2 + bx + c = (x + \square)(x + \square)$$

The sum of these numbers is b.

Example 1 Factor: $x^2 + 7x + 12$

Solution: We begin by writing the first terms of the binomial factors.

$(x + \square)(x + \square)$

Next we look for two numbers whose product is 12 and whose sum is 7. Since our numbers must have a positive product and a positive sum, we look at pairs of positive factors of 12 only.

Factors of 12	Sum of Factors
1, 12	13
2, 6	8
3, 4	7

Correct sum, so the numbers are 3 and 4.

Thus, $x^2 + 7x + 12 = (x + 3)(x + 4)$

Check: $(x + 3)(x + 4) = x^2 + 4x + 3x + 12 = x^2 + 7x + 12$

Work Practice 1

PRACTICE 1

Factor: $x^2 + 12x + 20$

Example 2 Factor: $x^2 - 12x + 35$

Solution: Again, we begin by writing the first terms of the binomials.

$(x + \square)(x + \square)$

Now we look for two numbers whose product is 35 and whose sum is -12. Since our numbers must have a positive product and a negative sum, we look at pairs of negative factors of 35 only.

Factors of 35	Sum of Factors
−1, −35	−36
−5, −7	−12

Correct sum, so the numbers are −5 and −7.

$x^2 - 12x + 35 = (x - 5)(x - 7)$

Check: To check, multiply $(x - 5)(x - 7)$.

Work Practice 2

PRACTICE 2

Factor each trinomial.

a. $x^2 - 23x + 22$

b. $x^2 - 27x + 50$

Example 3 Factor: $x^2 + 4x - 12$

Solution: $x^2 + 4x - 12 = (x + \square)(x + \square)$

We look for two numbers whose product is -12 and whose sum is 4. Since our numbers must have a negative product, we look at pairs of factors with opposite signs.

Factors of − 12	Sum of Factors
−1, 12	11
1, −12	−11
−2, 6	4
2, −6	−4
−3, 4	1
3, −4	−1

Correct sum, so the numbers are −2 and 6.

$x^2 + 4x - 12 = (x - 2)(x + 6)$

Work Practice 3

PRACTICE 3

Factor: $x^2 + 5x - 36$

Answers

1. $(x + 10)(x + 2)$
2. a. $(x - 1)(x - 22)$ b. $(x - 2)(x - 25)$
3. $(x + 9)(x - 4)$

PRACTICE 4

Factor each trinomial.

a. $q^2 - 3q - 40$

b. $y^2 + 2y - 48$

Example 4 Factor: $r^2 - r - 42$

Solution: Because the variable in this trinomial is r, the first term of each binomial factor is r.

$$r^2 - r - 42 = (r + \square)(r + \square)$$

Now we look for two numbers whose product is -42 and whose sum is -1, the numerical coefficient of r. The numbers are 6 and -7. Therefore,

$$r^2 - r - 42 = (r + 6)(r - 7)$$

Work Practice 4

PRACTICE 5

Factor: $x^2 + 6x + 15$

Example 5 Factor: $a^2 + 2a + 10$

Solution: Look for two numbers whose product is 10 and whose sum is 2. Neither 1 and 10 nor 2 and 5 give the required sum, 2. We conclude that $a^2 + 2a + 10$ is not factorable with integers. A polynomial such as $a^2 + 2a + 10$ is called a **prime polynomial.**

Work Practice 5

PRACTICE 6

Factor each trinomial.

a. $x^2 + 9xy + 14y^2$

b. $a^2 - 13ab + 30b^2$

Example 6 Factor: $x^2 + 5xy + 6y^2$

Solution: $x^2 + 5xy + 6y^2 = (x + \square)(x + \square)$

Recall that the middle term, $5xy$, is the same as $5yx$. Thus, we can see that $5y$ is the "coefficient" of x. We then look for two terms whose product is $6y^2$ and whose sum is $5y$. The terms are $2y$ and $3y$ because $2y \cdot 3y = 6y^2$ and $2y + 3y = 5y$. Therefore,

$$x^2 + 5xy + 6y^2 = (x + 2y)(x + 3y)$$

Work Practice 6

PRACTICE 7

Factor: $x^4 + 8x^2 + 12$

Example 7 Factor: $x^4 + 5x^2 + 6$

Solution: As usual, we begin by writing the first terms of the binomials. Since the greatest power of x in this polynomial is x^4, we write

$$(x^2 + \square)(x^2 + \square) \quad \text{Since } x^2 \cdot x^2 = x^4$$

Now we look for two factors of 6 whose sum is 5. The numbers are 2 and 3. Thus,

$$x^4 + 5x^2 + 6 = (x^2 + 2)(x^2 + 3)$$

Work Practice 7

If the terms of a polynomial are not written in descending powers of the variable, you may want to rearrange the terms before factoring.

PRACTICE 8

Factor: $48 - 14x + x^2$

Example 8 Factor: $40 - 13t + t^2$

Solution: First, we rearrange terms so that the trinomial is written in descending powers of t.

$$40 - 13t + t^2 = t^2 - 13t + 40$$

Next, try to factor.

$$t^2 - 13t + 40 = (t + \square)(t + \square)$$

Now we look for two factors of 40 whose sum is -13. The numbers are -8 and -5. Thus,

$$t^2 - 13t + 40 = (t - 8)(t - 5)$$

Work Practice 8

Answers

4. **a.** $(q - 8)(q + 5)$ **b.** $(y + 8)(y - 6)$
5. prime polynomial
6. **a.** $(x + 2y)(x + 7y)$ **b.** $(a - 3b)(a - 10b)$
7. $(x^2 + 6)(x^2 + 2)$
8. $(x - 6)(x - 8)$

The following sign patterns may be useful when factoring trinomials.

Helpful Hint

A positive constant in a trinomial tells us to look for two numbers with the same sign. The sign of the coefficient of the middle term tells us whether the signs are both positive or both negative.

both positive ↓ same sign ↙ $x^2 + 10x + 16 = (x + 2)(x + 8)$

both negative ↓ same sign ↓ $x^2 - 10x + 16 = (x - 2)(x - 8)$

A negative constant in a trinomial tells us to look for two numbers with opposite signs.

opposite signs ↓ $x^2 + 6x - 16 = (x + 8)(x - 2)$

opposite signs ↓ $x^2 - 6x - 16 = (x - 8)(x + 2)$

Objective B Factoring Out the Greatest Common Factor

Remember that the first step in factoring any polynomial is to factor out the greatest common factor (if there is one other than 1 or −1).

Example 9 Factor: $3m^2 - 24m - 60$

Solution: First we factor out the greatest common factor, 3, from each term.

$$3m^2 - 24m - 60 = 3(m^2 - 8m - 20)$$

Now we factor $m^2 - 8m - 20$ by looking for two factors of −20 whose sum is −8. The factors are −10 and 2. Therefore, the complete factored form is

$$3m^2 - 24m - 60 = 3(m + 2)(m - 10)$$

Work Practice 9

Helpful Hint

Remember to write the common factor, 3, as part of the factored form.

Example 10 Factor: $2x^4 - 26x^3 + 84x^2$

Solution:

$$2x^4 - 26x^3 + 84x^2 = 2x^2(x^2 - 13x + 42) \quad \text{Factor out common factor, } 2x^2.$$
$$= 2x^2(x - 6)(x - 7) \quad \text{Factor } x^2 - 13x + 42.$$

Work Practice 10

PRACTICE 9

Factor each trinomial.

a. $4x^2 - 24x + 36$

b. $x^3 + 3x^2 - 4x$

PRACTICE 10

Factor: $5x^5 - 25x^4 - 30x^3$

Answers

9. a. $4(x - 3)(x - 3)$ **b.** $x(x + 4)(x - 1)$

10. $5x^3(x + 1)(x - 6)$

Vocabulary and Readiness Check

Fill in each blank with "true" or "false."

1. To factor $x^2 + 7x + 6$, we look for two numbers whose product is 6 and whose sum is 7. ______
2. We can write the factorization $(y + 2)(y + 4)$ also as $(y + 4)(y + 2)$. ______
3. The factorization $(4x - 12)(x - 5)$ is completely factored. ______
4. The factorization $(x + 2y)(x + y)$ may also be written as $(x + 2y)^2$. ______

Complete each factored form.

5. $x^2 + 9x + 20 = (x + 4)(x \quad)$
6. $x^2 + 12x + 35 = (x + 5)(x \quad)$
7. $x^2 - 7x + 12 = (x - 4)(x \quad)$
8. $x^2 - 13x + 22 = (x - 2)(x \quad)$
9. $x^2 + 4x + 4 = (x + 2)(x \quad)$
10. $x^2 + 10x + 24 = (x + 6)(x \quad)$

4.2 Exercise Set

FOR EXTRA HELP

PRACTICE

WATCH

DOWNLOAD

READ

REVIEW

Objective A *Factor each trinomial completely. If a polynomial can't be factored, write "prime." See Examples 1 through 8.*

1. $x^2 + 7x + 6$
2. $x^2 + 6x + 8$
3. $y^2 - 10y + 9$
4. $y^2 - 12y + 11$
5. $x^2 - 6x + 9$
6. $x^2 - 10x + 25$
7. $x^2 - 3x - 18$
8. $x^2 - x - 30$
9. $x^2 + 3x - 70$
10. $x^2 + 4x - 32$
11. $x^2 + 5x + 2$
12. $x^2 - 7x + 5$
13. $x^2 + 8xy + 15y^2$
14. $x^2 + 6xy + 8y^2$
15. $a^4 - 2a^2 - 15$
16. $y^4 - 3y^2 - 70$
17. $13 + 14m + m^2$
18. $17 + 18n + n^2$
19. $10t - 24 + t^2$
20. $6q - 27 + q^2$
21. $a^2 - 10ab + 16b^2$
22. $a^2 - 9ab + 18b^2$

Objectives A B Mixed Practice *Factor each trinomial completely. Some of these trinomials contain a greatest common factor (other than 1). Don't forget to factor out the GCF first. See Examples 1 through 10.*

23. $2z^2 + 20z + 32$
24. $3x^2 + 30x + 63$
25. $2x^3 - 18x^2 + 40x$
26. $3x^3 - 12x^2 - 36x$
27. $x^2 - 3xy - 4y^2$
28. $x^2 - 4xy - 77y^2$
29. $x^2 + 15x + 36$
30. $x^2 + 19x + 60$
31. $x^2 - x - 2$
32. $x^2 - 5x - 14$
33. $r^2 - 16r + 48$
34. $r^2 - 10r + 21$
35. $x^2 + xy - 2y^2$
36. $x^2 - xy - 6y^2$
37. $3x^2 + 9x - 30$
38. $4x^2 - 4x - 48$

39. $3x^2 - 60x + 108$

40. $2x^2 - 24x + 70$

41. $x^2 - 18x - 144$

42. $x^2 + x - 42$

43. $r^2 - 3r + 6$

44. $x^2 + 4x - 10$

45. $x^2 - 8x + 15$

46. $x^2 - 9x + 14$

47. $6x^3 + 54x^2 + 120x$

48. $3x^3 + 3x^2 - 126x$

49. $4x^2y + 4xy - 12y$

50. $3x^2y - 9xy + 45y$

51. $x^2 - 4x - 21$

52. $x^2 - 4x - 32$

53. $x^2 + 7xy + 10y^2$

54. $x^2 - 3xy - 4y^2$

55. $64 + 24t + 2t^2$

56. $50 + 20t + 2t^2$

57. $x^3 - 2x^2 - 24x$

58. $x^3 - 3x^2 - 28x$

59. $2t^5 - 14t^4 + 24t^3$

60. $3x^6 + 30x^5 + 72x^4$

61. $5x^3y - 25x^2y^2 - 120xy^3$

62. $7a^3b - 35a^2b^2 + 42ab^3$

63. $162 - 45m + 3m^2$

64. $48 - 20n + 2n^2$

65. $-x^2 + 12x - 11$
(Factor out -1 first.)

66. $-x^2 + 8x - 7$
(Factor out -1 first.)

67. $\frac{1}{2}y^2 - \frac{9}{2}y - 11$
(Factor out $\frac{1}{2}$ first.)

68. $\frac{1}{3}y^2 - \frac{5}{3}y - 8$
(Factor out $\frac{1}{3}$ first.)

69. $x^3y^2 + x^2y - 20x$

70. $a^2b^3 + ab^2 - 30b$

Review

Multiply. See Section 3.5.

71. $(2x + 1)(x + 5)$

72. $(3x + 2)(x + 4)$

73. $(5y - 4)(3y - 1)$

74. $(4z - 7)(7z - 1)$

75. $(a + 3b)(9a - 4b)$

76. $(y - 5x)(6y + 5x)$

Concept Extensions

77. Write a polynomial that factors as $(x - 3)(x + 8)$.

78. To factor $x^2 + 13x + 42$, think of two numbers whose ______ is 42 and whose ______ is 13.

Complete each sentence in your own words.

79. If $x^2 + bx + c$ is factorable and c is negative, then the signs of the last-term factors of the binomials are opposite because...

80. If $x^2 + bx + c$ is factorable and c is positive, then the signs of the last-term factors of the binomials are the same because . . .

Remember that perimeter means distance around. Write the perimeter of each rectangle as a simplified polynomial. Then factor the polynomial completely.

△ **81.**

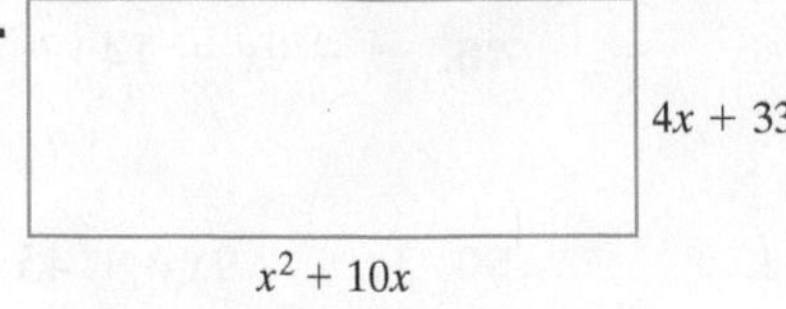

△ **82.**

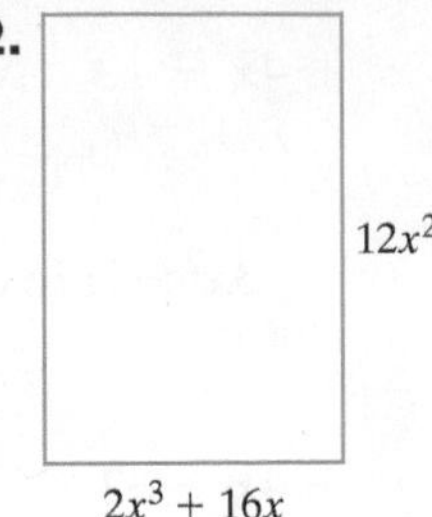

83. An object is thrown upward from the top of an 80-foot building with an initial velocity of 64 feet per second. Neglecting air resistance, the height of the object after t seconds is given by $-16t^2 + 64t + 80$. Factor this polynomial.

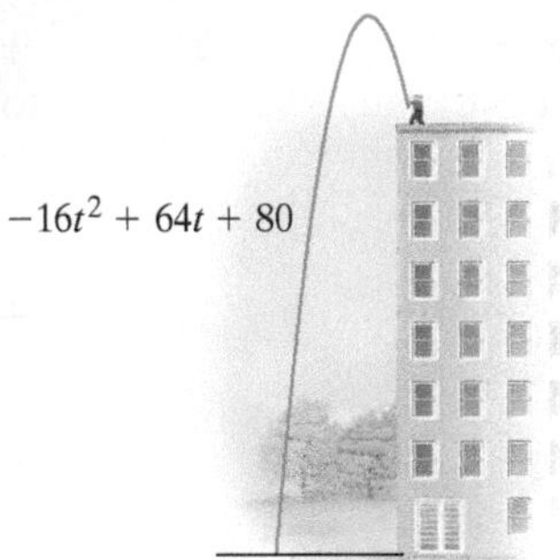

84. An object is thrown upward from the top of a 112-foot building with an initial velocity of 96 feet per second. Neglecting air resistance, the height of the object after t seconds is given by $-16t^2 + 96t + 112$. Factor this polynomial.

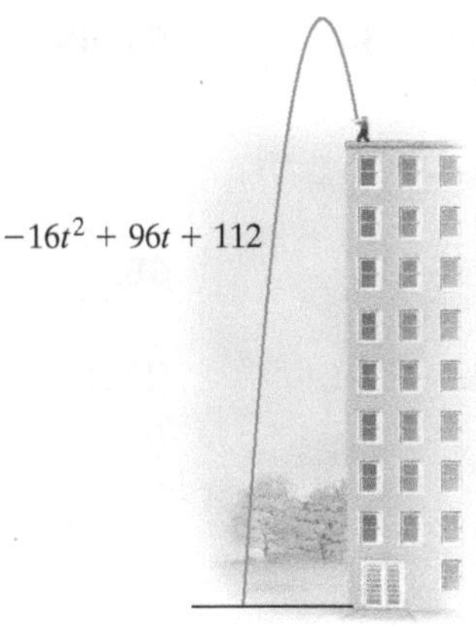

Factor each trinomial completely.

85. $x^2 + \frac{1}{2}x + \frac{1}{16}$

86. $x^2 + x + \frac{1}{4}$

87. $z^2(x + 1) - 3z(x + 1) - 70(x + 1)$

88. $y^2(x + 1) - 2y(x + 1) - 15(x + 1)$

Find all positive values of c so that each trinomial is factorable.

89. $n^2 - 16n + c$

90. $y^2 - 4y + c$

Find all positive values of b so that each trinomial is factorable.

91. $y^2 + by + 20$

92. $x^2 + bx + 15$

Factor each trinomial. (Hint: *Notice that $x^{2n} + 4x^n + 3$ factors as $(x^n + 1)(x^n + 3)$.* Remember: $x^n \cdot x^n = x^{n+n}$ *or* x^{2n}.)

93. $x^{2n} + 8x^n - 20$

94. $x^{2n} + 5x^n + 6$

4.3 FACTORING TRINOMIALS OF THE FORM $ax^2 + bx + c$

Objectives

A **Factor Trinomials of the Form $ax^2 + bx + c$, where $a \neq 1$.**

B **Factor Out the GCF Before Factoring a Trinomial of the Form $ax^2 + bx + c$.**

Objective A Factoring Trinomials of the Form $ax^2 + bx + c$

In this section, we factor trinomials of the form $ax^2 + bx + c$, such as

$$3x^2 + 11x + 6, \quad 8x^2 - 22x + 5, \quad \text{and} \quad 2x^2 + 13x - 7$$

Notice that the coefficient of the squared variable in these trinomials is a number other than 1. We will factor these trinomials using a trial-and-check method based on our work in the last section.

To begin, let's review the relationship between the numerical coefficients of the trinomial and the numerical coefficients of its factored form. For example, since

$$(2x + 1)(x + 6) = 2x^2 + 13x + 6,$$

a factored form of $2x^2 + 13x + 6$ is $(2x + 1)(x + 6)$.

Notice that $2x$ and x are factors of $2x^2$, the first term of the trinomial. Also, 6 and 1 are factors of 6, the last term of the trinomial, as shown:

$$2x^2 + 13x + 6 = (2x + 1)(x + 6)$$

$2x \cdot x$

$1 \cdot 6$

Also notice that $13x$, the middle term, is the sum of the following products:

$$2x^2 + 13x + 6 = (2x + 1)(x + 6)$$

$$\begin{array}{r} 1x \\ +12x \\ \hline 13x \end{array}$$ Middle term

Let's use this pattern to factor $5x^2 + 7x + 2$. First, we find factors of $5x^2$. Since all numerical coefficients in this trinomial are positive, we will use factors with positive numerical coefficients only. Thus, the factors of $5x^2$ are $5x$ and x. Let's try these factors as first terms of the binomials. Thus far, we have

$$5x^2 + 7x + 2 = (5x + \square)(x + \square)$$

Next, we need to find positive factors of 2. Positive factors of 2 are 1 and 2. Now we try possible combinations of these factors as second terms of the binomials until we obtain a middle term of $7x$.

$$(5x + 1)(x + 2) = 5x^2 + 11x + 2$$

$$\begin{array}{r} 1x \\ +10x \\ \hline 11x \end{array}$$ ⟶ **Incorrect** middle term

Let's try switching factors 2 and 1.

$$(5x + 2)(x + 1) = 5x^2 + 7x + 2$$

$$\begin{array}{r} 2x \\ +5x \\ \hline 7x \end{array}$$ ⟶ **Correct** middle term

Thus a factored form of $5x^2 + 7x + 2$ is $(5x + 2)(x + 1)$. To check, we multiply $(5x + 2)$ and $(x + 1)$. The product is $5x^2 + 7x + 2$.

PRACTICE 1

Factor each trinomial.

a. $5x^2 + 27x + 10$

b. $4x^2 + 12x + 5$

Example 1 Factor: $3x^2 + 11x + 6$

Solution: Since all numerical coefficients are positive, we use factors with positive numerical coefficients. We first find factors of $3x^2$.

Factors of $3x^2$: $3x^2 = 3x \cdot x$

If factorable, the trinomial will be of the form

$$3x^2 + 11x + 6 = (3x + \square)(x + \square)$$

Next we factor 6.

Factors of 6: $6 = 1 \cdot 6, \quad 6 = 2 \cdot 3$

Now we try combinations of factors of 6 until a middle term of $11x$ is obtained. Let's try 1 and 6 first.

$$(3x + 1)(x + 6) = 3x^2 + 19x + 6$$

$1x$
$+18x$
$19x$ ⟶ **Incorrect** middle term

Now let's next try 6 and 1.

$$(3x + 6)(x + 1)$$

Before multiplying, notice that the terms of the factor $3x + 6$ have a common factor of 3. The terms of the original trinomial $3x^2 + 11x + 6$ have no common factor other than 1, so the terms of its factors will also contain no common factor other than 1. This means that $(3x + 6)(x + 1)$ is not a factored form.

Next let's try 2 and 3 as last terms.

$$(3x + 2)(x + 3) = 3x^2 + 11x + 6$$

$2x$
$+9x$
$11x$ ⟶ **Correct** middle term

Thus a factored form of $3x^2 + 11x + 6$ is $(3x + 2)(x + 3)$.

Work Practice 1

Helpful Hint This is true in general: If the terms of a trinomial have no common factor (other than 1), then the terms of each of its binomial factors will contain no common factor (other than 1).

✓**Concept Check** Do the terms of $3x^2 + 29x + 18$ have a common factor? Without multiplying, decide which of the following factored forms could not be a factored form of $3x^2 + 29x + 18$.

a. $(3x + 18)(x + 1)$ **b.** $(3x + 2)(x + 9)$

c. $(3x + 6)(x + 3)$ **d.** $(3x + 9)(x + 2)$

PRACTICE 2

Factor each trinomial.

a. $2x^2 - 11x + 12$

b. $6x^2 - 5x + 1$

Example 2 Factor: $8x^2 - 22x + 5$

Solution: Factors of $8x^2$: $8x^2 = 8x \cdot x, \quad 8x^2 = 4x \cdot 2x$

We'll try $8x$ and x.

$$8x^2 - 22x + 5 = (8x + \square)(x + \square)$$

Since the middle term, $-22x$, has a negative numerical coefficient, we factor 5 into negative factors.

Factors of 5: $5 = -1 \cdot -5$

Answers

1. a. $(5x + 2)(x + 5)$ **b.** $(2x + 5)(2x + 1)$

2. a. $(2x - 3)(x - 4)$ **b.** $(3x - 1)(2x - 1)$

✓ **Concept Check Answer**

no; **a, c, d**

Let's try −1 and −5.

$$(8x - 1)(x - 5) = 8x^2 - 41x + 5$$

$-1x$
$+(-40x)$
$-41x$ ⟶ **Incorrect** middle term

Now let's try −5 and −1.

$$(8x - 5)(x - 1) = 8x^2 - 13x + 5$$

$-5x$
$+(-8x)$
$-13x$ ⟶ **Incorrect** middle term

Don't give up yet! We can still try other factors of $8x^2$. Let's try $4x$ and $2x$ with −1 and −5.

$$(4x - 1)(2x - 5) = 8x^2 - 22x + 5$$

$-2x$
$+(-20x)$
$-22x$ ⟶ **Correct** middle term

A factored form of $8x^2 - 22x + 5$ is $(4x - 1)(2x - 5)$.

Work Practice 2

Example 3 Factor: $2x^2 + 13x - 7$

Solution: Factors of $2x^2$: $2x^2 = 2x \cdot x$

Factors of −7: $-7 = -1 \cdot 7, \quad -7 = 1 \cdot -7$

We try possible combinations of these factors:

$(2x + 1)(x - 7) = 2x^2 - 13x - 7$ **Incorrect** middle term
$(2x - 1)(x + 7) = 2x^2 + 13x - 7$ **Correct** middle term

A factored form of $2x^2 + 13x - 7$ is $(2x - 1)(x + 7)$.

Work Practice 3

Example 4 Factor: $10x^2 - 13xy - 3y^2$

Solution: Factors of $10x^2$: $10x^2 = 10x \cdot x, \quad 10x^2 = 2x \cdot 5x$

Factors of $-3y^2$: $-3y^2 = -3y \cdot y, \quad -3y^2 = 3y \cdot -y$

We try some combinations of these factors:

Correct ↓ Correct ↓

$(10x - 3y)(x + y) = 10x^2 + 7xy - 3y^2$
$(x + 3y)(10x - y) = 10x^2 + 29xy - 3y^2$
$(5x + 3y)(2x - y) = 10x^2 + xy - 3y^2$
$(2x - 3y)(5x + y) = 10x^2 - 13xy - 3y^2$ **Correct** middle term

A factored form of $10x^2 - 13xy - 3y^2$ is $(2x - 3y)(5x + y)$.

Work Practice 4

Example 5 Factor: $3x^4 - 5x^2 - 8$

Solution: Factors of $3x^4$: $3x^4 = 3x^2 \cdot x^2$

Factors of −8: $-8 = -2 \cdot 4, 2 \cdot -4, -1 \cdot 8, 1 \cdot -8$

Continued on next page

PRACTICE 3

Factor each trinomial.

a. $3x^2 + 14x - 5$

b. $35x^2 + 4x - 4$

PRACTICE 4

Factor each trinomial.

a. $14x^2 - 3xy - 2y^2$

b. $12a^2 - 16ab - 3b^2$

PRACTICE 5

Factor: $2x^4 - 5x^2 - 7$

Answers

3. a. $(3x - 1)(x + 5)$
b. $(5x + 2)(7x - 2)$

4. a. $(7x + 2y)(2x - y)$
b. $(6a + b)(2a - 3b)$

5. $(2x^2 - 7)(x^2 + 1)$

Try combinations of these factors:

Correct ↓ Correct ↓

$(3x^2 - 2)(x^2 + 4) = 3x^4 + 10x^2 - 8$ **Incorrect** middle term

$(3x^2 + 4)(x^2 - 2) = 3x^4 - 2x^2 - 8$ **Incorrect** middle term

$(3x^2 + 8)(x^2 - 1) = 3x^4 + 5x^2 - 8$ **Incorrect sign** on middle term, so switch signs in binomial factors.

$(3x^2 - 8)(x^2 + 1) = 3x^4 - 5x^2 - 8$ **Correct** middle term

Work Practice 5

Helpful Hint

Study the last two lines of Example 5. If a factoring attempt gives you a middle term whose numerical coefficient is the opposite of the desired numerical coefficient, try switching the signs of the last terms in the binomials.

Switched signs

$(3x^2 + 8)(x^2 - 1) = 3x^4 + 5x^4 - 8$ Middle term: $+5x$

$(3x^2 - 8)(x^2 + 1) = 3x^4 - 5x^2 - 8$ Middle term: $-5x$

Objective B Factoring Out the Greatest Common Factor

Don't forget that the first step in factoring any polynomial is to look for a common factor to factor out.

PRACTICE 6

Factor each trinomial.

a. $3x^3 + 17x^2 + 10x$

b. $6xy^2 + 33xy - 18x$

Example 6 Factor: $24x^4 + 40x^3 + 6x^2$

Solution: Notice that all three terms have a common factor of $2x^2$. Thus we factor out $2x^2$ first.

$$24x^4 + 40x^3 + 6x^2 = 2x^2(12x^2 + 20x + 3)$$

Next we factor $12x^2 + 20x + 3$.

Factors of $12x^2$: $12x^2 = 4x \cdot 3x$, $12x^2 = 12x \cdot x$, $12x^2 = 6x \cdot 2x$

Since all terms in the trinomial have positive numerical coefficients, we factor 3 using positive factors only.

Factors of 3: $3 = 1 \cdot 3$

We try some combinations of the factors.

$2x^2(4x + 3)(3x + 1) = 2x^2(12x^2 + 13x + 3)$

$2x^2(12x + 1)(x + 3) = 2x^2(12x^2 + 37x + 3)$

$2x^2(2x + 3)(6x + 1) = 2x^2(12x^2 + 20x + 3)$ **Correct** middle term

A factored form of $24x^4 + 40x^3 + 6x^2$ is $2x^2(2x + 3)(6x + 1)$.

Helpful Hint Don't forget to include the common factor in the factored form.

Work Practice 6

When the term containing the squared variable has a negative coefficient, you may want to first factor out a common factor of -1.

PRACTICE 7

Factor: $-5x^2 - 19x + 4$

Example 7 Factor: $-6x^2 - 13x + 5$

Solution: We begin by factoring out a common factor of -1.

$-6x^2 - 13x + 5 = -1(6x^2 + 13x - 5)$ Factor out -1.

$= -1(3x - 1)(2x + 5)$ Factor $6x^2 + 13x - 5$.

Work Practice 7

Answers

6. a. $x(3x + 2)(x + 5)$
b. $3x(2y - 1)(y + 6)$
7. $-1(x + 4)(5x - 1)$

Vocabulary and Readiness Check

Complete each factorization.

1. $2x^2 + 5x + 3$ factors as $(2x + 3)(\ ?\ )$.
   a. $(x + 3)$ b. $(2x + 1)$ c. $(3x + 4)$ d. $(x + 1)$
2. $7x^2 + 9x + 2$ factors as $(7x + 2)(\ ?\ )$.
   a. $(3x + 1)$ b. $(x + 1)$ c. $(x + 2)$ d. $(7x + 1)$
3. $3x^2 + 31x + 10$ factors as ________.
   a. $(3x + 2)(x + 5)$ b. $(3x + 5)(x + 2)$ c. $(3x + 1)(x + 10)$
4. $5x^2 + 61x + 12$ factors as ________.
   a. $(5x + 1)(x + 12)$ b. $(5x + 3)(x + 4)$ c. $(5x + 2)(x + 6)$

4.3 Exercise Set

FOR EXTRA HELP

Powered by CourseCompass and MathXL

MyMathLab

PRACTICE

WATCH

DOWNLOAD

READ

REVIEW

Objective A *Complete each factored form. See Examples 1 through 5.*

1. $5x^2 + 22x + 8 = (5x + 2)(\qquad)$

2. $2y^2 + 15y + 25 = (2y + 5)(\qquad)$

3. $50x^2 + 15x - 2 = (5x + 2)(\qquad)$

4. $6y^2 + 11y - 10 = (2y + 5)(\qquad)$

5. $20x^2 - 7x - 6 = (5x + 2)(\qquad)$

6. $8y^2 - 2y - 55 = (2y + 5)(\qquad)$

Factor each trinomial completely. See Examples 1 through 5.

7. $2x^2 + 13x + 15$

8. $3x^2 + 8x + 4$

9. $8y^2 - 17y + 9$

10. $21x^2 - 41x + 10$

11. $2x^2 - 9x - 5$

12. $36r^2 - 5r - 24$

13. $20r^2 + 27r - 8$

14. $3x^2 + 20x - 63$

15. $10x^2 + 31x + 3$

16. $12x^2 + 17x + 5$

17. $x + 3x^2 - 2$

18. $y + 8y^2 - 9$

19. $6x^2 - 13xy + 5y^2$

20. $8x^2 - 14xy + 3y^2$

21. $15m^2 - 16m - 15$

22. $25n^2 - 5n - 6$

23. $-9x + 20 + x^2$

24. $-7x + 12 + x^2$

25. $2x^2 - 7x - 99$

26. $2x^2 + 7x - 72$

27. $-27t + 7t^2 - 4$

28. $-3t + 4t^2 - 7$

29. $3a^2 + 10ab + 3b^2$

30. $2a^2 + 11ab + 5b^2$

31. $49p^2 - 7p - 2$

32. $3r^2 + 10r - 8$

33. $18x^2 - 9x - 14$

34. $42a^2 - 43a + 6$

35. $2m^2 + 17m + 10$

36. $3n^2 + 20n + 5$

37. $24x^2 + 41x + 12$

38. $24x^2 - 49x + 15$

Objectives A B **Mixed Practice** *Factor each trinomial completely. See Examples 1 through 7.*

39. $12x^3 + 11x^2 + 2x$

40. $8a^3 + 14a^2 + 3a$

41. $21b^2 - 48b - 45$

42. $12x^2 - 14x - 10$

43. $7z + 12z^2 - 12$

44. $16t + 15t^2 - 15$

45. $6x^2y^2 - 2xy^2 - 60y^2$

46. $8x^2y + 34xy - 84y$

47. $4x^2 - 8x - 21$

48. $6x^2 - 11x - 10$

49. $3x^2 - 42x + 63$

50. $5x^2 - 75x + 60$

51. $8x^2 + 6xy - 27y^2$

52. $54a^2 + 39ab - 8b^2$

53. $-x^2 + 2x + 24$

54. $-x^2 + 4x + 21$

55. $4x^3 - 9x^2 - 9x$

56. $6x^3 - 31x^2 + 5x$

57. $24x^2 - 58x + 9$

58. $36x^2 + 55x - 14$

59. $40a^2b + 9ab - 9b$

60. $24y^2x + 7yx - 5x$

61. $30x^3 + 38x^2 + 12x$

62. $6x^3 - 28x^2 + 16x$

63. $6y^3 - 8y^2 - 30y$

64. $12x^3 - 34x^2 + 24x$

65. $10x^4 + 25x^3y - 15x^2y^2$

66. $42x^4 - 99x^3y - 15x^2y^2$

67. $-14x^2 + 39x - 10$

68. $-15x^2 + 26x - 8$

69. $16p^4 - 40p^3 + 25p^2$

70. $9q^4 - 42q^3 + 49q^2$

71. $-2x^2 + 9x + 5$

72. $-3x^2 + 8x + 16$

73. $-4 + 52x - 48x^2$

74. $-5 + 55x - 50x^2$

75. $2t^4 + 3t^2 - 27$

76. $4r^4 - 17r^2 - 15$

77. $5x^2y^2 + 20xy + 1$

78. $3a^2b^2 + 12ab + 1$

79. $6a^5 + 37a^3b^2 + 6ab^4$

80. $5m^5 + 26m^3h^2 + 5mh^4$

Review

Multiply. See Section 3.6.

81. $(x - 4)(x + 4)$

82. $(2x - 9)(2x + 9)$

83. $(x + 2)^2$

84. $(x + 3)^2$

85. $(2x - 1)^2$

86. $(3x - 5)^2$

Concept Extensions

See the Concept Check in this section.

87. Do the terms of $4x^2 + 19x + 12$ have a common factor (other than 1)?

88. Without multiplying, decide which of the following factored forms is not a factored form of $4x^2 + 19x + 12$.

a. $(2x + 4)(2x + 3)$
b. $(4x + 4)(x + 3)$
c. $(4x + 3)(x + 4)$
d. $(2x + 2)(2x + 6)$

Write the perimeter of each figure as a simplified polynomial. Then factor the polynomial completely.

89.

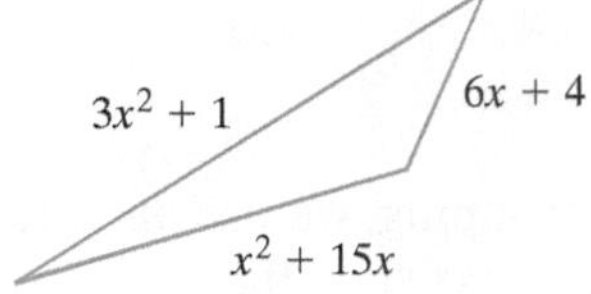

90.

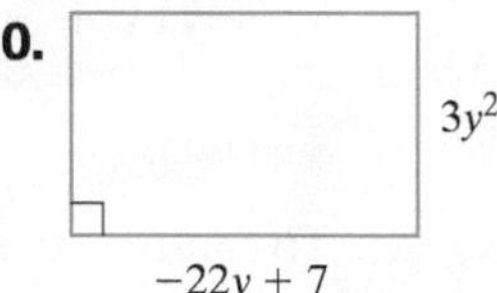

Factor each trinomial completely.

91. $4x^2 + 2x + \frac{1}{4}$

92. $27x^2 + 2x - \frac{1}{9}$

93. $4x^2(y - 1)^2 + 25x(y - 1)^2 + 25(y - 1)^2$

94. $3x^2(a + 3)^3 - 28x(a + 3)^3 + 25(a + 3)^3$

Find all positive values of b so that each trinomial is factorable.

95. $3x^2 + bx - 5$

96. $2z^2 + bz - 7$

Find all positive values of c so that each trinomial is factorable.

97. $5x^2 + 7x + c$

98. $3x^2 - 8x + c$

99. In your own words, describe the steps you use to factor a trinomial.

100. A student in your class factored $6x^2 + 7x + 1$ as $(3x + 1)(2x + 1)$. Write down how you would explain the student's error.

Objective

A Use the Grouping Method to Factor Trinomials of the Form $ax^2 + bx + c$.

4.4 FACTORING TRINOMIALS OF THE FORM $ax^2 + bx + c$ BY GROUPING

Objective A Using the Grouping Method

There is an alternative method that can be used to factor trinomials of the form $ax^2 + bx + c, a \neq 1$. This method is called the **grouping method** because it uses factoring by grouping as we learned in Section 4.1.

To see how this method works, recall from Section 4.2 that to factor a trinomial such as $x^2 + 11x + 30$, we find two numbers such that

Product is 30.

$$x^2 + 11x + 30$$

Sum is 11.

To factor a trinomial such as $2x^2 + 11x + 12$ by grouping, we use an extension of the method in Section 4.1. Here we look for two numbers such that

Product is $2 \cdot 12 = 24$.

$$2x^2 + 11x + 12$$

Sum is 11.

This time, we use the two numbers to write

$$2x^2 + 11x + 12 \text{ as}$$
$$= 2x^2 + \square x + \square x + 12$$

Then we factor by grouping. Since we want a positive product, 24, and a positive sum, 11, we consider pairs of positive factors of 24 only.

Factors of 24	Sum of Factors	
1, 24	25	
2, 12	14	
3, 8	11	Correct sum

The factors are 3 and 8. Now we use these factors to write the middle term, $11x$, as $3x + 8x$ (or $8x + 3x$). We replace $11x$ with $3x + 8x$ in the original trinomial and then we can factor by grouping.

$$\begin{aligned} 2x^2 + 11x + 12 &= 2x^2 + 3x + 8x + 12 \\ &= (2x^2 + 3x) + (8x + 12) && \text{Group the terms.} \\ &= x(2x + 3) + 4(2x + 3) && \text{Factor each group.} \\ &= (2x + 3)(x + 4) && \text{Factor out } (2x + 3). \end{aligned}$$

In general, we have the following procedure.

To Factor Trinomials by Grouping

Step 1: Factor out a greatest common factor, if there is one other than 1.

Step 2: For the resulting trinomial $ax^2 + bx + c$, find two numbers whose product is $a \cdot c$ and whose sum is b.

Step 3: Write the middle term, bx, using the factors found in Step 2.

Step 4: Factor by grouping.

Example 1 Factor $8x^2 - 14x + 5$ by grouping.

Solution:

Step 1: The terms of this trinomial contain no greatest common factor other than 1.

Step 2: This trinomial is of the form $ax^2 + bx + c$, with $a = 8$, $b = -14$, and $c = 5$. Find two numbers whose product is $a \cdot c$ or $8 \cdot 5 = 40$, and whose sum is b or -14.

The numbers are -4 and -10.

Factors of 40	Sum of Factors
−40, −1	−41
−20, −2	−22
−10, −4	−14

Correct sum

Step 3: Write $-14x$ as $-4x - 10x$ so that

$$8x^2 - 14x + 5 = 8x^2 - 4x - 10x + 5$$

Step 4: Factor by grouping.

$$8x^2 - 4x - 10x + 5 = 4x(2x - 1) - 5(2x - 1)$$
$$= (2x - 1)(4x - 5)$$

Work Practice 1

PRACTICE 1

Factor each trinomial by grouping.

a. $3x^2 + 14x + 8$

b. $12x^2 + 19x + 5$

Example 2 Factor $6x^2 - 2x - 20$ by grouping.

Solution:

Step 1: First factor out the greatest common factor, 2.

$$6x^2 - 2x - 20 = 2(3x^2 - x - 10)$$

Step 2: Next notice that $a = 3$, $b = -1$, and $c = -10$ in the resulting trinomial. Find two numbers whose product is $a \cdot c$ or $3(-10) = -30$ and whose sum is b, -1. The numbers are -6 and 5.

Step 3: $3x^2 - x - 10 = 3x^2 - 6x + 5x - 10$

Step 4: $3x^2 - 6x + 5x - 10 = 3x(x - 2) + 5(x - 2)$

$$= (x - 2)(3x + 5)$$

The factored form of $6x^2 - 2x - 20 = 2(x - 2)(3x + 5)$.

Don't forget to include the common factor of 2.

Work Practice 2

PRACTICE 2

Factor each trinomial by grouping.

a. $30x^2 - 26x + 4$

b. $6x^2y - 7xy - 5y$

Example 3 Factor $18y^4 + 21y^3 - 60y^2$ by grouping.

Solution:

Step 1: First factor out the greatest common factor, $3y^2$.

$$18y^4 + 21y^3 - 60y^2 = 3y^2(6y^2 + 7y - 20)$$

Step 2: Notice that $a = 6$, $b = 7$, and $c = -20$ in the resulting trinomial. Find two numbers whose product is $a \cdot c$ or $6(-20) = -120$ and whose sum is 7. It may help to factor -120 as a product of primes and -1.

$$-120 = 2 \cdot 2 \cdot 2 \cdot 3 \cdot 5 \cdot (-1)$$

Then choose pairings of factors until you have two pairings whose sum is 7.

$$2 \cdot 2 \cdot 2 \cdot 3 \cdot 5 \cdot (-1)$$

−8 (from $2 \cdot 2 \cdot 2 \cdot (-1)$), 15 (from $3 \cdot 5$). The numbers are −8 and 15.

Step 3: $6y^2 + 7y - 20 = 6y^2 - 8y + 15y - 20$

Step 4: $6y^2 - 8y + 15y - 20 = 2y(3y - 4) + 5(3y - 4)$

$$= (3y - 4)(2y + 5)$$

The factored form of $18y^4 + 21y^3 - 60y^2$ is $3y^2(3y - 4)(2y + 5)$.

Don't forget to include the common factor of $3y^2$.

Work Practice 3

PRACTICE 3

Factor $12y^5 + 10y^4 - 42y^3$ by grouping.

Answers

1. **a.** $(x + 4)(3x + 2)$ **b.** $(4x + 5)(3x + 1)$
2. **a.** $2(5x - 1)(3x - 2)$ **b.** $y(2x + 1)(3x - 5)$
3. $2y^3(3y + 7)(2y - 3)$

Vocabulary and Readiness Check

For each trinomial ax^2+bx+c, *choose two numbers whose product is* $a \cdot c$ *and whose sum is b.*

1. $x^2 + 6x + 8$

a. 4, 2 **b.** 7, 1 **c.** 6, 2 **d.** 6, 8

2. $x^2 + 11x + 24$

a. 6, 4 **b.** 24, 1 **c.** 8, 3 **d.** 2, 12

3. $2x^2 + 13x + 6$

a. 2, 6 **b.** 12, 1 **c.** 13, 1 **d.** 3, 4

4. $4x^2 + 8x + 3$

a. 4, 3 **b.** 4, 4 **c.** 12, 1 **d.** 2, 6

4.4 Exercise Set

FOR EXTRA HELP

MyMathLab

PRACTICE

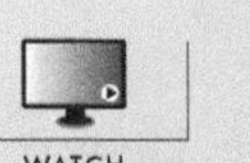
WATCH

DOWNLOAD

READ

REVIEW

Objective A *Factor each polynomial by grouping. Notice that Step 3 has already been done in these exercises. See Examples 1 through 3.*

1. $x^2 + 3x + 2x + 6$

2. $x^2 + 5x + 3x + 15$

3. $y^2 + 8y - 2y - 16$

4. $z^2 + 10z - 7z - 70$

5. $8x^2 - 5x - 24x + 15$

6. $4x^2 - 9x - 32x + 72$

7. $5x^4 - 3x^2 + 25x^2 - 15$

8. $2y^4 - 10y^2 + 7y^2 - 35$

Factor each trinomial by grouping. Exercises 9 through 12 are broken into parts to help you get started. See Examples 1 through 3.

9. $6x^2 + 11x + 3$

a. Find two numbers whose product is $6 \cdot 3 = 18$ and whose sum is 11.

b. Write $11x$ using the factors from part (a).

c. Factor by grouping.

10. $8x^2 + 14x + 3$

a. Find two numbers whose product is $8 \cdot 3 = 24$ and whose sum is 14.

b. Write $14x$ using the factors from part (a).

c. Factor by grouping.

11. $15x^2 - 23x + 4$

a. Find two numbers whose product is $15 \cdot 4 = 60$ and whose sum is -23.

b. Write $-23x$ using the factors from part (a).

c. Factor by grouping.

12. $6x^2 - 13x + 5$

a. Find two numbers whose product is $6 \cdot 5 = 30$ and whose sum is -13.

b. Write $-13x$ using the factors from part (a).

c. Factor by grouping.

13. $21y^2 + 17y + 2$

14. $15x^2 + 11x + 2$

15. $7x^2 - 4x - 11$

16. $8x^2 - x - 9$

17. $10x^2 - 9x + 2$

18. $30x^2 - 23x + 3$

19. $2x^2 - 7x + 5$

20. $2x^2 - 7x + 3$

21. $12x + 4x^2 + 9$

22. $20x + 25x^2 + 4$

23. $4x^2 - 8x - 21$

24. $6x^2 - 11x - 10$

25. $10x^2 - 23x + 12$

26. $21x^2 - 13x + 2$

27. $2x^3 + 13x^2 + 15x$

28. $3x^3 + 8x^2 + 4x$

29. $16y^2 - 34y + 18$

30. $4y^2 - 2y - 12$

31. $-13x + 6 + 6x^2$

32. $-25x + 12 + 12x^2$

33. $54a^2 - 9a - 30$

34. $30a^2 + 38a - 20$

35. $20a^3 + 37a^2 + 8a$

36. $10a^3 + 17a^2 + 3a$

37. $12x^3 - 27x^2 - 27x$

38. $30x^3 - 155x^2 + 25x$

39. $3x^2y + 4xy^2 + y^3$

40. $6r^2t + 7rt^2 + t^3$

41. $20z^2 + 7z + 1$

42. $36z^2 + 6z + 1$

43. $24a^2 - 6ab - 30b^2$

44. $30a^2 + 5ab - 25b^2$

45. $15p^4 + 31p^3q + 2p^2q^2$

46. $20s^4 + 61s^3t + 3s^2t^2$

47. $35 + 12x + x^2$

48. $33 + 14x + x^2$

49. $6 - 11x + 5x^2$

50. $5 - 12x + 7x^2$

Review

Multiply. See Section 3.6.

51. $(x - 2)(x + 2)$

52. $(y - 5)(y + 5)$

53. $(y + 4)(y + 4)$

54. $(x + 7)(x + 7)$

55. $(9z + 5)(9z - 5)$

56. $(8y + 9)(8y - 9)$

57. $(4x - 3)^2$

58. $(2z - 1)^2$

Concept Extensions

Write the perimeter of each figure as a simplified polynomial. Then factor the polynomial.

59.

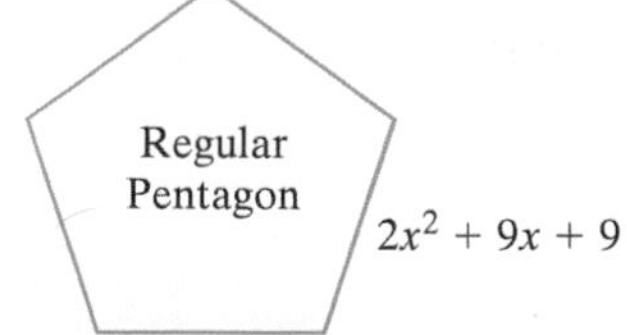

60.

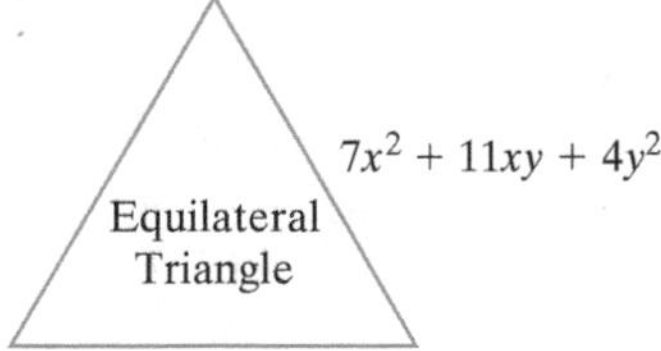

Factor each polynomial by grouping.

61. $x^{2n} + 2x^n + 3x^n + 6$
(*Hint:* Don't forget that $x^{2n} = x^n \cdot x^n$.)

62. $x^{2n} + 6x^n + 10x^n + 60$

63. $3x^{2n} + 16x^n - 35$

64. $12x^{2n} - 40x^n + 25$

65. In your own words, explain how to factor a trinomial by grouping.

Objectives

A Recognize Perfect Square Trinomials.

B Factor Perfect Square Trinomials.

C Factor the Difference of Two Squares.

4.5 FACTORING PERFECT SQUARE TRINOMIALS AND THE DIFFERENCE OF TWO SQUARES

Objective A Recognizing Perfect Square Trinomials

A trinomial that is the square of a binomial is called a **perfect square trinomial.** For example,

$$(x + 3)^2 = (x + 3)(x + 3)$$
$$= x^2 + 6x + 9$$

Thus $x^2 + 6x + 9$ is a perfect square trinomial.

In Chapter 3, we discovered special product formulas for squaring binomials.

$$(a + b)^2 = a^2 + 2ab + b^2 \quad \text{and} \quad (a - b)^2 = a^2 - 2ab + b^2$$

Because multiplication and factoring are reverse processes, we can now use these special products to help us factor perfect square trinomials. If we reverse these equations, we have the following.

Factoring Perfect Square Trinomials

$$a^2 + 2ab + b^2 = (a + b)^2$$
$$a^2 - 2ab + b^2 = (a - b)^2$$

Helpful Hint

Notice that for both given forms of a perfect square trinomial, the last term is positive. This is because the last term is a square.

To use these equations to help us factor, we must first be able to recognize a perfect square trinomial. A trinomial is a perfect square when

1. two terms, a^2 and b^2, are squares and
2. another term is $2 \cdot a \cdot b$ or $-2 \cdot a \cdot b$. That is, this term is twice the product of a and b, or its opposite.

PRACTICE 1

Decide whether each trinomial is a perfect square trinomial.

a. $x^2 + 12x + 36$
b. $x^2 + 20x + 100$

Example 1 Decide whether $x^2 + 8x + 16$ is a perfect square trinomial.

Solution:

1. Two terms, x^2 and 16, are squares $(16 = 4^2)$.
2. Twice the product of x and 4 is the other term of the trinomial.

$2 \cdot x \cdot 4 = 8x$

Thus, $x^2 + 8x + 16$ is a perfect square trinomial.

Work Practice 1

PRACTICE 2

Decide whether each trinomial is a perfect square trinomial.

a. $9x^2 + 20x + 25$
b. $4x^2 + 8x + 11$

Example 2 Decide whether $4x^2 + 10x + 9$ is a perfect square trinomial.

Solution:

1. Two terms, $4x^2$ and 9, are squares.

$4x^2 = (2x)^2 \quad \text{and} \quad 9 = 3^2$

2. Twice the product of $2x$ and 3 is *not* the other term of the trinomial.

$2 \cdot 2x \cdot 3 = 12x$, *not* $10x$

The trinomial is *not* a perfect square trinomial.

Work Practice 2

Answers
1. a. yes b. yes 2. a. no b. no

Example 3 Decide whether $9x^2 - 12xy + 4y^2$ is a perfect square trinomial.

Solution:

1. Two terms, $9x^2$ and $4y^2$, are squares.
   $9x^2 = (3x)^2$ and $4y^2 = (2y)^2$
2. Twice the product of $3x$ and $2y$ is the opposite of the other term of the trinomial.
   $2 \cdot 3x \cdot 2y = 12xy$, the opposite of $-12xy$

Thus, $9x^2 - 12xy + 4y^2$ is a perfect square trinomial.

Work Practice 3

PRACTICE 3

Decide whether each trinomial is a perfect square trinomial.

a. $25x^2 - 10x + 1$

b. $9x^2 - 42x + 49$

Objective B Factoring Perfect Square Trinomials

Now that we can recognize perfect square trinomials, we are ready to factor them.

Example 4 Factor: $x^2 + 12x + 36$

Solution:

$$x^2 + 12x + 36 = x^2 + 2 \cdot x \cdot 6 + 6^2 \quad 36 = 6^2 \text{ and } 12x = 2 \cdot x \cdot 6$$

$$a^2 + 2 \cdot a \cdot b + b^2$$

$$= (x + 6)^2$$

$$(a + b)^2$$

Work Practice 4

PRACTICE 4

Factor: $x^2 + 16x + 64$

Example 5 Factor: $25x^2 + 20xy + 4y^2$

Solution:

$$25x^2 + 20xy + 4y^2 = (5x)^2 + 2 \cdot 5x \cdot 2y + (2y)^2$$

$$= (5x + 2y)^2$$

Work Practice 5

PRACTICE 5

Factor: $9r^2 + 24rs + 16s^2$

Example 6 Factor: $4m^4 - 4m^2 + 1$

Solution:

$$4m^4 - 4m^2 + 1 = (2m^2)^2 - 2 \cdot 2m^2 \cdot 1 + 1^2$$

$$a^2 \quad - 2 \cdot a \cdot b + b^2$$

$$= (2m^2 - 1)^2$$

$$(a - b)^2$$

Work Practice 6

PRACTICE 6

Factor: $9n^4 - 6n^2 + 1$

Example 7 Factor: $25x^2 + 50x + 9$

Solution: Notice that this trinomial is not a perfect square trinomial.

$25x^2 = (5x)^2, 9 = 3^2$

but

$2 \cdot 5x \cdot 3 = 30x$

and $30x$ is not the middle term, $50x$.

Continued on next page

PRACTICE 7

Factor: $9x^2 + 15x + 4$

Answers

3. a. yes **b.** yes **4.** $(x + 8)^2$ **5.** $(3r + 4s)^2$ **6.** $(3n^2 - 1)^2$ **7.** $(3x + 1)(3x + 4)$

Helpful Hint A perfect square trinomial can also be factored by the methods found in Sections 4.2 through 4.4.

PRACTICE 8

Factor:

a. $8n^2 + 40n + 50$

b. $12x^3 - 84x^2 + 147x$

Although $25x^2 + 50x + 9$ is not a perfect square trinomial, it is factorable. Using techniques we learned in Sections 4.3 or 4.4, we find that

$$25x^2 + 50x + 9 = (5x + 9)(5x + 1)$$

Work Practice 7

Example 8 Factor: $162x^3 - 144x^2 + 32x$

Solution: Don't forget to first look for a common factor. There is a greatest common factor of $2x$ in this trinomial.

$$\begin{aligned} 162x^3 - 144x^2 + 32x &= 2x(81x^2 - 72x + 16) \\ &= 2x[(9x)^2 - 2\cdot 9x\cdot 4 + 4^2] \\ &= 2x(9x - 4)^2 \end{aligned}$$

Work Practice 8

Objective C Factoring the Difference of Two Squares

In Chapter 3, we discovered another special product, the product of the sum and difference of two terms a and b:

$$(a + b)(a - b) = a^2 - b^2$$

Reversing this equation gives us another factoring pattern, which we use to factor the difference of two squares.

Factoring the Difference of Two Squares

$$a^2 - b^2 = (a + b)(a - b)$$

To use this equation to help us factor, we must first be able to recognize the difference of two squares. A binomial is a difference of two squares if

1. both terms are squares and
2. the signs of the terms are different.

Let's practice using this pattern.

PRACTICE 9–12

Factor each binomial.

9. $x^2 - 9$ **10.** $a^2 - 16$

11. $c^2 - \frac{9}{25}$ **12.** $s^2 + 9$

Helpful Hint After the greatest common factor has been removed, the *sum* of two squares cannot be factored further using real numbers.

Examples Factor each binomial.

9. $z^2 - 4 = z^2 - 2^2 = (z + 2)(z - 2)$

$$\uparrow \quad \uparrow \qquad \uparrow \quad \uparrow \quad \uparrow \quad \uparrow$$
$$a^2 - b^2 = (a + b)(a - b)$$

10. $y^2 - 25 = y^2 - 5^2 = (y + 5)(y - 5)$

11. $y^2 - \frac{4}{9} = y^2 - \left(\frac{2}{3}\right)^2 = \left(y + \frac{2}{3}\right)\left(y - \frac{2}{3}\right)$

12. $x^2 + 4$

Note that the binomial $x^2 + 4$ is the *sum* of two squares since we can write $x^2 + 4$ as $x^2 + 2^2$. We might try to factor using $(x + 2)(x + 2)$ or $(x - 2)(x - 2)$. But when we multiply to check, we find that neither factoring is correct.

$$(x + 2)(x + 2) = x^2 + 4x + 4$$
$$(x - 2)(x - 2) = x^2 - 4x + 4$$

In both cases, the product is a trinomial, not the required binomial. In fact, $x^2 + 4$ is a prime polynomial.

Work Practice 9–12

Answers

8. a. $2(2n + 5)^2$ **b.** $3x(2x - 7)^2$

9. $(x - 3)(x + 3)$

10. $(a - 4)(a + 4)$

11. $\left(c - \frac{3}{5}\right)\left(c + \frac{3}{5}\right)$

12. prime polynomial

Examples Factor each difference of two squares.

13. $4x^2 - 1 = (2x)^2 - 1^2 = (2x + 1)(2x - 1)$

14. $25a^2 - 9b^2 = (5a)^2 - (3b)^2 = (5a + 3b)(5a - 3b)$

15. $y^4 - 16 = (y^2)^2 - 4^2$

$= (y^2 + 4)(y^2 - 4)$ Factor the difference of two squares.

$= (y^2 + 4)(y + 2)(y - 2)$ Factor the difference of two squares.

Work Practice 13–15

PRACTICE 13–15

Factor each difference of two squares.

13. $9s^2 - 1$

14. $16x^2 - 49y^2$

15. $p^4 - 81$

Helpful Hint

1. Don't forget to first see whether there's a greatest common factor (other than 1) that can be factored out.
2. Factor completely. In other words, check to see whether any factors can be factored further (as in Example 15).

Examples Factor each binomial.

16. $4x^3 - 49x = x(4x^2 - 49)$ Factor out the common factor, x.

$= x[(2x)^2 - 7^2]$

$= x(2x + 7)(2x - 7)$ Factor the difference of two squares.

17. $162x^4 - 2 = 2(81x^4 - 1)$ Factor out the common factor, 2.

$= 2(9x^2 + 1)(9x^2 - 1)$ Factor the difference of two squares.

$= 2(9x^2 + 1)(3x + 1)(3x - 1)$ Factor the difference of two squares.

18. $-49x^2 + 16 = -1(49x^2 - 16)$ Factor out -1.

$= -1(7x + 4)(7x - 4)$ Factor the difference of two squares.

Work Practice 16–18

PRACTICE 16–18

Factor each binomial.

16. $9x^3 - 25x$

17. $48x^4 - 3$

18. $-9x^2 + 100$

Example 19 Factor: $36 - x^2$

Solution: This is the difference of two squares. Factor as is or if you like, first write the binomial with the variable term first.

Factor as is: $36 - x^2 = 6^2 - x^2 = (6 + x)(6 - x)$

Rewrite binomial: $36 - x^2 = -x^2 + 36 = -1(x^2 - 36)$

$= -1(x + 6)(x - 6)$

Both factorizations are correct and are equal. To see this, factor -1 from $(6 - x)$ in the first factorization.

Work Practice 19

PRACTICE 19

Factor: $121 - m^2$

Helpful Hint

When rearranging terms, keep in mind that the sign of a term is in front of the term.

Answers

13. $(3s - 1)(3s + 1)$
14. $(4x - 7y)(4x + 7y)$
15. $(p^2 + 9)(p + 3)(p - 3)$
16. $x(3x - 5)(3x + 5)$
17. $3(4x^2 + 1)(2x + 1)(2x - 1)$
18. $-1(3x - 10)(3x + 10)$
19. $(11 + m)(11 - m)$ or $-1(m + 11)(m - 11)$

Calculator Explorations Graphing

A graphing calculator is a convenient tool for evaluating an expression at a given replacement value. For example, let's evaluate $x^2 - 6x$ when $x = 2$. To do so, store the value 2 in the variable x and then enter and evaluate the algebraic expression.

```
2→X
                2
X²-6X
               -8
```

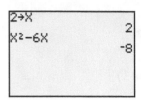

The value of $x^2 - 6x$ when $x = 2$ is -8. You may want to use this method for evaluating expressions as you explore the following.

We can use a graphing calculator to explore factoring patterns numerically. Use your calculator to evaluate $x^2 - 2x + 1$, $x^2 - 2x - 1$, and $(x - 1)^2$ for each value of x given in the table. What do you observe?

	$x^2 - 2x + 1$	$x^2 - 2x - 1$	$(x - 1)^2$
$x = 5$			
$x = -3$			
$x = 2.7$			
$x = -12.1$			
$x = 0$			

Notice in each case that $x^2 - 2x - 1 \neq (x - 1)^2$. Because for each x in the table the value of $x^2 - 2x + 1$ and the value of $(x - 1)^2$ are the same, we might guess that $x^2 - 2x + 1 = (x - 1)^2$. We can verify our guess algebraically with multiplication:

$$(x - 1)(x - 1) = x^2 - x - x + 1 = x^2 - 2x + 1$$

Vocabulary and Readiness Check

Use the choices below to fill in each blank. Some choices may be used more than once and some choices may not be used at all.

perfect square trinomial	true	$(5y)^2$	$(x + 5y)^2$
difference of two squares	false	$(x - 5y)^2$	$5y^2$

1. A ____________________ is a trinomial that is the square of a binomial.
2. The term $25y^2$ written as a square is ____________________.
3. The expression $x^2 + 10xy + 25y^2$ is called a ____________________.
4. The expression $x^2 - 49$ is called a ____________________.
5. The factorization $(x + 5y)(x + 5y)$ may also be written as ____________________.
6. True or false: The factorization $(x - 5y)(x + 5y)$ may also be written as $(x - 5y)^2$. ____________________
7. The trinomial $x^2 - 6x - 9$ is a perfect square trinomial. ____________________
8. The binomial $y^2 + 9$ factors as $(y + 3)^2$. ____________________

Write each number or term as a square. For example, 16 written as a square is 4^2.

9. 64 **10.** 9 **11.** $121a^2$

12. $81b^2$ **13.** $36p^4$ **14.** $4q^4$

4.5 Exercise Set

FOR EXTRA HELP

Objective A *Determine whether each trinomial is a perfect square trinomial. See Examples 1 through 3.*

1. $x^2 + 16x + 64$ **2.** $x^2 + 22x + 121$ **3.** $y^2 + 5y + 25$ **4.** $y^2 + 4y + 16$

5. $m^2 - 2m + 1$ **6.** $p^2 - 4p + 4$ **7.** $a^2 - 16a + 49$ **8.** $n^2 - 20n + 144$

9. $4x^2 + 12xy + 8y^2$ **10.** $25x^2 + 20xy + 2y^2$ **11.** $25a^2 - 40ab + 16b^2$ **12.** $36a^2 - 12ab + b^2$

Objective B *Factor each trinomial completely. See Examples 4 through 8.*

13. $x^2 + 22x + 121$ **14.** $x^2 + 18x + 81$ **15.** $x^2 - 16x + 64$ **16.** $x^2 - 12x + 36$

17. $16a^2 - 24a + 9$ **18.** $25x^2 - 20x + 4$ **19.** $x^4 + 4x^2 + 4$ **20.** $m^4 + 10m^2 + 25$

21. $2n^2 - 28n + 98$ **22.** $3y^2 - 6y + 3$ **23.** $16y^2 + 40y + 25$ **24.** $9y^2 + 48y + 64$

25. $x^2y^2 - 10xy + 25$ **26.** $4x^2y^2 - 28xy + 49$ **27.** $m^3 + 18m^2 + 81m$ **28.** $y^3 + 12y^2 + 36y$

29. $1 + 6x^2 + x^4$ **30.** $1 + 16x^2 + x^4$ **31.** $9x^2 - 24xy + 16y^2$ **32.** $25x^2 - 60xy + 36y^2$

Objective C *Factor each binomial completely. See Examples 9 through 19.*

33. $x^2 - 4$ **34.** $x^2 - 36$ **35.** $81 - p^2$ **36.** $100 - t^2$

37. $-4r^2 + 1$ **38.** $-9t^2 + 1$ **39.** $9x^2 - 16$ **40.** $36y^2 - 25$

41. $16r^2 + 1$ **42.** $49y^2 + 1$ **43.** $-36 + x^2$ **44.** $-1 + y^2$

45. $m^4 - 1$ **46.** $n^4 - 16$ **47.** $x^2 - 169y^2$ **48.** $x^2 - 225y^2$

49. $18r^2 - 8$ **50.** $32t^2 - 50$ **51.** $9xy^2 - 4x$ **52.** $36x^2y - 25y$

53. $16x^4 - 64x^2$ **54.** $25y^4 - 100y^2$ **55.** $xy^3 - 9xyz^2$ **56.** $x^3y - 4xy^3$

57. $36x^2 - 64y^2$ **58.** $225a^2 - 81b^2$ **59.** $144 - 81x^2$ **60.** $12x^2 - 27$

61. $25y^2 - 9$ **62.** $49a^2 - 16$ **63.** $121m^2 - 100n^2$ **64.** $169a^2 - 49b^2$

65. $x^2y^2 - 1$ **66.** $a^2b^2 - 16$ **67.** $x^2 - \frac{1}{4}$

68. $y^2 - \frac{1}{16}$ **69.** $49 - \frac{9}{25}m^2$ **70.** $100 - \frac{4}{81}n^2$

Objectives B C **Mixed Practice** *Factor each binomial or trinomial completely. See Examples 4 through 19.*

71. $81a^2 - 25b^2$

72. $49y^2 - 100z^2$

73. $x^2 + 14xy + 49y^2$

74. $x^2 + 10xy + 25y^2$

75. $32n^4 - 112n^2 + 98$

76. $162a^4 - 72a^2 + 8$

77. $x^6 - 81x^2$

78. $n^9 - n^5$

79. $64p^3q - 81pq^3$

80. $100x^3y - 49xy^3$

Review

Solve each equation. See Section 2.3.

81. $x - 6 = 0$

82. $y + 5 = 0$

83. $2m + 4 = 0$

84. $3x - 9 = 0$

85. $5z - 1 = 0$

86. $4a + 2 = 0$

Concept Extensions

Factor each expression completely.

87. $x^2 - \frac{2}{3}x + \frac{1}{9}$

88. $x^2 - \frac{1}{25}$

89. $(x + 2)^2 - y^2$

90. $(y - 6)^2 - z^2$

91. $a^2(b - 4) - 16(b - 4)$

92. $m^2(n + 8) - 9(n + 8)$

93. $(x^2 + 6x + 9) - 4y^2$ (*Hint:* Factor the trinomial in parentheses first.)

94. $(x^2 + 2x + 1) - 36y^2$ (See the hint for Exercise 93.)

95. $x^{2n} - 100$

96. $x^{2n} - 81$

97. Fill in the blank so that $x^2 +$ ______ $x + 16$ is a perfect square trinomial.

98. Fill in the blank so that $9x^2 +$ ______ $x + 25$ is a perfect square trinomial.

99. Describe a perfect square trinomial.

100. Write a perfect square trinomial that factors as $(x + 3y)^2$.

101. What binomial multiplied by $(x - 6)$ gives the difference of two squares?

102. What binomial multiplied by $(5 + y)$ gives the difference of two squares?

The area of the largest square in the figure is $(a + b)^2$. Use this figure to answer Exercises 103 and 104.

103. Write the area of the largest square as the sum of the areas of the smaller squares and rectangles.

104. What factoring formula from this section is visually represented by this square?

	a	b
a		
b		

105. The Toroweap Overlook, on the North Rim of the Grand Canyon, lies 3000 vertical feet above the Colorado River. The view is spectacular, and the sheer drop is dramatic. A film crew creating a documentary about the Grand Canyon has suspended a camera platform 296 feet below the Overlook. A camera filter comes loose and falls to the river below. The height of the filter above the river after t seconds is given by the expression $2704 - 16t^2$.

a. Find the height of the filter above the river after 3 seconds.

b. Find the height of the filter above the river after 7 seconds.

c. To the nearest whole second, estimate when the filter lands in the river.

d. Factor $2704 - 16t^2$.

106. An object is dropped from the top of Pittsburgh's USX Towers, which is 841 feet tall. (*Source: World Almanac* research) The height of the object after t seconds is given by the expression $841 - 16t^2$.

a. Find the height of the object after 2 seconds.

b. Find the height of the object after 5 seconds.

c. To the nearest whole second, estimate when the object hits the ground.

d. Factor $841 - 16t^2$.

107. The world's second tallest building is the Taipei 101 in Taipei, Taiwan, at a height of 1671 feet. (*Source:* Council on Tall Buildings and Urban Habitat) Suppose a worker is suspended 71 feet below the top of the pinnacle atop the building, at a height of 1600 feet above the ground. If the worker accidentally drops a bolt, the height of the bolt after t seconds is given by the expression $1600 - 16t^2$. (*Note:* As of January 2010, the Burj Khalifa was officially the tallest building at 2684 feet.)

a. Find the height of the bolt after 3 seconds.

b. Find the height of the bolt after 7 seconds.

c. To the nearest whole second, estimate when the bolt hits the ground.

d. Factor $1600 - 16t^2$.

108. A performer with the Moscow Circus is planning a stunt involving a free fall from the top of the Moscow State University building, which is 784 feet tall. (*Source:* Council on Tall Buildings and Urban Habitat) Neglecting air resistance, the performer's height above gigantic cushions positioned at ground level after t seconds is given by the expression $784 - 16t^2$.

a. Find the performer's height after 2 seconds.

b. Find the performer's height after 5 seconds.

c. To the nearest whole second, estimate when the performer reaches the cushions positioned at ground level.

d. Factor $784 - 16t^2$.

Integrated Review Sections 4.1–4.5

Choosing a Factoring Strategy

The following steps may be helpful when factoring polynomials.

To Factor a Polynomial

Step 1: Are there any common factors? If so, factor out the GCF.

Step 2: How many terms are in the polynomial?

a. Two terms: Is it the difference of two squares? $a^2 - b^2 = (a - b)(a + b)$

b. Three terms: Try one of the following.

i. Perfect square trinomial: $a^2 + 2ab + b^2 = (a + b)^2$

$a^2 - 2ab + b^2 = (a - b)^2$

ii. If not a perfect square trinomial, factor using the methods presented in Sections 4.2 through 4.4.

c. Four terms: Try factoring by grouping.

Step 3: See if any factors in the factored polynomial can be factored further.

Step 4: Check by multiplying.

Factor each polynomial completely.

1. $x^2 + x - 12$ **2.** $x^2 - 10x + 16$ **3.** $x^2 + 2x + 1$

4. $x^2 - 6x + 9$ **5.** $x^2 - x - 6$ **6.** $x^2 + x - 2$

7. $x^2 + x - 6$ **8.** $x^2 + 7x + 12$ **9.** $x^2 - 7x + 10$

10. $x^2 - x - 30$ **11.** $2x^2 - 98$ **12.** $3x^2 - 75$

13. $x^2 + 3x + 5x + 15$ **14.** $3y - 21 + xy - 7x$ **15.** $x^2 + 6x - 16$

16. $x^2 - 3x - 28$ **17.** $4x^3 + 20x^2 - 56x$ **18.** $6x^3 - 6x^2 - 120x$

19. $12x^2 + 34x + 24$ **20.** $24a^2 + 18ab - 15b^2$ **21.** $4a^2 - b^2$

22. $x^2 - 25y^2$ **23.** $28 - 13x - 6x^2$ **24.** $20 - 3x - 2x^2$

25. $4 - 2x + x^2$ **26.** $a + a^2 - 3$ **27.** $6y^2 + y - 15$

28. $4x^2 - x - 5$ **29.** $18x^3 - 63x^2 + 9x$ **30.** $12a^3 - 24a^2 + 4a$

31. $16a^2 - 56a + 49$ **32.** $25p^2 - 70p + 49$ **33.** $14 + 5x - x^2$

34. $3 - 2x - x^2$ **35.** $3x^4y + 6x^3y - 72x^2y$ **36.** $2x^3y + 8x^2y^2 - 10xy^3$

Answers

1. ______
2. ______
3. ______
4. ______
5. ______
6. ______
7. ______
8. ______
9. ______
10. ______
11. ______
12. ______
13. ______
14. ______
15. ______
16. ______
17. ______
18. ______
19. ______
20. ______
21. ______
22. ______
23. ______
24. ______
25. ______
26. ______
27. ______
28. ______
29. ______
30. ______
31. ______
32. ______
33. ______
34. ______
35. ______
36. ______

37. ______
38. ______
39. ______
40. ______
41. ______
42. ______
43. ______
44. ______
45. ______
46. ______
47. ______
48. ______
49. ______
50. ______
51. ______
52. ______
53. ______
54. ______
55. ______
56. ______
57. ______
58. ______
59. ______
60. ______
61. ______
62. ______
63. ______
64. ______
65. ______
66. ______
67. ______
68. ______
69. ______
70. ______
71. ______
72. ______
73. ______
74. ______
75. ______
76. ______

37. $12x^3y + 243xy$

38. $6x^3y^2 + 8xy^2$

39. $2xy - 72x^3y$

40. $2x^3 - 18x$

41. $x^3 + 6x^2 - 4x - 24$

42. $x^3 - 2x^2 - 36x + 72$

43. $6a^3 + 10a^2$

44. $4n^2 - 6n$

45. $3x^3 - x^2 + 12x - 4$

46. $x^3 - 2x^2 + 3x - 6$

47. $6x^2 + 18xy + 12y^2$

48. $12x^2 + 46xy - 8y^2$

49. $5(x + y) + x(x + y)$

50. $7(x - y) + y(x - y)$

51. $14t^2 - 9t + 1$

52. $3t^2 - 5t + 1$

53. $-3x^2 - 2x + 5$

54. $-7x^2 - 19x + 6$

55. $1 - 8a - 20a^2$

56. $1 - 7a - 60a^2$

57. $x^4 - 10x^2 + 9$

58. $x^4 - 13x^2 + 36$

59. $x^2 - 23x + 120$

60. $y^2 + 22y + 96$

61. $25p^2 - 70pq + 49q^2$

62. $16a^2 - 56ab + 49b^2$

63. $x^2 - 14x - 48$

64. $7x^2 + 24xy + 9y^2$

65. $-x^2 - x + 30$

66. $-x^2 + 6x - 8$

67. $3rs - s + 12r - 4$

68. $x^3 - 2x^2 + x - 2$

69. $4x^2 - 8xy - 3x + 6y$

70. $4x^2 - 2xy - 7yz + 14xz$

71. $x^2 + 9xy - 36y^2$

72. $3x^2 + 10xy - 8y^2$

73. $x^4 - 14x^2 - 32$

74. $x^4 - 22x^2 - 75$

75. Explain why it makes good sense to factor out the GCF first, before using other methods of factoring.

76. The sum of two squares usually does not factor. Is the sum of two squares $9x^2 + 81y^2$ factorable?

4.6 SOLVING QUADRATIC EQUATIONS BY FACTORING

Objectives

A Solve Quadratic Equations by Factoring.

B Solve Equations with Degree Greater than Two by Factoring.

In this section, we introduce a new type of equation—the **quadratic equation.**

Quadratic Equation

A quadratic equation is one that can be written in the form

$$ax^2 + bx + c = 0$$

where a, b, and c are real numbers and $a \neq 0$.

Some examples of quadratic equations are shown below.

$$x^2 - 9x - 22 = 0 \qquad 4x^2 - 28 = -49 \qquad x(2x - 7) = 4$$

The form $ax^2 + bx + c = 0$ is called the **standard form** of a quadratic equation. The quadratic equation $x^2 - 9x - 22 = 0$ is the only equation above that is in standard form.

Quadratic equations model many real-life situations. For example, let's suppose we want to know how long before a person diving from a 144-foot cliff reaches the ocean. The answer to this question is found by solving the quadratic equation $-16t^2 + 144 = 0$. (See Example 1 in Section 4.7.)

Objective A Solving Quadratic Equations by Factoring

Some quadratic equations can be solved by making use of factoring and the **zero-factor property.**

Zero-Factor Property

If a and b are real numbers and if $ab = 0$, then $a = 0$ or $b = 0$.

In other words, if the product of two numbers is 0, then at least one of the numbers must be 0.

Example 1 Solve: $(x - 3)(x + 1) = 0$

Solution: If this equation is to be a true statement, then either the factor $x - 3$ must be 0 or the factor $x + 1$ must be 0. In other words, either

$$x - 3 = 0 \qquad \text{or} \qquad x + 1 = 0$$

If we solve these two linear equations, we have

$$x = 3 \qquad \text{or} \qquad x = -1$$

Continued on next page

PRACTICE 1

Solve: $(x - 7)(x + 2) = 0$

Answer

1. 7 and −2

Thus, 3 and −1 are both solutions of the equation $(x - 3)(x + 1) = 0$. To check, we replace x with 3 in the original equation. Then we replace x with −1 in the original equation.

Check:

$$(x - 3)(x + 1) = 0 \qquad\qquad (x - 3)(x + 1) = 0$$

$$(3 - 3)(3 + 1) \stackrel{?}{=} 0 \quad \text{Replace } x \text{ with } 3. \qquad (-1 - 3)(-1 + 1) \stackrel{?}{=} 0 \quad \text{Replace } x \text{ with } -1.$$

$$0(4) = 0 \quad \text{True} \qquad\qquad (-4)(0) = 0 \quad \text{True}$$

The solutions are 3 and −1.

Work Practice 1

Helpful Hint

The zero-factor property says that *if a product is 0, then a factor is 0.*

If $a \cdot b = 0$, then $a = 0$ or $b = 0$.

If $x(x + 5) = 0$, then $x = 0$ or $x + 5 = 0$.

If $(x + 7)(2x - 3) = 0$, then $x + 7 = 0$ or $2x - 3 = 0$.

Use this property only when the product is 0. For example, if $a \cdot b = 8$, we do not know the value of a or b. The values may be $a = 2, b = 4$ or $a = 8, b = 1$, or any other two numbers whose product is 8.

PRACTICE 2

Solve: $(x - 10)(3x + 1) = 0$

Example 2 Solve: $(x - 5)(2x + 7) = 0$

Solution: The product is 0. By the zero-factor property, this is true only when a factor is 0. To solve, we set each factor equal to 0 and solve the resulting linear equations.

$$(x - 5)(2x + 7) = 0$$

$$x - 5 = 0 \quad \text{or} \quad 2x + 7 = 0$$

$$x = 5 \qquad\qquad 2x = -7$$

$$x = -\frac{7}{2}$$

Check: Let $x = 5$.

$$(x - 5)(2x + 7) = 0$$

$$(5 - 5)(2 \cdot 5 + 7) \stackrel{?}{=} 0 \quad \text{Replace } x \text{ with } 5.$$

$$0 \cdot 17 \stackrel{?}{=} 0$$

$$0 = 0 \quad \text{True}$$

Let $x = -\frac{7}{2}$.

$$(x - 5)(2x + 7) = 0$$

$$\left(-\frac{7}{2} - 5\right)\left(2\left(-\frac{7}{2}\right) + 7\right) \stackrel{?}{=} 0 \quad \text{Replace } x \text{ with } -\frac{7}{2}.$$

$$\left(-\frac{17}{2}\right)(-7 + 7) \stackrel{?}{=} 0$$

$$\left(-\frac{17}{2}\right) \cdot 0 \stackrel{?}{=} 0$$

$$0 = 0 \quad \text{True}$$

The solutions are 5 and $-\frac{7}{2}$.

Work Practice 2

Answer

2. 10 and $-\frac{1}{3}$

Example 3 Solve: $x(5x - 2) = 0$

Solution: $x(5x - 2) = 0$

$x = 0$ or $5x - 2 = 0$ Use the zero-factor property.

$5x = 2$

$x = \frac{2}{5}$

Check these solutions in the original equation. The solutions are 0 and $\frac{2}{5}$.

Work Practice 3

PRACTICE 3

Solve each equation.

a. $y(y + 3) = 0$

b. $x(4x - 3) = 0$

Example 4 Solve: $x^2 - 9x - 22 = 0$

Solution: One side of the equation is 0. However, to use the zero-factor property, one side of the equation must be 0 *and* the other side must be written as a product (must be factored). Thus, we must first factor this polynomial.

$x^2 - 9x - 22 = 0$

$(x - 11)(x + 2) = 0$ Factor.

Now we can apply the zero-factor property.

$x - 11 = 0$ or $x + 2 = 0$

$x = 11$ $\quad$ $x = -2$

Check: Let $x = 11$.

$x^2 - 9x - 22 = 0$

$11^2 - 9 \cdot 11 - 22 \stackrel{?}{=} 0$

$121 - 99 - 22 \stackrel{?}{=} 0$

$22 - 22 \stackrel{?}{=} 0$

$0 = 0$ True

Let $x = -2$.

$x^2 - 9x - 22 = 0$

$(-2)^2 - 9(-2) - 22 \stackrel{?}{=} 0$

$4 + 18 - 22 \stackrel{?}{=} 0$

$22 - 22 \stackrel{?}{=} 0$

$0 = 0$ True

The solutions are 11 and −2.

Work Practice 4

PRACTICE 4

Solve: $x^2 - 3x - 18 = 0$

Example 5 Solve: $4x^2 - 28x = -49$

Solution: First we rewrite the equation in standard form so that one side is 0. Then we factor the polynomial.

$4x^2 - 28x = -49$

$4x^2 - 28x + 49 = 0$ Write in standard form by adding 49 to both sides.

$(2x - 7)(2x - 7) = 0$ Factor.

Next we use the zero-factor property and set each factor equal to 0. Since the factors are the same, the related equations will give the same solution.

$2x - 7 = 0$ or $2x - 7 = 0$ Set each factor equal to 0.

$2x = 7$ $\quad$ $2x = 7$ Solve.

$x = \frac{7}{2}$ $\quad$ $x = \frac{7}{2}$

Check this solution in the original equation. The solution is $\frac{7}{2}$.

Work Practice 5

PRACTICE 5

Solve: $9x^2 - 24x = -16$

Answers

3. a. 0 and −3 **b.** 0 and $\frac{3}{4}$

4. 6 and −3 **5.** $\frac{4}{3}$

The following steps may be used to solve a quadratic equation by factoring.

To Solve Quadratic Equations by Factoring

Step 1: Write the equation in standard form so that one side of the equation is 0.

Step 2: Factor the quadratic equation completely.

Step 3: Set each factor containing a variable equal to 0.

Step 4: Solve the resulting equations.

Step 5: Check each solution in the original equation.

Since it is not always possible to factor a quadratic polynomial, not all quadratic equations can be solved by factoring. Other methods of solving quadratic equations are presented in Chapter 9.

PRACTICE 6

Solve each equation.

a. $x(x - 4) = 5$

b. $x(3x + 7) = 6$

Example 6 Solve: $x(2x - 7) = 4$

Solution: First we write the equation in standard form; then we factor.

$$x(2x - 7) = 4$$

$$2x^2 - 7x = 4 \quad \text{Multiply.}$$

$$2x^2 - 7x - 4 = 0 \quad \text{Write in standard form.}$$

$$(2x + 1)(x - 4) = 0 \quad \text{Factor.}$$

$$2x + 1 = 0 \quad \text{or} \quad x - 4 = 0 \quad \text{Set each factor equal to zero.}$$

$$2x = -1 \qquad x = 4 \quad \text{Solve.}$$

$$x = -\frac{1}{2}$$

Check the solutions in the original equation. The solutions are $-\frac{1}{2}$ and 4.

Work Practice 6

Helpful Hint

To solve the equation $x(2x - 7) = 4$, do **not** set each factor equal to 4. Remember that to apply the zero-factor property, one side of the equation must be 0 and the other side of the equation must be in factored form.

✓Concept Check Explain the error and solve the equation correctly.

$$(x - 3)(x + 1) = 5$$

$$x - 3 = 0 \quad \text{or} \quad x + 1 = 0$$

$$x = 3 \quad \text{or} \quad x = -1$$

Objective B Solving Equations with Degree Greater than Two by Factoring

Some equations with degree greater than 2 can be solved by factoring and then using the zero-factor property.

Answers

6. a. 5 and −1 **b.** $\frac{2}{3}$ and −3

✓ Concept Check Answer

To use the zero-factor property, one side of the equation must be 0, not 5. Correctly, $(x - 3)(x + 1) = 5$, $x^2 - 2x - 3 = 5$, $x^2 - 2x - 8 = 0$, $(x - 4)(x + 2) = 0$, $x - 4 = 0$ or $x + 2 = 0$, $x = 4$ or $x = -2$.

Example 7 Solve: $3x^3 - 12x = 0$

Solution: To factor the left side of the equation, we begin by factoring out the greatest common factor, $3x$.

$$3x^3 - 12x = 0$$
$$3x(x^2 - 4) = 0 \quad \text{Factor out the GCF, } 3x.$$
$$3x(x + 2)(x - 2) = 0 \quad \text{Factor } x^2 - 4 \text{, a difference of two squares.}$$
$$3x = 0 \quad \text{or} \quad x + 2 = 0 \quad \text{or} \quad x - 2 = 0 \quad \text{Set each factor equal to 0.}$$
$$x = 0 \qquad x = -2 \qquad x = 2 \quad \text{Solve.}$$

Thus, the equation $3x^3 - 12x = 0$ has three solutions: 0, −2, and 2.

Check: Replace x with each solution in the original equation.

Let $x = 0$.

$$3(0)^3 - 12(0) \stackrel{?}{=} 0$$
$$0 = 0 \quad \text{True}$$

Let $x = -2$.

$$3(-2)^3 - 12(-2) \stackrel{?}{=} 0$$
$$3(-8) + 24 \stackrel{?}{=} 0$$
$$0 = 0 \quad \text{True}$$

Let $x = 2$.

$$3(2)^3 - 12(2) \stackrel{?}{=} 0$$
$$3(8) - 24 \stackrel{?}{=} 0$$
$$0 = 0 \quad \text{True}$$

The solutions are 0, −2, and 2.

Work Practice 7

PRACTICE 7

Solve: $2x^3 - 18x = 0$

Example 8 Solve: $(5x - 1)(2x^2 + 15x + 18) = 0$

Solution:

$$(5x - 1)(2x^2 + 15x + 18) = 0$$
$$(5x - 1)(2x + 3)(x + 6) = 0 \quad \text{Factor the trinomial.}$$
$$5x - 1 = 0 \quad \text{or} \quad 2x + 3 = 0 \quad \text{or} \quad x + 6 = 0 \quad \text{Set each factor equal to 0.}$$
$$5x = 1 \qquad 2x = -3 \qquad x = -6 \quad \text{Solve.}$$
$$x = \frac{1}{5} \qquad x = -\frac{3}{2}$$

Check each solution in the original equation. The solutions are $\frac{1}{5}$, $-\frac{3}{2}$, and −6.

Work Practice 8

PRACTICE 8

Solve:
$(x + 3)(3x^2 - 20x - 7) = 0$

Answers
7. 0, 3, and −3 **8.** −3, $-\frac{1}{3}$, and 7

Vocabulary and Readiness Check

Use the choices below to fill in each blank. Not all choices will be used.

−3, 5	$a = 0$ or $b = 0$	0	linear
3, −5	quadratic	1	

1. An equation that can be written in the form $ax^2 + bx + c = 0$ (with $a \neq 0$) is called a ______________ equation.
2. If the product of two numbers is 0, then at least one of the numbers must be ______________.
3. The solutions to $(x - 3)(x + 5) = 0$ are ______________.
4. If $a \cdot b = 0$, then ______________.

4.6 Exercise Set

FOR EXTRA HELP

MyMathLab

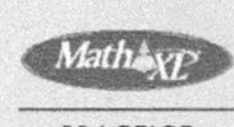
PRACTICE

WATCH

DOWNLOAD

READ

REVIEW

Objective A *Solve each equation. See Examples 1 through 3.*

1. $(x - 2)(x + 1) = 0$

2. $(x + 3)(x + 2) = 0$

3. $(x - 6)(x - 7) = 0$

4. $(x + 4)(x - 10) = 0$

5. $(x + 9)(x + 17) = 0$

6. $(x - 11)(x - 1) = 0$

7. $x(x + 6) = 0$

8. $x(x - 7) = 0$

9. $3x(x - 8) = 0$

10. $2x(x + 12) = 0$

11. $(2x + 3)(4x - 5) = 0$

12. $(3x - 2)(5x + 1) = 0$

13. $(2x - 7)(7x + 2) = 0$

14. $(9x + 1)(4x - 3) = 0$

15. $\left(x - \frac{1}{2}\right)\left(x + \frac{1}{3}\right) = 0$

16. $\left(x + \frac{2}{9}\right)\left(x - \frac{1}{4}\right) = 0$

17. $(x + 0.2)(x + 1.5) = 0$

18. $(x + 1.7)(x + 2.3) = 0$

Solve. See Examples 4 through 6.

19. $x^2 - 13x + 36 = 0$

20. $x^2 + 2x - 63 = 0$

21. $x^2 + 2x - 8 = 0$

22. $x^2 - 5x + 6 = 0$

23. $x^2 - 7x = 0$

24. $x^2 - 3x = 0$

25. $x^2 + 20x = 0$

26. $x^2 + 15x = 0$

27. $x^2 = 16$

28. $x^2 = 9$

29. $x^2 - 4x = 32$

30. $x^2 - 5x = 24$

31. $(x + 4)(x - 9) = 4x$

32. $(x + 3)(x + 8) = x$

33. $x(3x - 1) = 14$

34. $x(4x - 11) = 3$

35. $3x^2 + 19x - 72 = 0$

36. $36x^2 + x - 21 = 0$

Objectives A B and Section 2.3 **Mixed Practice** *Solve each equation. See Examples 1 through 8. (A few exercises are linear equations.)*

37. $4x^3 - x = 0$

38. $4y^3 - 36y = 0$

39. $4(x - 7) = 6$

40. $5(3 - 4x) = 9$

41. $(4x - 3)(16x^2 - 24x + 9) = 0$

42. $(2x + 5)(4x^2 + 20x + 25) = 0$

43. $4y^2 - 1 = 0$

44. $4y^2 - 81 = 0$

45. $(2x + 3)(2x^2 - 5x - 3) = 0$

46. $(2x - 9)(x^2 + 5x - 36) = 0$

47. $x^2 - 15 = -2x$

48. $x^2 - 26 = -11x$

49. $30x^2 - 11x = 30$

50. $9x^2 + 7x = 2$

51. $5x^2 - 6x - 8 = 0$

52. $12x^2 + 7x - 12 = 0$

53. $6y^2 - 22y - 40 = 0$

54. $3x^2 - 6x - 9 = 0$

55. $(y - 2)(y + 3) = 6$

56. $(y - 5)(y - 2) = 28$

57. $x^3 - 12x^2 + 32x = 0$

58. $x^3 - 14x^2 + 49x = 0$

59. $x^2 + 14x + 49 = 0$

60. $x^2 + 22x + 121 = 0$

61. $12y = 8y^2$

62. $9y = 6y^2$

63. $7x^3 - 7x = 0$

64. $3x^3 - 27x = 0$

65. $3x^2 + 8x - 11 = 13 - 6x$

66. $2x^2 + 12x - 1 = 4 + 3x$

67. $3x^2 - 20x = -4x^2 - 7x - 6$

68. $4x^2 - 20x = -5x^2 - 6x - 5$

Review

Perform each indicated operation. Write all results in lowest terms. See Section R.2.

69. $\frac{3}{5} + \frac{4}{9}$

70. $\frac{2}{3} + \frac{3}{7}$

71. $\frac{7}{10} - \frac{5}{12}$

72. $\frac{5}{9} - \frac{5}{12}$

73. $\frac{4}{5} \cdot \frac{7}{8}$

74. $\frac{3}{7} \cdot \frac{12}{17}$

Concept Extensions

For Exercises 75 and 76, see the Concept Check in this section.

75. Explain the error and solve correctly:

$x(x - 2) = 8$

$x = 8$ or $x - 2 = 8$

$x = 10$

76. Explain the error and solve correctly:

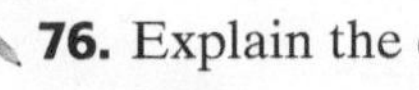

$(x - 4)(x + 2) = 0$

$x = -4$ or $x = 2$

77. Write a quadratic equation that has two solutions, 6 and -1. Leave the polynomial in the equation in factored form.

78. Write a quadratic equation that has two solutions, 0 and -2. Leave the polynomial in the equation in factored form.

79. Write a quadratic equation in standard form that has two solutions, 5 and 7.

80. Write an equation that has three solutions, 0, 1, and 2.

81. A compass is accidentally thrown upward and out of an air balloon at a height of 300 feet. The height, y, of the compass at time x is given by the equation $y = -16x^2 + 20x + 300$.

a. Find the height of the compass at the given times by filling in the table below.

Time, x (in seconds)	0	1	2	3	4	5	6
Height, y (in feet)							

b. Use the table to determine when the compass strikes the ground.

c. Use the table to approximate the maximum height of the compass.

82. A rocket is fired upward from the ground with an initial velocity of 100 feet per second. The height, y, of the rocket at any time x is given by the equation $y = -16x^2 + 100x$.

a. Find the height of the rocket at the given times by filling in the table below.

Time, x (in seconds)	0	1	2	3	4	5	6	7
Height, y (in feet)								

b. Use the table to determine between what two whole-numbered seconds the rocket strikes the ground.

c. Use the table to approximate the maximum height of the rocket.

Solve each equation.

83. $(x - 3)(3x + 4) = (x + 2)(x - 6)$

84. $(2x - 3)(x + 6) = (x - 9)(x + 2)$

85. $(2x - 3)(x + 8) = (x - 6)(x + 4)$

86. $(x + 6)(x - 6) = (2x - 9)(x + 4)$

4.7 QUADRATIC EQUATIONS AND PROBLEM SOLVING

Objective

A Solve Problems That Can Be Modeled by Quadratic Equations.

Objective A Solving Problems Modeled by Quadratic Equations

Some problems may be modeled by quadratic equations. To solve these problems, we use the same problem-solving steps that were introduced in Section 2.4. When solving these problems, keep in mind that a solution of an equation that models a problem may not be a solution to the problem. For example, a person's age or the length of a rectangle is always a positive number. Thus we discard solutions that do not make sense as solutions of the problem.

Example 1 Finding Free-Fall Time

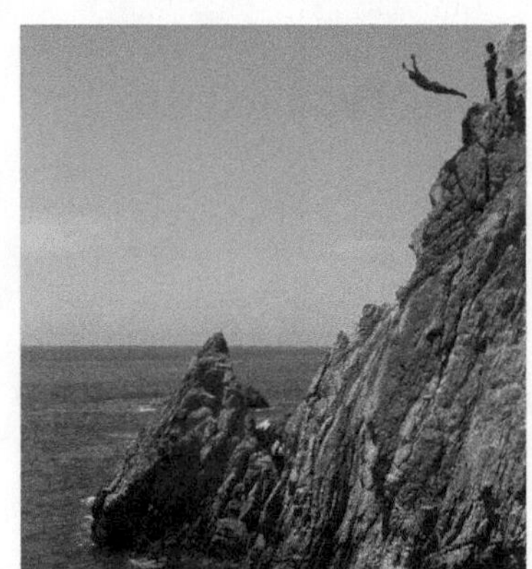

Since the 1940s, one of the top tourist attractions in Acapulco, Mexico, is watching the cliff divers off La Quebrada. The divers' platform is about 144 feet above the sea. These divers must time their descent just right, since they land in the crashing Pacific, in an inlet that is at most $9\frac{1}{2}$ feet deep. Neglecting air resistance, the height h in feet of a cliff diver above the ocean after t seconds is given by the quadratic equation $h = -16t^2 + 144$.

Find out how long it takes the diver to reach the ocean.

Solution:

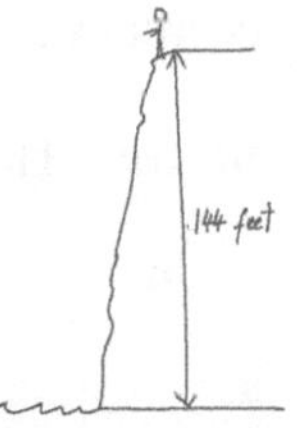

1. UNDERSTAND. Read and reread the problem. Then draw a picture of the problem.

   The equation $h = -16t^2 + 144$ models the height of the falling diver at time t. Familiarize yourself with this equation by finding the height of the diver at time $t = 1$ second and $t = 2$ seconds.

   When $t = 1$ second, the height of the diver is $h = -16(1)^2 + 144 = 128$ feet.

   When $t = 2$ seconds, the height of the diver is $h = -16(2)^2 + 144 = 80$ feet.

2. TRANSLATE. To find out how long it takes the diver to reach the ocean, we want to know the value of t for which $h = 0$.

3. SOLVE. Solve the equation.

$$0 = -16t^2 + 144$$

$$0 = -16(t^2 - 9) \quad \text{Factor out } -16.$$

$$0 = -16(t - 3)(t + 3) \quad \text{Factor completely.}$$

$$t - 3 = 0 \quad \text{or} \quad t + 3 = 0 \quad \text{Set each factor containing a variable equal to 0.}$$

$$t = 3 \quad \text{or} \quad t = -3 \quad \text{Solve.}$$

4. INTERPRET. Since the time t cannot be negative, the proposed solution is 3 seconds.

Check: Verify that the height of the diver when t is 3 seconds is 0.

When $t = 3$ seconds, $h = -16(3)^2 + 144 = -144 + 144 = 0$.

Work Practice 1

PRACTICE 1

Cliff divers also frequent the falls at Waimea Falls Park in Oahu, Hawaii. Here, a diver can jump from a ledge 64 feet up the waterfall into a rocky pool below. Neglecting air resistance, the height of a diver above the pool after t seconds is $h = -16t^2 + 64$. Find how long it takes the diver to reach the pool.

Answer

1. 2 sec

PRACTICE 2

The square of a number minus twice the number is 63. Find the number.

Example 2 Finding a Number

The square of a number plus three times the number is 70. Find the number.

Solution:

1. UNDERSTAND. Read and reread the problem. Suppose that the number is 5. The square of 5 is 5^2 or 25. Three times 5 is 15. Then $25 + 15 = 40$, not 70, so the number must be greater than 5. Remember, the purpose of proposing a number, such as 5, is to better understand the problem. Now that we do, we will let $x =$ the number.
2. TRANSLATE.

the square of a number	plus	three times the number	is	70
↓	↓	↓	↓	↓
x^2	$+$	$3x$	$=$	70

3. SOLVE.

$$x^2 + 3x = 70$$

$$x^2 + 3x - 70 = 0 \qquad \text{Subtract 70 from both sides.}$$

$$(x + 10)(x - 7) = 0 \qquad \text{Factor.}$$

$$x + 10 = 0 \quad \text{or} \quad x - 7 = 0 \qquad \text{Set each factor equal to 0.}$$

$$x = -10 \qquad x = 7 \qquad \text{Solve.}$$

4. INTERPRET.

Check: The square of -10 is $(-10)^2$, or 100. Three times -10 is $3(-10)$ or -30. Then $100 + (-30) = 70$, the correct sum, so -10 checks.

The square of 7 is 7^2 or 49. Three times 7 is $3(7)$, or 21. Then $49 + 21 = 70$, the correct sum, so 7 checks.

State: There are two numbers. They are -10 and 7.

Work Practice 2

PRACTICE 3

The length of a rectangular garden is 5 feet more than its width. The area of the garden is 176 square feet. Find the length and the width of the garden.

Example 3 Finding the Dimensions of a Sail

The height of a triangular sail is 2 meters less than twice the length of the base. If the sail has an area of 30 square meters, find the length of its base and the height.

Solution:

1. UNDERSTAND. Read and reread the problem. Since we are finding the length of the base and the height, we let

   $x =$ the length of the base

   Since the height is 2 meters less than twice the length of the base,

   $2x - 2 =$ the height

   An illustration is shown in the margin.

Height $= 2x - 2$

Base $= x$

2. TRANSLATE. We are given that the area of the triangle is 30 square meters, so we use the formula for area of a triangle.

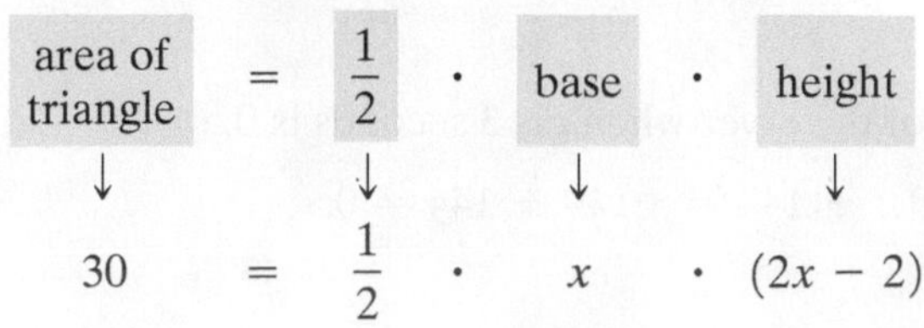

area of triangle	$=$	$\frac{1}{2}$	$\cdot$	base	$\cdot$	height
↓		↓		↓		↓
30	$=$	$\frac{1}{2}$	$\cdot$	x	$\cdot$	$(2x - 2)$

Answers

2. 9 and -7
3. length: 16 ft; width: 11 ft

3. SOLVE. Now we solve the quadratic equation.

$$30 = \frac{1}{2}x(2x - 2)$$

$$30 = x^2 - x \quad \text{Multiply.}$$

$$0 = x^2 - x - 30 \quad \text{Write in standard form.}$$

$$0 = (x - 6)(x + 5) \quad \text{Factor.}$$

$$x - 6 = 0 \quad \text{or} \quad x + 5 = 0 \quad \text{Set each factor equal to 0.}$$

$$x = 6 \qquad x = -5$$

4. INTERPRET. Since x represents the length of the base, we discard the solution -5. The base of a triangle cannot be negative. The base is then 6 meters and the height is $2(6) - 2 = 10$ meters.

Check: To check this problem, we recall that

$$\text{area} = \frac{1}{2} \cdot \text{base} \cdot \text{height or}$$

$$30 \stackrel{?}{=} \frac{1}{2}(6)(10)$$

$$30 = 30 \quad \text{True}$$

State: The base of the triangular sail is 6 meters and the height is 10 meters.

Work Practice 3

The next example has to do with consecutive integers. Study the following diagrams for a review of consecutive integers.

Examples

If x is the first integer, then consecutive integers are $x, x + 1, x + 2, \ldots$

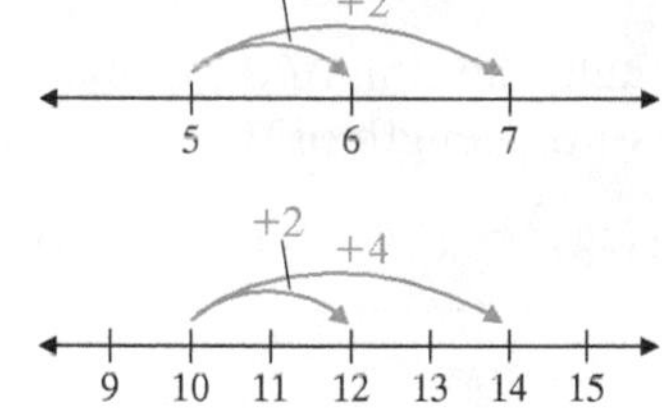

If x is the first even integer, then consecutive even integers are $x, x + 2, x + 4, \ldots$

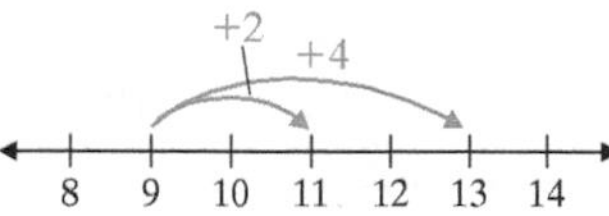

If x is the first odd integer, then consecutive odd integers are $x, x + 2, x + 4, \ldots$

+2 +4

8 9 10 11 12 13 14

Example 4 Finding Consecutive Even Integers

Find two consecutive even integers whose product is 34 more than their sum.

Solution:

1. UNDERSTAND. Read and reread the problem. Let's just choose two consecutive even integers to help us better understand the problem. Let's choose 10 and 12. Their product is $10(12) = 120$ and their sum is $10 + 12 = 22$. The product is $120 - 22$, or 98 greater than the sum. Thus our guess is incorrect, but we have a better understanding of this example.

   Let's let x and $x + 2$ be the consecutive even integers.

2. TRANSLATE.

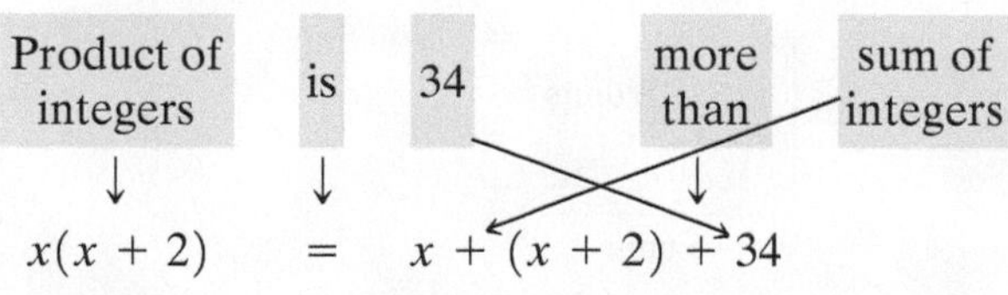

$$x(x + 2) \quad = \quad x + (x + 2) + 34$$

Continued on next page

PRACTICE 4

Find two consecutive odd integers whose product is 23 more than their sum.

Answer

4. 5 and 7 or -5 and -3

3. SOLVE. Now we solve the equation.

$$x(x + 2) = x + (x + 2) + 34 \quad \text{Multiply.}$$
$$x^2 + 2x = x + x + 2 + 34 \quad \text{Combine like terms.}$$
$$x^2 + 2x = 2x + 36 \quad \text{Write in standard form.}$$
$$x^2 - 36 = 0 \quad \text{Factor.}$$
$$(x + 6)(x - 6) = 0 \quad \text{Set each factor equal to 0.}$$
$$x + 6 = 0 \quad \text{or} \quad x - 6 = 0 \quad \text{Solve.}$$
$$x = -6 \qquad\qquad x = 6$$

4. INTERPRET. If $x = -6$, then $x + 2 = -6 + 2$, or -4.
If $x = 6$, then $x + 2 = 6 + 2$, or 8.

Check: $-6, -4$

$$-6(-4) \stackrel{?}{=} -6 + (-4) + 34$$
$$24 \stackrel{?}{=} -10 + 34$$
$$24 = 24 \quad \text{True}$$

$6, 8$

$$6(8) \stackrel{?}{=} 6 + 8 + 34$$
$$48 \stackrel{?}{=} 14 + 34$$
$$48 = 48 \quad \text{True}$$

State: The two consecutive even integers are -6 and -4 or 6 and 8.

Work Practice 4

The next example makes use of the **Pythagorean theorem.** Before we review this theorem, recall that a **right triangle** is a triangle that contains a 90° or right angle. The **hypotenuse** of a right triangle is the side opposite the right angle and is the longest side of the triangle. The **legs** of a right triangle are the other sides of the triangle.

Pythagorean Theorem

In a right triangle, the sum of the squares of the lengths of the two legs is equal to the square of the length of the hypotenuse.

$$(\text{leg})^2 + (\text{leg})^2 = (\text{hypotenuse})^2 \quad \text{or} \quad a^2 + b^2 = c^2$$

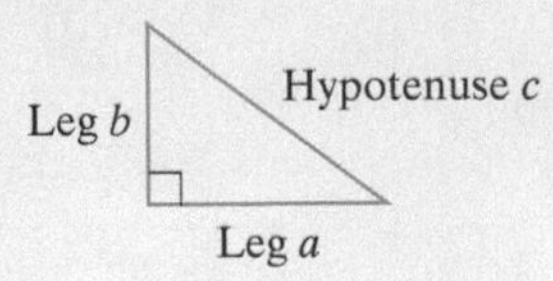

Helpful Hint If you use this formula, don't forget that c represents the length of the hypotenuse.

PRACTICE 5

The length of one leg of a right triangle is 7 meters less than the length of the other leg. The length of the hypotenuse is 13 meters. Find the lengths of the legs.

Example 5 Finding the Dimensions of a Triangle

Find the lengths of the sides of a right triangle if the lengths can be expressed as three consecutive even integers.

Solution:

1. UNDERSTAND. Read and reread the problem. Let's suppose that the length of one leg of the right triangle is 4 units. Then the other leg is the next even integer, or 6 units, and the hypotenuse of the triangle is the next even integer, or 8 units. Remember that the hypotenuse is the longest side. Let's see if a triangle with sides of these lengths forms a right triangle. To do this, we check to see whether the Pythagorean theorem holds true.

$$4^2 + 6^2 \stackrel{?}{=} 8^2$$
$$16 + 36 \stackrel{?}{=} 64$$
$$52 = 64 \quad \text{False}$$

4 units
8 units
6 units

Answer

5. 5 meters, 12 meters

Our proposed numbers do not check, but we now have a better understanding of the problem.

We let x, $x + 2$, and $x + 4$ be three consecutive even integers. Since these integers represent lengths of the sides of a right triangle, we have the following.

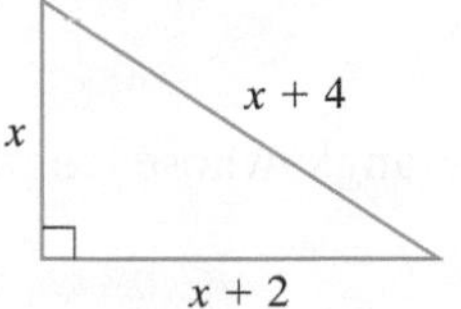

x = one leg
$x + 2$ = other leg
$x + 4$ = hypotenuse (longest side)

2. TRANSLATE. By the Pythagorean theorem, we have that

$$(\text{leg})^2 + (\text{leg})^2 = (\text{hypotenuse})^2$$
$$(x)^2 + (x + 2)^2 = (x + 4)^2$$

3. SOLVE. Now we solve the equation.

$$x^2 + (x + 2)^2 = (x + 4)^2$$
$$x^2 + x^2 + 4x + 4 = x^2 + 8x + 16 \quad \text{Multiply.}$$
$$2x^2 + 4x + 4 = x^2 + 8x + 16 \quad \text{Combine like terms.}$$
$$x^2 - 4x - 12 = 0 \quad \text{Write in standard form.}$$
$$(x - 6)(x + 2) = 0 \quad \text{Factor.}$$
$$x - 6 = 0 \quad \text{or} \quad x + 2 = 0 \quad \text{Set each factor equal to 0.}$$
$$x = 6 \qquad x = -2$$

4. INTERPRET. We discard $x = -2$ since length cannot be negative. If $x = 6$, then $x + 2 = 8$ and $x + 4 = 10$.

Check: Verify that

$$(\text{leg})^2 + (\text{leg})^2 = (\text{hypotenuse})^2$$
$$6^2 + 8^2 \stackrel{?}{=} 10^2$$
$$36 + 64 \stackrel{?}{=} 100$$
$$100 = 100 \quad \text{True}$$

State: The sides of the right triangle have lengths 6 units, 8 units, and 10 units.

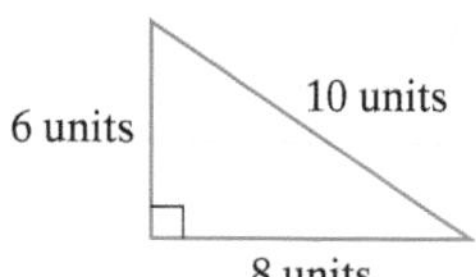

Work Practice 5

4.7 Exercise Set

FOR EXTRA HELP

PRACTICE

WATCH

DOWNLOAD

READ

REVIEW

Objective A *See Examples 1 through 5 for all exercises.*

Translating *For Exercises 1 through 6, represent each given condition using a single variable, x.*

△ **1.** The length and width of a rectangle whose length is 4 centimeters more than its width

△ **2.** The length and width of a rectangle whose length is twice its width

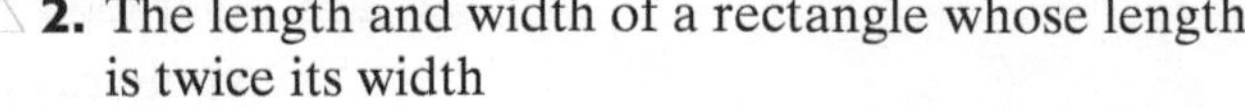

3. Two consecutive odd integers

4. Two consecutive even integers

△ **5.** The base and height of a triangle whose height is one more than four times its base

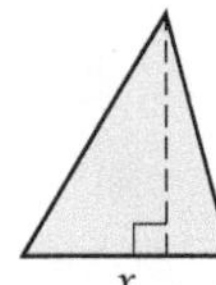

△ **6.** The base and height of a trapezoid whose base is three less than five times its height

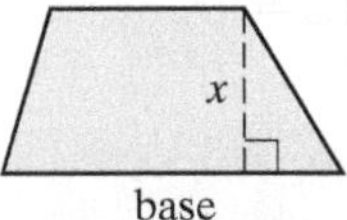

Use the information given to find the dimensions of each figure.

△ **7.**

The *area* of the square is 121 square units. Find the length of its sides.

△ **8.**

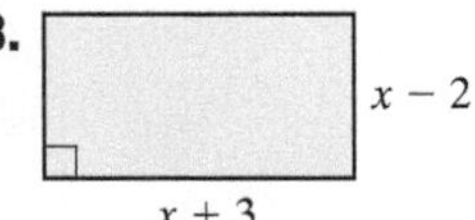

The *area* of the rectangle is 84 square inches. Find its length and width.

△ **9.**

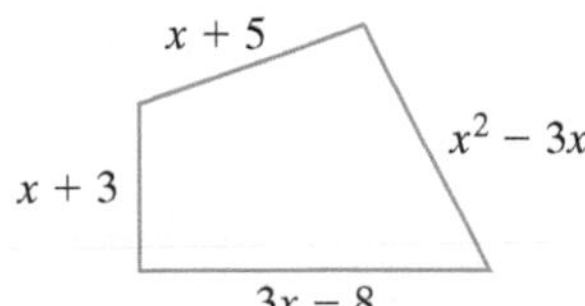

The *perimeter* of the quadrilateral is 120 centimeters. Find the lengths of its sides.

10.

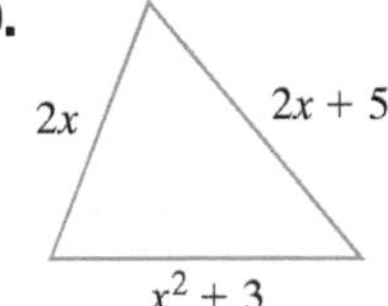

The *perimeter* of the triangle is 85 feet. Find the lengths of its sides.

△ **11.**

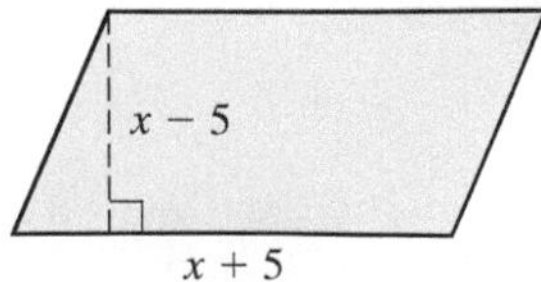

The *area* of the parallelogram is 96 square miles. Find its base and height.

△ **12.**

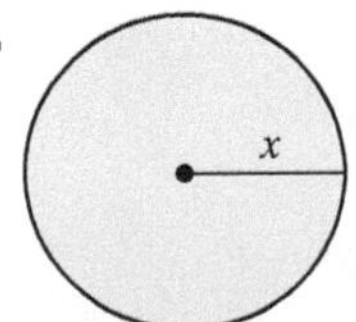

The *area* of the circle is 25p square kilometers. Find its radius.

Solve.

13. An object is thrown upward from the top of an 80-foot building with an initial velocity of 64 feet per second. The height h of the object after t seconds is given by the quadratic equation $h = -16t^2 + 64t + 80$. When will the object hit the ground?

14. A hang glider accidentally drops her compass from the top of a 400-foot cliff. The height h of the compass after t seconds is given by the quadratic equation $h = -16t^2 + 400$. When will the compass hit the ground?

15. The width of a rectangle is 7 centimeters less than twice its length. Its area is 30 square centimeters. Find the dimensions of the rectangle.

16. The length of a rectangle is 9 inches more than its width. Its area is 112 square inches. Find the dimensions of the rectangle.

The equation $D = \frac{1}{2}n(n - 3)$ *gives the number of diagonals D for a polygon with n sides. For example, a polygon with 6 sides has* $D = \frac{1}{2} \cdot 6(6 - 3)$ *or* $D = 9$ *diagonals. (See if you can count all 9 diagonals. Some are shown in the figure.) Use this equation,* $D = \frac{1}{2}n(n - 3)$, *for Exercises 17 through 20.*

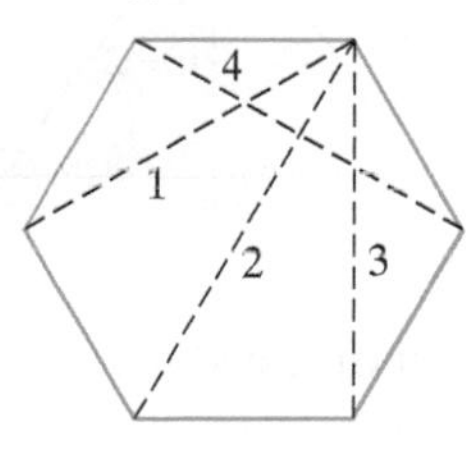

17. Find the number of diagonals for a polygon that has 12 sides.

18. Find the number of diagonals for a polygon that has 15 sides.

19. Find the number of sides n for a polygon that has 35 diagonals.

20. Find the number of sides n for a polygon that has 14 diagonals.

21. The sum of a number and its square is 132. Find the number.

22. The sum of a number and its square is 182. Find the number.

23. The product of two consecutive room numbers is 210. Find the room numbers.

24. The product of two consecutive page numbers is 420. Find the page numbers.

25. A ladder is leaning against a building so that the distance from the ground to the top of the ladder is one foot less than the length of the ladder. Find the length of the ladder if the distance from the bottom of the ladder to the building is 5 feet.

26. Use the given figure to find the length of the guy wire.

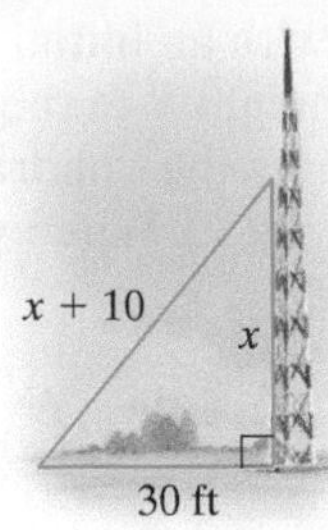

27. If the sides of a square are increased by 3 inches, the area becomes 64 square inches. Find the length of the sides of the original square.

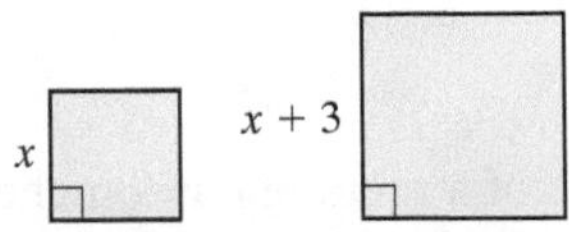

28. If the sides of a square are increased by 5 meters, the area becomes 100 square meters. Find the length of the sides of the original square.

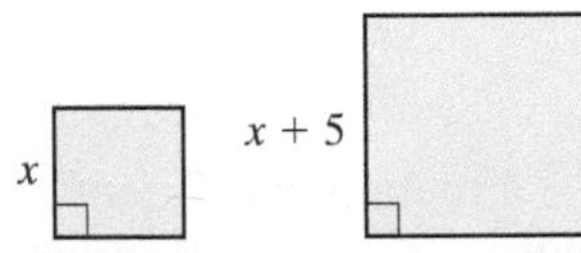

29. One leg of a right triangle is 4 millimeters longer than the smaller leg and the hypotenuse is 8 millimeters longer than the smaller leg. Find the lengths of the sides of the triangle.

30. One leg of a right triangle is 9 centimeters longer than the other leg and the hypotenuse is 45 centimeters. Find the lengths of the legs of the triangle.

31. The length of the base of a triangle is twice its height. If the area of the triangle is 100 square kilometers, find the height.

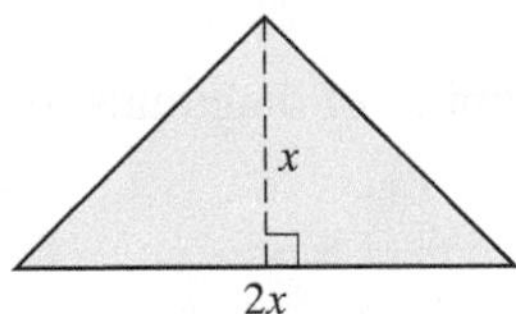

32. The height of a triangle is 2 millimeters less than the base. If the area is 60 square millimeters, find the base.

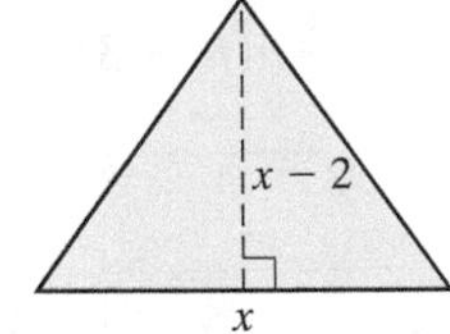

33. Find the length of the shorter leg of a right triangle if the longer leg is 12 feet more than the shorter leg and the hypotenuse is 12 feet less than twice the shorter leg.

34. Find the length of the shorter leg of a right triangle if the longer leg is 10 miles more than the shorter leg and the hypotenuse is 10 miles less than twice the shorter leg.

35. An object is dropped from 39 feet below the tip of the pinnacle atop one of the 1483-foot-tall Petronas Twin Towers in Kuala Lumpur, Malaysia. (*Source:* Council on Tall Buildings and Urban Habitat) The height h of the object after t seconds is given by the equation $h = -16t^2 + 1444$. Find how many seconds pass before the object reaches the ground.

36. An object is dropped from the top of 311 South Wacker Drive, a 961-foot-tall office building in Chicago. (*Source:* Council on Tall Buildings and Urban Habitat) The height h of the object after t seconds is given by the equation $h = -16t^2 + 961$. Find how many seconds pass before the object reaches the ground.

37. At the end of 2 years, P dollars invested at an interest rate r compounded annually increases to an amount, A dollars, given by

$$A = P(1 + r)^2$$

Find the interest rate if \$100 increased to \$144 in 2 years. Write your answer as a percent.

38. At the end of 2 years, P dollars invested at an interest rate r compounded annually increases to an amount, A dollars, given by

$$A = P(1 + r)^2$$

Find the interest rate if \$2000 increased to \$2420 in 2 years. Write your answer as a percent.

△ **39.** Find the dimensions of a rectangle whose width is 7 miles less than its length and whose area is 120 square miles.

△ **40.** Find the dimensions of a rectangle whose width is 2 inches less than half its length and whose area is 160 square inches.

41. If the cost, C, for manufacturing x units of a certain product is given by $C = x^2 - 15x + 50$, find the number of units manufactured at a cost of \$9500.

42. If a switchboard handles n telephones, the number C of telephone connections it can make simultaneously is given by the equation $C = \frac{n(n-1)}{2}$. Find how many telephones are handled by a switchboard making 120 telephone connections simultaneously.

Review

The following double line graph shows a comparison of the number of annual visitors (in millions) to Glacier National Park and Gettysburg National Military Park for the years shown. Use this graph to answer Exercises 43 through 49. See Section 2.4.

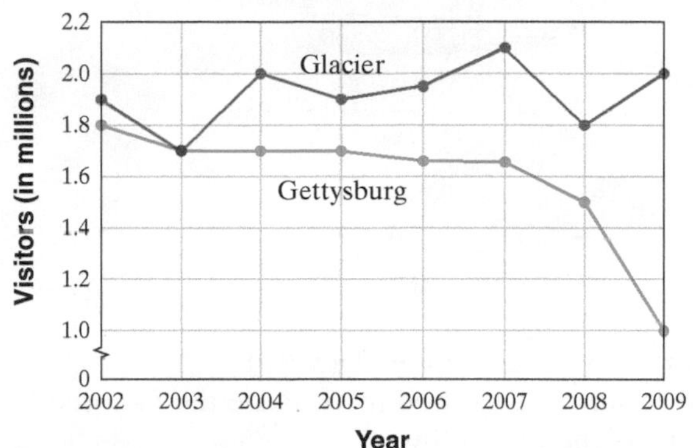

43. Approximate the number of visitors to Glacier National Park in 2002.

44. Approximate the number of visitors to Gettysburg National Military Park in 2009.

45. Approximate the number of visitors to Glacier National Park in 2005.

46. Approximate the number of visitors to Gettysburg National Military Park in 2005.

47. Determine the year that the colored lines in this graph intersect.

48. In your own words, explain the meaning of the point of intersection in the graph.

49. Describe the trends shown in this graph and speculate as to why these trends have occurred.

Concept Extensions

△ **50.** Two boats travel at right angles to each other after leaving the same dock at the same time. One hour later the boats are 17 miles apart. If one boat travels 7 miles per hour faster than the other boat, find the rate of each boat.

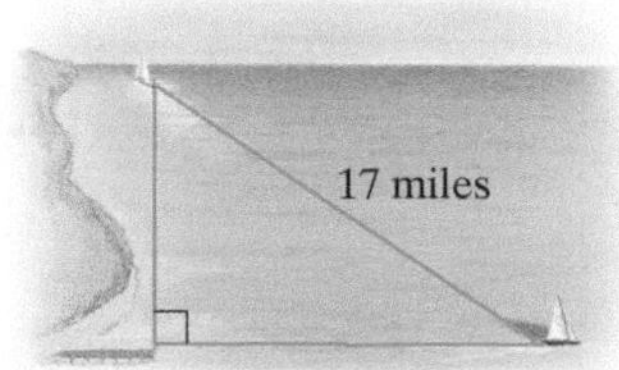

△ **51.** The side of a square equals the width of a rectangle. The length of the rectangle is 6 meters longer than its width. The sum of the areas of the square and the rectangle is 176 square meters. Find the side of the square.

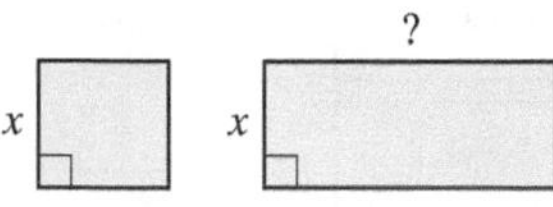

52. The sum of two numbers is 20, and the sum of their squares is 218. Find the numbers.

53. The sum of two numbers is 25, and the sum of their squares is 325. Find the numbers.

△ **54.** A rectangular garden is surrounded by a walk of uniform width. The area of the garden is 180 square yards. If the dimensions of the garden plus the walk are 16 yards by 24 yards, find the width of the walk.

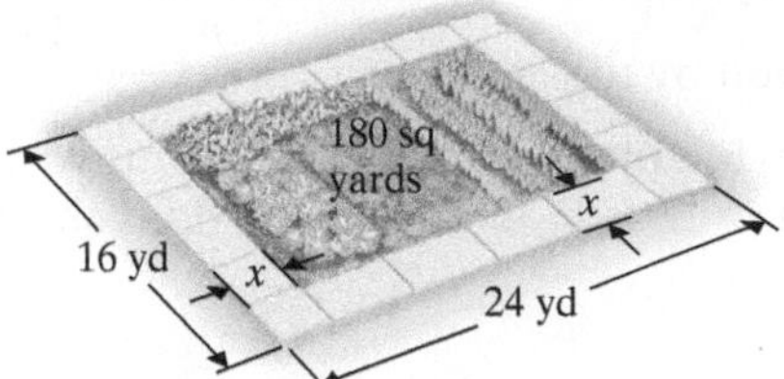

△ **55.** A rectangular pool is surrounded by a walk 4 meters wide. The pool is 6 meters longer than its width. If the total area of the pool and walk is 576 square meters more than the area of the pool, find the dimensions of the pool.

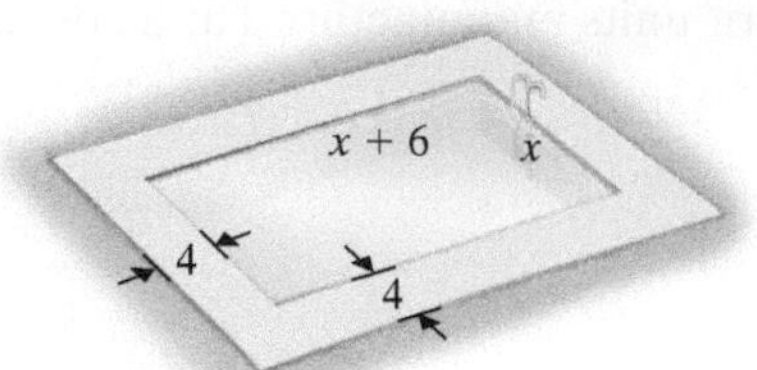

△ **56.** According to the International America's Cup Class (IACC) rule, a sailboat competing in the America's Cup match must have a 110-foot-tall mast and a combined mainsail and jib sail area of 3000 square feet. (*Source:* America's Cup Organizing Committee) A design for an IACC-class sailboat calls for the mainsail to be 60% of the combined sail area. If the height of the triangular mainsail is 28 feet more than twice the length of the boom, find the length of the boom and the height of the mainsail.

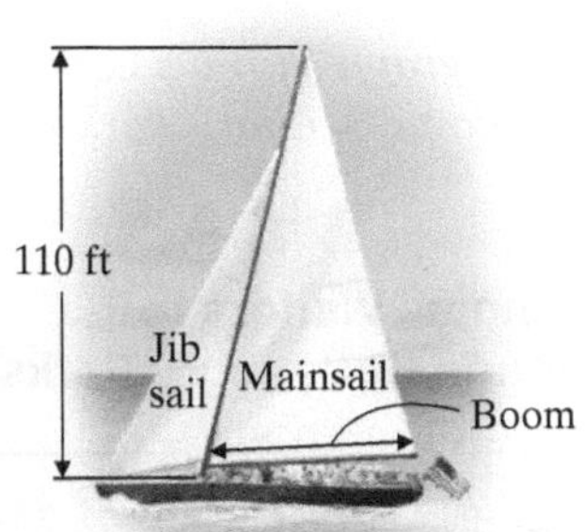

Chapter 4 Group Activity

Factoring polynomials can be visualized using areas of rectangles. To see this, let's first find the areas of the following squares and rectangles. (Recall that Area = Length · Width.)

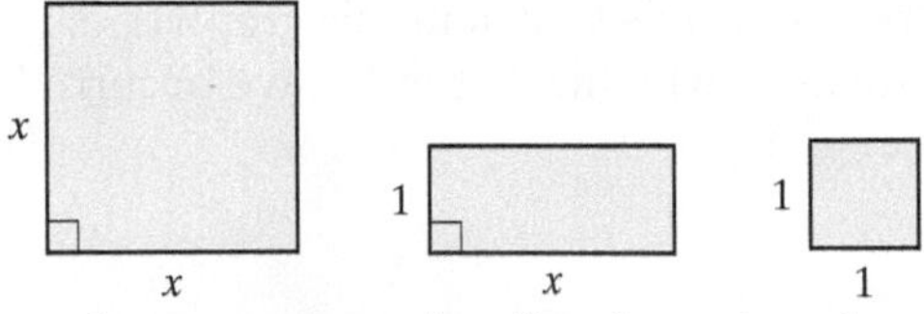

To use these areas to visualize factoring the polynomial $x^2 + 3x + 2$, for example, use the shapes below to form a rectangle. The factored form is found by reading the length and the width of the rectangle as shown below.

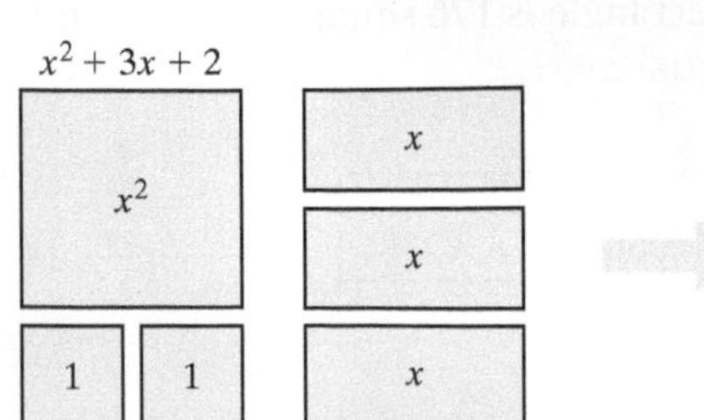

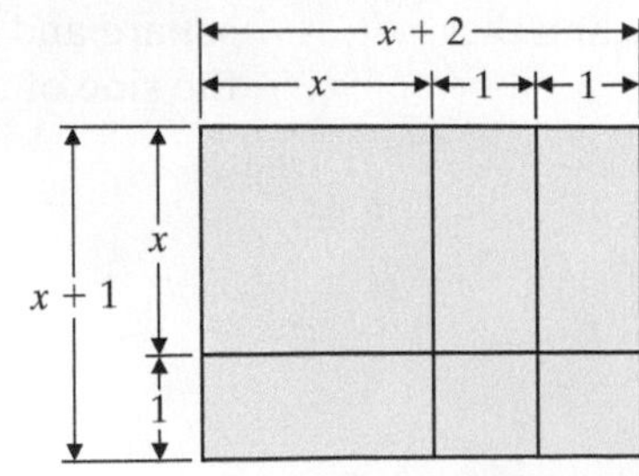

Thus, $x^2 + 3x + 2 = (x + 2)(x + 1)$.

Try using this method to visualize the factored form of each polynomial below.

Work in a group and use tiles to find the factored form of the polynomials below. (Tiles can be handmade from index cards.)

1. $x^2 + 6x + 5$
2. $x^2 + 5x + 6$
3. $x^2 + 5x + 4$
4. $x^2 + 4x + 3$
5. $x^2 + 6x + 9$
6. $x^2 + 4x + 4$

Chapter 4 Vocabulary Check

Fill in each blank with one of the words or phrases listed below. Some words or phrases may be used more than once.

factoring	leg	hypotenuse
greatest common factor	perfect square trinomial	quadratic equation

1. An equation that can be written in the form $ax^2 + bx + c = 0$ (with a not 0) is called a ____________________.
2. ____________________ is the process of writing an expression as a product.
3. The ____________________ of a list of terms is the product of all common factors.
4. A trinomial that is the square of some binomial is called a ____________________.
5. In a right triangle, the side opposite the right angle is called the ____________________.
6. In a right triangle, each side adjacent to the right angle is called a ____________________.
7. The Pythagorean theorem states that $(\text{leg})^2 + (\text{leg})^2 =$ (____________________$)^2$.

Helpful Hint Are you preparing for your test? Don't forget to take the Chapter 4 Test on page 332. Then check your answers at the back of the text and use the Chapter Test Prep Videos to see the fully worked-out solutions to any of the exercises you want to review.

4 Chapter Highlights

Definitions and Concepts	Examples
Section 4.1 The Greatest Common Factor	
Factoring is the process of writing an expression as a product.	Factor: $6 = 2 \cdot 3$ Factor: $x^2 + 5x + 6 = (x + 2)(x + 3)$
The GCF of a list of variable terms contains the smallest exponent on each common variable.	The GCF of z^5, z^3, and z^{10} is z^3.
The GCF of a list of terms is the product of all common factors.	Find the GCF of $8x^2y$, $10x^3y^2$, and $50x^2y^3$. $8x^2y = 2 \cdot 2 \cdot 2 \cdot x^2 \cdot y$ $10x^3y^2 = 2 \cdot 5 \cdot x^3 \cdot y^2$ $50x^2y^3 = 2 \cdot 5 \cdot 5 \cdot x^2 \cdot y^3$ $\text{GCF} = 2 \cdot x^2 \cdot y$ or $2x^2y$
To Factor by Grouping **Step 1.** Group the terms in two groups so that each group has a common factor. **Step 2.** Factor out the GCF from each group. **Step 3.** If there is a common binomial factor, factor it out. **Step 4.** If not, rearrange the terms and try these steps again.	Factor: $10ax + 15a - 6xy - 9y$ **Step 1.** $(10ax + 15a) + (-6xy - 9y)$ **Step 2.** $5a(2x + 3) - 3y(2x + 3)$ **Step 3.** $(2x + 3)(5a - 3y)$
Section 4.2 Factoring Trinomials of the Form $x^2 + bx + c$	
The product of these numbers is c. $x^2 + bx + c = (x + \square)(x + \square)$ The sum of these numbers is b.	Factor: $x^2 + 7x + 12$ $3 + 4 = 7$ $3 \cdot 4 = 12$ $x^2 + 7x + 12 = (x + 3)(x + 4)$

Definitions and Concepts	Examples
Section 4.3 Factoring Trinomials of the Form $ax^2 + bx + c$	
To factor $ax^2 + bx + c$, try various combinations of factors of ax^2 and c until a middle term of bx is obtained when checking.	Factor: $3x^2 + 14x - 5$ Factors of $3x^2$: $3x, x$ Factors of -5: $-1, 5$ and $1, -5$ $(3x - 1)(x + 5)$ $-1x$ $+15x$ **Correct** middle term $14x$
Section 4.4 Factoring Trinomials of the Form $ax^2 + bx + c$ by Grouping	
To Factor $ax^2 + bx + c$ by Grouping **Step 1.** Find two numbers whose product is $a \cdot c$ and whose sum is b. **Step 2.** Rewrite bx, using the factors found in Step 1. **Step 3.** Factor by grouping.	Factor: $3x^2 + 14x - 5$ **Step 1.** Find two numbers whose product is $3 \cdot (-5)$ or -15 and whose sum is 14. They are 15 and -1. **Step 2.** $3x^2 + 14x - 5$ $= 3x^2 + 15x - 1x - 5$ **Step 3.** $= 3x(x + 5) - 1(x + 5)$ $= (x + 5)(3x - 1)$
Section 4.5 Factoring Perfect Square Trinomials and the Difference of Two Squares	
A **perfect square trinomial** is a trinomial that is the square of some binomial.	**Perfect Square Trinomial = Square of Binomial** $x^2 + 4x + 4 = (x + 2)^2$ $25x^2 - 10x + 1 = (5x - 1)^2$
Factoring Perfect Square Trinomials $a^2 + 2ab + b^2 = (a + b)^2$ $a^2 - 2ab + b^2 = (a - b)^2$	Factor. $x^2 + 6x + 9 = x^2 + 2 \cdot x \cdot 3 + 3^2 = (x + 3)^2$ $4x^2 - 12x + 9 = (2x)^2 - 2 \cdot 2x \cdot 3 + 3^2$ $= (2x - 3)^2$
Difference of Two Squares $a^2 - b^2 = (a + b)(a - b)$	Factor. $x^2 - 9 = x^2 - 3^2 = (x + 3)(x - 3)$
Section 4.6 Solving Quadratic Equations by Factoring	
A **quadratic equation** is an equation that can be written in the form $ax^2 + bx + c = 0$ with a not 0. The form $ax^2 + bx + c = 0$ is called the **standard form** of a quadratic equation.	**Quadratic Equation** — **Standard Form** $x^2 = 16$ — $x^2 - 16 = 0$ $y = -2y^2 + 5$ — $2y^2 + y - 5 = 0$
Zero-Factor Property If a and b are real numbers and if $ab = 0$, then $a = 0$ or $b = 0$.	If $(x + 3)(x - 1) = 0$, then $x + 3 = 0$ or $x - 1 = 0$.

Definitions and Concepts	Examples
Section 4.6 Solving Quadratic Equations by Factoring (*continued*)	
TO SOLVE QUADRATIC EQUATIONS BY FACTORING	Solve: $3x^2 = 13x - 4$
Step 1. Write the equation in standard form so that one side of the equation is 0.	**Step 1.** $3x^2 - 13x + 4 = 0$
Step 2. Factor completely.	**Step 2.** $(3x - 1)(x - 4) = 0$
Step 3. Set each factor containing a variable equal to 0.	**Step 3.** $3x - 1 = 0$ or $x - 4 = 0$
Step 4. Solve the resulting equations.	**Step 4.** $3x = 1$ $\quad x = 4$ $x = \frac{1}{3}$
Step 5. Check solutions in the original equation.	**Step 5.** Check both $\frac{1}{3}$ and 4 in the original equation.
Section 4.7 Quadratic Equations and Problem Solving	
PROBLEM-SOLVING STEPS	A garden is in the shape of a rectangle whose length is two feet more than its width. If the area of the garden is 35 square feet, find its dimensions.
1. UNDERSTAND the problem.	1. Read and reread the problem. Guess a solution and check your guess. Draw a diagram. Let x be the width of the rectangular garden. Then $x + 2$ is the length. 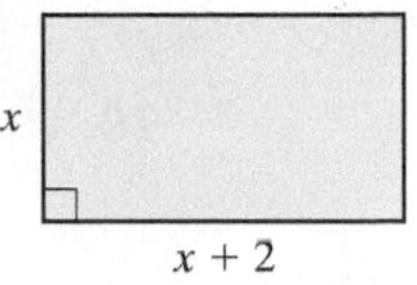
2. TRANSLATE.	2. length · width = area ↓ ↓ ↓ $(x + 2) \cdot x = 35$
3. SOLVE.	3. $(x + 2)x = 35$ $x^2 + 2x - 35 = 0$ $(x - 5)(x + 7) = 0$ $x - 5 = 0$ or $x + 7 = 0$ $x = 5$ $\quad x = -7$
4. INTERPRET.	4. Discard the solution $x = -7$ since x represents width. *Check:* If x is 5 feet, then $x + 2 = 5 + 2 = 7$ feet. The area of a rectangle whose width is 5 feet and whose length is 7 feet is (5 feet)(7 feet) or 35 square feet. *State:* The garden is 5 feet by 7 feet.

Chapter 4 Review

(4.1) *Complete each factoring.*

1. $6x^2 - 15x = 3x(\qquad)$

2. $4x^5 + 2x - 10x^4 = 2x(\qquad)$

Factor out the GCF from each polynomial.

3. $5m + 30$

4. $20x^3 + 12x^2 + 24x$

5. $3x(2x + 3) - 5(2x + 3)$

6. $5x(x + 1) - (x + 1)$

Factor each polynomial by grouping.

7. $3x^2 - 3x + 2x - 2$

8. $3a^2 + 9ab + 3b^2 + ab$

9. $10a^2 + 5ab + 7b^2 + 14ab$

10. $6x^2 + 10x - 3x - 5$

(4.2) *Factor each trinomial.*

11. $x^2 + 6x + 8$

12. $x^2 - 11x + 24$

13. $x^2 + x + 2$

14. $x^2 - 5x - 6$

15. $x^2 + 2x - 8$

16. $x^2 + 4xy - 12y^2$

17. $x^2 + 8xy + 15y^2$

18. $72 - 18x - 2x^2$

19. $32 + 12x - 4x^2$

20. $5y^3 - 50y^2 + 120y$

21. To factor $x^2 + 2x - 48$, think of two numbers whose product is ______ and whose sum is ______.

22. What is the first step in factoring $3x^2 + 15x + 30$?

(4.3) or (4.4) *Factor each trinomial.*

23. $2x^2 + 13x + 6$

24. $4x^2 + 4x - 3$

25. $6x^2 + 5xy - 4y^2$

26. $x^2 - x + 2$

27. $2x^2 - 23x - 39$

28. $18x^2 - 9xy - 20y^2$

29. $10y^3 + 25y^2 - 60y$

30. $60y^3 - 39y^2 + 6y$

Write the perimeter of each figure as a simplified polynomial. Then factor each polynomial completely.

△ **31.**

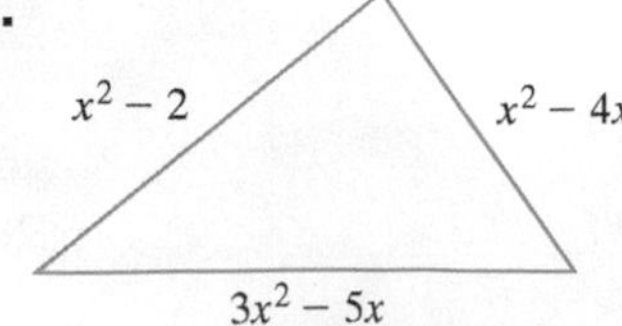

△ **32.**

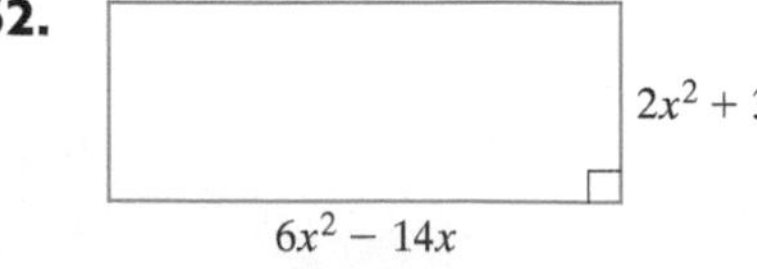

(4.5) *Determine whether each polynomial is a perfect square trinomial.*

33. $x^2 + 6x + 9$
34. $x^2 + 8x + 64$
35. $9m^2 - 12m + 16$
36. $4y^2 - 28y + 49$

Determine whether each binomial is a difference of two squares.

37. $x^2 - 9$
38. $x^2 + 16$
39. $4x^2 - 25y^2$
40. $9a^3 - 1$

Factor each polynomial completely.

41. $x^2 - 81$
42. $x^2 + 12x + 36$
43. $4x^2 - 9$
44. $9t^2 - 25s^2$
45. $16x^2 + y^2$
46. $n^2 - 18n + 81$
47. $3r^2 + 36r + 108$
48. $9y^2 - 42y + 49$
49. $5m^8 - 5m^6$
50. $4x^2 - 28xy + 49y^2$
51. $3x^2y + 6xy^2 + 3y^3$
52. $16x^4 - 1$

(4.6) *Solve each equation.*

53. $(x + 6)(x - 2) = 0$
54. $(x - 7)(x + 11) = 0$
55. $3x(x + 1)(7x - 2) = 0$
56. $4(5x + 1)(x + 3) = 0$
57. $x^2 + 8x + 7 = 0$
58. $x^2 - 2x - 24 = 0$
59. $x^2 + 10x = -25$
60. $x(x - 10) = -16$
61. $(3x - 1)(9x^2 + 3x + 1) = 0$
62. $56x^2 - 5x - 6 = 0$
63. $m^2 = 6m$
64. $r^2 = 25$
65. Write a quadratic equation that has the two solutions 4 and 5.
66. Write a quadratic equation that has two solutions, both -1.

(4.7) *Use the given information to choose the correct dimensions.*

△ **67.** The perimeter of a rectangle is 24 inches. The length is twice the width. Find the dimensions of the rectangle.

a. 5 inches by 7 inches
b. 5 inches by 10 inches
c. 4 inches by 8 inches
d. 2 inches by 10 inches

△ **68.** The area of a rectangle is 80 meters. The length is one more than three times the width. Find the dimensions of the rectangle.

a. 8 meters by 10 meters
b. 4 meters by 13 meters
c. 4 meters by 20 meters
d. 5 meters by 16 meters

Use the given information to find the dimensions of each figure.

△ **69.** The *area* of the square is 81 square units. Find the length of a side.

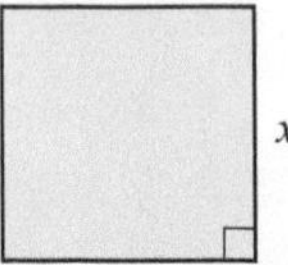

△ **70.** The *perimeter* of the quadrilateral is 47 units. Find the lengths of the sides.

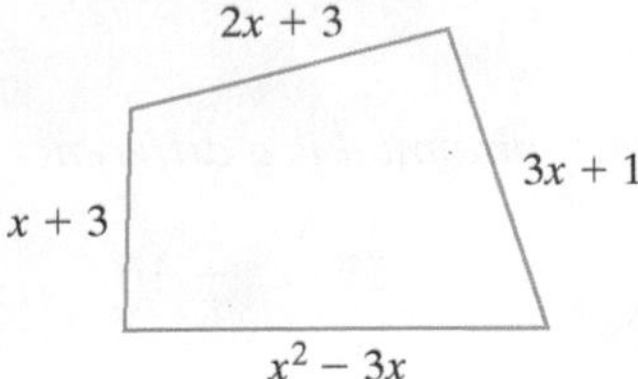

Solve.

△ **71.** A flag for a local organization is in the shape of a rectangle whose length is 15 inches less than twice its width. If the area of the flag is 500 square inches, find its dimensions.

△ **72.** The base of a triangular sail is four times its height. If the area of the triangle is 162 square yards, find the base.

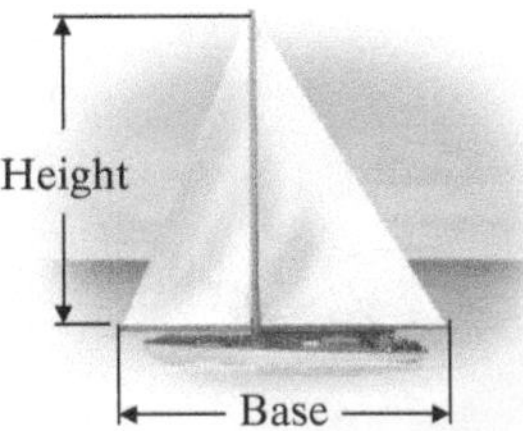

73. Find two consecutive positive integers whose product is 380.

74. Find two consecutive positive even integers whose product is 440.

75. A rocket is fired from the ground with an initial velocity of 440 feet per second. Its height h after t seconds is given by the equation $h = -16t^2 + 440t$.

a. Find how many seconds pass before the rocket reaches a height of 2800 feet. Explain why two answers are obtained.

b. Find how many seconds pass before the rocket reaches the ground again.

△ **76.** An architect's squaring instrument is in the shape of a right triangle. Find the length of the longer leg of the right triangle if the hypotenuse is 8 centimeters longer than the longer leg and the shorter leg is 8 centimeters shorter than the longer leg.

Mixed Review

Factor completely.

77. $6x + 24$

78. $7x - 63$

79. $11x(4x - 3) - 6(4x - 3)$

80. $2x(x - 5) - (x - 5)$

81. $3x^3 - 4x^2 + 6x - 8$

82. $xy + 2x - y - 2$

83. $2x^2 + 2x - 24$

84. $3x^3 - 30x^2 + 27x$

85. $4x^2 - 81$

86. $2x^2 - 18$

87. $16x^2 - 24x + 9$

88. $5x^2 + 20x + 20$

Solve.

89. $2x^2 - x - 28 = 0$

90. $x^2 - 2x = 15$

91. $2x(x + 7)(x + 4) = 0$

92. $x(x - 5) = -6$

93. $x^2 = 16x$

94. The perimeter of the following triangle is 48 inches. Find the lengths of its sides.

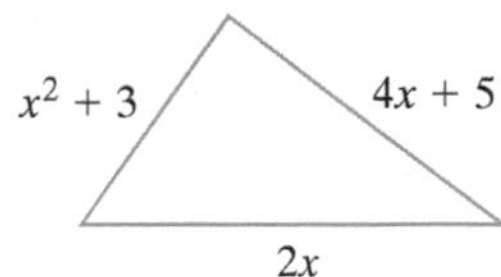

95. The width of a rectangle is 4 inches less than its length. Its area is 12 square inches. Find the dimensions of the rectangle.

Chapter 4 Test

Step-by-step test solutions are found on the Chapter Test Prep Videos available via the Interactive DVD Lecture Series, in MyMathLab or on YouTube (search "MartinGayIntroAlg" and click on "Channels").

Answers

1. ______
2. ______
3. ______
4. ______
5. ______
6. ______
7. ______
8. ______
9. ______
10. ______
11. ______
12. ______
13. ______
14. ______
15. ______
16. ______
17. ______
18. ______
19. ______
20. ______
21. ______
22. ______
23. ______

Factor each polynomial completely. If a polynomial cannot be factored, write "prime."

1. $9x^2 - 3x$

2. $x^2 + 11x + 28$

3. $49 - m^2$

4. $y^2 + 22y + 121$

5. $x^4 - 16$

6. $4(a + 3) - y(a + 3)$

7. $x^2 + 4$

8. $y^2 - 8y - 48$

9. $3a^2 + 3ab - 7a - 7b$

10. $3x^2 - 5x + 2$

11. $180 - 5x^2$

12. $3x^3 - 21x^2 + 30x$

13. $6t^2 - t - 5$

14. $xy^2 - 7y^2 - 4x + 28$

15. $x - x^5$

16. $x^2 + 14xy + 24y^2$

Solve each equation.

17. $(x - 3)(x + 9) = 0$

18. $x^2 + 5x = 14$

19. $x(x + 6) = 7$

20. $3x(2x - 3)(3x + 4) = 0$

21. $5t^3 - 45t = 0$

22. $t^2 - 2t - 15 = 0$

23. $6x^2 = 15x$

Solve.

24. A deck for a home is in the shape of a triangle. The length of the base of the triangle is 9 feet longer than its height. If the area of the triangle is 68 square feet, find the length of the base.

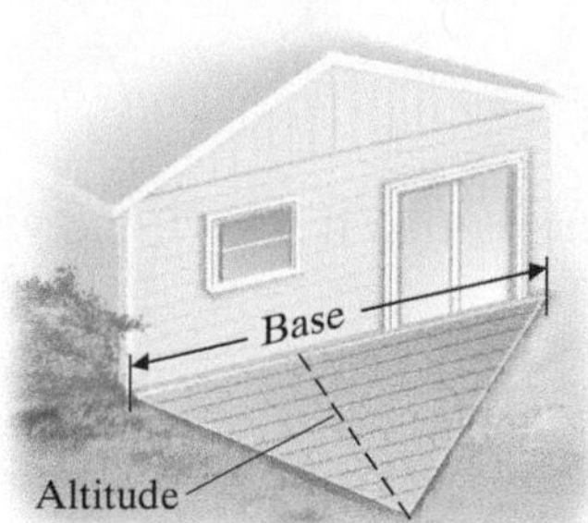

△ **25.** The *area* of the rectangle is 54 square units. Find the dimensions of the rectangle.

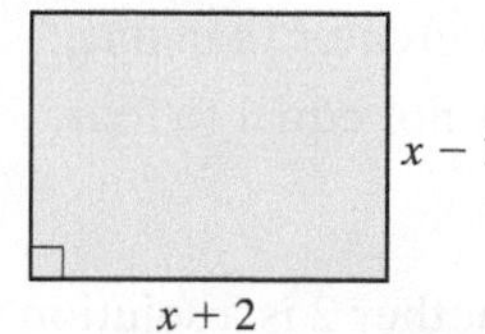

26. An object is dropped from the top of the Woolworth Building on Broadway in New York City. The height h of the object after t seconds is given by the equation

$$h = -16t^2 + 784$$

Find how many seconds pass before the object reaches the ground.

△ **27.** Find the lengths of the sides of a right triangle if the hypotenuse is 10 centimeters longer than the shorter leg and 5 centimeters longer than the longer leg.

28. A window washer is suspended 38 feet below the roof of the 1127-foot-tall John Hancock Center in Chicago. (*Source:* Council on Tall Buildings and Urban Habitat) If the window washer drops an object from this height, the object's height h after t seconds is given by the equation $h = -16t^2 + 1089$. Find how many seconds pass before the object reaches the ground.

24. ______

25. ______

26. ______

27. ______

28. ______

Answers

1. a. ______
b. ______
c. ______
2. a. ______
b. ______
3. ______
4. ______
5. ______
6. ______
7. a. ______
b. ______
c. ______
8. ______
9. ______
10. ______
11. ______
12. ______
13. ______
14. ______
15. ______
16. ______
17. ______
18. ______
19. ______
20. ______

Cumulative Review Chapters 1–4

1. Translate each sentence into a mathematical statement.

a. Nine is less than or equal to eleven.

b. Eight is greater than one.

c. Three is not equal to four.

2. Insert $<$ or $>$ in the space to make each statement true.

a. $|-5| \quad |-3|$

b. $|0| \quad |-2|$

3. Decide whether 2 is a solution of $3x + 10 = 8x$.

4. Evaluate $\frac{x}{y} + 5x$ if $x = 20$ and $y = 10$.

5. Subtract 8 from -4.

6. Evaluate $\frac{x}{y} + 5x$ if $x = -20$ and $y = 10$.

7. Evaluate each expression when $x = -2$ and $y = -4$.

a. $\frac{3x}{2y}$

b. $x^3 - y^2$

c. $\frac{x - y}{-x}$

8. Evaluate $\frac{x}{y} + 5x$ if $x = -20$ and $y = -10$.

Simplify each expression by combining like terms.

9. $2x + 3x + 5 + 2$

10. $5 - 2(3x - 7)$

11. $-5a - 3 + a + 2$

12. $5(x - 6) + 9(-2x + 1)$

13. $2.3x + 5x - 6$

Solve each equation.

14. $0.8y + 0.2(y - 1) = 1.8$

15. $-3x = 33$

16. $\frac{x}{-7} = -4$

17. $3(x - 4) = 3x - 12$

18. $-\frac{2}{3}x = -22$

19. Solve $V = lwh$ for l.

20. Solve for y: $3x + 2y = -7$

Simplify each expression.

21. $(5^3)^6$

22. $5^2 + 5^1$

23. $(y^8)^2$

24. $y^8 \cdot y^2$

Simplify the following expressions. Write each result using positive exponents only.

25. $\dfrac{(2x^3)^4 x}{x^7}$

26. 3^{-2}

27. $(y^{-3}z^6)^{-6}$

28. $\dfrac{x^{-3}}{x^{-7}}$

29. $\dfrac{x^{-7}}{(x^4)^3}$

30. $\dfrac{(5a^7)^2}{a^5}$

Simplify each polynomial by combining any like terms.

31. $-3x + 7x$

32. $\dfrac{2}{3}x + 23 + \dfrac{1}{6}x - 100$

33. $11x^2 + 5 + 2x^2 - 7$

34. $0.2x - 1.1 + 2.3 - 0.7x$

35. Multiply: $(2x - y)^2$

36. Multiply: $(3x - 7y)^2$

Use a special product to square each binomial.

37. $(t + 2)^2$

38. $(x - 13)^2$

39. $(x^2 - 7y)^2$

40. $(7x + y)^2$

41. Divide: $\dfrac{8x^2y^2 - 16xy + 2x}{4xy}$

21. ______
22. ______
23. ______
24. ______
25. ______
26. ______
27. ______
28. ______
29. ______
30. ______
31. ______
32. ______
33. ______
34. ______
35. ______
36. ______
37. ______
38. ______
39. ______
40. ______
41. ______

42. ________

43. ________

44. ________

45. ________

46. ________

47. ________

48. ________

49. ________

50. ________

Factor each polynomial. For Exercise 47, factor by grouping.

42. $z^3 + 7z + z^2 + 7$

43. $5(x + 3) + y(x + 3)$

44. $2x^3 + 2x^2 - 84x$

45. $x^4 + 5x^2 + 6$

46. $-4x^2 - 23x + 6$

47. $6x^2 - 2x - 20$

48. $9xy^2 - 16x$

49. The platform for the cliff divers in Acapulco, Mexico, is about 144 feet above the sea. Neglecting air resistance, the height h in feet of a cliff diver above the ocean after t seconds is given by the quadratic equation $h = -16t^2 + 144$. Find how long it takes the diver to reach the ocean.

50. Solve $x^2 - 13x = -36$.

Rational Expressions

In this chapter, we expand our knowledge of algebraic expressions to include algebraic fractions, called *rational expressions*. We explore the operations of addition, subtraction, multiplication, and division using principles similar to the principles for numerical fractions.

Sections

Check Your Progress

Many sport statistics are calculated using formulas containing rational expressions. Below are a few examples:

Sport	Formula	Explanation
Baseball	$S = \frac{h + d + 2t + 3r}{b}$	A baseball player's slugging percentage S, where h = number of hits, d = number of doubles, t = number of triples, r = number of home runs, and b = number of at bats
NCAA Football	$R_{\text{NCAA}} = \frac{100C + 330T - 200I + 8.4Y}{A}$	A quarterback's rating in NCAA football R, where C = the number of completed passes, A = the number of attempted passes, T = the number of touchdown passes, Y = the number of yards in the completed passes, and I = the number of interceptions
NFL Football	$R_{\text{NFL}} = \frac{a + b + c + d}{6} \times 100$	A quarterback's rating in NFL football R, where a, b, c, and d are each formulas containing rational expressions.

(*Source:* Wikipedia.org.)

In Section 5.1, Exercises 87 and 88, you will have the opportunity to calculate some sport statistics.

Objectives

A Find the Value of a Rational Expression Given a Replacement Number.

B Identify Values for Which a Rational Expression Is Undefined.

C Simplify, or Write Rational Expressions in Lowest Terms.

D Write Equivalent Forms of Rational Expressions.

5.1 SIMPLIFYING RATIONAL EXPRESSIONS

Objective A Evaluating Rational Expressions

A rational number is a number that can be written as a quotient of integers. A *rational expression* is also a quotient; it is a quotient of polynomials. Examples are

$$\frac{2}{3}, \quad \frac{3y^3}{8}, \quad \frac{-4p}{p^3 + 2p + 1}, \quad \text{and} \quad \frac{5x^2 - 3x + 2}{3x + 7}$$

Rational Expression

A **rational expression** is an expression that can be written in the form

$$\frac{P}{Q}$$

where P and Q are polynomials and $Q \neq 0$.

Rational expressions have different numerical values depending on what values replace the variables.

PRACTICE 1

Find the value of $\frac{x-3}{5x+1}$ for each replacement value.

a. $x = 4$

b. $x = -3$

Example 1 Find the numerical value of $\frac{x+4}{2x-3}$ for each replacement value.

a. $x = 5$ **b.** $x = -2$

Solution:

a. We replace each x in the expression with 5 and then simplify.

$$\frac{x+4}{2x-3} = \frac{5+4}{2(5)-3} = \frac{9}{10-3} = \frac{9}{7}$$

b. We replace each x in the expression with -2 and then simplify.

$$\frac{x+4}{2x-3} = \frac{-2+4}{2(-2)-3} = \frac{2}{-7} \quad \text{or} \quad -\frac{2}{7}$$

Work Practice 1

In the example above, we wrote $\frac{2}{-7}$ as $-\frac{2}{7}$. For a negative fraction such as $\frac{2}{-7}$, recall from Section 1.6 that

$$\frac{2}{-7} = \frac{-2}{7} = -\frac{2}{7}$$

In general, for any fraction,

$$\frac{-a}{b} = \frac{a}{-b} = -\frac{a}{b}, \qquad b \neq 0$$

This is also true for rational expressions. For example,

$$\underbrace{\frac{-(x+2)}{x}}_{\uparrow} = \frac{x+2}{-x} = -\frac{x+2}{x}$$

Notice the parentheses.

Answers

1. a. $\frac{1}{21}$ **b.** $\frac{3}{7}$

Objective B Identifying When a Rational Expression Is Undefined

In the definition of rational expression (first "box" in this section), notice that we wrote $Q \neq 0$ for the denominator Q. The denominator of a rational expression must not equal 0 since division by 0 is not defined. (See the Helpful Hint to the right.) This means we must be careful when replacing the variable in a rational expression by a number. For example, suppose we replace x with 5 in the rational expression $\frac{3+x}{x-5}$. The expression becomes

$$\frac{3+x}{x-5} = \frac{3+5}{5-5} = \frac{8}{0}$$

But division by 0 is undefined. Therefore, in this expression we can allow x to be any real number *except* 5. **A rational expression is undefined for values that make the denominator 0.** Thus,

> To find values for which a rational expression is undefined, find values for which the denominator is 0.

Helpful Hint **Do you recall why division by 0 is not defined?** Remember, for example, that

$\frac{8}{4} = 2$ because $2 \cdot 4 = 8$.

Thus, if $\frac{8}{0} = \textit{a number}$,

then $\textit{the number} \cdot 0 = 8$.

There is no number that when multiplied by 0 equals 8; thus $\frac{8}{0}$ is undefined. This is true in general for fractions and rational expressions.

Example 2 Are there any values for x for which each expression is undefined?

a. $\frac{x}{x-3}$ **b.** $\frac{x^2+2}{x^2-3x+2}$ **c.** $\frac{x^3-6x^2-10x}{3}$

Solution: To find values for which a rational expression is undefined, we find values that make the denominator 0.

a. The denominator of $\frac{x}{x-3}$ is 0 when $x - 3 = 0$ or when $x = 3$. Thus, when $x = 3$, the expression $\frac{x}{x-3}$ is undefined.

b. We set the denominator equal to 0.

$$x^2 - 3x + 2 = 0$$
$$(x-2)(x-1) = 0 \quad \text{Factor.}$$
$$x - 2 = 0 \quad \text{or} \quad x - 1 = 0 \quad \text{Set each factor equal to 0.}$$
$$x = 2 \qquad\qquad x = 1 \quad \text{Solve.}$$

Thus, when $x = 2$ or $x = 1$, the denominator $x^2 - 3x + 2$ is 0. So the rational expression $\frac{x^2+2}{x^2-3x+2}$ is undefined when $x = 2$ or when $x = 1$.

c. The denominator of $\frac{x^3-6x^2-10x}{3}$ is never 0, so there are no values of x for which this expression is undefined.

Work Practice 2

PRACTICE 2

Are there any values for x for which each rational expression is undefined?

a. $\frac{x}{x+8}$

b. $\frac{x-3}{x^2+5x+4}$

c. $\frac{x^2-3x+2}{5}$

Note: Unless otherwise stated, we will now assume that variables in rational expressions are replaced only by values for which the expressions are defined.

Objective C Simplifying Rational Expressions

A fraction is said to be written in lowest terms or simplest form when the numerator and denominator have no common factors other than 1 (or −1). For example, the fraction $\frac{7}{10}$ is written in lowest terms since the numerator and denominator have no common factors other than 1 (or −1).

The process of writing a rational expression in lowest terms or simplest form is called **simplifying** a rational expression.

Answers

2. a. $x = -8$ **b.** $x = -4, x = -1$ **c.** no

Simplifying a rational expression is similar to simplifying a fraction. Recall from Section R.2 that to simplify a fraction, we essentially "remove factors of 1." Our ability to do this comes from these facts:

- Any nonzero number over itself simplifies to 1 $\left(\frac{5}{5} = 1, \frac{-7.26}{-7.26} = 1, \text{ and } \frac{c}{c} = 1 \text{ as long as } c \text{ is not } 0\right)$, and
- The product of any number and 1 is that number $\left(19 \cdot 1 = 19, -8.9 \cdot 1 = -8.9, \frac{a}{b} \cdot 1 = \frac{a}{b}\right)$.

In other words, we have the following:

$$\frac{a \cdot c}{b \cdot c} = \frac{a}{b} \cdot \frac{c}{c} = \frac{a}{b}$$

Since $\frac{a}{b} \cdot 1 = \frac{a}{b}$

Simplify: $\frac{15}{20}$

$$\frac{15}{20} = \frac{3 \cdot 5}{2 \cdot 2 \cdot 5}$$ Factor the numerator and the denominator.

$$= \frac{3 \cdot 5}{2 \cdot 2 \cdot 5}$$ Look for common factors.

$$= \frac{3}{2 \cdot 2} \cdot \frac{5}{5}$$ Common factors in the numerator and denominator form factors of 1.

$$= \frac{3}{2 \cdot 2} \cdot 1$$ Write $\frac{5}{5}$ as 1.

$$= \frac{3}{2 \cdot 2} = \frac{3}{4}$$ Multiply.

Before we use the same technique to simplify a rational expression, remember that as long as the denominator is not 0, $\frac{a^3b}{a^3b} = 1, \frac{x+3}{x+3} = 1, \text{ and } \frac{7x^2 + 5x - 100}{7x^2 + 5x - 100} = 1.$

Simplify: $\frac{x^2 - 9}{x^2 + x - 6}$

$$\frac{x^2 - 9}{x^2 + x - 6} = \frac{(x-3)(x+3)}{(x-2)(x+3)}$$ Factor the numerator and the denominator.

$$= \frac{(x-3)\,(x+3)}{(x-2)\,(x+3)}$$ Look for common factors.

$$= \frac{x-3}{x-2} \cdot \frac{x+3}{x+3}$$

$$= \frac{x-3}{x-2} \cdot 1$$ Write $\frac{x+3}{x+3}$ as 1.

$$= \frac{x-3}{x-2}$$ Multiply.

Just as for numerical fractions, we can use a shortcut notation. Remember that as long as exact factors in both the numerator and denominator are divided out, we are "removing a factor of 1." We will use the following notation to show this:

$$\frac{x^2 - 9}{x^2 + x - 6} = \frac{(x-3)\,(x+3)}{(x-2)\,(x+3)}$$ A factor of 1 is identified by the shading.

$$= \frac{x-3}{x-2}$$ Remove a factor of 1.

Thus, the rational expression $\frac{x^2 - 9}{x^2 + x - 6}$ has the same value as the rational expression $\frac{x - 3}{x - 2}$ for all values of x except 2 and -3. (Remember that when x is 2, the denominator of both rational expressions is 0 and when x is -3, the original rational expression has a denominator of 0.)

As we simplify rational expressions, we will assume that the simplified rational expression is equal to the original rational expression for all real numbers except those for which either denominator is 0. The following steps may be used to simplify rational expressions.

To Simplify a Rational Expression

Step 1: Completely factor the numerator and denominator.

Step 2: Divide out factors common to the numerator and denominator. (This is the same as "removing a factor of 1.")

Example 3 Simplify: $\frac{5x - 5}{x^3 - x^2}$

Solution: To begin, we factor the numerator and denominator if possible. Then we look for common factors.

$$\frac{5x - 5}{x^3 - x^2} = \frac{5(x - 1)}{x^2(x - 1)} = \frac{5}{x^2}$$

Work Practice 3

PRACTICE 3

Simplify: $\frac{x^4 + x^3}{5x + 5}$

Example 4 Simplify: $\frac{x^2 + 8x + 7}{x^2 - 4x - 5}$

Solution: We factor the numerator and denominator and then look for common factors.

$$\frac{x^2 + 8x + 7}{x^2 - 4x - 5} = \frac{(x + 7)(x + 1)}{(x - 5)(x + 1)} = \frac{x + 7}{x - 5}$$

Work Practice 4

PRACTICE 4

Simplify: $\frac{x^2 + 11x + 18}{x^2 + x - 2}$

Example 5 Simplify: $\frac{x^2 + 4x + 4}{x^2 + 2x}$

Solution: We factor the numerator and denominator and then look for common factors.

$$\frac{x^2 + 4x + 4}{x^2 + 2x} = \frac{(x + 2)(x + 2)}{x(x + 2)} = \frac{x + 2}{x}$$

Work Practice 5

PRACTICE 5

Simplify: $\frac{x^2 + 10x + 25}{x^2 + 5x}$

Helpful Hint

When simplifying a rational expression, we look for **common *factors,* not common *terms.***

$$\frac{x \cdot (x + 2)}{x \cdot x} = \frac{x + 2}{x}$$

Common factors. These can be divided out.

$$\frac{x + 2}{x}$$

Common terms. There is no factor of 1 that can be generated.

Answers

3. $\frac{x^3}{5}$ **4.** $\frac{x + 9}{x - 1}$ **5.** $\frac{x + 5}{x}$

✓Concept Check Recall that we can remove only *factors* of 1. Which of the following are *not* true? Explain why.

a. $\frac{3-1}{3+5}$ simplifies to $-\frac{1}{5}$ **b.** $\frac{2x+10}{2}$ simplifies to $x+5$

c. $\frac{37}{72}$ simplifies to $\frac{3}{2}$ **d.** $\frac{2x+3}{2}$ simplifies to $x+3$

PRACTICE 6

Simplify: $\frac{x+5}{x^2-25}$

Example 6 Simplify: $\frac{x+9}{x^2-81}$

Solution: We factor and then divide the numerator and denominator by all common factors.

$$\frac{x+9}{x^2-81} = \frac{x+9}{(x+9)(x-9)} = \frac{1}{x-9}$$

Work Practice 6

PRACTICE 7

Simplify each rational expression.

a. $\frac{x+4}{4+x}$

b. $\frac{x-4}{4-x}$

Example 7 Simplify each rational expression.

a. $\frac{x+y}{y+x}$ **b.** $\frac{x-y}{y-x}$

Solution:

a. The expression $\frac{x+y}{y+x}$ can be simplified by using the commutative property of addition to rewrite the denominator $y+x$ as $x+y$.

$$\frac{x+y}{y+x} = \frac{x+y}{x+y} = 1$$

b. The expression $\frac{x-y}{y-x}$ can be simplified by recognizing that $y-x$ and $x-y$ are opposites. In other words, $y-x=-1(x-y)$. We proceed as follows:

$$\frac{x-y}{y-x} = \frac{1\cdot(x-y)}{(-1)(x-y)} = \frac{1}{-1} = -1$$

Work Practice 7

Objective D Writing Equivalent Forms of Rational Expressions

From Example 7a, we have $y+x=x+y$. $y+x$ and $x+y$ are equivalent.

From Example 7b, we have $y-x=-1(x-y)$. $y-x$ and $x-y$ are opposites.

Thus, $\frac{x+y}{y+x} = \frac{x+y}{x+y} = 1$ and $\frac{x-y}{y-x} = \frac{x-y}{-1(x-y)} = \frac{1}{-1} = -1$.

When performing operations on rational expressions, equivalent forms of answers often result. For this reason, it is very important to be able to recognize equivalent answers.

Answers

6. $\frac{1}{x-5}$ 7. a. 1 b. −1

✓ **Concept Check Answer**

a, c, d

Example 8 List some equivalent forms of $-\frac{5x - 1}{x + 9}$.

Solution: To do so, recall that $-\frac{a}{b} = \frac{-a}{b} = \frac{a}{-b}$. Thus

$$-\frac{5x - 1}{x + 9} = \frac{-(5x - 1)}{x + 9} = \frac{-5x + 1}{x + 9} \quad \text{or} \quad \frac{1 - 5x}{x + 9}$$

Also,

$$-\frac{5x - 1}{x + 9} = \frac{5x - 1}{-(x + 9)} = \frac{5x - 1}{-x - 9} \quad \text{or} \quad \frac{5x - 1}{-9 - x}$$

Thus $-\frac{5x - 1}{x + 9} = \frac{-(5x - 1)}{x + 9} = \frac{-5x + 1}{x + 9} = \frac{5x - 1}{-(x + 9)} = \frac{5x - 1}{-x - 9}$

Work Practice 8

Keep in mind that many rational expressions may look different but in fact are equivalent.

PRACTICE 8

List 4 equivalent forms of $-\frac{3x + 7}{x - 6}$.

Helpful Hint Remember, a negative sign in front of a fraction or rational expression may be moved to the numerator or the denominator, but *not* both.

Answer

8. $\frac{-(3x + 7)}{x - 6}$; $\frac{-3x - 7}{x - 6}$; $\frac{3x + 7}{-(x - 6)}$; $\frac{3x + 7}{-x + 6}$

Vocabulary and Readiness Check

Use the choices below to fill in each blank. Not all choices will be used.

-1	0	simplifying	$\frac{-a}{-b}$	$\frac{-a}{b}$	$\frac{a}{-b}$
1	2	rational expression			

1. A ________________ is an expression that can be written in the form $\frac{P}{Q}$ where P and Q are polynomials and $Q \neq 0$.

2. The expression $\frac{x + 3}{3 + x}$ simplifies to ________________.

3. The expression $\frac{x - 3}{3 - x}$ simplifies to ________________.

4. A rational expression is undefined for values that make the denominator ________________.

5. The expression $\frac{7x}{x - 2}$ is undefined for $x =$ ________________.

6. The process of writing a rational expression in lowest terms is called ________________.

7. For a rational expression, $-\frac{a}{b} =$ ________________ $=$ ________________.

Decide which rational expression can be simplified. (Do not actually simplify.)

8. $\frac{x}{x + 7}$ **9.** $\frac{3 + x}{x + 3}$ **10.** $\frac{5 - x}{x - 5}$ **11.** $\frac{x + 2}{x + 8}$

5.1 Exercise Set

FOR EXTRA HELP

PRACTICE WATCH DOWNLOAD READ REVIEW

Objective A *Find the value of the following expressions when $x = 2$, $y = -2$, and $z = -5$. See Example 1.*

1. $\frac{x + 5}{x + 2}$

2. $\frac{x + 8}{x + 1}$

3. $\frac{y^3}{y^2 - 1}$

4. $\frac{z}{z^2 - 5}$

5. $\frac{x^2 + 8x + 2}{x^2 - x - 6}$

6. $\frac{x + 5}{x^2 + 4x - 8}$

7. The average cost per DVD, in dollars, for a company to produce x DVDs on exercising is given by the formula $A = \frac{3x + 400}{x}$, where A is the average cost per DVD and x is the number of DVDs produced.

a. Find the cost for producing 1 DVD.

b. Find the average cost for producing 100 DVDs.

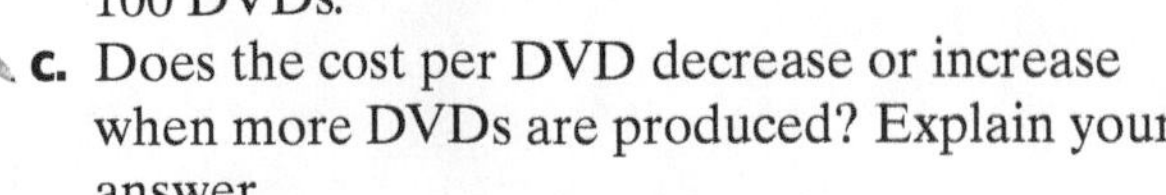

c. Does the cost per DVD decrease or increase when more DVDs are produced? Explain your answer.

8. For a certain model of fax machine, the manufacturing cost C per machine is given by the equation

$$C = \frac{250x + 10{,}000}{x}$$

where x is the number of fax machines manufactured and cost C is in dollars per machine.

a. Find the cost per fax machine when manufacturing 100 fax machines.

b. Find the cost per fax machine when manufacturing 1000 fax machines.

c. Does the cost per machine decrease or increase when more machines are manufactured? Explain why this is so.

Objective B *Find any numbers for which each rational expression is undefined. See Example 2.*

9. $\frac{7}{2x}$

10. $\frac{3}{5x}$

11. $\frac{x+3}{x+2}$

12. $\frac{5x+1}{x-9}$

13. $\frac{x-4}{2x-5}$

14. $\frac{x+1}{5x-2}$

15. $\frac{9x^3+4}{15x^2+30x}$

16. $\frac{19x^3+2}{x^2-x}$

17. $\frac{x^2-5x-2}{4}$

18. $\frac{9y^5+y^3}{9}$

19. $\frac{3x^2+9}{x^2-5x-6}$

20. $\frac{11x^2+1}{x^2-5x-14}$

21. $\frac{x}{3x^2+13x+14}$

22. $\frac{x}{2x^2+15x+27}$

Objective C *Simplify each expression. See Examples 3 through 7.*

23. $\frac{x+7}{7+x}$

24. $\frac{y+9}{9+y}$

25. $\frac{x-7}{7-x}$

26. $\frac{y-9}{9-y}$

27. $\frac{2}{8x+16}$

28. $\frac{3}{9x+6}$

29. $\frac{x-2}{x^2-4}$

30. $\frac{x+5}{x^2-25}$

31. $\frac{2x-10}{3x-30}$

32. $\frac{3x-9}{4x-16}$

33. $\frac{-5a-5b}{a+b}$

34. $\frac{-4x-4y}{x+y}$

35. $\frac{7x+35}{x^2+5x}$

36. $\frac{9x+99}{x^2+11x}$

37. $\frac{x+5}{x^2-4x-45}$

38. $\frac{x-3}{x^2-6x+9}$

39. $\frac{5x^2+11x+2}{x+2}$

40. $\frac{12x^2+4x-1}{2x+1}$

41. $\frac{x^3+7x^2}{x^2+5x-14}$

42. $\frac{x^4-10x^3}{x^2-17x+70}$

43. $\frac{14x^2-21x}{2x-3}$

44. $\frac{4x^2+24x}{x+6}$

45. $\frac{x^2+7x+10}{x^2-3x-10}$

46. $\frac{2x^2+7x-4}{x^2+3x-4}$

47. $\frac{3x^2+7x+2}{3x^2+13x+4}$

48. $\frac{4x^2-4x+1}{2x^2+9x-5}$

49. $\frac{2x^2-8}{4x-8}$

50. $\frac{5x^2-500}{35x+350}$

51. $\frac{4-x^2}{x-2}$

52. $\frac{49-y^2}{y-7}$

53. $\frac{x^2-1}{x^2-2x+1}$

54. $\frac{x^2-16}{x^2-8x+16}$

Simplify each expression. Each exercise contains a four-term polynomial that should be factored by grouping. See Examples 3 through 7.

55. $\frac{x^2+xy+2x+2y}{x+2}$

56. $\frac{ab+ac+b^2+bc}{b+c}$

57. $\frac{5x + 15 - xy - 3y}{2x + 6}$

58. $\frac{xy - 6x + 2y - 12}{y^2 - 6y}$

59. $\frac{2xy + 5x - 2y - 5}{3xy + 4x - 3y - 4}$

60. $\frac{2xy + 2x - 3y - 3}{2xy + 4x - 3y - 6}$

Objective D *Study Example 8. Then list four equivalent forms for each rational expression.*

61. $-\frac{x - 10}{x + 8}$

62. $-\frac{x + 11}{x - 4}$

63. $-\frac{5y - 3}{y - 12}$

64. $-\frac{8y - 1}{y - 15}$

Objectives C D Mixed Practice *Simplify each expression. Then determine whether the given answer is correct. See Examples 3 through 8.*

65. $\frac{9 - x^2}{x - 3}$; Answer: $-3 - x$

66. $\frac{100 - x^2}{x - 10}$; Answer: $-10 - x$

67. $\frac{7 - 34x - 5x^2}{25x^2 - 1}$; Answer: $\frac{x + 7}{-5x - 1}$

68. $\frac{2 - 15x - 8x^2}{64x^2 - 1}$; Answer: $\frac{x + 2}{-8x - 1}$

Review

Perform each indicated operation. See Section R.2.

69. $\frac{1}{3} \cdot \frac{9}{11}$

70. $\frac{5}{27} \cdot \frac{2}{5}$

71. $\frac{1}{3} \div \frac{1}{4}$

72. $\frac{7}{8} \div \frac{1}{2}$

73. $\frac{13}{20} \div \frac{2}{9}$

74. $\frac{8}{15} \div \frac{5}{8}$

Concept Extensions

Which of the following are incorrect and why? See the Concept Check in this section.

75. $\frac{5a - 15}{5}$ simplifies to $a - 3$

76. $\frac{7m - 9}{7}$ simplifies to $m - 9$

77. $\frac{1 + 2}{1 + 3}$ simplifies to $\frac{2}{3}$

78. $\frac{46}{54}$ simplifies to $\frac{6}{5}$

79. Explain how to write a fraction in lowest terms.

80. Explain how to write a rational expression in lowest terms.

81. Explain why the denominator of a fraction or a rational expression must not equal 0.

82. Does $\frac{(x - 3)(x + 3)}{x - 3}$ have the same value as $x + 3$ for all real numbers? Explain why or why not.

83. The dose of medicine prescribed for a child depends on the child's age A in years and the adult dose D for the medication. Young's Rule is a formula used by pediatricians that gives a child's dose C as

$$C = \frac{DA}{A + 12}$$

Suppose that an 8-year-old child needs medication, and the normal adult dose is 1000 mg. What size dose should the child receive?

84. Calculating body-mass index is a way to gauge whether a person should lose weight. Doctors recommend that body-mass index values fall between 19 and 25. The formula for body-mass index B is

$$B = \frac{705w}{h^2}$$

where w is weight in pounds and h is height in inches. Should a 148-pound person who is 5 feet 6 inches tall lose weight?

85. Anthropologists and forensic scientists use a measure called the cephalic index to help classify skulls. The cephalic index of a skull with width W and length L from front to back is given by the formula

$$C = \frac{100W}{L}$$

A long skull has an index value less than 75, a medium skull has an index value between 75 and 85, and a broad skull has an index value over 85. Find the cephalic index of a skull that is 5 inches wide and 6.4 inches long. Classify the skull.

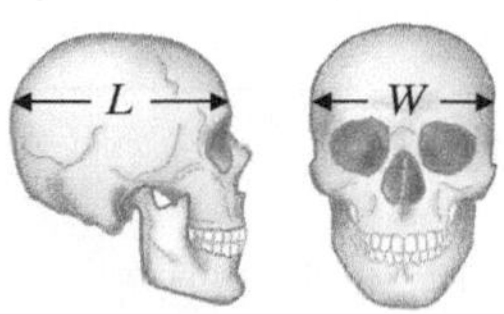

86. A company's gross profit margin P can be computed with the formula $P = \dfrac{R - C}{R}$, where R = the company's revenue and C = cost of goods sold. For the fiscal year 2008, computer company Apple had revenues of $32.5 billion and cost of goods sold $21.3 billion. (*Source:* Apple, Inc.) What was Apple's gross profit margin in 2008? Express the answer as a percent, rounded to the nearest tenth of a percent.

87. A baseball player's slugging percentage S can be calculated with the following formula: $S = \dfrac{h + d + 2t + 3r}{b}$, where h = number of hits, d = number of doubles, t = number of triples, r = number of home runs, and b = number of at bats. In 2008, Albert Pujols of the St. Louis Cardinals led Major League Baseball in slugging percentage. During the 2008 season, Pujols had 524 at bats, 187 hits, 44 doubles, no triples, and 37 home runs. (*Source:* Major League Baseball) Calculate Pujols' 2008 slugging percentage. Round to the nearest tenth of a percent.

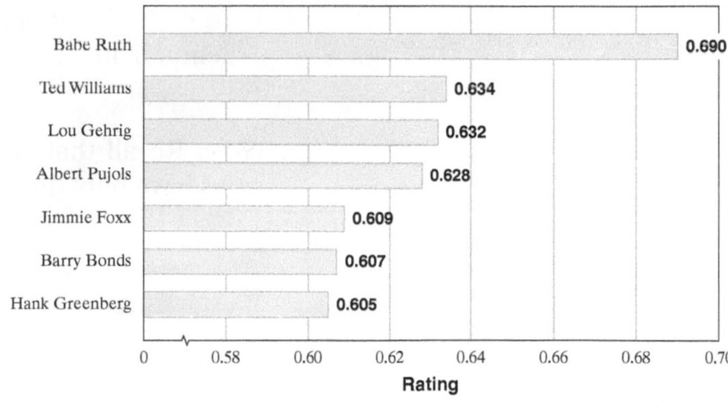

Source: Baseball Almanac

88. To calculate a quarterback's rating in NCAA football, you may use the formula $\dfrac{100C + 330T - 200I + 8.4Y}{A}$, where C = the number of completed passes, A = the number of attempted passes, T = the number of touchdown passes, Y = the number of yards in the completed passes, and I = the number of interceptions. Sam Bradford of the University of Oklahoma was selected as the 2008 winner of the Heisman Memorial Trophy as the Most Outstanding Football Player. Bradford, a sophomore quarterback with the Sooners, ended the season with 442 attempts, 302 completions, 4464 yards, 53 touchdowns, and only 6 interceptions. Calculate Bradford's quarterback rating for the 2008 season. (*Source:* NCAA) Round the answer to the nearest tenth.

Objectives

A Multiply Rational Expressions.

B Divide Rational Expressions.

C Multiply and Divide Rational Expressions.

D Convert Between Units of Measure.

5.2 MULTIPLYING AND DIVIDING RATIONAL EXPRESSIONS

Objective A Multiplying Rational Expressions

Just as simplifying rational expressions is similar to simplifying number fractions, multiplying and dividing rational expressions is similar to multiplying and dividing number fractions.

Fractions	**Rational Expressions**
Multiply: $\frac{3}{5}\cdot\frac{10}{11}$	Multiply: $\frac{x-3}{x+5}\cdot\frac{2x+10}{x^2-9}$

Multiply numerators and then multiply denominators.

$\frac{3}{5}\cdot\frac{10}{11}=\frac{3\cdot 10}{5\cdot 11}$	$\frac{x-3}{x+5}\cdot\frac{2x+10}{x^2-9}=\frac{(x-3)\cdot(2x+10)}{(x+5)\cdot(x^2-9)}$

Simplify by factoring numerators and denominators.

$=\frac{3\cdot 2\cdot 5}{5\cdot 11}$	$=\frac{(x-3)\cdot 2(x+5)}{(x+5)(x+3)(x-3)}$

Divide numerators and denominators by all common factors.

$=\frac{3\cdot 2}{11}$ or $\frac{6}{11}$	$=\frac{2}{x+3}$

Multiplying Rational Expressions

If $\frac{P}{Q}$ and $\frac{R}{S}$ are rational expressions, then

$$\frac{P}{Q}\cdot\frac{R}{S}=\frac{PR}{QS}$$

To multiply rational expressions, multiply the numerators and then multiply the denominators.

Note: Recall that, unless otherwise stated, we assume variables in rational expressions have only those replacement values for which the expressions are defined.

PRACTICE 1

Multiply.

a. $\frac{16y}{3}\cdot\frac{1}{x^2}$

b. $\frac{-5a^3}{3b^3}\cdot\frac{2b^2}{15a}$

Example 1 Multiply.

a. $\frac{25x}{2}\cdot\frac{1}{y^3}$ **b.** $\frac{-7x^2}{5y}\cdot\frac{3y^5}{14x^2}$

Solution: To multiply rational expressions, we first multiply the numerators and then multiply the denominators of both expressions. Then we write the product in lowest terms.

a. $\frac{25x}{2}\cdot\frac{1}{y^3}=\frac{25x\cdot 1}{2\cdot y^3}=\frac{25x}{2y^3}$

The expression $\frac{25x}{2y^3}$ is in lowest terms.

b. $\frac{-7x^2}{5y}\cdot\frac{3y^5}{14x^2}=\frac{-7x^2\cdot 3y^5}{5y\cdot 14x^2}$ Multiply.

Answers

1. a. $\frac{16y}{3x^2}$ b. $-\frac{2a^2}{9b}$

The expression $\frac{-7x^2 \cdot 3y^5}{5y \cdot 14x^2}$ is not in lowest terms, so we factor the numerator and the denominator and "remove factors of 1."

$$= \frac{-1 \cdot 7 \cdot 3 \cdot x^2 \cdot y \cdot y^4}{5 \cdot 2 \cdot 7 \cdot x^2 \cdot y}$$ Common factors in the numerator and denominator form factors of 1.

$$= -\frac{3y^4}{10}$$ Divide out common factors. (This is the same as "removing a factor of 1.")

Work Practice 1

When multiplying rational expressions, it is usually best to factor each numerator and denominator first. This will help us write the product in lowest terms.

Example 2 Multiply: $\frac{x^2 + x}{3x} \cdot \frac{6}{5x + 5}$

Solution:

$$\frac{x^2 + x}{3x} \cdot \frac{6}{5x + 5} = \frac{x(x + 1)}{3x} \cdot \frac{2 \cdot 3}{5(x + 1)}$$ Factor numerators and denominators.

$$= \frac{x(x + 1) \cdot 2 \cdot 3}{3x \cdot 5(x + 1)}$$ Multiply.

$$= \frac{2}{5}$$ Divide out common factors.

Work Practice 2

The following steps may be used to multiply rational expressions.

To Multiply Rational Expressions

Step 1: Completely factor numerators and denominators.

Step 2: Multiply numerators and multiply denominators.

Step 3: Simplify or write the product in lowest terms by dividing out common factors.

✓Concept Check Which of the following is a true statement?

a. $\frac{1}{3} \cdot \frac{1}{2} = \frac{1}{5}$ **b.** $\frac{2}{x} \cdot \frac{5}{x} = \frac{10}{x}$ **c.** $\frac{3}{x} \cdot \frac{1}{2} = \frac{3}{2x}$ **d.** $\frac{x}{7} \cdot \frac{x + 5}{4} = \frac{2x + 5}{28}$

Example 3 Multiply: $\frac{3x + 3}{5x^2 - 5x} \cdot \frac{2x^2 + x - 3}{4x^2 - 9}$

Solution:

$$\frac{3x + 3}{5x^2 - 5x} \cdot \frac{2x^2 + x - 3}{4x^2 - 9} = \frac{3(x + 1)}{5x(x - 1)} \cdot \frac{(2x + 3)(x - 1)}{(2x - 3)(2x + 3)}$$ Factor.

$$= \frac{3(x + 1)(2x + 3)(x - 1)}{5x(x - 1)(2x - 3)(2x + 3)}$$ Multiply.

$$= \frac{3(x + 1)}{5x(2x - 3)}$$ Simplify.

Work Practice 3

PRACTICE 2

Multiply: $\frac{3x + 6}{14} \cdot \frac{7x^2}{x^3 + 2x^2}$

PRACTICE 3

Multiply:

$\frac{4x + 8}{7x^2 - 14x} \cdot \frac{3x^2 - 5x - 2}{9x^2 - 1}$

Answers

2. $\frac{3}{2}$ **3.** $\frac{4(x + 2)}{7x(3x - 1)}$

✓ Concept Check Answer

c

Objective B Dividing Rational Expressions

We can divide by a rational expression in the same way we divide by a number fraction. Recall that to divide by a fraction, we multiply by its reciprocal.

For example, to divide $\frac{3}{2}$ by $\frac{7}{8}$, we multiply $\frac{3}{2}$ by $\frac{8}{7}$.

$$\frac{3}{2} \div \frac{7}{8} = \frac{3}{2} \cdot \frac{8}{7} = \frac{3 \cdot 4 \cdot 2}{2 \cdot 7} = \frac{12}{7}$$

Helpful Hint

Don't forget how to find reciprocals. The reciprocal of $\frac{a}{b}$ is $\frac{b}{a}$, $a \neq 0, b \neq 0$.

Dividing Rational Expressions

If $\frac{P}{Q}$ and $\frac{R}{S}$ are rational expressions and $\frac{R}{S}$ is not 0, then

$$\frac{P}{Q} \div \frac{R}{S} = \frac{P}{Q} \cdot \frac{S}{R} = \frac{PS}{QR}$$

To divide two rational expressions, multiply the first rational expression by the reciprocal of the second rational expression.

PRACTICE 4

Divide: $\frac{7x^2}{6} \div \frac{x}{2y}$

Example 4 Divide: $\frac{3x^3}{40} \div \frac{4x^3}{y^2}$

Solution:

$$\frac{3x^3}{40} \div \frac{4x^3}{y^2} = \frac{3x^3}{40} \cdot \frac{y^2}{4x^3} \quad \text{Multiply by the reciprocal of } \frac{4x^3}{y^2}.$$

$$= \frac{3x^3 \cdot y^2}{160x^3}$$

$$= \frac{3y^2}{160} \quad \text{Simplify.}$$

Work Practice 4

PRACTICE 5

Divide: $\frac{(x-4)^2}{6} \div \frac{3x-12}{2}$

Helpful Hint

Remember, **to Divide by a Rational Expression**, multiply by its reciprocal.

Example 5 Divide: $\frac{(x+2)^2}{10} \div \frac{2x+4}{5}$

Solution:

$$\frac{(x+2)^2}{10} \div \frac{2x+4}{5} = \frac{(x+2)^2}{10} \cdot \frac{5}{2x+4} \quad \text{Multiply by the reciprocal of } \frac{2x+4}{5}.$$

$$= \frac{(x+2)(x+2) \cdot 5}{5 \cdot 2 \cdot 2 \cdot (x+2)} \quad \text{Factor and multiply.}$$

$$= \frac{x+2}{4} \quad \text{Simplify.}$$

Work Practice 5

Answers

4. $\frac{7xy}{3}$ 5. $\frac{x-4}{9}$

Example 6 Divide: $\frac{6x+2}{x^2-1} \div \frac{3x^2+x}{x-1}$

Solution:

$$\frac{6x+2}{x^2-1} \div \frac{3x^2+x}{x-1} = \frac{6x+2}{x^2-1} \cdot \frac{x-1}{3x^2+x}$$ Multiply by the reciprocal.

$$= \frac{2(3x+1)(x-1)}{(x+1)(x-1) \cdot x(3x+1)}$$ Factor and multiply.

$$= \frac{2}{x(x+1)}$$ Simplify.

Work Practice 6

PRACTICE 6

Divide: $\frac{10x+4}{x^2-4} \div \frac{5x^3+2x^2}{x+2}$

Example 7 Divide: $\frac{2x^2-11x+5}{5x-25} \div \frac{4x-2}{10}$

Solution:

$$\frac{2x^2-11x+5}{5x-25} \div \frac{4x-2}{10} = \frac{2x^2-11x+5}{5x-25} \cdot \frac{10}{4x-2}$$ Multiply by the reciprocal.

$$= \frac{(2x-1)(x-5) \cdot 2 \cdot 5}{5(x-5) \cdot 2(2x-1)}$$ Factor and multiply.

$$= \frac{1}{1} \text{ or } 1$$ Simplify.

Work Practice 7

PRACTICE 7

Divide:

$\frac{3x^2-10x+8}{7x-14} \div \frac{9x-12}{21}$

Objective C Multiplying and Dividing Rational Expressions

Let's make sure that we understand the difference between multiplying and dividing rational expressions.

Rational Expressions	
Multiplication	Multiply the numerators and multiply the denominators.
Division	Multiply by the reciprocal of the divisor.

Example 8 Multiply or divide as indicated.

a. $\frac{x-4}{5} \cdot \frac{x}{x-4}$

b. $\frac{x-4}{5} \div \frac{x}{x-4}$

c. $\frac{x^2-4}{2x+6} \cdot \frac{x^2+4x+3}{2-x}$

Solution:

a. $\frac{x-4}{5} \cdot \frac{x}{x-4} = \frac{(x-4) \cdot x}{5 \cdot (x-4)} = \frac{x}{5}$

b. $\frac{x-4}{5} \div \frac{x}{x-4} = \frac{x-4}{5} \cdot \frac{x-4}{x} = \frac{(x-4)^2}{5x}$

c. $\frac{x^2-4}{2x+6} \cdot \frac{x^2+4x+3}{2-x} = \frac{(x-2)(x+2) \cdot (x+1)(x+3)}{2(x+3) \cdot (2-x)}$ Factor and multiply.

Continued on next page

PRACTICE 8

Multiply or divide as indicated.

a. $\frac{x+3}{x} \cdot \frac{7}{x+3}$

b. $\frac{x+3}{x} \div \frac{7}{x+3}$

c. $\frac{3-x}{x^2+6x+5} \cdot \frac{2x+10}{x^2-7x+12}$

Answers

6. $\frac{2}{x^2(x-2)}$ 7. 1

8. a. $\frac{7}{x}$ b. $\frac{(x+3)^2}{7x}$

c. $-\frac{2}{(x+1)(x-4)}$

Recall from Section 5.1 that $x - 2$ and $2 - x$ are opposites. This means that $\frac{x-2}{2-x} = -1$. Thus,

$$\frac{(x-2)(x+2)\cdot(x+1)(x+3)}{2(x+3)\cdot(2-x)} = \frac{-1(x+2)(x+1)}{2}$$
$$= -\frac{(x+2)(x+1)}{2}$$

Work Practice 8

Objective D Converting Between Units of Measure

How many square inches are in 1 square foot?

How many cubic feet are in a cubic yard?

If you have trouble answering these questions, this section will be helpful to you.

Now that we know how to multiply fractions and rational expressions, we can use this knowledge to help us convert between units of measure. To do so, we will use **unit fractions.** A unit fraction is a fraction that equals 1. For example, since 12 in. = 1 ft, we have the unit fractions

$$\frac{12 \text{ in.}}{1 \text{ ft}} = 1 \quad \text{and} \quad \frac{1 \text{ ft}}{12 \text{ in.}} = 1$$

PRACTICE 9

288 square inches = _____ square feet

Example 9 18 square feet = _____ square yards

Solution: Let's multiply 18 square feet by a unit fraction that has square feet in the denominator and square yards in the numerator. From the diagram, you can see that

1 square yard = 9 square feet

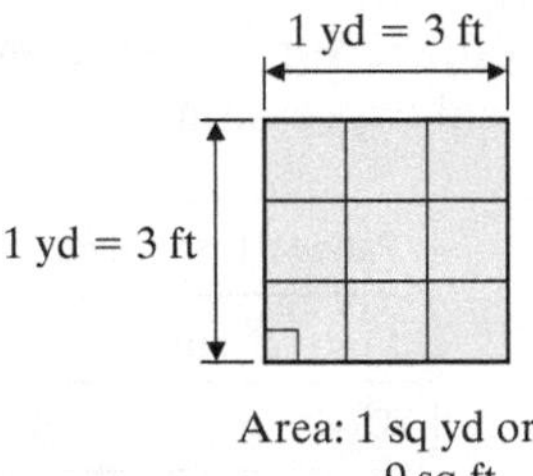

Area: 1 sq yd or 9 sq ft

Thus,

$$18 \text{ sq ft} = \frac{18 \text{ sq ft}}{1} \cdot 1 = \frac{\overset{2}{\cancel{18}} \cancel{\text{sq ft}}}{1} \cdot \frac{1 \text{ sq yd}}{\underset{1}{\cancel{9}} \cancel{\text{sq ft}}}$$
$$= \frac{2 \cdot 1}{1 \cdot 1} \text{ sq yd} = 2 \text{ sq yd}$$

Thus, 18 sq ft = 2 sq yd.

Draw a diagram of 18 sq ft to help you see that this is reasonable.

Work Practice 9

PRACTICE 10

3.5 square feet = _____ square inches

Example 10 5.2 square yards = _____ square feet

Solution:

$$5.2 \text{ sq yd} = \frac{5.2 \text{ sq yd}}{1} \cdot 1 = \frac{5.2 \cancel{\text{sq yd}}}{1} \cdot \frac{9 \text{ sq ft}}{1 \cancel{\text{sq yd}}} \begin{array}{l} \leftarrow \text{Units converting to} \\ \leftarrow \text{Units given} \end{array}$$
$$= \frac{5.2 \cdot 9}{1 \cdot 1} \text{ sq ft}$$
$$= 46.8 \text{ sq ft}$$

Thus, 5.2 sq yd = 46.8 sq ft.

Draw a diagram to see that this is reasonable.

Work Practice 10

Answers

9. 2 sq ft 10. 504 sq in.

Example 11 Converting from Cubic Feet to Cubic Yards

The largest building in the world by volume is The Boeing Company's Everett, Washington, factory complex, where Boeing's wide-body jetliners, the 747, 767, and 777, are built. The volume of this factory complex is 472,370,319 cubic feet. Find the volume of this Boeing facility in cubic yards. (*Source:* The Boeing Company)

PRACTICE 11

The largest casino in the world is the Venetian, in Macau, on the southern tip of China. The gaming area for this casino is approximately 61,000 *square yards*. Find the size of the gaming area in *square feet*. (*Source: USA Today*)

Solution: There are 27 cubic feet in 1 cubic yard. (See the diagram.)

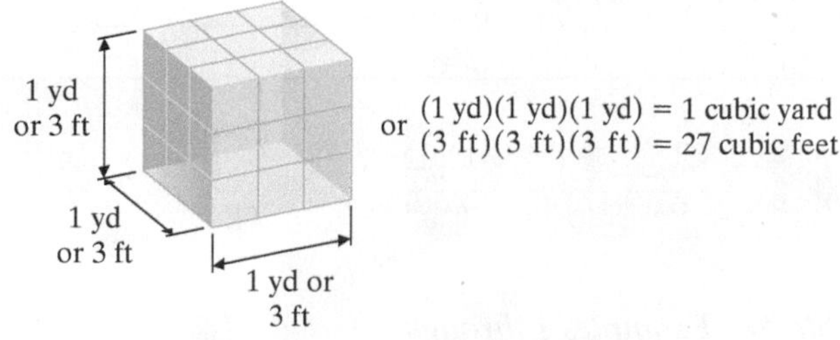

$$\begin{aligned}472{,}370{,}319 \text{ cu ft} &= 472{,}370{,}319 \cancel{\text{cu ft}} \cdot \frac{1 \text{ cu yd}}{27 \cancel{\text{cu ft}}}\\ &= \frac{472{,}370{,}319}{27} \text{ cu yd}\\ &= 17{,}495{,}197 \text{ cu yd}\end{aligned}$$

Work Practice 11

Helpful Hint

When converting among units of measurement, if possible write the unit fraction so that **the numerator contains the units you are converting to** and **the denominator contains the original units.**

$$\begin{aligned}48 \text{ in.} &= \frac{48 \cancel{\text{in.}}}{1} \cdot \overbrace{\frac{1 \text{ ft}}{12 \cancel{\text{in.}}}}^{\text{Unit fraction}} \begin{matrix}\leftarrow \text{Units converting to}\\ \leftarrow \text{Original units}\end{matrix}\\ &= \frac{48}{12} \text{ ft} = 4 \text{ ft}\end{aligned}$$

Example 12

At the 2008 Summer Olympics, Jamaican athlete Usain Bolt won the gold medal in the men's 100-meter track event. He ran the distance at an average speed of 33.9 feet per second. Convert this speed to miles per hour. (*Source:* Beijing 2008 Olympics Committee)

Solution: Recall that 1 mile = 5280 feet and 1 hour = 3600 seconds $(60 \cdot 60)$.

$$\begin{aligned}33.9 \text{ feet/second} &= \frac{33.9 \text{ feet}}{1 \text{ second}} \cdot \overbrace{\frac{3600 \text{ seconds}}{1 \text{ hour}} \cdot \frac{1 \text{ mile}}{5280 \text{ feet}}}^{\text{Unit fractions}}\\ &= \frac{33.9 \cdot 3600}{5280} \text{ miles/hour}\\ &\approx 23.1 \text{ miles/hour (rounded to the nearest tenth)}\end{aligned}$$

Work Practice 12

PRACTICE 12

The cheetah is the fastest land animal, being clocked at about 102.7 feet per second. Convert this to miles per hour. Round to the nearest tenth. (*Source: World Almanac and Book of Facts*)

Answers

11. 549,000 sq ft
12. 70.0 miles per hour

Vocabulary and Readiness Check

Use the choices below to fill in each blank. Not all choices will be used.

opposites $\quad \frac{a \cdot d}{b \cdot c} \quad \frac{a \cdot c}{b \cdot d} \quad \frac{x}{42} \quad \frac{x^2}{42} \quad \frac{2x}{42} \quad \frac{6}{7} \quad \frac{7}{6}$

reciprocals

1. The expressions $\frac{x}{2y}$ and $\frac{2y}{x}$ are called __________.

2. $\frac{a}{b} \cdot \frac{c}{d} =$ __________

3. $\frac{a}{b} \div \frac{c}{d} =$ __________

4. $\frac{x}{7} \cdot \frac{x}{6} =$ __________

5. $\frac{x}{7} \div \frac{x}{6} =$ __________

5.2 Exercise Set

FOR EXTRA HELP

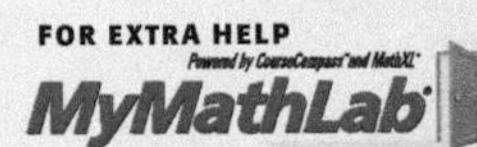

PRACTICE

WATCH

DOWNLOAD

READ

REVIEW

Objective A *Find each product and simplify if possible. See Examples 1 through 3.*

1. $\frac{3x}{y^2} \cdot \frac{7y}{4x}$

2. $\frac{9x^2}{y} \cdot \frac{4y}{3x^3}$

3. $\frac{8x}{2} \cdot \frac{x^5}{4x^2}$

4. $\frac{6x^2}{10x^3} \cdot \frac{5x}{12}$

5. $-\frac{5a^2b}{30a^2b^2} \cdot b^3$

6. $-\frac{9x^3y^2}{18xy^5} \cdot y^3$

7. $\frac{x}{2x - 14} \cdot \frac{x^2 - 7x}{5}$

8. $\frac{4x - 24}{20x} \cdot \frac{5}{x - 6}$

9. $\frac{6x + 6}{5} \cdot \frac{10}{36x + 36}$

10. $\frac{x^2 + x}{8} \cdot \frac{16}{x + 1}$

11. $\frac{(m + n)^2}{m - n} \cdot \frac{m}{m^2 + mn}$

12. $\frac{(m - n)^2}{m + n} \cdot \frac{m}{m^2 - mn}$

13. $\frac{x^2 - 25}{x^2 - 3x - 10} \cdot \frac{x + 2}{x}$

14. $\frac{a^2 - 4a + 4}{a^2 - 4} \cdot \frac{a + 3}{a - 2}$

15. $\frac{x^2 + 6x + 8}{x^2 + x - 20} \cdot \frac{x^2 + 2x - 15}{x^2 + 8x + 16}$

16. $\frac{x^2 + 9x + 20}{x^2 - 15x + 44} \cdot \frac{x^2 - 11x + 28}{x^2 + 12x + 35}$

Objective B *Find each quotient and simplify. See Examples 4 through 7.*

17. $\frac{5x^7}{2x^5} \div \frac{15x}{4x^3}$

18. $\frac{9y^4}{6y} \div \frac{y^2}{3}$

19. $\frac{8x^2}{y^3} \div \frac{4x^2y^3}{6}$

20. $\frac{7a^2b}{3ab^2} \div \frac{21a^2b^2}{14ab}$

21. $\frac{(x - 6)(x + 4)}{4x} \div \frac{2x - 12}{8x^2}$

22. $\frac{(x + 3)^2}{5} \div \frac{5x + 15}{25}$

23. $\frac{3x^2}{x^2 - 1} \div \frac{x^5}{(x + 1)^2}$

24. $\frac{9x^5}{a^2 - b^2} \div \frac{27x^2}{3b - 3a}$

25. $\frac{m^2 - n^2}{m + n} \div \frac{m}{m^2 + nm}$

26. $\frac{(m - n)^2}{m + n} \div \frac{m^2 - mn}{m}$

27. $\frac{x+2}{7-x} \div \frac{x^2-5x+6}{x^2-9x+14}$

28. $\frac{x-3}{2-x} \div \frac{x^2+3x-18}{x^2+2x-8}$

29. $\frac{x^2+7x+10}{x-1} \div \frac{x^2+2x-15}{x-1}$

30. $\frac{x+1}{2x^2+5x+3} \div \frac{20x+100}{2x+3}$

Objective C **Mixed Practice** *Multiply or divide as indicated. See Example 8.*

31. $\frac{5x-10}{12} \div \frac{4x-8}{8}$

32. $\frac{6x+6}{5} \div \frac{9x+9}{10}$

33. $\frac{x^2+5x}{8} \cdot \frac{9}{3x+15}$

34. $\frac{3x^2+12x}{6} \cdot \frac{9}{2x+8}$

35. $\frac{7}{6p^2+q} \div \frac{14}{18p^2+3q}$

36. $\frac{3x+6}{20} \div \frac{4x+8}{8}$

37. $\frac{3x+4y}{x^2+4xy+4y^2} \cdot \frac{x+2y}{2}$

38. $\frac{x^2-y^2}{3x^2+3xy} \cdot \frac{3x^2+6x}{3x^2-2xy-y^2}$

39. $\frac{(x+2)^2}{x-2} \div \frac{x^2-4}{2x-4}$

40. $\frac{x+3}{x^2-9} \div \frac{5x+15}{(x-3)^2}$

41. $\frac{x^2-4}{24x} \div \frac{2-x}{6xy}$

42. $\frac{3y}{3-x} \div \frac{12xy}{x^2-9}$

43. $\frac{a^2+7a+12}{a^2+5a+6} \cdot \frac{a^2+8a+15}{a^2+5a+4}$

44. $\frac{b^2+2b-3}{b^2+b-2} \cdot \frac{b^2-4}{b^2+6b+8}$

45. $\frac{5x-20}{3x^2+x} \cdot \frac{3x^2+13x+4}{x^2-16}$

46. $\frac{9x+18}{4x^2-3x} \cdot \frac{4x^2-11x+6}{x^2-4}$

47. $\frac{8n^2-18}{2n^2-5n+3} \div \frac{6n^2+7n-3}{n^2-9n+8}$

48. $\frac{36n^2-64}{3n^2-10n+8} \div \frac{3n^2-5n-12}{n^2-9n+14}$

Objective D *Convert as indicated. See Examples 9 through 12.*

49. 10 square feet = ________ square inches.

50. 1008 square inches = ________ square feet.

51. 45 square feet = ________ square yards.

52. 2 square yards = ________ square inches.

53. 3 cubic yards = ________ cubic feet.

54. 2 cubic yards = ________ cubic inches.

55. 50 miles per hour = ________ feet per second (round to the nearest whole).

56. 10 feet per second = ________ miles per hour (round to the nearest tenth).

57. 6.3 square yards = ________ square feet.

58. 3.6 square yards = ________ square feet.

59. In January 2010, the Burj Khalifa Tower officially became the tallest building in the world. This tower has a curtain wall (the exterior skin of the building) that is approximately 133,500 square yards. Convert this to square feet. (*Source:* Burj Khalifa)

60. The Pentagon, headquarters for the Department of Defense, contains 3,705,793 square feet of office and storage space. Convert this to square yards. Round to the nearest square yard. (*Source:* U.S. Department of Defense)

61. On October 9, 2007, Russ Wicks set a new stock car world speed record of 359.2 feet/second on the Bonneville Salt Flats in Utah. Convert this speed to miles/hour. Round to the nearest tenth. (*Source:* RussWicks.com)

62. On October 4, 2004, the rocket plane *SpaceShipOne* shot to an altitude of more than 100 km for the second time inside a week to claim the $10 million Ansari X-Prize. At one point in its flight, *SpaceShipOne* was traveling past Mach 1, about 930 miles per hour. Find this speed in feet per second. (*Source:* Space.com)

Review

Perform each indicated operation. See Section R.2.

63. $\frac{1}{5}+\frac{4}{5}$

64. $\frac{3}{15}+\frac{6}{15}$

65. $\frac{9}{9}-\frac{19}{9}$

66. $\frac{4}{3}-\frac{8}{3}$

67. $\frac{6}{5}+\left(\frac{1}{5}-\frac{8}{5}\right)$

68. $-\frac{3}{2}+\left(\frac{1}{2}-\frac{3}{2}\right)$

Concept Extensions

Identify each statement as true or false. If false, correct the multiplication. See the Concept Check in this section.

69. $\frac{4}{a}\cdot\frac{1}{b}=\frac{4}{ab}$

70. $\frac{2}{3}\cdot\frac{2}{4}=\frac{2}{7}$

71. $\frac{x}{5}\cdot\frac{x+3}{4}=\frac{2x+3}{20}$

72. $\frac{7}{a}\cdot\frac{3}{a}=\frac{21}{a}$

73. Find the area of the rectangle.

$\frac{2x}{x^2-25}$ feet

$\frac{x+5}{9x}$ feet

74. Find the area of the square.

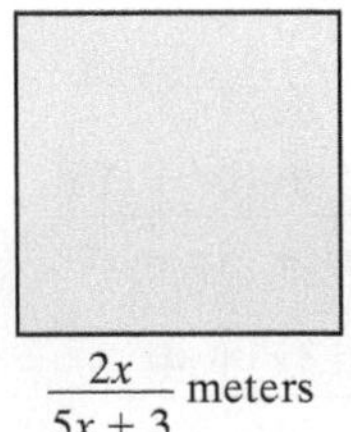

$\frac{2x}{5x+3}$ meters

Multiply or divide as indicated.

75. $\left(\frac{x^2-y^2}{x^2+y^2}\div\frac{x^2-y^2}{3x}\right)\cdot\frac{x^2+y^2}{6}$

76. $\left(\frac{x^2-9}{x^2-1}\cdot\frac{x^2+2x+1}{2x^2+9x+9}\right)\div\frac{2x+3}{1-x}$

77. $\left(\frac{2a+b}{b^2}\cdot\frac{3a^2-2ab}{ab+2b^2}\right)\div\frac{a^2-3ab+2b^2}{5ab-10b^2}$

78. $\left(\frac{x^2y^2-xy}{4x-4y}\div\frac{3y-3x}{8x-8y}\right)\cdot\frac{y-x}{8}$

79. In your own words, explain how you multiply rational expressions.

80. Explain how dividing rational expressions is similar to dividing rational numbers.

81. During a day in 2010, 1 euro was equivalent to 1.3245 American dollars. If you wanted to exchange \$2000 U.S. for euros on that day for a European vacation, how many would you have received? Round to the nearest whole. (*Source:* Barclay's Bank)

82. An environmental technician finds that warm water from an industrial process is being discharged into a nearby pond at a rate of 30 gallons per minute. Plant regulations state that the flow rate should be no more than 0.1 cubic feet per second. Is the flow rate of 30 gallons per minute in violation of the plant regulations? (*Hint:* 1 cubic foot is equivalent to 7.48 gallons.)

5.3 ADDING AND SUBTRACTING RATIONAL EXPRESSIONS WITH THE SAME DENOMINATOR AND LEAST COMMON DENOMINATOR

Objectives

A Add and Subtract Rational Expressions with Common Denominators.

B Find the Least Common Denominator of a List of Rational Expressions.

C Write a Rational Expression as an Equivalent Expression Whose Denominator Is Given.

Objective A Adding and Subtracting Rational Expressions with the Same Denominator

Like multiplication and division, addition and subtraction of rational expressions is similar to addition and subtraction of rational numbers. In this section, we add and subtract rational expressions with a common denominator.

Add: $\frac{6}{5} + \frac{2}{5}$ | Add: $\frac{9}{x+2} + \frac{3}{x+2}$

Add the numerators and place the sum over the common denominator.

$$\frac{6}{5} + \frac{2}{5} = \frac{6+2}{5}$$
$$= \frac{8}{5} \quad \text{Simplify.}$$

$$\frac{9}{x+2} + \frac{3}{x+2} = \frac{9+3}{x+2}$$
$$= \frac{12}{x+2} \quad \text{Simplify.}$$

Adding and Subtracting Rational Expressions with Common Denominators

If $\frac{P}{R}$ and $\frac{Q}{R}$ are rational expressions, then

$$\frac{P}{R} + \frac{Q}{R} = \frac{P+Q}{R} \quad \text{and} \quad \frac{P}{R} - \frac{Q}{R} = \frac{P-Q}{R}$$

To add or subtract rational expressions, add or subtract numerators and place the sum or difference over the common denominator.

Example 1 Add: $\frac{5m}{2n} + \frac{m}{2n}$

Solution:

$$\frac{5m}{2n} + \frac{m}{2n} = \frac{5m+m}{2n} \quad \text{Add the numerators.}$$
$$= \frac{6m}{2n} \quad \text{Simplify the numerator by combining like terms.}$$
$$= \frac{3m}{n} \quad \text{Simplify by dividing out the common factor.}$$

Work Practice 1

PRACTICE 1

Add: $\frac{8x}{3y} + \frac{x}{3y}$

Example 2 Subtract: $\frac{2y}{2y-7} - \frac{7}{2y-7}$

Solution:

$$\frac{2y}{2y-7} - \frac{7}{2y-7} = \frac{2y-7}{2y-7} \quad \text{Subtract the numerators.}$$
$$= \frac{1}{1} \text{ or } 1 \quad \text{Simplify.}$$

Work Practice 2

PRACTICE 2

Subtract: $\frac{3x}{3x-7} - \frac{7}{3x-7}$

Answers

1. $\frac{3x}{y}$ 2. 1

PRACTICE 3

Subtract: $\dfrac{2x^2 + 5x}{x + 2} - \dfrac{4x + 6}{x + 2}$

Example 3 Subtract: $\dfrac{3x^2 + 2x}{x - 1} - \dfrac{10x - 5}{x - 1}$

Solution:

$$\frac{3x^2 + 2x}{x - 1} - \frac{10x - 5}{x - 1} = \frac{3x^2 + 2x - (10x - 5)}{x - 1}$$ Subtract the numerators. Notice the parentheses.

$$= \frac{3x^2 + 2x - 10x + 5}{x - 1}$$ Use the distributive property.

$$= \frac{3x^2 - 8x + 5}{x - 1}$$ Combine like terms.

$$= \frac{(x - 1)(3x - 5)}{x - 1}$$ Factor.

$$= 3x - 5$$ Simplify.

Work Practice 3

Helpful Hint

Notice how the numerator $10x - 5$ was subtracted in Example 3.

This $-$ sign applies to the entire numerator $10x - 5$.

So parentheses are inserted here to indicate this.

$$\frac{3x^2 + 2x}{x - 1} - \frac{10x - 5}{x - 1} = \frac{3x^2 + 2x - (10x - 5)}{x - 1}$$

Objective B Finding the Least Common Denominator

Recall from Section R.2 that to add and subtract fractions with different denominators, we first find the least common denominator (LCD). Then we write all fractions as equivalent fractions with the LCD.

For example, suppose we want to add $\frac{3}{8}$ and $\frac{1}{6}$. To find the LCD of the denominators, factor 8 and 6. Remember, the LCD is the same as the least common multiple, LCM. It is the smallest number that is a multiple of 6 and also 8.

$8 = 2 \cdot 2 \cdot 2$
$6 = 2 \cdot 3$

The LCM is a multiple of 6.

$\text{LCM} = 2 \cdot 2 \cdot 2 \cdot 3 = 24$

The LCM is a multiple of 8.

In the next section, we will continue and find the sum $\frac{3}{8} + \frac{1}{6}$, but for now, let's concentrate on the LCD.

To add or subtract rational expressions with different denominators, we also first find the LCD and then write all rational expressions as equivalent expressions with the LCD. The **least common denominator (LCD) of a list of rational expressions** is a polynomial of least degree whose factors include all the factors of the denominators in the list.

To Find the Least Common Denominator (LCD)

Step 1: Factor each denominator completely.

Step 2: The least common denominator (LCD) is the product of all unique factors found in Step 1, each raised to a power equal to the greatest number of times that the factor appears in any one factored denominator.

Answer

3. $2x - 3$

Example 4 Find the LCD for each pair.

a. $\frac{1}{8}, \frac{3}{22}$ **b.** $\frac{7}{5x}, \frac{6}{15x^2}$

Solution:

a. We start by finding the prime factorization of each denominator.

$8 = 2^3$ and
$22 = 2 \cdot 11$

Next we write the product of all the unique factors, each raised to a power equal to the greatest number of times that the factor appears.

The greatest number of times that the factor 2 appears is 3.
The greatest number of times that the factor 11 appears is 1.

$\text{LCD} = 2^3 \cdot 11^1 = 8 \cdot 11 = 88$

b. We factor each denominator.

$5x = 5 \cdot x$ and
$15x^2 = 3 \cdot 5 \cdot x^2$

The greatest number of times that the factor 5 appears is 1.
The greatest number of times that the factor 3 appears is 1.
The greatest number of times that the factor x appears is 2.

$\text{LCD} = 3^1 \cdot 5^1 \cdot x^2 = 15x^2$

Work Practice 4

PRACTICE 4

Find the LCD for each pair.

a. $\frac{2}{9}, \frac{7}{15}$

b. $\frac{5}{6x^3}, \frac{11}{8x^5}$

Example 5 Find the LCD of $\frac{7x}{x+2}$ and $\frac{5x^2}{x-2}$.

Solution: The denominators $x + 2$ and $x - 2$ are completely factored already. The factor $x + 2$ appears once and the factor $x - 2$ appears once.

$\text{LCD} = (x + 2)(x - 2)$

Work Practice 5

PRACTICE 5

Find the LCD of $\frac{3a}{a+5}$ and $\frac{7a}{a-5}$.

Example 6 Find the LCD of $\frac{6m^2}{3m+15}$ and $\frac{2}{(m+5)^2}$.

Solution: We factor each denominator.

$3m + 15 = 3(m + 5)$

$(m + 5)^2 = (m + 5)^2$ This denominator is already factored.

The greatest number of times that the factor 3 appears is 1.
The greatest number of times that the factor $m + 5$ appears *in any one denominator* is 2.

$\text{LCD} = 3(m + 5)^2$

Work Practice 6

PRACTICE 6

Find the LCD of $\frac{7x^2}{(x-4)^2}$ and $\frac{5x}{3x-12}$.

✓Concept Check Choose the correct LCD of $\frac{x}{(x+1)^2}$ and $\frac{5}{x+1}$.

a. $x + 1$ **b.** $(x + 1)^2$ **c.** $(x + 1)^3$ **d.** $5x(x + 1)^2$

Answers

4. a. 45 **b.** $24x^5$
5. $(a + 5)(a - 5)$ **6.** $3(x - 4)^2$

✓ Concept Check Answer

b

PRACTICE 7

Find the LCD of $\frac{y+5}{y^2+2y-3}$ and $\frac{y+4}{y^2-3y+2}$.

Example 7 Find the LCD of $\frac{t-10}{2t^2+t-6}$ and $\frac{t+5}{t^2+3t+2}$.

Solution:

$2t^2 + t - 6 = (2t-3)(t+2)$

$t^2 + 3t + 2 = (t+1)(t+2)$

$\text{LCD} = (2t-3)(t+2)(t+1)$

Work Practice 7

PRACTICE 8

Find the LCD of $\frac{6}{x-4}$ and $\frac{9}{4-x}$.

Example 8 Find the LCD of $\frac{2}{x-2}$ and $\frac{10}{2-x}$.

Solution: The denominators $x-2$ and $2-x$ are opposites. That is, $2-x = -1(x-2)$. We can use either $x-2$ or $2-x$ as the LCD.

$\text{LCD} = x-2 \quad \text{or} \quad \text{LCD} = 2-x$

Work Practice 8

Objective C Writing Equivalent Rational Expressions

Next we practice writing a rational expression as an equivalent rational expression with a given denominator. To do this, we multiply by a form of 1. Recall that multiplying an expression by 1 produces an equivalent expression. In other words,

$$\frac{P}{Q} = \frac{P}{Q}\cdot 1 = \frac{P}{Q}\cdot\frac{R}{R} = \frac{PR}{QR}$$

PRACTICE 9

Write the rational expression as an equivalent rational expression with the given denominator.

$$\frac{2x}{5y} = \frac{}{20x^2y^2}$$

Example 9 Write each rational expression as an equivalent rational expression with the given denominator.

a. $\frac{4b}{9a} = \frac{}{27a^2b}$ **b.** $\frac{7x}{2x+5} = \frac{}{6x+15}$

Solution:

a. We can ask ourselves: "What do we multiply $9a$ by to get $27a^2b$?" The answer is $3ab$, since $9a(3ab) = 27a^2b$. So we multiply by 1 in the form of $\frac{3ab}{3ab}$.

$$\frac{4b}{9a} = \frac{4b}{9a}\cdot 1 = \frac{4b}{9a}\cdot\frac{3ab}{3ab} = \frac{4b(3ab)}{9a(3ab)} = \frac{12ab^2}{27a^2b}$$

b. First, factor the denominator on the right.

$$\frac{7x}{2x+5} = \frac{}{3(2x+5)}$$

To obtain the denominator on the right from the denominator on the left, we multiply by 1 in the form of $\frac{3}{3}$.

$$\frac{7x}{2x+5} = \frac{7x}{2x+5}\cdot\frac{3}{3} = \frac{7x\cdot 3}{(2x+5)\cdot 3} = \frac{21x}{3(2x+5)}$$

Work Practice 9

Answers

7. $(y+3)(y-1)(y-2)$
8. $x-4$ or $4-x$
9. $\frac{8x^3y}{20x^2y^2}$

Example 10 Write the rational expression as an equivalent rational expression with the given denominator.

$$\frac{5}{x^2 - 4} = \frac{}{(x - 2)(x + 2)(x - 4)}$$

Solution: First we factor the denominator $x^2 - 4$ as $(x - 2)(x + 2)$. If we multiply the original denominator $(x - 2)(x + 2)$ by $x - 4$, the result is the new denominator $(x - 2)(x + 2)(x - 4)$. Thus, we multiply by 1 in the form of $\frac{x - 4}{x - 4}$.

$$\frac{5}{x^2 - 4} = \frac{5}{(x - 2)(x + 2)} = \frac{5}{(x - 2)(x + 2)} \cdot \frac{x - 4}{x - 4}$$

$$= \frac{5(x - 4)}{(x - 2)(x + 2)(x - 4)}$$

$$= \frac{5x - 20}{(x - 2)(x + 2)(x - 4)}$$

Work Practice 10

PRACTICE 10

Write the rational expression as an equivalent rational expression with the given denominator.

$$\frac{3}{x^2 - 25} = \frac{}{(x + 5)(x - 5)(x - 3)}$$

Answer

10. $\frac{3x - 9}{(x + 5)(x - 5)(x - 3)}$

Vocabulary and Readiness Check

Use the choices below to fill in each blank. Not all choices will be used.

$\frac{9}{22}$ $\frac{5}{22}$ $\frac{9}{11}$ $\frac{5}{11}$ $\frac{ac}{b}$ $\frac{a-c}{b}$ $\frac{a+c}{b}$ $\frac{5-6+x}{x}$ $\frac{5-(6+x)}{x}$

1. $\frac{7}{11} + \frac{2}{11} =$ ________
2. $\frac{7}{11} - \frac{2}{11} =$ ________
3. $\frac{a}{b} + \frac{c}{b} =$ ________
4. $\frac{a}{b} - \frac{c}{b} =$ ________
5. $\frac{5}{x} - \frac{6+x}{x} =$ ________

5.3 Exercise Set

FOR EXTRA HELP MyMathLab

PRACTICE WATCH DOWNLOAD READ REVIEW

Objective A *Add or subtract as indicated. Simplify the result if possible. See Examples 1 through 3.*

1. $\frac{a}{13} + \frac{9}{13}$
2. $\frac{x+1}{7} + \frac{6}{7}$
3. $\frac{4m}{3n} + \frac{5m}{3n}$
4. $\frac{3p}{2q} + \frac{11p}{2q}$
5. $\frac{4m}{m-6} - \frac{24}{m-6}$
6. $\frac{8y}{y-2} - \frac{16}{y-2}$
7. $\frac{9}{3+y} + \frac{y+1}{3+y}$
8. $\frac{9}{y+9} + \frac{y-5}{y+9}$
9. $\frac{5x^2+4x}{x-1} - \frac{6x+3}{x-1}$
10. $\frac{x^2+9x}{x+7} - \frac{4x+14}{x+7}$
11. $\frac{4a}{a^2+2a-15} - \frac{12}{a^2+2a-15}$
12. $\frac{3y}{y^2+3y-10} - \frac{6}{y^2+3y-10}$
13. $\frac{2x+3}{x^2-x-30} - \frac{x-2}{x^2-x-30}$
14. $\frac{3x-1}{x^2+5x-6} - \frac{2x-7}{x^2+5x-6}$

Objective B *Find the LCD for each list of rational expressions. See Examples 4 through 8.*

15. $\frac{19}{2x}, \frac{5}{4x^3}$
16. $\frac{17x}{4y^5}, \frac{2}{8y}$
17. $\frac{9}{8x}, \frac{3}{2x+4}$
18. $\frac{1}{6y}, \frac{3x}{4y+12}$
19. $\frac{2}{x+3}, \frac{5}{x-2}$
20. $\frac{-6}{x-1}, \frac{4}{x+5}$

21. $\frac{x}{x+6}, \frac{10}{3x+18}$

22. $\frac{12}{x+5}, \frac{x}{4x+20}$

23. $\frac{8x^2}{(x-6)^2}, \frac{13x}{5x-30}$

24. $\frac{9x^2}{7x-14}, \frac{6x}{(x-2)^2}$

25. $\frac{1}{3x+3}, \frac{8}{2x^2+4x+2}$

26. $\frac{19x+5}{4x-12}, \frac{3}{2x^2-12x+18}$

27. $\frac{5}{x-8}, \frac{3}{8-x}$

28. $\frac{2x+5}{3x-7}, \frac{5}{7-3x}$

29. $\frac{5x+1}{x^2+3x-4}, \frac{3x}{x^2+2x-3}$

30. $\frac{4}{x^2+4x+3}, \frac{4x-2}{x^2+10x+21}$

31. $\frac{2x}{3x^2+4x+1}, \frac{7}{2x^2-x-1}$

32. $\frac{3x}{4x^2+5x+1}, \frac{5}{3x^2-2x-1}$

33. $\frac{1}{x^2-16}, \frac{x+6}{2x^3-8x^2}$

34. $\frac{5}{x^2-25}, \frac{x+9}{3x^3-15x^2}$

Objective C *Rewrite each rational expression as an equivalent rational expression with the given denominator. See Examples 9 and 10.*

35. $\frac{3}{2x} = \frac{}{4x^2}$

36. $\frac{3}{9y^5} = \frac{}{72y^9}$

37. $\frac{6}{3a} = \frac{}{12ab^2}$

38. $\frac{5}{4y^2x} = \frac{}{32y^3x^2}$

39. $\frac{9}{2x+6} = \frac{}{2y(x+3)}$

40. $\frac{4x+1}{3x+6} = \frac{}{3y(x+2)}$

41. $\frac{9a+2}{5a+10} = \frac{}{5b(a+2)}$

42. $\frac{5+y}{2x^2+10} = \frac{}{4(x^2+5)}$

43. $\frac{x}{x^3+6x^2+8x} = \frac{}{x(x+4)(x+2)(x+1)}$

44. $\frac{5x}{x^3+2x^2-3x} = \frac{}{x(x-1)(x-5)(x+3)}$

45. $\frac{9y-1}{15x^2-30} = \frac{}{30x^2-60}$

46. $\frac{6m-5}{3x^2-9} = \frac{}{12x^2-36}$

Mixed Practice (*Sections 5.2, 5.3*) *Perform the indicated operations.*

47. $\frac{5x}{7} + \frac{9x}{7}$

48. $\frac{5x}{7} \cdot \frac{9x}{7}$

49. $\frac{x+3}{4} \div \frac{2x-1}{4}$

50. $\frac{x+3}{4} - \frac{2x-1}{4}$

51. $\frac{x^2}{x-6} - \frac{5x+6}{x-6}$

52. $\frac{-2x}{x^3-8x} + \frac{3x}{x^3-8x}$

53. $\frac{x^2+5x}{x^2-25} \cdot \frac{3x-15}{x^2}$

54. $\frac{-2x}{x^3-8x} \div \frac{3x}{x^3-8x}$

55. $\frac{x^3+7x^2}{3x^3-x^2} \div \frac{5x^2+36x+7}{9x^2-1}$

56. $\frac{12x-6}{x^2+3x} \cdot \frac{4x^2+13x+3}{4x^2-1}$

Review

Perform each indicated operation. See Section R.2.

57. $\frac{2}{3} + \frac{5}{7}$

58. $\frac{9}{10} - \frac{3}{5}$

59. $\frac{2}{6} - \frac{3}{4}$

60. $\frac{11}{15} + \frac{5}{9}$

61. $\frac{1}{12} + \frac{3}{20}$

62. $\frac{7}{30} + \frac{3}{18}$

Concept Extensions

For Exercises 63 and 64, see the Concept Check in this section.

63. Choose the correct LCD of $\frac{11a^3}{4a-20}$ and $\frac{15a^3}{(a-5)^2}$.

a. $4a(a-5)(a+5)$ **b.** $a-5$
c. $(a-5)^2$ **d.** $4(a-5)^2$
e. $(4a-20)(a-5)^2$

64. Choose the correct LCD of $\frac{5}{14x^2}$ and $\frac{y}{6x^3}$.

a. $84x^5$ **b.** $84x^3$
c. $42x^3$ **d.** $42x^5$

For Exercises 65 and 66, an algebra student approaches you with each incorrect solution. Find the error and correct the work shown below.

65. $\frac{2x-6}{x-5} - \frac{x+4}{x-5}$

$= \frac{2x-6-x+4}{x-5}$

$= \frac{x-2}{x-5}$

66. $\frac{x}{x+3} + \frac{2}{x+3}$

$= \frac{x+2}{x+3}$

$= \frac{2}{3}$

67. A square has a side of length $\frac{5}{x-2}$ meters. Express its perimeter as a rational expression.

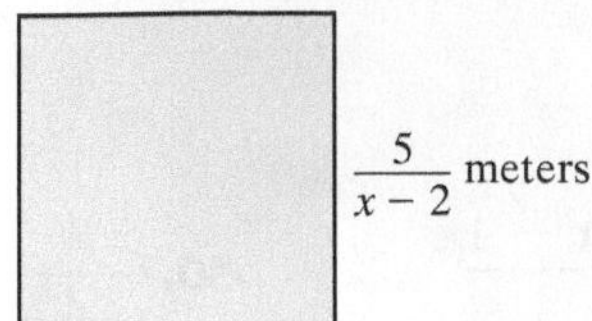

68. A trapezoid has sides of the indicated lengths. Find its perimeter.

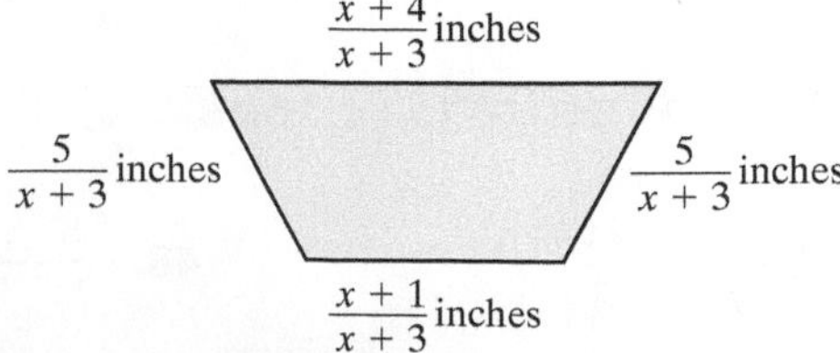

69. Write two rational expressions with the same denominator whose sum is $\frac{5}{3x-1}$.

70. Write two rational expressions with the same denominator whose difference is $\frac{x-7}{x^2+1}$.

71. The planet Mercury revolves around the Sun in 88 Earth days. It takes Jupiter 4332 Earth days to make one revolution around the Sun. (*Source:* National Space Science Data Center) If the two planets are aligned as shown in the figure, how long will it take for them to align again?

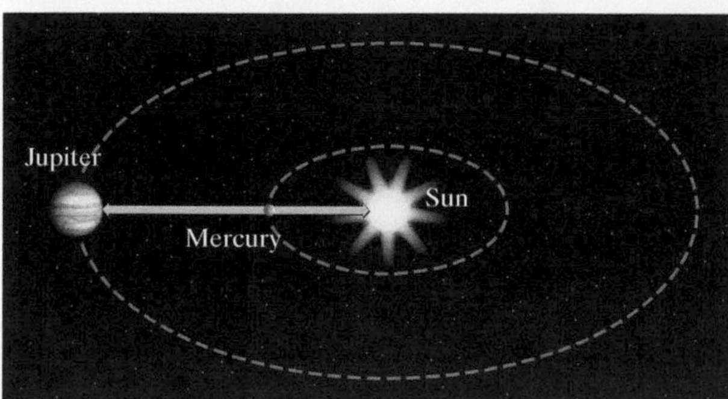

72. You are throwing a barbecue and you want to make sure that you purchase the same number of hot dogs as hot dog buns. Hot dogs come 8 to a package and hot dog buns come 12 to a package. What is the least number of each type of package you should buy?

73. Write some instructions to help a friend who is having difficulty finding the LCD of two rational expressions.

74. In your own words, describe how to add or subtract two rational expressions with the same denominator.

75. Explain why the LCD of the rational expressions $\frac{7}{x+1}$ and $\frac{9x}{(x+1)^2}$ is $(x+1)^2$ and not $(x+1)^3$.

76. Explain the similarities between subtracting $\frac{3}{8}$ from $\frac{7}{8}$ and subtracting $\frac{6}{x+3}$ from $\frac{9}{x+3}$.

5.6 PROPORTIONS AND PROBLEM SOLVING WITH RATIONAL EQUATIONS

Objectives

A Solve Proportions.

B Use Proportions to Solve Problems, Including Similar Triangle Problems.

C Solve Problems about Numbers.

D Solve Problems about Work.

E Solve Problems about Distance.

Objective A Solving Proportions

A **ratio** is the quotient of two numbers or two quantities. For example, the ratio of 2 to 5 can be written in fraction form as $\frac{2}{5}$, the quotient of 2 and 5.

A **rate** is a special type of ratio with different kinds of measurement. For example, the ratio "110 miles in 2 hours" written as a fraction in simplest form is $\frac{110 \text{ miles}}{2 \text{ hours}} = \frac{55 \text{ mi}}{1 \text{ hr}}$ or 55 mph.

If two ratios are equal, we say the ratios are **in proportion** to each other. A **proportion** is a mathematical statement that two ratios are equal.

For example, the equation $\frac{1}{2} = \frac{4}{8}$ is a proportion, as is $\frac{x}{5} = \frac{8}{10}$, because both sides of the equations are ratios. When we want to emphasize the equation as a proportion, we

read the proportion $\frac{1}{2} = \frac{4}{8}$ as "one is to two as four is to eight"

In a proportion, cross products are equal. To understand cross products, let's start with the proportion

$$\frac{a}{b} = \frac{c}{d}$$

and multiply both sides by the LCD, bd.

$$bd\left(\frac{a}{b}\right) = bd\left(\frac{c}{d}\right) \quad \text{Multiply both sides by the LCD, } bd.$$

$$\underbrace{ad}_{\text{Cross product}} = \underbrace{bc}_{\text{Cross product}} \quad \text{Simplify.}$$

Notice why ad and bc are called cross products.

ad $\qquad$ bc

$$\frac{a}{b} = \frac{c}{d}$$

Cross Products

If $\frac{a}{b} = \frac{c}{d}$, then $ad = bc$.

For example, if

$\frac{1}{2} = \frac{4}{8}$, then $1 \cdot 8 = 2 \cdot 4$ or $8 = 8$

Notice that a proportion contains four numbers (or expressions). If any three numbers are known, we can solve and find the fourth number.

PRACTICE 1

Solve for x: $\frac{3}{8} = \frac{63}{x}$

Example 1 Solve for x: $\frac{45}{x} = \frac{5}{7}$

Solution: This is an equation with rational expressions, and also a proportion. Below are two ways to solve.

Since this is a rational equation, we can use the methods of the previous section.

$$\frac{45}{x} = \frac{5}{7}$$

$$7x \cdot \frac{45}{x} = 7x \cdot \frac{5}{7}$$ Multiply both sides by LCD, $7x$.

$$7 \cdot 45 = x \cdot 5$$ Divide out common factors.

$$315 = 5x$$ Multiply.

$$\frac{315}{5} = \frac{5x}{5}$$ Divide both sides by 5.

$$63 = x$$ Simplify.

Since this is also a proportion, we may set cross products equal.

$$\frac{45}{x} = \frac{5}{7}$$

$$45 \cdot 7 = x \cdot 5$$ Set cross products equal.

$$315 = 5x$$ Multiply.

$$\frac{315}{5} = \frac{5x}{5}$$ Divide both sides by 5.

$$63 = x$$ Simplify.

Check: Both methods give us a solution of 63. To check, substitute 63 for x in the original proportion. The solution is 63.

Work Practice 1

In this section, if the rational equation is a proportion, we will use cross products to solve.

PRACTICE 2

Solve for x: $\frac{2x+1}{7} = \frac{x-3}{5}$

Example 2 Solve for x: $\frac{x-5}{3} = \frac{x+2}{5}$

Solution:

$$\frac{x-5}{3} = \frac{x+2}{5}$$

$$5(x-5) = 3(x+2)$$ Set cross products equal.

$$5x - 25 = 3x + 6$$ Multiply.

$$5x = 3x + 31$$ Add 25 to both sides.

$$2x = 31$$ Subtract $3x$ from both sides.

$$\frac{2x}{2} = \frac{31}{2}$$ Divide both sides by 2.

$$x = \frac{31}{2}$$

Check: Verify that $\frac{31}{2}$ is the solution.

Work Practice 2

Objective B Using Proportions to Solve Problems

Proportions can be used to model and solve many real-life problems. When using proportions in this way, it is important to judge whether the solution is reasonable. Doing so helps us to decide if the proportion has been formed correctly. We use the same problem-solving steps that were introduced in Section 2.4.

Answers

1. $x = 168$ 2. $x = -\frac{26}{3}$

Example 3 Calculating the Cost of Recordable Compact Discs

Three boxes of CD-Rs (recordable compact discs) cost \$37.47. How much should 5 boxes cost?

Solution:

1. UNDERSTAND. Read and reread the problem. We know that the cost of 5 boxes is more than the cost of 3 boxes, or \$37.47, and less than the cost of 6 boxes, which is double the cost of 3 boxes, or 2(\$37.47) = \$74.94. Let's suppose that 5 boxes cost \$60.00. To check, we see if 3 boxes is to 5 boxes as the *price* of 3 boxes is to the *price* of 5 boxes. In other words, we see if

$$\frac{\text{3 boxes}}{\text{5 boxes}} = \frac{\text{price of 3 boxes}}{\text{price of 5 boxes}}$$

or

$$\frac{3}{5} = \frac{37.47}{60.00}$$

$$3(60.00) = 5(37.47)$$ Set cross products equal.

or

$$180.00 = 187.35$$ Not a true statement.

Thus, \$60 is not correct, but we now have a better understanding of the problem.

Let x = price of 5 boxes of CD-Rs.

2. TRANSLATE.

$$\frac{\text{3 boxes}}{\text{5 boxes}} = \frac{\text{price of 3 boxes}}{\text{price of 5 boxes}}$$

$$\frac{3}{5} = \frac{37.47}{x}$$

3. SOLVE.

$$\frac{3}{5} = \frac{37.47}{x}$$

$$3x = 5(37.47)$$ Set cross products equal.

$$3x = 187.35$$

$$x = 62.45$$ Divide both sides by 3.

4. INTERPRET.

Check: Verify that 3 boxes is to 5 boxes as \$37.47 is to \$62.45. Also, notice that our solution is a reasonable one as discussed in Step 1.

State: Five boxes of CD-Rs cost \$62.45.

Work Practice 3

PRACTICE 3

To estimate the number of people in Jackson, population 50,000, who have a flu shot, 250 people were polled. Of those polled, 26 had a flu shot. How many people in the city might we expect to have a flu shot?

Answer

3. 5200 people

Helpful Hint

The proportion $\frac{5 \text{ boxes}}{3 \text{ boxes}} = \frac{\text{price of 5 boxes}}{\text{price of 3 boxes}}$ could also have been used to solve Example 3. Notice that the cross products are the same.

Similar triangles have the same shape but not necessarily the same size. In similar triangles, the measures of corresponding angles are equal, and corresponding sides are in proportion.

If triangle ABC and triangle XYZ shown are similar, then we know that the measure of angle A = the measure of angle X, the measure of angle B = the measure of angle Y, and the measure of angle C = the measure of angle Z. We also know that corresponding sides are in proportion: $\frac{a}{x} = \frac{b}{y} = \frac{c}{z}$.

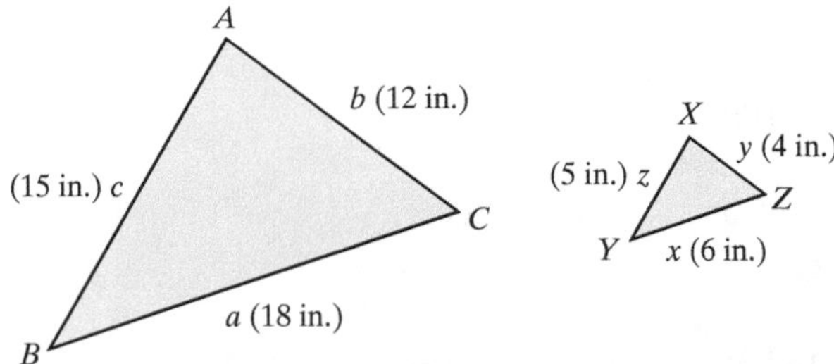

In this section, we will position similar triangles so that they have the same orientation.

To show that corresponding sides are in proportion for the triangles above, we write the ratios of the corresponding sides.

$$\frac{a}{x} = \frac{18}{6} = 3 \quad \frac{b}{y} = \frac{12}{4} = 3 \quad \frac{c}{z} = \frac{15}{5} = 3$$

PRACTICE 4

For the similar triangles, find x.

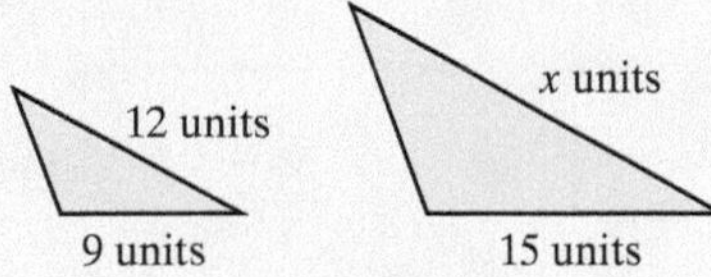

Example 4 Finding the Length of a Side of a Triangle

If the following two triangles are similar, find the missing length x.

2 yards | 10 yards | 3 yards | x yards

Solution:

1. UNDERSTAND. Read the problem and study the figure.
2. TRANSLATE. Since the triangles are similar, their corresponding sides are in proportion and we have

$$\frac{2}{3} = \frac{10}{x}$$

3. SOLVE. To solve, we multiply both sides by the LCD, $3x$, or cross multiply.

$$2x = 30$$

$$x = 15 \quad \text{Divide both sides by 2.}$$

4. INTERPRET.

Check: To check, replace x with 15 in the original proportion and see that a true statement results.

State: The missing length is 15 yards.

Work Practice 4

Answer

4. 20 units

Objective C Solving Problems about Numbers

Let's continue to solve problems. The remaining problems are all modeled by rational equations.

Example 5 Finding an Unknown Number

The quotient of a number and 6, minus $\frac{5}{3}$, is the quotient of the number and 2. Find the number.

Solution:

1. UNDERSTAND. Read and reread the problem. Suppose that the unknown number is 2; then we see if the quotient of 2 and 6, or $\frac{2}{6}$, minus $\frac{5}{3}$ is equal to the quotient of 2 and 2, or $\frac{2}{2}$.

   $\frac{2}{6} - \frac{5}{3} = \frac{1}{3} - \frac{5}{3} = -\frac{4}{3}$, not $\frac{2}{2}$

   Don't forget that the purpose of a proposed solution is to better understand the problem.

   Let $x =$ the unknown number.

2. TRANSLATE.

In words:	the quotient of x and 6	minus	$\frac{5}{3}$	is	the quotient of x and 2
	↓	↓	↓	↓	↓
Translate:	$\frac{x}{6}$	$-$	$\frac{5}{3}$	$=$	$\frac{x}{2}$

3. SOLVE. Here, we solve the equation $\frac{x}{6} - \frac{5}{3} = \frac{x}{2}$. We begin by multiplying both sides of the equation by the LCD, 6.

$$6\left(\frac{x}{6} - \frac{5}{3}\right) = 6\left(\frac{x}{2}\right)$$

$$6\left(\frac{x}{6}\right) - 6\left(\frac{5}{3}\right) = 6\left(\frac{x}{2}\right) \quad \text{Apply the distributive property.}$$

$$x - 10 = 3x \quad \text{Simplify.}$$

$$-10 = 2x \quad \text{Subtract } x \text{ from both sides.}$$

$$\frac{-10}{2} = \frac{2x}{2} \quad \text{Divide both sides by 2.}$$

$$-5 = x \quad \text{Simplify.}$$

4. INTERPRET.

Check: To check, we verify that "the quotient of -5 and 6 minus $\frac{5}{3}$ is the quotient of -5 and 2," or $-\frac{5}{6} - \frac{5}{3} = -\frac{5}{2}$.

State: The unknown number is -5.

Work Practice 5

PRACTICE 5

The quotient of a number and 2, minus $\frac{1}{3}$, is the quotient of the number and 6. Find the number.

Answer

5. 1

Objective D Solving Problems about Work

The next example is often called a work problem. Work problems usually involve people or machines doing a certain task.

PRACTICE 6

Andrew and Timothy Larson volunteer at a local recycling plant. Andrew can sort a batch of recyclables in 2 hours alone while his brother Timothy needs 3 hours to complete the same job. If they work together, how long will it take them to sort one batch?

Example 6 Finding Work Rates

Sam Waterton and Frank Schaffer work in a plant that manufactures automobiles. Sam can complete a quality control tour of the plant in 3 hours while his assistant, Frank, needs 7 hours to complete the same job. The regional manager is coming to inspect the plant facilities, so both Sam and Frank are directed to complete a quality control tour together. How long will this take?

Solution:

1. UNDERSTAND. Read and reread the problem. The key idea here is the relationship between the **time** (hours) it takes to complete the job and the **part of the job** completed in 1 unit of time (hour). For example, if the **time** it takes Sam to complete the job is 3 hours, the **part of the job** he can complete in 1 hour is $\frac{1}{3}$. Similarly, Frank can complete $\frac{1}{7}$ of the job in 1 hour.

   Let $x =$ the **time** in hours it takes Sam and Frank to complete the job together.

   Then $\frac{1}{x} =$ the **part of the job** they complete in 1 hour.

	Hours to Complete Total Job	Part of Job Completed in 1 Hour
Sam	3	$\frac{1}{3}$
Frank	7	$\frac{1}{7}$
Together	x	$\frac{1}{x}$

2. TRANSLATE.

In words:	part of job Sam completes in 1 hour	added to	part of job Frank completes in 1 hour	is equal to	part of job they complete together in 1 hour
	↓	↓	↓	↓	↓
Translate:	$\frac{1}{3}$	+	$\frac{1}{7}$	=	$\frac{1}{x}$

3. SOLVE. Here, we solve the equation $\frac{1}{3} + \frac{1}{7} = \frac{1}{x}$. We begin by multiplying both sides of the equation by the LCD, $21x$.

$$21x\left(\frac{1}{3}\right) + 21x\left(\frac{1}{7}\right) = 21x\left(\frac{1}{x}\right)$$

$$7x + 3x = 21 \quad \text{Simplify.}$$

$$10x = 21$$

$$x = \frac{21}{10} \text{ or } 2\frac{1}{10} \text{ hours}$$

Answer

6. $1\frac{1}{5}$ hours

4. INTERPRET.

Check: Our proposed solution is $2\frac{1}{10}$ hours. This proposed solution is reasonable since $2\frac{1}{10}$ hours is more than half of Sam's time and less than half of Frank's time. Check this solution in the originally *stated* problem.

State: Sam and Frank can complete the quality control tour in $2\frac{1}{10}$ hours.

Work Practice 6

✓Concept Check Solve $E = mc^2$

a. for m **b.** for c^2

Objective E Solving Problems about Distance

Next we look at a problem solved by the distance formula,

$$d = r \cdot t$$

Example 7 Finding Speeds of Vehicles

A car travels 180 miles in the same time that a truck travels 120 miles. If the car's speed is 20 miles per hour faster than the truck's, find the car's speed and the truck's speed.

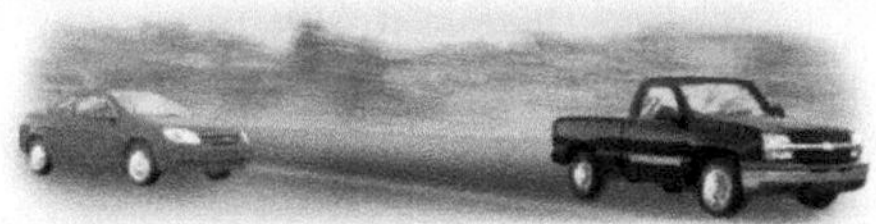

Solution:

1. UNDERSTAND. Read and reread the problem. Suppose that the truck's speed is 45 miles per hour. Then the car's speed is 20 miles per hour more, or 65 miles per hour.

We are given that the car travels 180 miles in the same time that the truck travels 120 miles. To find the time it takes the car to travel 180 miles, remember that since $d = rt$, we know that $\frac{d}{r} = t$.

Car's Time

$$t = \frac{d}{r} = \frac{180}{65} = 2\frac{50}{65} = 2\frac{10}{13} \text{ hours}$$

Truck's Time

$$t = \frac{d}{r} = \frac{120}{45} = 2\frac{30}{45} = 2\frac{2}{3} \text{ hours}$$

Since the times are not the same, our proposed solution is not correct. But we have a better understanding of the problem.

Let $x =$ the speed of the truck.

Since the car's speed is 20 miles per hour faster than the truck's, then

$x + 20 =$ the speed of the car

Use the formula $d = r \cdot t$ or **d**istance = **r**ate · **t**ime. Prepare a chart to organize the information in the problem.

	Distance	=	Rate	·	Time
Truck	120		x		$\frac{120}{x}$ ← distance / ← rate
Car	180		$x + 20$		$\frac{180}{x + 20}$ ← distance / ← rate

Helpful Hint

If $d = r \cdot t$,

then $t = \frac{d}{r}$

or $time = \frac{distance}{rate}$.

PRACTICE 7

A car travels 600 miles in the same time that a motorcycle travels 450 miles. If the car's speed is 15 miles per hour more than the motorcycle's, find the speed of the car and the speed of the motorcycle.

Answer

7. car: 60 mph; motorcycle: 45 mph

✓ Concept Check Answers

a. $m = \frac{E}{c^2}$ **b.** $c^2 = \frac{E}{m}$

Continued on next page

2. TRANSLATE. Since the car and the truck traveled the same amount of time, we have that

In words: car's time = truck's time

$$\downarrow \qquad \downarrow$$

Translate: $\dfrac{180}{x+20} = \dfrac{120}{x}$

3. SOLVE. We begin by setting cross products equal.

$$\frac{180}{x+20} = \frac{120}{x}$$

$$180x = 120(x + 20)$$

$$180x = 120x + 2400 \quad \text{Use the distributive property.}$$

$$60x = 2400 \quad \text{Subtract } 120x \text{ from both sides.}$$

$$x = 40 \quad \text{Divide both sides by 60.}$$

4. INTERPRET. The speed of the truck is 40 miles per hour. The speed of the car must then be $x + 20$ or 60 miles per hour.

Check: Find the time it takes the car to travel 180 miles and the time it takes the truck to travel 120 miles.

Car's Time

$$t = \frac{d}{r} = \frac{180}{60} = 3 \text{ hours}$$

Truck's Time

$$t = \frac{d}{r} = \frac{120}{40} = 3 \text{ hours}$$

Since both travel the same amount of time, the proposed solution is correct.

State: The car's speed is 60 miles per hour and the truck's speed is 40 miles per hour.

Work Practice 7

Vocabulary and Readiness Check

Without solving algebraically, select the best choice for each exercise.

1. One person can complete a job in 7 hours. A second person can complete the same job in 5 hours. How long will it take them to complete the job if they work together?

a. more than 7 hours
b. between 5 and 7 hours
c. less than 5 hours

2. One inlet pipe can fill a pond in 30 hours. A second inlet pipe can fill the same pond in 25 hours. How long before the pond is filled if both inlet pipes are on?

a. less than 25 hours
b. between 25 and 30 hours
c. more than 30 hours

Given the variable in the first column, use the phrase in the second column to translate to an expression, and then continue to the phrase in the third column to translate to another expression.

3.	A number: x	The reciprocal of the number:	The reciprocal of the number, decreased by 3:
4.	A number: y	The reciprocal of the number:	The reciprocal of the number, increased by 2:
5.	A number: z	The sum of the number and 5:	The reciprocal of the sum of the number and 5:
6.	A number: x	The difference of the number and 1:	The reciprocal of the difference of the number and 1:
7.	A number: y	Twice the number:	Eleven divided by twice the number:
8.	A number: z	Triple the number:	Negative ten divided by triple the number:

5.6 Exercise set

FOR EXTRA HELP

PRACTICE

WATCH

DOWNLOAD

READ

REVIEW

Objective A *Solve each proportion. See Examples 1 and 2.*

1. $\frac{2}{3} = \frac{x}{6}$

2. $\frac{x}{2} = \frac{16}{6}$

3. $\frac{x}{10} = \frac{5}{9}$

4. $\frac{9}{4x} = \frac{6}{2}$

5. $\frac{x + 1}{2x + 3} = \frac{2}{3}$

6. $\frac{x + 1}{x + 2} = \frac{5}{3}$

7. $\frac{9}{5} = \frac{12}{3x + 2}$

8. $\frac{6}{11} = \frac{27}{3x - 2}$

Objective B *Solve. See Example 3.*

9. The ratio of the weight of an object on Earth to the weight of the same object on Pluto is 100 to 3. If an elephant weighs 4100 pounds on Earth, find the elephant's weight on Pluto.

10. If a 170-pound person weighs approximately 65 pounds on Mars, about how much does a 9000-pound satellite weigh? Round your answer to the nearest pound.

11. There are 110 calories per 28.4 grams of Crispy Rice cereal. Find how many calories are in 42.6 grams of this cereal.

12. On an architect's blueprint, 1 inch corresponds to 4 feet. Find the length of a wall represented by a line that is $3\frac{7}{8}$ inches long on the blueprint.

Find the unknown length x or y in the following pairs of similar triangles. See Example 4.

13.

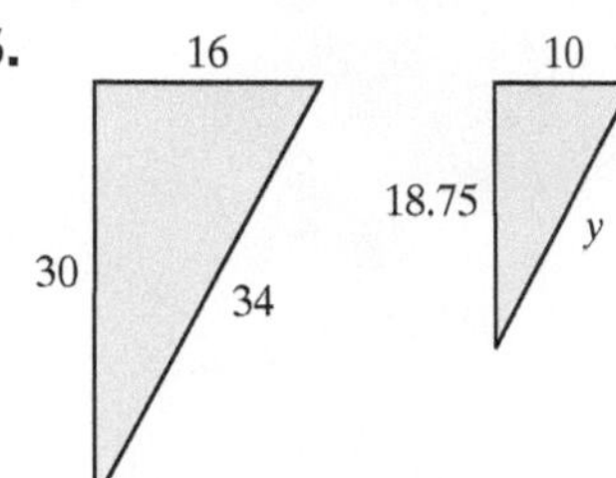

14.

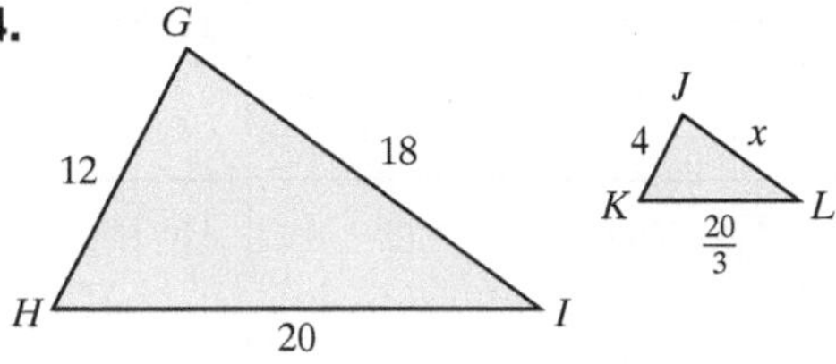

15.

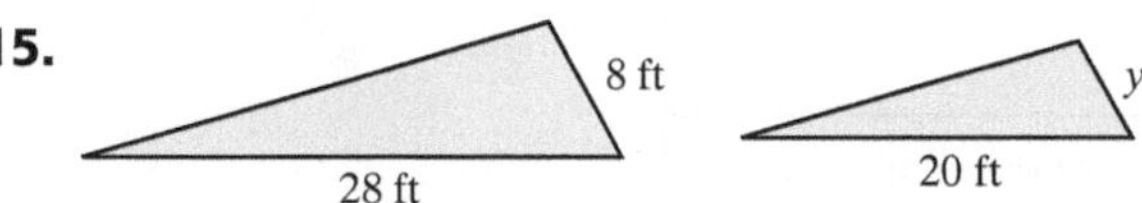

16.

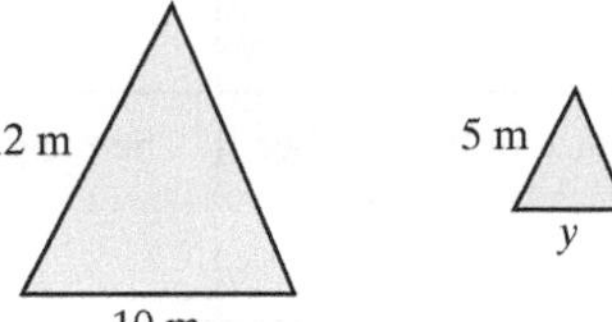

Objective C *Solve the following. See Example 5.*

17. Three times the reciprocal of a number equals 9 times the reciprocal of 6. Find the number.

18. Twelve divided by the sum of x and 2 equals the quotient of 4 and the difference of x and 2. Find x.

19. If twice a number added to 3 is divided by the number plus 1, the result is three halves. Find the number.

20. A number added to the product of 6 and the reciprocal of the number equals -5. Find the number.

Objective D *See Example 6.*

21. Smith Engineering found that an experienced surveyor surveys a roadbed in 4 hours. An apprentice surveyor needs 5 hours to survey the same stretch of road. If the two work together, find how long it takes them to complete the job.

22. An experienced bricklayer constructs a small wall in 3 hours. The apprentice completes the job in 6 hours. Find how long it takes if they work together.

23. In 2 minutes, a conveyor belt moves 300 pounds of recyclable aluminum from the delivery truck to a storage area. A smaller belt moves the same quantity of cans the same distance in 6 minutes. If both belts are used, find how long it takes to move the cans to the storage area.

24. Find how long it takes the conveyor belts described in Exercise 23 to move 1200 pounds of cans. (*Hint:* Think of 1200 pounds as four 300-pound jobs.)

Objective E *See Example 7.*

25. A jogger begins her workout by jogging to the park, a distance of 12 miles. She then jogs home at the same speed but along a different route. This return trip is 18 miles and her time is one hour longer. Find her jogging speed. Complete the accompanying chart and use it to find her jogging speed.

	Distance	=	Rate	·	Time
Trip to Park	12				
Return Trip	18				

26. A boat can travel 9 miles upstream in the same amount of time it takes to travel 11 miles downstream. If the current of the river is 3 miles per hour, complete the chart below and use it to find the speed of the boat in still water.

	Distance	=	Rate	·	Time
Upstream	9		$r - 3$		
Downstream	11		$r + 3$		

27. A cyclist rode the first 20-mile portion of his workout at a constant speed. For the 16-mile cooldown portion of his workout, he reduced his speed by 2 miles per hour. Each portion of the workout took the same time. Find the cyclist's speed during the first portion and find his speed during the cooldown portion.

28. A semi-truck travels 300 miles through the flatland in the same amount of time that it travels 180 miles through mountains. The rate of the truck is 20 miles per hour slower in the mountains than in the flatland. Find both the flatland rate and mountain rate.

Objectives A B C D E **Mixed Practice** *Solve the following. See Examples 1 through 7. (Note: Some exercises can be modeled by equations without rational expressions.)*

29. A human factors expert recommends that there be at least 9 square feet of floor space in a college classroom for every student in the class. Find the minimum floor space that 40 students need.

30. Due to space problems at a local university, a 20-foot by 12-foot conference room is converted into a classroom. Find the maximum number of students the room can accommodate. (See Exercise 29.)

31. One-fourth equals the quotient of a number and 8. Find the number.

32. Four times a number added to 5 is divided by 6. The result is $\frac{7}{2}$. Find the number.

33. Marcus and Tony work for Lombardo's Pipe and Concrete. Mr. Lombardo is preparing an estimate for a customer. He knows that Marcus lays a slab of concrete in 6 hours. Tony lays the same size slab in 4 hours. If both work on the job and the cost of labor is \$45.00 per hour, decide what the labor estimate should be.

34. Mr. Dodson can paint his house by himself in 4 days. His son needs an additional day to complete the job if he works by himself. If they work together, find how long it takes to paint the house.

35. A pilot can travel 400 miles with the wind in the same amount of time as 336 miles against the wind. Find the speed of the wind if the pilot's speed in still air is 230 miles per hour.

36. A fisherman on Pearl River rows 9 miles downstream in the same amount of time he rows 3 miles upstream. If the current is 6 miles per hour, find how long it takes him to cover the 12 miles.

37. Find the unknown length y.

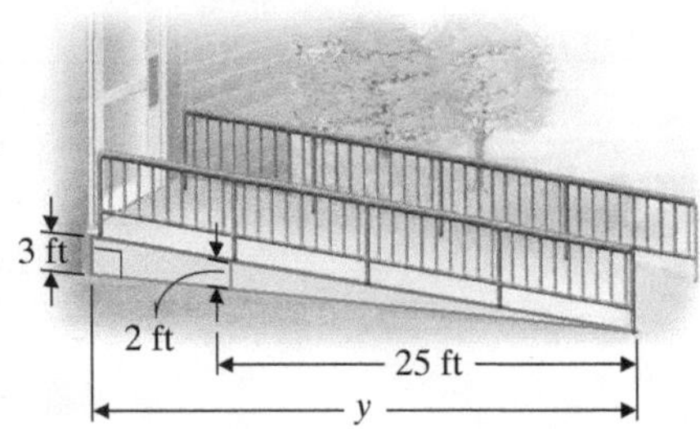

△ **38.** Find the unknown length y.

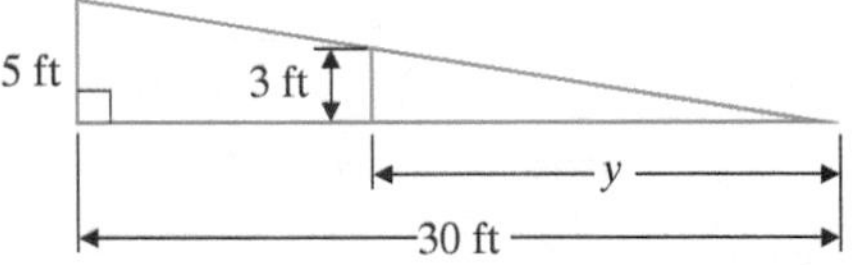

39. Suppose two trains leave Holbrook, Arizona, at the same time, traveling in opposite directions. One train travels 10 mph faster than the other. In 3.5 hours, the trains are 322 miles apart. Find the speed of each train.

40. Suppose two cars leave Brinkley, Arkansas, at the same time, traveling in opposite directions. One car travels 8 mph faster than the other car. In 2.5 hours, the cars are 280 miles apart. Find the speed of each car.

41. Two divided by the difference of a number and 3 minus 4 divided by the number plus 3, equals 8 times the reciprocal of the difference of the number squared and 9. What is the number?

42. If 15 times the reciprocal of a number is added to the ratio of 9 times the number minus 7 and the number plus 2, the result is 9. What is the number?

43. A pilot flies 630 miles with a tailwind of 35 miles per hour. Against the wind, he flies only 455 miles in the same amount of time. Find the rate of the plane in still air.

44. A marketing manager travels 1080 miles in a corporate jet and then an additional 240 miles by car. If the car ride takes one hour longer than the jet ride takes, and if the rate of the jet is 6 times the rate of the car, find the time the manager travels by jet and find the time the manager travels by car.

45. To mix weed killer with water correctly, it is necessary to mix 8 teaspoons of weed killer with 2 gallons of water. Find how many gallons of water are needed to mix with the entire box if it contains 36 teaspoons of weed killer.

46. The directions for a certain bug spray concentrate are to mix 3 ounces of concentrate with 2 gallons of water. How many ounces of concentrate are needed to mix with 5 gallons of water?

47. A boater travels 16 miles per hour on the water on a still day. During one particularly windy day, he finds that he travels 48 miles with the wind behind him in the same amount of time that he travels 16 miles into the wind. Find the rate of the wind.

Let x be the rate of the wind.

	$r \times t = d$	
with wind	$16 + x$	48
into wind	$16 - x$	16

48. The current on a portion of the Mississippi River is 3 miles per hour. A barge can go 6 miles upstream in the same amount of time it takes to go 10 miles downstream. Find the speed of the boat in still water.

Let x be the speed of the boat in still water.

	$r \times t = d$	
upstream	$x - 3$	6
downstream	$x + 3$	10

49. Two hikers are 11 miles apart and walking toward each other. They meet in 2 hours. Find the rate of each hiker if one hiker walks 1.1 mph faster than the other.

50. On a 255-mile trip, Gary Alessandrini traveled at an average speed of 70 mph, got a speeding ticket, and then traveled at 60 mph for the remainder of the trip. If the entire trip took 4.5 hours and the speeding ticket stop took 30 minutes, how long did Gary speed before getting stopped?

51. One custodian cleans a suite of offices in 3 hours. When a second worker is asked to join the regular custodian, the job takes only $1\frac{1}{2}$ hours. How long does it take the second worker to do the same job alone?

52. One person proofreads copy for a small newspaper in 4 hours. If a second proofreader is also employed, the job can be done in $2\frac{1}{2}$ hours. How long does it take for the second proofreader to do the same job alone?

△ **53.** An architect is completing the plans for a triangular deck. Use the diagram below to find the missing dimension.

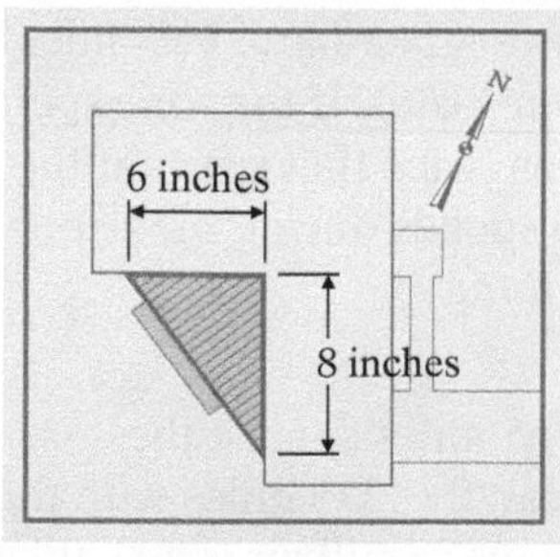

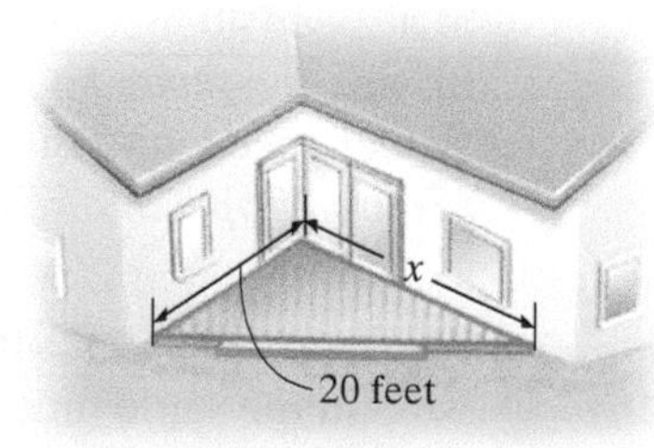

△ **54.** A student wishes to make a small model of a triangular mainsail in order to study the effects of wind on the sail. The smaller model will be the same shape as a regular-size sailboat's mainsail. Use the following diagram to find the missing dimensions.

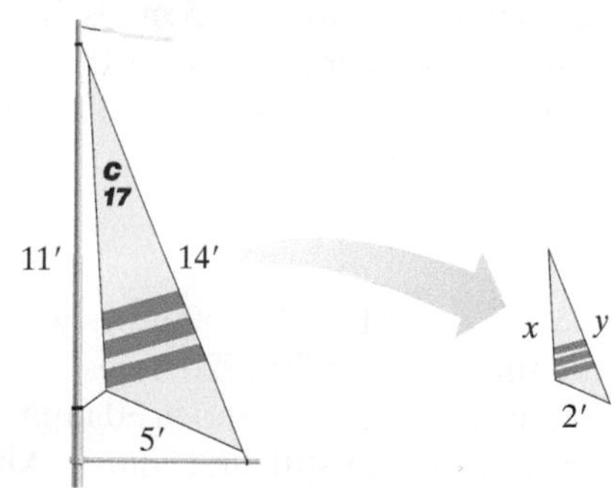

55. A manufacturer of cans of salted mixed nuts states that the ratio of peanuts to other nuts is 3 to 2. If 324 peanuts are in a can, find how many other nuts should also be in the can.

56. There are 1280 calories in a 14-ounce portion of Eagle Brand Milk. Find how many calories are in 2 ounces of Eagle Brand Milk.

57. A jet plane traveling at 500 mph overtakes a propeller plane traveling at 200 mph that had a 2-hour head start. How far from the starting point are the planes?

58. How long will it take a bus traveling at 60 miles per hour to overtake a car traveling at 40 mph if the car had a 1.5-hour head start?

59. One pipe fills a storage pool in 20 hours. A second pipe fills the same pool in 15 hours. When a third pipe is added and all three are used to fill the pool, it takes only 6 hours. Find how long it takes the third pipe to do the job.

60. One pump fills a tank in 9 hours. A second pump fills the same tank in 6 hours. When a third pump is added and all three are used to fill the tank, it takes only 3 hours. Find how long it takes the third pump to fill the tank.

61. A car travels 280 miles in the same time that a motorcycle travels 240 miles. If the car's speed is 10 miles per hour more than the motorcycle's, find the speed of the car and the speed of the motorcycle.

62. A bus traveled on a level road for 3 hours at an average speed 20 miles per hour faster than it traveled on a winding road. The time spent on the winding road was 4 hours. Find the average speed on the level road if the entire trip was 305 miles.

63. In 6 hours, an experienced cook prepares enough pies to supply a local restaurant's daily order. Another cook prepares the same number of pies in 7 hours. Together with a third cook, they prepare the pies in 2 hours. Find how long it takes the third cook to prepare the pies alone.

64. Mrs. Smith balances the company books in 8 hours. It takes her assistant 12 hours to do the same job. If they work together, find how long it takes them to balance the books.

65. The quotient of a number and 3, minus 1, equals $\frac{5}{3}$. Find the number.

66. The quotient of a number and 5, minus 1, equals $\frac{7}{5}$. Find the number.

67. Currently, the Toyota Corolla is the best-selling car in the world. Suppose that during a test drive of two Corollas, one car travels 224 miles in the same time that the second car travels 175 miles. If the speed of one car is 14 miles per hour faster than the speed of the second car, find the speed of both cars. (*Source: Top Ten of Everything*)

68. The second best-selling car is the Volkswagen Golf. A driver of this car took a day trip around the California coastline driving at two different speeds. He drove 70 miles at a slower speed and 300 miles at a speed 40 miles per hour faster. If the time spent driving the faster speed was twice that spent at the slower speed, find the two speeds during the trip. (*Source: Top Ten of Everything*)

69. A pilot can fly an MD-11 2160 miles with the wind in the same time she can fly 1920 miles against the wind. If the speed of the wind is 30 mph, find the speed of the plane in still air. (*Source*: Air Transport Association of America)

70. A pilot can fly a DC-10 1365 miles against the wind in the same time he can fly 1575 miles with the wind. If the speed of the plane in still air is 490 miles per hour, find the speed of the wind. (*Source*: Air Transport Association of America)

Given that the following pairs of triangles are similar, find each missing length.

71.

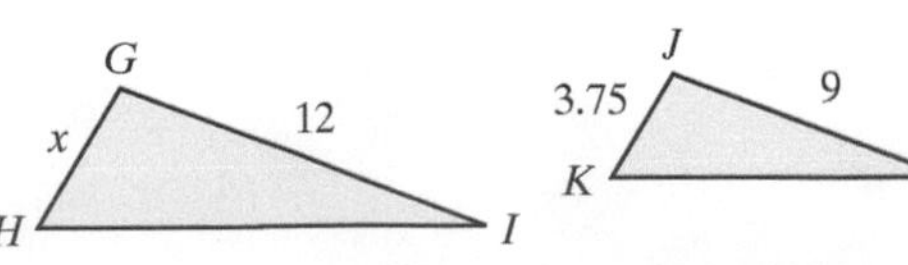

72.

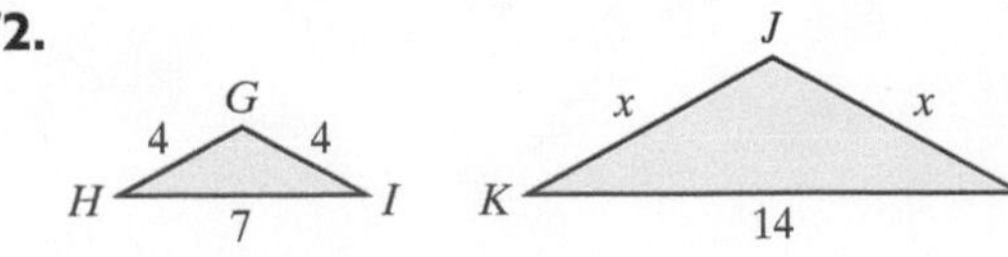

△ **73.**

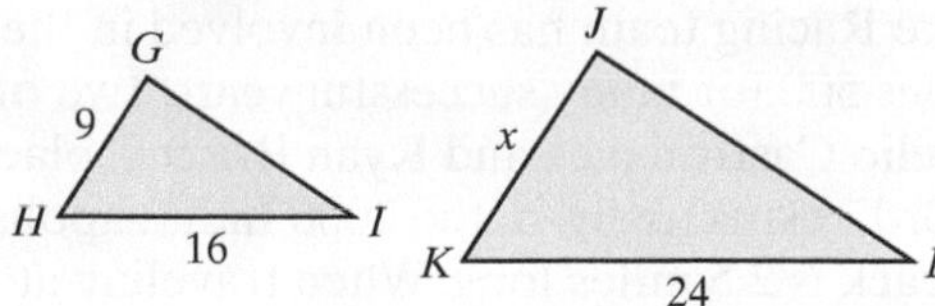

△ **74.**

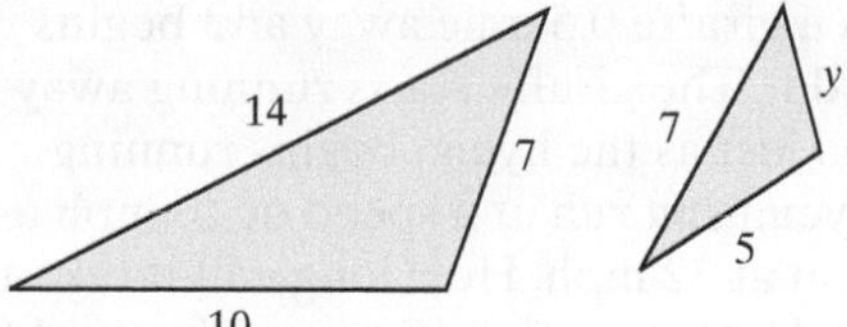

Review

Simplify. Follow the circled steps in the order shown. See Section R.2.

75. $\dfrac{\frac{3}{4}+\frac{1}{4}}{\frac{3}{8}+\frac{13}{8}}$ ← ① Add. ← ② Add.

76. $\dfrac{\frac{9}{5}+\frac{6}{5}}{\frac{17}{6}+\frac{7}{6}}$ ← ① Add. ← ② Add.

77. $\dfrac{\frac{2}{5}+\frac{1}{5}}{\frac{7}{10}+\frac{7}{10}}$ ① Add. ← ③ Divide. ② Add.

78. $\dfrac{\frac{1}{4}+\frac{5}{4}}{\frac{3}{8}+\frac{7}{8}}$ ① Add. ← ③ Divide. ② Add.

Concept Extensions

79. Onc pump fills a tank 3 times as fast as another pump. If the pumps work together, they fill the tank in 21 minutes. How long does it take each pump to fill the tank?

80. For which of the following equations can we immediately use cross products to solve for x?

a. $\dfrac{2-x}{5}=\dfrac{1+x}{3}$

b. $\dfrac{2}{5}-x=\dfrac{1+x}{3}$

81. Person A can complete a job in 5 hours, and person B can complete the same job in 3 hours. Without solving algebraically, discuss reasonable and unreasonable answers for how long it would take them to complete the job together.

82. For what value of x is $\dfrac{x}{x-1}$ in proportion to $\dfrac{x+1}{x}$? Explain your result.

Solve. See the Concept Check in this section.

Solve $D = RT$

83. for R

84. for T

85. A hyena spots a giraffe 0.5 mile away and begins running toward it. The giraffe starts running away from the hyena just as the hyena begins running toward it. A hyena can run at a speed of 40 mph and a giraffe can run at 32 mph. How long will it take the hyena to overtake the giraffe? (*Source: The World Almanac and Book of Facts*)

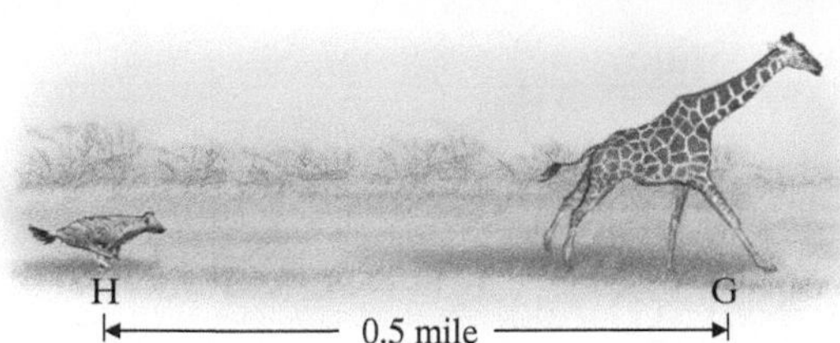

86. The Penske Racing team has been involved in the Indianapolis 500 for many successful years. Two of its drivers, Helio Castroneves and Ryan Briscoe, placed 4th and 23rd, respectively, in the 2008 Indianapolis 500. The track is 2.5 miles long. When traveling at their fastest lap speeds, Briscoe drove 2.492 miles in the same time that Castroneves completed an entire 2.5-mile lap. Castroneves' fastest lap speed was 0.694 mph faster than Briscoe's fastest lap speed. Find each driver's fastest lap speed. Round each speed to the nearest tenth. (*Source:* Indy Racing League)

Chapter 5 Group Activity

Fast-Growing Careers

According to U.S. Bureau of Labor Statistics projections, the careers listed below will have the largest job growth in the years shown.

Occupation	Employment (number in thousands)		
	2006	2016	Change
1. Registered nurses	2505	3092	+587
2. Retail salespersons	4477	5034	+557
3. Customer service representatives	2202	2747	+545
4. Combined food preparation and serving workers, including fast food	2503	2955	+452
5. Office clerks, general	3200	3604	+404
6. Personal and home care aides	767	1156	+389
7. Home health aides	787	1171	+384
8. Postsecondary teachers	1672	2054	+382
9. Janitors and cleaners, except maids and housekeeping cleaners	2387	2732	+345
10. Nursing aides, orderlies, and attendants	1447	1711	+264

What do all of these in-demand occupations have in common? They all require a knowledge of math! For some careers, like nurses, postsecondary teachers, and salespersons, the ways math is used on the job may be obvious. For other occupations, the use of math may not be quite as obvious. However, tasks common to many jobs, such as filling in a time sheet or a medication log, writing up an expense report, planning a budget, figuring a bill, ordering supplies, and even making a work schedule, all require math.

Activity

Suppose that your college placement office is planning to publish an occupational handbook on math in popular occupations. Choose one of the occupations from the given list that interests you. Research the occupation. Then write a brief entry for the occupational handbook that describes how a person in that career would use math in his or her job. Include an example if possible.

Chapter 5 Vocabulary Check

Fill in each blank with one of the words or phrases listed below. Not all choices will be used.

least common denominator	simplifying	reciprocals	numerator	$\frac{-a}{b}$
cross products	ratio	proportion	rate	
rational expression	unit	complex fraction	denominator	$\frac{-a}{-b}$ $\frac{a}{-b}$

1. A(n) __________________ is an expression that can be written in the form $\frac{P}{Q}$, where P and Q are polynomials and Q is not 0.
2. In a(n) __________________, the numerator or denominator or both may contain fractions.
3. For a rational expression, $-\frac{a}{b} =$ __________________ $=$ __________________.
4. A rational expression is undefined when the __________________ is 0.
5. The process of writing a rational expression in lowest terms is called __________________.
6. The expressions $\frac{2x}{7}$ and $\frac{7}{2x}$ are called __________________.
7. The __________________ of a list of rational expressions is a polynomial of least degree whose factors include all factors of the denominators in the list.
8. A(n) __________________ fraction is a fraction that equals 1.
9. A(n) __________________ is the quotient of two numbers.
10. $\frac{x}{2} = \frac{7}{16}$ is an example of a(n) __________________.
11. If $\frac{a}{b} = \frac{c}{d}$, then ad and bc are called __________________.
12. A(n) __________________ is a special type of ratio where different measurements are used.

Helpful Hint Are you preparing for your test? Don't forget to take the Chapter 5 Test on page 416. Then check your answers at the back of the text and use the Chapter Test Prep Videos to see the fully worked-out solutions to any of the exercises you want to review.

5 Chapter Highlights

Definitions and Concepts	Examples
Section 5.1 Simplifying Rational Expressions	
A **rational expression** is an expression that can be written in the form $\frac{P}{Q}$, where P and Q are polynomials and Q does not equal 0.	$\frac{7y^3}{4}, \frac{x^2+6x+1}{x-3}, \frac{-5}{s^3+8}$
To find values for which a rational expression is undefined, find values for which the denominator is 0.	Find any values for which the expression $\frac{5y}{y^2-4y+3}$ is undefined. $y^2 - 4y + 3 = 0$ Set the denominator equal to 0. $(y-3)(y-1) = 0$ Factor. $y - 3 = 0$ or $y - 1 = 0$ Set each factor equal to 0. $y = 3$ $\quad y = 1$ Solve. The expression is undefined when y is 3 and when y is 1.

(continued)

Definitions and Concepts	Examples
Section 5.1 Simplifying Rational Expressions (*continued*)	
To Simplify a Rational Expression **Step 1.** Factor the numerator and denominator. **Step 2.** Divide out factors common to the numerator and denominator. (This is the same as removing a factor of 1.)	Simplify: $\frac{4x+20}{x^2-25}$ $\frac{4x+20}{x^2-25}=\frac{4(x+5)}{(x+5)(x-5)}=\frac{4}{x-5}$
Section 5.2 Multiplying and Dividing Rational Expressions	
To Multiply Rational Expressions **Step 1.** Factor numerators and denominators. **Step 2.** Multiply numerators and multiply denominators. **Step 3.** Write the product in lowest terms. $\frac{P}{Q}\cdot\frac{R}{S}=\frac{PR}{QS}$	Multiply: $\frac{4x+4}{2x-3}\cdot\frac{2x^2+x-6}{x^2-1}$ $\frac{4x+4}{2x-3}\cdot\frac{2x^2+x-6}{x^2-1}$ $=\frac{4(x+1)}{2x-3}\cdot\frac{(2x-3)(x+2)}{(x+1)(x-1)}$ $=\frac{4(x+1)(2x-3)(x+2)}{(2x-3)(x+1)(x-1)}$ $=\frac{4(x+2)}{x-1}$
To divide by a rational expression, multiply by the reciprocal. $\frac{P}{Q}\div\frac{R}{S}=\frac{P}{Q}\cdot\frac{S}{R}=\frac{PS}{QR}$	Divide: $\frac{15x+5}{3x^2-14x-5}\div\frac{15}{3x-12}$ $\frac{15x+5}{3x^2-14x-5}\div\frac{15}{3x-12}$ $=\frac{5(3x+1)}{(3x+1)(x-5)}\cdot\frac{3(x-4)}{3\cdot 5}$ $=\frac{x-4}{x-5}$
Section 5.3 Adding and Subtracting Rational Expressions with the Same Denominator and Least Common Denominator	
To add or subtract rational expressions with the same denominator, add or subtract numerators, and place the sum or difference over the common denominator. $\frac{P}{R}+\frac{Q}{R}=\frac{P+Q}{R}$ $\frac{P}{R}-\frac{Q}{R}=\frac{P-Q}{R}$	Perform each indicated operation. $\frac{5}{x+1}+\frac{x}{x+1}=\frac{5+x}{x+1}$ $\frac{2y+7}{y^2-9}-\frac{y+4}{y^2-9}$ $=\frac{(2y+7)-(y+4)}{y^2-9}$ $=\frac{2y+7-y-4}{y^2-9}$ $=\frac{y+3}{(y+3)(y-3)}$ $=\frac{1}{y-3}$

Definitions and Concepts	Examples
Section 5.3 Adding and Subtracting Rational Expressions with the Same Denominator and Least Common Denominator (*continued*)	
To Find the Least Common Denominator (LCD) **Step 1.** Factor the denominators. **Step 2.** The LCD is the product of all unique factors, each raised to a power equal to the greatest number of times that it appears in any one factored denominator.	Find the LCD for $\frac{7x}{x^2 + 10x + 25}$ and $\frac{11}{3x^2 + 15x}$ $x^2 + 10x + 25 = (x + 5)(x + 5)$ $3x^2 + 15x = 3x(x + 5)$ $\text{LCD} = 3x(x + 5)(x + 5)$ or $3x(x + 5)^2$
Section 5.4 Adding and Subtracting Rational Expressions with Different Denominators	
To Add or Subtract Rational Expressions with Different Denominators **Step 1.** Find the LCD. **Step 2.** Rewrite each rational expression as an equivalent expression whose denominator is the LCD. **Step 3.** Add or subtract numerators and place the sum or difference over the common denominator. **Step 4.** Write the result in lowest terms.	Perform the indicated operation. $\frac{9x + 3}{x^2 - 9} - \frac{5}{x - 3}$ $= \frac{9x + 3}{(x + 3)(x - 3)} - \frac{5}{x - 3}$ LCD is $(x + 3)(x - 3)$. $= \frac{9x + 3}{(x + 3)(x - 3)} - \frac{5(x + 3)}{(x - 3)(x + 3)}$ $= \frac{9x + 3 - 5(x + 3)}{(x + 3)(x - 3)}$ $= \frac{9x + 3 - 5x - 15}{(x + 3)(x - 3)}$ $= \frac{4x - 12}{(x + 3)(x - 3)}$ $= \frac{4(x - 3)}{(x + 3)(x - 3)} = \frac{4}{x + 3}$
Section 5.5 Solving Equations Containing Rational Expressions	
To Solve an Equation Containing Rational Expressions **Step 1.** Multiply both sides of the equation by the LCD of all rational expressions in the equation. **Step 2.** Remove any grouping symbols and solve the resulting equation. **Step 3.** Check the solution in the original equation.	Solve: $\frac{5x}{x + 2} + 3 = \frac{4x - 6}{x + 2}$ The LCD is $x + 2$. $(x + 2)\left(\frac{5x}{x + 2} + 3\right) = (x + 2)\left(\frac{4x - 6}{x + 2}\right)$ $(x + 2)\left(\frac{5x}{x + 2}\right) + (x + 2)(3) = (x + 2)\left(\frac{4x - 6}{x + 2}\right)$ $5x + 3x + 6 = 4x - 6$ $4x = -12$ $x = -3$ The solution checks; the solution is -3.

Definitions and Concepts	Examples

Section 5.6 Proportions and Problem Solving with Rational Equations

A **ratio** is the quotient of two numbers or two quantities.

A **proportion** is a mathematical statement that two ratios are equal.

Proportions

$$\frac{2}{3} = \frac{8}{12} \qquad \frac{x}{7} = \frac{15}{35}$$

Cross products:

If $\frac{a}{b} = \frac{c}{d}$, then $ad = bc$.

Cross Products

$2 \cdot 12$ or 24 $\qquad$ $3 \cdot 8$ or 24

$$\frac{2}{3} = \frac{8}{12}$$

Solve: $\frac{3}{4} = \frac{x}{x-1}$

$$\frac{3}{4} = \frac{x}{x-1}$$

$$3(x-1) = 4x \quad \text{Set cross products equal.}$$
$$3x - 3 = 4x$$
$$-3 = x$$

Problem-Solving Steps

1. UNDERSTAND. Read and reread the problem.

A small plane and a car leave Kansas City, Missouri, and head for Minneapolis, Minnesota, a distance of 450 miles. The speed of the plane is 3 times the speed of the car, and the plane arrives 6 hours ahead of the car. Find the speed of the car.

Let $x =$ the speed of the car.

Then $3x =$ the speed of the plane.

	Distance	= Rate	· Time
Car	450	x	$\frac{450}{x} \left(\frac{\text{distance}}{\text{rate}}\right)$
Plane	450	$3x$	$\frac{450}{3x} \left(\frac{\text{distance}}{\text{rate}}\right)$

2. TRANSLATE.

In words: plane's time + 6 hours = car's time

Translate: $\frac{450}{3x} + 6 = \frac{450}{x}$

3. SOLVE.

$$\frac{450}{3x} + 6 = \frac{450}{x}$$
$$3x\left(\frac{450}{3x}\right) + 3x(6) = 3x\left(\frac{450}{x}\right)$$
$$450 + 18x = 1350$$
$$18x = 900$$
$$x = 50$$

4. INTERPRET.

Check this solution in the originally stated problem. **State** the conclusion: The speed of the car is 50 miles per hour.

Definitions and Concepts	Examples
Section 5.7 Simplifying Complex Fractions	
METHOD 1: TO SIMPLIFY A COMPLEX FRACTION **Step 1:** Add or subtract fractions in the numerator and the denominator of the complex fraction. **Step 2:** Perform the indicated division. **Step 3:** Write the result in lowest terms.	Simplify: $\dfrac{\dfrac{1}{x}+2}{\dfrac{1}{x}-\dfrac{1}{y}} = \dfrac{\dfrac{1}{x}+\dfrac{2x}{x}}{\dfrac{y}{xy}-\dfrac{x}{xy}}$ $= \dfrac{\dfrac{1+2x}{x}}{\dfrac{y-x}{xy}}$ $= \dfrac{1+2x}{x}\cdot\dfrac{xy}{y-x}$ $= \dfrac{y(1+2x)}{y-x}$
METHOD 2: TO SIMPLIFY A COMPLEX FRACTION **Step 1:** Find the LCD of all fractions in the complex fraction. **Step 2:** Multiply the numerator and the denominator of the complex fraction by the LCD. **Step 3:** Perform the indicated operations and write the result in lowest terms.	$\dfrac{\dfrac{1}{x}+2}{\dfrac{1}{x}-\dfrac{1}{y}} = \dfrac{xy\left(\dfrac{1}{x}+2\right)}{xy\left(\dfrac{1}{x}-\dfrac{1}{y}\right)}$ $= \dfrac{xy\left(\dfrac{1}{x}\right)+xy(2)}{xy\left(\dfrac{1}{x}\right)-xy\left(\dfrac{1}{y}\right)}$ $= \dfrac{y+2xy}{y-x}$ or $\dfrac{y(1+2x)}{y-x}$

Chapter 5 Review

(5.1) *Find any real number for which each rational expression is undefined.*

1. $\frac{x + 5}{x^2 - 4}$

2. $\frac{5x + 9}{4x^2 - 4x - 15}$

Find the value of each rational expression when $x = 5$, $y = 7$, and $z = -2$.

3. $\frac{2 - z}{z + 5}$

4. $\frac{x^2 + xy - y^2}{x + y}$

Simplify each rational expression.

5. $\frac{2x + 6}{x^2 + 3x}$

6. $\frac{3x - 12}{x^2 - 4x}$

7. $\frac{x + 2}{x^2 - 3x - 10}$

8. $\frac{x + 4}{x^2 + 5x + 4}$

9. $\frac{x^3 - 4x}{x^2 + 3x + 2}$

10. $\frac{5x^2 - 125}{x^2 + 2x - 15}$

11. $\frac{x^2 - x - 6}{x^2 - 3x - 10}$

12. $\frac{x^2 - 2x}{x^2 + 2x - 8}$

Simplify each expression. First, factor the four-term polynomials by grouping.

13. $\frac{x^2 + xa + xb + ab}{x^2 - xc + bx - bc}$

14. $\frac{x^2 + 5x - 2x - 10}{x^2 - 3x - 2x + 6}$

(5.2) *Perform each indicated operation and simplify.*

15. $\frac{15x^3y^2}{z} \cdot \frac{z}{5xy^3}$

16. $\frac{-y^3}{8} \cdot \frac{9x^2}{y^3}$

17. $\frac{x^2 - 9}{x^2 - 4} \cdot \frac{x - 2}{x + 3}$

18. $\frac{2x + 5}{x - 6} \cdot \frac{2x}{-x + 6}$

19. $\frac{x^2 - 5x - 24}{x^2 - x - 12} \div \frac{x^2 - 10x + 16}{x^2 + x - 6}$

20. $\frac{4x + 4y}{xy^2} \div \frac{3x + 3y}{x^2y}$

21. $\frac{x^2 + x - 42}{x - 3} \cdot \frac{(x - 3)^2}{x + 7}$

22. $\frac{2a + 2b}{3} \cdot \frac{a - b}{a^2 - b^2}$

23. $\frac{2x^2 - 9x + 9}{8x - 12} \div \frac{x^2 - 3x}{2x}$

24. $\frac{x^2 - y^2}{x^2 + xy} \div \frac{3x^2 - 2xy - y^2}{3x^2 + 6x}$

(5.3) *Perform each indicated operation and simplify.*

25. $\dfrac{x}{x^2 + 9x + 14} + \dfrac{7}{x^2 + 9x + 14}$

26. $\dfrac{x}{x^2 + 2x - 15} + \dfrac{5}{x^2 + 2x - 15}$

27. $\dfrac{4x - 5}{3x^2} - \dfrac{2x + 5}{3x^2}$

28. $\dfrac{9x + 7}{6x^2} - \dfrac{3x + 4}{6x^2}$

Find the LCD of each pair of rational expressions.

29. $\dfrac{x + 4}{2x}, \dfrac{3}{7x}$

30. $\dfrac{x - 2}{x^2 - 5x - 24}, \dfrac{3}{x^2 + 11x + 24}$

Rewrite each rational expression as an equivalent expression whose denominator is the given polynomial.

31. $\dfrac{5}{7x} = \dfrac{\quad}{14x^3y}$

32. $\dfrac{9}{4y} = \dfrac{\quad}{16y^3x}$

33. $\dfrac{x + 2}{x^2 + 11x + 18} = \dfrac{\quad}{(x + 2)(x - 5)(x + 9)}$

34. $\dfrac{3x - 5}{x^2 + 4x + 4} = \dfrac{\quad}{(x + 2)^2(x + 3)}$

(5.4) *Perform each indicated operation and simplify.*

35. $\dfrac{4}{5x^2} + \dfrac{6}{y}$

36. $\dfrac{2}{x - 3} - \dfrac{4}{x - 1}$

37. $\dfrac{4}{x + 3} - 2$

38. $\dfrac{3}{x^2 + 2x - 8} + \dfrac{2}{x^2 - 3x + 2}$

39. $\dfrac{2x - 5}{6x + 9} - \dfrac{4}{2x^2 + 3x}$

40. $\dfrac{x - 1}{x^2 - 2x + 1} - \dfrac{x + 1}{x - 1}$

(5.5) *Solve each equation.*

41. $\dfrac{n}{10} = 9 - \dfrac{n}{5}$

42. $\dfrac{2}{x + 1} - \dfrac{1}{x - 2} = -\dfrac{1}{2}$

43. $\dfrac{y}{2y + 2} + \dfrac{2y - 16}{4y + 4} = \dfrac{y - 3}{y + 1}$

44. $\dfrac{2}{x - 3} - \dfrac{4}{x + 3} = \dfrac{8}{x^2 - 9}$

45. $\dfrac{x - 3}{x + 1} - \dfrac{x - 6}{x + 5} = 0$

46. $x + 5 = \dfrac{6}{x}$

(5.6) *Solve each proportion.*

47. $\frac{2}{x-1} = \frac{3}{x+3}$

48. $\frac{4}{y-3} = \frac{2}{y-3}$

Solve.

49. A machine can process 300 parts in 20 minutes. Find how many parts can be processed in 45 minutes.

50. As his consulting fee, Mr. Visconti charges \$90.00 per day. Find how much he charges for 3 hours of consulting. Assume an 8-hour workday.

51. Five times the reciprocal of a number equals the sum of $\frac{3}{2}$ the reciprocal of the number and $\frac{7}{6}$. What is the number?

52. The reciprocal of a number equals the reciprocal of the difference of 4 and the number. Find the number.

53. A car travels 90 miles in the same time that a car traveling 10 miles per hour slower travels 60 miles. Find the speed of each car.

54. The current in a bayou near Lafayette, Louisiana, is 4 miles per hour. A paddleboat travels 48 miles upstream in the same amount of time it takes to travel 72 miles downstream. Find the speed of the boat in still water.

55. When Mark and Maria manicure Mr. Stergeon's lawn, it takes them 5 hours. If Mark works alone, it takes 7 hours. Find how long it takes Maria alone.

56. It takes pipe A 20 days to fill a fish pond. Pipe B takes 15 days. Find how long it takes both pipes together to fill the pond.

Given that the pairs of triangles are similar, find each missing length x.

57.

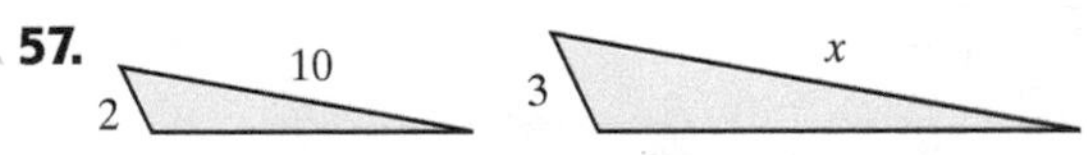

58.

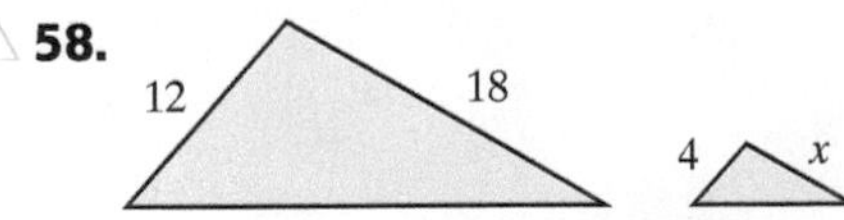

(5.7) *Simplify each complex fraction.*

59. $\dfrac{\frac{5x}{27}}{-\frac{10xy}{21}}$

60. $\dfrac{\frac{3}{5}+\frac{2}{7}}{\frac{1}{5}+\frac{5}{6}}$

61. $\dfrac{3-\frac{1}{y}}{2-\frac{1}{y}}$

62. $\dfrac{\frac{6}{x+2}+4}{\frac{8}{x+2}-4}$

Mixed Review

Simplify each rational expression.

63. $\frac{4x+12}{8x^2+24x}$

64. $\frac{x^3-6x^2+9x}{x^2+4x-21}$

Perform the indicated operations and simplify.

65. $\dfrac{x^2 + 9x + 20}{x^2 - 25} \cdot \dfrac{x^2 - 9x + 20}{x^2 + 8x + 16}$

66. $\dfrac{x^2 - x - 72}{x^2 - x - 30} \div \dfrac{x^2 + 6x - 27}{x^2 - 9x + 18}$

67. $\dfrac{x}{x^2 - 36} + \dfrac{6}{x^2 - 36}$

68. $\dfrac{5x - 1}{4x} - \dfrac{3x - 2}{4x}$

69. $\dfrac{4}{3x^2 + 8x - 3} + \dfrac{2}{3x^2 - 7x + 2}$

70. $\dfrac{3x}{x^2 + 9x + 14} - \dfrac{6x}{x^2 + 4x - 21}$

Solve.

71. $\dfrac{4}{a - 1} + 2 = \dfrac{3}{a - 1}$

72. $\dfrac{x}{x + 3} + 4 = \dfrac{x}{x + 3}$

Solve.

73. The quotient of twice a number and 3, minus one-sixth, is the quotient of the number and 2. Find the number.

74. Mr. Crocker can paint his shed by himself in three days. His son will need an additional day to complete the job if he works alone. If they work together, find how long it takes to paint the shed.

Given that the following pairs of triangles are similar, find each missing length.

75.

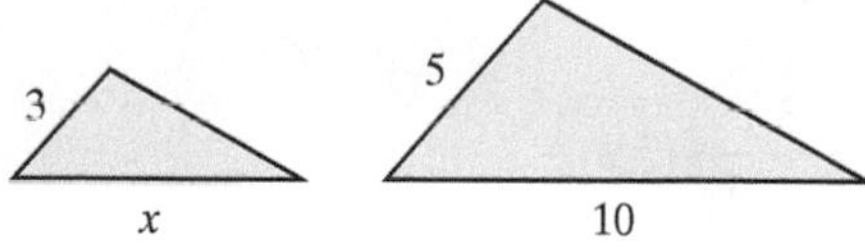

76.

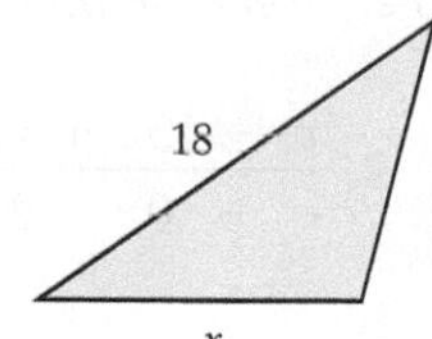

Simplify each complex fraction.

77. $\dfrac{\frac{1}{4}}{\frac{1}{3} + \frac{1}{2}}$

78. $\dfrac{4 + \frac{2}{x}}{6 + \frac{3}{x}}$

Chapter 5 Test

Step-by-step test solutions are found on the Chapter Test Prep Videos available via the Interactive DVD Lecture Series, in MyMathLab or on YouTube (search "MartinGayIntroAlg" and click on "Channels").

Answers

1. ______
2. a. ______
b. ______
3. ______
4. ______
5. ______
6. ______
7. ______
8. ______
9. ______
10. ______
11. ______
12. ______
13. ______
14. ______
15. ______
16. ______
17. ______

1. Find any real numbers for which the following expression is undefined.

$$\frac{x + 5}{x^2 + 4x + 3}$$

2. For a certain computer desk, the average manufacturing cost C per desk (in dollars) is

$$C = \frac{100x + 3000}{x}$$

where x is the number of desks manufactured.

a. Find the average cost per desk when manufacturing 200 computer desks.

b. Find the average cost per desk when manufacturing 1000 computer desks.

Simplify each rational expression.

3. $\dfrac{3x - 6}{5x - 10}$

4. $\dfrac{x + 6}{x^2 + 12x + 36}$

5. $\dfrac{7 - x}{x - 7}$

6. $\dfrac{y - x}{x^2 - y^2}$

7. $\dfrac{2m^3 - 2m^2 - 12m}{m^2 - 5m + 6}$

8. $\dfrac{ay + 3a + 2y + 6}{ay + 3a + 5y + 15}$

Perform each indicated operation and simplify if possible.

9. $\dfrac{x^2 - 13x + 42}{x^2 + 10x + 21} \div \dfrac{x^2 - 4}{x^2 + x - 6}$

10. $\dfrac{3}{x - 1} \cdot (5x - 5)$

11. $\dfrac{y^2 - 5y + 6}{2y + 4} \cdot \dfrac{y + 2}{2y - 6}$

12. $\dfrac{5}{2x + 5} - \dfrac{6}{2x + 5}$

13. $\dfrac{5a}{a^2 - a - 6} - \dfrac{2}{a - 3}$

14. $\dfrac{6}{x^2 - 1} + \dfrac{3}{x + 1}$

15. $\dfrac{x^2 - 9}{x^2 - 3x} \div \dfrac{x^2 + 4x + 1}{2x + 10}$

16. $\dfrac{x + 2}{x^2 + 11x + 18} + \dfrac{5}{x^2 - 3x - 10}$

17. $\dfrac{4y}{y^2 + 6y + 5} - \dfrac{3}{y^2 + 5y + 4}$

Solve each equation.

18. $\dfrac{4}{y} - \dfrac{5}{3} = \dfrac{-1}{5}$

19. $\dfrac{5}{y+1} = \dfrac{4}{y+2}$

20. $\dfrac{a}{a-3} = \dfrac{3}{a-3} - \dfrac{3}{2}$

21. $\dfrac{10}{x^2-25} = \dfrac{3}{x+5} + \dfrac{1}{x-5}$

22. $x - \dfrac{14}{x-1} = 4 - \dfrac{2x}{x-1}$

Simplify each complex fraction.

23. $\dfrac{\dfrac{5x^2}{yz^2}}{\dfrac{10x}{z^3}}$

24. $\dfrac{\dfrac{b}{a} - \dfrac{a}{b}}{\dfrac{1}{b} + \dfrac{1}{a}}$

25. $\dfrac{5 - \dfrac{1}{y^2}}{\dfrac{1}{y} + \dfrac{2}{y^2}}$

26. One number plus five times its reciprocal is equal to six. Find the number.

27. A pleasure boat traveling on the Red River takes the same time to go 14 miles upstream as it takes to go 16 miles downstream. If the current of the river is 2 miles per hour, find the speed of the boat in still water.

28. An inlet pipe can fill a tank in 12 hours. A second pipe can fill the tank in 15 hours. If both pipes are used, find how long it takes to fill the tank.

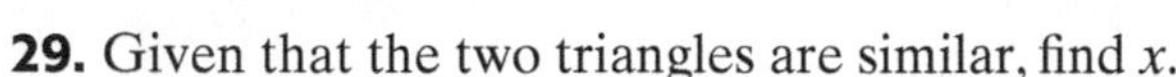

△ **29.** Given that the two triangles are similar, find x.

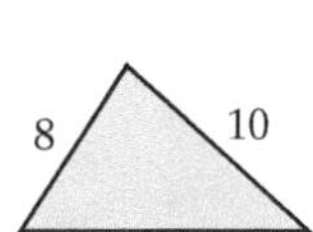

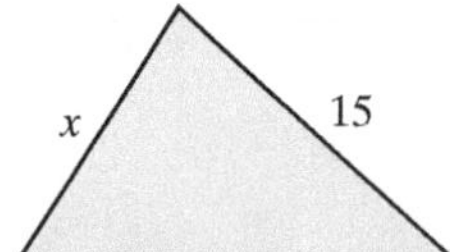

30. In a sample of 85 fluorescent bulbs, 3 were found to be defective. At this rate, how many defective bulbs should be found in 510 bulbs?

18. ______
19. ______
20. ______
21. ______
22. ______
23. ______
24. ______
25. ______
26. ______
27. ______
28. ______
29. ______
30. ______

Answers

1. a. ______
b. ______
c. ______
2. a. ______
b. ______
c. ______
3. a. ______
b. ______
4. a. ______
b. ______
5. ______
6. ______
7. ______
8. ______
9. ______
10. ______
11. ______
12. ______
13. ______
14. ______

Cumulative Review Chapters 1–5

1. Write each sentence as an equation. Let x represent the unknown number.

a. The quotient of 15 and a number is 4.

b. Three subtracted from 12 is a number.

c. 17 added to four times a number is 21.

2. Write each sentence as an equation. Let x represent the unknown number.

a. The difference of 12 and a number is -45.

b. The product of 12 and a number is -45.

c. A number less 10 is twice the number.

3. Find the sums.

a. $3 + (-7) + (-8)$

b. $[7 + (-10)] + [-2 + (-4)]$

4. Find the differences.

a. $28 - 6 - 30$

b. $7 - 2 - 22$

For Exercises 5 through 8, name the property illustrated by each true statement.

5. $3(x + y) = 3 \cdot x + 3 \cdot y$

6. $3 + y = y + 3$

7. $(x + 7) + 9 = x + (7 + 9)$

8. $(x \cdot 7) \cdot 9 = x \cdot (7 \cdot 9)$

9. Solve: $3 - x = 7$

10. Solve: $7x - 6 = 6x - 6$

11. A 10-foot board is to be cut into two pieces so that the length of the longer piece is 4 times the length of the shorter. Find the length of each piece.

12. Find two consecutive even integers whose sum is 382.

13. Solve: $y = mx + b$ for x.

14. Solve: $3x - 2y = 6$ for x.

15. Solve $x + 4 \leq -6$. Graph the solutions.

−10 −8 −6 −4 −2 0 2 4 6 8 10

16. Solve: $-3x + 7 > -x + 9$

Simplify.

17. $\frac{x^5}{x^2}$

18. $\frac{y^{14}}{y^{14}}$

19. $\frac{4^7}{4^3}$

20. $(x^5y^2)^3$

21. $\frac{(-3)^5}{(-3)^2}$

22. $\frac{x^{19}y^5}{xy}$

23. $\frac{2x^5y^2}{xy}$

24. $(-3a^2b)(5a^3b)$

Simplify by writing each expression with positive exponents only.

25. $2x^{-3}$

26. 7^{-2}

27. $(-2)^{-4}$

28. $5z^{-7}$

Multiply.

29. $5x(2x^3 + 6)$

30. $(x + 9)^2$

31. $-3x^2(5x^2 + 6x - 1)$

32. $(2x + 1)(2x - 1)$

Perform the indicated operations.

33. Divide: $\frac{4x^2 + 7 + 8x^3}{2x + 3}$

34. Divide $(4x^3 - 9x + 2)$ by $(x - 4)$.

35. Factor: $x^2 + 7x + 12$

36. Factor: $-2a^2 + 10a + 12$

15. ______

16. ______

17. ______

18. ______

19. ______

20. ______

21. ______

22. ______

23. ______

24. ______

25. ______

26. ______

27. ______

28. ______

29. ______

30. ______

31. ______

32. ______

33. ______

34. ______

35. ______

36. ______

37. ______
38. ______
39. ______
40. ______
41. ______
42. ______
43. ______
44. ______
45. ______
46. ______
47. ______
48. ______
49. ______
50. ______

37. Factor: $25x^2 + 20xy + 4y^2$

38. Factor: $x^2 - 4$

39. Solve: $x^2 - 9x - 22 = 0$

40. Solve: $3x^2 + 5x = 2$

41. Multiply: $\frac{x^2 + x}{3x} \cdot \frac{6}{5x + 5}$

42. Simplify: $\frac{2x^2 - 50}{4x^4 - 20x^3}$

43. Subtract: $\frac{3x^2 + 2x}{x - 1} - \frac{10x - 5}{x - 1}$

44. Factor: $7x^6 - 7x^5 + 7x^4$

45. Subtract: $\frac{6x}{x^2 - 4} - \frac{3}{x + 2}$

46. Factor: $4x^2 + 12x + 9$

47. Solve: $\frac{t - 4}{2} - \frac{t - 3}{9} = \frac{5}{18}$

48. Multiply: $\frac{6x^2 - 18x}{3x^2 - 2x} \cdot \frac{15x - 10}{x^2 - 9}$

49. Sam Waterton and Frank Schaffer work in a plant that manufactures automobiles. Sam can complete a quality control tour of the plant in 3 hours while his assistant, Frank, needs 7 hours to complete the same job. The regional manager is coming to inspect the plant facilities, so both Sam and Frank are directed to complete a quality control tour together. How long will this take?

50. Simplify: $\dfrac{\frac{m}{3} + \frac{n}{6}}{\frac{m + n}{12}}$

Graphing Equations and Inequalities

6

Sections

Check Your Progress

In Chapter 2 we learned to solve and graph the solutions of linear equations and inequalities in one variable on number lines. Now we define and present techniques for solving and graphing linear equations and inequalities in two variables on grids. Two-variable equations lead directly to the concept of *function*, perhaps the most important concept in all mathematics. Functions are introduced in Section 6.6.

"Neither snow, nor rain, nor heat, nor gloom of night stays these couriers from the swift completion of their appointed rounds." This familiar quotation, adapted from Herodotus, is inscribed in the New York City post office. By land and sea and air, on horseback, steamboats, and jets, the U.S. mail has been delivered to its destinations for more than 200 years. To this day, the most unusual delivery method is by mule, to the most remote mail location in the country, Supai, Arizona, located deep below the south rim of the Grand Canyon.

The Post Office Department, the predecessor of the U.S. Postal Service, was created by the Second Continental Congress on July 26, 1775. This agency was an arm of the U.S. government until 1982, the last year the Postal Service accepted public subsidy. In Exercises 39 through 44, Section 6.6, you will explore the way that some postage is calculated.

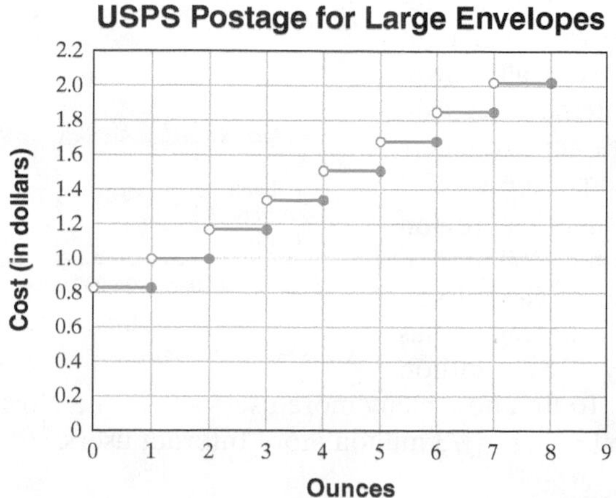

Objectives

A **Read Bar and Line Graphs.**

B **Plot Ordered Pairs of Numbers on the Rectangular Coordinate System.**

C **Graph Paired Data to Create a Scatter Diagram.**

D **Find the Missing Coordinate of an Ordered Pair Solution, Given One Coordinate of the Pair.**

6.1 READING GRAPHS AND THE RECTANGULAR COORDINATE SYSTEM

In today's world, where the exchange of information must be fast and entertaining, graphs are becoming increasingly popular. They provide a quick way of making comparisons, drawing conclusions, and approximating quantities.

Objective A Reading Bar and Line Graphs

A **bar graph** consists of a series of bars arranged vertically or horizontally. The bar graph in Example 1 shows a comparison of worldwide Internet users by region. The names of the regions are listed vertically and a bar is shown for each region. Corresponding to the length of the bar for each region is a number along a horizontal axis. These horizontal numbers are numbers of Internet users in millions.

PRACTICE 1

Use the graph from Example 1 to answer the following.

a. Find the region with the fewest Internet users and approximate the number of users.

b. How many more users are in the Asia/Oceania/Australia region than in the Africa/Middle East region?

Example 1

The following bar graph shows the estimated number of Internet users worldwide by region, as of a recent year.

a. Find the region that has the most Internet users and approximate the number of users.

b. How many more users are in the North America region than the Latin America/Caribbean region?

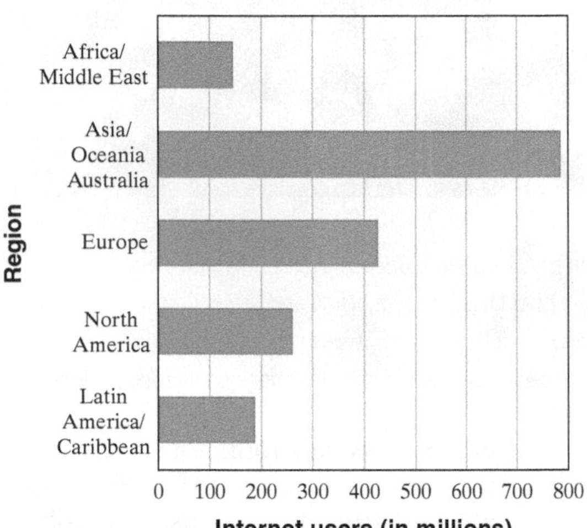

Source: Internet World Stats

Solution:

a. Since these bars are arranged horizontally, we look for the longest bar, which is the bar representing Asia/Oceania/Australia. To approximate the number associated with this region, we move from the right edge of this bar vertically downward to the Internet user axis. This region has approximately 785 million Internet users.

b. The North America region has approximately 260 million Internet users. The Latin America/Caribbean region has approximately 187 million Internet users. To find how many more users are in the North America region, we subtract $260 - 187 = 73$ million more Internet users.

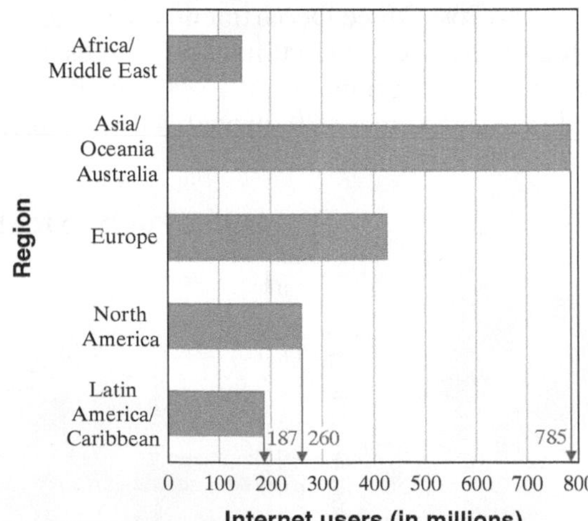

Source: Internet World Stats

Work Practice 1

Answers

1. a. Africa/Middle East region, 145 million Internet users, b. 640 million more Internet users

A **line graph** consists of a series of points connected by a line. The next graph is an example of a line graph. It is also sometimes called a **broken line graph.**

Example 2

The line graph shows the relationship between time since smoking a cigarette and pulse rate. Time is recorded along the horizontal axis in minutes, with 0 minutes being the moment a smoker lights a cigarette. Pulse is recorded along the vertical axis in heartbeats per minute.

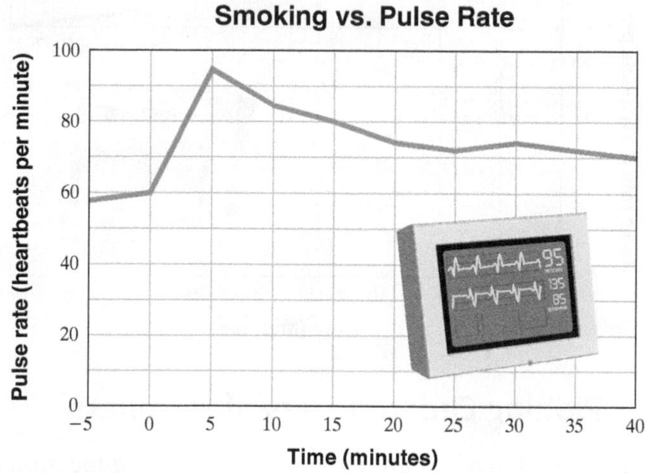

a. What is the pulse rate 15 minutes after a cigarette is lit?

b. When is the pulse rate the lowest?

c. When does the pulse rate show the greatest change?

Solution:

a. We locate the number 15 along the time axis and move vertically upward until the line is reached. From this point on the line, we move horizontally to the left until the pulse rate axis is reached. Reading the number of beats per minute, we find that the pulse rate is 80 beats per minute 15 minutes after a cigarette is lit.

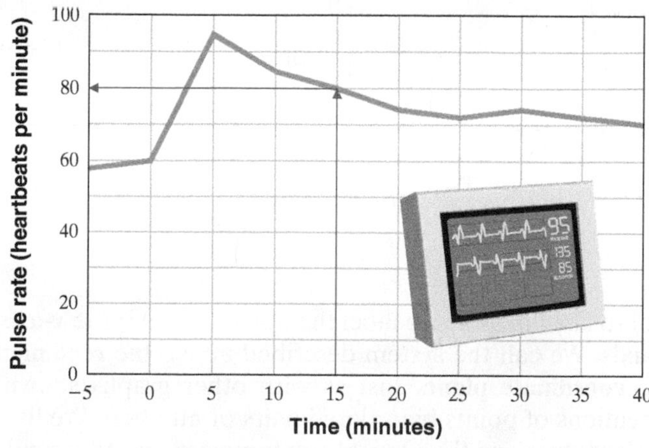

b. We find the lowest point of the line graph, which represents the lowest pulse rate. From this point, we move vertically downward to the time axis. We find that the pulse rate is the lowest at −5 minutes, which means 5 minutes *before* lighting a cigarette.

c. The pulse rate shows the greatest change during the 5 minutes between 0 and 5. Notice that the line graph is *steepest* between 0 and 5 minutes.

Work Practice 2

PRACTICE 2

Use the graph from Example 2 to answer the following.

a. What is the pulse rate 40 minutes after lighting a cigarette?

b. What is the pulse rate when the cigarette is being lit?

c. When is the pulse rate the highest?

Answers

2. a. 70 beats per minute **b.** 60 beats per minute **c.** 5 minutes after lighting

Notice in the graph on the previous page that there are two numbers associated with each point of the graph. For example, we discussed earlier that 15 minutes after "lighting up," the pulse rate is 80 beats per minute. If we agree to write the time first and the pulse rate second, we can say there is a point on the graph corresponding to the **ordered pair** of numbers (15, 80). A few more ordered pairs are shown alongside their corresponding points.

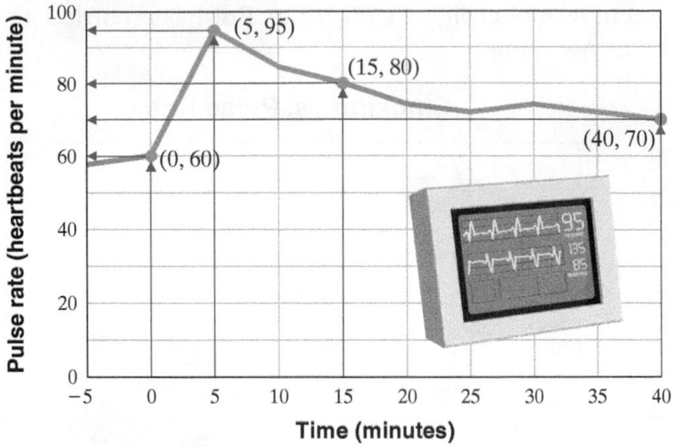

Objective B Plotting Ordered Pairs of Numbers

In general, we use the idea of ordered pairs to describe the location of a point in a plane (such as a piece of paper). We start with a horizontal and a vertical axis. Each axis is a number line, and for the sake of consistency we construct our axes to intersect at the 0 coordinate of both. This point of intersection is called the **origin.** Notice that these two number lines or axes divide the plane into four regions called **quadrants.** The quadrants are usually numbered with Roman numerals as shown. The axes are not considered to be in any quadrant.

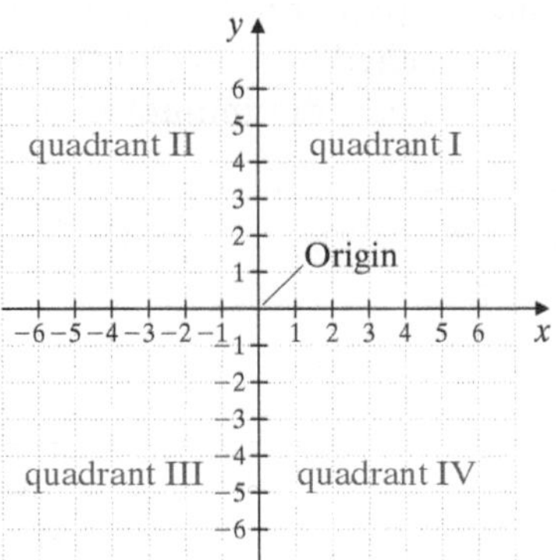

It is helpful to label axes, so we label the horizontal axis the ***x*-axis** and the vertical axis the ***y*-axis.** We call the system described above the **rectangular coordinate system,** or the **coordinate plane.** Just as with other graphs shown, we can then describe the locations of points by ordered pairs of numbers. We list the horizontal ***x*-axis** measurement first and the vertical ***y*-axis** measurement second.

To plot or graph the point corresponding to the ordered pair (a, b) we start at the origin. We then move a units left or right (right if a is positive, left if a is negative). From there, we move b units up or down (up if b is positive, down if b is negative). For example, to plot the point corresponding to the ordered pair (3, 2), we start at the origin, move 3 units right, and from there move 2 units up. (See the figure on the next page.) The x-value, 3, is also called the ***x*-coordinate** and the y-value, 2, is also called the ***y*-coordinate.** From now on, we will call the point with coordinates (3, 2) simply the point (3, 2). The point $(-2, 5)$ is also graphed on the next page.

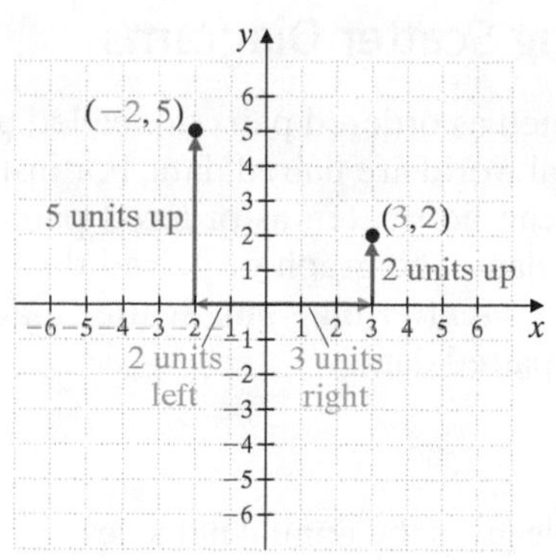

Helpful Hint

Don't forget that **each ordered pair corresponds to exactly one point in the plane and that each point in the plane corresponds to exactly one ordered pair.**

✓**Concept Check** Is the graph of the point $(-5, 1)$ in the same location as the graph of the point $(1, -5)$? Explain.

Example 3 On a single coordinate system, plot each ordered pair. State in which quadrant, or on which axis, each point lies.

a. $(5, 3)$ **b.** $(-2, -4)$ **c.** $(1, -2)$ **d.** $(-5, 3)$ **e.** $(0, 0)$

f. $(0, 2)$ **g.** $(-5, 0)$ **h.** $\left(0, -5\frac{1}{2}\right)$ **i.** $\left(4\frac{2}{3}, -3\right)$

Solution:

a. Point $(5, 3)$ lies in quadrant I.

b. Point $(-2, -4)$ lies in quadrant III.

c. Point $(1, -2)$ lies in quadrant IV.

d. Point $(-5, 3)$ lies in quadrant II.

e.–h. Points $(0, 0)$, $(0, 2)$, and $\left(0, -5\frac{1}{2}\right)$ lie on the y-axis. Points $(0, 0)$ and $(-5, 0)$ lie on the x-axis.

i. Point $\left(4\frac{2}{3}, -3\right)$ lies in quadrant IV.

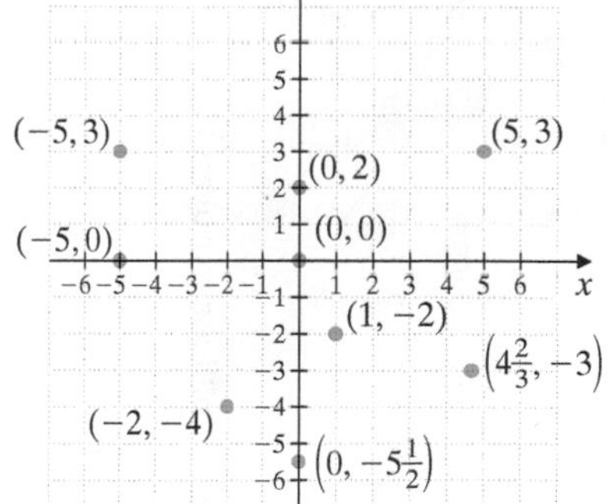

Work Practice 3

Helpful Hint

In Example 3, notice that the point $(0, 0)$ lies on both the x-axis and the y-axis. It is the only point in the entire rectangular coordinate system that has this feature. Why? It is the only point of intersection of the x-axis and the y-axis.

✓**Concept Check** For each description of a point in the rectangular coordinate system, write an ordered pair that represents it.

a. Point A is located three units to the left of the y-axis and five units above the x-axis.

b. Point B is located six units below the origin.

From Example 3, notice that the y-coordinate of any point on the x-axis is 0. For example, the point $(-5, 0)$ lies on the x-axis. Also, the x-coordinate of any point on the y-axis is 0. For example, the point $(0, 2)$ lies on the y-axis.

PRACTICE 3

On a single coordinate system, plot each ordered pair. State in which quadrant, or on which axis, each point lies.

a. $(4, 2)$ **b.** $(-1, -3)$

c. $(2, -2)$ **d.** $(-5, 1)$

e. $(0, 3)$ **f.** $(3, 0)$

g. $(0, -4)$ **h.** $\left(-2\frac{1}{2}, 0\right)$

i. $\left(1, -3\frac{3}{4}\right)$

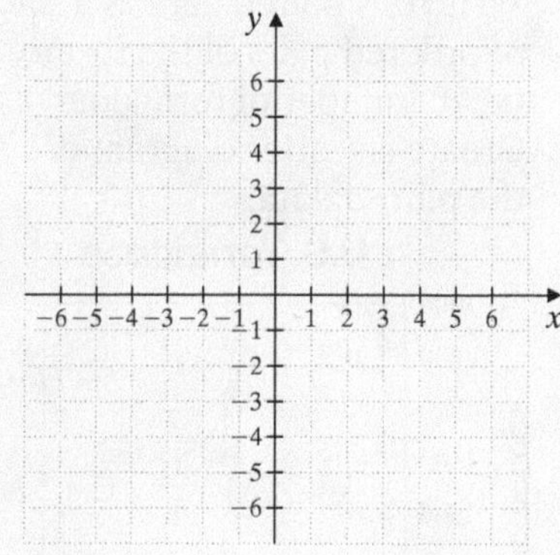

Answers

3.

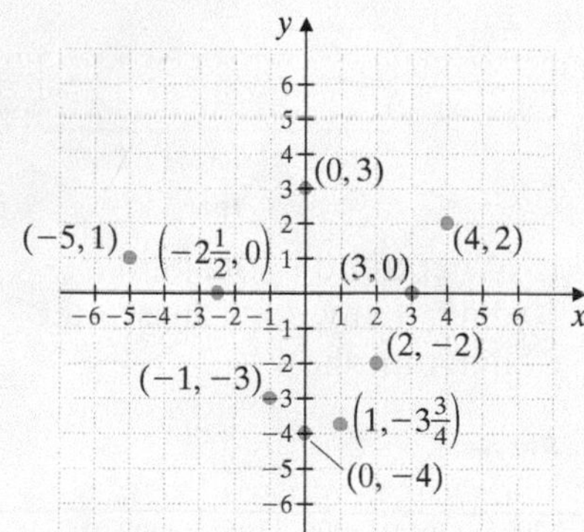

a. Point $(4, 2)$ lies in quadrant I.
b. Point $(-1, -3)$ lies in quadrant III.
c. Point $(2, -2)$ lies in quadrant IV.
d. Point $(-5, 1)$ lies in quadrant II.
e–h. Points $(3, 0)$ and $\left(-2\frac{1}{2}, 0\right)$ lie on the x-axis. Points $(0, 3)$ and $(0, -4)$ lie on the y-axis.
i. Point $\left(1, -3\frac{3}{4}\right)$ lies in quadrant IV.

✓ **Concept Check Answer**

The graph of point $(-5, 1)$ lies in quadrant II and the graph of point $(1, -5)$ lies in quadrant IV. They are *not* in the same location.

✓ **Concept Check Answers**

a. $(-3, 5)$ **b.** $(0, -6)$

PRACTICE 4

The table gives the number of tornadoes that have occurred in the United States for the years shown. (*Source:* Storm Prediction Center, National Weather Service)

Year	Tornadoes
2003	1376
2004	1817
2005	1264
2006	1106
2007	1093
2008	1621

a. Write this paired data as a set of ordered pairs of the form (year, number of tornadoes).
b. Create a scatter diagram of the paired data.

U.S. Tornadoes

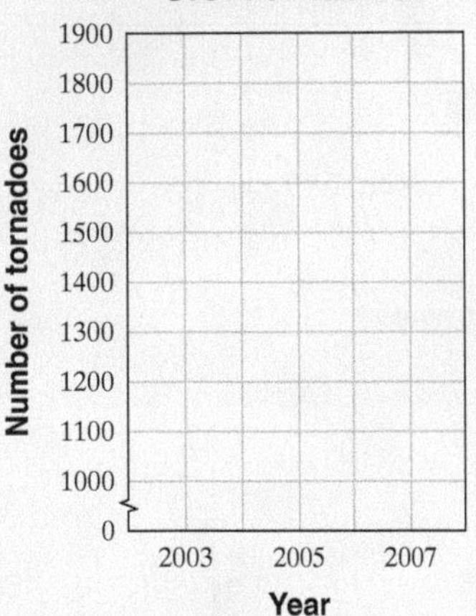

c. What trend in the paired data, if any, does the scatter diagram show?

Answers

4. a. (2003, 1376), (2004, 1817), (2005, 1264), (2006, 1106), (2007, 1093), (2008, 1621)

b. **U.S. Tornadoes**

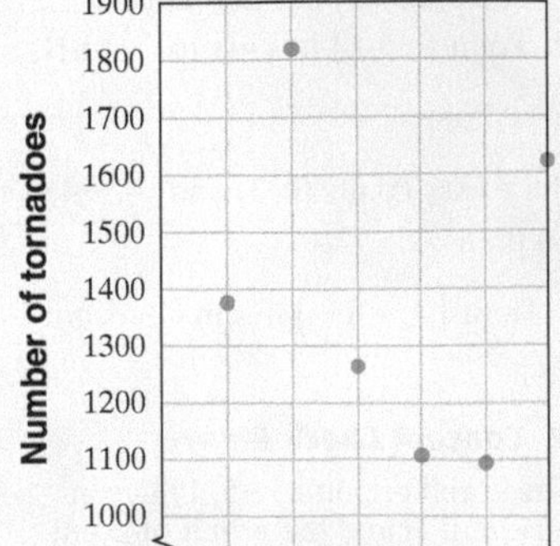

c. The number of tornadoes varies greatly from year to year.

Objective C Creating Scatter Diagrams

Data that can be represented as ordered pairs are called **paired data.** Many types of data collected from the real world are paired data. For instance, the annual measurements of a child's height can be written as ordered pairs of the form (year, height in inches) and are paired data. The graph of paired data as points in a rectangular coordinate system is called a **scatter diagram.** Scatter diagrams can be used to look for patterns and trends in paired data.

Example 4 The table gives the annual net sales for PetSmart for the years shown. (*Source:* PetSmart)

a. Write this paired data as a set of ordered pairs of the form (year, net sales in billions of dollars).
b. Create a scatter diagram of the paired data.
c. What trend in the paired data does the scatter diagram show?

Year	PetSmart Net Sales (in billions of dollars)
2003	3.0
2004	3.4
2005	3.8
2006	4.2
2007	4.7
2008	5.1

Solution:

a. The ordered pairs are (2003, 3.0), (2004, 3.4), (2005, 3.8), (2006, 4.2), (2007, 4.7), and (2008, 5.1).

b. We begin by plotting the ordered pairs. Because the x-coordinate in each ordered pair is a year, we label the x-axis "Year" and mark the horizontal axis with the years given. Then we label the y-axis or vertical axis "Net Sales (in billions of dollars)." In this case, it is convenient to mark the vertical axis in multiples of 0.5, starting with 0. In Practice 4, since there are no years when the number of tornadoes is less than 1000, we use the notation ⌇ to skip to 1000, and then proceed by multiples of 100.

PetSmart Net Sales

Net sales (in billions of dollars): 5.5, 5.0, 4.5, 4.0, 3.5, 3.0, 2.5, 2.0, 1.5, 1.0, 0.5

Year: 2003, 2004, 2005, 2006, 2007, 2008

c. The scatter diagram shows that PetSmart net sales steadily increased over the years 2003–2008.

Work Practice 4

Objective D Completing Ordered Pair Solutions

Let's see how we can use ordered pairs to record solutions of equations containing two variables. An equation in one variable such as $x + 1 = 5$ has one solution, 4: the number 4 is the value of the variable x that makes the equation true.

An equation in two variables, such as $2x + y = 8$, has solutions consisting of two values, one for x and one for y. For example, $x = 3$ and $y = 2$ is a solution of $2x + y = 8$ because, if x is replaced with 3 and y with 2, we get a true statement.

$$2x + y = 8$$
$$2(3) + 2 \stackrel{?}{=} 8 \quad \text{Replace } x \text{ with 3 and } y \text{ with 2.}$$
$$8 = 8 \quad \text{True}$$

The solution $x = 3$ and can be written as $(3, 2)$, an ordered pair of numbers.

In general, an ordered pair is a **solution** of an equation in two variables if replacing the variables by the values of the ordered pair results in a *true statement.*

For example, another ordered pair solution of $2x + y = 8$ is $(5, -2)$. Replacing x with 5 and y with -2 results in a true statement.

$$2x + y = 8$$
$$2(5) + (-2) \stackrel{?}{=} 8 \quad \text{Replace } x \text{ with 5 and } y \text{ with } -2.$$
$$10 - 2 \stackrel{?}{=} 8$$
$$8 = 8 \quad \text{True}$$

Example 5 Complete each ordered pair so that it is a solution to the equation $3x + y = 12$.

a. $(0, \;\;)$ **b.** $(\;\;, 6)$ **c.** $(-1, \;\;)$

Solution:

a. In the ordered pair $(0, \;\;)$, the x-value is 0. We let $x = 0$ in the equation and solve for y.

$$3x + y = 12$$
$$3(0) + y = 12 \quad \text{Replace } x \text{ with 0.}$$
$$0 + y = 12$$
$$y = 12$$

The completed ordered pair is $(0, 12)$.

b. In the ordered pair $(\;\;, 6)$, the y-value is 6. We let $y = 6$ in the equation and solve for x.

$$3x + y = 12$$
$$3x + 6 = 12 \quad \text{Replace } y \text{ with 6.}$$
$$3x = 6 \quad \text{Subtract 6 from both sides.}$$
$$x = 2 \quad \text{Divide both sides by 3.}$$

The ordered pair is $(2, 6)$.

c. In the ordered pair $(-1, \;\;)$, the x-value is -1. We let $x = -1$ in the equation and solve for y.

$$3x + y = 12$$
$$3(-1) + y = 12 \quad \text{Replace } x \text{ with } -1.$$
$$-3 + y = 12$$
$$y = 15 \quad \text{Add 3 to both sides.}$$

The ordered pair is $(-1, 15)$.

Work Practice 5

PRACTICE 5

Complete each ordered pair so that it is a solution to the equation $x + 2y = 8$.

a. $(0, \;\;)$
b. $(\;\;, 3)$
c. $(-4, \;\;)$

Solutions of equations in two variables can also be recorded in a **table of paired values,** as shown in the next example.

Answers

5. a. $(0, 4)$ **b.** $(2, 3)$ **c.** $(-4, 6)$

PRACTICE 6

Complete the table for the equation $y = -2x$.

	x	y
a.	−3	
b.		0
c.		10

Example 6 Complete the table for the equation $y = 3x$.

	x	y
a.	−1	
b.		0
c.		−9

Solution:

a. We replace x with -1 in the equation and solve for y.

$y = 3x$

$y = 3(-1)$ Let $x = -1$.

$y = -3$

The ordered pair is $(-1, -3)$.

b. We replace y with 0 in the equation and solve for x.

$y = 3x$

$0 = 3x$ Let $y = 0$.

$0 = x$ Divide both sides by 3.

The ordered pair is $(0, 0)$.

c. We replace y with -9 in the equation and solve for x.

$y = 3x$

$-9 = 3x$ Let $y = -9$.

$-3 = x$ Divide both sides by 3.

The ordered pair is $(-3, -9)$. The completed table is shown to the right.

x	y
−1	−3
0	0
−3	−9

Work Practice 6

PRACTICE 7

Complete the table for the equation $y = \frac{1}{3}x - 1$.

	x	y
a.	−3	
b.	0	
c.		0

Example 7 Complete the table for the equation

$$y = \frac{1}{2}x - 5.$$

	x	y
a.	−2	
b.	0	
c.		0

Solution:

a. Let $x = -2$.

$y = \frac{1}{2}x - 5$

$y = \frac{1}{2}(-2) - 5$

$y = -1 - 5$

$y = -6$

b. Let $x = 0$.

$y = \frac{1}{2}x - 5$

$y = \frac{1}{2}(0) - 5$

$y = 0 - 5$

$y = -5$

c. Let $y = 0$.

$y = \frac{1}{2}x - 5$

$0 = \frac{1}{2}x - 5$ Now, solve for x.

$5 = \frac{1}{2}x$ Add 5.

$10 = x$ Multiply by 2.

Ordered Pairs: $(-2, -6)$ $(0, -5)$ $(10, 0)$

The completed table is

x	y
−2	−6
0	−5
10	0

Work Practice 7

Answers

6.

	x	y
a.	−3	6
b.	0	0
c.	−5	10

7.

	x	y
a.	−3	−2
b.	0	−1
c.	3	0

By now, you have noticed that equations in two variables often have more than one solution. We discuss this more in the next section.

A table showing ordered pair solutions may be written vertically or horizontally, as shown in the next example.

Example 8 A small business purchased a computer for \$2000. The business predicts that the computer will be used for 5 years and the value in dollars y of the computer in x years is $y = -300x + 2000$. Complete the table.

x	0	1	2	3	4	5
y						

Solution:

To find the value of y when x is 0, we replace x with 0 in the equation. We use this same procedure to find y when x is 1 and when x is 2.

When $x = 0$,

$y = -300x + 2000$
$y = -300 \cdot 0 + 2000$
$y = 0 + 2000$
$y = 2000$

When $x = 1$,

$y = -300x + 2000$
$y = -300 \cdot 1 + 2000$
$y = -300 + 2000$
$y = 1700$

When $x = 2$,

$y = -300x + 2000$
$y = -300 \cdot 2 + 2000$
$y = -600 + 2000$
$y = 1400$

We have the ordered pairs (0, 2000), (1, 1700), and (2, 1400). This means that in 0 years the value of the computer is \$2000, in 1 year the value of the computer is \$1700, and in 2 years the value is \$1400. To complete the table of values, we continue the procedure for $x = 3$, $x = 4$, and $x = 5$.

When $x = 3$,

$y = -300x + 2000$
$y = -300 \cdot 3 + 2000$
$y = -900 + 2000$
$y = 1100$

When $x = 4$,

$y = -300x + 2000$
$y = -300 \cdot 4 + 2000$
$y = -1200 + 2000$
$y = 800$

When $x = 5$,

$y = -300x + 2000$
$y = -300 \cdot 5 + 2000$
$y = -1500 + 2000$
$y = 500$

The completed table is shown below.

x	0	1	2	3	4	5
y	2000	1700	1400	1100	800	500

Work Practice 8

PRACTICE 8

A company purchased a fax machine for \$400. The business manager of the company predicts that the fax machine will be used for 7 years and the value in dollars y of the machine in x years is $y = -50x + 400$. Complete the table.

x	1	2	3	4	5	6	7
y							

The ordered pair solutions recorded in the completed table for Example 8 are another set of paired data. They are graphed next. Notice that this scatter diagram gives a visual picture of the decrease in value of the computer.

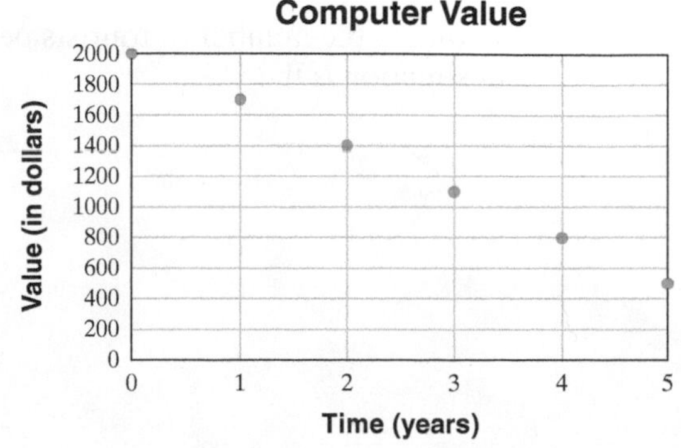

Answer

8.

x	1	2	3	4	5	6	7
y	350	300	250	200	150	100	50

Vocabulary and Readiness Check

Use the choices below to fill in each blank. The exercises below all have to do with the rectangular coordinate system.

origin	x-coordinate	x-axis	scatter diagram	four
quadrants	y-coordinate	y-axis	solution	one

1. The horizontal axis is called the ______________.

2. The vertical axis is called the ______________.

3. The intersection of the horizontal axis and the vertical axis is a point called the ______________.

4. The axes divide the plane into regions, called ______________. There are ______________ of these regions.

5. In the ordered pair of numbers $(-2, 5)$, the number -2 is called the ______________ and the number 5 is called the ______________.

6. Each ordered pair of numbers corresponds to ______________ point in the plane.

7. An ordered pair is a(n) ______________ of an equation in two variables if replacing the variables by the coordinates of the ordered pair results in a true statement.

8. The graph of paired data as points in a rectangular coordinate system is called a(n) ______________.

6.1 Exercise Set

FOR EXTRA HELP

PRACTICE

WATCH

DOWNLOAD

READ

REVIEW

Objective A *The following bar graph shows the top 10 tourist destinations and the number of tourists that visit each country per year. Use this graph to answer Exercises 1 through 6. See Example 1.*

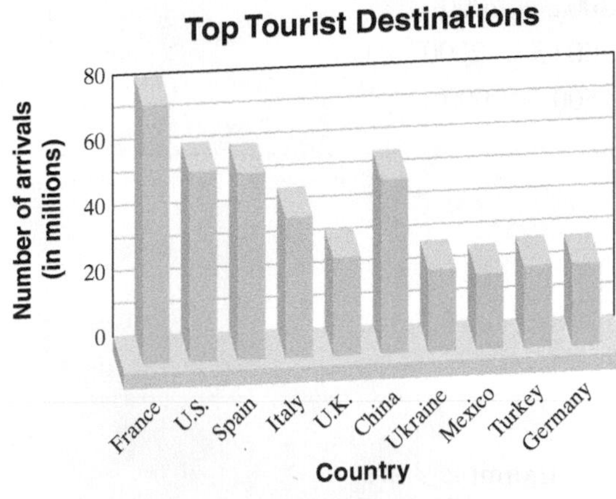

Source: Wikipedia

1. Which country shown is the most popular tourist destination?

2. Which country shown is the least popular tourist destination?

3. Which countries shown have more than 40 million tourists per year?

4. Which countries shown have fewer than 30 million tourists per year?

5. Estimate the number of tourists per year whose destination is Italy.

6. Estimate the number of tourists per year whose destination is the U.K.

The following line graph shows the paid attendance at each Super Bowl game from 2003 through 2009. Use this graph to answer Exercises 7 through 10. See Example 2.

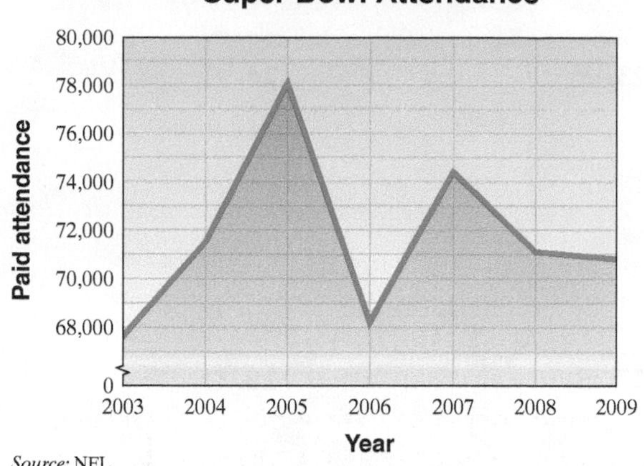

Source: NFL

7. Estimate the Super Bowl attendance in 2009.

8. Estimate the Super Bowl attendance in 2004.

9. Find the year on the graph with the greatest Super Bowl attendance and approximate that attendance.

10. Find the year on the graph with the least Super Bowl attendance and approximate that attendance.

The line graph below shows the number of students per computer in U.S. public schools. Use this graph for Exercises 11 through 16. See Example 2.

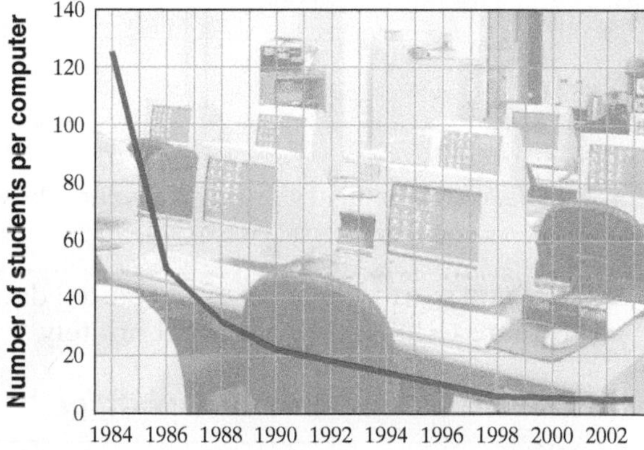

Source: World Almanac, 2005

11. Approximate the number of students per computer in 1986.

12. Approximate the number of students per computer in 2002.

13. Between what years did the greatest decrease in number of students per computer occur?

14. What was the first year that the number of students per computer fell below 20?

15. What was the first year that the number of students per computer fell below 15?

16. Discuss any trends shown by this line graph.

Objective B *Plot each ordered pair. State in which quadrant or on which axis each point lies. See Example 3.*

17. a. $(1, 5)$ **b.** $(-5, -2)$ **c.** $(-3, 0)$ **d.** $(0, -1)$
e. $(2, -4)$ **f.** $\left(-1, 4\frac{1}{2}\right)$ **g.** $(3.7, 2.2)$ **h.** $\left(\frac{1}{2}, -3\right)$

18. a. $(2, 4)$ **b.** $(0, 2)$ **c.** $(-2, 1)$ **d.** $(-3, -3)$
e. $\left(3\frac{3}{4}, 0\right)$ **f.** $(5, -4)$ **g.** $(-3.4, 4.8)$ **h.** $\left(\frac{1}{3}, -5\right)$

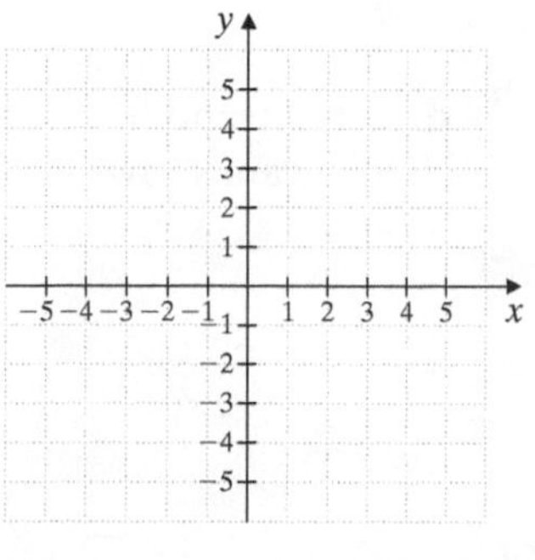

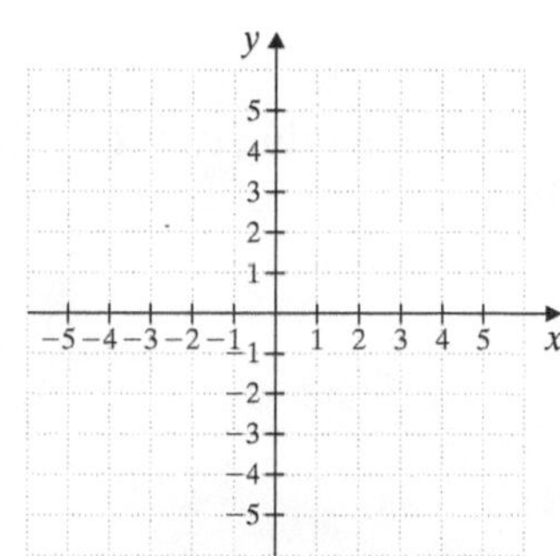

Find the x- and y-coordinates of each labeled point. See Example 3.

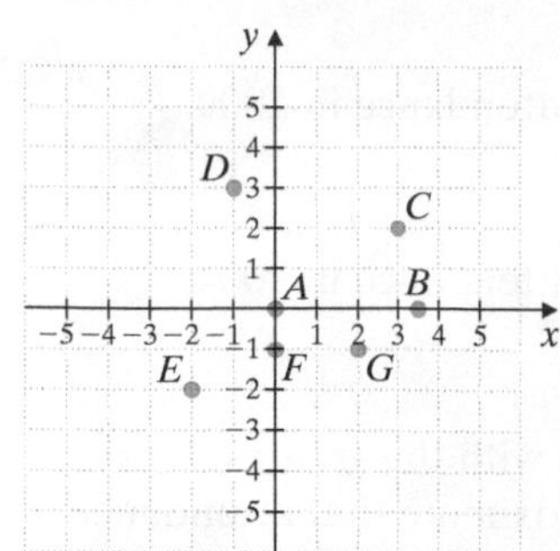

19. *A* **20.** *B* **21.** *C*

22. *D* **23.** *E* **24.** *F*

25. *G*

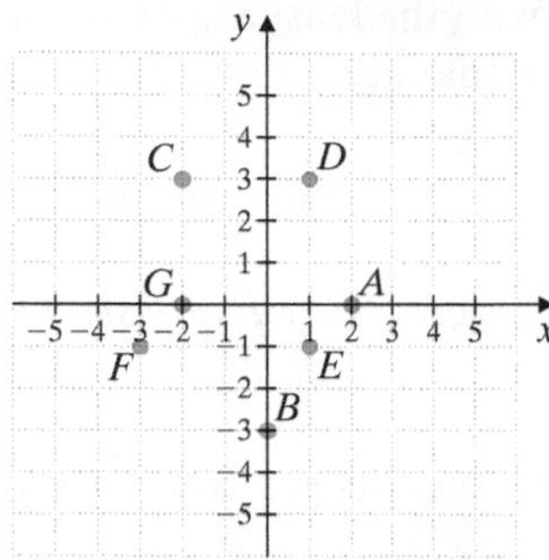

26. *A* **27.** *B* **28.** *C*

29. *D* **30.** *E* **31.** *F*

32. *G*

Objective C *Solve. See Example 4.*

33. The table shows the domestic box office (in billions of dollars) for the U.S. movie industry during the years shown. (*Source:* Motion Picture Association of America)

Year	Box Office (in billions of dollars)
2003	9.17
2004	9.22
2005	8.83
2006	9.14
2007	9.63
2008	9.79

a. Write this paired data as a set of ordered pairs of the form (year, box office).

b. In your own words, write the meaning of the ordered pair (2006, 9.14).

c. Create a scatter diagram of the paired data. Be sure to label the axes appropriately.

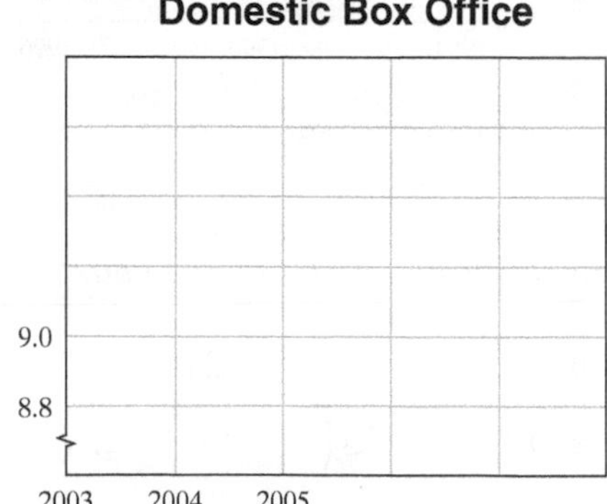

d. What trend in the paired data does the scatter diagram show?

34. The table shows the amount of money (in billions of dollars) that Americans spent on their pets for the years shown. (*Source:* American Pet Products Manufacturers Association)

Year	Pet-Related Expenditures (in billions of dollars)
2005	36.3
2006	38.5
2007	41.2
2008	43.4

a. Write this paired data as a set of ordered pairs of the form (year, pet-related expenditures).

b. In your own words, write the meaning of the ordered pair (2007, 41.2).

c. Create a scatter diagram of the paired data. Be sure to label the axes appropriately.

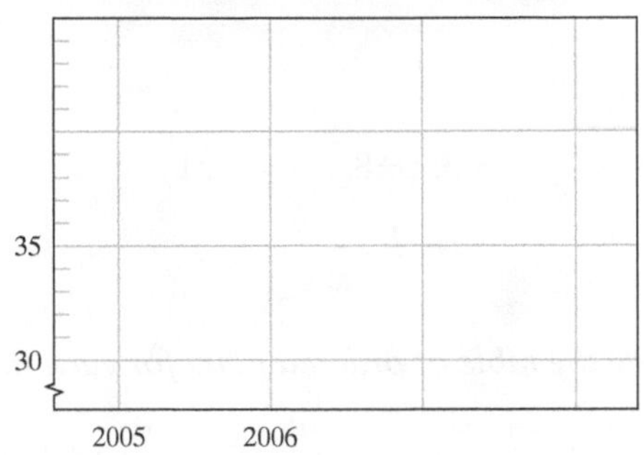

d. What trend in the paired data does the scatter diagram show?

35. Minh, a psychology student, kept a record of how much time she spent studying for each of her 20-point psychology quizzes and her score on each quiz.

Hours Spent Studying	0.50	0.75	1.00	1.25	1.50	1.50	1.75	2.00
Quiz Score	10	12	15	16	18	19	19	20

a. Write the data as ordered pairs of the form (hours spent studying, quiz score).

b. In your own words, write the meaning of the ordered pair (1.25, 16).

c. Create a scatter diagram of the paired data. Be sure to label the axes appropriately.

d. What might Minh conclude from the scatter diagram?

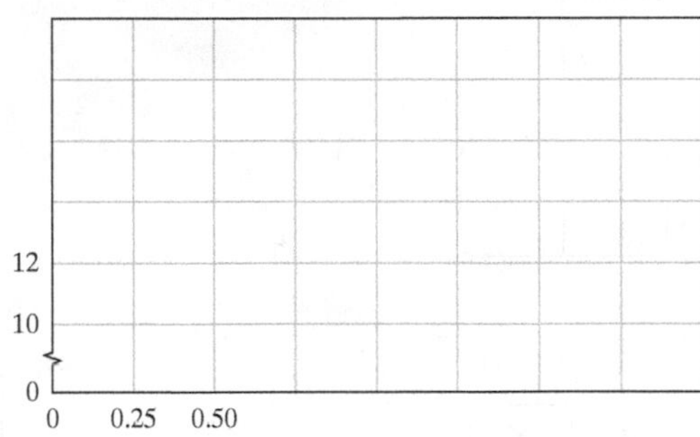

36. A local lumberyard uses quantity pricing. The table shows the price per board for different amounts of lumber purchased.

Price per Board (in dollars)	Number of Boards Purchased
8.00	1
7.50	10
6.50	25
5.00	50
2.00	100

a. Write the data as ordered pairs of the form (price per board, number of boards purchased).

b. In your own words, write the meaning of the ordered pair (2.00, 100).

c. Create a scatter diagram of the paired data. Be sure to label the axes appropriately.

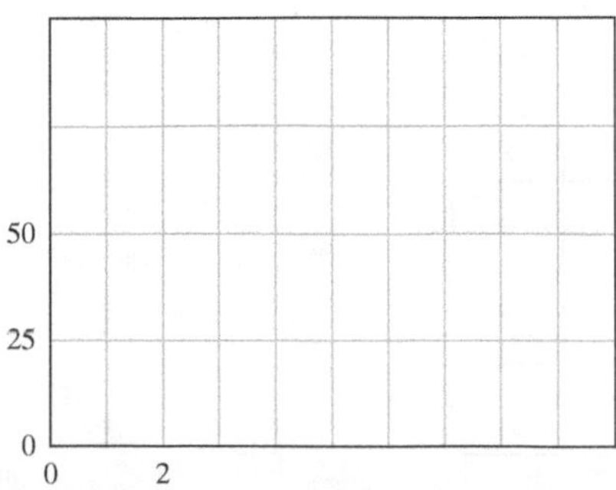

d. What trend in the paired data does the scatter diagram show?

Objective **D** *Complete each ordered pair so that it is a solution of the given linear equation. See Example 5.*

37. $x - 4y = 4$; (, −2), (4,)

38. $x - 5y = -1$; (, −2), (4,)

39. $y = \frac{1}{4}x - 3$; (−8,), (, 1)

40. $y = \frac{1}{5}x - 2$; (−10,), (, 1)

Complete the table of ordered pairs for each linear equation. See Examples 6 and 7.

41. $y = -7x$

x	y
0	
−1	
	2

42. $y = -9x$

x	y
	0
−3	
	2

43. $x = -y + 2$

x	y
0	
	0
−3	

44. $x = -y + 4$

x	y
	0
0	
	−3

45. $y = \frac{1}{2}x$

x	y
0	
−6	
	1

46. $y = \frac{1}{3}x$

x	y
0	
−6	
	1

47. $x + 3y = 6$

x	y
0	
	0
	1

48. $2x + y = 4$

x	y
0	
	0
	2

49. $y = 2x - 12$

x	y
0	
	−2
3	

50. $y = 5x + 10$

x	y
	0
	5
0	

51. $2x + 7y = 5$

x	y
0	
	0
	1

52. $x - 6y = 3$

x	y
0	
1	
	−1

Objectives B C D Mixed Practice *Complete the table of ordered pairs for each equation. Then plot the ordered pair solutions. See Examples 3 through 7.*

53. $x = -5y$

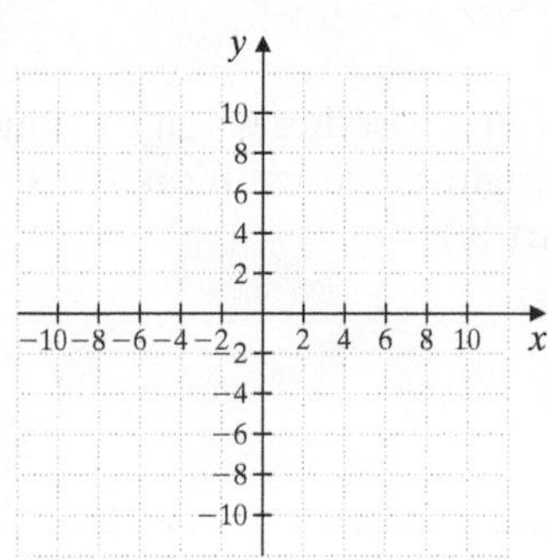

x	y
	0
	1
10	

54. $y = -3x$

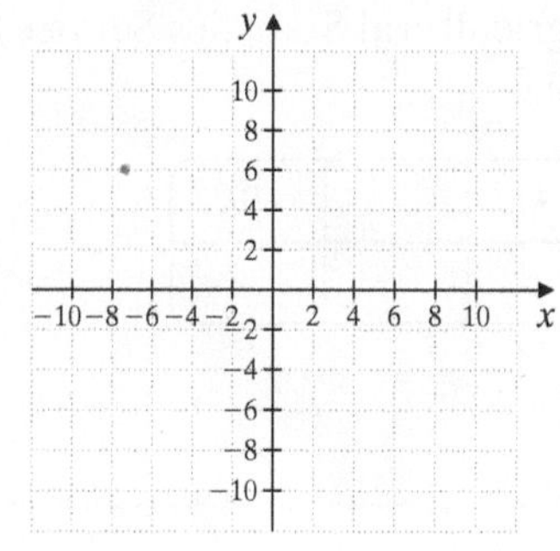

x	y
0	
−2	
	9

55. $y = \frac{1}{3}x + 2$

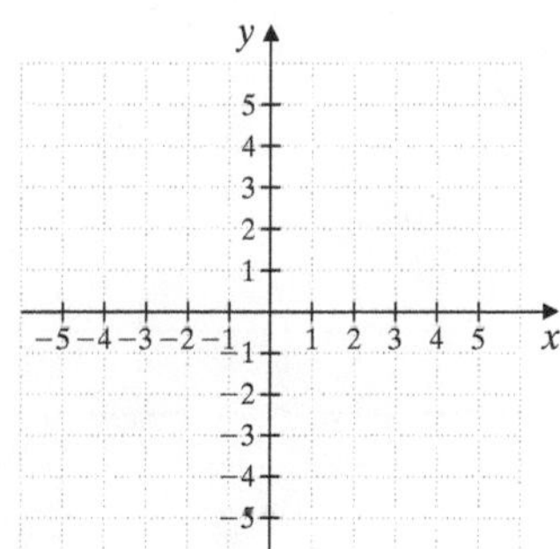

x	y
0	
−3	
	0

56. $y = \frac{1}{2}x + 3$

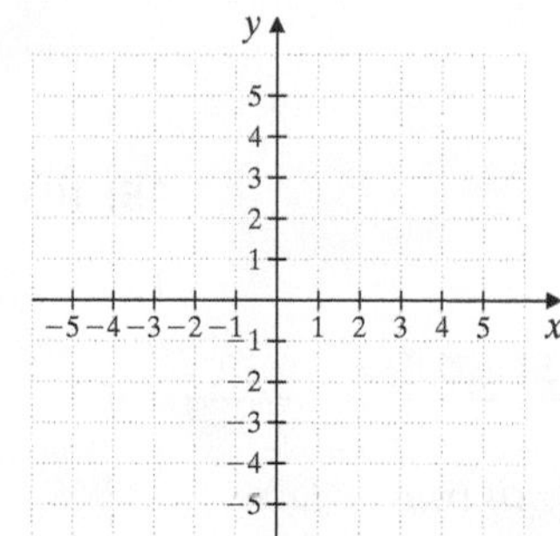

x	y
0	
−4	
	0

Solve. See Example 8.

57. The cost in dollars y of producing x computer desks is given by $y = 80x + 5000$.

a. Complete the table.

x	100	200	300
y			

b. Find the number of computer desks that can be produced for $8600. (*Hint:* Find x when $y = 8600$.)

58. The hourly wage y of an employee at a certain production company is given by $y = 0.25x + 9$ where x is the number of units produced by the employee in an hour.

a. Complete the table.

x	0	1	5	10
y				

b. Find the number of units that an employee must produce each hour to earn an hourly wage of $12.25. (*Hint:* Find x when $y = 12.25$.)

59. The average annual cinema admission price y (in dollars) from 2000 through 2008 is given by $y = 0.2x + 5.39$. In this equation, x represents the number of years after 2000. (*Source:* Motion Picture Association of America)

a. Complete the table.

x	1	3	5
y			

b. Find the year in which the average cinema admission price was approximately $6.40. (*Hint:* Find x when $y = 6.40$ and round to the nearest whole number.)

c. Use the given equation to predict when the cinema admission price might be $8.00. (Use the hint for part b.)

60. The amount y of land occupied by farms in the United States (in millions of acres) from 1997 through 2007 is given by $y = -4x + 967$. In the equation, x represents the number of years after 1997. (*Source:* National Agricultural Statistics Service)

a. Complete the table.

x	4	7	10
y			

b. Find the year in which there were approximately 930 million acres of land occupied by farms. (*Hint:* Find x when $y = 930$ and round to the nearest whole number.)

c. Use the given equation to predict when the land occupied by farms might be 900 million acres. (Use the hint for part b.)

Review

Solve each equation for y. See Section 2.5.

61. $x + y = 5$

62. $x - y = 3$

63. $2x + 4y = 5$

64. $5x + 2y = 7$

65. $10x = -5y$

66. $4y = -8x$

Concept Extensions

Answer each exercise with true or false.

67. Point $(-1, 5)$ lies in quadrant IV.

68. Point $(3, 0)$ lies on the y-axis.

69. For the point $\left(-\frac{1}{2}, 1.5\right)$, the first value, $-\frac{1}{2}$, is the x-coordinate and the second value, 1.5, is the y-coordinate.

70. The ordered pair $\left(2, \frac{2}{3}\right)$ is a solution of $2x - 3y = 6$.

For Exercises 71 through 75, fill in each blank with "0," "positive," or "negative." For Exercises 76 and 77, fill in each blank with "x" or "y."

	Point	Location
71.	(______, ______)	quadrant III
72.	(______, ______)	quadrant I
73.	(______, ______)	quadrant IV
74.	(______, ______)	quadrant II
75.	(______, ______)	origin
76.	(number, 0)	__-axis
77.	(0, number)	__-axis

78. Give an example of an ordered pair whose location is in (or on)

a. quadrant I **b.** quadrant II **c.** quadrant III
d. quadrant IV **e.** x-axis **f.** y-axis

Solve. See the Concept Checks in this section.

79. Is the graph of $(3, 0)$ in the same location as the graph of $(0, 3)$? Explain why or why not.

80. Give the coordinates of a point such that if the coordinates are reversed, the location is the same.

81. In general, what points can have coordinates reversed and still have the same location?

82. In your own words, describe how to plot or graph an ordered pair of numbers.

83. Discuss any similarities in the graphs of the ordered pair solutions for Exercises 53–56.

84. Discuss any differences in the graphs of the ordered pair solution for Exercises 53–56.

Write an ordered pair for each point described.

85. Point C is four units to the right of the y-axis and seven units below the x-axis.

86. Point D is three units to the left of the origin.

87. Find the perimeter of the rectangle whose vertices are the points with coordinates $(-1, 5)$, $(3, 5)$, $(3, -4)$, and $(-1, -4)$.

88. Find the area of the rectangle whose vertices are the points with coordinates $(5, 2)$, $(5, -6)$, $(0, -6)$, and $(0, 2)$.

The scatter diagram below shows Target's annual revenues. The horizontal axis represents the number of years after 2003.

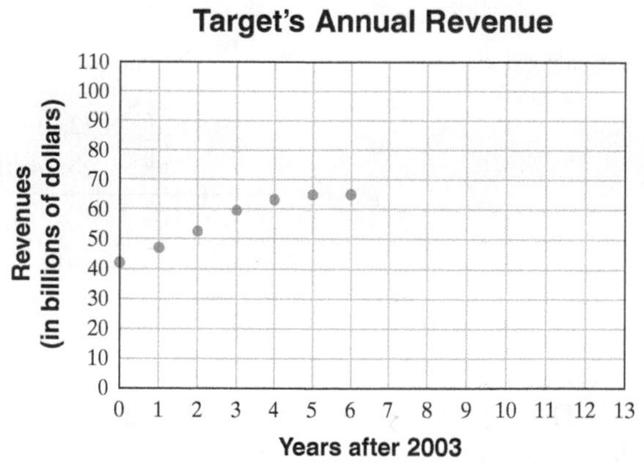

89. Estimate the annual revenues for years 1, 2, 3, and 4.

90. Use a straightedge or ruler and this scatter diagram to predict Target's revenue in the year 2015.

Objective

A **Graph a Linear Equation by Finding and Plotting Ordered Pair Solutions.**

6.2 GRAPHING LINEAR EQUATIONS

In the previous section, we found that equations in two variables may have more than one solution. For example, both (2, 2) and (0, 4) are solutions of the equation $x + y = 4$. In fact, this equation has an infinite number of solutions. Other solutions include $(-2, 6)$, $(4, 0)$, and $(6, -2)$. Notice the pattern that appears in the graph of these solutions.

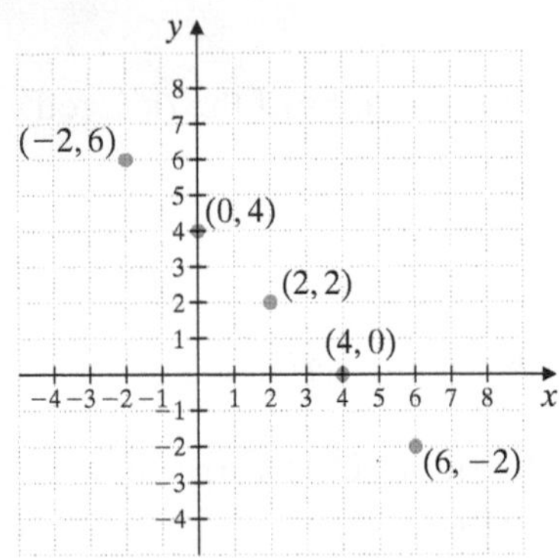

These solutions all appear to lie on the same line, as seen in the second graph. It can be shown that every ordered pair solution of the equation corresponds to a point on this line, and every point on this line corresponds to an ordered pair solution. Thus, we say that this line is the **graph of the equation** $x + y = 4$. Notice that we can show only a part of a line on a graph. The arrowheads on each end of the line below remind us that the line actually extends indefinitely in both directions.

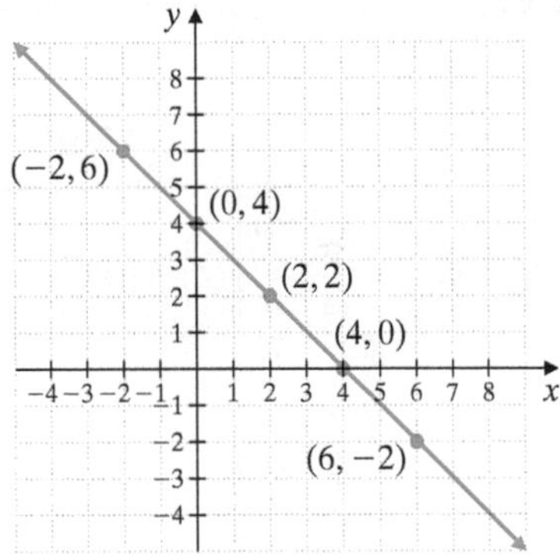

The equation $x + y = 4$ is called a *linear equation in two variables* and *the graph of every linear equation in two variables is a straight line.*

Linear Equation in Two Variables

A **linear equation in two variables** is an equation that can be written in the form

$$Ax + By = C$$

where A, B, and C are real numbers and A and B are not both 0. This form is called **standard form. The graph of a linear equation in two variables is a straight line.**

A linear equation in two variables may be written in many forms. Standard form, $Ax + By = C$, is just one of many of these forms.

Following are examples of linear equations in two variables.

$2x + y = 8$ (Standard Form) $\quad -2x = 7y \quad y = \frac{1}{3}x + 2 \quad y = 7$

Objective A Graphing Linear Equations

From geometry, we know that a straight line is determined by just two points. Thus, to graph a linear equation in two variables, we need to find just two of its infinitely many solutions. Once we do so, we plot the solution points and draw the line connecting the points. Usually, we find a third solution as well, as a check.

Example 1 Graph the linear equation $2x + y = 5$.

Solution: To graph this equation, we find three ordered pair solutions of $2x + y = 5$. To do this, we choose a value for one variable, x or y, and solve for the other variable. For example, if we let $x = 1$, then $2x + y = 5$ becomes

$2x + y = 5$
$2(1) + y = 5$ Replace x with 1.
$2 + y = 5$ Multiply.
$y = 3$ Subtract 2 from both sides.

Since $y = 3$ when $x = 1$, the ordered pair $(1, 3)$ is a solution of $2x + y = 5$. Next, we let $x = 0$.

$2x + y = 5$
$2(0) + y = 5$ Replace x with 0.
$0 + y = 5$
$y = 5$

The ordered pair $(0, 5)$ is a second solution.

The two solutions found so far allow us to draw the straight line that is the graph of all solutions of $2x + y = 5$. However, we will find a third ordered pair as a check. Let $y = -1$.

$2x + y = 5$
$2x + (-1) = 5$ Replace y with -1.
$2x - 1 = 5$
$2x = 6$ Add 1 to both sides.
$x = 3$ Divide both sides by 2.

The third solution is $(3, -1)$. These three ordered pair solutions are listed in the table and plotted on the coordinate plane. The graph of $2x + y = 5$ is the line through the three points.

x	y
1	3
0	5
3	−1

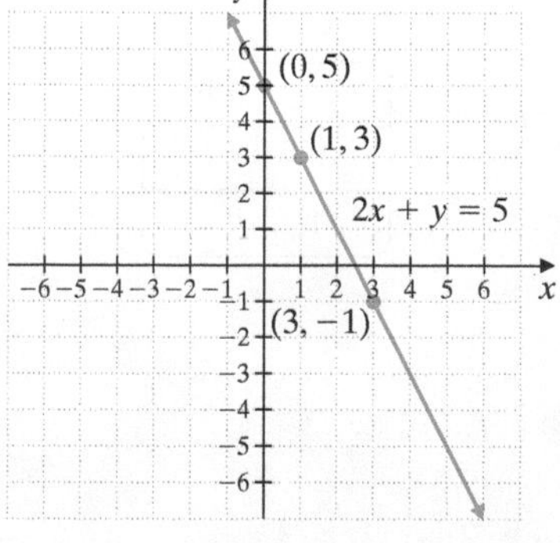

Work Practice 1

PRACTICE 1

Graph the linear equation $x + 3y = 6$.

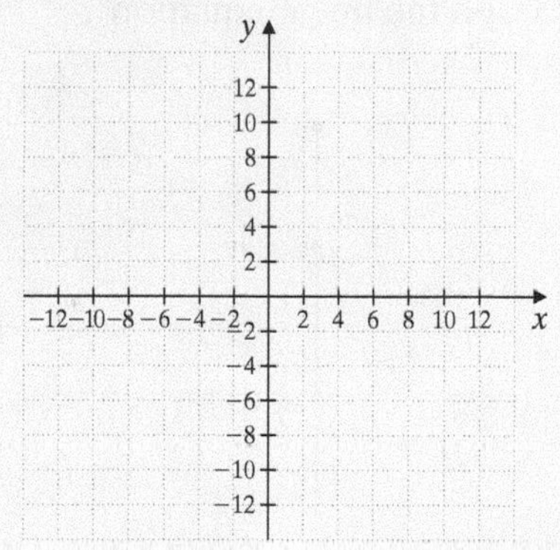

Helpful Hint All three points should fall on the same straight line. If not, check your ordered pair solutions for a mistake.

Answer

1.

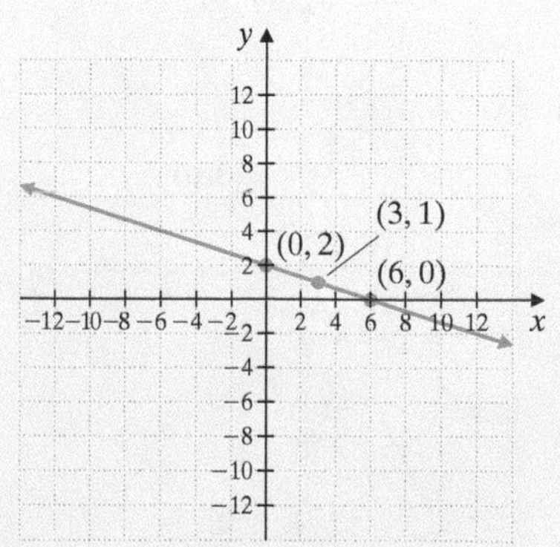

PRACTICE 2

Graph the linear equation $-2x + 4y = 8$.

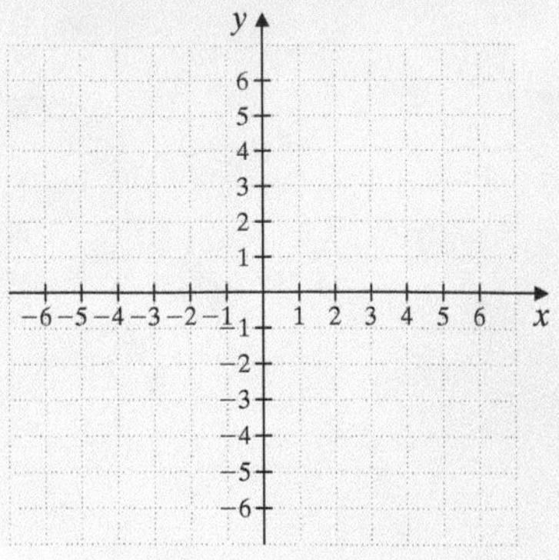

PRACTICE 3

Graph the linear equation $y = 2x$.

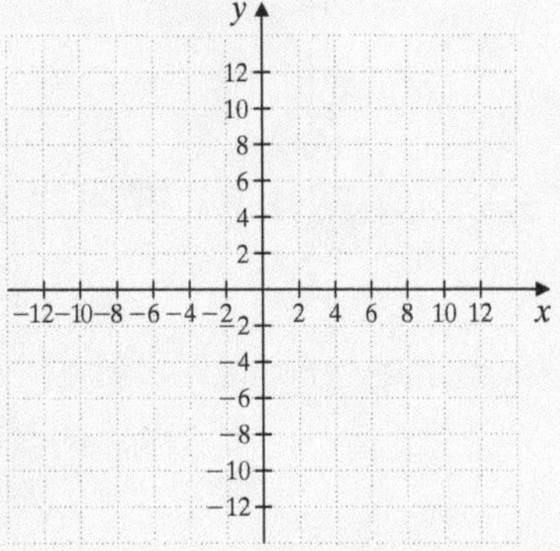

Answers

2.

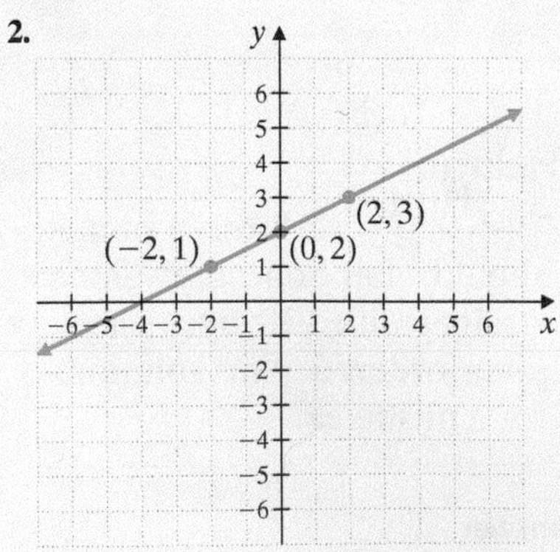

3.

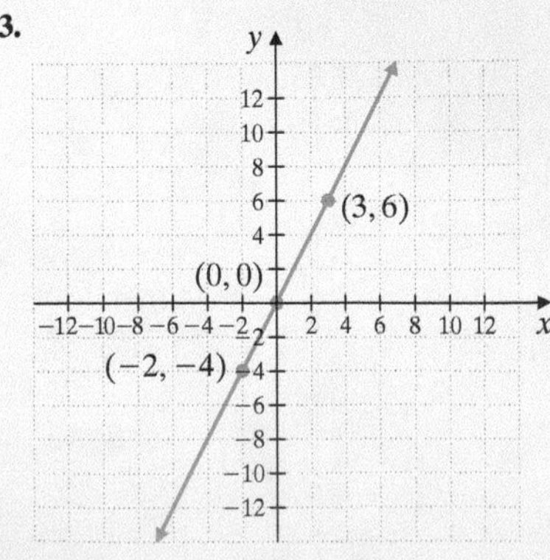

Example 2 Graph the linear equation $-5x + 3y = 15$.

Solution: We find three ordered pair solutions of $-5x + 3y = 15$.

Let $x = 0$.

$$-5x + 3y = 15$$
$$-5\cdot 0 + 3y = 15$$
$$0 + 3y = 15$$
$$3y = 15$$
$$y = 5$$

Let $y = 0$.

$$-5x + 3y = 15$$
$$-5x + 3\cdot 0 = 15$$
$$-5x + 0 = 15$$
$$-5x = 15$$
$$x = -3$$

Let $x = -2$.

$$-5x + 3y = 15$$
$$-5\cdot -2 + 3y = 15$$
$$10 + 3y = 15$$
$$3y = 5$$
$$y = \frac{5}{3} \text{ or } 1\frac{2}{3}$$

The ordered pairs are $(0, 5)$, $(-3, 0)$,and $\left(-2, 1\frac{2}{3}\right)$. The graph of $-5x + 3y = 15$ is the line through the three points.

x	y
0	5
−3	0
−2	$1\frac{2}{3}$

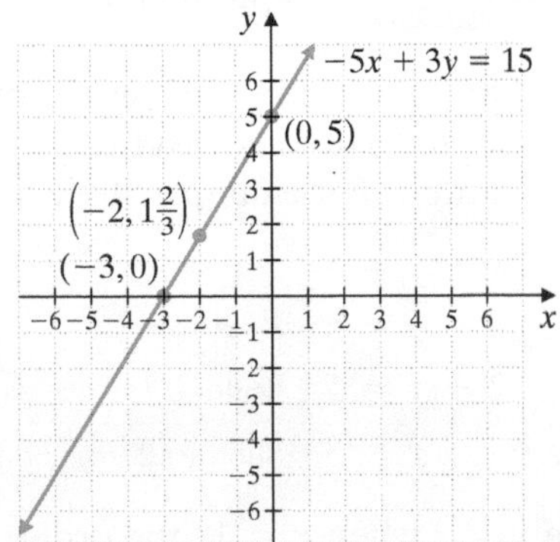

Work Practice 2

Example 3 Graph the linear equation $y = 3x$.

Solution: We find three ordered pair solutions. Since this equation is solved for y, we'll choose three x-values.

If $x = 2$, $y = 3\cdot 2 = 6$.
If $x = 0$, $y = 3\cdot 0 = 0$.
If $x = -1$, $y = 3\cdot -1 = -3$.

Next, we plot the ordered pair solutions and draw a line through the plotted points. The line is the graph of $y = 3x$.

Think about the following for a moment: A line is made up of an infinite number of points. Every point on the line defined by $y = 3x$ represents an ordered pair solution of the equation and every ordered pair solution is a point on this line.

x	y
2	6
0	0
−1	−3

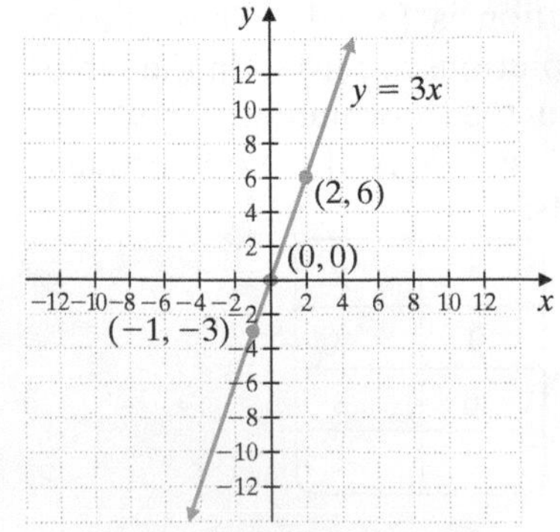

Work Practice 3

Helpful Hint

When graphing a linear equation in two variables, if it is

- solved for y, it may be easier to find ordered pair solutions by choosing x-values. If it is
- solved for x, it may be easier to find ordered pair solutions by choosing y-values.

Example 4 Graph the linear equation $y = -\frac{1}{3}x + 2$.

Solution: We find three ordered pair solutions, plot the solutions, and draw a line through the plotted solutions. To avoid fractions, we'll choose x-values that are multiples of 3 to substitute into the equation.

If $x = 6$, then $y = -\frac{1}{3}\cdot 6 + 2 = -2 + 2 = 0$

If $x = 0$, then $y = -\frac{1}{3}\cdot 0 + 2 = 0 + 2 = 2$

If $x = -3$, then $y = -\frac{1}{3}\cdot -3 + 2 = 1 + 2 = 3$

x	y
6	0
0	2
−3	3

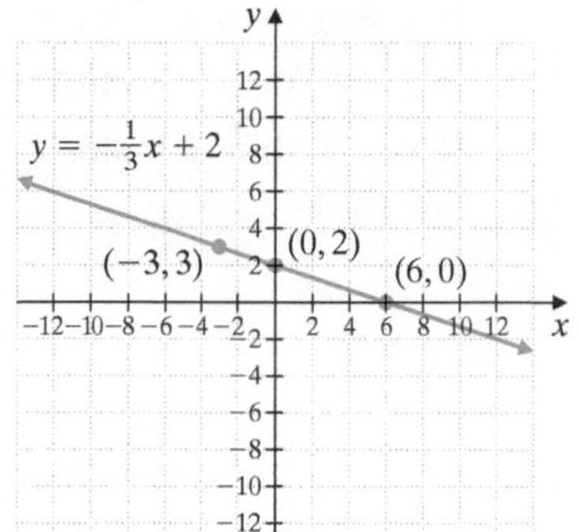

Work Practice 4

Let's take a moment and compare the graphs in Examples 3 and 4. The graph of $y = 3x$ tilts upward (as we follow the line from left to right) and the graph of $y = -\frac{1}{3}x + 2$ tilts downward (as we follow the line from left to right). We will learn more about the tilt, or slope, of a line in Section 6.4.

Example 5 Graph the linear equation $y = -2$.

Solution: The equation $y = -2$ can be written in standard form as $0x + y = -2$. No matter what value we replace x with, y is always -2.

x	y
0	−2
3	−2
−2	−2

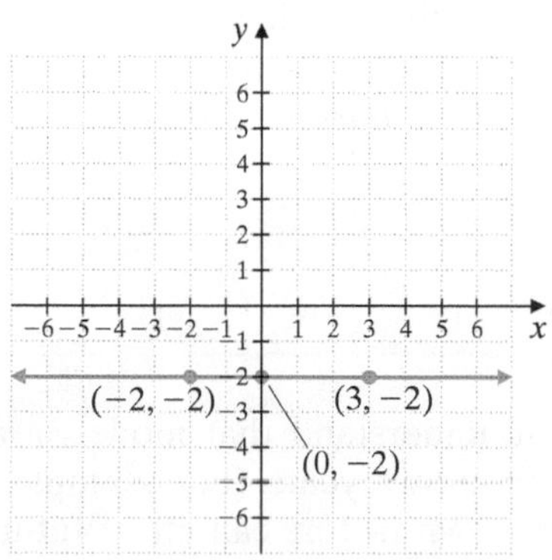

Notice that the graph of $y = -2$ is a horizontal line.

Work Practice 5

Linear equations are often used to model real data, as seen in the next example.

PRACTICE 4

Graph the linear equation $y = -\frac{1}{2}x + 4$.

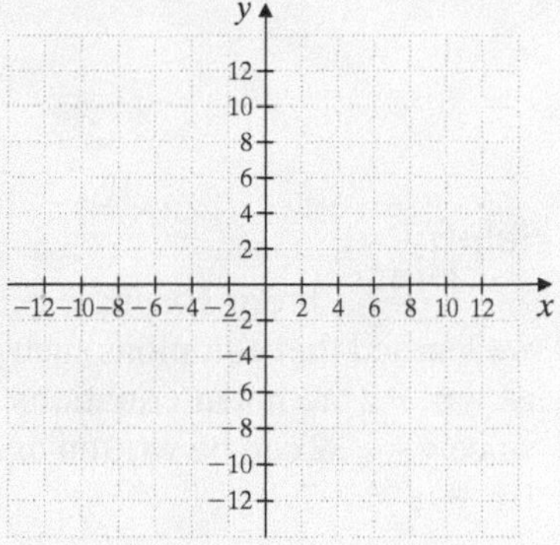

PRACTICE 5

Graph the linear equation $x = 3$.

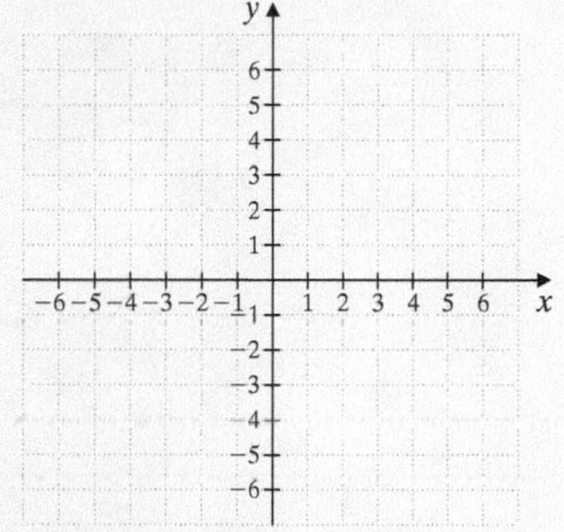

Answers

4.

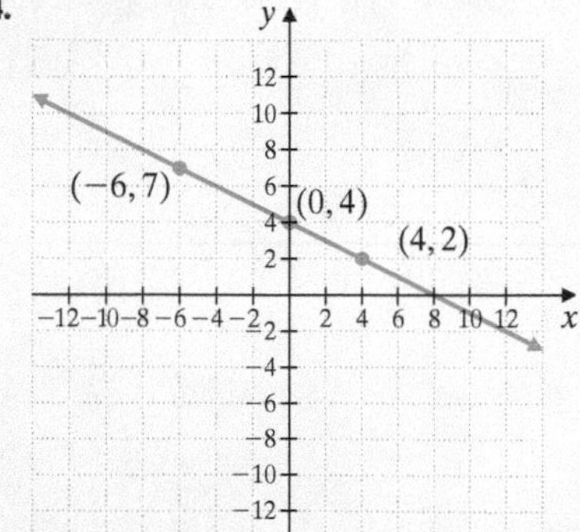

5.

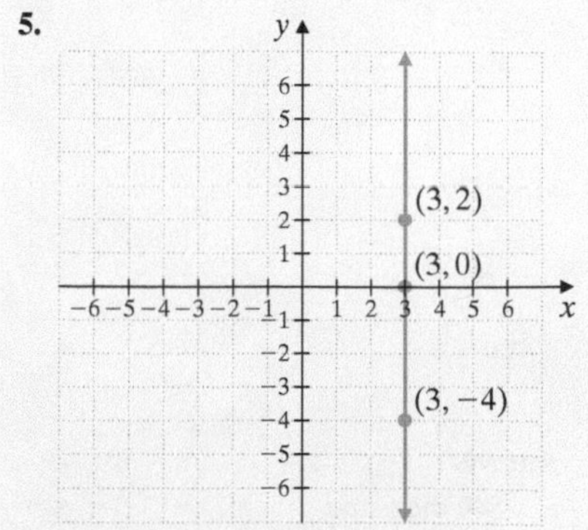

PRACTICE 6

Use the graph in Example 6 to predict the number of registered nurses in 2015.

Helpful Hint From Example 5, we learned that equations such as $y = -2$ are linear equations since $y = -2$ can be written as $0x + y = -2$.

Example 6 Estimating the Number of Registered Nurses

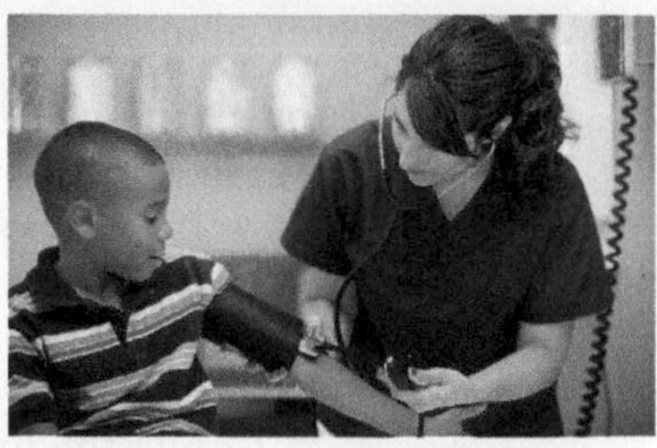

One of the occupations expected to have the most growth in the next few years is registered nurse. The number of people y (in thousands) employed as registered nurses in the United States can be estimated by the linear equation $y = 46.7x + 2279$, where x is the number of years after the year 2003. (*Source:* Based on data from the Bureau of Labor Statistics)

a. Graph the equation.

b. Use the graph to predict the number of registered nurses in the year 2014.

Solution:

a. To graph $y = 46.7x + 2279$, choose x-values and substitute in the equation.

If $x = 0$, then $y = 46.7(0) + 2279 = 2279$.

If $x = 2$, then $y = 46.7(2) + 2279 = 2372.4$.

If $x = 5$, then $y = 46.7(5) + 2279 = 2512.5$.

x	y
0	2279
2	2372.4
5	2512.5

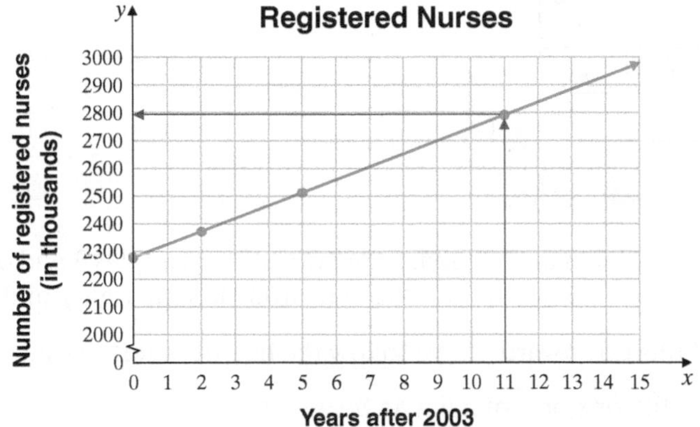

b. To use the graph to *predict* the number of registered nurses in the year 2014, we need to find the y-coordinate that corresponds to $x = 11$. (11 years after 2003 is the year 2014.) To do so, find 11 on the x-axis. Move vertically upward to the graphed line and then horizontally to the left. We approximate the number on the y-axis to be 2800. Thus, in the year 2014, we predict that there will be 2800 thousand registered nurses. (The actual value, using 11 for x, is 2792.7.)

Work Practice 6

Helpful Hint

Make sure you understand that models are mathematical approximations of the data for the known years. (For example, see the model in Example 6.) Any number of unknown factors can affect future years, so be cautious when using models to make predictions.

Answer

6. 2840 thousand

Calculator Explorations Graphing

In this section, we begin an optional study of graphing calculators and graphing software packages for computers. These graphers use the same point plotting technique that was introduced in this section. The advantage of this graphing technology is, of course, that graphing calculators and computers can find and plot ordered pair solutions much faster than we can. Note, however, that the features described in these boxes may not be available on all graphing calculators.

The rectangular screen where a portion of the rectangular coordinate system is displayed is called a **window.** We call it a **standard window** for graphing when both the x- and y-axes show coordinates between -10 and 10. This information is often displayed in the window menu on a graphing calculator as follows.

Xmin = −10
Xmax = 10
Xscl = 1 The scale on the x-axis is one unit per tick mark.
Ymin = −10
Ymax = 10
Yscl = 1 The scale on the y-axis is one unit per tick mark.

To use a graphing calculator to graph the equation $y = 2x + 3$, press the [Y=] key and enter the keystrokes [2] [x] [+] [3]. The top row should now read $Y_1 = 2x + 3$. Next press the [GRAPH] key, and the display should look like this:

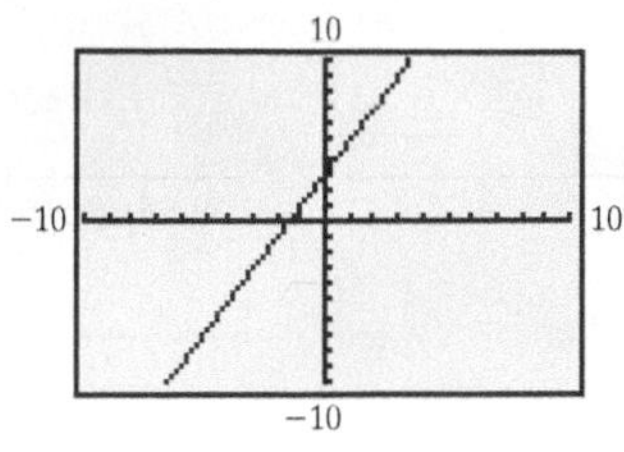

Graph the following linear equations. (Unless otherwise stated, use a standard window when graphing.)

1. $y = -3x + 7$

2. $y = -x + 5$

3. $y = 2.5x - 7.9$

4. $y = -1.3x + 5.2$

5. $y = -\frac{3}{10}x + \frac{32}{5}$

6. $y = \frac{2}{9}x - \frac{22}{3}$

6.2 Exercise Set

FOR EXTRA HELP

PRACTICE

WATCH

DOWNLOAD

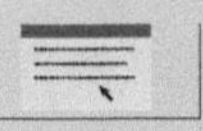
READ

REVIEW

Objective A *For each equation, find three ordered pair solutions by completing the table. Then use the ordered pairs to graph the equation. See Examples 1 through 5.*

1. $x - y = 6$

x	y
	0
4	
	−1

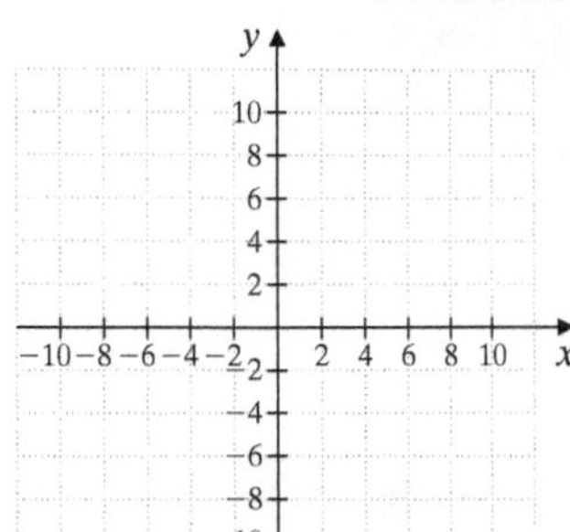

2. $x - y = 4$

x	y
0	
	2
−1	

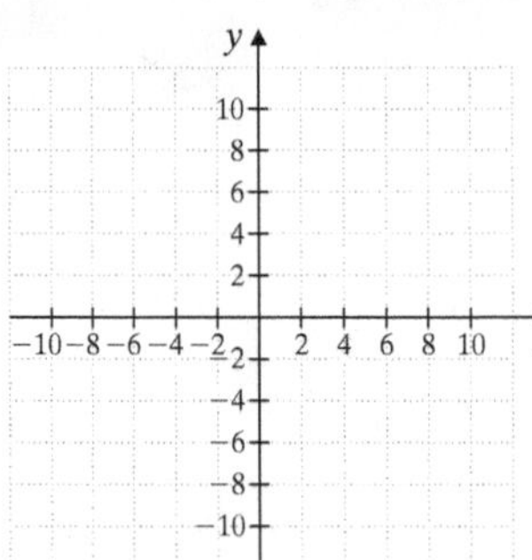

3. $y = -4x$

x	y
1	
0	
−1	

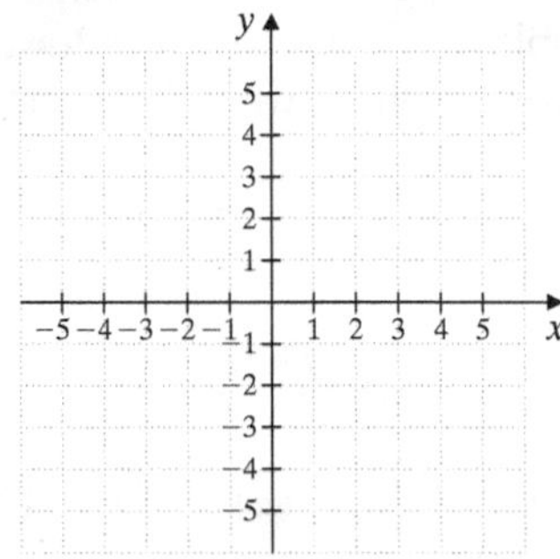

4. $y = -5x$

x	y
1	
0	
−1	

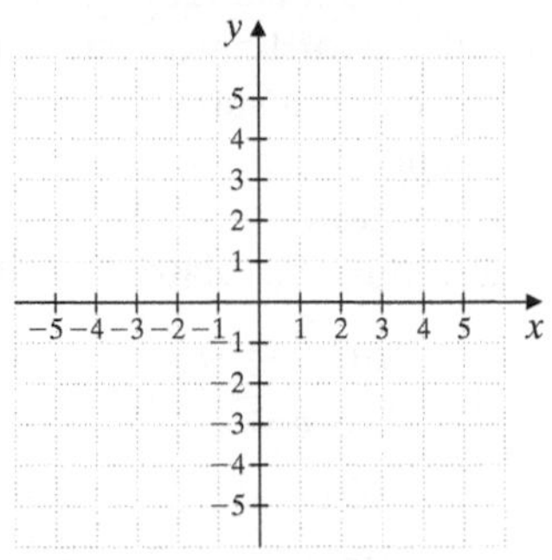

5. $y = \frac{1}{3}x$

x	y
0	
6	
−3	

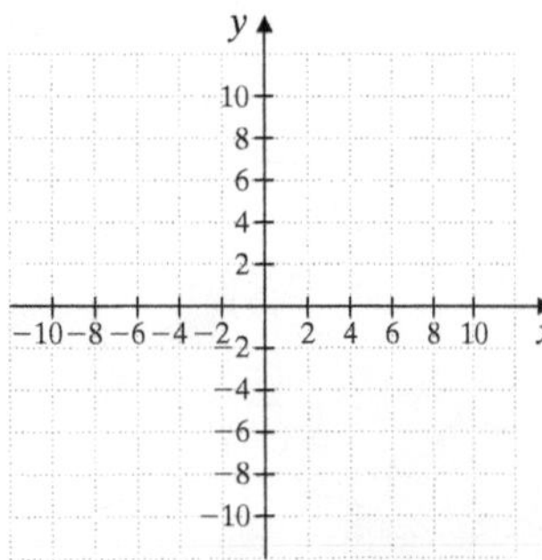

6. $y = \frac{1}{2}x$

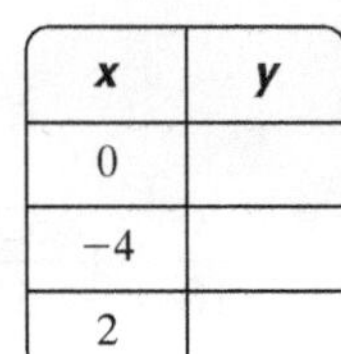

x	y
0	
−4	
2	

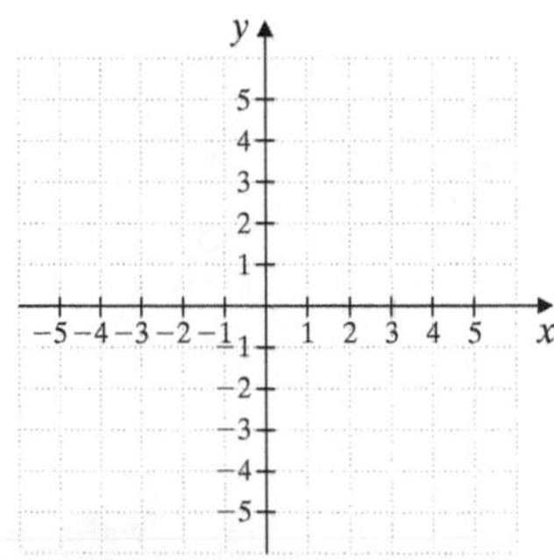

7. $y = -4x + 3$

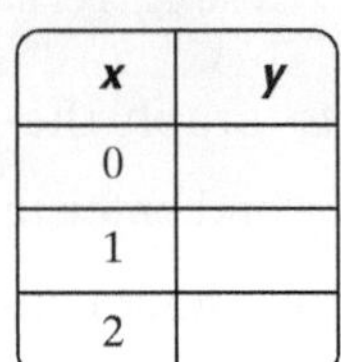

x	y
0	
1	
2	

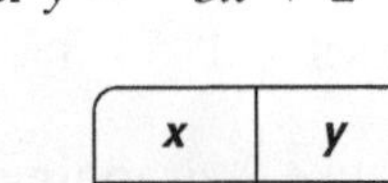

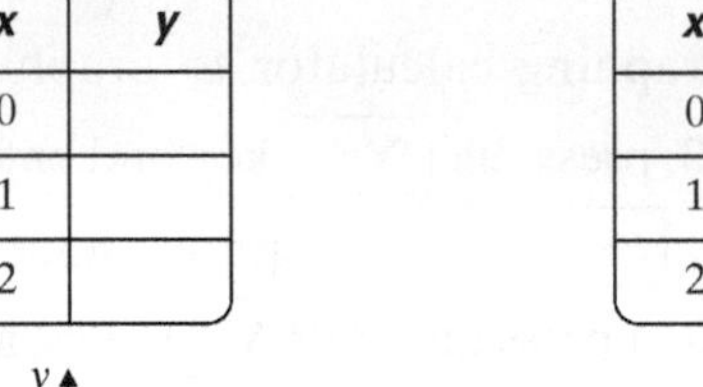

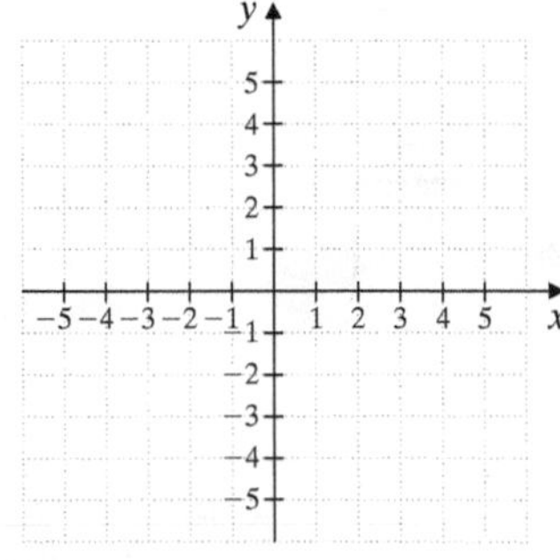

8. $y = -5x + 2$

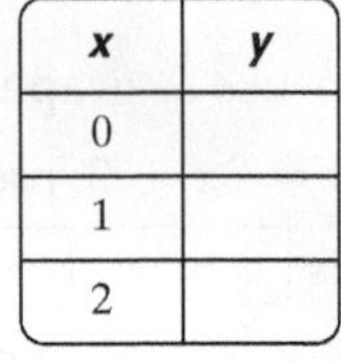

x	y
0	
1	
2	

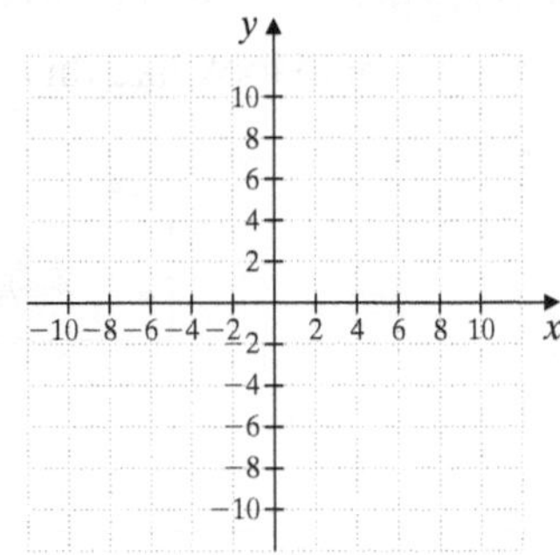

Graph each linear equation. See Examples 1 through 5.

9. $x + y = 1$

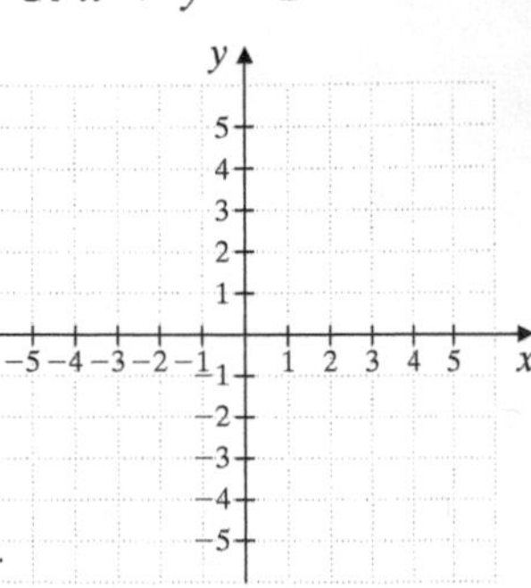

10. $x + y = 7$

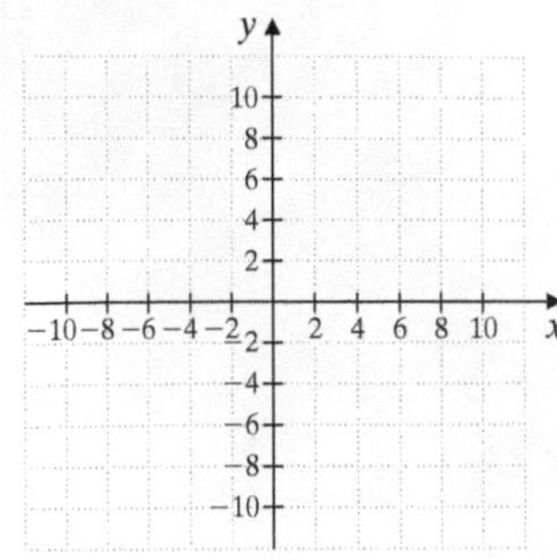

11. $x - y = -2$

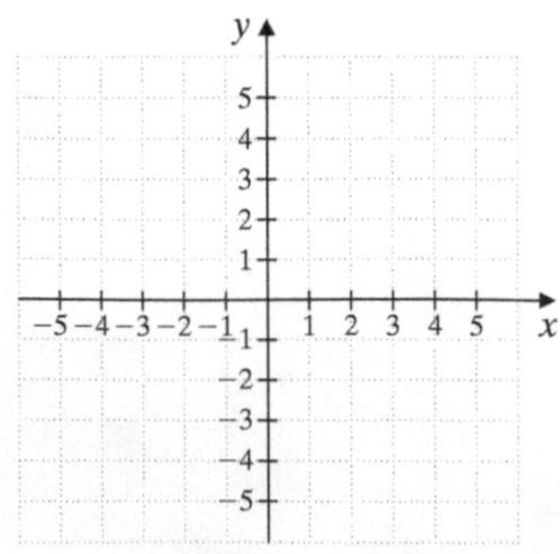

12. $-x + y = 6$

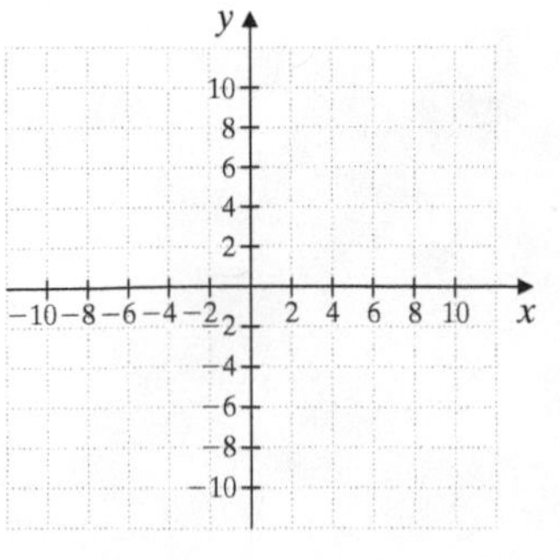

13. $x - 2y = 6$

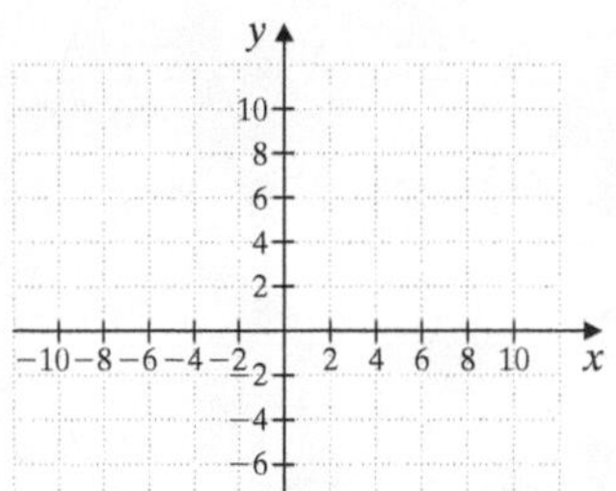

14. $-x + 5y = 5$

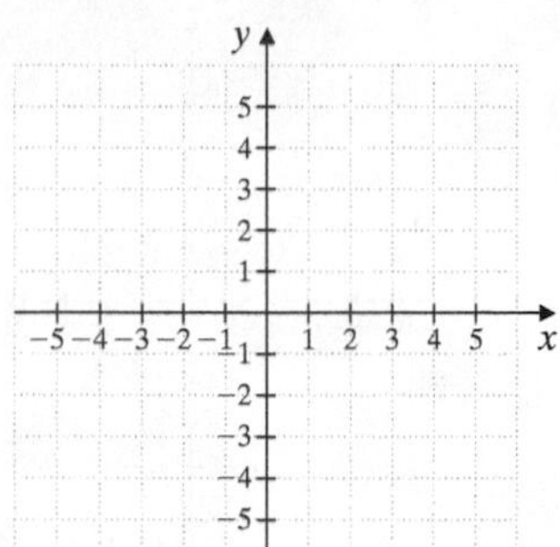

15. $y = 6x + 3$

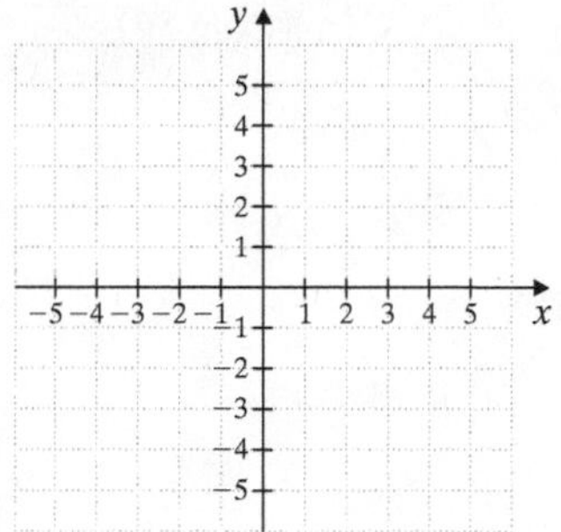

16. $y = -2x + 7$

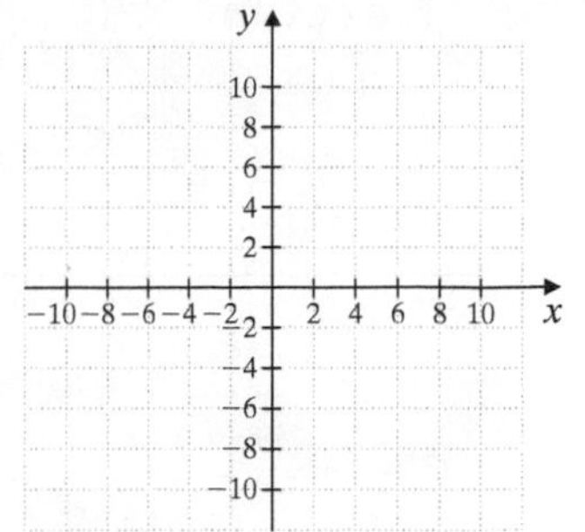

17. $x = -4$

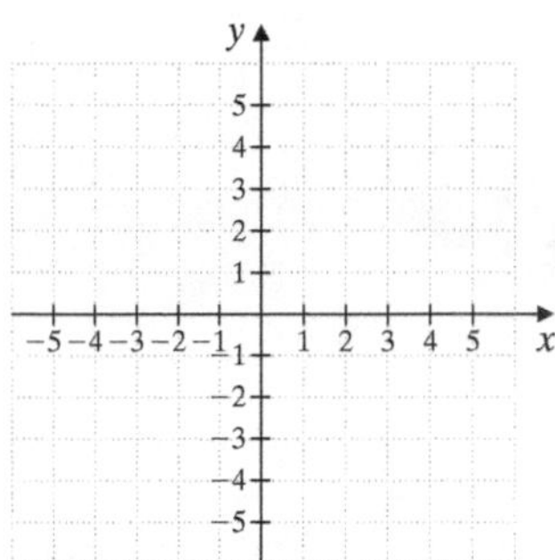

18. $y = 5$

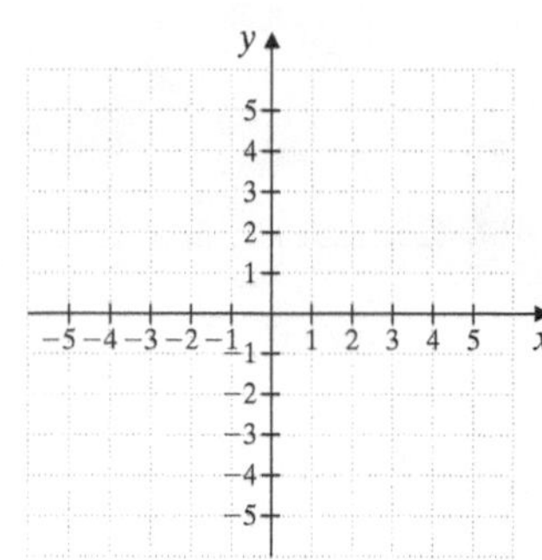

19. $y = 3$

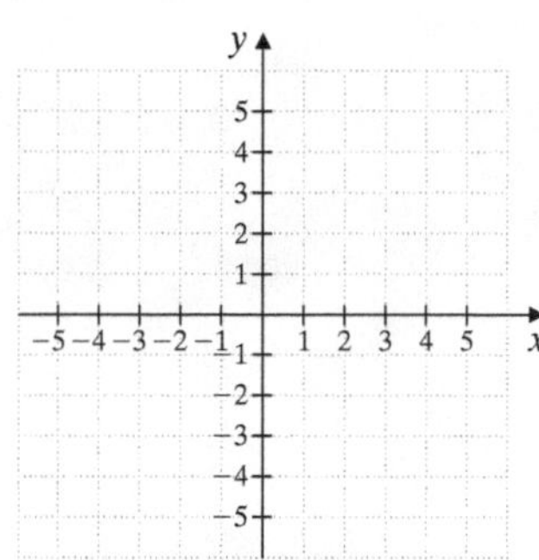

20. $x = -1$

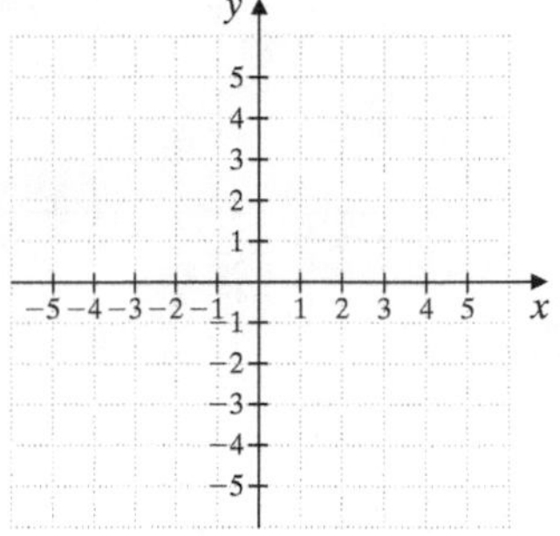

21. $y = x$

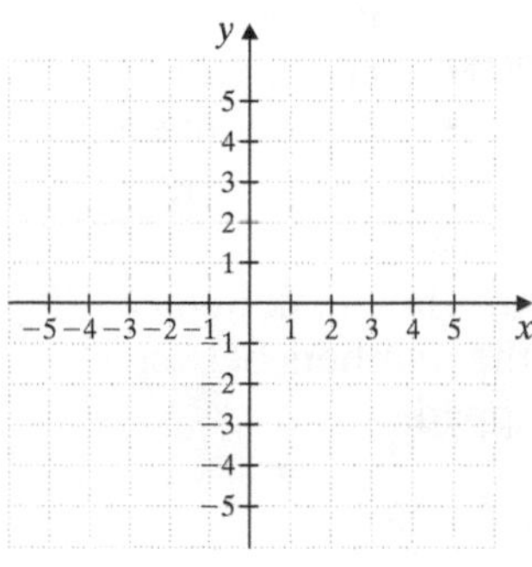

22. $y = -x$

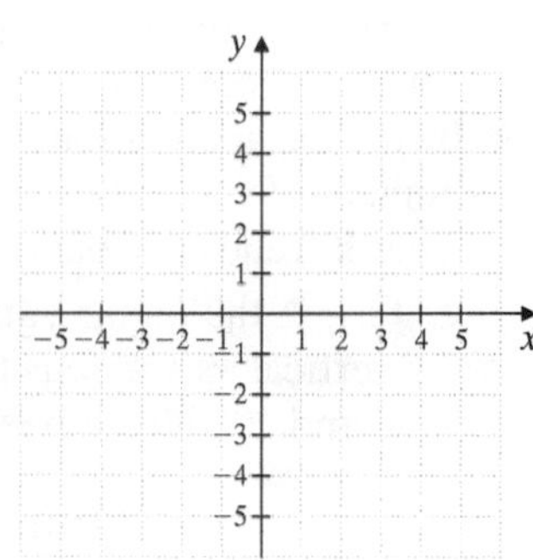

23. $x = -3y$

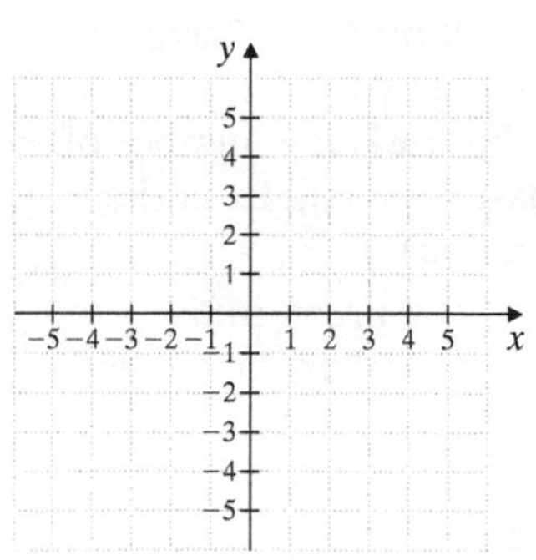

24. $x = 4y$

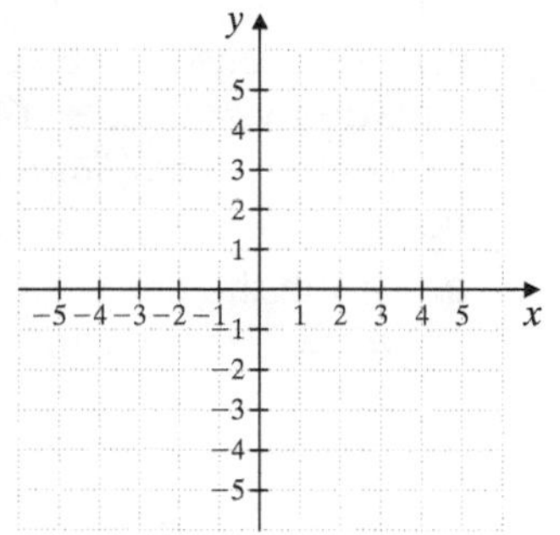

25. $x + 3y = 9$

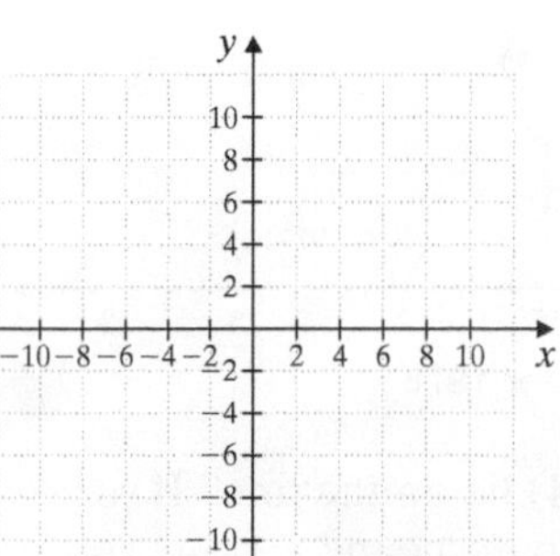

26. $2x + y = 2$

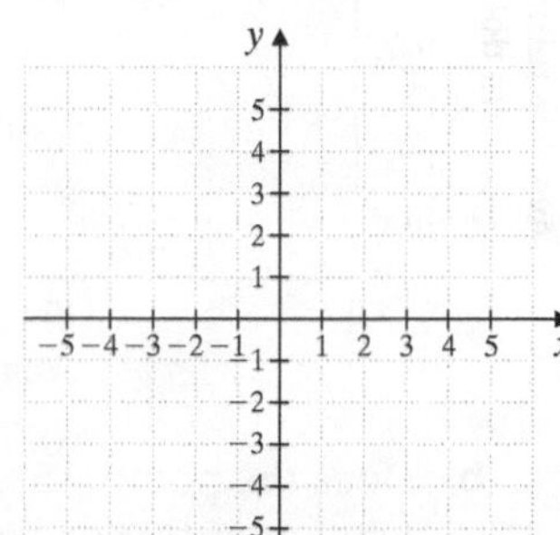

27. $y = \frac{1}{2}x + 2$

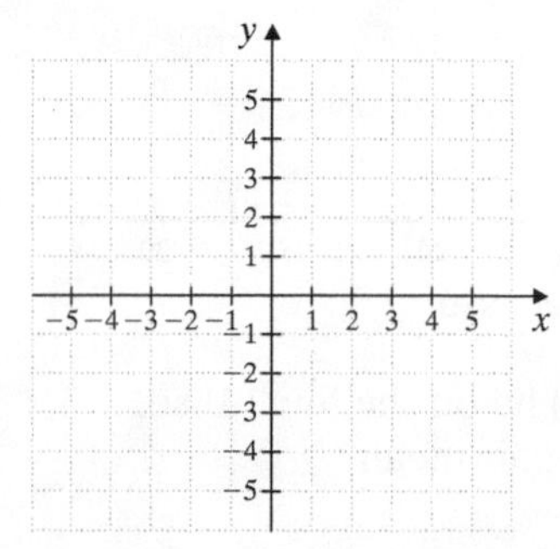

28. $y = \frac{1}{4}x + 3$

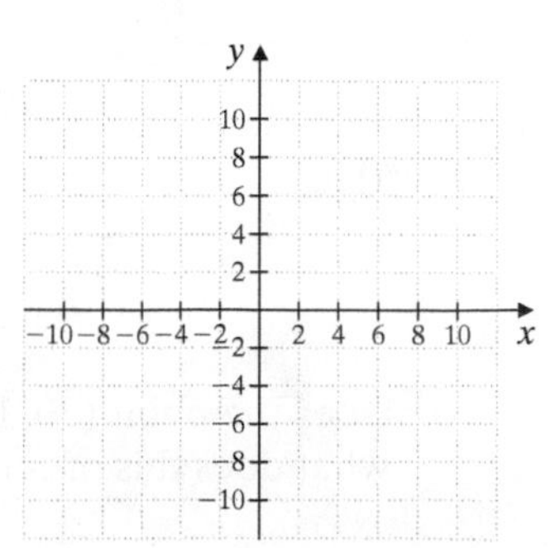

29. $3x - 2y = 12$

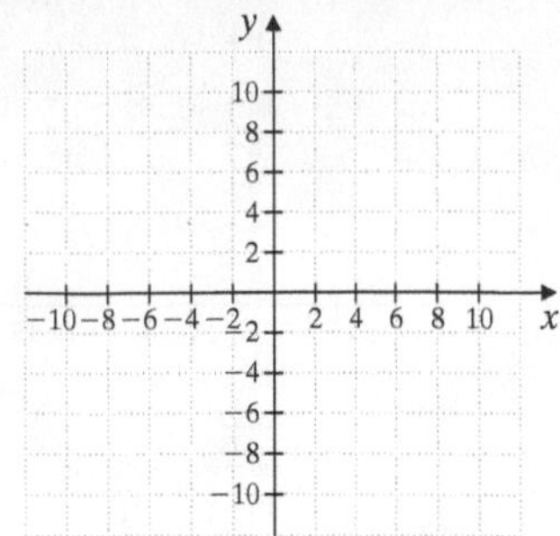

30. $2x - 7y = 14$

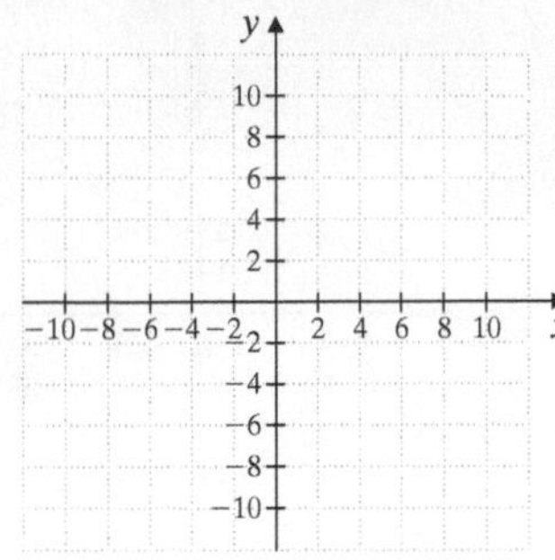

31. $y = -3.5x + 4$

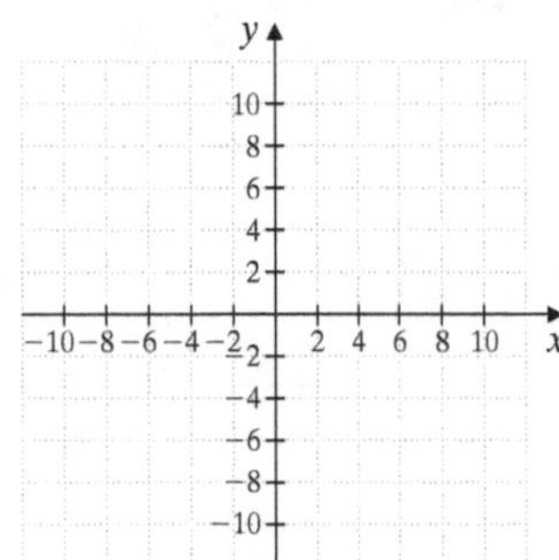

32. $y = -1.5x - 3$

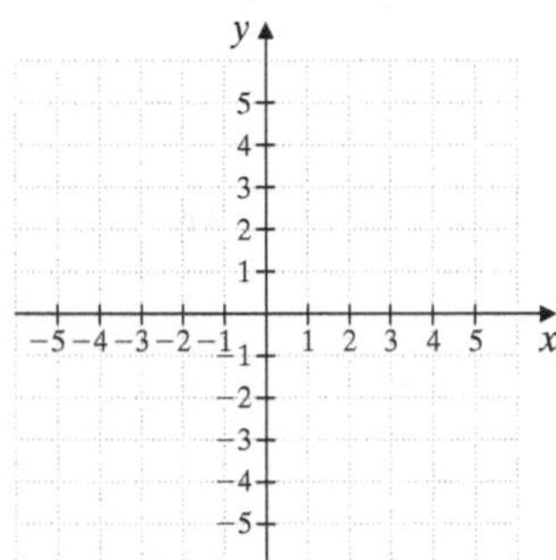

Solve. See Example 6.

33. One American rite of passage is a driver's license. The number of people y (in millions) who have a driver's license can be estimated by the linear equation $y = 2.2x + 145$, where x is the number of years after 1990. (*Source:* Based on data from the Federal Highway Administration)

a. Graph the linear equation. The break in the vertical axis means that the numbers between 0 and 100 have been skipped.

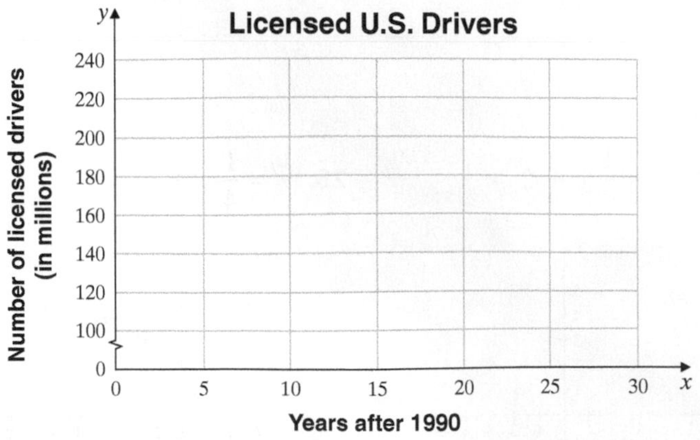

b. Does the point (20, 189) lie on the line? If so, what does this ordered pair mean?

34. College is getting more expensive every year. The average cost for tuition and fees at a public two-year college y from 1978 through 2009 can be approximated by the linear equation $y = 45x + 1089$, where x is the number of years after 1978. (*Source:* The College Board: Trends in College Pricing 2008)

a. Graph the linear equation. The break in the vertical axis means that the numbers between 0 and 1000 have been skipped.

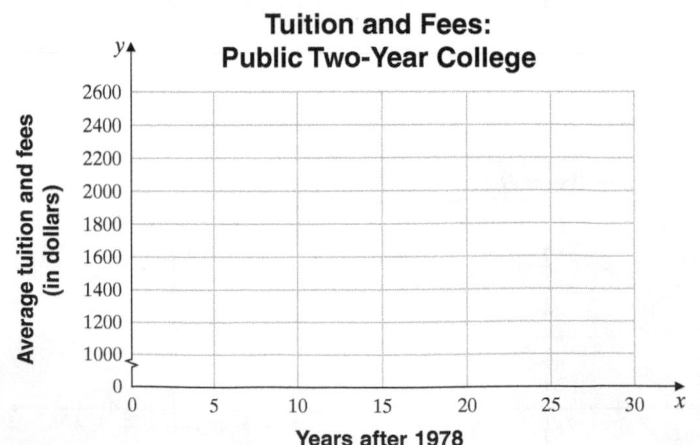

b. Does the point (15, 1764) lie on the line? If so, what does this ordered pair mean?

35. The percent of U.S. households y that have at least one computer can be approximated by the linear equation $y = 5.6x + 38.5$, where x is the number of years since 1998. (*Source: Statistical Abstract of the United States*)

a. Graph the linear equation.

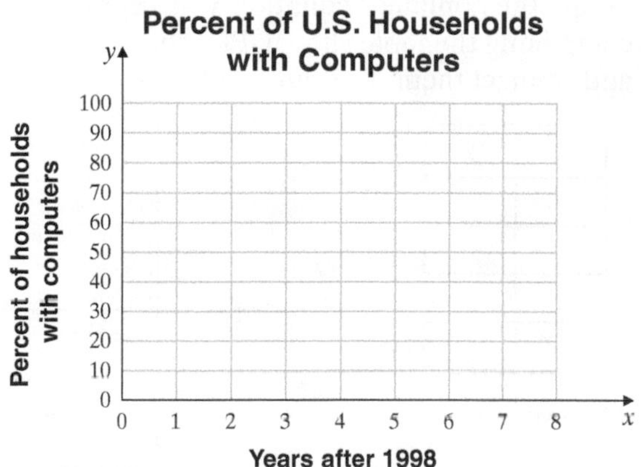

b. Complete the ordered pair (5,).

c. Write a sentence explaining the meaning of the ordered pair found in part b.

36. The restaurant industry is still busier than ever. The yearly revenue for restaurants in the United States can be estimated by $y = 13.4x + 6.2$, where x is the number of years after 1970 and y is the revenue in billions of dollars. (*Source:* National Restaurant Association)

a. Graph the linear equation.

b. Complete the ordered pair (25,).

c. Write a sentence explaining the meaning of the ordered pair found in part b.

Review

37. The coordinates of three vertices of a rectangle are $(-2, 5)$, $(4, 5)$, and $(-2, -1)$. Find the coordinates of the fourth vertex. See Section 6.1.

38. The coordinates of two vertices of a square are $(-3, -1)$ and $(2, -1)$. Find the coordinates of two pairs of points possible for the third and fourth vertices. See Section 6.1.

Complete each table. See Section 6.1.

39. $x - y = -3$

x	y
0	
	0

40. $y - x = 5$

x	y
0	
	0

41. $y = 2x$

x	y
0	
	0

42. $x = -3y$

x	y
0	
	0

Concept Extensions

Graph each pair of linear equations on the same set of axes. Discuss how the graphs are similar and how they are different.

43. $y = 5x$
$y = 5x + 4$

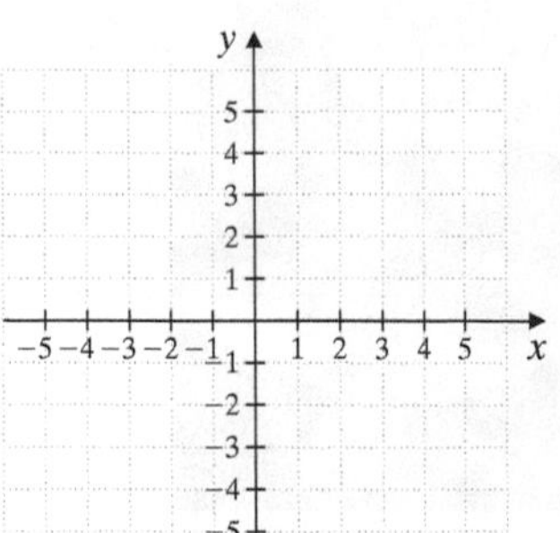

44. $y = 2x$
$y = 2x + 5$

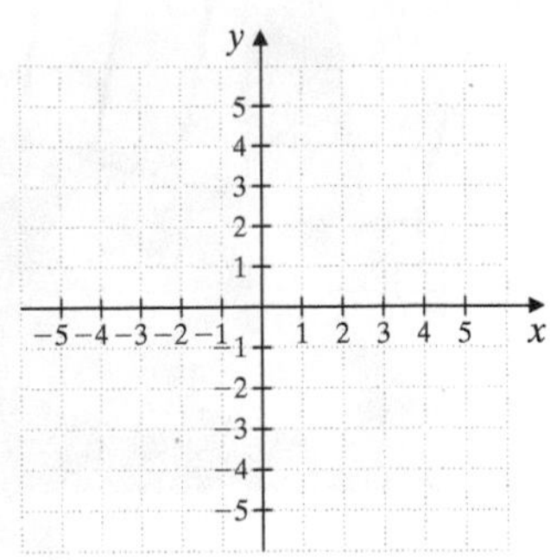

45. $y = -2x$
$y = -2x - 3$

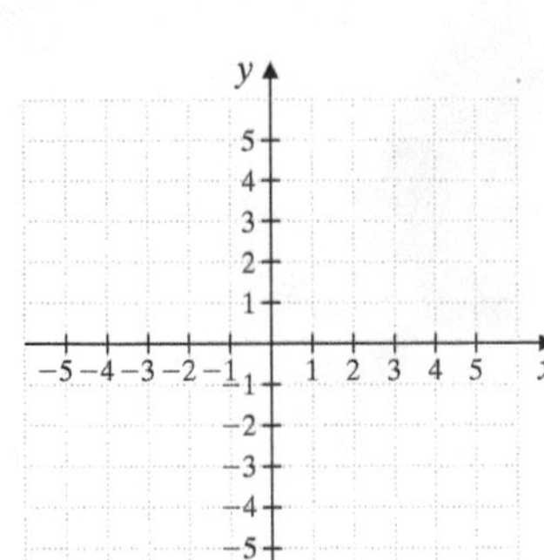

46. $y = x$
$y = x - 7$

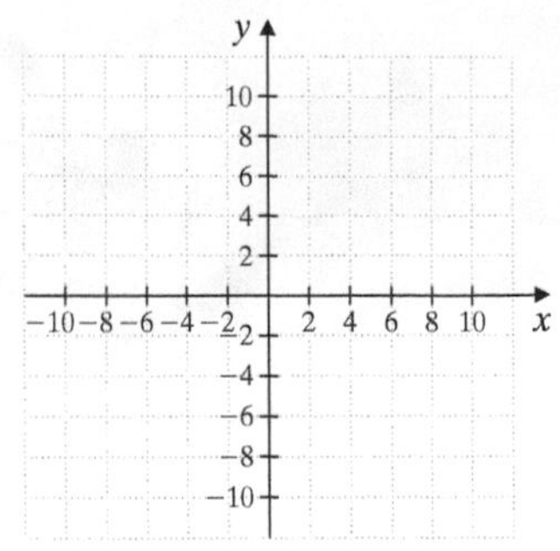

47. Graph the nonlinear equation $y = x^2$ by completing the table shown. Plot the ordered pairs and connect them with a smooth curve.

x	y
0	
1	
−1	
2	
−2	

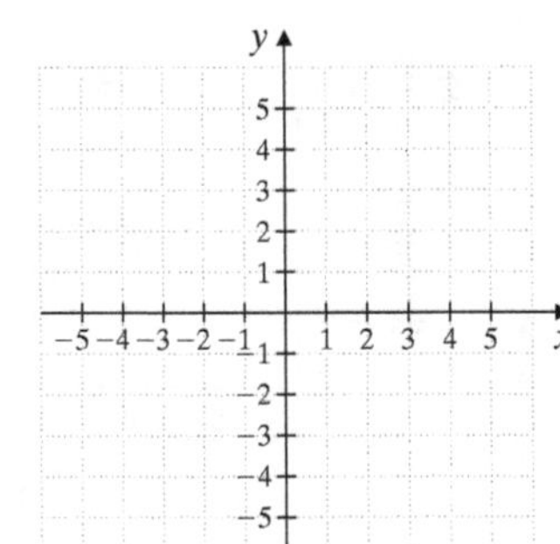

48. Graph the nonlinear equation $y = |x|$ by completing the table shown. Plot the ordered pairs and connect them. This curve is "V" shaped.

x	y
0	
1	
−1	
2	
−2	

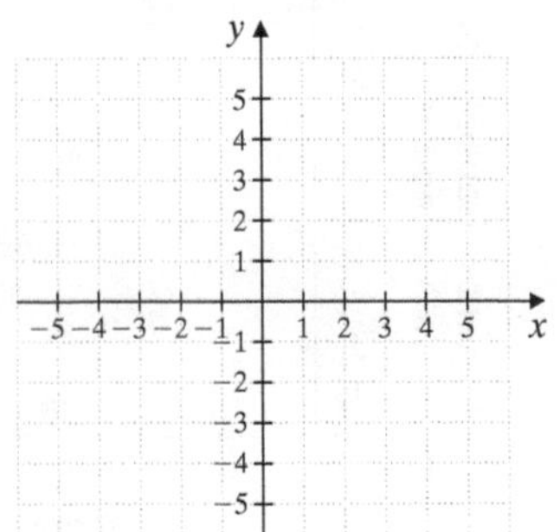

△ **49.** The perimeter of the trapezoid below is 22 centimeters. Write a linear equation in two variables for the perimeter. Find y if x is 3 centimeters.

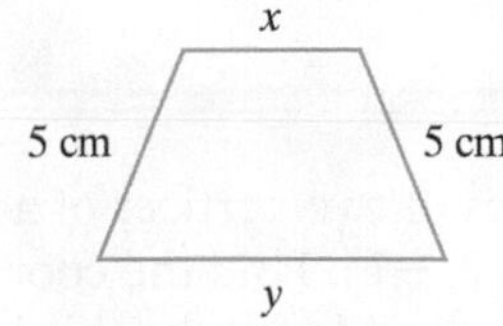

△ **50.** The perimeter of the rectangle below is 50 miles. Write a linear equation in two variables for the perimeter. Use this equation to find x when y is 20 miles.

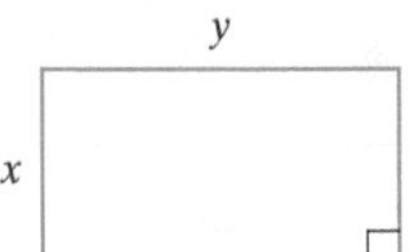

51. If (a, b) is an ordered pair solution of $x + y = 5$, is (b, a) also a solution? Explain why or why not.

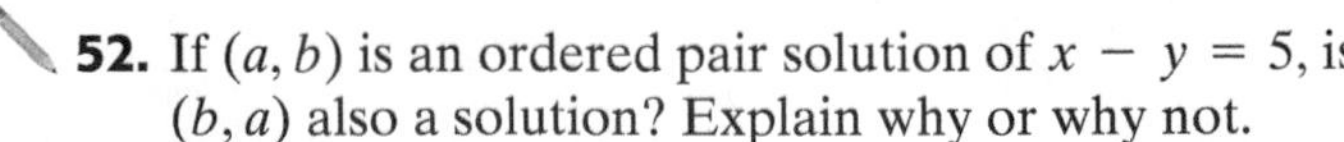

52. If (a, b) is an ordered pair solution of $x - y = 5$, is (b, a) also a solution? Explain why or why not.

6.3 INTERCEPTS

Objectives

A Identify Intercepts of a Graph.

B Graph a Linear Equation by Finding and Plotting Intercept Points.

C Identify and Graph Vertical and Horizontal Lines.

Objective A Identifying Intercepts

The graph of $y = 4x - 8$ is shown below. Notice that this graph crosses the y-axis at the point $(0, -8)$. This point is called the **y-intercept.** Likewise the graph crosses the x-axis at $(2, 0)$. This point is called the **x-intercept.**

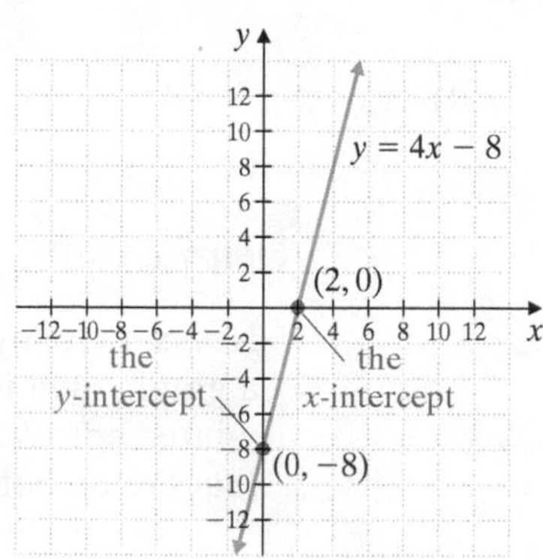

The intercepts are $(2, 0)$ and $(0, -8)$.

Helpful Hint

If a graph crosses the x-axis at $(2, 0)$ and the y-axis at $(0, -8)$, then

$(2, 0)$ ← x-intercept $(0, -8)$ ← y-intercept

Notice that for the x-intercept, the y-value is 0 and for the y-intercept, the x-value is 0.

Note: Sometimes in mathematics, you may see just the number -8 stated as the y-intercept, and 2 stated as the x-intercept.

Examples Identify the x- and y-intercepts.

1.

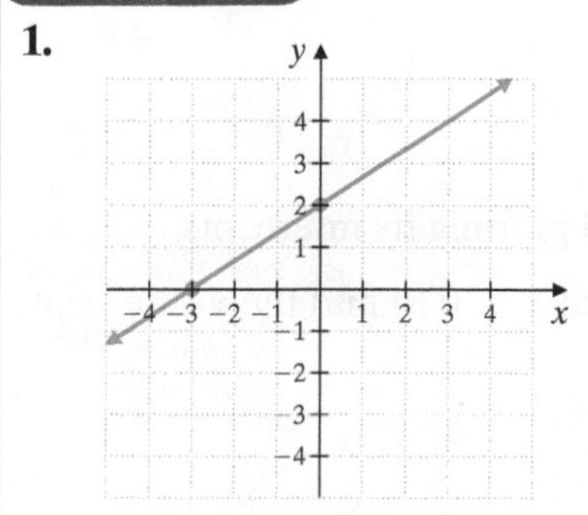

Solution:

x-intercept: $(-3, 0)$

y-intercept: $(0, 2)$

Continued on next page

PRACTICE 1

Identify the x- and y-intercepts.

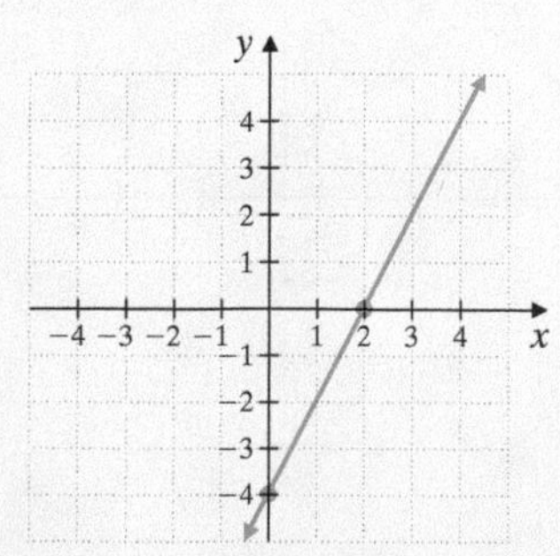

Answer

1. x-intercept: $(2, 0)$; y-intercept: $(0, -4)$

PRACTICE 2–3

Identify the x- and y-intercepts.

2.

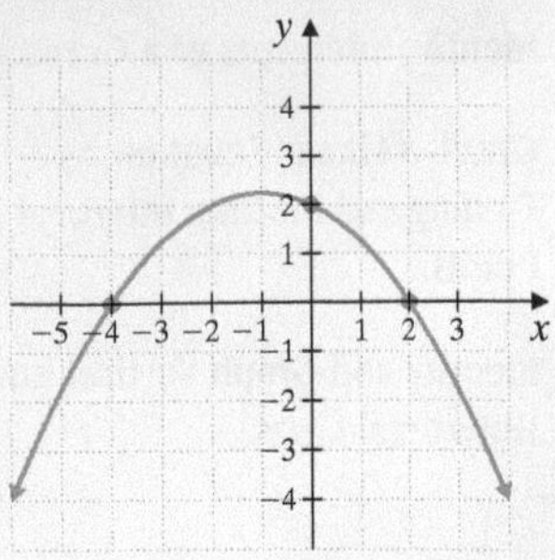

3.

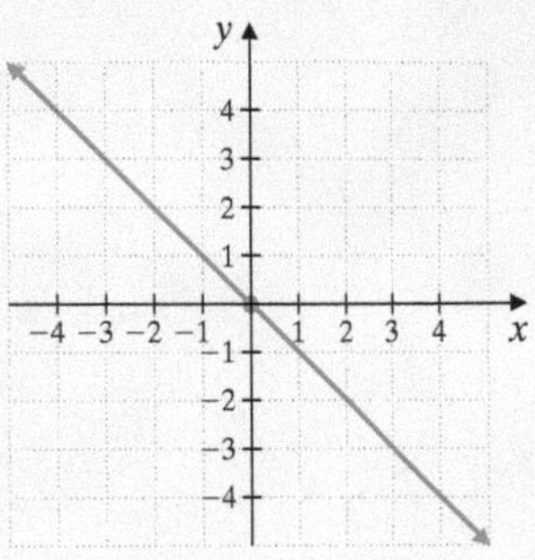

2.

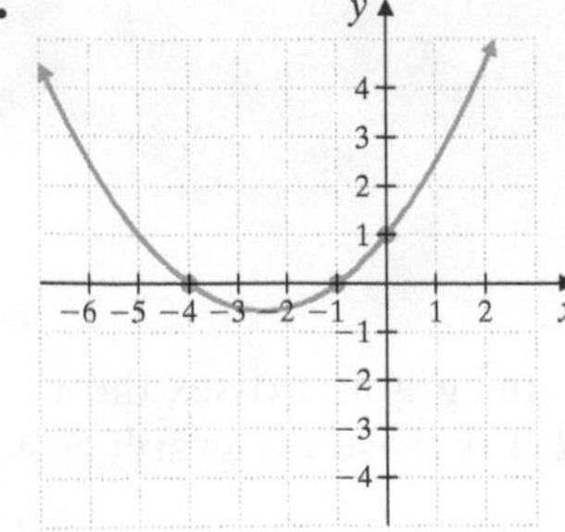

Solution:

x-intercepts: $(-4, 0), (-1, 0)$
y-intercept: $(0, 1)$

3.

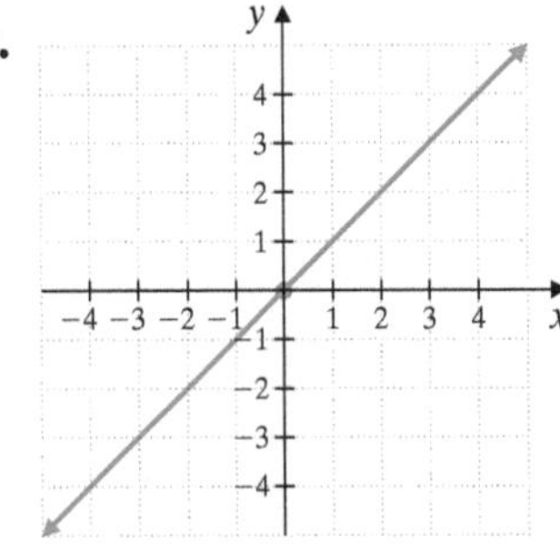

Solution:

x-intercept: $(0, 0)$
y-intercept: $(0, 0)$

Here, the x- and y-intercepts happen to be the same point.

Helpful Hint

Notice that any time $(0, 0)$ is a point of a graph, then it is an x-intercept and a y-intercept. Why? It is the *only* point that lies on both axes.

Work Practice 1–3

Objective B Finding and Plotting Intercepts

Given an equation of a line, we can usually find intercepts easily since one coordinate is 0.

To find the x-intercept of a line from its equation, let $y = 0$, since a point on the x-axis has a y-coordinate of 0. To find the y-intercept of a line from its equation, let $x = 0$, since a point on the y-axis has an x-coordinate of 0.

Finding x- and y-Intercepts

To find the x-intercept, let $y = 0$ and solve for x.
To find the y-intercept, let $x = 0$ and solve for y.

PRACTICE 4

Graph $2x - y = 4$ by finding and plotting its intercepts.

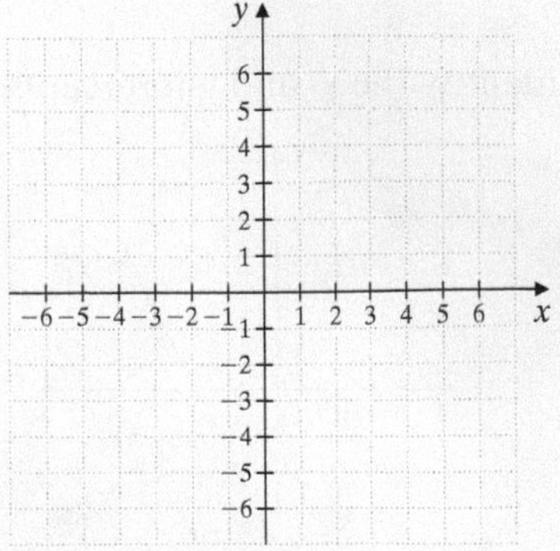

Example 4 Graph $x - 3y = 6$ by finding and plotting its intercepts.

Solution: We let $y = 0$ to find the x-intercept and $x = 0$ to find the y-intercept.

Let $y = 0$.	Let $x = 0$.
$x - 3y = 6$	$x - 3y = 6$
$x - 3(0) = 6$	$0 - 3y = 6$
$x - 0 = 6$	$-3y = 6$
$x = 6$	$y = -2$

The x-intercept is $(6, 0)$ and the y-intercept is $(0, -2)$. We find a third ordered pair solution to check our work. If we let $y = -1$, then $x = 3$. We plot the points $(6, 0)$,

Answers

2. x-intercepts: $(-4, 0)(2, 0)$; y-intercept: $(0, 2)$
3. x-intercept and y-intercept: $(0, 0)$
4. See page 451.

(0, −2), and (3, −1). The graph of $x - 3y = 6$ is the line drawn through these points as shown.

x	y
6	0
0	−2
3	−1

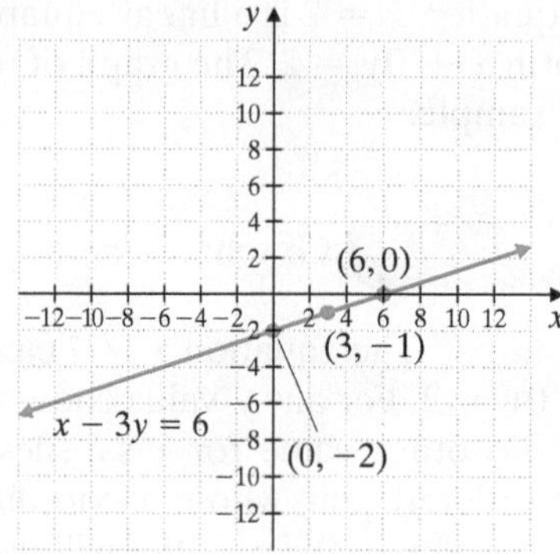

Work Practice 4

Example 5 Graph $x = -2y$ by finding and plotting its intercepts.

Solution: We let $y = 0$ to find the x-intercept and $x = 0$ to find the y-intercept.

Let $y = 0$.
$x = -2y$
$x = -2(0)$
$x = 0$

Let $x = 0$.
$x = -2y$
$0 = -2y$
$0 = y$

Both the x-intercept and y-intercept are (0, 0). In other words, when $x = 0$, then $y = 0$, which gives the ordered pair (0, 0). Also, when $y = 0$, then $x = 0$, which gives the same ordered pair, (0, 0). This happens when the graph passes through the origin. Since two points are needed to determine a line, we must find at least one more ordered pair that satisfies $x = -2y$. Since the equation is solved for x, we choose y-values so that there is no need to solve to find the corresponding x-value. We let $y = -1$ to find a second ordered pair solution and let $y = 1$ as a check point.

Let $y = -1$.
$x = -2(-1)$
$x = 2$ Multiply.

Let $y = 1$.
$x = -2(1)$
$x = -2$ Multiply.

The ordered pairs are (0, 0), (2, −1), and (−2, 1). We plot these points to graph $x = -2y$.

x	y
0	0
2	−1
−2	1

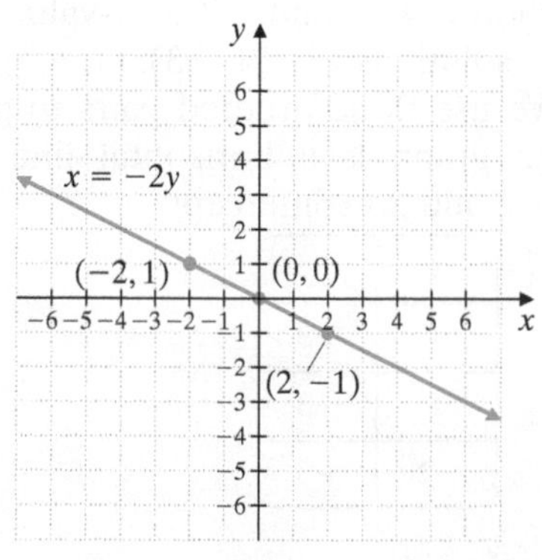

Work Practice 5

PRACTICE 5

Graph $y = 3x$ by finding and plotting its intercepts.

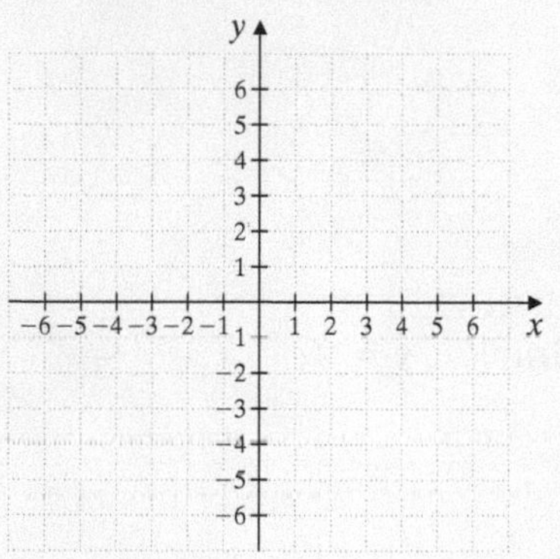

Answers

4.
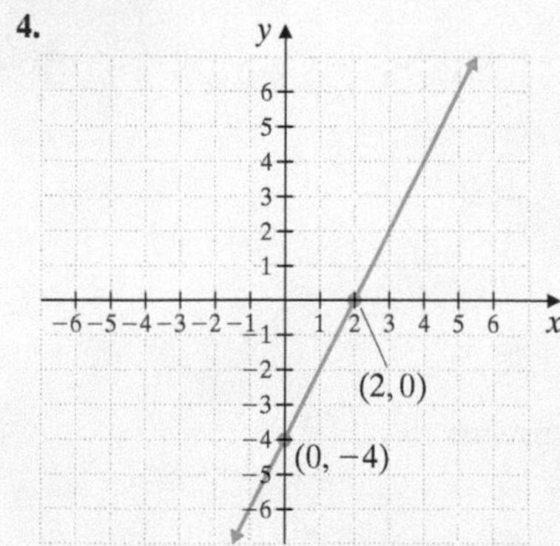

5.
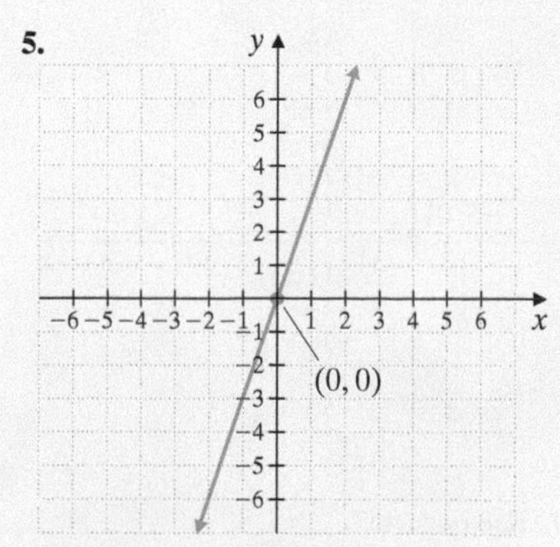

Objective C Graphing Vertical and Horizontal Lines

The equation $x = 2$ is a linear equation in two variables because it can be written in the form $x + 0y = 2$. The graph of this equation is a vertical line, as reviewed in the next example.

PRACTICE 6
Graph: $x = -3$

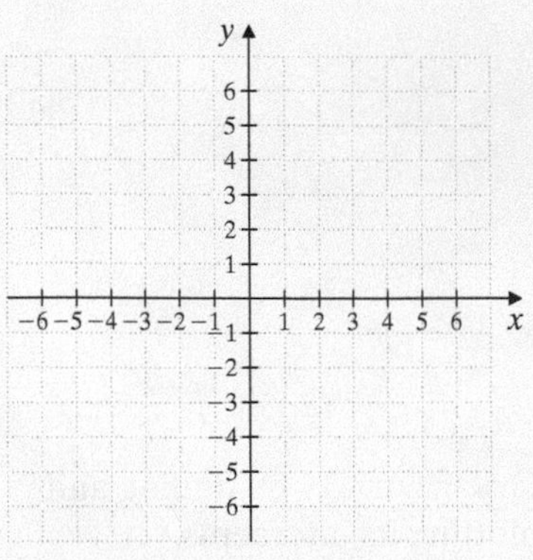

Example 6 Graph: $x = 2$

Solution: The equation $x = 2$ can be written as $x + 0y = 2$. For any y-value chosen, notice that x is 2. No other value for x satisfies $x + 0y = 2$. Any ordered pair whose x-coordinate is 2 is a solution of $x + 0y = 2$. We will use the ordered pair solutions (2, 3), (2, 0), and (2, −3) to graph $x = 2$.

x	y
2	3
2	0
2	−3

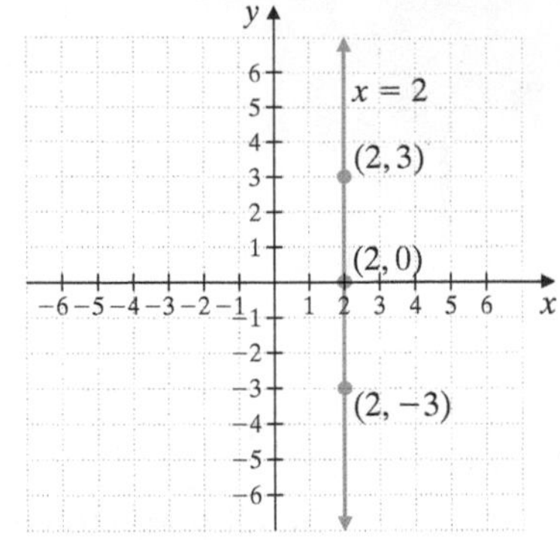

The graph is a vertical line with x-intercept 2. Note that this graph has no y-intercept because x is never 0.

Work Practice 6

PRACTICE 7
Graph: $y = 4$

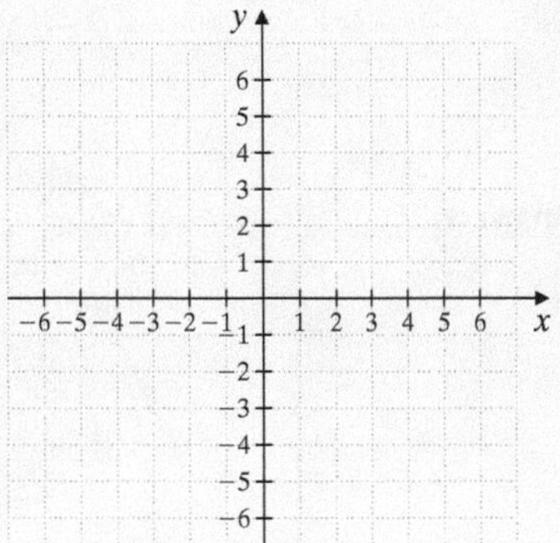

In general, we have the following.

Vertical Lines

The graph of $x = c$, where c is a real number, is a **vertical line** with x-intercept $(c, 0)$.

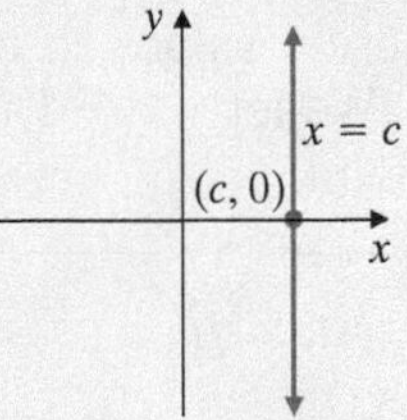

Example 7 Graph: $y = -3$

Solution: The equation $y = -3$ can be written as $0x + y = -3$. For any x-value chosen, y is −3. If we choose 4, 1, and −2 as x-values, the ordered pair solutions are (4, −3), (1, −3), and (−2, −3). We use these ordered pairs to graph $y = -3$. The graph is a horizontal line with y-intercept −3 and no x-intercept.

x	y
4	−3
1	−3
−2	−3

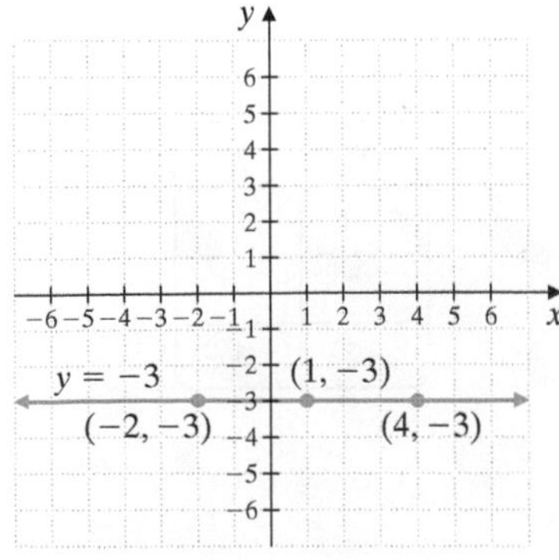

Work Practice 7

Answers

6.

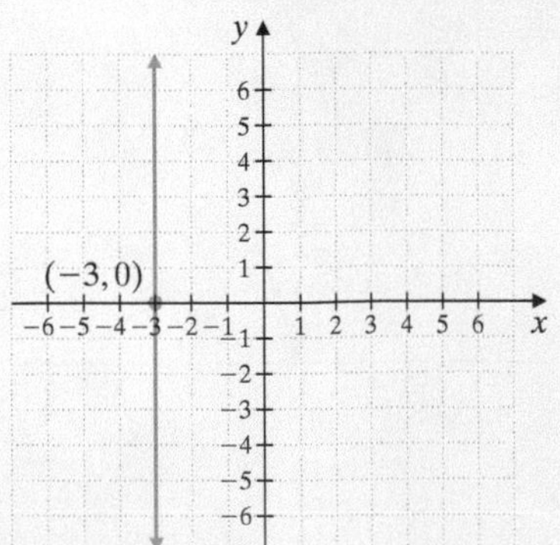

7. See page 453.

In general, we have the following.

Horizontal Lines

The graph of $y = c$, where c is a real number, is a **horizontal line** with y-intercept $(0, c)$.

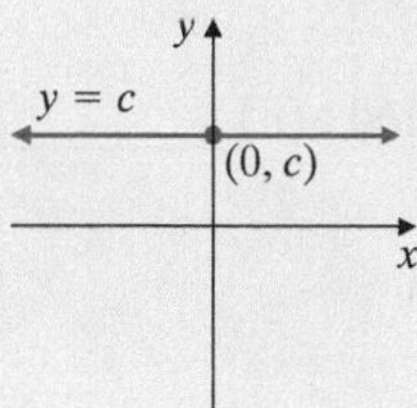

Answer

7.

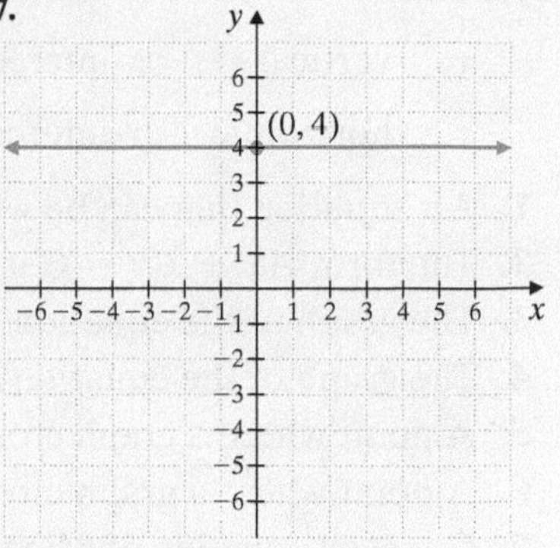

Calculator Explorations Graphing

You may have noticed that to use the $\boxed{\text{Y=}}$ key on a graphing calculator to graph an equation, the equation must be solved for y. For example, to graph $2x + 3y = 7$, we solve this equation for y.

$$2x + 3y = 7$$

$$3y = -2x + 7 \quad \text{Subtract } 2x \text{ from both sides.}$$

$$\frac{3y}{3} = -\frac{2x}{3} + \frac{7}{3} \quad \text{Divide both sides by 3.}$$

$$y = -\frac{2}{3}x + \frac{7}{3} \quad \text{Simplify.}$$

To graph $2x + 3y = 7$ or $y = -\frac{2}{3}x + \frac{7}{3}$, press the $\boxed{\text{Y=}}$ key and enter

$$Y_1 = -\frac{2}{3}x + \frac{7}{3}$$

$2x + 3y = 7$ or $y = -\frac{2}{3}x + \frac{7}{3}$

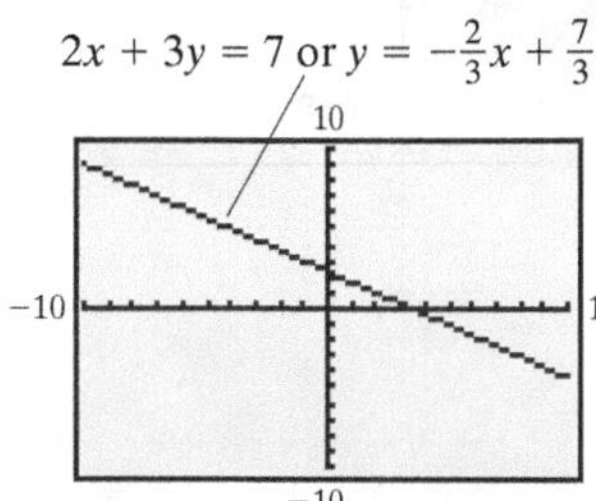

Graph each linear equation.

1. $x = 3.78y$
2. $-2.61y = x$
3. $3x + 7y = 21$
4. $-4x + 6y = 12$
5. $-2.2x + 6.8y = 15.5$
6. $5.9x - 0.8y = -10.4$

Vocabulary and Readiness Check

Use the choices below to fill in each blank. Some choices may be used more than once. Exercises 1 and 2 come from Section 6.2.

x	vertical	x-intercept	linear
y	horizontal	y-intercept	standard

1. An equation that can be written in the form $Ax + By = C$ is called a(n) __________ equation in two variables.
2. The form $Ax + By = C$ is called __________ form.
3. The graph of the equation $y = -1$ is a(n) __________ line.
4. The graph of the equation $x = 5$ is a(n) __________ line.
5. A point where a graph crosses the y-axis is called a(n) __________.
6. A point where a graph crosses the x-axis is called a(n) __________.
7. Given an equation of a line, to find the x-intercept (if there is one), let __________ = 0 and solve for __________.
8. Given an equation of a line, to find the y-intercept (if there is one), let __________ = 0 and solve for __________.

Answer the following true or false.

9. All lines have an x-intercept *and* a y-intercept.
10. The graph of $y = 4x$ contains the point $(0, 0)$.
11. The graph of $x + y = 5$ has an x-intercept of $(5, 0)$ and a y-intercept of $(0, 5)$.
12. The graph of $y = 5x$ contains the point $(5, 1)$.

6.3 Exercise Set

FOR EXTRA HELP MyMathLab

PRACTICE

WATCH

DOWNLOAD

READ

REVIEW

Objective A *Identify the intercepts. See Examples 1 through 3.*

1.

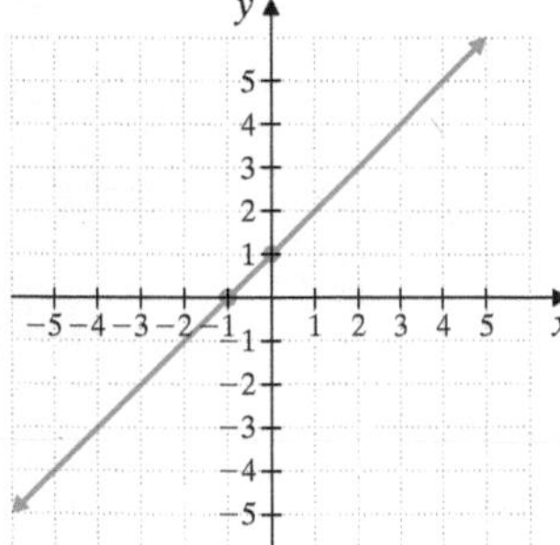

2.

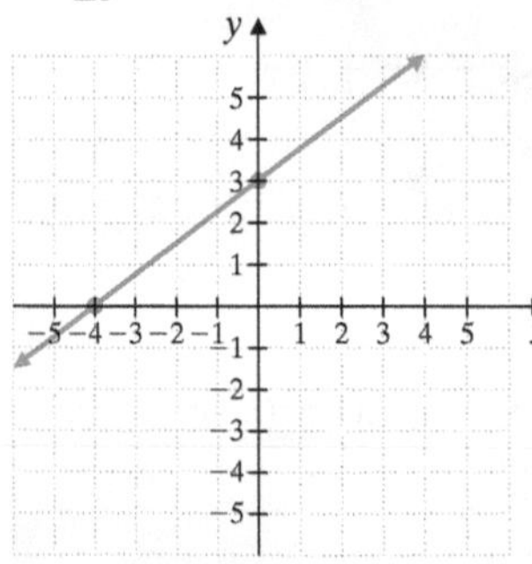

3.

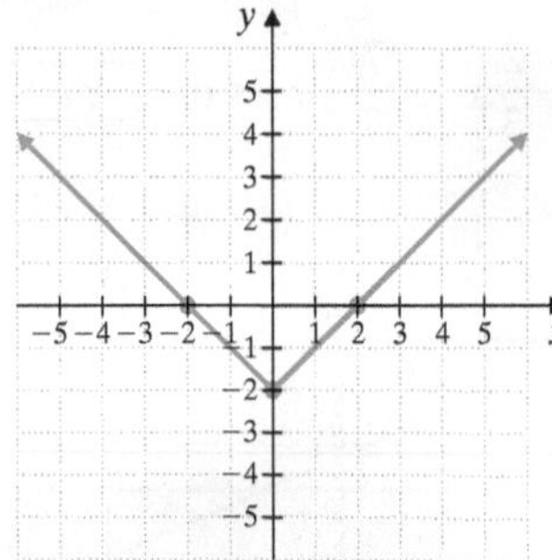

4.

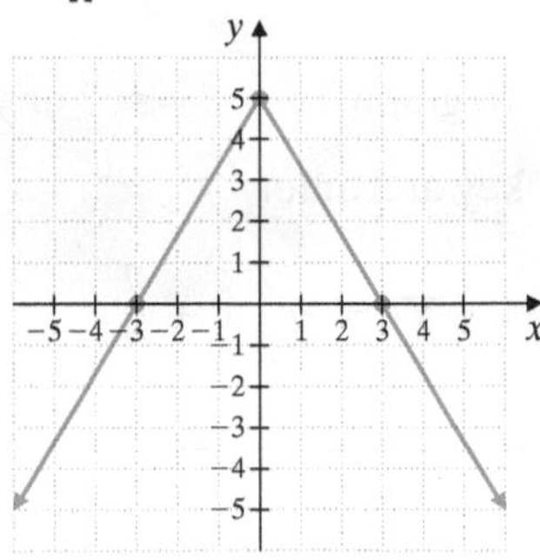

5.

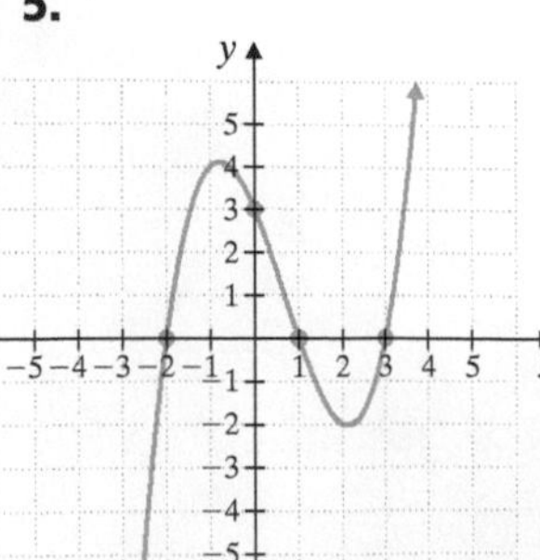

6.

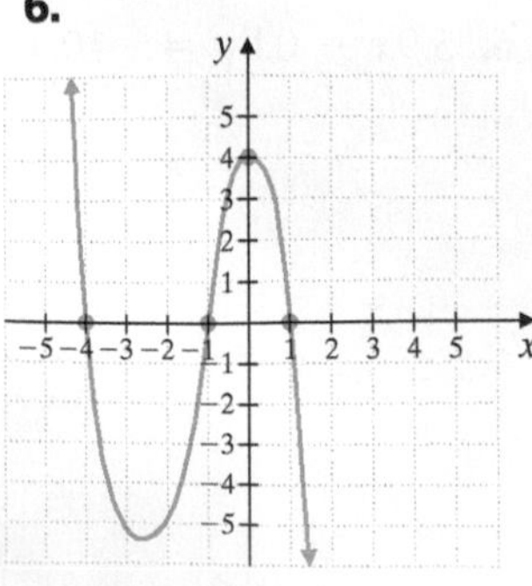

7.

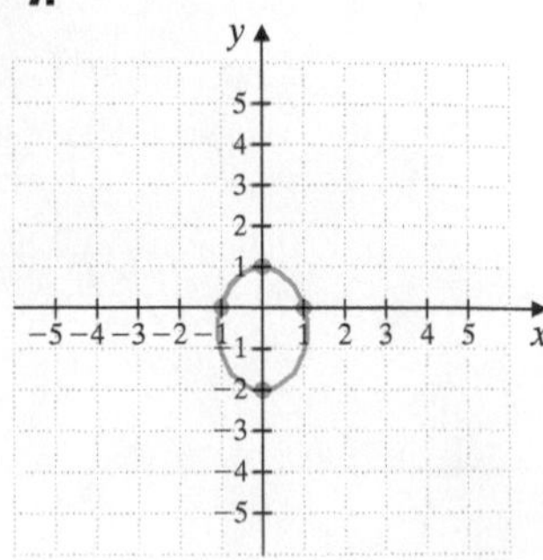

8.

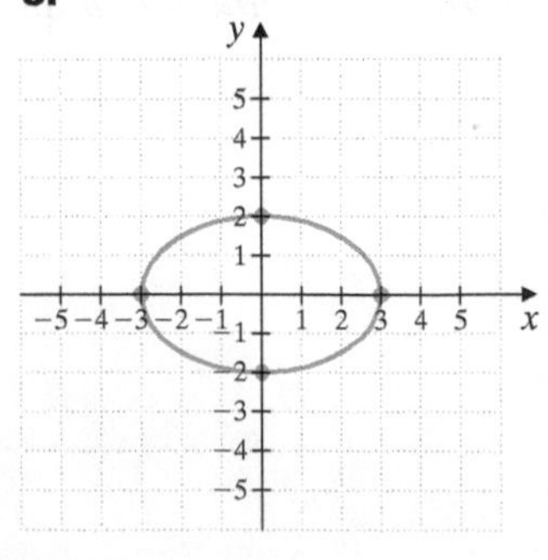

Objective B *Graph each linear equation by finding and plotting its intercepts. See Examples 4 and 5.*

9. $x - y = 3$

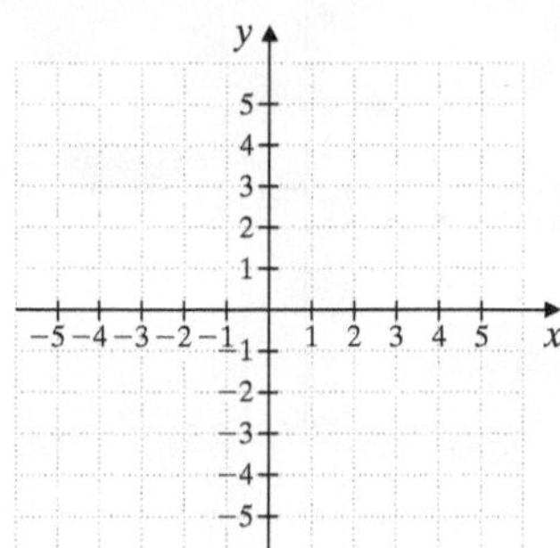

10. $x - y = -4$

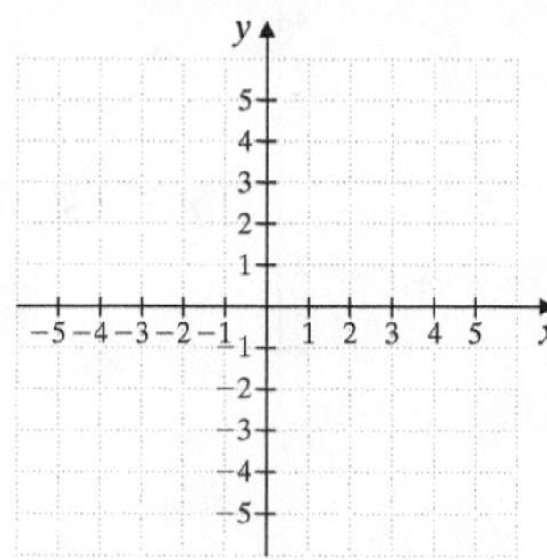

11. $x = 5y$

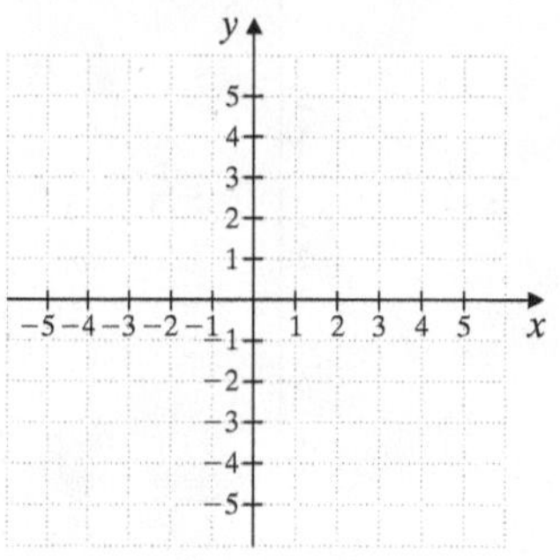

12. $x = 2y$

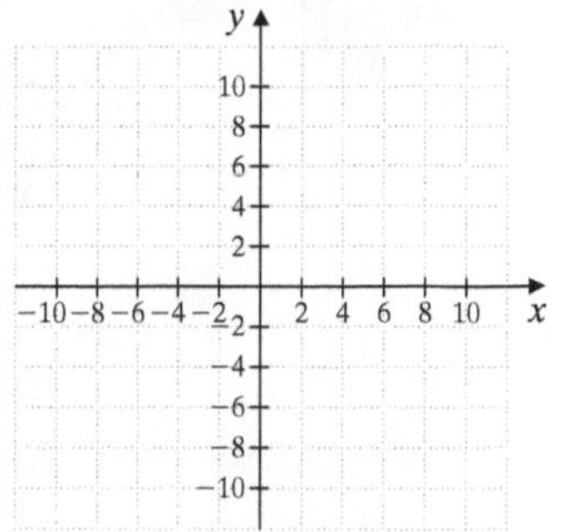

13. $-x + 2y = 6$

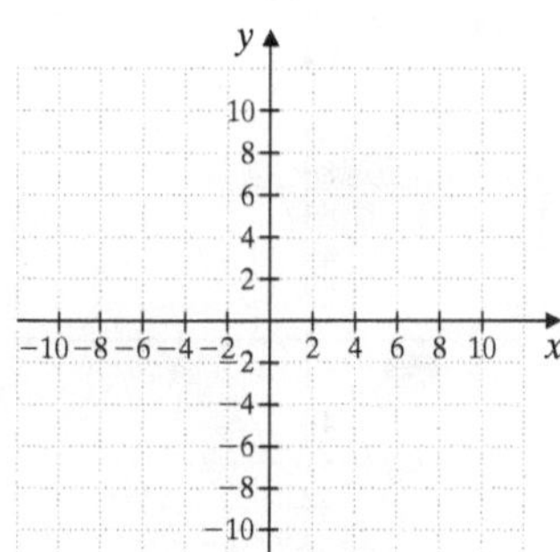

14. $x - 2y = -8$

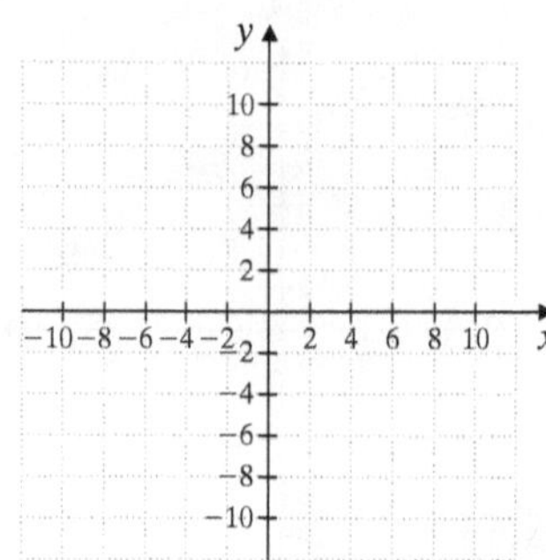

15. $2x - 4y = 8$

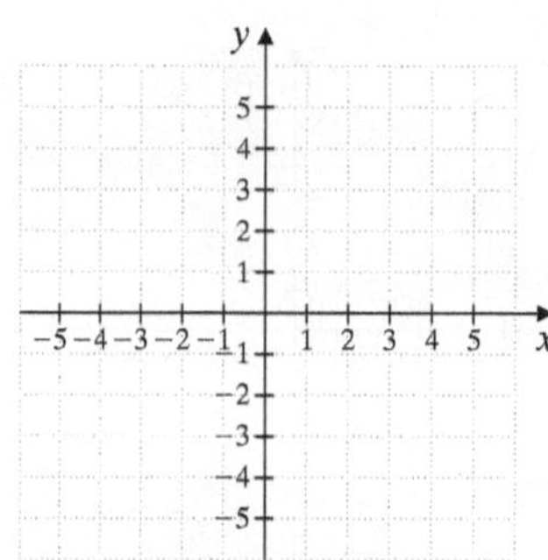

16. $2x + 3y = 6$

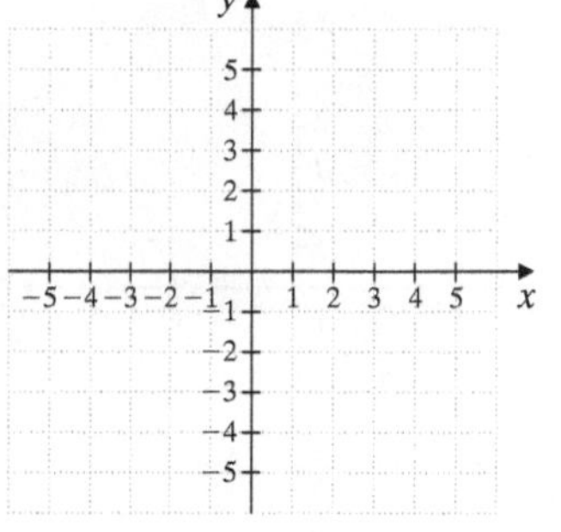

17. $y = 2x$

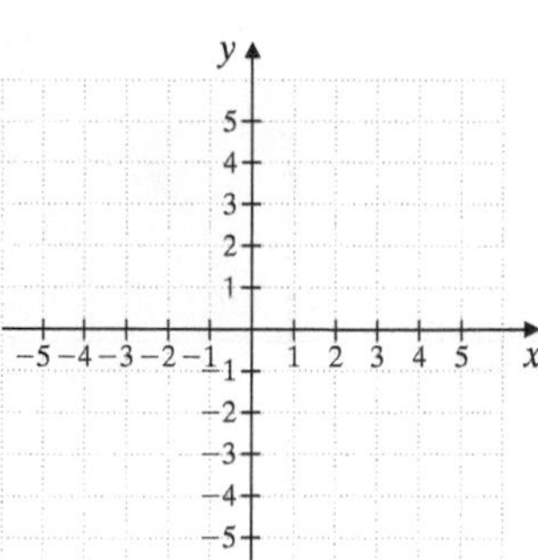

18. $y = -2x$

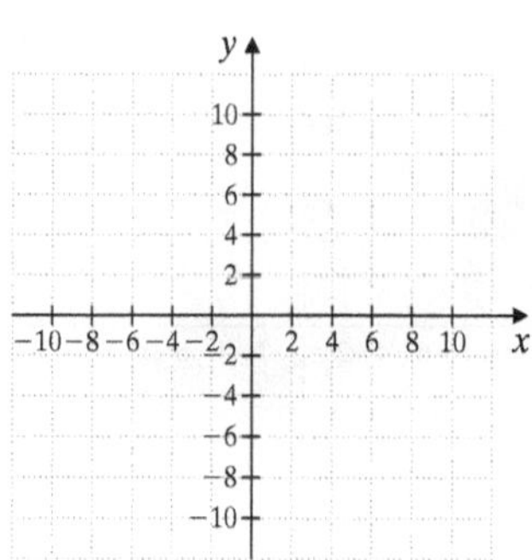

19. $y = 3x + 6$

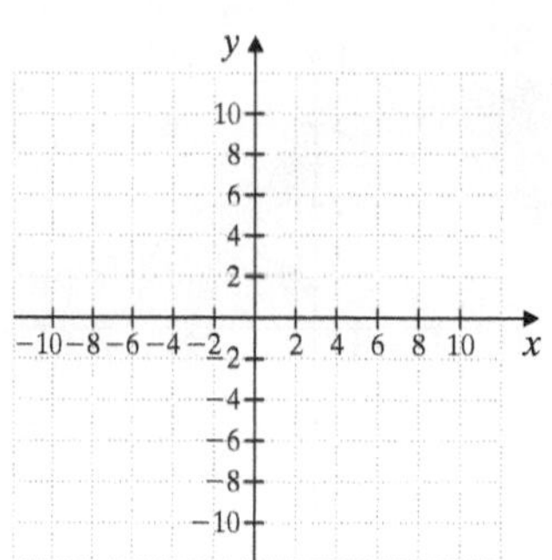

20. $y = 2x + 10$

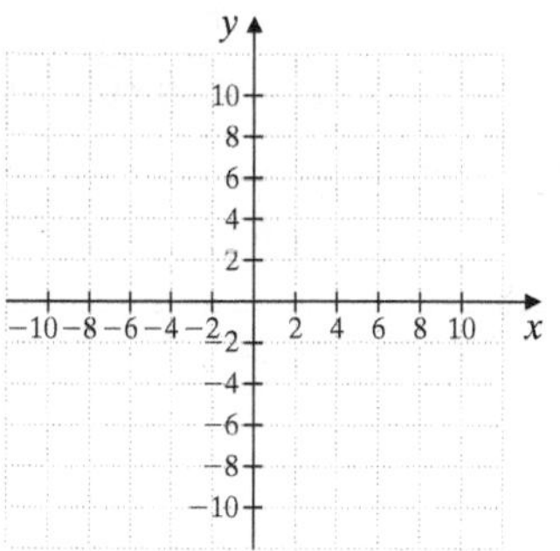

Objective C *Graph each linear equation. See Examples 6 and 7.*

21. $x = -1$

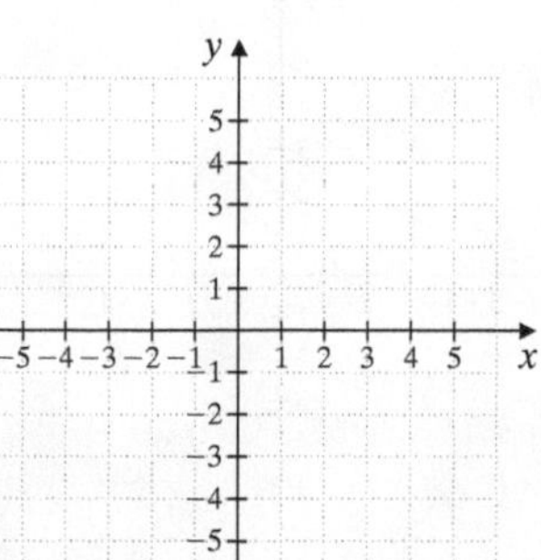

22. $y = 5$

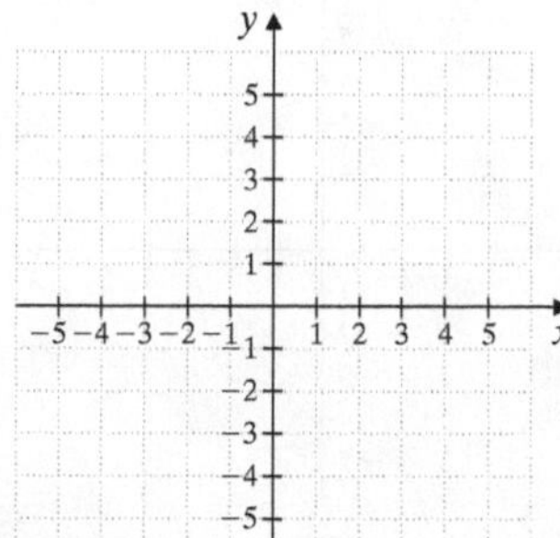

23. $y = 0$

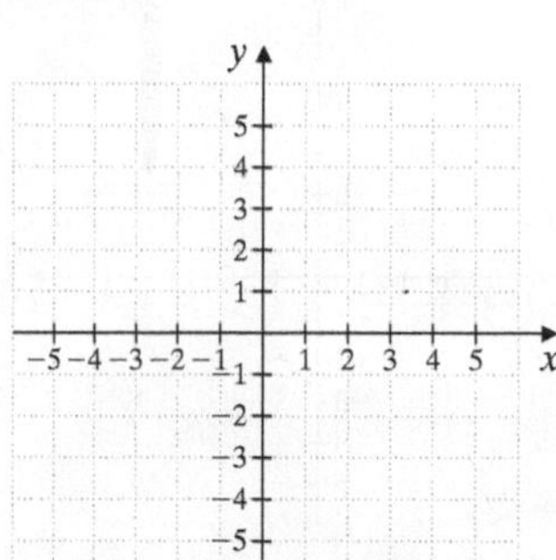

24. $x = 0$

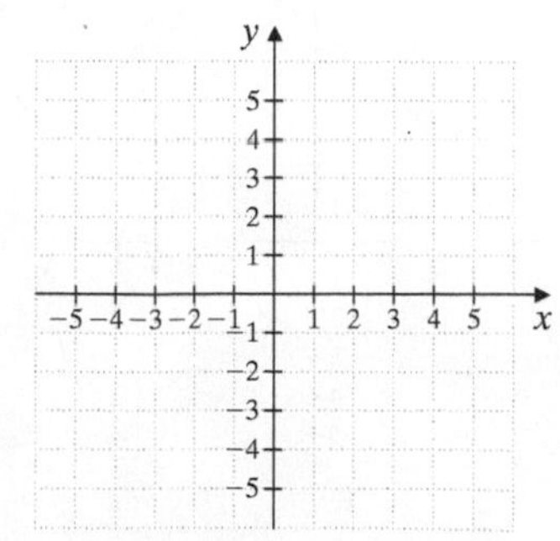

25. $y + 7 = 0$

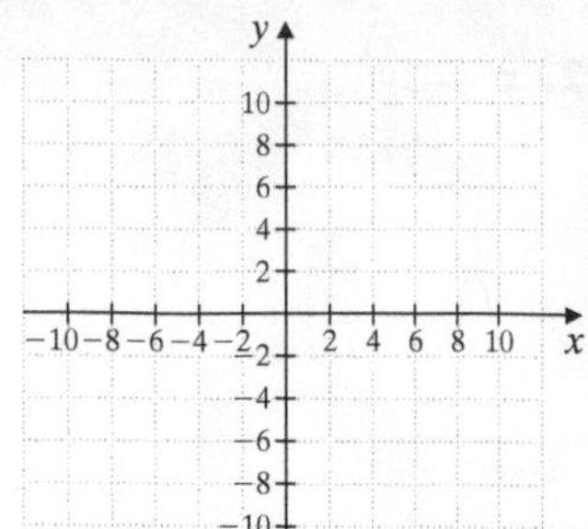

26. $x - 2 = 0$

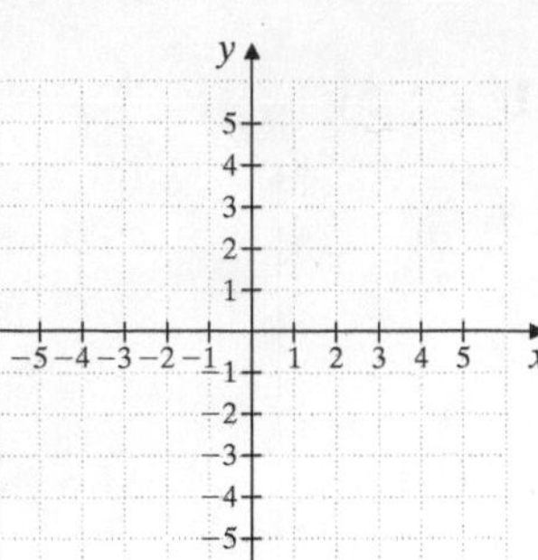

27. $x + 3 = 0$

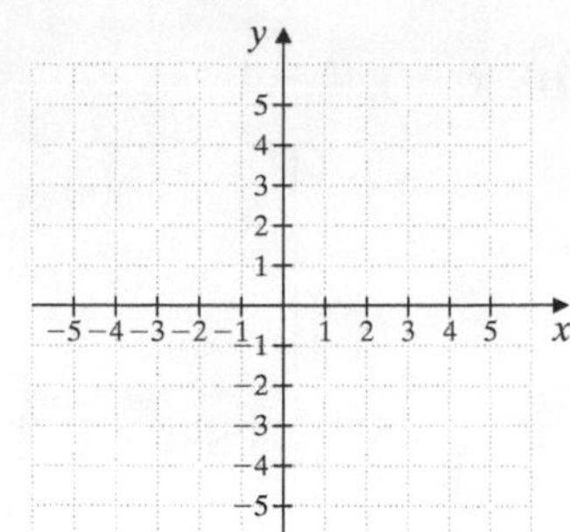

28. $y - 6 = 0$

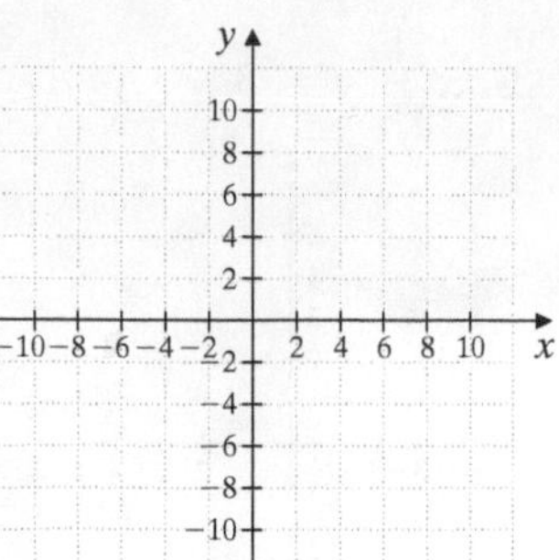

Objectives **B** **C** **Mixed Practice** *Graph each linear equation. See Examples 4 through 7.*

29. $x = y$

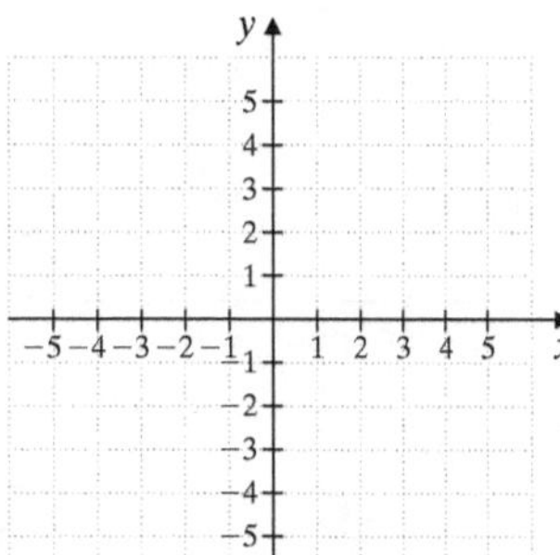

30. $x = -y$

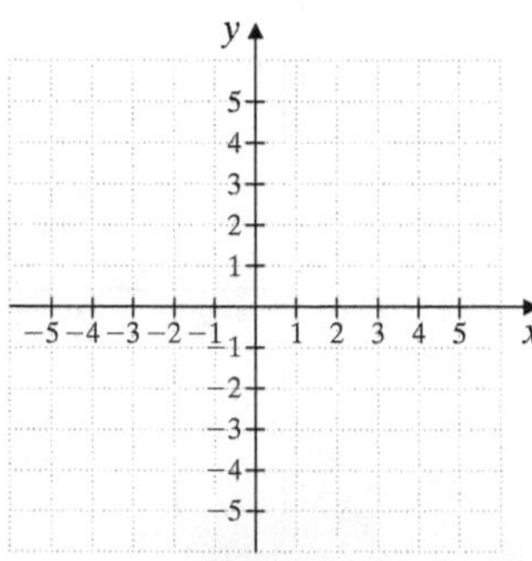

31. $x + 8y = 8$

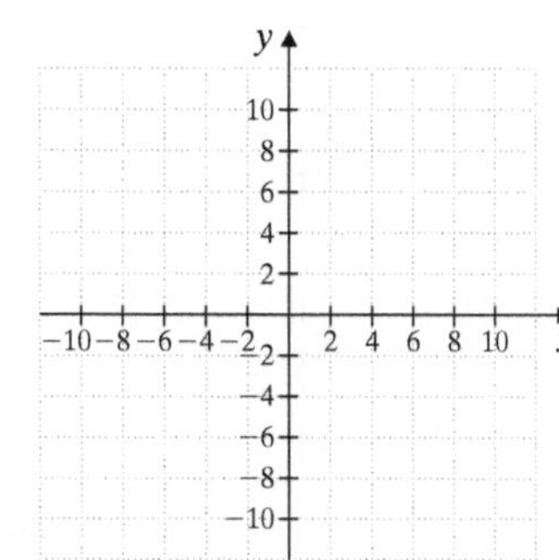

32. $x + 3y = 9$

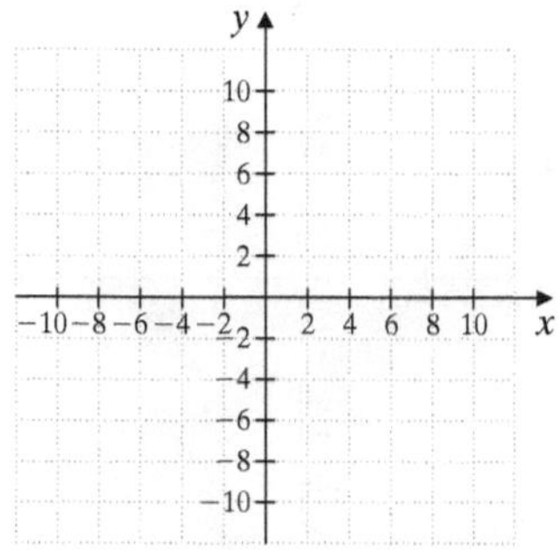

33. $5 = 6x - y$

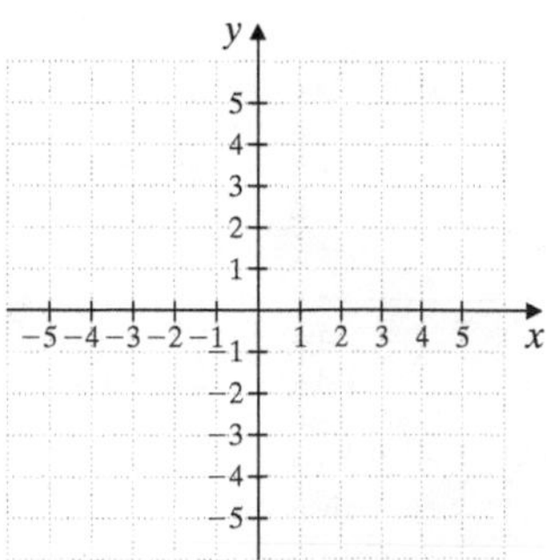

34. $4 = x - 3y$

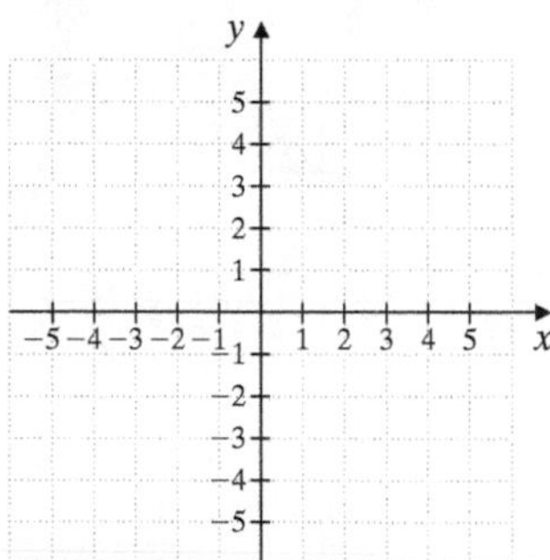

35. $-x + 10y = 11$

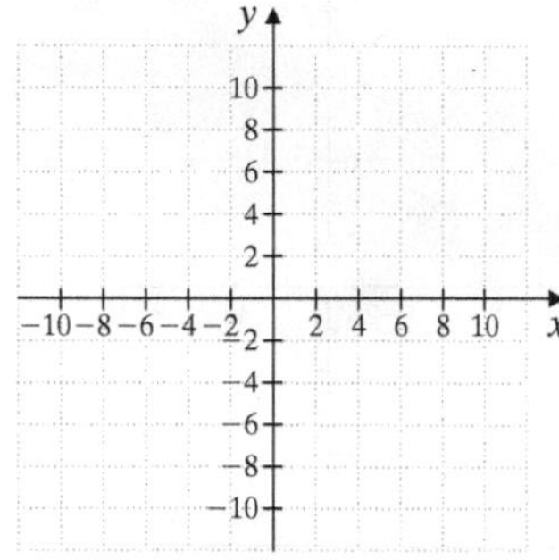

36. $-x + 9y = 10$

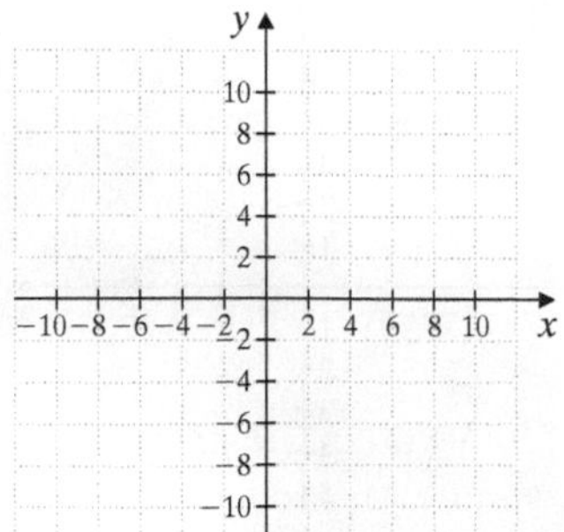

37. $x = -4\frac{1}{2}$

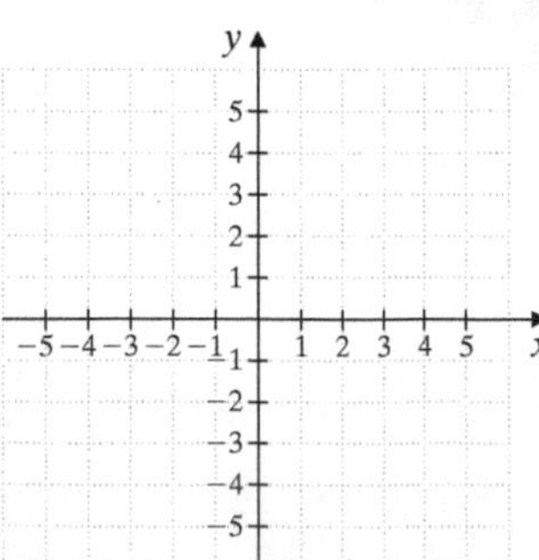

38. $x = -1\frac{3}{4}$

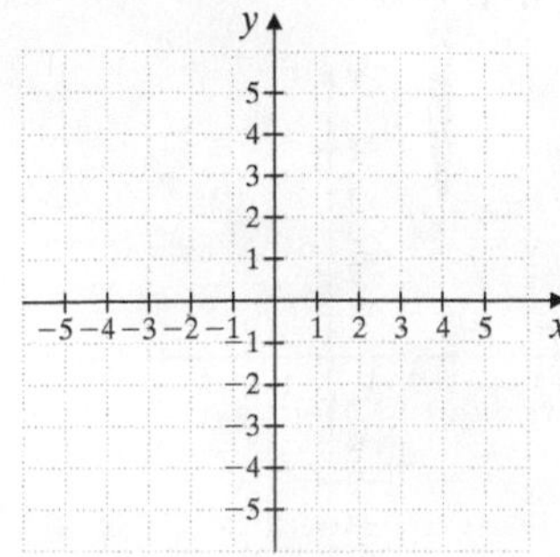

39. $y = 3\frac{1}{4}$

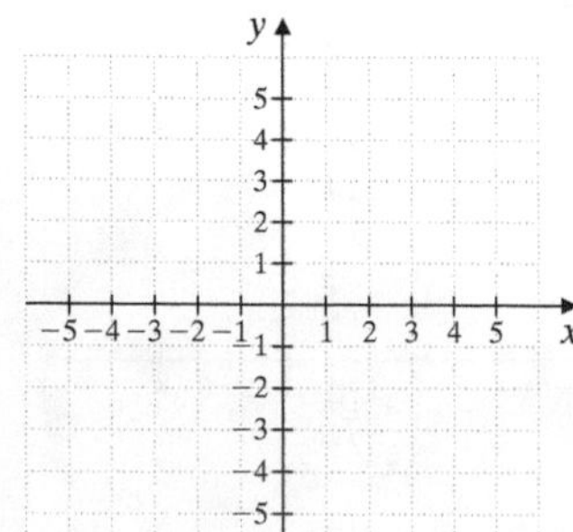

40. $y = 2\frac{1}{2}$

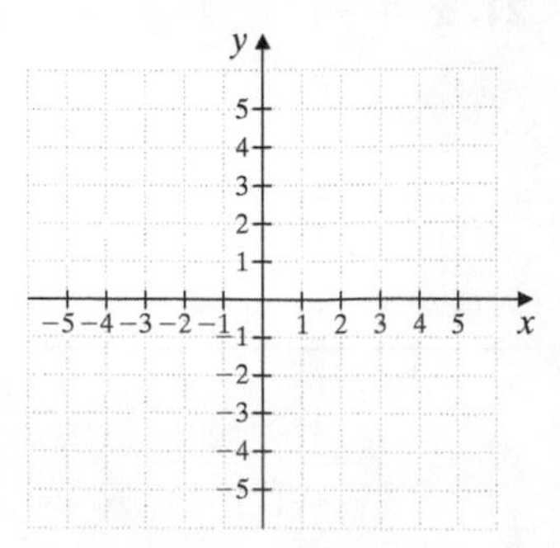

41. $y = -\frac{2}{3}x + 1$

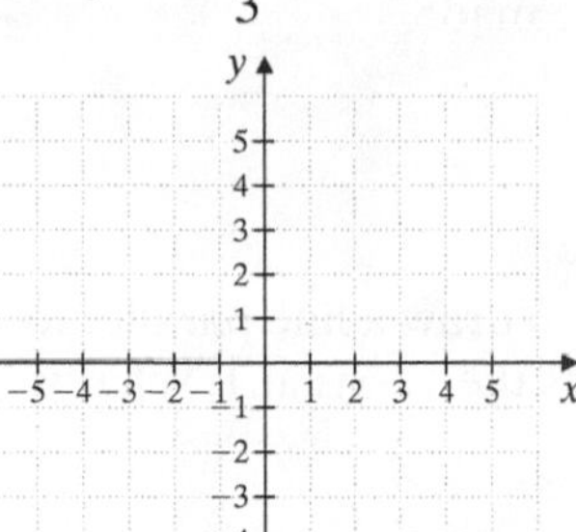

42. $y = -\frac{3}{5}x + 3$

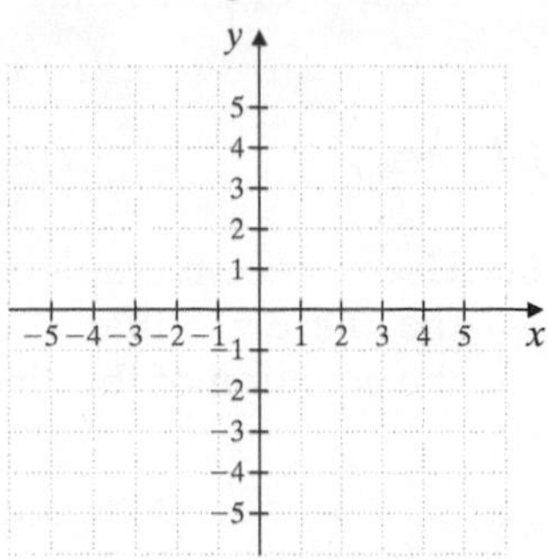

43. $4x - 6y + 2 = 0$

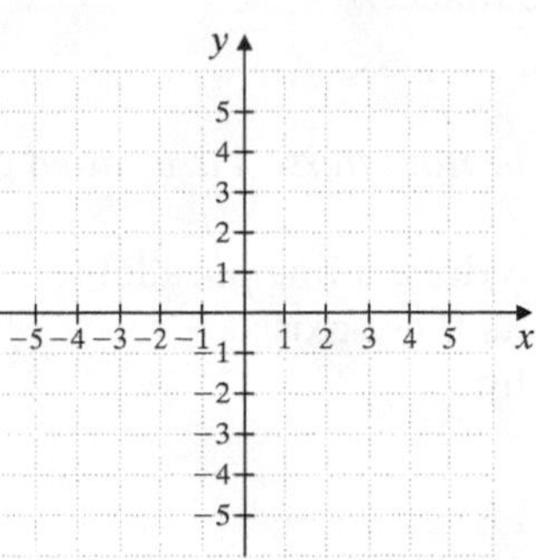

44. $9x - 6y + 3 = 0$

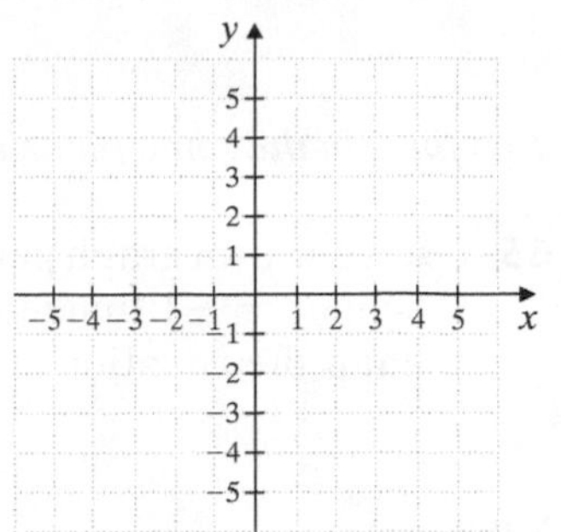

Review

Simplify. See Sections 1.5, and 1.6.

45. $\frac{-6 - 3}{2 - 8}$

46. $\frac{4 - 5}{-1 - 0}$

47. $\frac{-8 - (-2)}{-3 - (-2)}$

48. $\frac{12 - 3}{10 - 9}$

49. $\frac{0 - 6}{5 - 0}$

50. $\frac{2 - 2}{3 - 5}$

Concept Extensions

Match each equation with its graph.

51. $y = 3$

52. $y = 2x + 2$

53. $x = 3$

54. $y = 2x + 3$

a.

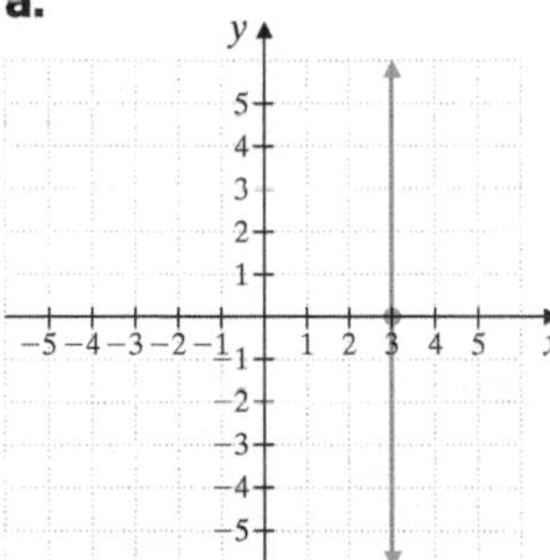

b.

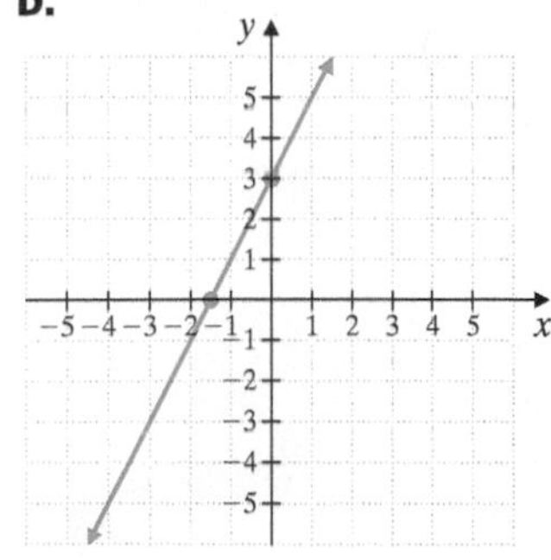

c.

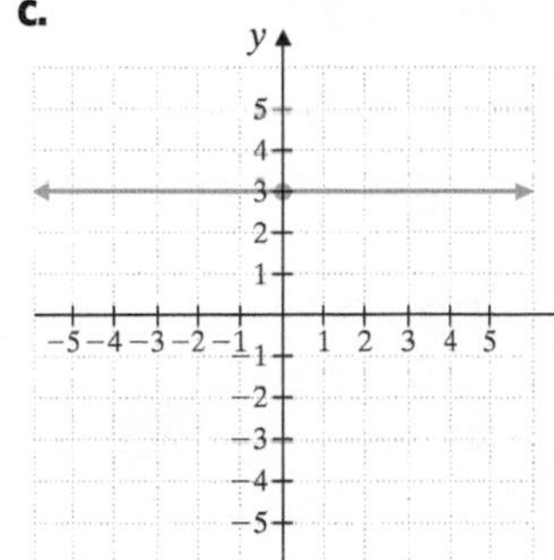

d.

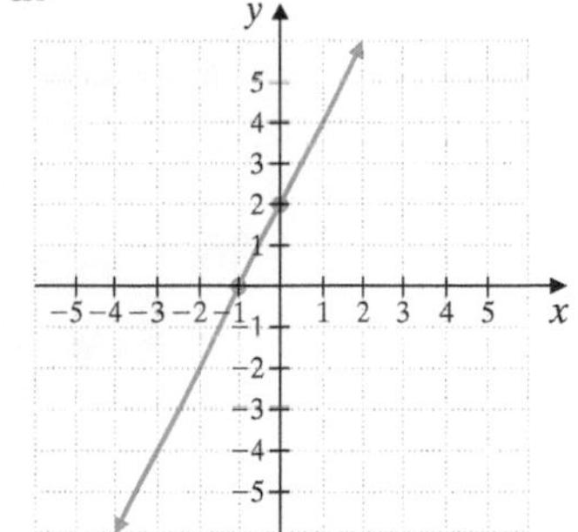

55. What is the greatest number of x- and y-intercepts that a line can have?

56. What is the smallest number of x- and y-intercepts that a line can have?

57. What is the smallest number of x- and y-intercepts that a circle can have?

58. What is the greatest number of x- and y-intercepts that a circle can have?

59. Discuss whether a vertical line ever has a y-intercept.

60. Discuss whether a horizontal line ever has an x-intercept.

The production supervisor at Alexandra's Office Products finds that it takes 3 hours to manufacture a particular office chair and 6 hours to manufacture an office desk. A total of 1200 hours is available to produce office chairs and desks of this style. The linear equation that models this situation is $3x + 6y = 1200$, *where x represents the number of chairs produced and y the number of desks manufactured.*

61. Complete the ordered pair solution (0,   ) of this equation. Describe the manufacturing situation that corresponds to this solution.

62. Complete the ordered pair solution (, 0) of this equation. Describe the manufacturing situation that corresponds to this solution.

63. If 50 desks are manufactured, find the greatest number of chairs that can be made.

64. If 50 chairs are manufactured, find the greatest number of desks that can be made.

Two lines in the same plane that do not intersect are called ***parallel lines.***

65. Use your own graph paper to draw a line parallel to the line $y = -1$ that intersects the y-axis at -4. What is the equation of this line?

66. Use your own graph paper to draw a line parallel to the line $x = 5$ that intersects the x-axis at 1. What is the equation of this line?

Solve.

67. It has been said that newspapers are disappearing, replaced by various electronic media. The average circulation of newspapers in the United States y, in millions, from 2003 to 2007 can be modeled by the equation $y = -1.9x + 59$, where x represents the number of years after 2003. (*Source:* Newspaper Association of America)

a. Find the x-intercept of this equation (round to the nearest tenth).

b. What does this x-intercept mean?

68. The number of a certain chain of stores y for the years 2003–2007 can be modeled by the equation $y = -198x + 3991$, where x represents the number of years after 2003. (*Source:* Limited Brands)

a. Find the y-intercept of this equation.

b. What does this y-intercept mean?

6.4 SLOPE AND RATE OF CHANGE

Objectives

- **A** Find the Slope of a Line Given Two Points of the Line.
- **B** Find the Slope of a Line Given Its Equation.
- **C** Find the Slopes of Horizontal and Vertical Lines.
- **D** Compare the Slopes of Parallel and Perpendicular Lines.
- **E** Slope as a Rate of Change.

Objective A Finding the Slope of a Line Given Two Points

Thus far, much of this chapter has been devoted to graphing lines. You have probably noticed by now that a key feature of a line is its slant or steepness. In mathematics, the slant or steepness of a line is formally known as its **slope.** We measure the slope of a line by the ratio of vertical change (rise) to the corresponding horizontal change (run) as we move along the line.

On the line below, for example, suppose that we begin at the point (1, 2) and move to the point (4, 6). The vertical change is the change in y-coordinates: $6 - 2$ or 4 units. The corresponding horizontal change is the change in x-coordinates: $4 - 1 = 3$ units. The ratio of these changes is

$$\text{slope} = \frac{\text{change in } y \text{ (vertical change or rise)}}{\text{change in } x \text{ (horizontal change or run)}} = \frac{4}{3}$$

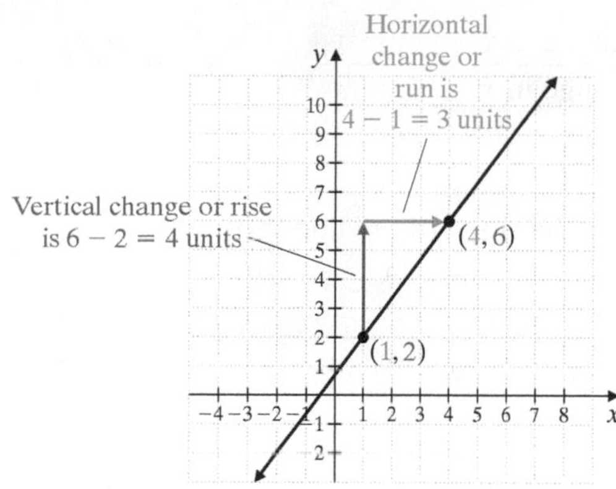

The slope of this line, then, is $\frac{4}{3}$. This means that for every 4 units of change in y-coordinates, there is a corresponding change of 3 units in x-coordinates.

Helpful Hint

It makes no difference what two points of a line are chosen to find its slope. The slope of a line is the same everywhere on the line.

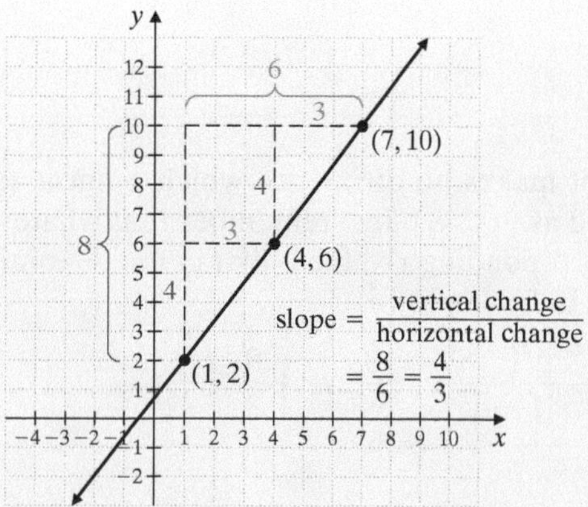

To find the slope of a line, then, choose two points of the line. Label the two x-coordinates of the two points x_1 and x_2 (read "x sub one" and "x sub two"), and label the corresponding y-coordinates y_1 and y_2.

The vertical change or **rise** between these points is the difference in the y-coordinates: $y_2 - y_1$. The horizontal change or **run** between the points is the difference of the x-coordinates: $x_2 - x_1$. The slope of the line is the ratio of $y_2 - y_1$ to $x_2 - x_1$, and we traditionally use the letter m to denote slope $m = \dfrac{y_2 - y_1}{x_2 - x_1}$.

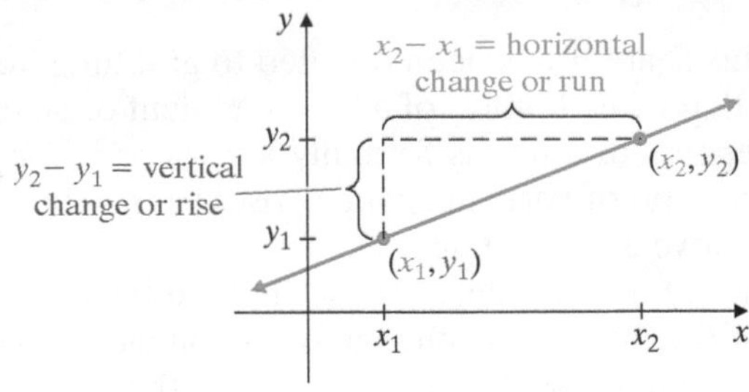

Slope of a Line

The slope m of the line containing the points (x_1, y_1) and (x_2, y_2) is given by

$$m = \frac{\text{rise}}{\text{run}} = \frac{\text{change in } y}{\text{change in } x} = \frac{y_2 - y_1}{x_2 - x_1}, \qquad \text{as long as } x_2 \neq x_1$$

PRACTICE 1

Find the slope of the line through $(-2, 3)$ and $(4, -1)$. Graph the line.

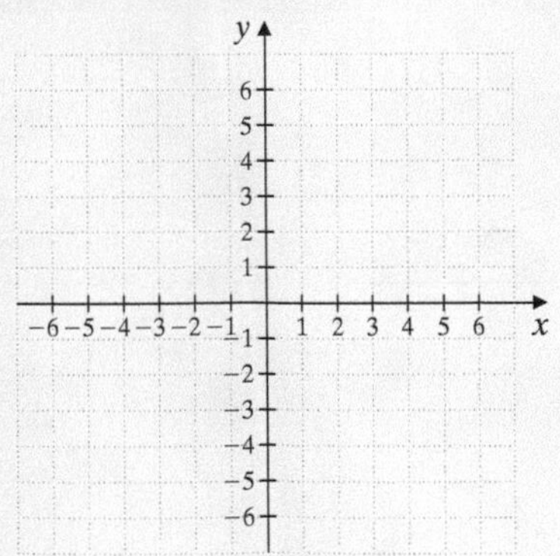

Example 1 Find the slope of the line through $(-1, 5)$ and $(2, -3)$. Graph the line.

Solution: Let (x_1, y_1) be $(-1, 5)$ and (x_2, y_2) be $(2, -3)$. Then, by the definition of slope, we have the following.

$$m = \frac{y_2 - y_1}{x_2 - x_1} = \frac{-3 - 5}{2 - (-1)} = \frac{-8}{3} = -\frac{8}{3}$$

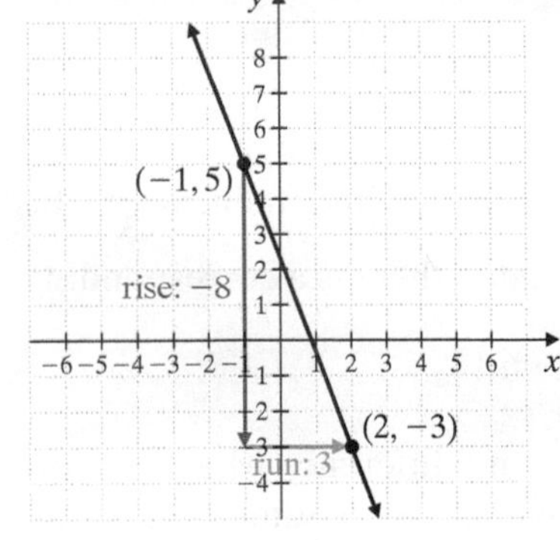

The slope of the line is $-\dfrac{8}{3}$.

Work Practice 1

Answer

1. $-\dfrac{2}{3}$

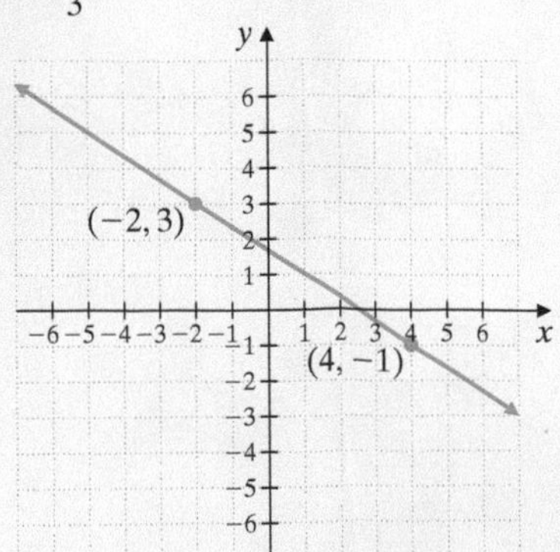

Helpful Hint

When finding slope, it makes no difference which point is identified as (x_1, y_1) and which is identified as (x_2, y_2). Just remember that whatever y-value is first in the numerator, its corresponding x-value is first in the denominator. Another way to calculate the slope in Example 1 is

$$m = \frac{y_2 - y_1}{x_2 - x_1} = \frac{5 - (-3)}{-1 - 2} = \frac{8}{-3} \text{ or } -\frac{8}{3} \quad \leftarrow \text{Same slope as found in Example 1}$$

✔ **Concept Check** The points $(-2, -5)$, $(0, -2)$, $(4, 4)$, and $(10, 13)$ all lie on the same line. Work with a partner and verify that the slope is the same no matter which points are used to find slope.

✔ **Concept Check Answer**

$m = \dfrac{3}{2}$

Example 2 Find the slope of the line through $(-1, -2)$ and $(2, 4)$. Graph the line.

Solution: Let (x_1, y_1) be $(2, 4)$ and (x_2, y_2) be $(-1, -2)$.

$$m = \frac{y_2 - y_1}{x_2 - x_1}$$

$$= \frac{-2 - 4}{-1 - 2} \quad \begin{matrix} y\text{-value} \\ \text{corresponding } x\text{-value} \end{matrix}$$

$$= \frac{-6}{-3} = 2$$

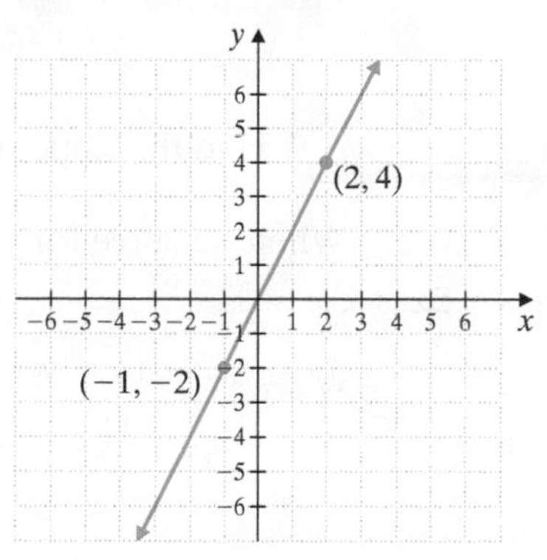

The slope is 2.

Work Practice 2

PRACTICE 2

Find the slope of the line through $(-2, 1)$ and $(3, 5)$. Graph the line.

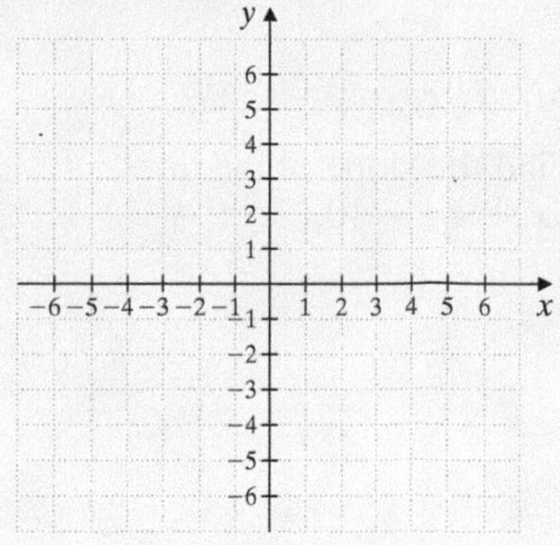

✓Concept Check What is wrong with the following slope calculation for the points $(3, 5)$ and $(-2, 6)$?

$$m = \frac{5 - 6}{-2 - 3} = \frac{-1}{-5} = \frac{1}{5}$$

Notice that the slope of the line in Example 1 is negative and that the slope of the line in Example 2 is positive. Let your eye follow the line with negative slope from left to right and notice that the line "goes down." If you follow the line with positive slope from left to right, you will notice that the line "goes up." This is true in general.

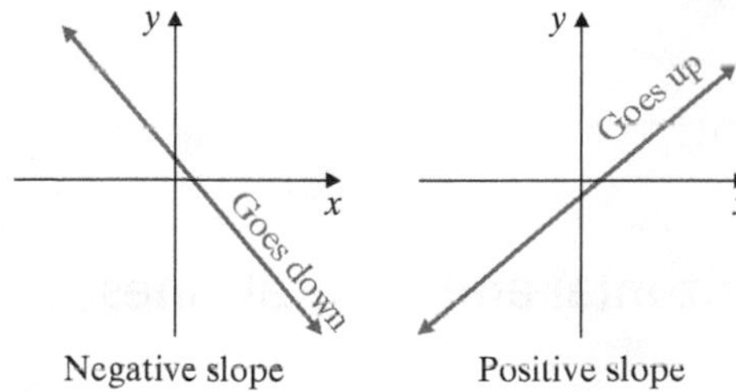

Helpful Hint To decide whether a line "goes up" or "goes down," always follow the line from left to right.

Objective B Finding the Slope of a Line Given Its Equation

As we have seen, the slope of a line is defined by two points on the line. Thus, if we know the equation of a line, we can find its slope by finding two of its points. For example, let's find the slope of the line

$$y = 3x - 2$$

To find two points, we can choose two values for x and substitute to find corresponding y-values. If $x = 0$, for example, $y = 3 \cdot 0 - 2$ or $y = -2$. If $x = 1$, $y = 3 \cdot 1 - 2$ or $y = 1$. This gives the ordered pairs $(0, -2)$ and $(1, 1)$. Using the definition for slope, we have

$$m = \frac{1 - (-2)}{1 - 0} = \frac{3}{1} = 3 \quad \text{The slope is 3.}$$

Notice that the slope, 3, is the same as the coefficient of x in the equation $y = 3x - 2$. This is true in general.

Answer

2. $\frac{4}{5}$

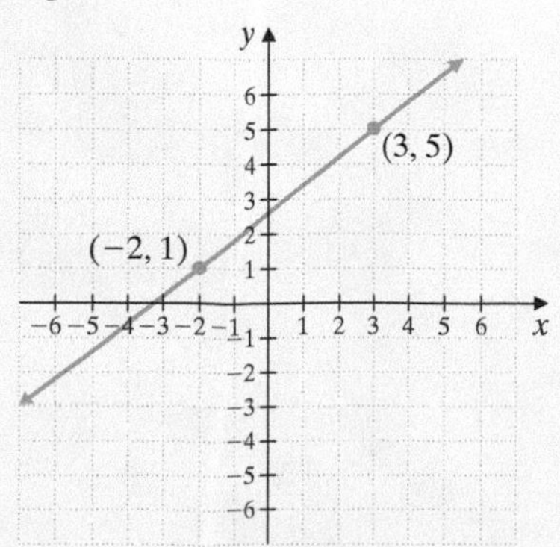

✓ Concept Check Answer

$$m = \frac{5 - 6}{3 - (-2)} = \frac{-1}{5} = -\frac{1}{5}$$

If a linear equation is solved for y, the coefficient of x is the line's slope. In other words, the slope of the line given by $y = mx + b$ is m, the coefficient of x.

$$y = mx + b$$
(m ← slope)

PRACTICE 3

Find the slope of the line $5x + 4y = 10$.

Example 3 Find the slope of the line $-2x + 3y = 11$.

Solution: When we solve for y, the coefficient of x is the slope.

$$-2x + 3y = 11$$

$$3y = 2x + 11 \quad \text{Add } 2x \text{ to both sides.}$$

$$y = \frac{2}{3}x + \frac{11}{3} \quad \text{Divide both sides by 3.}$$

The slope is $\frac{2}{3}$.

Work Practice 3

PRACTICE 4

Find the slope of the line $-y = -2x + 7$.

Example 4 Find the slope of the line $-y = 5x - 2$.

Solution: Remember, the equation must be solved for y (not $-y$) in order for the coefficient of x to be the slope.

To solve for y, let's divide both sides of the equation by -1.

$$-y = 5x - 2 \quad \text{Divide both sides by } -1.$$

$$\frac{-y}{-1} = \frac{5x}{-1} - \frac{2}{-1} \quad \text{Simplify.}$$

$$y = -5x + 2$$

The slope is -5.

Work Practice 4

Objective C Finding Slopes of Horizontal and Vertical Lines

PRACTICE 5

Find the slope of $y = 3$.

Example 5 Find the slope of the line $y = -1$.

Solution: Recall that $y = -1$ is a horizontal line with y-intercept -1. To find the slope, we find two ordered pair solutions of $y = -1$, knowing that solutions of $y = -1$ must have a y-value of -1. We will use $(2, -1)$ and $(-3, -1)$. We let (x_1, y_1) be $(2, -1)$ and (x_2, y_2) be $(-3, -1)$.

$$m = \frac{y_2 - y_1}{x_2 - x_1} = \frac{-1 - (-1)}{-3 - 2} = \frac{0}{-5} = 0$$

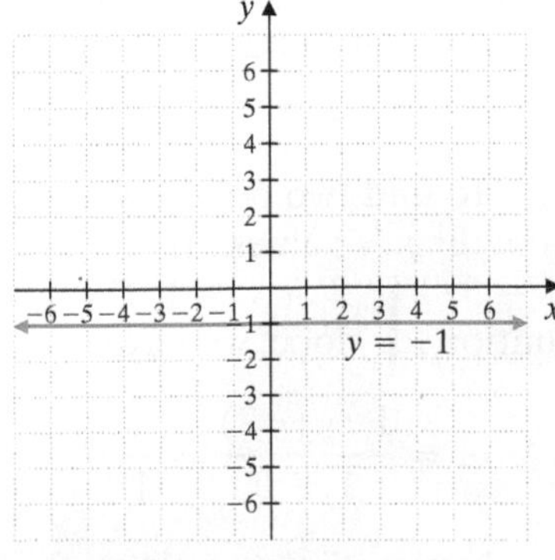

The slope of the line $y = -1$ is 0. Since the y-values will have a difference of 0 for every horizontal line, we can say that all **horizontal lines have a slope of 0.**

Work Practice 5

Answers

3. $-\frac{5}{4}$ 4. 2 5. 0

Example 6 Find the slope of the line $x = 5$.

Solution: Recall that the graph of $x = 5$ is a vertical line with x-intercept 5. To find the slope, we find two ordered pair solutions of $x = 5$. Ordered pair solutions of $x = 5$ must have an x-value of 5. We will use (5, 0) and (5, 4). We let $(x_1, y_1) = (5, 0)$ and $(x_2, y_2) = (5, 4)$.

$$m = \frac{y_2 - y_1}{x_2 - x_1} = \frac{4 - 0}{5 - 5} = \frac{4}{0}$$

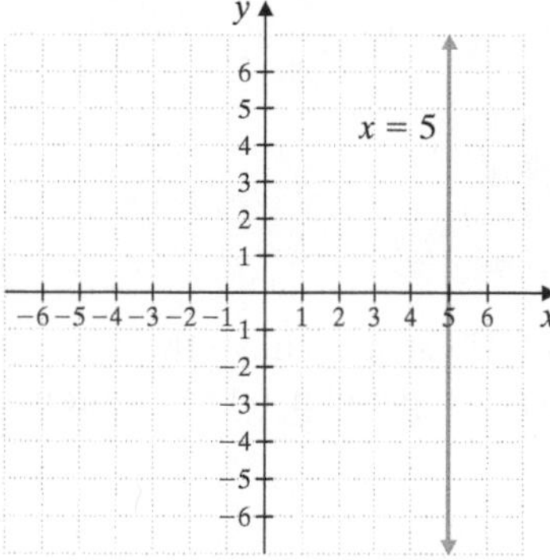

Since $\frac{4}{0}$ is undefined, we say that the slope of the vertical line $x = 5$ is undefined. Since the x-values will have a difference of 0 for every vertical line, we can say that all **vertical lines have undefined slope.**

Work Practice 6

PRACTICE 6

Find the slope of the line $x = -2$.

Helpful Hint

Slope of 0 and undefined slope are not the same. Vertical lines have undefined slope, while horizontal lines have a slope of 0.

Here is a general review of slope.

Summary of Slope

Slope m of the line through (x_1, y_1) and (x_2, y_2) is given by the equation

$$m = \frac{y_2 - y_1}{x_2 - x_1}.$$

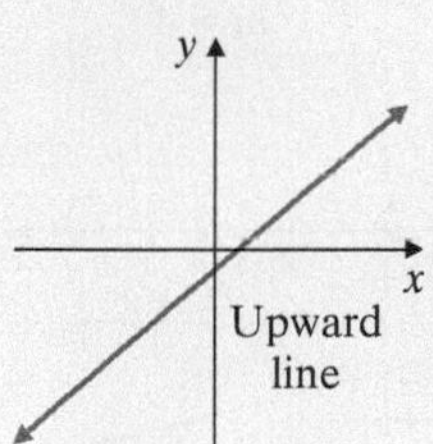

Positive slope: $m > 0$

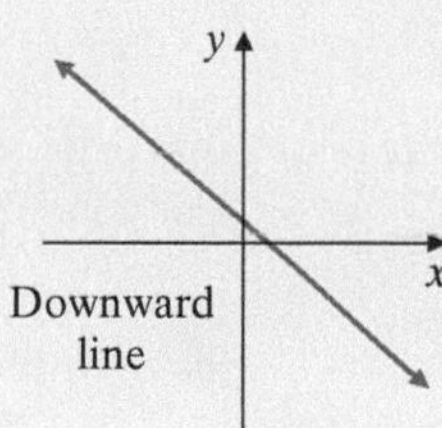

Negative slope: $m < 0$

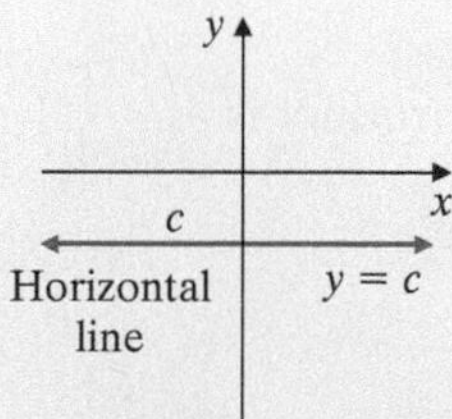

Zero slope: $m = 0$

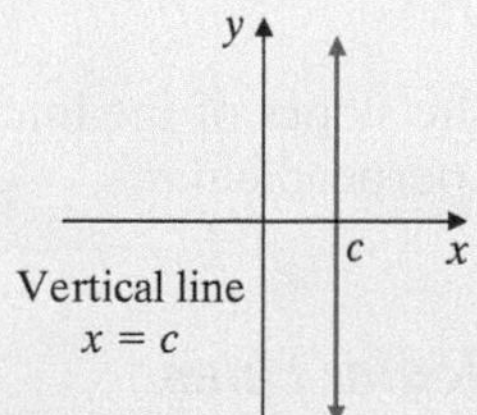

No slope or undefined slope

Objective D Slopes of Parallel and Perpendicular Lines

Two lines in the same plane are **parallel** if they do not intersect. Slopes of lines can help us determine whether lines are parallel. Since parallel lines have the same steepness, it follows that they have the same slope.

Answer

6. undefined slope

For example, the graphs of

$$y = -2x + 4$$

and

$$y = -2x - 3$$

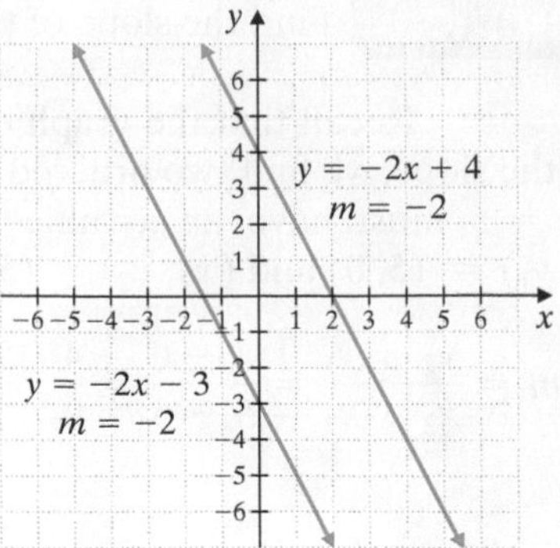

are shown. These lines have the same slope, −2. They also have different y-intercepts, so the lines are parallel. (If the y-intercepts were the same also, the lines would be the same.)

Parallel Lines

Nonvertical parallel lines have the same slope and different y-intercepts.

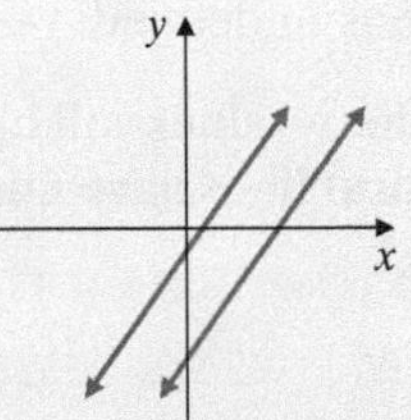

Two lines are **perpendicular** if they lie in the same plane and meet at a 90° (right) angle. How do the slopes of perpendicular lines compare? The product of the slopes of two perpendicular lines is −1.

For example, the graphs of

$$y = 4x + 1$$

and

$$y = -\frac{1}{4}x - 3$$

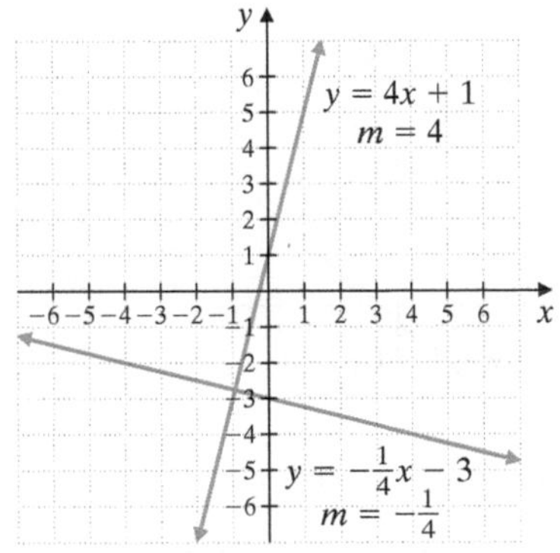

are shown. The slopes of the lines are 4 and $-\frac{1}{4}$. Their product is $4\left(-\frac{1}{4}\right) = -1$, so the lines are perpendicular.

Perpendicular Lines

If the product of the slopes of two lines is −1, then the lines are perpendicular.

(Two nonvertical lines are perpendicular if the slope of one is the negative reciprocal of the slope of the other.)

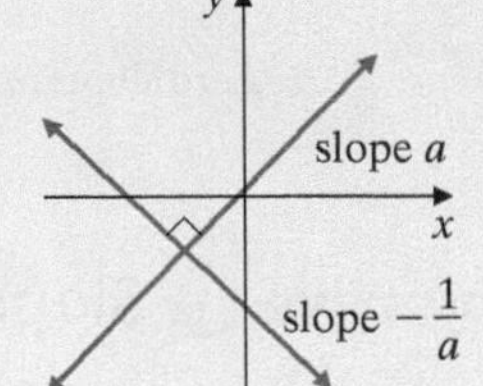

Helpful Hint

Here are examples of numbers that are negative (opposite) reciprocals.

Number	Negative Reciprocal	Their product is −1.
$\frac{2}{3}$	$-\frac{3}{2}$	$\frac{2}{3} \cdot -\frac{3}{2} = -\frac{6}{6} = -1$
-5 or $-\frac{5}{1}$	$\frac{1}{5}$	$-5 \cdot \frac{1}{5} = -\frac{5}{5} = -1$

Here are a few important points about vertical and horizontal lines.

- Two distinct vertical lines are parallel.
- Two distinct horizontal lines are parallel.
- A horizontal line and a vertical line are always perpendicular.

Example 7 Determine whether each pair of lines is parallel, perpendicular, or neither.

a. $y = -\frac{1}{5}x + 1$

$2x + 10y = 3$

b. $x + y = 3$

$-x + y = 4$

c. $3x + y = 5$

$2x + 3y = 6$

Solution:

a. The slope of the line $y = -\frac{1}{5}x + 1$ is $-\frac{1}{5}$. We find the slope of the second line by solving its equation for y.

$2x + 10y = 3$

$10y = -2x + 3$ Subtract $2x$ from both sides.

$y = \frac{-2}{10}x + \frac{3}{10}$ Divide both sides by 10.

$y = -\frac{1}{5}x + \frac{3}{10}$ Simplify.

The slope of this line is $-\frac{1}{5}$ also. Since the lines have the same slope and different y-intercepts, they are parallel, as shown in the figure on the left below.

b. To find each slope, we solve each equation for y.

$x + y = 3$

$y = -x + 3$

The slope is −1.

$-x + y = 4$

$y = x + 4$

The slope is 1.

The slopes are not the same, so the lines are not parallel. Next we check the product of the slopes: $(-1)(1) = -1$. Since the product is −1, the lines are perpendicular, as shown in the figure on the right below.

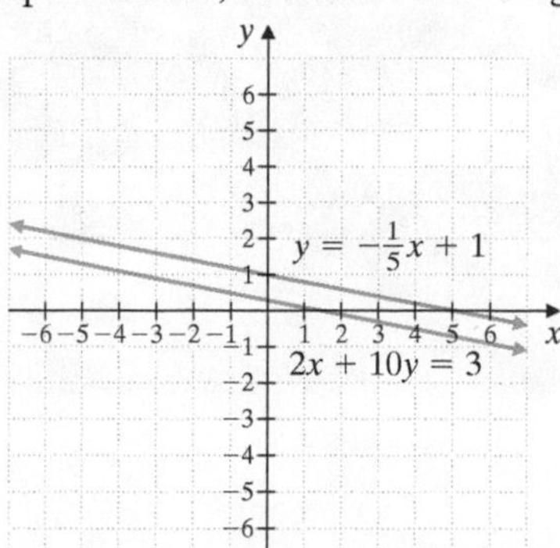

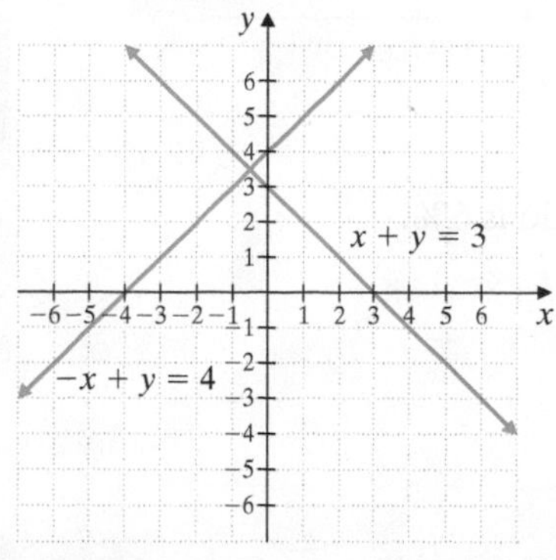

Continued on next page

PRACTICE 7

Determine whether each pair of lines is parallel, perpendicular, or neither.

a. $x + y = 5$

$2x + y = 5$

b. $5y = 2x - 3$

$5x + 2y = 1$

c. $y = 2x + 1$

$4x - 2y = 8$

Answers

7. a. neither **b.** perpendicular **c.** parallel

c. We solve each equation for y to find each slope. The slopes are -3 and $-\frac{2}{3}$. The slopes are not the same and their product is not -1. Thus, the lines are neither parallel nor perpendicular.

Work Practice 7

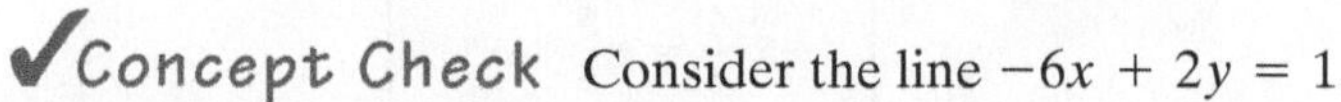

✓Concept Check Consider the line $-6x + 2y = 1$.

a. Write the equations of two lines parallel to this line.

b. Write the equations of two lines perpendicular to this line.

Objective E Slope as a Rate of Change

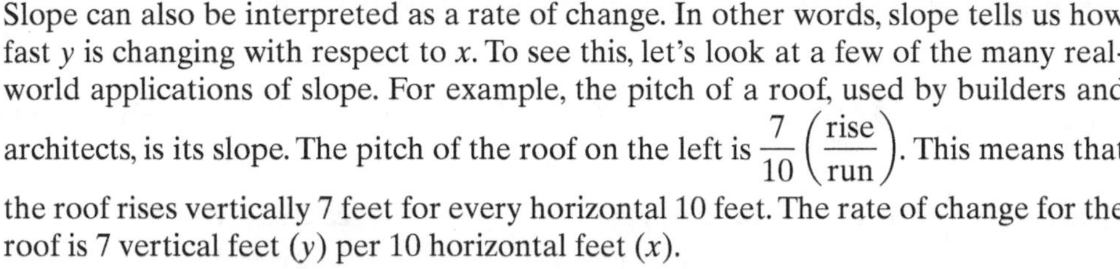

Slope can also be interpreted as a rate of change. In other words, slope tells us how fast y is changing with respect to x. To see this, let's look at a few of the many real-world applications of slope. For example, the pitch of a roof, used by builders and architects, is its slope. The pitch of the roof on the left is $\frac{7}{10}\left(\frac{\text{rise}}{\text{run}}\right)$. This means that the roof rises vertically 7 feet for every horizontal 10 feet. The rate of change for the roof is 7 vertical feet (y) per 10 horizontal feet (x).

The grade of a road is its slope written as a percent. A 7% grade, as shown below, means that the road rises (or falls) 7 feet for every horizontal 100 feet. $\left(\text{Recall that } 7\% = \frac{7}{100}.\right)$ Here, the slope of $\frac{7}{100}$ gives us the rate of change. The road rises (in our diagram) 7 vertical feet (y) for every 100 horizontal feet (x).

PRACTICE 8

Find the grade of the road shown.

Example 8 Finding the Grade of a Road

At one part of the road to the summit of Pike's Peak, the road rises 15 feet for a horizontal distance of 250 feet. Find the grade of the road.

Solution: Recall that the grade of a road is its slope written as a percent.

$$\text{grade} = \frac{\text{rise}}{\text{run}} = \frac{15}{250} = 0.06 = 6\%$$

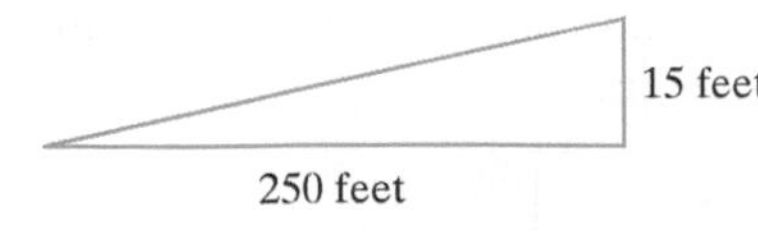

The grade is 6%.

Work Practice 8

Answer

8. 15%

✓ Concept Check Answers

Answers may vary; for example,

a. $y = 3x - 3,\ y = 3x - 1$

b. $y = -\frac{1}{3}x,\ y = -\frac{1}{3}x + 1$

Slope can also be interpreted as a rate of change. In other words, slope tells us how fast y is changing with respect to x.

Example 9 Finding the Slope of a Line

The following graph shows the cost y (in cents) of a nationwide long-distance telephone call from Texas with a certain telephone-calling plan, where x is the length of the call in minutes. Find the slope of the line and attach the proper units for the rate of change. Then write a sentence explaining the meaning of slope in this application.

Solution: Use (2, 34) and (6, 62) to calculate slope.

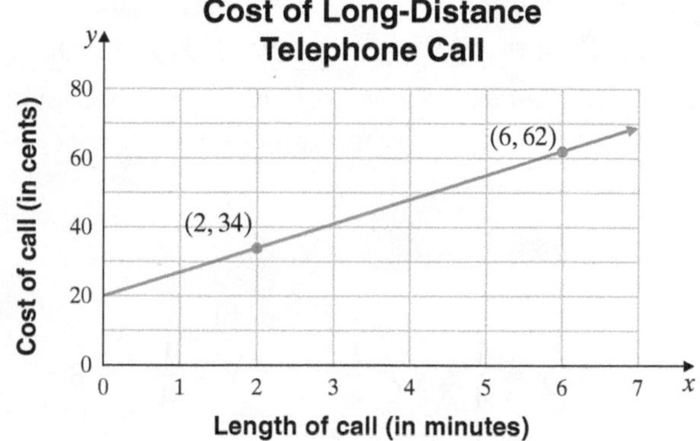

$$m = \frac{62 - 34}{6 - 2} = \frac{28}{4} = \frac{7 \text{ cents}}{1 \text{ minute}}$$

This means that the rate of change of a phone call is 7 cents per 1 minute, or the cost of the phone call is 7 cents per minute.

Work Practice 9

PRACTICE 9

Find the slope of the line and write the slope as a rate of change. This graph represents annual food and drink sales y (in billions of dollars) for year x. Write a sentence explaining the meaning of slope in this application.

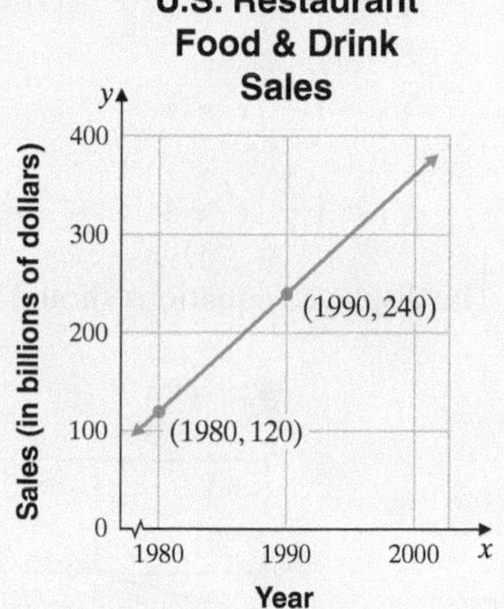

Source: National Restaurant Assn.

Answer

9. $m = 12$; The sales of food and drink from restaurants increases by \$12 billion per year.

Calculator Explorations Graphing

It is possible to use a graphing calculator and sketch the graph of more than one equation on the same set of axes. This feature can be used to see that parallel lines have the same slope. For example, graph the equations $y = \frac{2}{5}x$, $y = \frac{2}{5}x + 7$, and $y = \frac{2}{5}x - 4$ on the same set of axes. To do so, press the $\boxed{Y=}$ key and enter the equations on the first three lines.

$$Y_1 = \left(\frac{2}{5}\right)x$$

$$Y_2 = \left(\frac{2}{5}\right)x + 7$$

$$Y_3 = \left(\frac{2}{5}\right)x - 4$$

The displayed equations should look like this:

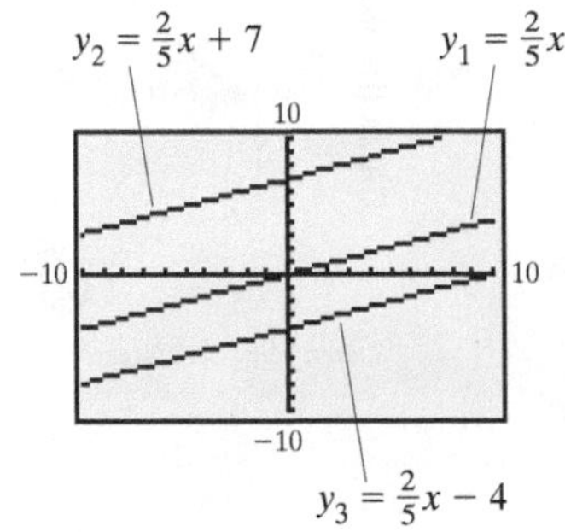

These lines are parallel as expected since they all have a slope of $\frac{2}{5}$. The graph of $y = \frac{2}{5}x + 7$ is the graph of $y = \frac{2}{5}x$ moved 7 units upward with a y-intercept of 7. Also, the graph of $y = \frac{2}{5}x - 4$ is the graph of $y = \frac{2}{5}x$ moved 4 units downward with a y-intercept of -4.

Graph the parallel lines on the same set of axes. Describe the similarities and differences in their graphs.

1. $y = 3.8x$, $y = 3.8x - 3$, $y = 3.8x + 9$

2. $y = -4.9x$, $y = -4.9x + 1$, $y = -4.9x + 8$

3. $y = \frac{1}{4}x$, $y = \frac{1}{4}x + 5$, $y = \frac{1}{4}x - 8$

4. $y = -\frac{3}{4}x$, $y = -\frac{3}{4}x - 5$, $y = -\frac{3}{4}x + 6$

Vocabulary and Readiness Check

Use the choices below to fill in each blank. Not all choices will be used.

m	x	0	positive	undefined
b	y	slope	negative	

1. The measure of the steepness or tilt of a line is called ____________.

2. If an equation is written in the form $y = mx + b$, the value of the letter ____________ is the value of the slope of the graph.

3. The slope of a horizontal line is ____________.

4. The slope of a vertical line is ____________.

5. If the graph of a line moves upward from left to right, the line has ____________ slope.

6. If the graph of a line moves downward from left to right, the line has ____________ slope.

7. Given two points of a line, slope $= \dfrac{\text{change in \_\_\_\_\_\_\_\_}}{\text{change in \_\_\_\_\_\_\_\_}}$.

State whether the slope of the line is positive, negative, 0, or undefined.

8.

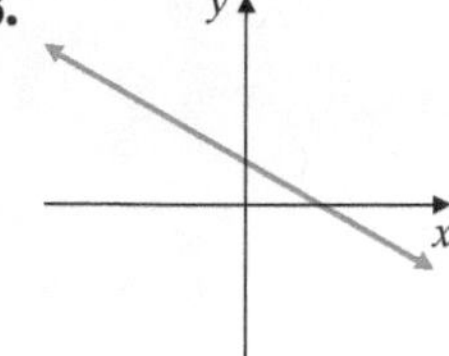

9.

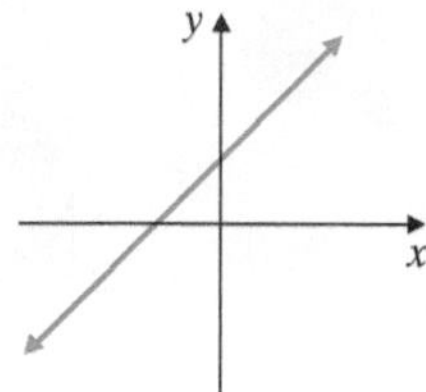

10.

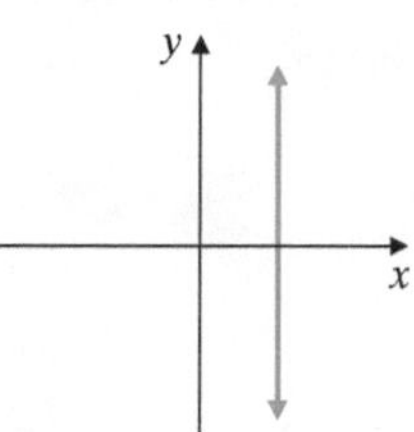

11.

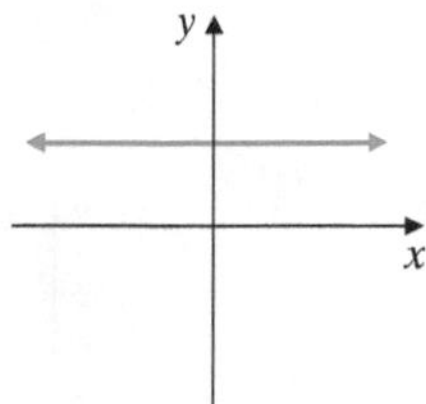

Decide whether a line with the given slope slants upward or downward or is horizontal or vertical.

12. $m = \dfrac{7}{6}$ ____________ **13.** $m = -3$ ____________ **14.** $m = 0$ ____________ **15.** m is undefined. ____________

6.4 Exercise Set

FOR EXTRA HELP

PRACTICE

WATCH

DOWNLOAD

READ

REVIEW

Objective A *Find the slope of the line that passes through the given points. See Examples 1 and 2.*

1. $(-1, 5)$ and $(6, -2)$ **2.** $(-1, 16)$ and $(3, 4)$ **3.** $(1, 4)$ and $(5, 3)$ **4.** $(3, 1)$ and $(2, 6)$

5. $(5, 1)$ and $(-2, 1)$ **6.** $(-8, 3)$ and $(-2, 3)$ **7.** $(-4, 3)$ and $(-4, 5)$ **8.** $(-2, -3)$ and $(-2, 5)$

Use the points shown on each graph to find the slope of each line. See Examples 1 and 2.

9.

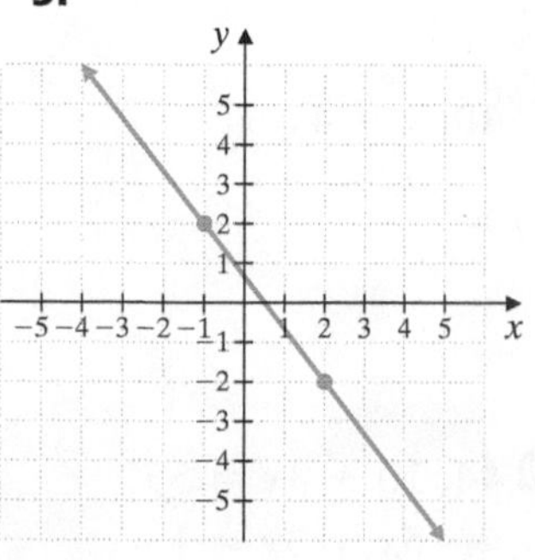

10.

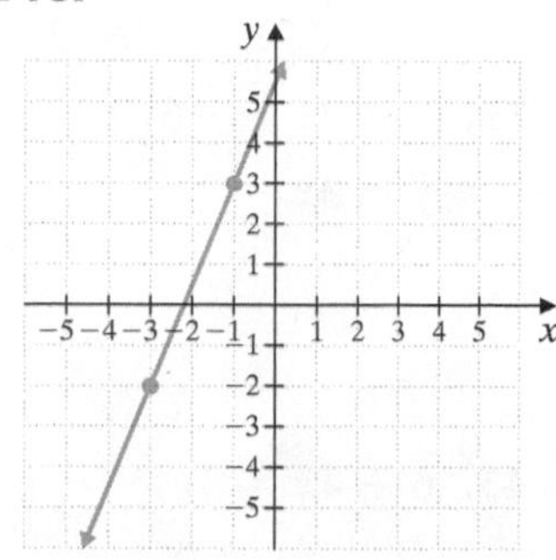

11.

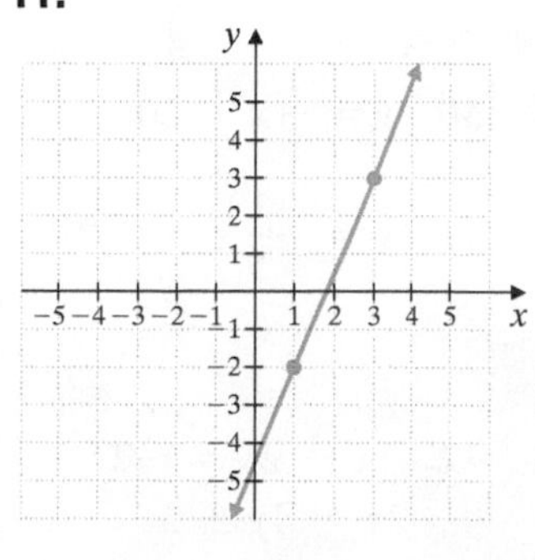

12.

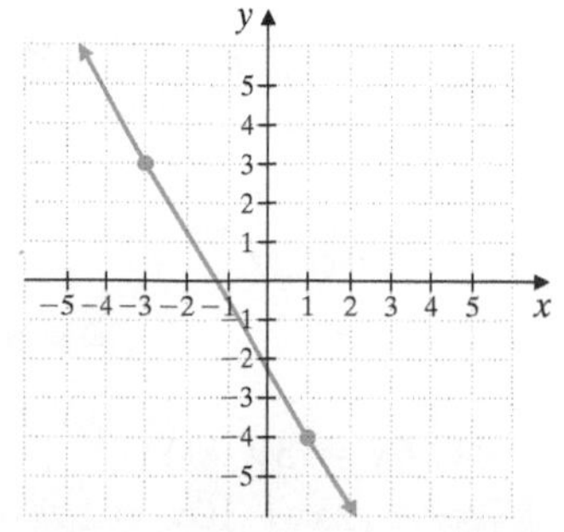

For each graph, determine which line has the greater slope.

13.

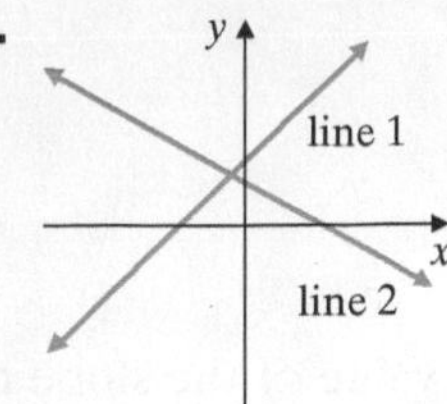

14.

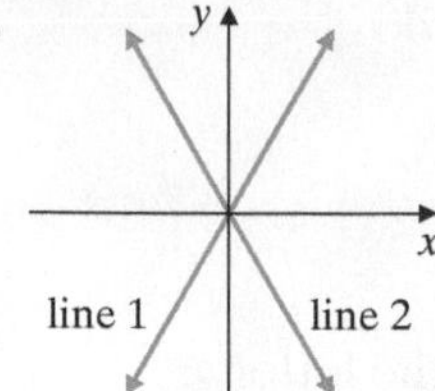

15.

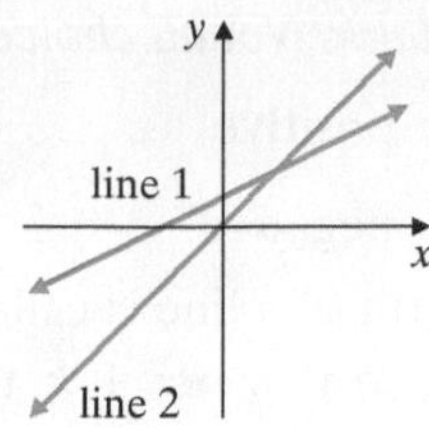

16.

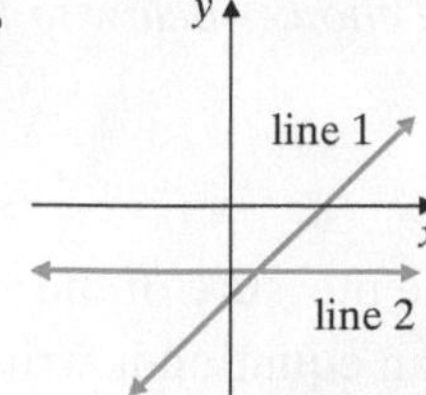

Objectives **B** **C** **Mixed Practice** *Find the slope of each line. See Examples 3 through 6.*

17. $y = 5x - 2$

18. $y = -2x + 6$

19. $y = -0.3x + 2.5$

20. $y = -7.6x - 0.1$

21. $2x + y = 7$

22. $-5x + y = 10$

23.

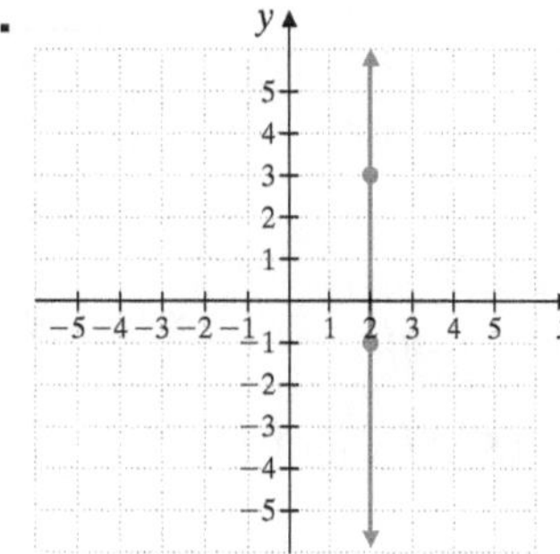

24.

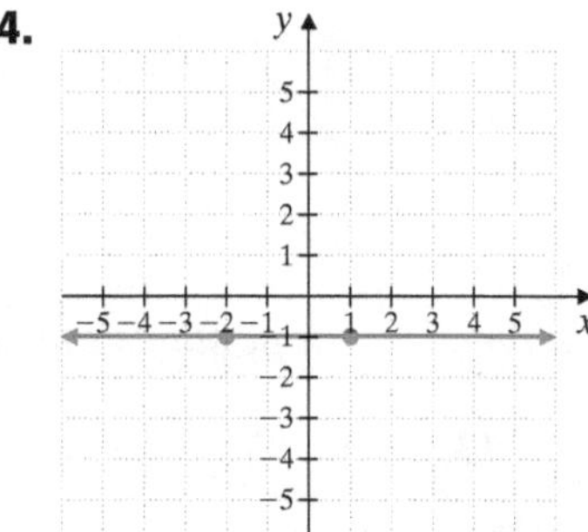

25. $2x - 3y = 10$

26. $3x - 5y = 1$

27. $x = 1$

28. $y = -2$

29. $x = 2y$

30. $x = -4y$

31. $y = -3$

32. $x = 5$

33. $-3x - 4y = 6$

34. $-4x - 7y = 9$

35. $20x - 5y = 1.2$

36. $24x - 3y = 5.7$

△ Objective **D** *Determine whether each pair of lines is parallel, perpendicular, or neither. See Example 7.*

37. $y = \frac{2}{9}x + 3$
$y = -\frac{2}{9}x$

38. $y = \frac{1}{5}x + 20$
$y = -\frac{1}{5}x$

39. $x - 3y = -6$
$y = 3x - 9$

40. $y = 4x - 2$
$4x + y = 5$

41. $6x = 5y + 1$
$-12x + 10y = 1$

42. $-x + 2y = -2$
$2x = 4y + 3$

43. $6 + 4x = 3y$
$3x + 4y = 8$

44. $10 + 3x = 5y$
$5x + 3y = 1$

△ *Find the slope of the line that is (a) parallel and (b) perpendicular to the line through each pair of points. See Example 7.*

45. $(-3, -3)$ and $(0, 0)$

46. $(6, -2)$ and $(1, 4)$

47. $(-8, -4)$ and $(3, 5)$

48. $(6, -1)$ and $(-4, -10)$

Objective **E** *The pitch of a roof is its slope. Find the pitch of each roof shown. See Example 8.*

49.

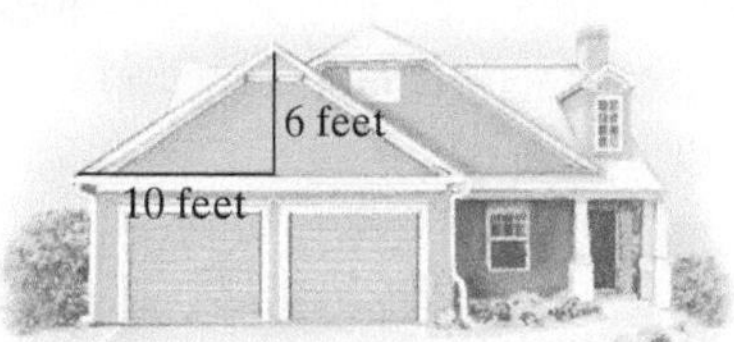

50.

The grade of a road is its slope written as a percent. Find the grade of each road shown. See Example 8.

51.

52.

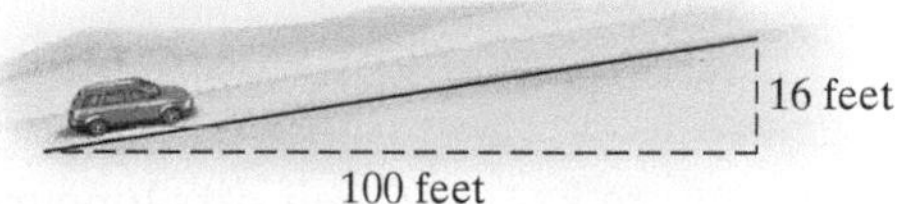

53. One of Japan's superconducting "bullet" trains is researched and tested at the Yamanashi Maglev Test Line near Otsuki City. The steepest section of the track has a rise of 2580 meters for a horizontal distance of 6450 meters. What is the grade (slope written as a percent) of this section of track? (*Source:* Japan Railways Central Co.)

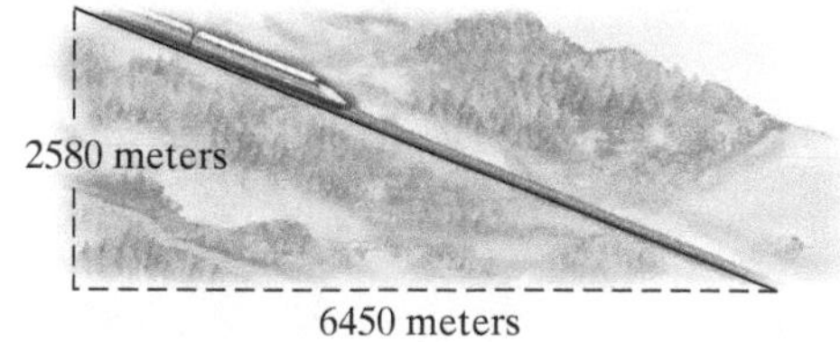

54. Professional plumbers suggest that a sewer pipe should rise 0.25 inch for every horizontal foot. Find the recommended slope for a sewer pipe and write the slope as a grade, or percent. Round to the nearest percent.

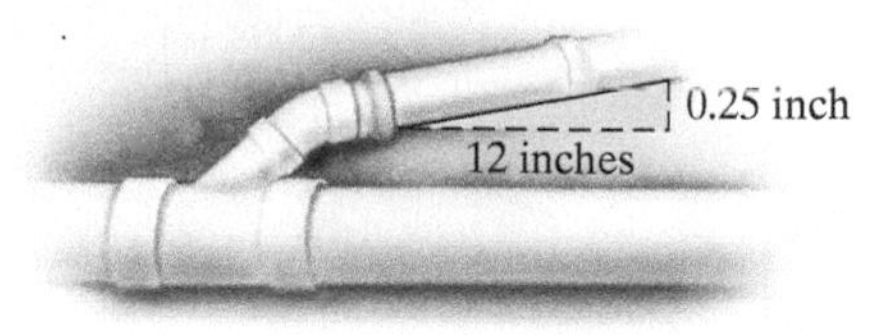

55. There has been controversy over the past few years about the world's steepest street. The *Guinness Book of Records* actually listed Baldwin Street, in Dunedin, New Zealand, as the world's steepest street, but Canton Avenue in the Pittsburgh neighborhood of Beechview may be steeper. Calculate each grade to the nearest percent.

		Grade (%)
Canton Avenue	for every 30 meters of horizontal distance, the vertical change is 11 meters	
Baldwin Street	for every 2.86 meters of horizontal distance, the vertical change is 1 meter	

56. According to federal regulations, a wheelchair ramp should rise no more than 1 foot for a horizontal distance of 12 feet. Write the slope as a grade. Round to the nearest tenth of a percent.

Find the slope of each line and write a sentence using the slope as a rate of change. Don't forget to attach the proper units. See Example 9.

57. This graph approximates the number of U.S. households that have televisions y (in millions) for year x.

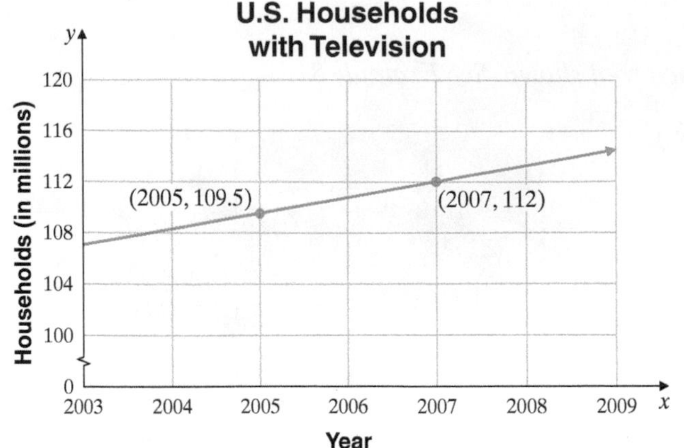

58. The graph approximates the amount of money y (in billions of dollars) spent worldwide on tourism for year x. (*Source:* World Tourism Organization)

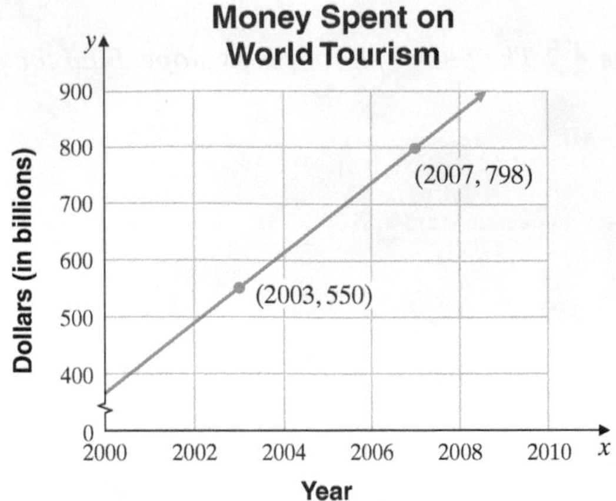

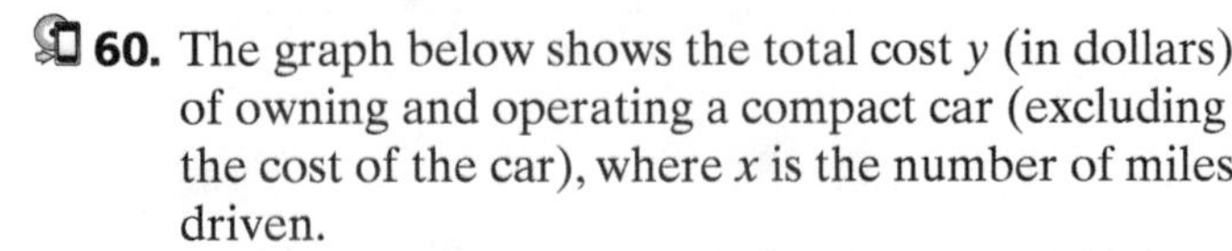

59. Americans are keeping their cars longer. The graph below shows the median age y (in years) of automobiles in the United States for the years shown. (*Source:* Bureau of Transportation Statistics)

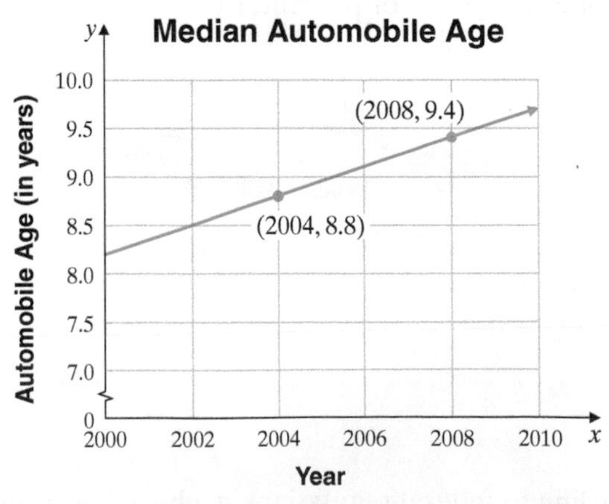

60. The graph below shows the total cost y (in dollars) of owning and operating a compact car (excluding the cost of the car), where x is the number of miles driven.

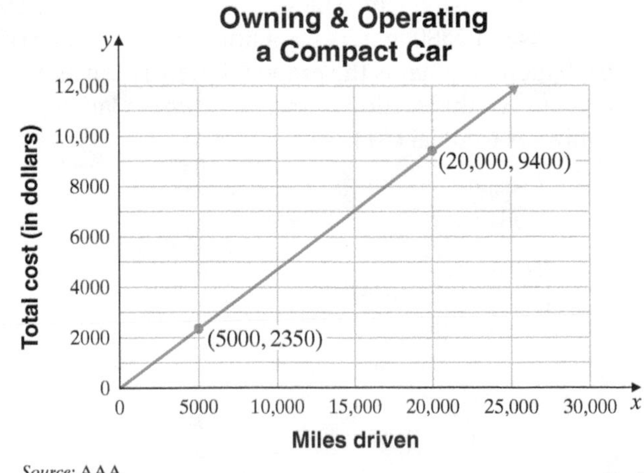

Review

Solve each equation for y. See Section 2.5.

61. $y - (-6) = 2(x - 4)$

62. $y - 7 = -9(x - 6)$

63. $y - 1 = -6(x - (-2))$

64. $y - (-3) = 4(x - (-5))$

Concept Extensions

Match each line with its slope.

a. $m = 0$

b. undefined slope

c. $m = 3$

d. $m = 1$

e. $m = -\frac{1}{2}$

f. $m = -\frac{3}{4}$

65.

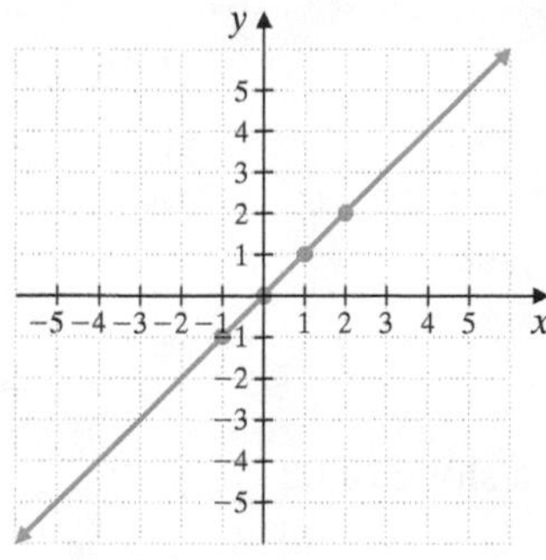

66.

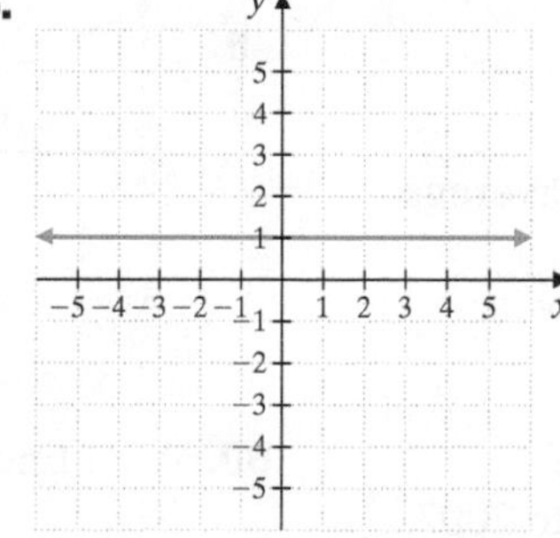

67.

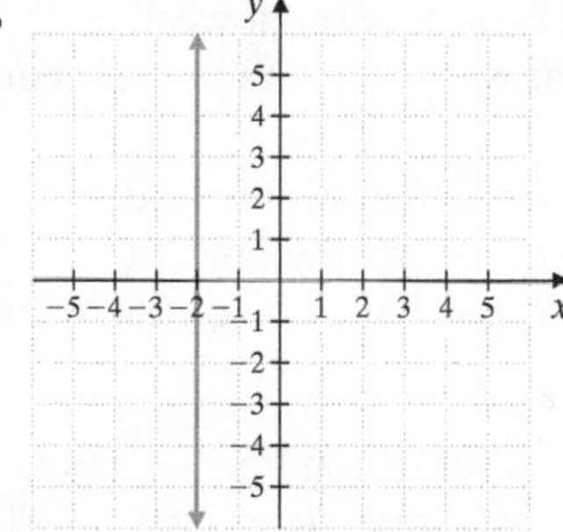

68.

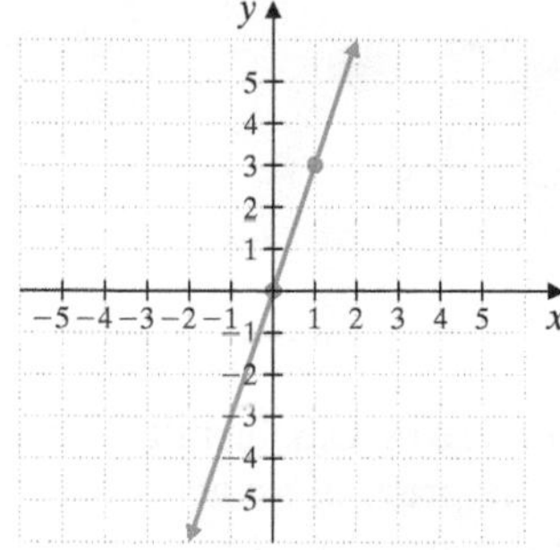

69.

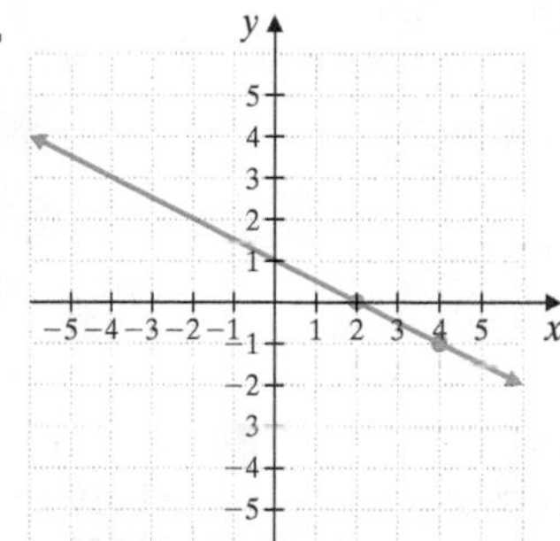

70.

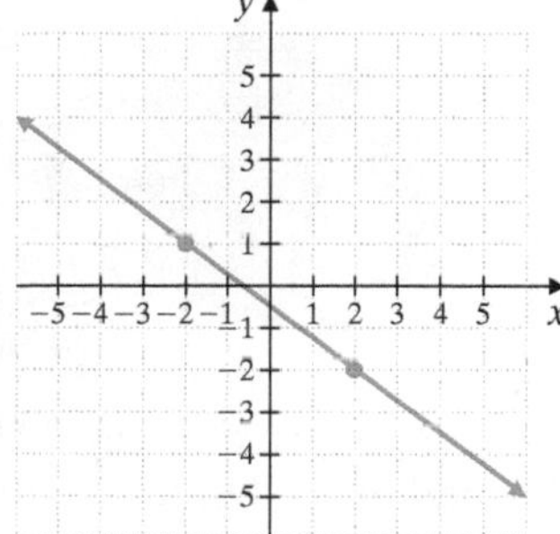

Solve. See a Concept Check in this section.

71. Verify that the points $(2, 1)$, $(0, 0)$, $(-2, -1)$, and $(-4, -2)$ are all on the same line by computing the slope between each pair of points. (See the first Concept Check.)

72. Given the points $(2, 3)$ and $(-5, 1)$, can the slope of the line through these points be calculated by $\frac{1 - 3}{2 - (-5)}$? Why or why not? (See the second Concept Check.)

73. Write the equations of three lines parallel to $10x - 5y = -7$. (See the third Concept Check.)

74. Write the equations of two lines perpendicular to $10x - 5y = -7$. (See the third Concept Check.)

The following line graph shows the average fuel economy (in miles per gallon) of passenger automobiles produced during each of the model years shown. Use this graph to answer Exercises 75 through 80.

75. What was the average fuel economy (in miles per gallon) for automobiles produced during 2004?

76. Find the decrease in average fuel economy for automobiles between the years 1998 and 1999.

77. During which of the model years shown was average fuel economy the lowest?
What was the average fuel economy for that year?

78. During which of the model years shown was average fuel economy the highest?
What was the average fuel economy for that year?

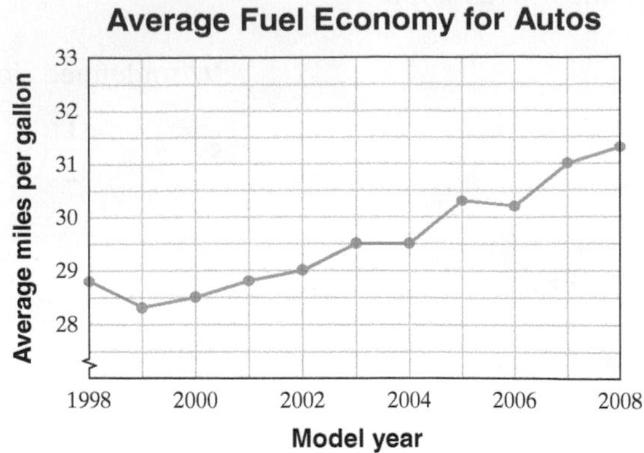

Source: Bureau of Transportation Statistics

79. Of the following line segments, which has the greatest slope: from 2002 to 2003, from 2006 to 2007, or from 2007 to 2008?

80. What line segment has a slope of 0?

81. Find x so that the pitch of the roof is $\frac{2}{5}$.

82. Find x so that the pitch of the roof is $\frac{1}{3}$.

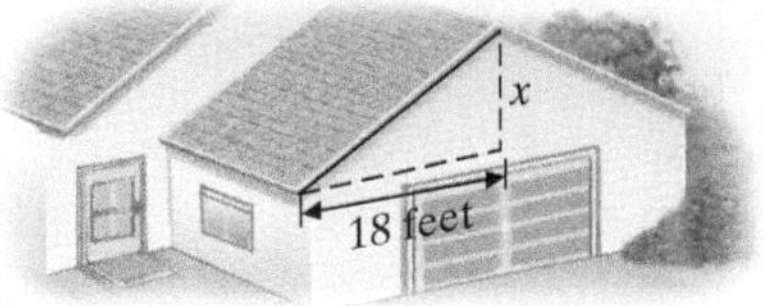

83. There were approximately 2025 heart transplants performed in the United States in 2004. In 2007, the number of heart transplants in the United States rose to 2208. (*Source:* Organ Procurement and Transplantation Network)

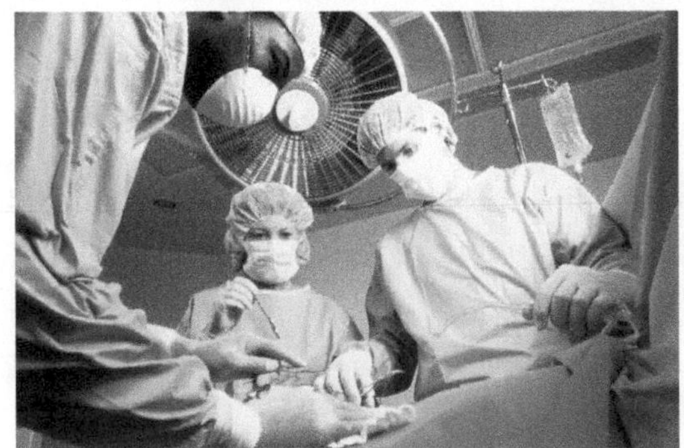

a. Write two ordered pairs of the form (year, number of heart transplants).

b. Find the slope of the line between the two points.

c. Write a sentence explaining the meaning of the slope as a rate of change.

84. The average price of an acre of U.S. farmland was \$1210 in 2002. In 2008, the price of an acre rose to \$2350. (*Source:* National Agricultural Statistics Services)

a. Write two ordered pairs of the form (year, price of an acre).

b. Find the slope of the line through the two points.

c. Write a sentence explaining the meaning of the slope as a rate of change.

85. Show that the quadrilateral with vertices $(1, 3)$, $(2, 1)$, $(-4, 0)$, and $(-3, -2)$ is a parallelogram.

86. Show that a triangle with vertices at the points $(1, 1)$, $(-4, 4)$, and $(-3, 0)$ is a right triangle.

Find the slope of the line through the given points.

87. $(-3.8, 1.2)$ and $(-2.2, 4.5)$

88. $(2.1, 6.7)$ and $(-8.3, 9.3)$

89. $(14.3, -10.1)$ and $(9.8, -2.9)$

90. $(2.3, 0.2)$ and $(7.9, 5.1)$

91. The graph of $y = \frac{1}{2}x$ has a slope of $\frac{1}{2}$. The graph of $y = 3x$ has a slope of 3. The graph of $y = 5x$ has a slope of 5. Graph all three equations on a single coordinate system. As the slope becomes larger, how does the steepness of the line change?

92. The graph of $y = -\frac{1}{3}x + 2$ has a slope of $-\frac{1}{3}$. The graph of $y = -2x + 2$ has a slope of -2. The graph of $y = -4x + 2$ has a slope of -4. Graph all three equations on a single coordinate system. As the absolute value of the slope becomes larger, how does the steepness of the line change?

Objectives

A **Use the Slope-Intercept Form to Graph a Linear Equation.**

B **Use the Slope-Intercept Form to Write an Equation of a Line.**

C **Use the Point-Slope Form to Find an Equation of a Line Given Its Slope and a Point of the Line.**

D **Use the Point-Slope Form to Find an Equation of a Line Given Two Points of the Line.**

E **Use the Point-Slope Form to Solve Problems.**

6.5 EQUATIONS OF LINES

We know that when a linear equation is solved for y, the coefficient of x is the slope of the line. For example, the slope of the line whose equation is $y = 3x + 1$ is 3. In this equation, $y = 3x + 1$, what does 1 represent? To find out, let $x = 0$ and watch what happens.

$$y = 3x + 1$$

$$y = 3 \cdot 0 + 1 \quad \text{Let } x = 0.$$

$$y = 1$$

We now have the ordered pair $(0, 1)$, which means that 1 is the y-intercept.

This is true in general. To see this, let $x = 0$ and solve for y in $y = mx + b$.

$$y = m \cdot 0 + b \quad \text{Let } x = 0.$$

$$y = b$$

We obtain the ordered pair $(0, b)$, which means that point is the y-intercept.

The form $y = mx + b$ is appropriately called the *slope-intercept form* of a linear equation. (m: slope; b: y-intercept is $(0, b)$)

Slope-Intercept Form

When a linear equation in two variables is written in **slope-intercept form,**

$$y = mx + b$$

(m: slope; $(0, b)$, y-intercept)

then m is the slope of the line and $(0, b)$ is the y-intercept of the line.

Objective A Using the Slope-Intercept Form to Graph an Equation

We can use the slope-intercept form of the equation of a line to graph a linear equation.

Example 1 Use the slope-intercept form to graph the equation

$$y = \frac{3}{5}x - 2.$$

Solution: Since the equation $y = \frac{3}{5}x - 2$ is written in slope-intercept form $y = mx + b$, the slope of its graph is $\frac{3}{5}$ and the y-intercept is $(0, -2)$. To graph this equation, we begin by plotting the point $(0, -2)$. From this point, we can find another point of the graph by using the slope $\frac{3}{5}$ and recalling that slope is $\frac{\text{rise}}{\text{run}}$. We start at the y-intercept and move 3 units up since the

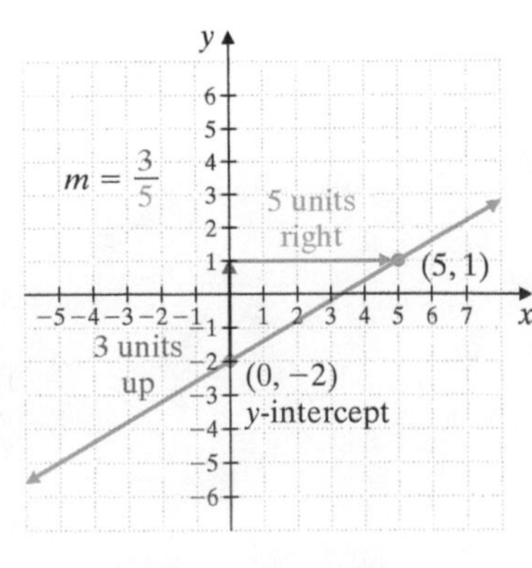

PRACTICE 1

Use the slope-intercept form to graph the equation $y = \frac{2}{3}x - 4$.

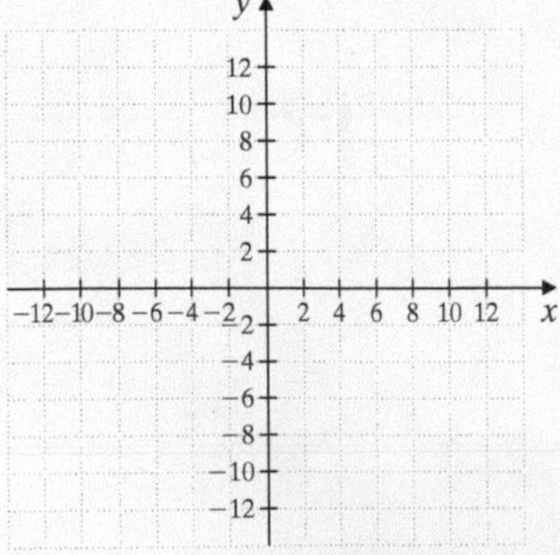

Answer

1.

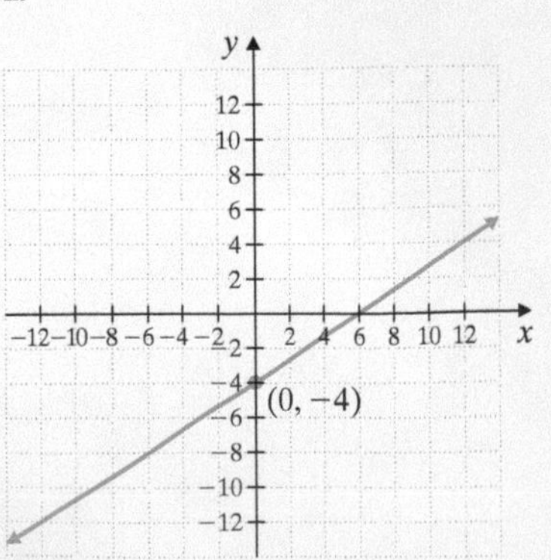

numerator of the slope is 3; then we move 5 units to the right since the denominator of the slope is 5. We stop at the point (5, 1). The line through (0, −2) and (5, 1) is the graph of $y = \frac{3}{5}x - 2$.

Work Practice 1

Example 2 Use the slope-intercept form to graph the equation $4x + y = 1$.

Solution: First we write the given equation in slope-intercept form.

$$4x + y = 1$$
$$y = -4x + 1$$

The graph of this equation will have slope −4 and y-intercept (0, 1). To graph this line, we first plot the point (0, 1). To find another point of the graph, we use the slope −4, which can be written as $\frac{-4}{1}$ $\left(\frac{4}{-1} \text{ could also be used}\right)$. We start at the point (0, 1) and move 4 units down (since the numerator of the slope is −4), and then 1 unit to the right (since the denominator of the slope is 1).

We arrive at the point (1, −3). The line through (0, 1) and (1, −3) is the graph of $4x + y = 1$.

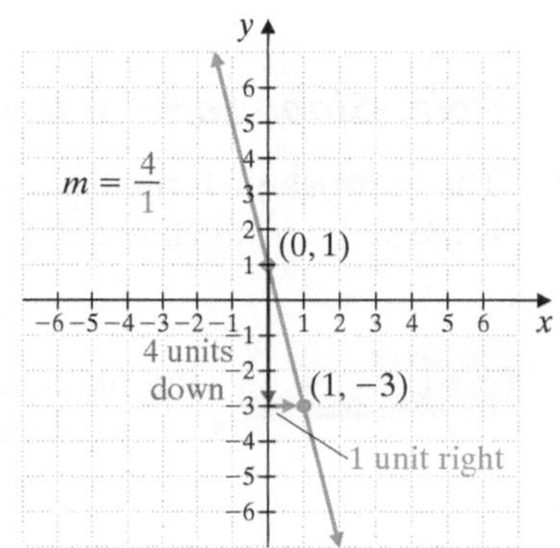

Work Practice 2

PRACTICE 2

Use the slope-intercept form to graph $3x + y = 2$.

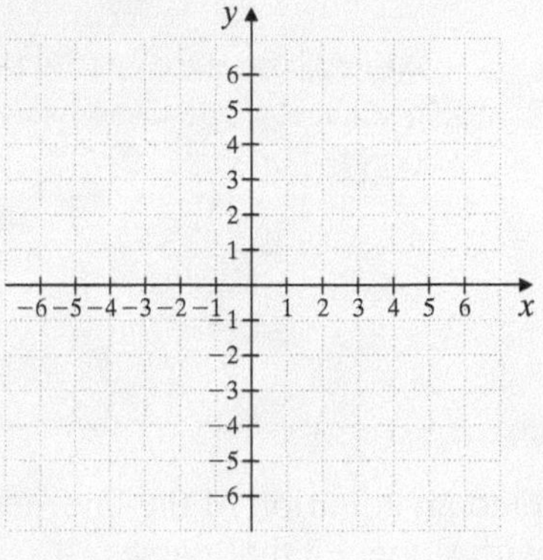

Helpful Hint

In Example 2, if we interpret the slope of −4 as $\frac{4}{-1}$, we arrive at (−1, 5) for a second point. Notice that this point is also on the line.

PRACTICE 3

Find an equation of the line with y-intercept (0, −4) and slope of $\frac{1}{5}$.

Objective B Using the Slope-Intercept Form to Write an Equation

The slope-intercept form can also be used to write the equation of a line when we know its slope and y-intercept.

Example 3 Find an equation of the line with y-intercept (0, −3) and slope of $\frac{1}{4}$.

Solution: We are given the slope and the y-intercept. We let $m = \frac{1}{4}$ and $b = -3$ and write the equation in slope-intercept form, $y = mx + b$.

$$y = mx + b$$
$$y = \frac{1}{4}x + (-3) \quad \text{Let } m = \frac{1}{4} \text{ and } b = -3.$$
$$y = \frac{1}{4}x - 3 \quad \text{Simplify.}$$

Work Practice 3

Answers

2.

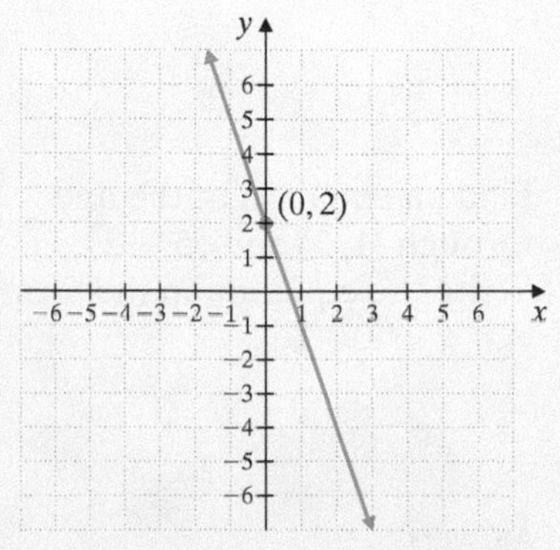

3. $y = \frac{1}{5}x - 4$

Objective C Writing an Equation Given Its Slope and a Point

Thus far, we have written an equation of a line by knowing its slope and y-intercept. We can also write an equation of a line if we know its slope and any point on the line. To see how we do this, let m represent slope and (x_1, y_1) represent the point on the line. Then if (x, y) is any other point of the line, we have that

$$\frac{y - y_1}{x - x_1} = m$$

$$y - y_1 = m(x - x_1) \quad \text{Multiply both sides by } (x - x_1).$$

$\uparrow$ slope

This is the *point-slope form* of the equation of a line.

Point-Slope Form of the Equation of a Line

The **point-slope form** of the equation of a line is $y - y_1 = m(x - x_1)$, where m is the slope of the line and (x_1, y_1) is a point on the line.

PRACTICE 4

Find an equation of the line with slope -3 that passes through $(2, -4)$. Write the equation in slope-intercept form, $y = mx + b$, and in standard form, $Ax + By = C$.

Example 4 Find an equation of the line with slope -2 that passes through $(-1, 5)$. Write the equation in slope-intercept form, $y = mx + b$, and in standard form, $Ax + By = C$.

Solution: Since the slope and a point on the line are given, we use point-slope form $y - y_1 = m(x - x_1)$ to write the equation. Let $m = -2$ and $(-1, 5) = (x_1, y_1)$.

$$y - y_1 = m(x - x_1)$$

$$y - 5 = -2[x - (-1)] \quad \text{Let } m = -2 \text{ and } (x_1, y_1) = (-1, 5).$$

$$y - 5 = -2(x + 1) \quad \text{Simplify.}$$

$$y - 5 = -2x - 2 \quad \text{Use the distributive property.}$$

To write the equation in slope-intercept form, $y = mx + b$, we simply solve the equation for y. To do this, we add 5 to both sides.

$$y - 5 = -2x - 2$$

$$y = -2x + 3 \quad \text{Slope-intercept form}$$

$$2x + y = 3 \quad \text{Add } 2x \text{ to both sides and we have standard form.}$$

Work Practice 4

Objective D Writing an Equation Given Two Points

We can also find the equation of a line when we are given any two points of the line.

PRACTICE 5

Find an equation of the line through $(1, 3)$ and $(5, -2)$. Write the equation in the form $Ax + By = C$.

Example 5 Find an equation of the line through $(2, 5)$ and $(-3, 4)$. Write the equation in the form $Ax + By = C$.

Solution: First, use the two given points to find the slope of the line.

$$m = \frac{4 - 5}{-3 - 2} = \frac{-1}{-5} = \frac{1}{5}$$

Next we use the slope $\frac{1}{5}$ and either one of the given points to write the equation in point-slope form. We use $(2, 5)$. Let $x_1 = 2$, $y_1 = 5$, and $m = \frac{1}{5}$.

Answers

4. $y = -3x + 2$; $3x + y = 2$
5. $5x + 4y = 17$

$y - y_1 = m(x - x_1)$ Use point-slope form.

$y - 5 = \frac{1}{5}(x - 2)$ Let $x_1 = 2$, $y_1 = 5$, and $m = \frac{1}{5}$.

$5(y - 5) = 5 \cdot \frac{1}{5}(x - 2)$ Multiply both sides by 5 to clear fractions.

$5y - 25 = x - 2$ Use the distributive property and simplify.

$-x + 5y - 25 = -2$ Subtract x from both sides.

$-x + 5y = 23$ Add 25 to both sides.

Work Practice 5

Helpful Hint

When you multiply both sides of the equation from Example 5, $-x + 5y = 23$, by -1, it becomes $x - 5y = -23$.

Both $-x + 5y = 23$ and $x - 5y = -23$ are in the form $Ax + By = C$ and both are equations of the same line.

Objective E Using the Point-Slope Form to Solve Problems

Problems occurring in many fields can be modeled by linear equations in two variables. The next example is from the field of marketing and shows how consumer demand for a product depends on the price of the product.

Example 6 The Whammo Company has learned that by pricing a newly released Frisbee at \$6, sales will reach 2000 Frisbees per day. Raising the price to \$8 will cause the sales to fall to 1500 Frisbees per day.

a. Assume that the relationship between sales price and number of Frisbees sold is linear and write an equation describing this relationship. Write the equation in slope-intercept form. Use ordered pairs of the form (sales price, number sold).

b. Predict the daily sales of Frisbees if the sales price is \$7.50.

Solution:

a. We use the given information and write two ordered pairs. Our ordered pairs are (6, 2000) and (8, 1500). To use the point-slope form to write an equation, we find the slope of the line that contains these points.

$$m = \frac{2000 - 1500}{6 - 8} = \frac{500}{-2} = -250$$

Next we use the slope and either one of the points to write the equation in point-slope form. We use (6, 2000).

Continued on next page

PRACTICE 6

The Pool Entertainment Company learned that by pricing a new pool toy at \$10, local sales will reach 200 a week. Lowering the price to \$9 will cause sales to rise to 250 a week.

a. Assume that the relationship between sales price and number of toys sold is linear, and write an equation describing this relationship. Write the equation in slope-intercept form. Use ordered pairs of the form (sales price, number sold).

b. Predict the weekly sales of the toy if the price is \$7.50.

Answers

6. a. $y = -50x + 700$ **b.** 325

$$y - y_1 = m(x - x_1) \quad \text{Use point-slope form.}$$
$$y - 2000 = -250(x - 6) \quad \text{Let } x_1 = 6,\ y_1 = 2000, \text{ and } m = -250.$$
$$y - 2000 = -250x + 1500 \quad \text{Use the distributive property.}$$
$$y = -250x + 3500 \quad \text{Write in slope-intercept form.}$$

b. To predict the sales if the price is \$7.50, we find y when $x = 7.50$.

$y = -250x + 3500$

$y = -250(7.50) + 3500$ Let $x = 7.50$.

$y = -1875 + 3500$

$y = 1625$

If the sales price is \$7.50, sales will reach 1625 Frisbees per day.

Work Practice 6

We could have solved Example 6 by using ordered pairs of the form (number sold, sales price).

Here is a summary of our discussion on linear equations thus far.

Forms of Linear Equations

$Ax + By = C$	**Standard form** of a linear equation. A and B are not both 0.
$y = mx + b$	**Slope-intercept form** of a linear equation. The slope is m and the y-intercept is $(0, b)$.
$y - y_1 = m(x - x_1)$	**Point-slope form** of a linear equation. The slope is m and (x_1, y_1) is a point on the line.
$y = c$	**Horizontal line** The slope is 0 and the y-intercept is $(0, c)$.
$x = c$	**Vertical line** The slope is undefined and the x-intercept is $(c, 0)$.

Parallel and Perpendicular Lines

Nonvertical parallel lines have the same slope.
The product of the slopes of two nonvertical perpendicular lines is -1.

Calculator Explorations Graphing

A graphing calculator is a very useful tool for discovering patterns. To discover the change in the graph of a linear equation caused by a change in slope, try the following. Use a standard window and graph a linear equation in the form $y = mx + b$. Recall that the graph of such an equation will have slope m and y-intercept $(0, b)$.

First graph $y = x + 3$. To do so, press the Y= key and enter $Y_1 = x + 3$. Notice that this graph has slope 1 and that the y-intercept is 3. Next, on the same set of axes, graph $y = 2x + 3$ and $y = 3x + 3$ by pressing Y= and entering $Y_2 = 2x + 3$ and $Y_3 = 3x + 3$.

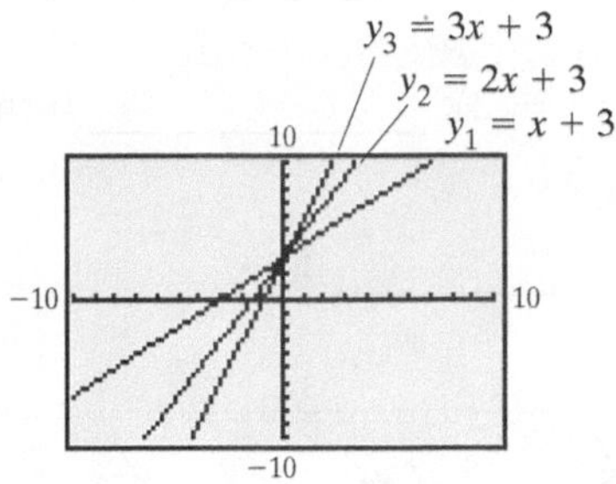

Notice the difference in the graph of each equation as the slope changes from 1 to 2 to 3. How would the graph of $y = 5x + 3$ appear? To see the change in the graph caused by a change in negative slope, try graphing $y = -x + 3$, $y = -2x + 3$, and $y = -3x + 3$ on the same set of axes.

Use a graphing calculator to graph the following equations. For each exercise, graph the first equation and use its graph to predict the appearance of the other equations. Then graph the other equations on the same set of axes and check your prediction.

1. $y = x$; $y = 6x$, $y = -6x$

2. $y = -x$; $y = -5x$, $y = -10x$

3. $y = \frac{1}{2}x + 2$; $y = \frac{3}{4}x + 2$, $y = x + 2$

4. $y = x + 1$; $y = \frac{5}{4}x + 1$, $y = \frac{5}{2}x + 1$

Vocabulary and Readiness Check

Use the choices below to fill in each blank. Some choices may be used more than once and some not at all.

b	(y_1, x_1)	point-slope	vertical	standard
m	(x_1, y_1)	slope-intercept	horizontal	

1. The form $y = mx + b$ is called ____________ form. When a linear equation in two variables is written in this form, ____________ is the slope of its graph and (0, ____________) is its y-intercept.

2. The form $y - y_1 = m(x - x_1)$ is called ____________ form. When a linear equation in two variables is written in this form, ____________ is the slope of its graph and ____________ is a point on the graph.

For Exercises 3 through 6 identify the form that the linear equation in two variables is written in. For Exercises 7 and 8, identify the appearance of the graph of the equation.

3. $y - 7 = 4(x + 3)$; ____________ form

4. $5x - 9y = 11$; ____________ form

5. $y = \frac{3}{4}x - \frac{1}{3}$; ____________ form

6. $y + 2 = \frac{-1}{3}(x - 2)$; ____________ form

7. $y = \frac{1}{2}$; ____________ line

8. $x = -17$; ____________ line

6.5 Exercise Set

FOR EXTRA HELP

PRACTICE

WATCH

DOWNLOAD

READ

REVIEW

Objective A *Use the slope-intercept form to graph each equation. See Examples 1 and 2.*

1. $y = 2x + 1$

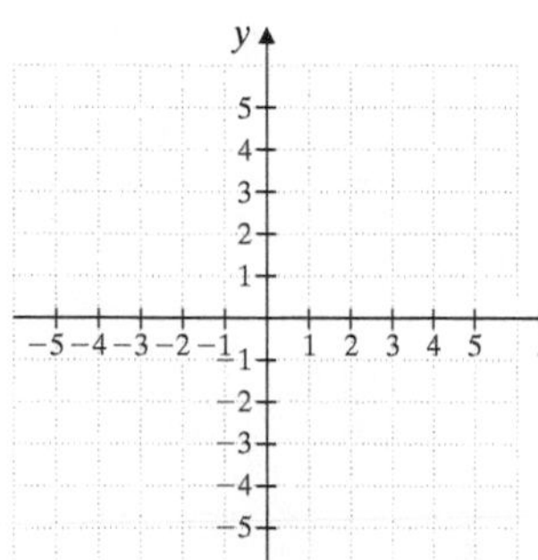

2. $y = -4x - 1$

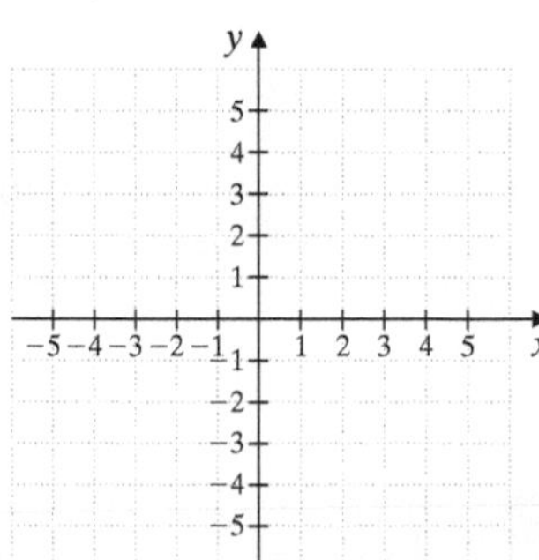

3. $y = \frac{2}{3}x + 5$

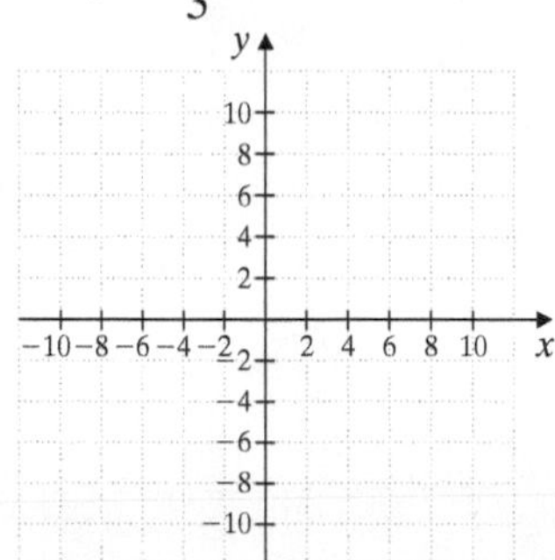

4. $y = \frac{1}{4}x - 3$

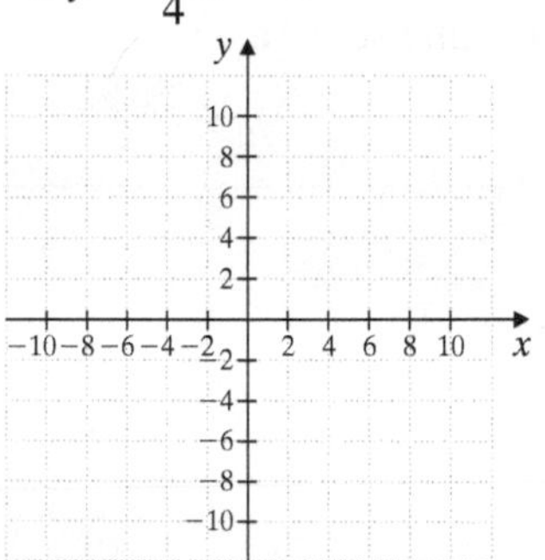

5. $y = -5x$

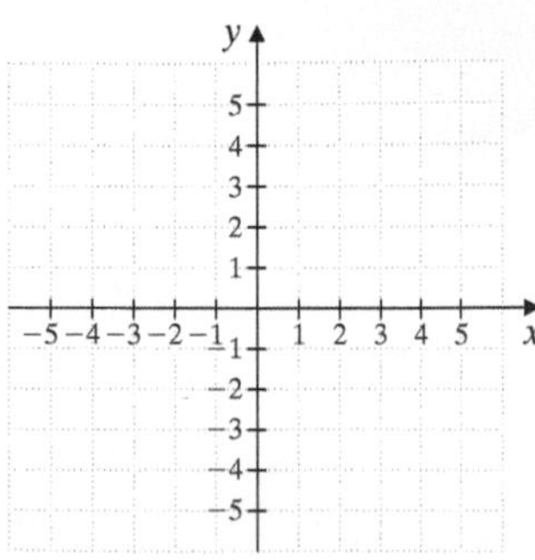

6. $y = -6x$

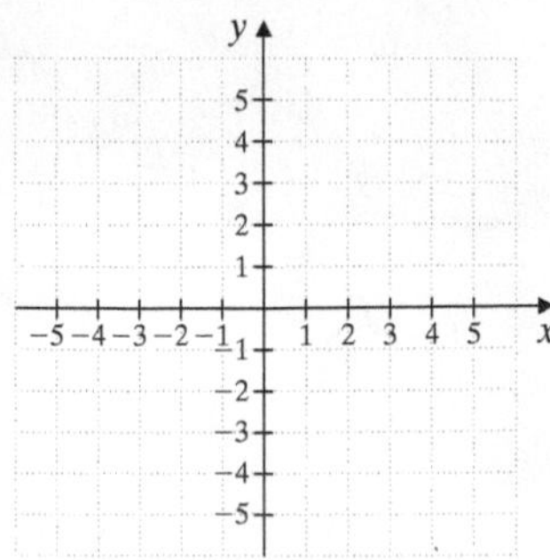

7. $4x + y = 6$

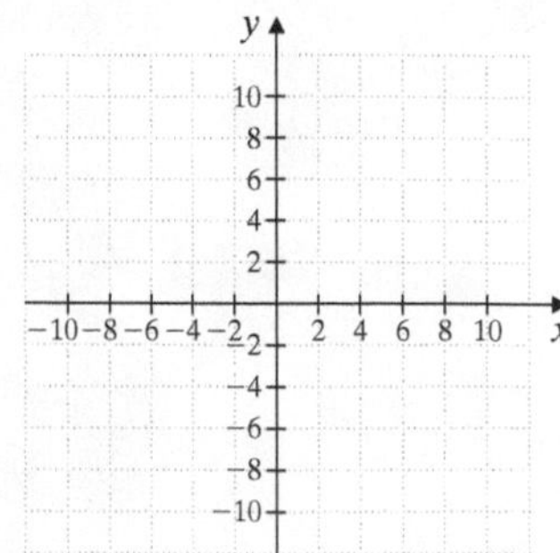

8. $-3x + y = 2$

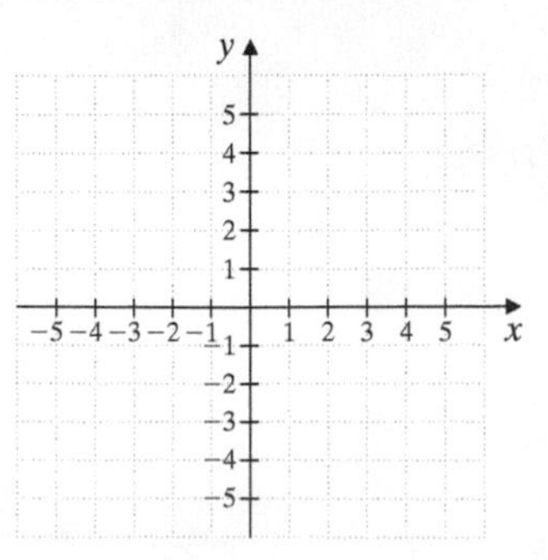

9. $4x - 7y = -14$

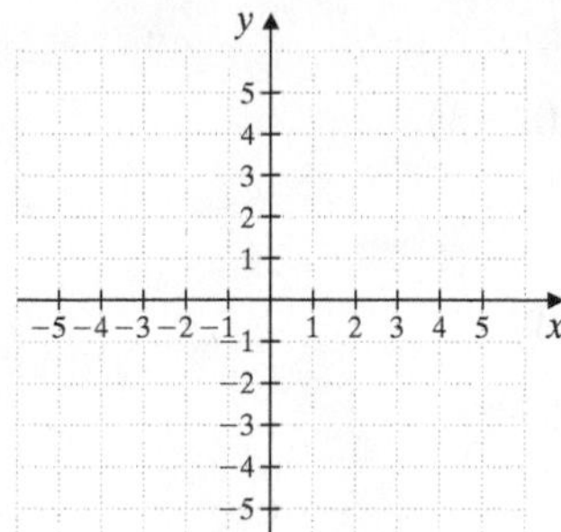

10. $3x - 4y = 4$

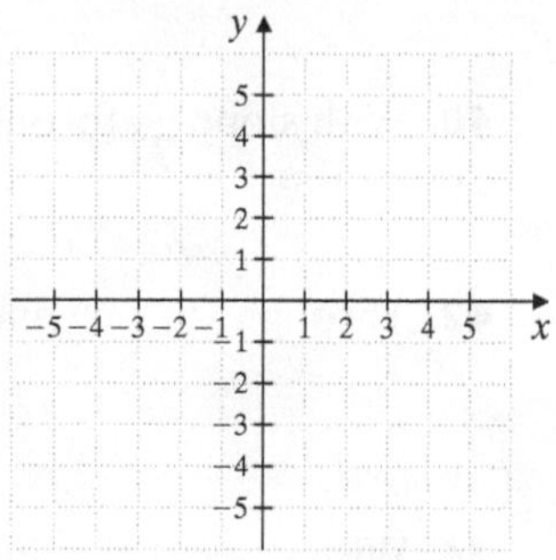

11. $x = \frac{5}{4}y$

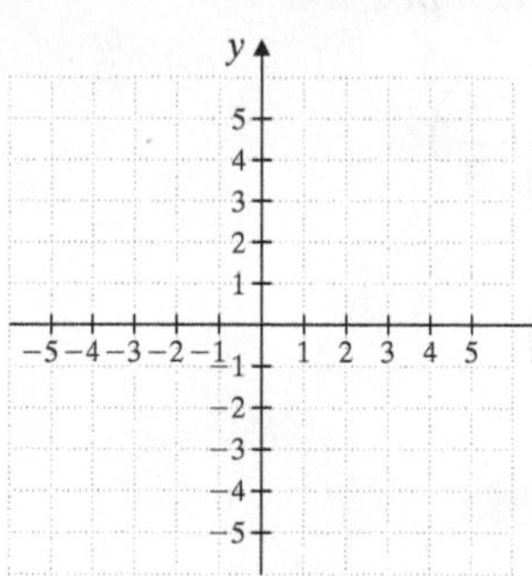

12. $x = \frac{3}{2}y$

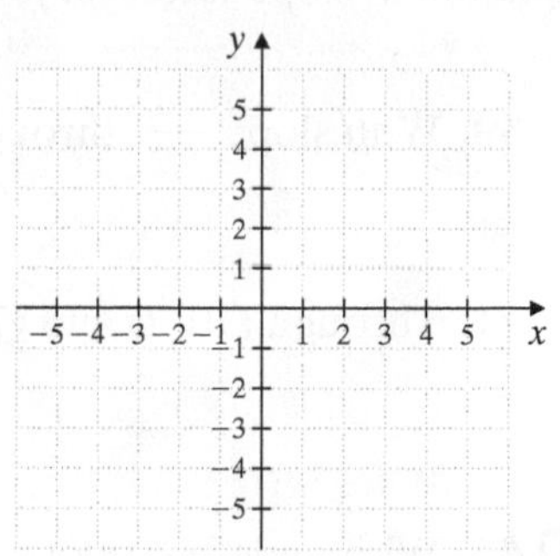

Objective B *Write an equation of the line with each given slope, m, and y-intercept, (0, b). See Example 3.*

13. $m = 5, b = 3$

14. $m = -3, b = -3$

15. $m = -4, b = -\frac{1}{6}$

16. $m = 2, b = \frac{3}{4}$

17. $m = \frac{2}{3}, b = 0$

18. $m = -\frac{4}{5}, b = 0$

19. $m = 0, b = -8$

20. $m = 0, b = -2$

21. $m = -\frac{1}{5}, b = \frac{1}{9}$

22. $m = \frac{1}{2}, b = -\frac{1}{3}$

Objective C *Find an equation of each line with the given slope that passes through the given point. Write the equation in the form $Ax + By = C$. See Example 4.*

23. $m = 6;\quad (2, 2)$

24. $m = 4;\quad (1, 3)$

25. $m = -8;\quad (-1, -5)$

26. $m = -2;\quad (-11, -12)$

27. $m = \frac{3}{2};\quad (5, -6)$

28. $m = \frac{2}{3};\quad (-8, 9)$

29. $m = -\frac{1}{2};\quad (-3, 0)$

30. $m = -\frac{1}{5};\quad (4, 0)$

Objective D *Find an equation of the line passing through each pair of points. Write the equation in the form $Ax + By = C$. See Example 5.*

31. $(3, 2)$ and $(5, 6)$

32. $(6, 2)$ and $(8, 8)$

33. $(-1, 3)$ and $(-2, -5)$

34. $(-4, 0)$ and $(6, -1)$

35. $(2, 3)$ and $(-1, -1)$

36. $(7, 10)$ and $(-1, -1)$

37. $(0, 0)$ and $\left(-\frac{1}{8}, \frac{1}{13}\right)$

38. $(0, 0)$ and $\left(-\frac{1}{2}, \frac{1}{3}\right)$

Objectives **B C D Mixed Practice** *See Examples 3 through 5. Find an equation of each line described. Write each equation in slope-intercept form when possible.*

39. With slope $-\frac{1}{2}$, through $\left(0, \frac{5}{3}\right)$

40. With slope $\frac{5}{7}$, through $(0, -3)$

41. Through $(10, 7)$ and $(7, 10)$

42. Through $(5, -6)$ and $(-6, 5)$

43. With undefined slope, through $\left(-\frac{3}{4}, 1\right)$

44. With slope 0, through $(6.7, 12.1)$

45. Slope 1, through $(-7, 9)$

46. Slope 5, through $(6, -8)$

47. Slope -5, y-intercept $(0, 7)$

48. Slope -2, y-intercept $(0, -4)$

49. Through $(1, 2)$, parallel to $y = 5$

50. Through $(1, -5)$, parallel to the y-axis

51. Through $(2, 3)$ and $(0, 0)$

52. Through $(4, 7)$ and $(0, 0)$

53. Through $(-2, -3)$, perpendicular to the y-axis

54. Through $(0, 12)$, perpendicular to the x-axis

55. Slope $-\frac{4}{7}$, through $(-1, -2)$

56. Slope $-\frac{3}{5}$, through $(4, 4)$

Objective **E** *Solve. Assume each exercise describes a linear relationship. Write the equations in slope-intercept form. See Example 6.*

57. In 2003, there were 302 million magazine subscriptions in the United States. By 2007, this number was 322 million. (*Source:* Audit Bureau of Circulation, Magazine Publishers Association)

a. Write two ordered pairs of the form (years after 2003, millions of magazine subscriptions) for this situation.

b. Assume the relationship between years after 2003 and millions of magazine subscriptions is linear over this period. Use the ordered pairs from part (a) to write an equation for the line relating year after 2003 to millions of magazine subscriptions.

c. Use this linear equation in part (b) to estimate the millions of magazine subscriptions in 2005.

58. In 2000, crude oil field production in the United States was 2130 thousand barrels. In 2007, U.S. crude oil field production dropped to 1850 thousand barrels. (*Source:* Energy Information Administration)

a. Write two ordered pairs of the form (years after 2000, crude oil production).

b. Assume the relationship between years after 2000 and crude oil production is linear over this period. Use the ordered pairs from part (a) to write an equation of the line relating years after 2000 to crude oil production.

c. Use the linear equation from part (b) to estimate crude oil production in the United States in 2010, if this trend were to continue.

59. A rock is dropped from the top of a 400-foot cliff. After 1 second, the rock is traveling 32 feet per second. After 3 seconds, the rock is traveling 96 feet per second.

a. Assume that the relationship between time and speed is linear and write an equation describing this relationship. Use ordered pairs of the form (time, speed).

b. Use this equation to determine the speed of the rock 4 seconds after it is dropped.

60. A Hawaiian fruit company is studying the sales of a pineapple sauce to see if this product is to be continued. At the end of its first year, profits on this product amounted to $30,000. At the end of the fourth year, profits were $66,000.

a. Assume that the relationship between years on the market and profit is linear and write an equation describing this relationship. Use ordered pairs of the form (years on the market, profit).

b. Use this equation to predict the profit at the end of 7 years.

61. In 2004 there were approximately 83,000 gas-electric hybrid vehicles sold in the United States. In 2007, there were approximately 353,000 such vehicles sold. (*Source:* Energy Information Administration, Department of Energy)

a. Assume the relationship between years past 2004 and the number of vehicles sold is linear over this period. Write an equation describing the relationship between time and the number of gas-electric hybrid vehicles sold. Use ordered pairs of the form (years past 2004, number of vehicles sold).

b. Use this equation to estimate the number of gas-electric hybrid sales in 2009.

62. In 2008, there were approximately 945 thousand restaurants in the United States. In 2004, there were 875 thousand restaurants. (*Source:* National Restaurant Association)

a. Assume the relationship between years past 2004 and the number of restaurants is linear over this period. Write an equation describing the relationship between time and the number of restaurants. Use ordered pairs of the form (years past 2004, numbers of restaurants in thousands).

b. Use this equation to predict the number of eating establishments in 2012.

63. In 2007 there were approximately 5540 cinema sites in the United States. In 2003 there were 5700 cinema sites. (*Source:* National Association of Theater Owners)

a. Assume the relationship between years past 2003 and the number of cinema sites is linear over this period. Write an equation describing this relationship. Use ordered pairs of the form (years past 2003, number of cinema sites).

b. Use this equation to predict the number of cinema sites in 2010.

64. In 2006, the U.S. population per square mile of land area was approximately 83.6. In 2000, the population per square mile was 79.6.

a. Assume the relationship between years past 2000 and population per square mile is linear over this period. Write an equation describing the relationship between year and population per square mile. Use ordered pairs of the form (years past 2000, population per square mile).

b. Use this equation to predict the population per square mile in 2010.

65. The Pool Fun Company has learned that, by pricing a newly released Fun Noodle at \$3, sales will reach 10,000 Fun Noodles per day during the summer. Raising the price to \$5 will cause sales to fall to 8000 Fun Noodles per day.

a. Assume that the relationship between price and number of Fun Noodles sold is linear and write an equation describing this relationship. Use ordered pairs of the form (price, number sold).

b. Predict the daily sales of Fun Noodles if the price is \$3.50.

66. The value of a building bought in 1995 may be depreciated (or decreased) as time passes for income tax purposes. Seven years after the building was bought, this value was \$225,000 and 12 years after it was bought, this value was \$195,000.

a. If the relationship between number of years past 1995 and the depreciated value of the building is linear, write an equation describing this relationship. Use ordered pairs of the form (years past 1995, value of building).

b. Use this equation to estimate the depreciated value of the building in 2013.

Review

Find the value of $x^2 - 3x + 1$ for each given value of x. See Section 1.3.

67. 2

68. 5

69. -1

70. -3

Concept Extensions

Match each linear equation with its graph.

71. $y = 2x + 1$

72. $y = -x + 1$

73. $y = -3x - 2$

74. $y = \frac{5}{3}x - 2$

a.

b.

c.

d.

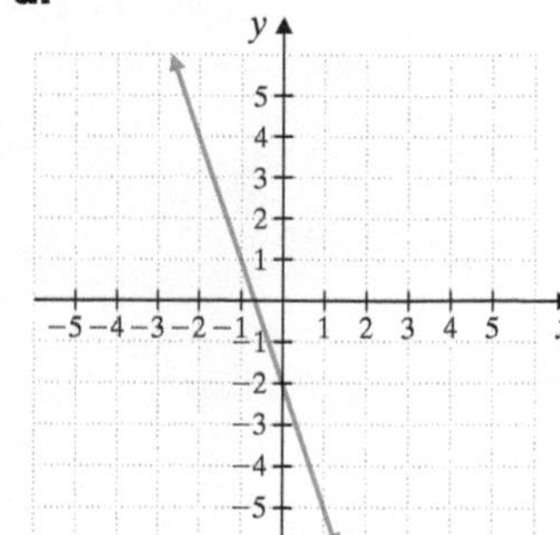

75. Write an equation in standard form of the line that contains the point $(-1, 2)$ and is parallel to (has the same slope as) the line $y = 3x - 1$.

76. Write an equation in standard form of the line that contains the point $(4, 0)$ and is parallel to (has the same slope as) the line $y = -2x + 3$.

△ **77.** Write an equation in standard form of the line that contains the point $(-1, 2)$ and is perpendicular to the line $y = 3x - 1$.

△ **78.** Write an equation in standard form of the line that contains the point $(4, 0)$ and is perpendicular to the line $y = -2x + 3$.

Integrated Review Sections 6.1–6.5

Answers

1. ______

2. ______

3. ______

4. ______

5. ______

6. ______

7. ______

8. ______

Summary on Linear Equations

Find the slope of each line.

1.

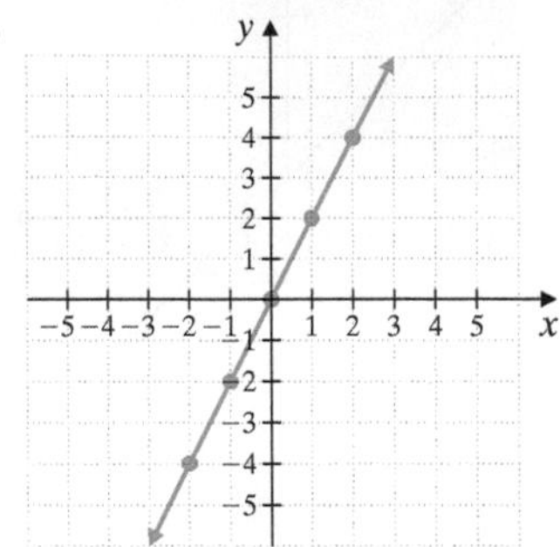

2.

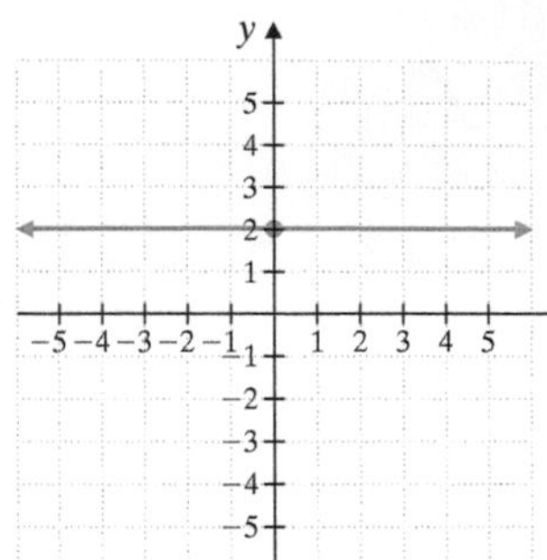

3.

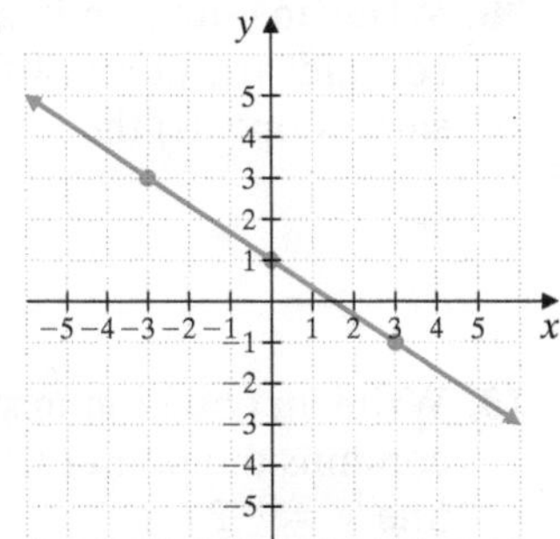

4.

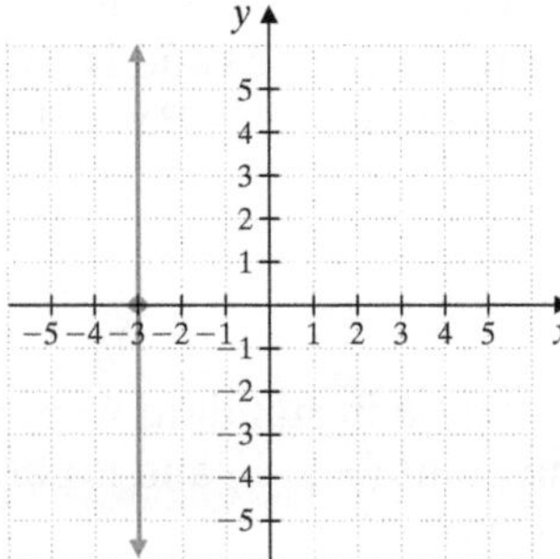

Graph each linear equation. For Exercises 11 and 12, label the intercepts.

5. $y = -2x$

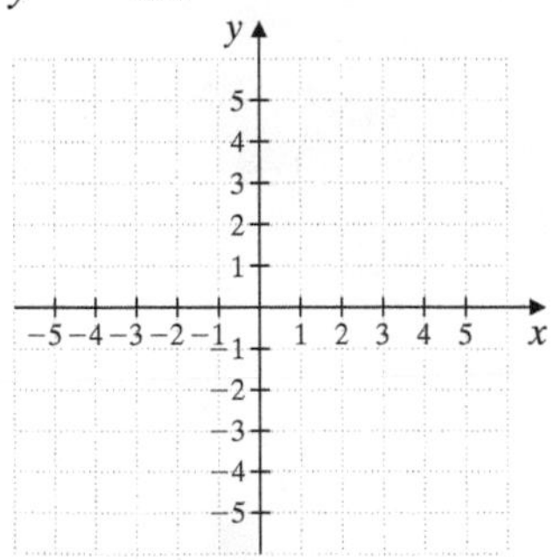

6. $x + y = 3$

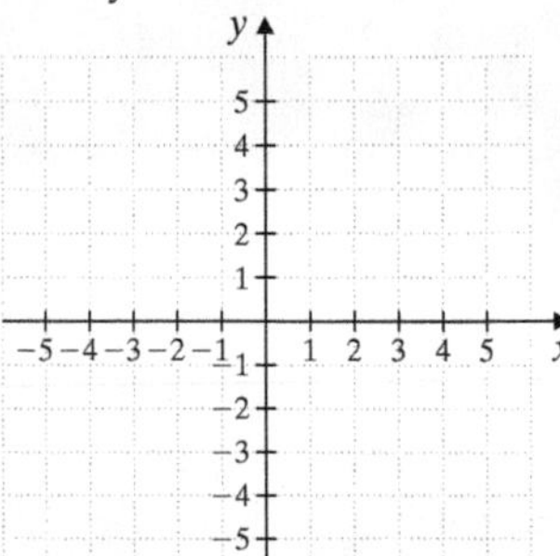

7. $x = -1$

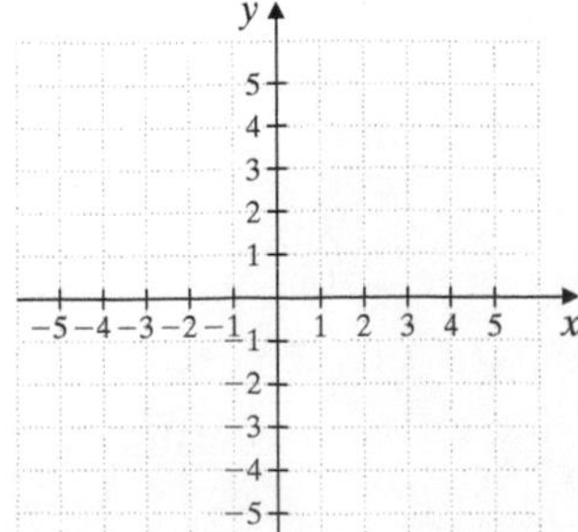

8. $y = 4$

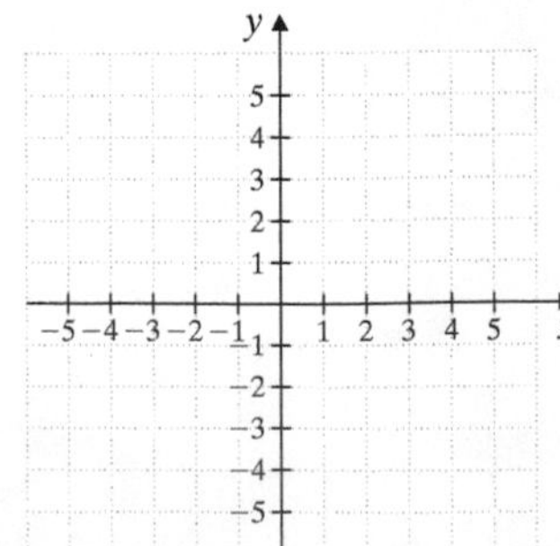

9. $x - 2y = 6$

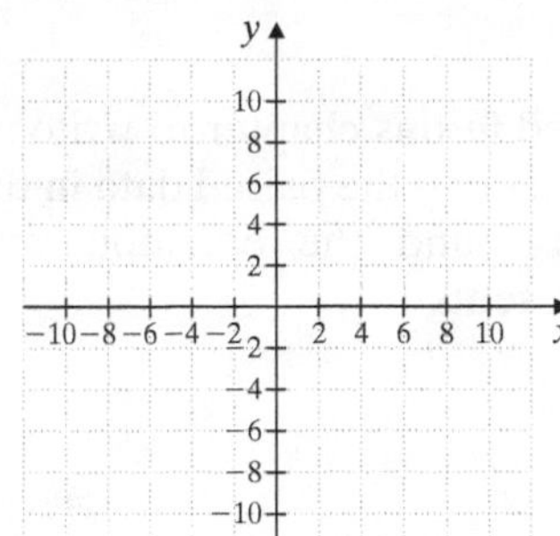
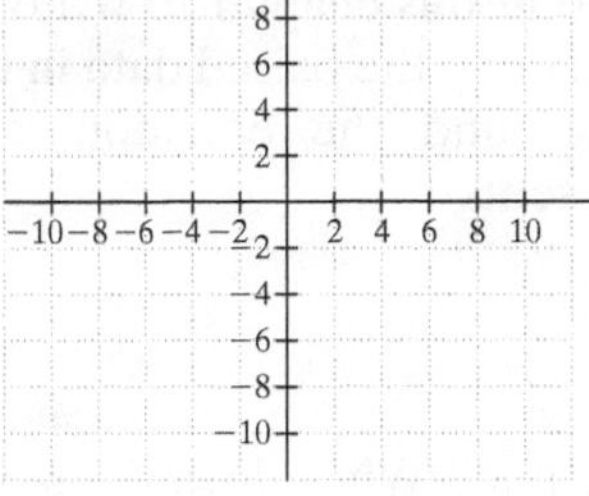

10. $y = 3x + 2$

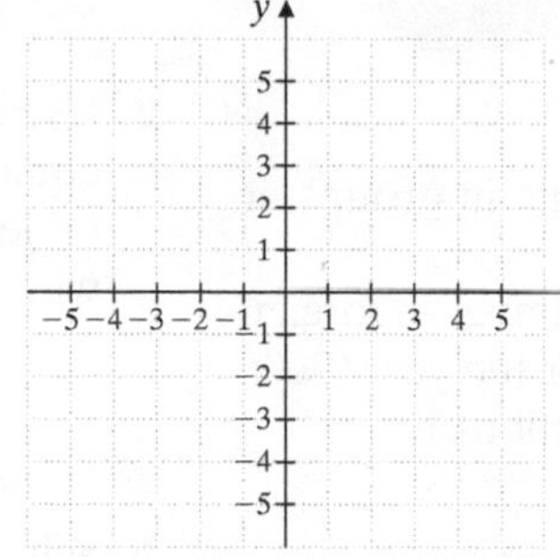

11. $y = -\frac{3}{4}x + 3$

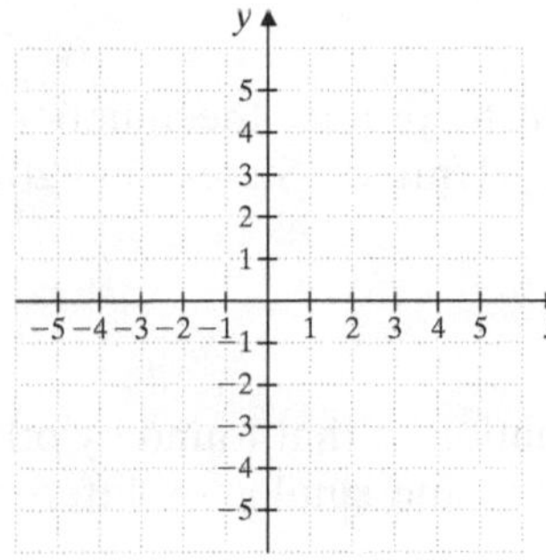

12. $5x - 2y = 8$

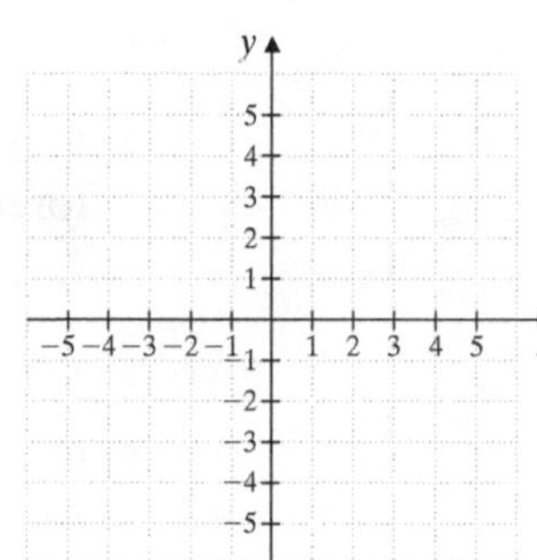

Find the slope of each line by writing the equation in slope-intercept form.

13. $y = 3x - 1$ **14.** $y = -6x + 2$ **15.** $7x + 2y = 11$ **16.** $2x - y = 0$

Find the slope of each line.

17. $x = 2$ **18.** $y = -4$

19. Write an equation of the line with slope $m = 2$ and y-intercept $\left(0, -\frac{1}{3}\right)$. Write the equation in the form $y = mx + b$.

20. Find an equation of the line with slope $m = -4$ that passes through the point $(-1, 3)$. Write the equation in the form $y = mx + b$.

21. Find an equation of the line that passes through the points $(2, 0)$ and $(-1, -3)$. Write the equation in the form $Ax + By = C$.

Determine whether each pair of lines is parallel, perpendicular, or neither.

22. $6x - y = 7$
$2x + 3y = 4$

23. $3x - 6y = 4$
$y = -2x$

24. Yogurt is an ever more popular food item. In 2002, American Dairy affiliates produced 2133 million pounds of yogurt. In 2007, this number rose to 3478 million pounds of yogurt.

a. Write two ordered pairs of the form (year, millions of pounds of yogurt produced).
b. Find the slope of the line between these two points.
c. Write a sentence explaining the meaning of the slope as a rate of change.

9. ______
10. ______
11. ______
12. ______
13. ______
14. ______
15. ______
16. ______
17. ______
18. ______
19. ______
20. ______
21. ______
22. ______
23. ______
24. a. ______
b. ______
c. ______

Chapter 6 Group Activity

Finding a Linear Model

This activity may be completed by working in groups or individually.

The following table shows the actual number of foreign visitors (in millions) to the United States for the years 2005 through 2011. (The last two years are predictions.)

Year	Foreign Visitors to the United States (in millions)
2005	48.1
2006	51.0
2007	56.0
2008	61.1
2009	57.4
2010	59.5
2011	61.4

(*Source:* Tourism Industries/International Trade Administration, U.S. Department of Commerce)

1. Make a scatter diagram of the paired data in the table.
2. Use what you have learned in this chapter to write an equation of the line representing the paired data in the table. Explain how you found the equation, and what each variable represents.
3. What is the slope of your line? What does the slope mean in this context?
4. Use your linear equation to predict the number of foreign visitors to the United States in 2014.
5. Compare your linear equation to that found by other students or groups. Is it the same, similar, or different? How?
6. Compare your prediction from question 4 to that of other students or groups. Describe what you find.
7. The number of visitors to the United States for 2012 was estimated to be 65.1 million. If this data point is added to the chart, how does it affect your results?

Chapter 6 Vocabulary Check

Fill in each blank with one of the words listed below.

y-axis	x-axis	solution	linear	standard	point-slope
x-intercept	y-intercept	y	x	slope	relation
domain	range	direct	inverse	slope-intercept	function

1. An ordered pair is a(n) ____________ of an equation in two variables if replacing the variables by the coordinates of the ordered pair results in a true statement.
2. The vertical number line in the rectangular coordinate system is called the ____________.
3. A(n) ____________ equation can be written in the form $Ax + By = C$.
4. A(n) ____________ is a point of the graph where the graph crosses the x-axis.
5. The form $Ax + By = C$ is called ____________ form.
6. A(n) ____________ is a point of the graph where the graph crosses the y-axis.
7. A set of ordered pairs that assigns to each x-value exactly one y-value is called a(n) ____________.
8. The equation $y = 7x - 5$ is written in ____________ form.
9. The set of all x-coordinates of a relation is called the ____________ of the relation.
10. The set of all y-coordinates of a relation is called the ____________ of the relation.
11. A set of ordered pairs is called a(n) ____________.
12. The equation $y + 1 = 7(x - 2)$ is written in ____________ form.
13. To find an x-intercept of a graph, let ____________ = 0.
14. The horizontal number line in the rectangular coordinate system is called the ____________.
15. To find a y-intercept of a graph, let ____________ = 0.
16. The ____________ of a line measures the steepness or tilt of the line.
17. The equation $y = kx$ is an example of ____________ variation.
18. The equation $y = \frac{k}{x}$ is an example of ____________ variation.

Helpful Hint Are you preparing for your test? Don't forget to take the Chapter 6 Test on page 534. Then check your answers at the back of the text and use the Chapter Test Prep Videos to see the fully worked-out solutions to any of the exercises you want to review.

6 Chapter Highlights

Definitions and Concepts	Examples
Section 6.1 Reading Graphs and the Rectangular Coordinate System	
The **rectangular coordinate system** consists of a plane and a vertical and a horizontal number line intersecting at their 0 coordinates. The vertical number line is called the **y-axis** and the horizontal number line is called the **x-axis.** The point of intersection of the axes is called the **origin.** To **plot** or **graph** an ordered pair means to find its corresponding point on a rectangular coordinate system. To plot or graph an ordered pair such as $(3, -2)$, start at the origin. Move 3 units to the right and from there, 2 units down. To plot or graph $(-3, 4)$, start at the origin. Move 3 units to the left and from there, 4 units up. An ordered pair is a **solution** of an equation in two variables if replacing the variables with the coordinates of the ordered pair results in a true statement.	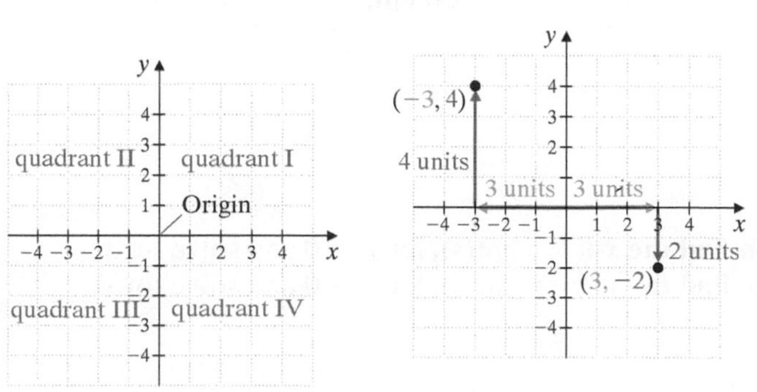

Definitions and Concepts	Examples

Section 6.1 Reading Graphs and the Rectangular Coordinate System (*continued*)

If one coordinate of an ordered pair solution of an equation is known, the other value can be determined by substitution.

Complete the ordered pair (0,) for the equation $x - 6y = 12$.

$$x - 6y = 12$$
$$0 - 6y = 12 \quad \text{Let } x = 0.$$
$$\frac{-6y}{-6} = \frac{12}{-6} \quad \text{Divide by } -6.$$
$$y = -2$$

The ordered pair solution is $(0, -2)$.

Section 6.2 Graphing Linear Equations

A **linear equation in two variables** is an equation that can be written in the form $Ax + By = C$, where A and B are not both 0. The form $Ax + By = C$ is called **standard form.**

$3x + 2y = -6 \qquad x = -5$

$y = 3 \qquad y = -x + 10$

$x + y = 10$ is in standard form.

To graph a linear equation in two variables, find three ordered pair solutions. Plot the solution points and draw the line connecting the points.

Graph: $x - 2y = 5$

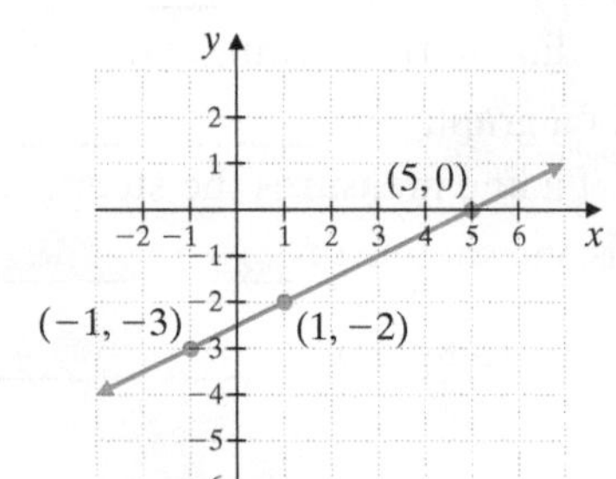

x	y
5	0
1	−2
−1	−3

Section 6.3 Intercepts

An **intercept** of a graph is a point where the graph intersects an axis. If a graph intersects the x-axis at a, then $(a, 0)$ is an **x-intercept.** If a graph intersects the y-axis at b, then $(0, b)$ is a **y-intercept.**

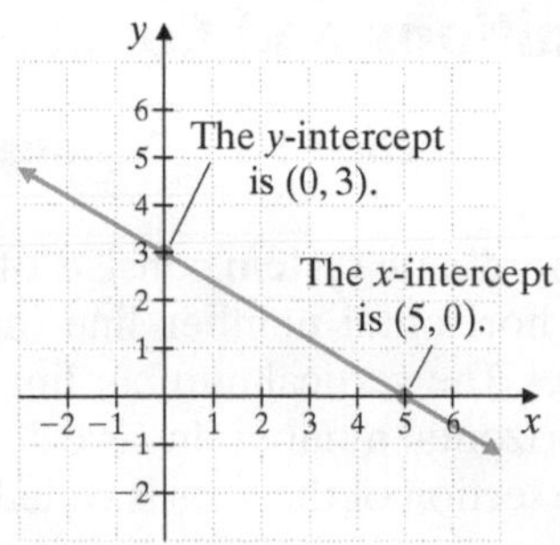

To find the x-intercept(s), let $y = 0$ and solve for x.
To find the y-intercept(s), let $x = 0$ and solve for y.

Find the intercepts for $2x - 5y = -10$ and graph the line.

If $y = 0$, then

$$2x - 5 \cdot 0 = -10$$
$$2x = -10$$
$$\frac{2x}{2} = \frac{-10}{2}$$
$$x = -5$$

If $x = 0$, then

$$2 \cdot 0 - 5y = -10$$
$$-5y = -10$$
$$\frac{-5y}{-5} = \frac{-10}{-5}$$
$$y = 2$$

Definitions and Concepts	Examples

Section 6.3 Intercepts (*continued*)

The x-intercept is $(-5, 0)$. The y-intercept is $(0, 2)$.

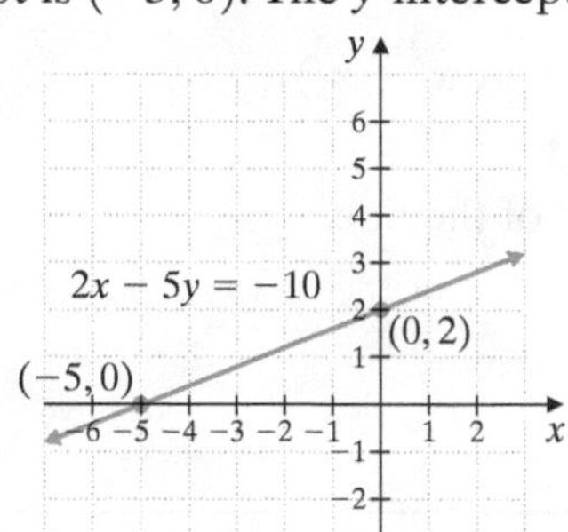

The graph of $x = c$ is a vertical line with x-intercept $(c, 0)$.
The graph of $y = c$ is a horizontal line with y-intercept $(0, c)$.

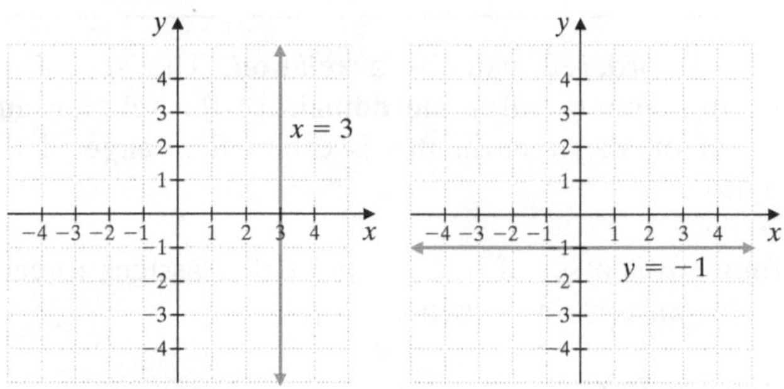

Section 6.4 Slope and Rate of Change

The **slope m** of the line through points (x_1, y_1) and (x_2, y_2) is given by

$$m = \frac{y_2 - y_1}{x_2 - x_1} \quad \text{as long as } x_2 \neq x_1$$

A horizontal line has slope 0.
The slope of a vertical line is undefined.
Nonvertical parallel lines have the same slope.
Two nonvertical lines are perpendicular if the slope of one is the negative reciprocal of the slope of the other.

The slope of the line through points $(-1, 6)$ and $(-5, 8)$ is

$$m = \frac{y_2 - y_1}{x_2 - x_1} = \frac{8 - 6}{-5 - (-1)} = \frac{2}{-4} = -\frac{1}{2}$$

The slope of the line $y = -5$ is 0.
The line $x = 3$ has undefined slope.

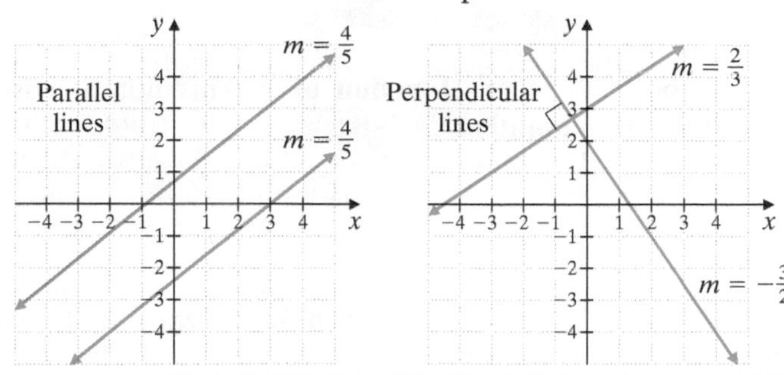

Section 6.5 Equations of Lines

Slope-Intercept Form

$$y = mx + b$$

m is the slope of the line.
$(0, b)$ is the y-intercept.

Find the slope and the y-intercept of the line $2x + 3y = 6$.
Solve for y:

$$2x + 3y = 6$$

$$3y = -2x + 6 \quad \text{Subtract } 2x.$$

$$y = -\frac{2}{3}x + 2 \quad \text{Divide by 3.}$$

The slope of the line is $-\frac{2}{3}$ and the y-intercept is $(0, 2)$.

(*continued*)

Definitions and Concepts	Examples
Section 6.5 Equations of Lines (*continued*)	
POINT-SLOPE FORM $y - y_1 = m(x - x_1)$ m is the slope. (x_1, y_1) is a point of the line.	Find an equation of the line with slope $\frac{3}{4}$ that contains the point $(-1, 5)$. $y - 5 = \frac{3}{4}[x - (-1)]$ $4(y - 5) = 3(x + 1)$ Multiply by 4. $4y - 20 = 3x + 3$ Distribute. $-3x + 4y = 23$ Subtract $3x$ and add 20.
Section 6.6 Introduction to Functions	
A set of ordered pairs is a **relation.** The set of all x-coordinates is called the **domain** of the relation and the set of all y-coordinates is called the **range** of the relation.	The domain of the relation $\{(0, 5), (2, 5), (4, 5), (5, -2)\}$ is $\{0, 2, 4, 5\}$. The range is $\{-2, 5\}$.
A **function** is a set of ordered pairs that assigns to each x-value exactly one y-value. **VERTICAL LINE TEST** If a vertical line can be drawn so that it intersects a graph more than once, the graph is not the graph of a function. (If no such line can be drawn, the graph is that of a function.)	Which are graphs of functions? 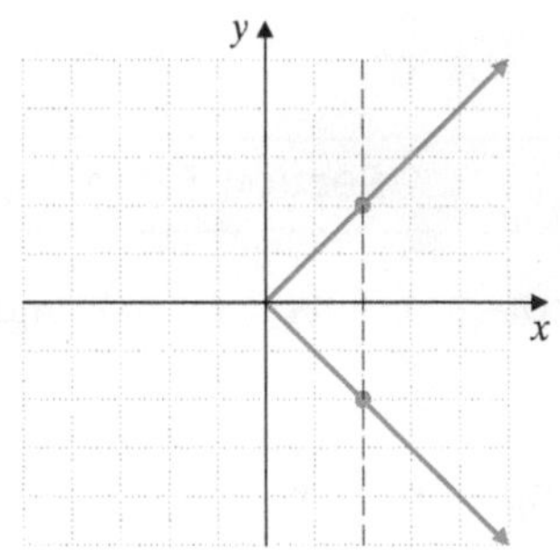 This graph is not the graph of a function. 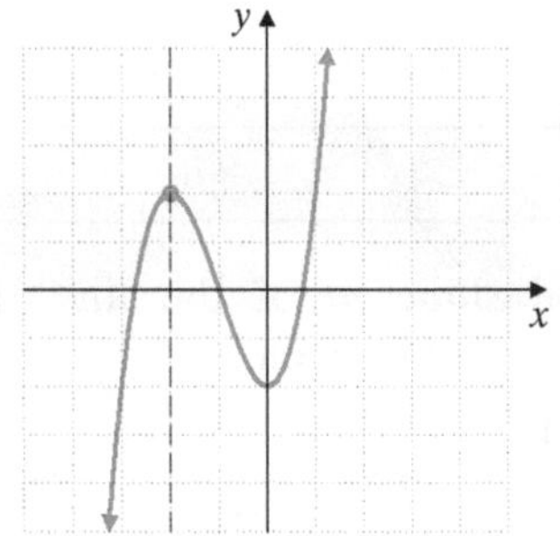 This graph is the graph of a function.
The symbol $f(x)$ means **function of *x*.** This notation is called **function notation.**	If $f(x) = 3x - 7$, then $f(-1) = 3(-1) - 7$ $= -3 - 7$ $= -10$
Section 6.7 Graphing Linear Inequalities in Two Variables	
A **linear inequality in two variables** is an inequality that can be written in one of these forms: $Ax + By < C$ $Ax + By \le C$ $Ax + By > C$ $Ax + By \ge C$ where A and B are not both 0.	$2x - 5y < 6$ $x \ge -5$ $y > -8x$ $y \le 2$

Definitions and Concepts	Examples

Section 6.7 Graphing Linear Inequalities in Two Variables (*continued*)

To Graph a Linear Inequality

1. Graph the boundary line by graphing the related equation. Draw the line solid if the inequality symbol is $\leq$ or $\geq$. Draw the line dashed if the inequality symbol is $<$ or $>$.
2. Choose a test point not on the line. Substitute its coordinates into the original inequality.
3. If the resulting inequality is true, shade the half-plane that contains the test point. If the inequality is not true, shade the half-plane that does not contain the test point.

Graph: $2x - y \leq 4$

1. Graph $2x - y = 4$. Draw a solid line because the inequality symbol is $\leq$.
2. Check the test point $(0, 0)$ in the original inequality, $2x - y \leq 4$.

   $2 \cdot 0 - 0 \leq 4$ Let $x = 0$ and $y = 0$.

   $0 \leq 4$ True

3. The inequality is true, so shade the half-plane containing $(0, 0)$ as shown.

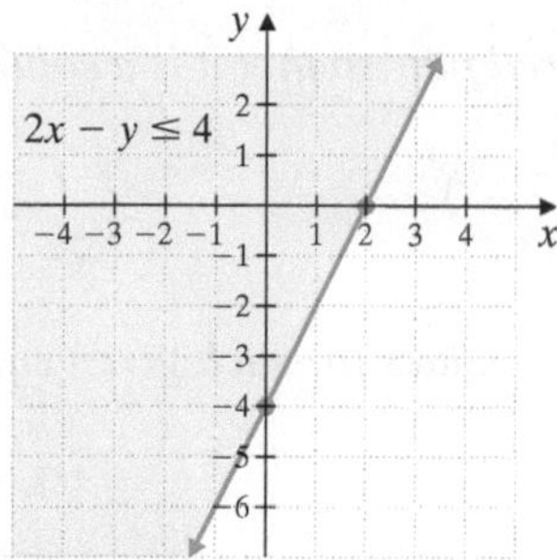

Section 6.8 Direct and Inverse Variation

y **varies directly as** x, or y is **directly proportional to** x, if there is a nonzero constant k such that

$$y = kx$$

y **varies inversely as** x, or y is **inversely proportional to** x, if there is a nonzero constant k such that

$$y = \frac{k}{x}$$

The circumference of a circle C varies directly as its radius r.

$$C = \underbrace{2\pi}_{k} r$$

Pressure P varies inversely with volume V.

$$P = \frac{k}{V}$$

Chapter 6 Review

(6.1) *Plot each ordered pair on the same rectangular coordinate system.*

1. $(-7, 0)$

2. $\left(0, 4\frac{4}{5}\right)$

3. $(-2, -5)$

4. $(1, -3)$

5. $(0.7, 0.7)$

6. $(-6, 4)$

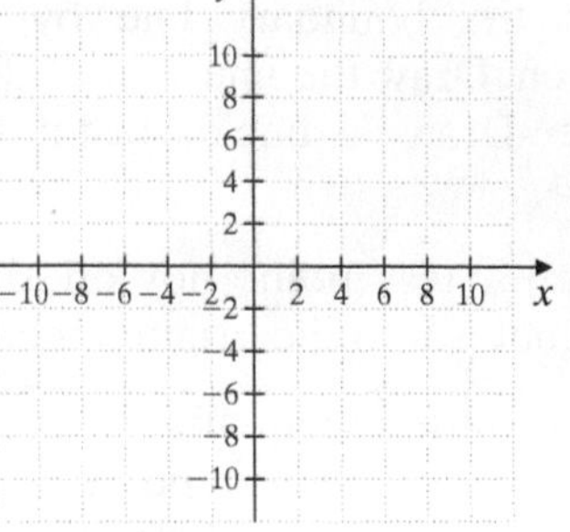

Complete each ordered pair so that it is a solution of the given equation.

7. $-2 + y = 6x; (7, \quad)$

8. $y = 3x + 5; (\quad , -8)$

Complete the table of values for each given equation.

9. $9 = -3x + 4y$

x	y
	0
	3
9	

10. $y = 5$

x	y
7	
−7	
0	

11. $x = 2y$

x	y
	0
	5
	−5

12. The cost in dollars of producing x compact disc holders is given by $y = 5x + 2000$.

a. Complete the table.

x	1	100	1000
y			

b. Find the number of compact disc holders that can be produced for $6430.

(6.2) *Graph each linear equation.*

13. $x - y = 1$

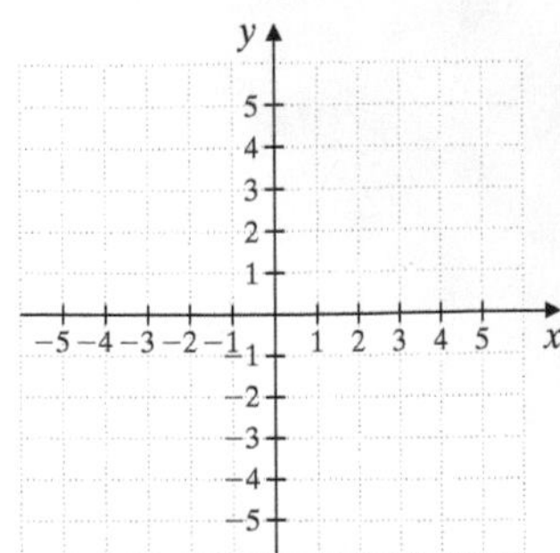

14. $x + y = 6$

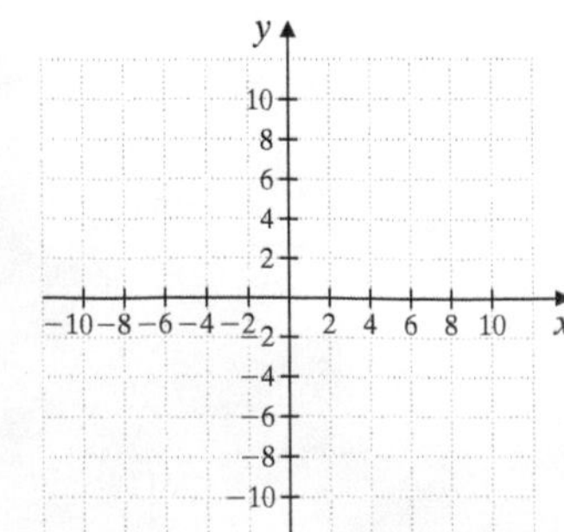

15. $x - 3y = 12$

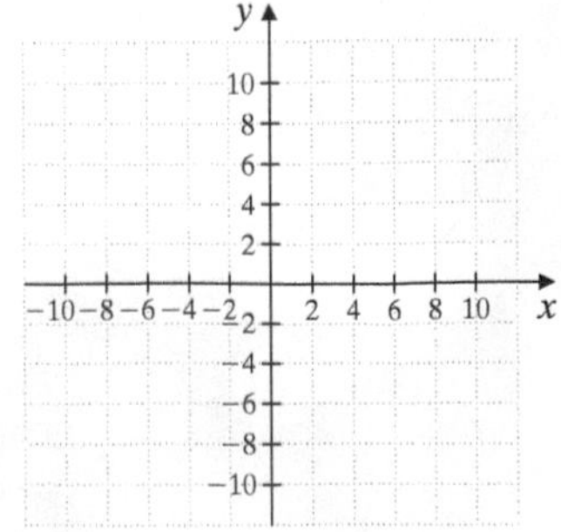

16. $5x - y = -8$

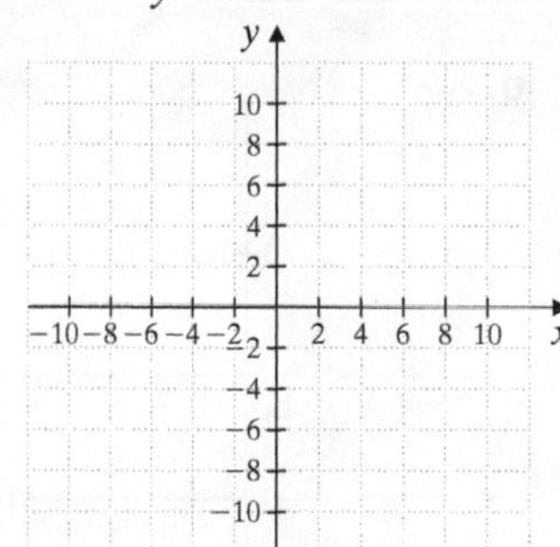

17. $x = 3y$

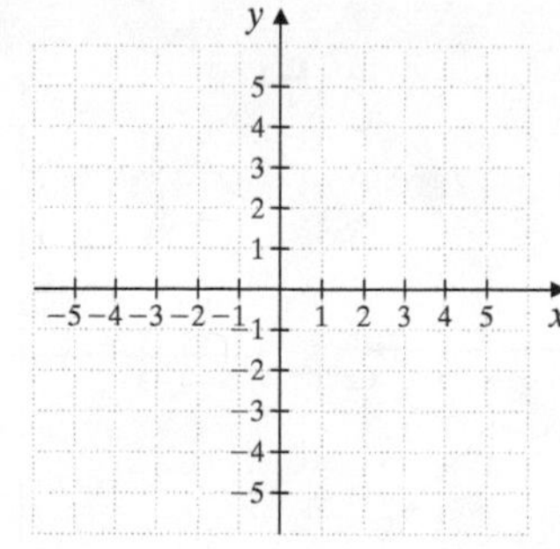

18. $y = -2x$

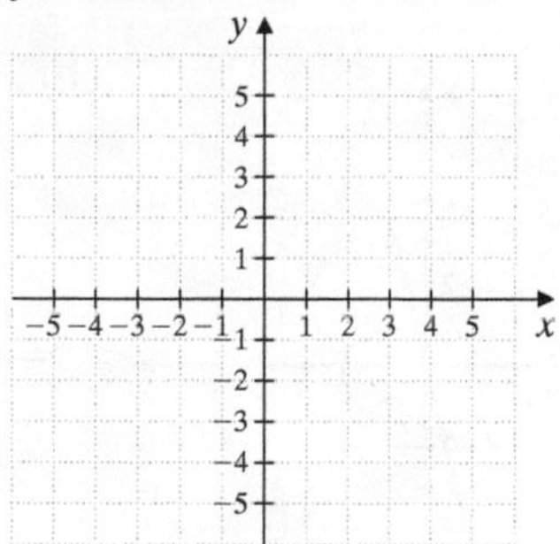

(6.3) *Identify the intercepts in each graph.*

19.

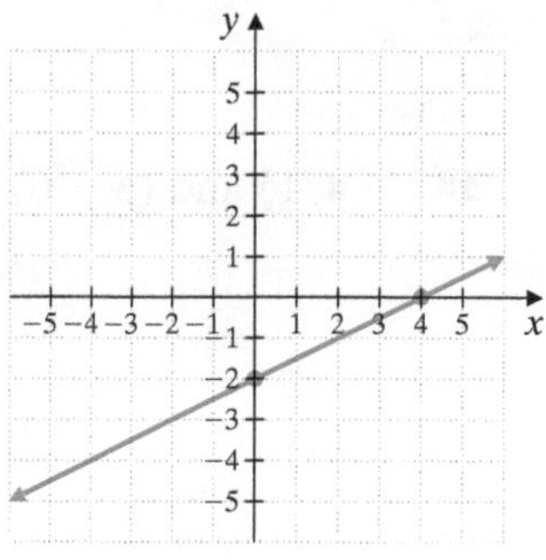

20.

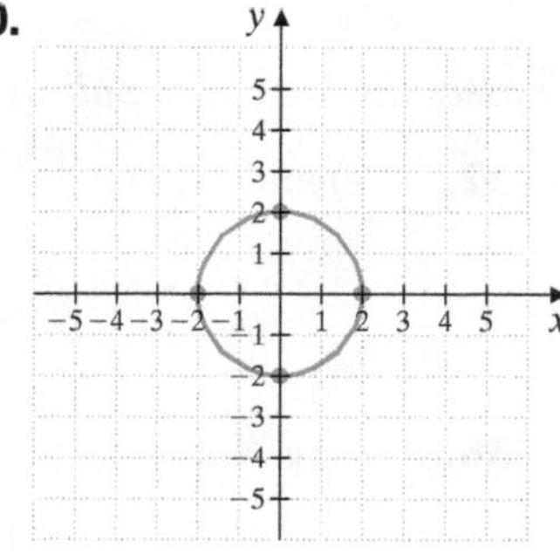

Graph each linear equation.

21. $y = -3$

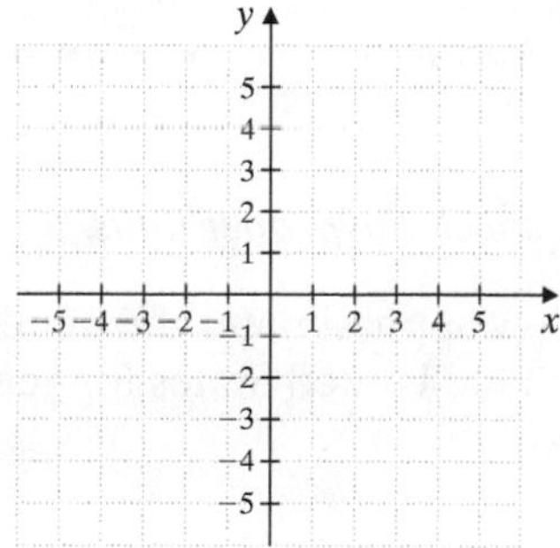

22. $x = 5$

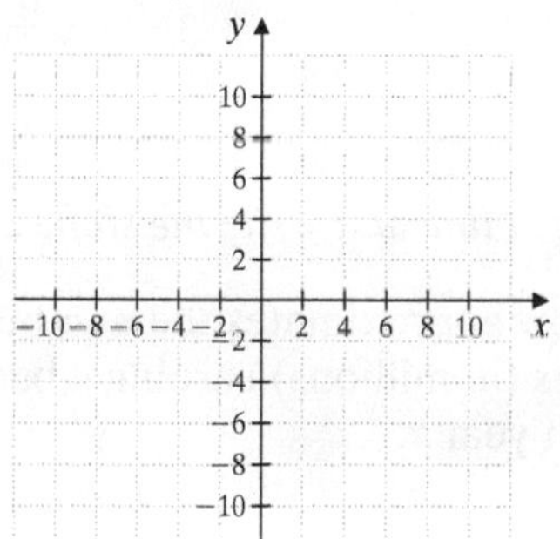

Find the intercepts of each equation.

23. $x - 3y = 12$

24. $-4x + y = 8$

(6.4) *Find the slope of each line.*

25.

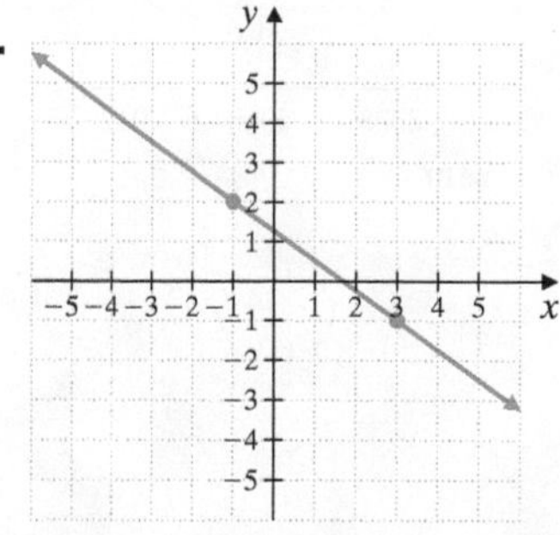

26.

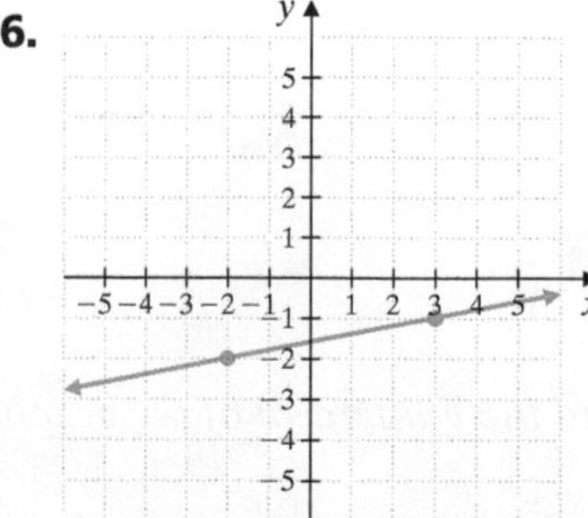

Match each line with its slope.

a.

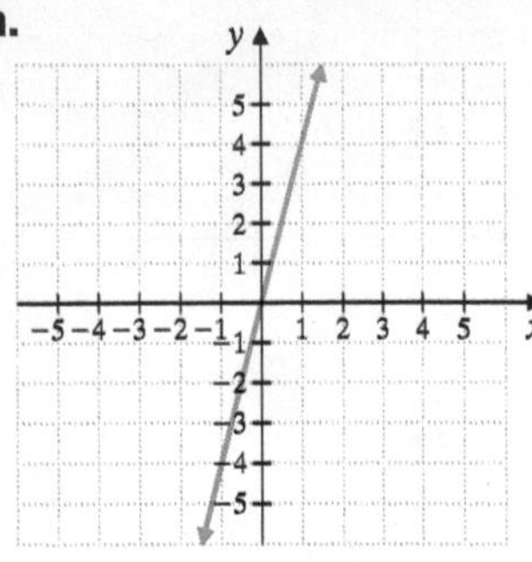

b.

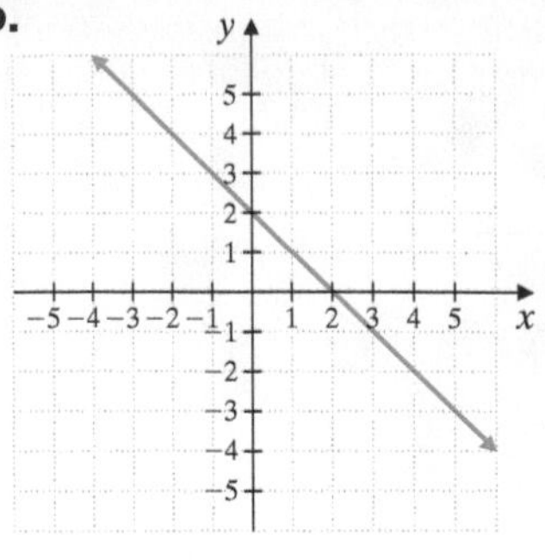

c.

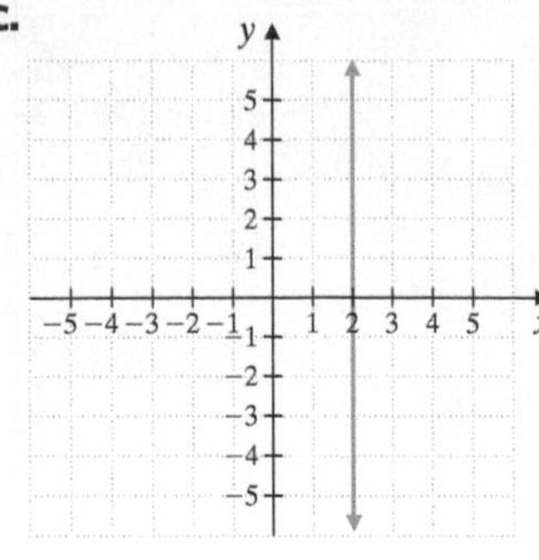

d.

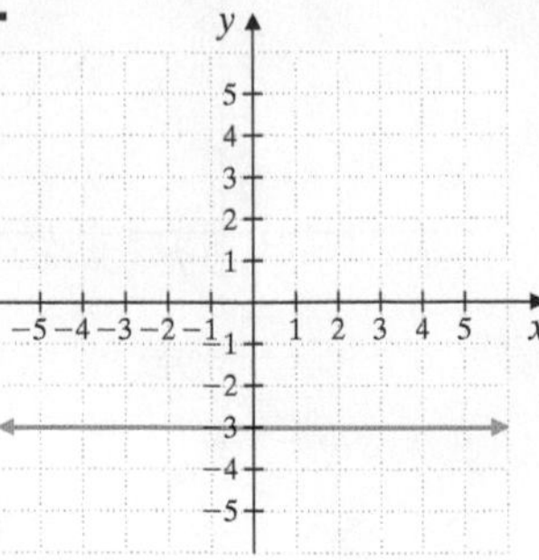

27. $m = 0$ **28.** $m = -1$ **29.** undefined slope **30.** $m = 4$

Find the slope of the line that passes through each pair of points.

31. $(2, 5)$ and $(6, 8)$ **32.** $(4, 7)$ and $(1, 2)$ **33.** $(1, 3)$ and $(-2, -9)$ **34.** $(-4, 1)$ and $(3, -6)$

Find the slope of each line.

35. $y = 3x + 7$ **36.** $x - 2y = 4$ **37.** $y = -2$ **38.** $x = 0$

△ *Determine whether each pair of lines is parallel, perpendicular, or neither.*

39. $x - y = -6$
$x + y = 3$

40. $3x + y = 7$
$-3x - y = 10$

41. $y = 4x + \frac{1}{2}$
$4x + 2y = 1$

42. $y = 6x - \frac{1}{3}$
$x + 6y = 6$

Find the slope of each line and write the slope as a rate of change. Don't forget to attach the proper units.

43. The graph below approximates the number of U.S. college students (in millions) earning a bachelor's degree for each year x.

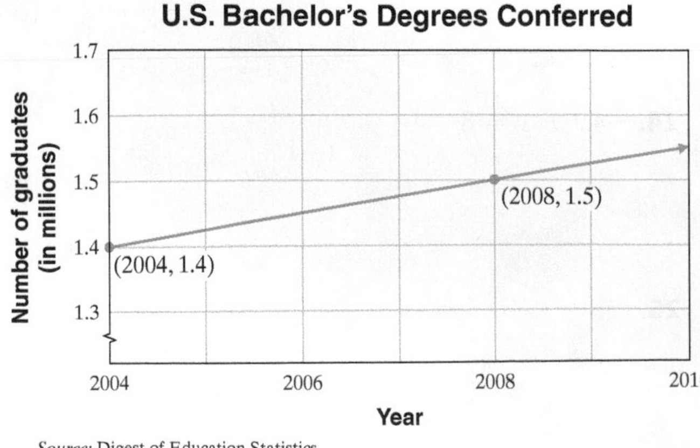

44. The graph below approximates the number of kidney transplants y in the United States for year x.

U.S. Kidney Transplants
Number of Kidney Transplants
(2007, 16,600)
(2004, 14,800)
Year

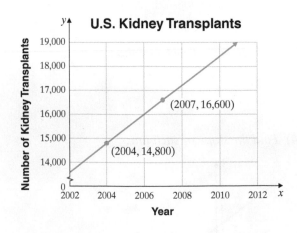

(6.5) *Determine the slope and the y-intercept of the graph of each equation.*

45. $x - 6y = -1$ **46.** $3x + y = 7$

Write an equation of each line.

47. slope -5; y-intercept $\left(0, \frac{1}{2}\right)$

48. slope $\frac{2}{3}$; y-intercept $(0, 6)$

Match each equation with its graph.

49. $y = 2x + 1$

50. $y = -4x$

51. $y = 2x$

52. $y = 2x - 1$

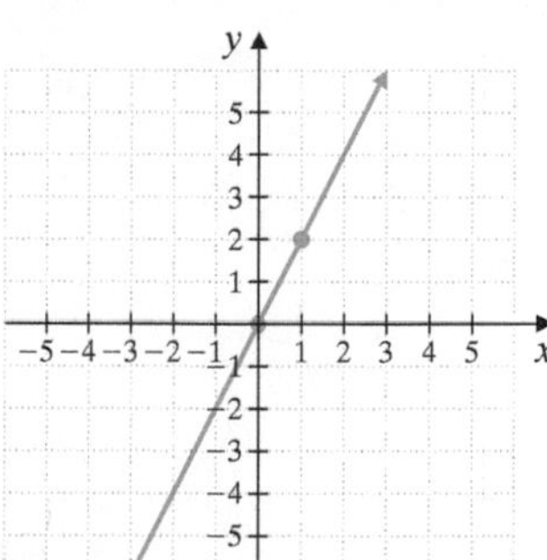

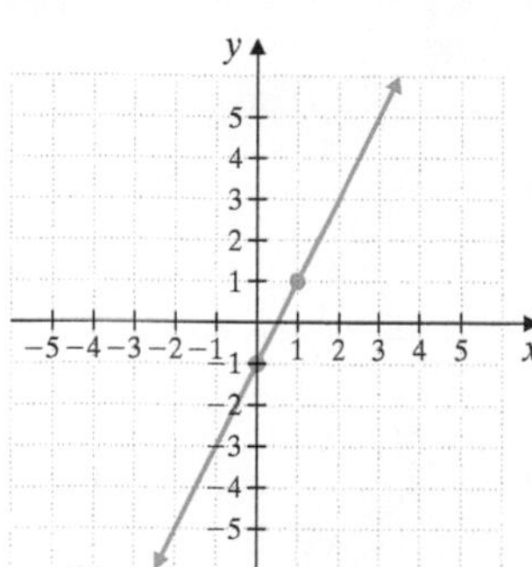

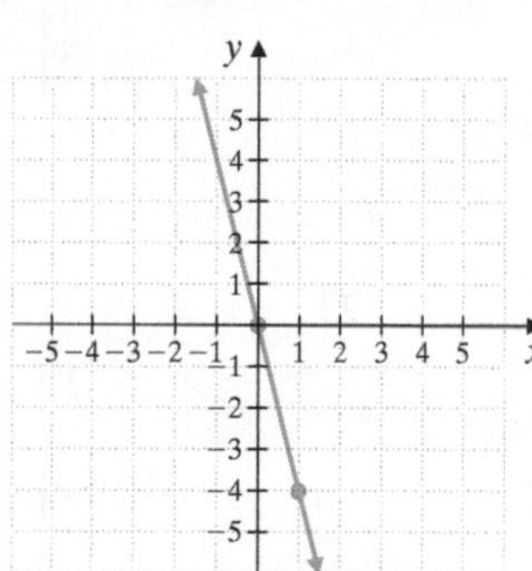

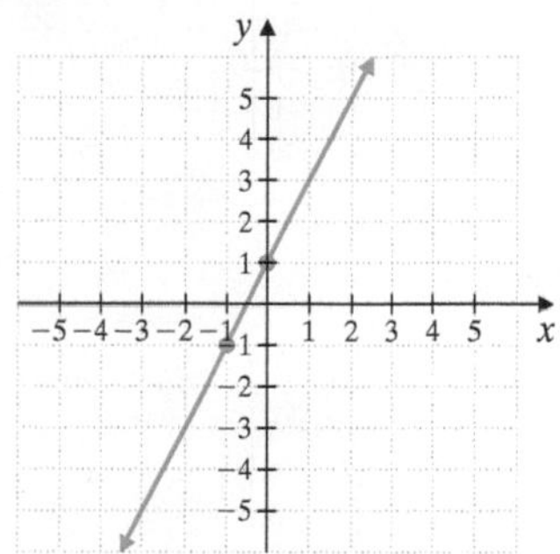

Write an equation of the line with the given slope that passes through the given point. Write the equation in the form $Ax + By = C$.

53. $m = 4$; $(2, 0)$

54. $m = -3$; $(0, -5)$

55. $m = \frac{3}{5}$; $(1, 4)$

56. $m = -\frac{1}{3}$; $(-3, 3)$

Write an equation of the line passing through each pair of points. Write the equation in the form $y = mx + b$.

57. $(1, 7)$ and $(2, -7)$

58. $(-2, 5)$ and $(-4, 6)$

(6.6) *Determine whether each relation or graph is a function.*

59. $\{(7, 1), (7, 5), (2, 6)\}$

60. $\{(0, -1), (5, -1), (2, 2)\}$

61.

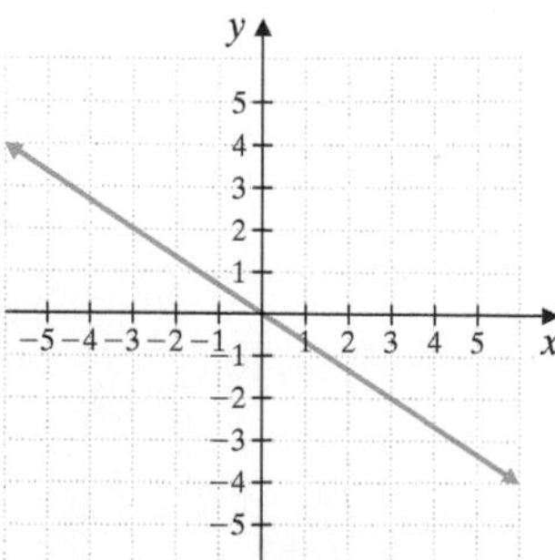

62.

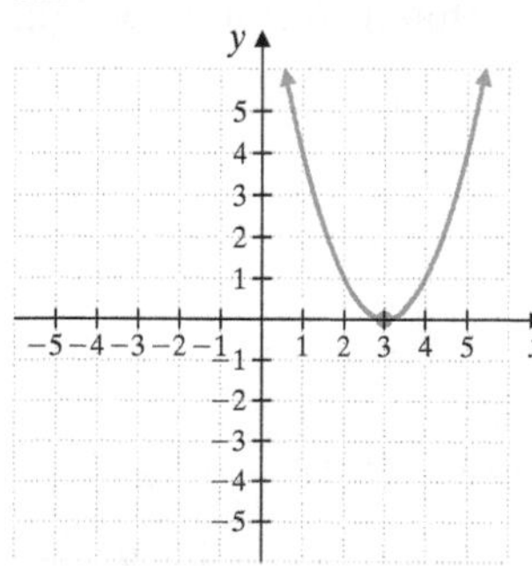

63.

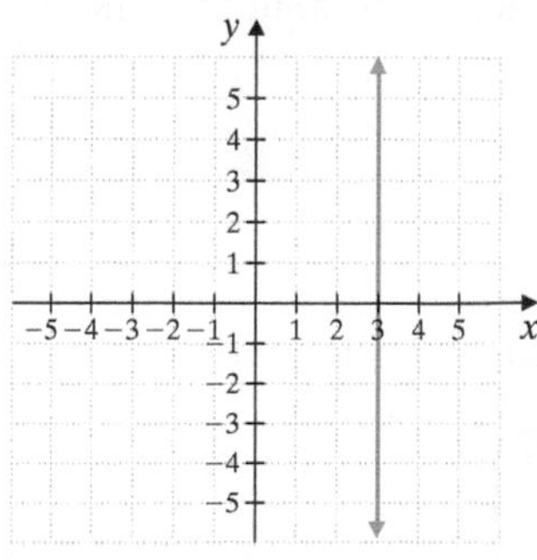

64.

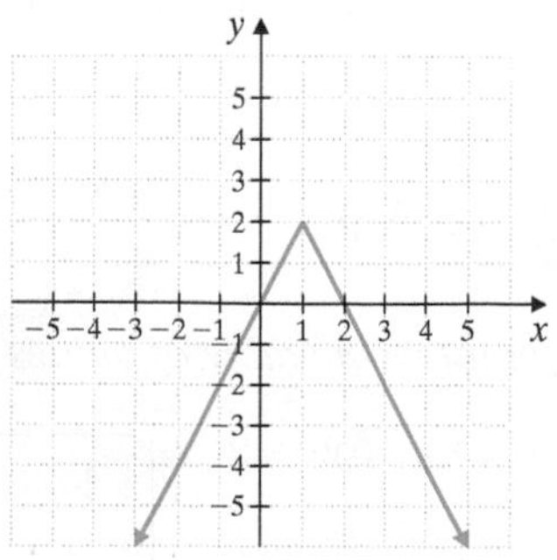

Find each indicated function value for the function $f(x) = -2x + 6$.

65. $f(0)$

66. $f(-2)$

67. $f\left(\frac{1}{2}\right)$

68. $f\left(-\frac{1}{2}\right)$

(6.7) *Graph each inequality.*

69. $x + 6y < 6$

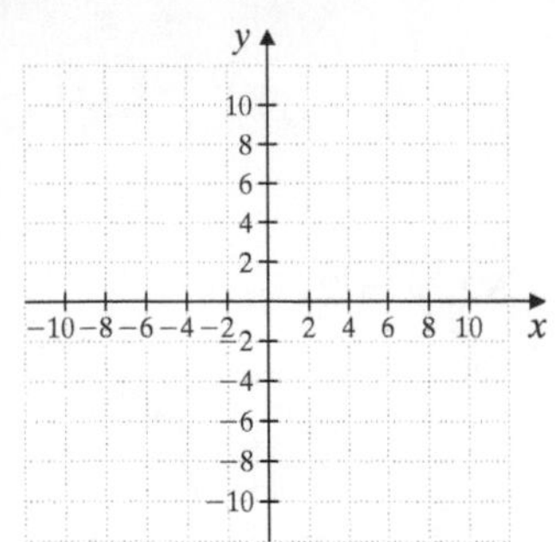

70. $x + y > -2$

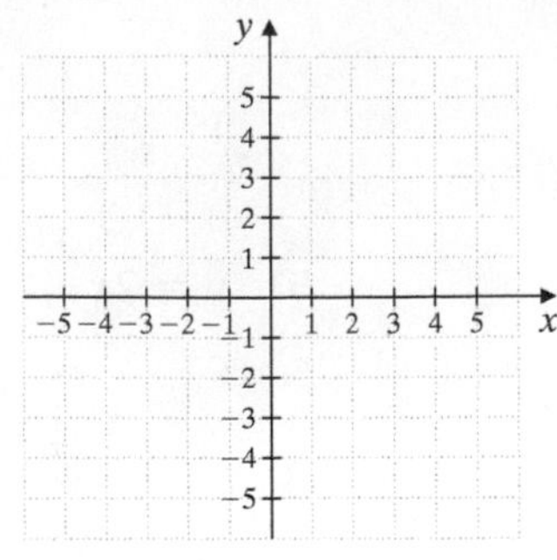

71. $y \geq -7$

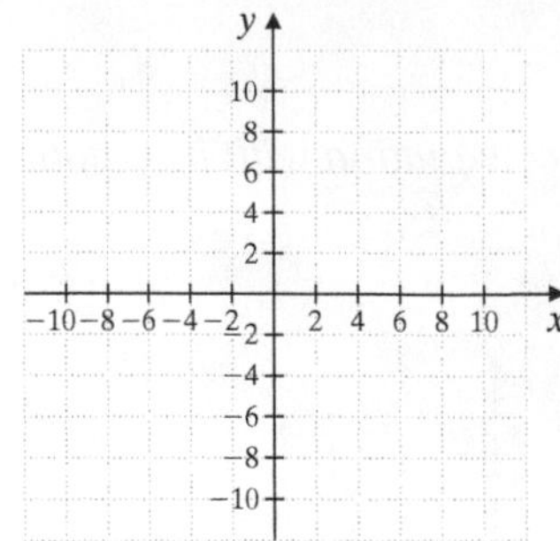

72. $y \leq -4$

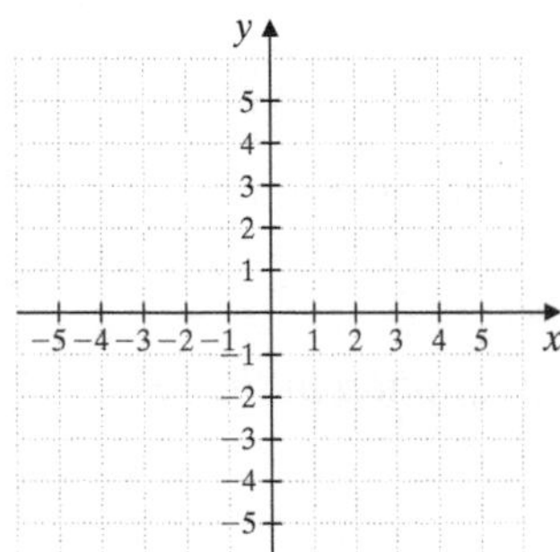

73. $-x \leq y$

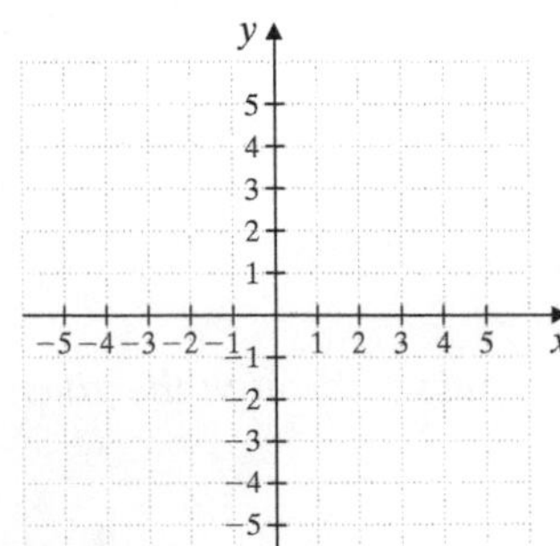

74. $x \geq -y$

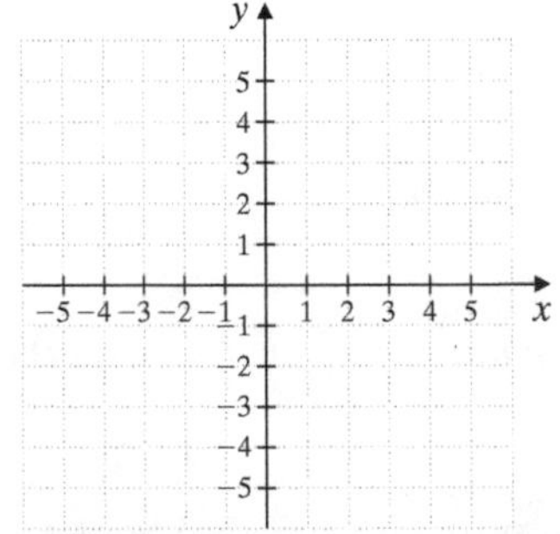

(6.8) *Solve.*

75. y varies directly as x. If $y = 40$ when $x = 4$, find y when x is 11.

76. y varies inversely as x. If $y = 4$ when $x = 6$, find y when x is 48.

77. y varies inversely as x^3. If $y = 12.5$ when $x = 2$, find y when x is 3.

78. y varies directly as x^2. If $y = 175$ when $x = 5$, find y when $x = 10$.

79. The cost of manufacturing a certain medicine varies inversely as the amount of medicine manufactured increases. If 3000 milliliters can be manufactured for \$6600, find the cost to manufacture 5000 milliliters.

80. The distance a spring stretches varies directly with the weight attached to the spring. If a 150-pound weight stretches the spring 8 inches, find the distance that a 90-pound weight stretches the spring.

Mixed Review

Complete the table of values for each given equation.

81. $2x - 5y = 9$

x	y
	1
2	
	−3

82. $x = -3y$

x	y
0	
	1
6	

Find the intercepts for each equation.

83. $2x - 3y = 6$

84. $-5x + y = 10$

Graph each linear equation.

85. $x - 5y = 10$

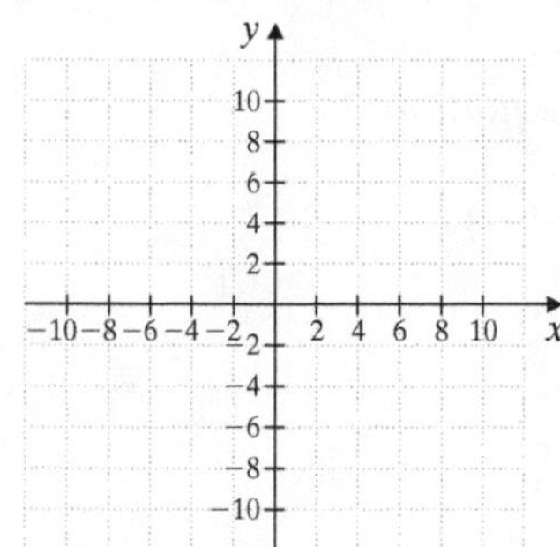

86. $x + y = 4$

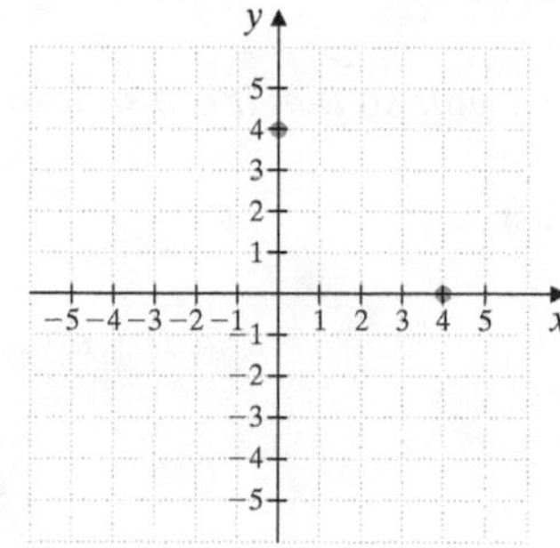

87. $y = -4x$

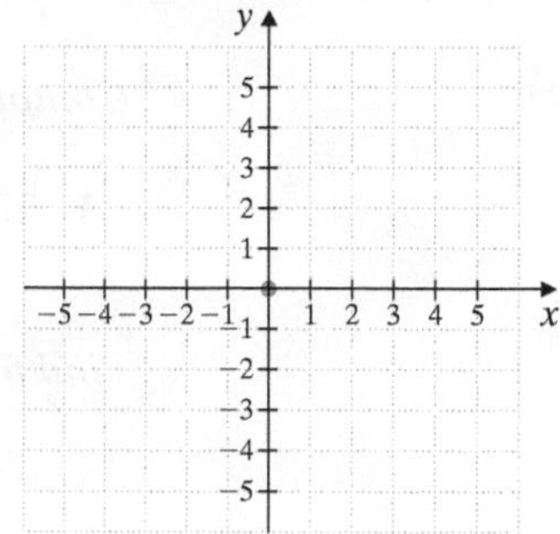

88. $2x + 3y = -6$

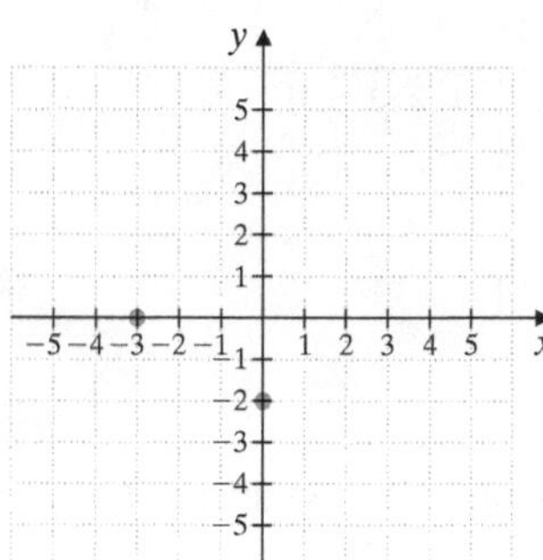

89. $x = 3$

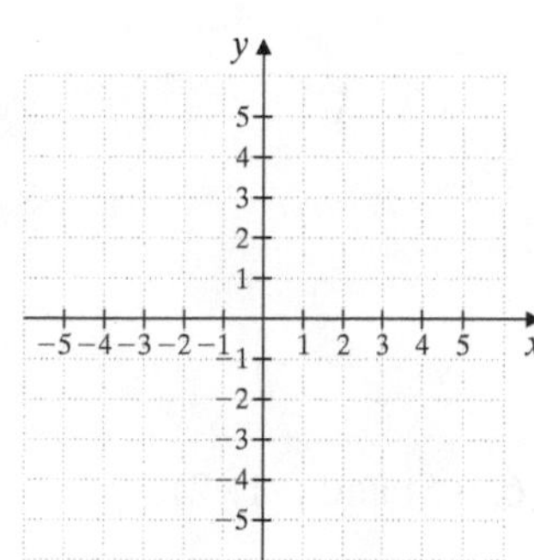

90. $y = -2$

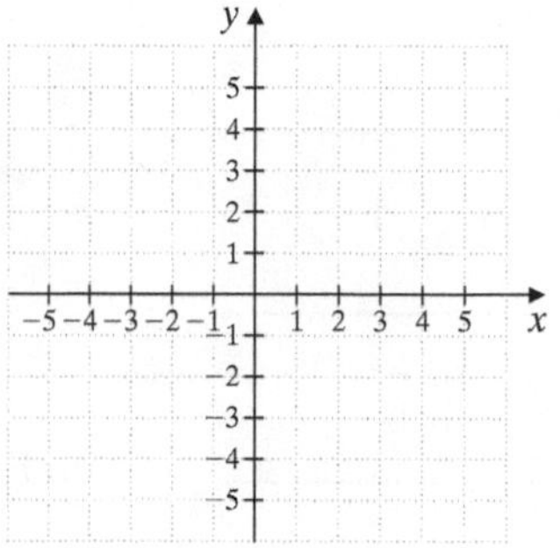

Find the slope of the line that passes through each pair of points.

91. $(3, -5)$ and $(-4, 2)$

92. $(1, 3)$ and $(-6, -8)$

Find the slope of each line.

93.

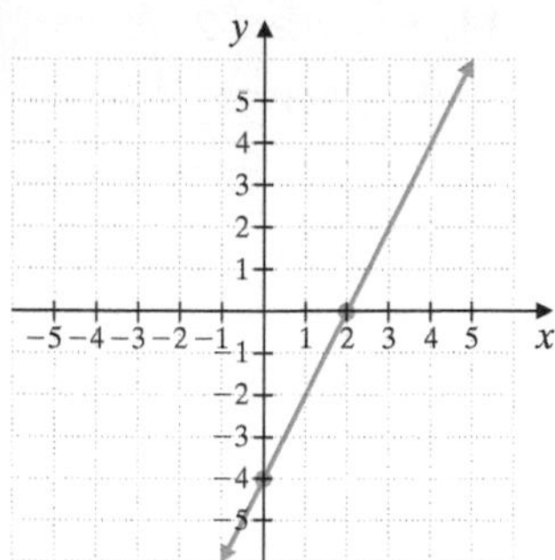

94.

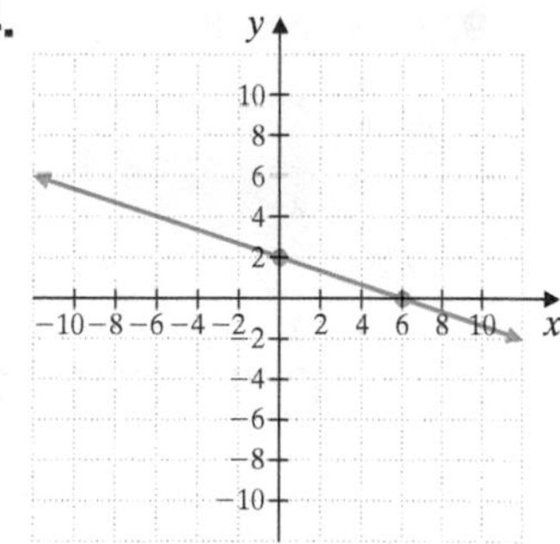

Determine the slope and y-intercept of the graph of each equation.

95. $-2x + 3y = -15$

96. $6x + y - 2 = 0$

Write an equation of the line with the given slope that passes through the given point. Write the equation in the form $Ax + By = C$.

97. $m = -5$; $(3, -7)$

98. $m = 3$; $(0, 6)$

Write an equation of the line passing through each pair of points. Write the equation in the form $Ax + By = C$.

99. $(-3, 9)$ and $(-2, 5)$

100. $(3, 1)$ and $(5, -9)$

Chapter 6 Test

Step-by-step test solutions are found on the Chapter Test Prep Videos available via the Interactive DVD Lecture Series, in MyMathLab or on YouTube (search "MartinGayIntroAlg" and click on "Channels").

Answers

1. ______

2. ______

3. ______

4. ______

5. ______

6. ______

7. ______

8. ______

9. ______

10. ______

11. ______

12. ______

13. ______

14. ______

Complete each ordered pair so that it is a solution of the given equation.

1. $12y - 7x = 5$; $(1, \ )$

2. $y = 17$; $(-4, \ )$

Find the slope of each line.

3.

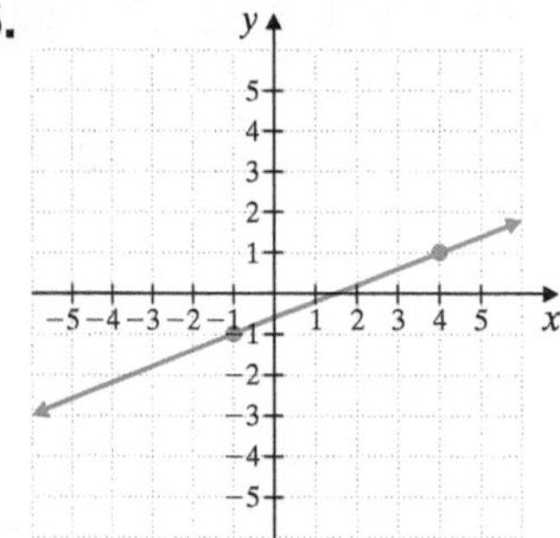

4.

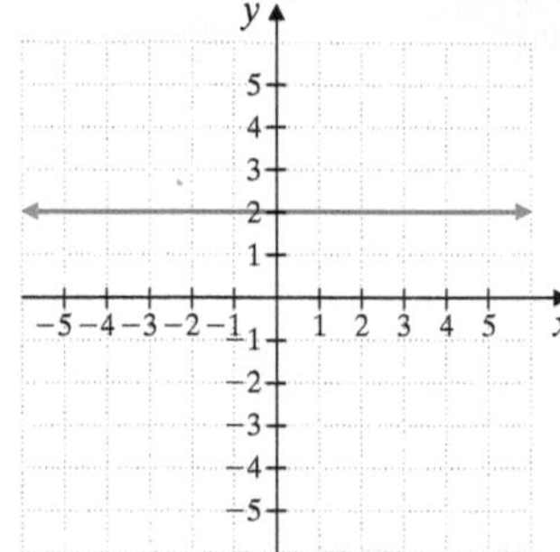

5. Passes through $(6, -5)$ and $(-1, 2)$

6. Passes through $(0, -8)$ and $(-1, -1)$

7. $2x + y = 8$

8. $(x = 6)$

Graph.

9. $2x + y = 8$

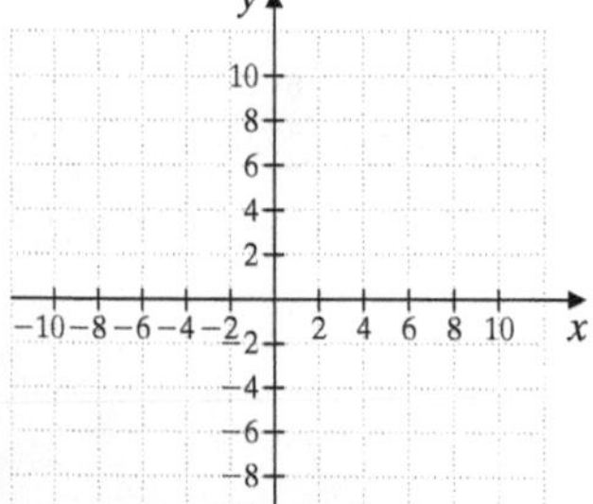

10. $-x + 4y = 5$

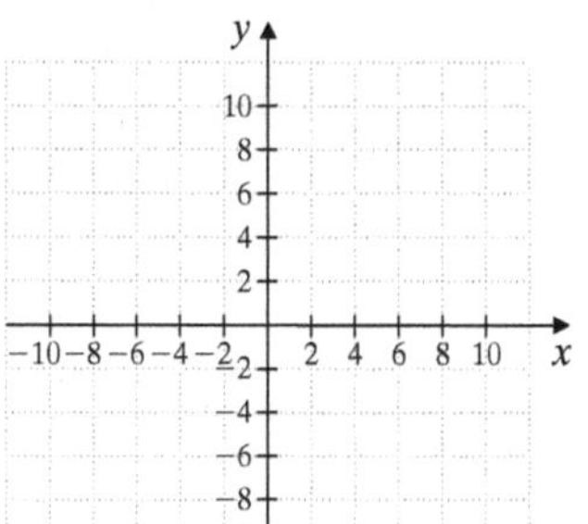

11. $x - y \geq -2$

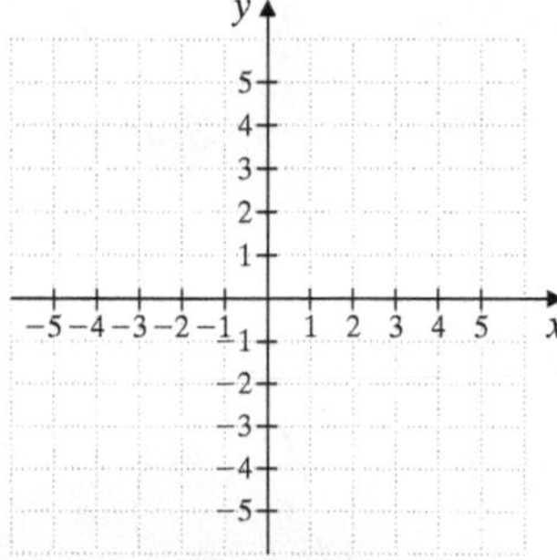

12. $y \geq -4x$

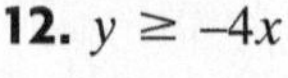

13. $5x - 7y = 5$

14. $2x - 3y > -6$

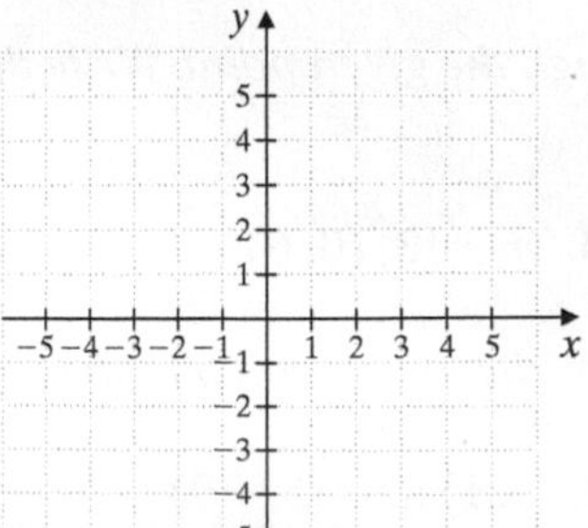

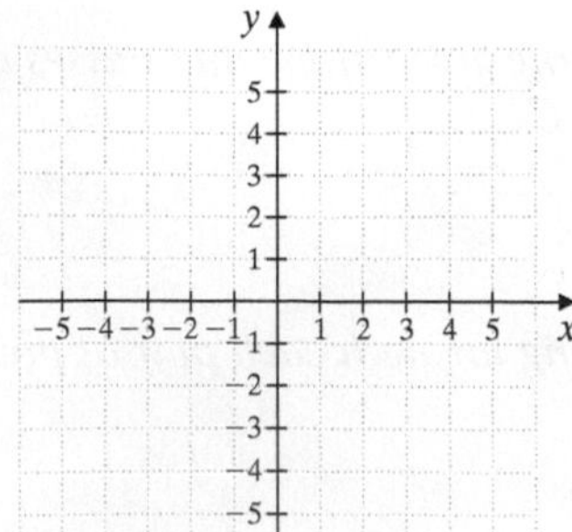

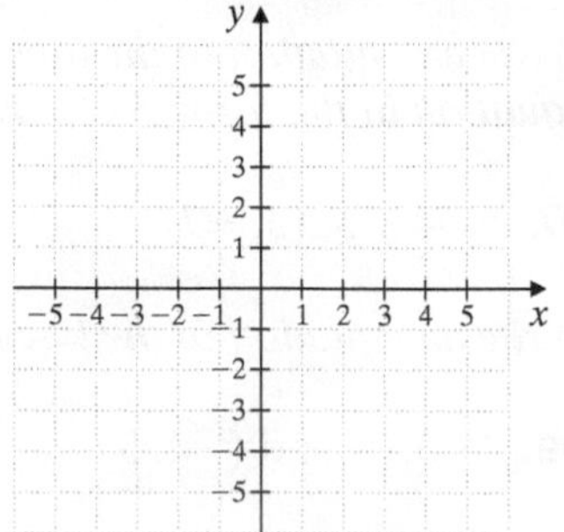

15. $6x + y > -1$

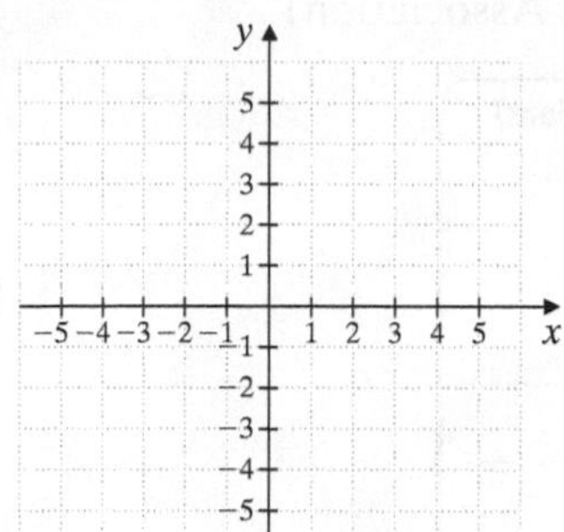

16. $y = -1$

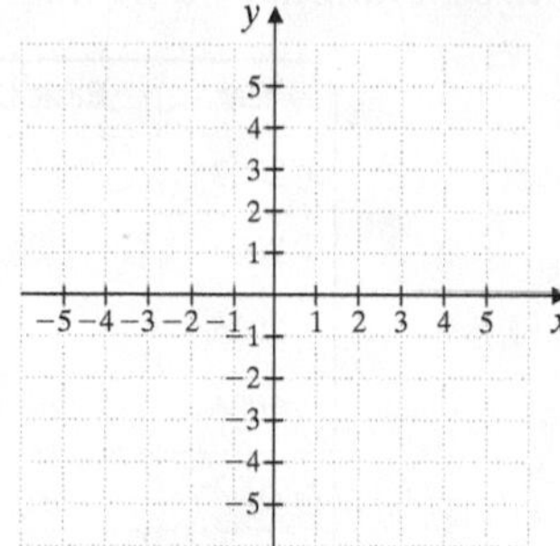
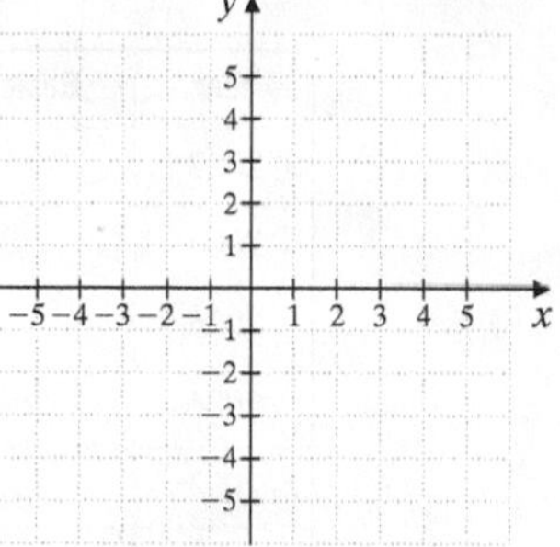

17. Determine whether the graphs of $y = 2x - 6$ and $-4x = 2y$ are parallel lines, perpendicular lines, or neither.

Find the equation of each line. Write the equation in the form $Ax + By = C$.

18. Slope $-\frac{1}{4}$, passes through $(2, 2)$

19. Passes through the origin and $(6, -7)$

20. Passes through $(2, -5)$ and $(1, 3)$

21. Slope $\frac{1}{8}$; y-intercept $(0, 12)$

Determine whether each relation is a function. For Exercises 24 and 25, if a function, find the domain and range.

22. $\{(-1, 2), (-2, 4), (-3, 6), (-4, 8)\}$

23. $\{(-3, -3), (0, 5), (-3, 2), (0, 0)\}$

24. The graph shown in Exercise 3.

25. The graph shown in Exercise 4.

Find the indicated function values for each function.

26. $f(x) = 2x - 4$

a. $f(-2)$

b. $f(0.2)$

c. $f(0)$

27. $f(x) = x^3 - x$

a. $f(-1)$

b. $f(0)$

c. $f(4)$

△ **28.** The perimeter of the parallelogram below is 42 meters. Write a linear equation in two variables for the perimeter. Use this equation to find x when y is 8 meters.

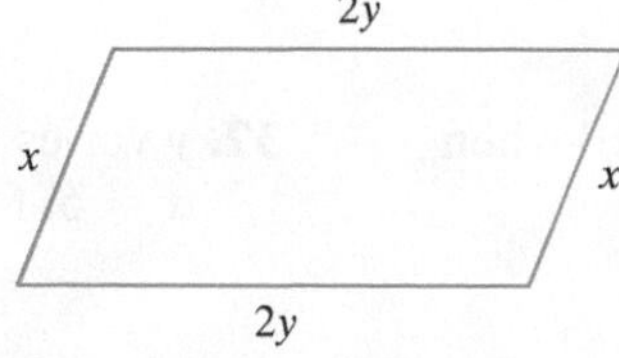

15. ____________

16. ____________

17. ____________

18. ____________

19. ____________

20. ____________

21. ____________

22. ____________

23. ____________

24. ____________

25. ____________

26. a. ____________

b. ____________

c. ____________

27. a. ____________

b. ____________

c. ____________

28. ____________

29. The table gives the number of basic cable TV subscribers (in millions) for the years shown. (*Source:* National Cable and Telecommunications Association)

Year	Basic Cable TV Subscribers (in millions)
2003	66.0
2004	65.4
2005	65.4
2006	65.6
2007	64.9
2008	63.7
2009	62.1

a. Write this data as a set of ordered pairs of the form (year, number of basic cable TV subscribers in millions).

b. Create a scatter diagram of the data. Be sure to label the axes properly.

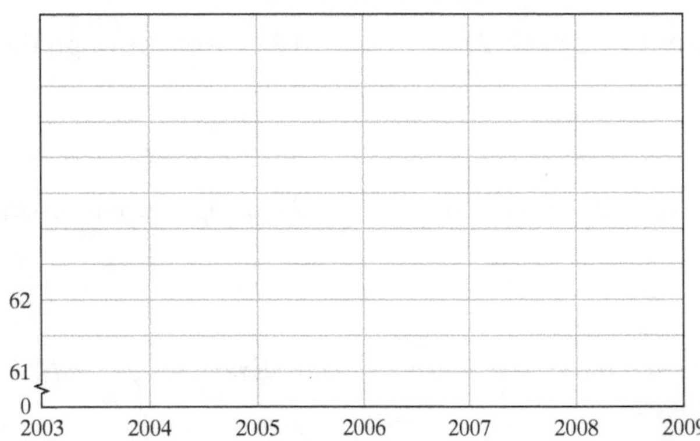

30. This graph approximates the movie ticket sales y (in millions) for the year x. Find the slope of the line and write the slope as a rate of change. Don't forget to attach the proper units.

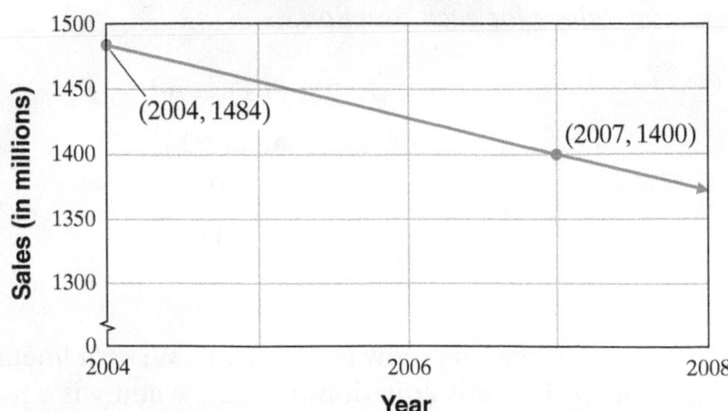

Source: National Association of Theater Owners

31. y varies directly as x. If $y = 10$ when $x = 15$, find y when x is 42.

32. y varies inversely as x^2. If $y = 8$ when $x = 5$, find y when x is 15.

29. a. ______

b. ______

30. ______

31. ______

32. ______

Cumulative Review Chapters 1–6

Simplify each expression.

1. $6 \div 3 + 5^2$

2. $\frac{10}{3} + \frac{5}{21}$

3. $1 + 2[5(2 \cdot 3 + 1) - 10]$

4. $16 - 3 \cdot 3 + 2^4$

5. The highest point in the United States is the top of Mount McKinley, at a height of 20,320 feet above sea level. The lowest point is Death Valley, California, which is 282 feet below sea level. How much higher is Mount McKinley than Death Valley? (*Source:* U.S. Geological Society)

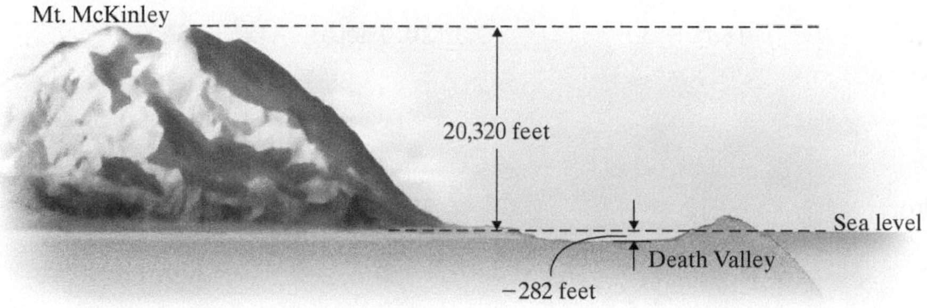

6. Simplify: $1.7x - 11 - 0.9x - 25$

Write each phrase as an algebraic expression and simplify if possible. Let x represent the unknown number.

7. Twice a number, plus 6.

8. The product of −15 and the sum of a number and $\frac{2}{3}$.

9. The difference of a number and 4, divided by 7.

10. The quotient of −9 and twice a number.

11. Five plus the sum of a number and 1.

12. A number subtracted from −86.

13. Solve for x: $\frac{5}{2}x = 15$

14. Solve for x: $\frac{x}{4} - 1 = -7$

15. Solve $2x < -4$. Graph the solutions.

−5 −4 −3 −2 −1 0 1 2 3 4 5

16. Solve: $5(x + 4) \geq 4(2x + 3)$

17. Find the degree of each polynomial and tell whether the polynomial is a monomial, binomial, trinomial, or none of these.

a. $-2t^2 + 3t + 6$

b. $15x - 10$

c. $7x + 3x^3 + 2x^2 - 1$

18. Solve $x + 2y = 6$ for y.

Answers

1. ______
2. ______
3. ______
4. ______
5. ______
6. ______
7. ______
8. ______
9. ______
10. ______
11. ______
12. ______
13. ______
14. ______
15. ______
16. ______
17. a. ______
b. ______
c. ______
18. ______

19. ______

20. ______

21. ______

22. ______

23. ______

24. ______

25. ______

26. ______

27. ______

28. ______

29. ______

30. ______

31. ______

32. ______

33. ______

34. ______

35. ______

36. ______

37. ______

38. ______

19. Add: $(-2x^2 + 5x - 1) + (-2x^2 + x + 3)$

20. Subtract: $(-2x^2 + 5x - 1) - (-2x^2 + x + 3)$

21. Multiply: $(3y + 1)^2$

22. Multiply: $(x - 12)^2$

23. Factor: $-9a^5 + 18a^2 - 3a$

24. Factor: $4x^2 - 36$

25. Factor: $x^2 + 4x - 12$

26. Factor: $3x^2 - 20xy - 7y^2$

27. Factor: $8x^2 - 22x + 5$

28. Factor: $18x^2 + 35x - 2$

29. Solve: $x^2 - 9x - 22 = 0$

30. Solve: $x^2 = x$

31. Divide: $\dfrac{2x^2 - 11x + 5}{5x - 25} \div \dfrac{4x - 2}{10}$

32. Simplify: $\dfrac{2x^2 - 50}{4x^4 - 20x^3}$

Write the rational expression as an equivalent rational expression with the given denominator.

33. $\dfrac{4b}{9a} = \dfrac{\quad}{27a^2b}$

34. $\dfrac{1}{2x} = \dfrac{\quad}{14x^3}$

35. Add: $1 + \dfrac{m}{m + 1}$

36. Subtract: $\dfrac{2x + 1}{x - 6} - \dfrac{x - 4}{x - 6}$

37. Solve: $3 - \dfrac{6}{x} = x + 8$

38. Solve: $3x^2 + 5x = 2$

39. Simplify: $\dfrac{\dfrac{x+1}{y}}{\dfrac{x}{y}+2}$

40. Simplify: $\dfrac{\dfrac{x}{2}-\dfrac{y}{6}}{\dfrac{x}{12}-\dfrac{y}{3}}$

41. Complete each ordered pair so that it is a solution to the equation $3x + y = 12$.

a. $(0, \quad)$

b. $(\quad, 6)$

c. $(-1, \quad)$

42. Complete the table for $y = -5x$.

x	*y*
0	
−1	
	10

43. Graph: $2x + y = 5$

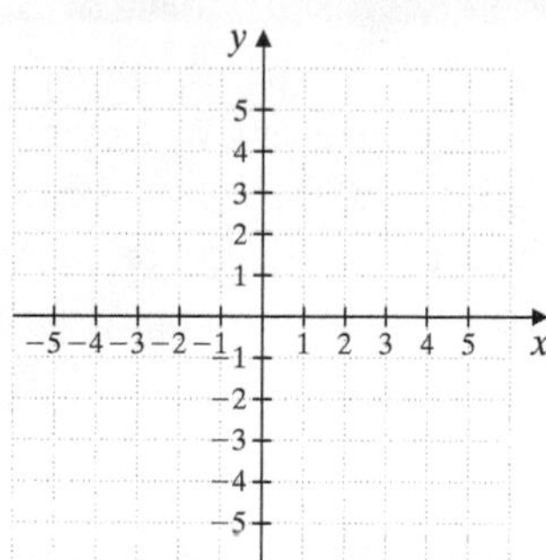

44. Find the slope of the line through $(0, 5)$ and $(-5, 4)$.

45. Find the slope of the line $-2x + 3y = 11$.

46. Find the slope of the line $x = -10$.

47. Find an equation of the line with slope -2 that passes through $(-1, 5)$. Write the equation in slope-intercept form, $y = mx + b$, and in standard form, $Ax + By = C$.

48. Find the slope and y-intercept of the line whose equation is $2x - 5y = 10$.

49. Given find each function value and list the corresponding ordered pair.

a. $g(2)$ **b.** $g(-2)$ **c.** $g(0)$

50. Write an equation of the line through $(2, 3)$ and $(0, 0)$. Write the equation in standard form.

39. ____

40. ____

41. a. ____

b. ____

c. ____

42. ____

43. ____

44. ____

45. ____

46. ____

47. ____

48. ____

49. a. ____

b. ____

c. ____

50. ____

8 Roots and Radicals

Sections

Check Your Progress

Having spent the last chapter studying equations, we return now to algebraic expressions. We expand on our skills of operating on expressions–adding, subtracting, multiplying, dividing, and raising to powers–to include finding roots. Just as subtraction is defined by addition and division by multiplication, finding roots is defined by raising to powers. As we master finding roots, we will work with equations that contain roots and solve problems that can be modeled by such equations.

One of the structures at the Beijing Olympics that captured everyone's imagination was the swimming and diving competition venue, the National Aquatics Center, better known as the Water Cube. It has a concrete and steel base, but it is the outside membrane of the center that makes it special. The complete structure of the Water Cube is covered with a plastic skin that is meant to simulate the shape of soap bubbles. The bubble covering is not just for looks; rather, the temperature of the building is regulated by controlling the air temperature lodged within the bubbles. Many people believe the Water Cube to be the fastest Olympic pool in the world; and in fact, between this pool and the faster Speedo swimsuit, 25 world records were broken. (*Source:* ARUP East Asia) In Section 8.2, Exercises 89 and 90, we will explore some of the dimensions of this most unusual Olympic venue.

Selected New World Records at 2008 Olympics in Beijing "Water Cube"

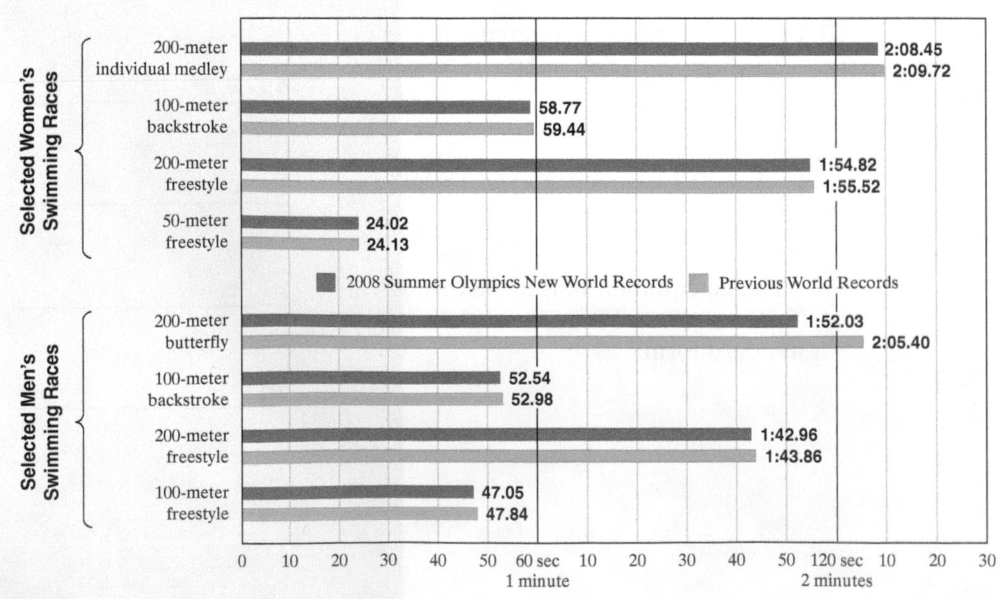

8.1 INTRODUCTION TO RADICALS

Objectives

A Find Square Roots.

B Find Cube Roots.

C Find nth Roots.

D Approximate Square Roots.

E Simplify Radicals Containing Variables.

Objective A Finding Square Roots

In this section, we define finding the **root** of a number by its reverse operation, raising a number to a power. We begin with squares and square roots.

The *square* of 5 is $5^2 = 25$.
The *square* of -5 is $(-5)^2 = 25$.
The *square* of $\frac{1}{2}$ is $\left(\frac{1}{2}\right)^2 = \frac{1}{4}$.

The reverse operation of squaring a number is finding a **square root** of a number. For example,

A *square root* of 25 is 5, because $5^2 = 25$.
A *square root* of 25 is also -5, because $(-5)^2 = 25$.
A *square root* of $\frac{1}{4}$ is $\frac{1}{2}$, because $\left(\frac{1}{2}\right)^2 = \frac{1}{4}$.

In general, the number b is a square root of a number a if $b^2 = a$.

The symbol $\sqrt{\ }$ is used to denote the **positive** or **principal square root** of a number. For example,

$\sqrt{25} = 5$ only, since $5^2 = 25$ and 5 is positive.

The symbol $-\sqrt{\ }$ is used to denote the **negative square root.** For example,

$-\sqrt{25} = -5$

The symbol $\sqrt{\ }$ is called a **radical** or **radical sign.** The expression within or under a radical sign is called the **radicand.** An expression containing a radical is called a **radical expression.**

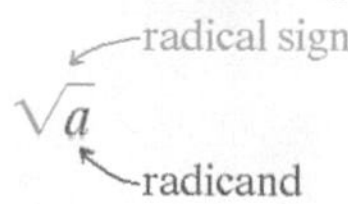

Square Root

If a is a positive number, then

$\sqrt{a}$ is the **positive square root** of a and

$-\sqrt{a}$ is the **negative square root** of a.

Also, $\sqrt{0} = 0$.

Examples Find each square root.

1. $\sqrt{36} = 6$, because $6^2 = 36$ and 6 is positive.
2. $-\sqrt{16} = -4$. The negative sign in front of the radical indicates the negative square root of 16.
3. $\sqrt{\frac{9}{100}} = \frac{3}{10}$ because $\left(\frac{3}{10}\right)^2 = \frac{9}{100}$ and $\frac{3}{10}$ is positive.
4. $\sqrt{0} = 0$ because $0^2 = 0$.
5. $\sqrt{0.64} = 0.8$ because $(0.8)^2 = 0.64$ and 0.8 is positive.

Work Practice 1–5

PRACTICE 1–5

Find each square root.

1. $\sqrt{100}$
2. $-\sqrt{81}$
3. $\sqrt{\frac{25}{81}}$
4. $\sqrt{1}$
5. $\sqrt{0.81}$

Answers
1. 10 **2.** -9 **3.** $\frac{5}{9}$ **4.** 1 **5.** 0.9

Is the square root of a negative number a real number? For example, is $\sqrt{-4}$ a real number? To answer this question, we ask ourselves, is there a real number whose square is -4? Since there is no real number whose square is -4, we say that $\sqrt{-4}$ is not a real number. In general,

A square root of a negative number is not a real number.

Study the following table to make sure you understand the differences discussed earlier.

Number	Square Roots of Number	$\sqrt{\text{number}}$	$-\sqrt{\text{number}}$
25	$-5, 5$	$\sqrt{25} = 5$ only	$-\sqrt{25} = -5$
$\frac{1}{4}$	$-\frac{1}{2}, \frac{1}{2}$	$\sqrt{\frac{1}{4}} = \frac{1}{2}$ only	$-\sqrt{\frac{1}{4}} = -\frac{1}{2}$
-9	No real square roots.	$\sqrt{-9}$ is not a real number.	

Objective B Finding Cube Roots

We can find roots other than square roots. For example, since $2^3 = 8$, we call 2 the **cube root** of 8. In symbols, we write

$\sqrt[3]{8} = 2$ The number 3 is called the **index.**

Also,

$\sqrt[3]{-64} = -4$ Since $(-4)^3 = -64$

Notice that unlike the square root of a negative number, the cube root of a negative number is a real number. This is so because while we cannot find a real number whose *square* is negative, we *can* find a real number whose *cube* is negative. In fact, the cube of a negative number is a negative number. Therefore, the cube root of a negative number is a negative number.

PRACTICE 6–8

Find each cube root.

6. $\sqrt[3]{27}$
7. $\sqrt[3]{-8}$
8. $\sqrt[3]{\frac{1}{64}}$

Examples Find each cube root.

6. $\sqrt[3]{1} = 1$ because $1^3 = 1$.
7. $\sqrt[3]{-27} = -3$ because $(-3)^3 = -27$.
8. $\sqrt[3]{\frac{1}{125}} = \frac{1}{5}$ because $\left(\frac{1}{5}\right)^3 = \frac{1}{125}$.

Work Practice 6–8

Objective C Finding *n*th Roots

Just as we can raise a real number to powers other than 2 or 3, we can find roots other than square roots and cube roots. In fact, we can take the nth root of a number where n is any natural number. An ***n*th root** of a number a is a number whose nth power is a.

In symbols, the nth root of a is written as $\sqrt[n]{a}$. Recall that n is called the **index.** The index 2 is usually omitted for square roots.

Helpful Hint

If the index is even, as it is in $\sqrt{}$, $\sqrt[4]{}$, $\sqrt[6]{}$, and so on, the radicand must be nonnegative for the root to be a real number. For example,

$\sqrt[4]{81} = 3$ but $\sqrt[4]{-81}$ is not a real number.

$\sqrt[6]{64} = 2$ but $\sqrt[6]{-64}$ is not a real number.

Answers

6. 3 7. -2 8. $\frac{1}{4}$

✓Concept Check Which of the following is a real number?

a. $\sqrt{-64}$ **b.** $\sqrt[4]{-64}$ **c.** $\sqrt[5]{-64}$ **d.** $\sqrt[6]{-64}$

Examples Find each root.

9. $\sqrt[4]{16} = 2$ because $2^4 = 16$ and 2 is positive.

10. $\sqrt[5]{-32} = -2$ because $(-2)^5 = -32$.

11. $-\sqrt[6]{1} = -1$ because $\sqrt[6]{1} = 1$.

12. $\sqrt[4]{-81}$ is not a real number since the index, 4, is even and the radicand, -81, is negative. In other words, there is no real number that when raised to the 4th power gives -81.

Work Practice 9–12

PRACTICE 9–12

Find each root.

9. $\sqrt[4]{-16}$

10. $\sqrt[5]{-1}$

11. $\sqrt[4]{256}$

12. $\sqrt[6]{-1}$

Objective D Approximating Square Roots

Recall that numbers such as 1, 4, 9, 25, and $\frac{4}{25}$ are called **perfect squares,** since $1^2 = 1, 2^2 = 4, 3^2 = 9, 5^2 = 25$, and $\left(\frac{2}{5}\right)^2 = \frac{4}{25}$. Square roots of perfect square radicands simplify to rational numbers.

What happens when we try to simplify a root such as $\sqrt{3}$? Since 3 is not a perfect square, $\sqrt{3}$ is not a rational number. It cannot be written as a quotient of integers. It is called an **irrational number** and we can find a decimal **approximation** of it. To find decimal approximations, use a calculator or Appendix E.1. (For calculator help, see the next example or the box at the end of this section.)

Example 13 Use a calculator or Appendix E.1 to approximate $\sqrt{3}$ to three decimal places.

Solution: We may use Appendix E.1 or a calculator to approximate $\sqrt{3}$. To use a calculator, find the square root key $\boxed{\sqrt{\ }}$.

$$\sqrt{3} \approx 1.732050808$$

To three decimal places, $\sqrt{3} \approx 1.732$.

Work Practice 13

PRACTICE 13

Use a calculator or Appendix E.1 to approximate $\sqrt{22}$ to three decimal places.

From Example 13, we found that

$$\sqrt{3} \approx 1.732$$

To see if the approximation is reasonable, notice that since

$$1 < 3 < 4, \text{ then}$$

$$\sqrt{1} < \sqrt{3} < \sqrt{4}, \text{ or}$$

$$1 < \sqrt{3} < 2.$$

Since $\sqrt{3}$ is a number between 1 and 2, our result of $\sqrt{3} \approx 1.732$ is reasonable.

Objective E Simplifying Radicals Containing Variables

Radicals can also contain variables. To simplify radicals containing variables, special care must be taken. To see how we simplify $\sqrt{x^2}$, let's look at a few examples in this form.

If $x = 3$, we have $\sqrt{3^2} = \sqrt{9} = 3$, or x.

If x is 5, we have $\sqrt{5^2} = \sqrt{25} = 5$, or x.

From these two examples, you may think that $\sqrt{x^2}$ simplifies to x. Let's now look at an example where x is a negative number. If $x = -3$, we have $\sqrt{(-3)^2} = \sqrt{9} = 3$, not -3, our original x. To make sure that $\sqrt{x^2}$ simplifies to a nonnegative number, we have the following.

Answers

9. not a real number **10.** -1 **11.** 4 **12.** not a real number **13.** 4.690

✓ Concept Check Answer

c

For any real number a,

$$\sqrt{a^2} = |a|$$

Thus,

$$\sqrt{x^2} = |x|,$$
$$\sqrt{(-8)^2} = |-8| = 8,$$
$$\sqrt{(7y)^2} = |7y|, \quad \text{and so on.}$$

To avoid this confusion, for the rest of the chapter we assume that **if a variable appears in the radicand of a radical expression, it represents positive numbers only.** Then

$\sqrt{x^2} = |x| = x$ since x is a positive number.

$\sqrt{y^2} = y$ Because $(y)^2 = y^2$

$\sqrt{x^8} = x^4$ Because $(x^4)^2 = x^8$

$\sqrt{9x^2} = 3x$ Because $(3x)^2 = 9x^2$

Examples Simplify each expression. Assume that all variables represent positive numbers.

14. $\sqrt{z^2} = z$ because $(z)^2 = z^2$.
15. $\sqrt{x^6} = x^3$ because $(x^3)^2 = x^6$.
16. $\sqrt[3]{27y^6} = 3y^2$ because $(3y^2)^3 = 27y^6$.
17. $\sqrt{16x^{16}} = 4x^8$ because $(4x^8)^2 = 16x^{16}$.
18. $\sqrt{\frac{x^4}{25}} = \frac{x^2}{5}$ because $\left(\frac{x^2}{5}\right)^2 = \frac{x^4}{25}$.
19. $\sqrt[3]{-125a^{12}b^{15}} = -5a^4b^5$ because $(-5a^4b^5)^3 = -125a^{12}b^{15}$.

Work Practice 14–19

PRACTICE 14–19

Simplify each expression. Assume that all variables represent positive numbers.

14. $\sqrt{z^8}$ **15.** $\sqrt{x^{20}}$

16. $\sqrt{4x^6}$ **17.** $\sqrt[3]{8y^{12}}$

18. $\sqrt{\frac{z^8}{81}}$ **19.** $\sqrt[3]{-64x^9y^{24}}$

Answers

14. z^4 **15.** x^{10} **16.** $2x^3$ **17.** $2y^4$ **18.** $\frac{z^4}{9}$ **19.** $-4x^3y^8$

Calculator Explorations Simplifying Square Roots

To simplify or approximate square roots using a calculator, locate the key marked [√]. To simplify $\sqrt{25}$ using a scientific calculator, press [25] [√]. The display should read [5]. To simplify $\sqrt{25}$ using a graphing calculator, press [√] [25] [ENTER].

To approximate $\sqrt{30}$, press [30] [√] (or [√] [30]). The display should read [5.477225575]. This is an approximation for $\sqrt{30}$. A three-decimal-place approximation is

$$\sqrt{30} \approx 5.477$$

Is this answer reasonable? Since 30 is between perfect squares 25 and 36, $\sqrt{30}$ is between $\sqrt{25} = 5$ and $\sqrt{36} = 6$. The calculator result is then reasonable since 5.477225575 is between 5 and 6.

Use a calculator to approximate each expression to three decimal places. Decide whether each result is reasonable.

1. $\sqrt{6}$ **2.** $\sqrt{14}$

3. $\sqrt{11}$ **4.** $\sqrt{200}$

5. $\sqrt{82}$ **6.** $\sqrt{46}$

Many scientific calculators have a key, such as [$\sqrt[x]{y}$], that can be used to approximate roots other than square roots. To approximate these roots using a graphing calculator, look under the [MATH] menu or consult your manual. To use a [$\sqrt[x]{y}$] key to find $\sqrt[3]{8}$, press [3] [$\sqrt[x]{y}$] [8] (press [ENTER] if needed). The display should read [2].

Use a calculator to approximate each expression to three decimal places. Decide whether each result is reasonable.

7. $\sqrt[3]{40}$ **8.** $\sqrt[3]{71}$

9. $\sqrt[4]{20}$ **10.** $\sqrt[4]{15}$

11. $\sqrt[5]{18}$ **12.** $\sqrt[6]{2}$

Vocabulary and Readiness Check

Use the choices below to fill in each blank.

positive	index	radical sign	power
negative	principal	square root	radicand

1. The symbol $\sqrt{}$ is used to denote the positive, or __________, square root.
2. In the expression $\sqrt[4]{16}$, the number 4 is called the __________, the number 16 is called the __________, and $\sqrt{}$ is called the __________.
3. The reverse operation of squaring a number is finding a(n) __________ of a number.
4. For a positive number a,

   $-\sqrt{a}$ is the ________ square root of a and

   $\sqrt{a}$ is the ________ square root of a.
5. An nth root of a number a is a number whose nth __________ is a.

Answer each true or false.

6. $\sqrt{4} = -2$ __________
7. $\sqrt{-9} = -3$ __________
8. $\sqrt{1000} = 100$ __________
9. $\sqrt{1} = 1$ and $\sqrt{0} = 0$ __________
10. $\sqrt{64} = 8$ and $\sqrt[3]{64} = 4$ __________

8.1 Exercise Set

FOR EXTRA HELP

Objective **A** *Find each square root. See Examples 1 through 5.*

1. $\sqrt{16}$
2. $\sqrt{64}$
3. $\sqrt{\frac{1}{25}}$
4. $\sqrt{\frac{1}{64}}$
5. $-\sqrt{100}$
6. $-\sqrt{36}$
7. $\sqrt{-4}$
8. $\sqrt{-25}$
9. $-\sqrt{121}$
10. $-\sqrt{49}$
11. $\sqrt{\frac{9}{25}}$
12. $\sqrt{\frac{4}{81}}$
13. $\sqrt{900}$
14. $\sqrt{400}$
15. $\sqrt{144}$
16. $\sqrt{169}$
17. $\sqrt{\frac{1}{100}}$
18. $\sqrt{\frac{1}{121}}$
19. $\sqrt{0.25}$
20. $\sqrt{0.49}$

Objective **B** *Find each cube root. See Examples 6 through 8.*

21. $\sqrt[3]{125}$
22. $\sqrt[3]{64}$
23. $\sqrt[3]{-64}$
24. $\sqrt[3]{-27}$
25. $-\sqrt[3]{8}$
26. $-\sqrt[3]{27}$
27. $\sqrt[3]{\frac{1}{8}}$
28. $\sqrt[3]{\frac{1}{64}}$
29. $\sqrt[3]{-125}$
30. $\sqrt[3]{-1}$

Objectives A B C **Mixed Practice** *Find each root. See Examples 1 through 12.*

31. $\sqrt[5]{32}$ **32.** $\sqrt[4]{81}$ **33.** $\sqrt{81}$ **34.** $\sqrt{49}$

35. $\sqrt[4]{-16}$ **36.** $\sqrt{-9}$ **37.** $\sqrt[3]{-\frac{27}{64}}$ **38.** $\sqrt[3]{-\frac{8}{27}}$

39. $-\sqrt[4]{625}$ **40.** $-\sqrt[5]{32}$ **41.** $\sqrt[6]{1}$ **42.** $\sqrt[5]{1}$

Objective D *Approximate each square root to three decimal places. See Example 13.*

43. $\sqrt{7}$ **44.** $\sqrt{10}$ **45.** $\sqrt{37}$ **46.** $\sqrt{27}$ **47.** $\sqrt{136}$ **48.** $\sqrt{8}$

49. A standard baseball diamond is a square with 90-foot sides connecting the bases. The distance from home plate to second base is $90 \cdot \sqrt{2}$ feet. Approximate $\sqrt{2}$ to two decimal places and use your result to approximate the distance $90 \cdot \sqrt{2}$ feet.

50. The roof of the warehouse shown needs to be shingled. The total area of the roof is exactly $480 \cdot \sqrt{29}$ square feet. Approximate $\sqrt{29}$ to two decimal places and use your result to approximate the area $480 \cdot \sqrt{29}$ square feet. Approximate this area to the nearest whole number.

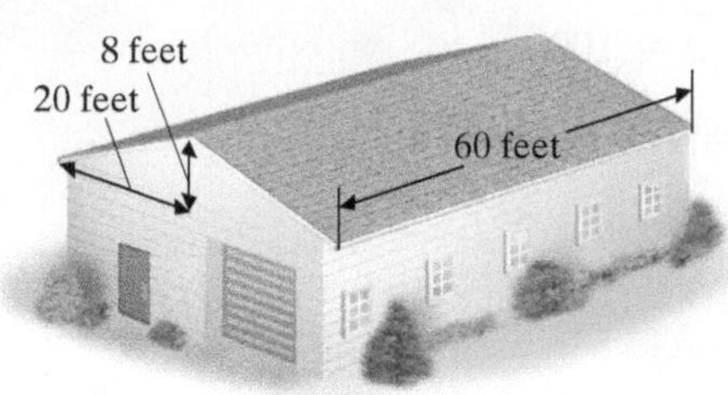

Objective E *Find each root. Assume that all variables represent positive numbers. See Examples 14 through 19.*

51. $\sqrt{m^2}$ **52.** $\sqrt{y^{10}}$ **53.** $\sqrt{x^4}$ **54.** $\sqrt{x^6}$

55. $\sqrt{9x^8}$ **56.** $\sqrt{36x^{12}}$ **57.** $\sqrt{81x^2}$ **58.** $\sqrt{100z^4}$

59. $\sqrt{a^2b^4}$ **60.** $\sqrt{x^{12}y^{20}}$ **61.** $\sqrt{16a^6b^4}$ **62.** $\sqrt{4m^{14}n^2}$

63. $\sqrt[3]{a^6b^{18}}$ **64.** $\sqrt[3]{x^{12}y^{18}}$ **65.** $\sqrt[3]{-8x^3y^{27}}$ **66.** $\sqrt[3]{-27a^6b^{30}}$

67. $\sqrt{\frac{x^6}{36}}$ **68.** $\sqrt{\frac{y^8}{49}}$ **69.** $\sqrt{\frac{25y^2}{9}}$ **70.** $\sqrt{\frac{4x^2}{81}}$

Review

Write each integer as a product of two integers such that one of the factors is a perfect square. For example, we can write $18 = 9 \cdot 2$, *where 9 is a perfect square. See Section R.1.*

71. 50 **72.** 8 **73.** 32 **74.** 75

75. 28 **76.** 44 **77.** 27 **78.** 90

Concept Extensions

Solve. See the Concept Check in this section.

79. Which of the following is a real number?

a. $\sqrt[7]{-1}$ **b.** $\sqrt[3]{-125}$

c. $\sqrt[6]{-128}$ **d.** $\sqrt[8]{-1}$

80. Which of the following is a real number?

a. $\sqrt{-1}$ **b.** $\sqrt[3]{-1}$

c. $\sqrt[4]{-1}$ **d.** $\sqrt[5]{-1}$

The length of a side of a square is given by the expression $\sqrt{A}$, where A is the square's area. Use this expression for Exercises 81 through 84. Be sure to attach the appropriate units.

△ **81.** The area of a square is 49 square miles. Find the length of a side of the square.

Square

$\sqrt{A}$

△ **82.** The area of a square is $\frac{1}{81}$ square meters. Find the length of a side of the square.

△ **83.** Sony currently makes the smallest portable mini disc player. It is approximately in the shape of a square with top area of 9.61 square inches. Find the length of a side. (*Source:* SONY)

△ **84.** A parking lot is in the shape of a square with area 2500 square yards. Find the length of a side.

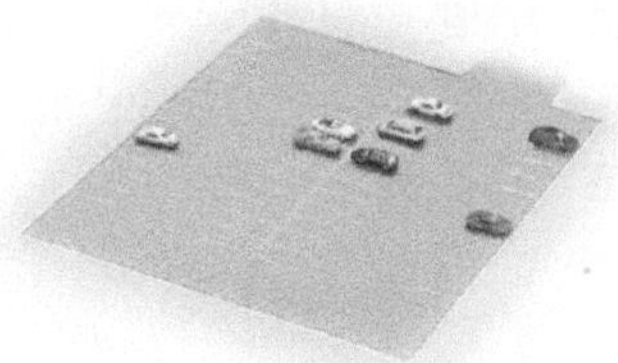

85. Simplify $\sqrt{\sqrt{81}}$.

86. Simplify $\sqrt[3]{\sqrt[3]{1}}$.

87. Simplify $\sqrt{\sqrt{10{,}000}}$.

88. Simplify $\sqrt{\sqrt{1{,}600{,}000{,}000}}$.

For each square root below, give two whole numbers that the square root lies between. For example,

since $\sqrt{11}$ is between $\sqrt{9}$ and $\sqrt{16}$, then

$\sqrt{11}$ is between 3 and 4.

89. $\sqrt{18}$

90. $\sqrt{28}$

91. $\sqrt{80}$

92. $\sqrt{98}$

93. The formula for calculating the period (one back-and-forth swing) of a pendulum is $T = 2\pi\sqrt{\frac{L}{g}}$, where T is time of the period of the swing, L is the length of the pendulum, and g is the acceleration of gravity. At the California Academy of Sciences, one can see a Foucault's pendulum with length = 30 ft and $g = 32$ ft/sec^2. Using $\pi \approx 3.14$, find the period of this pendulum. (Round to the nearest tenth of a second.)

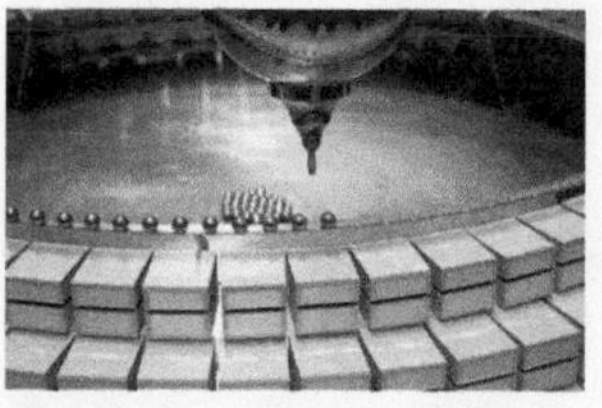

94. If the amount of gold discovered by humankind could be assembled in one place, it would be a cube with a volume of 195,112 cubic feet. Each side of the cube would be $\sqrt[3]{195{,}112}$ feet long. How long would one side of the cube be? (*Source: Reader's Digest*)

95. Explain why the square root of a negative number is not a real number.

96. Explain why the cube root of a negative number is a real number.

97. Graph $y = \sqrt{x}$. (Complete the table below, plot the ordered pair solutions, and draw a smooth curve through the points. Remember that since the radicand cannot be negative, this particular graph begins at the point with coordinates (0, 0).)

x	y	
0	0	
1		
3		(approximate)
4		
9		

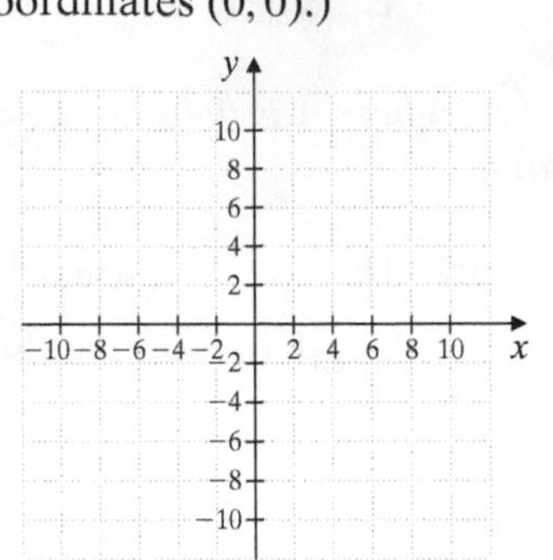

98. Graph $y = \sqrt[3]{x}$. (Complete the table below, plot the ordered pair solutions, and draw a smooth curve through the points.)

x	y	
−8		
−2		(approximate)
−1		
0		
1		
2		(approximate)
8		

Recall from this section that $\sqrt{a^2} = |a|$ for any real number a. Simplify the following given that x represents any real number.

99. $\sqrt{x^2}$

100. $\sqrt{4x^2}$

101. $\sqrt{(x + 2)^2}$

102. $\sqrt{x^2 + 6x + 9}$
(*Hint:* First factor $x^2 + 6x + 9$.)

Use a graphing calculator and graph each function. Observe the graph from left to right and give the ordered pair that corresponds to the "beginning" of the graph. Then tell why the graph starts at that point.

103. $y = \sqrt{x - 2}$

104. $y = \sqrt{x + 3}$

105. $y = \sqrt{x + 4}$

106. $y = \sqrt{x - 5}$

8.2 SIMPLIFYING RADICALS

Objectives

A Use the Product Rule to Simplify Radicals.

B Use the Quotient Rule to Simplify Radicals.

C Use Both Rules to Simplify Radicals Containing Variables.

D Simplify Cube Roots.

Objective A Simplifying Radicals Using the Product Rule

A square root is simplified when the radicand contains no perfect square factors (other than 1). For example, $\sqrt{20}$ is not simplified because $\sqrt{20} = \sqrt{4 \cdot 5}$ and 4 is a perfect square.

To begin simplifying square roots, we notice the following pattern.

$$\sqrt{9 \cdot 16} = \sqrt{144} = 12$$
$$\sqrt{9} \cdot \sqrt{16} = 3 \cdot 4 = 12$$

Since both expressions simplify to 12, we can write

$$\sqrt{9 \cdot 16} = \sqrt{9} \cdot \sqrt{16}$$

This suggests the following product rule for square roots.

Product Rule for Square Roots

If $\sqrt{a}$ and $\sqrt{b}$ are real numbers, then

$$\sqrt{a \cdot b} = \sqrt{a} \cdot \sqrt{b}$$

In other words, the square root of a product is equal to the product of the square roots.

To simplify $\sqrt{45}$, for example, we factor 45 so that one of its factors is a perfect square factor.

$\sqrt{45} = \sqrt{9 \cdot 5}$ Factor 45.

$= \sqrt{9} \cdot \sqrt{5}$ Use the product rule.

$= 3\sqrt{5}$ Write $\sqrt{9}$ as 3.

The notation $3\sqrt{5}$ means $3 \cdot \sqrt{5}$. Since the radicand 5 has no perfect square factor other than 1, the expression $3\sqrt{5}$ is in simplest form.

Helpful Hint

A radical expression in simplest form *does not mean* a decimal approximation. The simplest form of a radical expression is an exact form and may still contain a radical.

$$\underbrace{\sqrt{45} = 3\sqrt{5}}_{\text{exact}} \qquad \underbrace{\sqrt{45} \approx 6.71}_{\text{decimal approximation}}$$

Examples Simplify.

1. $\sqrt{54} = \sqrt{9 \cdot 6}$ Factor 54 so that one factor is a perfect square. 9 is a perfect square.

$= \sqrt{9} \cdot \sqrt{6}$ Use the product rule.

$= 3\sqrt{6}$ Write $\sqrt{9}$ as 3.

2. $\sqrt{12} = \sqrt{4 \cdot 3}$ Factor 12 so that one factor is a perfect square. 4 is a perfect square.

$= \sqrt{4} \cdot \sqrt{3}$ Use the product rule.

$= 2\sqrt{3}$ Write $\sqrt{4}$ as 2.

Continued on next page

PRACTICE 1–4

Simplify.

1. $\sqrt{40}$ **2.** $\sqrt{18}$

3. $\sqrt{500}$ **4.** $\sqrt{15}$

Answers

1. $2\sqrt{10}$ **2.** $3\sqrt{2}$ **3.** $10\sqrt{5}$ **4.** $\sqrt{15}$

3. $\sqrt{200} = \sqrt{100 \cdot 2}$ Factor 200 so that one factor is a perfect square. 100 is a perfect square.

$= \sqrt{100} \cdot \sqrt{2}$ Use the product rule.

$= 10\sqrt{2}$ Write $\sqrt{100}$ as 10.

4. $\sqrt{35}$ The radicand 35 contains no perfect square factors other than 1. Thus $\sqrt{35}$ is in simplest form.

Work Practice 1–4

In Example 3, 100 is the largest perfect square factor of 200. What happens if we don't use the largest perfect square factor? Although using the largest perfect square factor saves time, the result is the same no matter what perfect square factor is used. For example, it is also true that $200 = 4 \cdot 50$. Then

$$\sqrt{200} = \sqrt{4} \cdot \sqrt{50}$$
$$= 2 \cdot \sqrt{50}$$

Since $\sqrt{50}$ is not in simplest form, we continue.

$$\sqrt{200} = 2 \cdot \sqrt{50}$$
$$= 2 \cdot \sqrt{25 \cdot 2}$$
$$= 2 \cdot \sqrt{25} \cdot \sqrt{2}$$
$$= 2 \cdot 5 \cdot \sqrt{2}$$
$$= 10\sqrt{2}$$

PRACTICE 5

Simplify $7\sqrt{75}$.

Example 5 Simplify $3\sqrt{8}$.

Solution: Remember that $3\sqrt{8}$ means $3 \cdot \sqrt{8}$.

$3 \cdot \sqrt{8} = 3 \cdot \sqrt{4 \cdot 2}$ Factor 8 so that one factor is a perfect square.

$= 3 \cdot \sqrt{4} \cdot \sqrt{2}$ Use the product rule.

$= 3 \cdot 2 \cdot \sqrt{2}$ Write $\sqrt{4}$ as 2.

$= 6 \cdot \sqrt{2}$ or $6\sqrt{2}$ Write $3 \cdot 2$ as 6.

Work Practice 5

Objective B Simplifying Radicals Using the Quotient Rule

Next, let's examine the square root of a quotient.

$$\sqrt{\frac{16}{4}} = \sqrt{4} = 2$$

Also,

$$\frac{\sqrt{16}}{\sqrt{4}} = \frac{4}{2} = 2$$

Since both expressions equal 2, we can write

$$\sqrt{\frac{16}{4}} = \frac{\sqrt{16}}{\sqrt{4}}$$

This suggests the following quotient rule.

Answer

5. $35\sqrt{3}$

Quotient Rule for Square Roots

If $\sqrt{a}$ and $\sqrt{b}$ are real numbers and $b \neq 0$, then

$$\sqrt{\frac{a}{b}} = \frac{\sqrt{a}}{\sqrt{b}}$$

In other words, the square root of a quotient is equal to the quotient of the square roots.

Examples Use the quotient rule to simplify.

6. $\sqrt{\frac{25}{36}} = \frac{\sqrt{25}}{\sqrt{36}} = \frac{5}{6}$

7. $\sqrt{\frac{3}{64}} = \frac{\sqrt{3}}{\sqrt{64}} = \frac{\sqrt{3}}{8}$

8. $\sqrt{\frac{40}{81}} = \frac{\sqrt{40}}{\sqrt{81}}$ Use the quotient rule.

$= \frac{\sqrt{4} \cdot \sqrt{10}}{9}$ Use the product rule and write $\sqrt{81}$ as 9.

$= \frac{2\sqrt{10}}{9}$ Write $\sqrt{4}$ as 2.

Work Practice 6–8

PRACTICE 6–8

Use the quotient rule to simplify.

6. $\sqrt{\frac{16}{81}}$

7. $\sqrt{\frac{2}{25}}$

8. $\sqrt{\frac{45}{49}}$

Objective C Simplifying Radicals Containing Variables

Recall that $\sqrt{x^6} = x^3$ because $(x^3)^2 = x^6$. If a variable radicand in a square root has an odd exponent, we write the exponential expression so that one factor is the greatest even power contained in the expression. Then we use the product rule to simplify.

Examples Simplify each radical. Assume that all variables represent positive numbers.

9. $\sqrt{x^5} = \sqrt{x^4 \cdot x} = \sqrt{x^4} \cdot \sqrt{x} = x^2\sqrt{x}$

10. $\sqrt{8y^2} = \sqrt{4 \cdot 2 \cdot y^2} = \sqrt{4y^2 \cdot 2} = \sqrt{4y^2} \cdot \sqrt{2} = 2y\sqrt{2}$ 4 and y^2 are both perfect square factors so we grouped them under one radical.

11. $\sqrt{\frac{45}{x^6}} = \frac{\sqrt{45}}{\sqrt{x^6}} = \frac{\sqrt{9 \cdot 5}}{x^3} = \frac{\sqrt{9} \cdot \sqrt{5}}{x^3} = \frac{3\sqrt{5}}{x^3}$

12. $\sqrt{\frac{5p^3}{9}} = \frac{\sqrt{5p^3}}{\sqrt{9}} = \frac{\sqrt{p^2 \cdot 5p}}{3} = \frac{\sqrt{p^2} \cdot \sqrt{5p}}{3} = \frac{p\sqrt{5p}}{3}$

Work Practice 9–12

PRACTICE 9–12

Simplify each radical. Assume that all variables represent positive numbers.

9. $\sqrt{x^{11}}$

10. $\sqrt{18x^4}$

11. $\sqrt{\frac{27}{x^8}}$

12. $\sqrt{\frac{7y^7}{25}}$

Answers

6. $\frac{4}{9}$ 7. $\frac{\sqrt{2}}{5}$ 8. $\frac{3\sqrt{5}}{7}$ 9. $x^5\sqrt{x}$ 10. $3x^2\sqrt{2}$ 11. $\frac{3\sqrt{3}}{x^4}$ 12. $\frac{y^3\sqrt{7y}}{5}$

Objective D Simplifying Cube Roots

The product and quotient rules also apply to roots other than square roots. For example, to simplify cube roots, we look for perfect cube factors of the radicand. Recall that 8 is a perfect cube since $2^3 = 8$. Therefore, to simplify $\sqrt[3]{48}$, we factor 48 as $8 \cdot 6$.

$$\sqrt[3]{48} = \sqrt[3]{8 \cdot 6} \quad \text{Factor 48.}$$
$$= \sqrt[3]{8} \cdot \sqrt[3]{6} \quad \text{Use the product rule.}$$
$$= 2\sqrt[3]{6} \quad \text{Write } \sqrt[3]{8} \text{ as 2.}$$

$2\sqrt[3]{6}$ is in simplest form since the radicand, 6, contains no perfect cube factors other than 1.

PRACTICE 13–16

Simplify each radical.

13. $\sqrt[3]{88}$ **14.** $\sqrt[3]{50}$

15. $\sqrt[3]{\dfrac{10}{27}}$ **16.** $\sqrt[3]{\dfrac{81}{8}}$

Examples Simplify each radical.

13. $\sqrt[3]{54} = \sqrt[3]{27 \cdot 2} = \sqrt[3]{27} \cdot \sqrt[3]{2} = 3\sqrt[3]{2}$

14. $\sqrt[3]{18}$ The number 18 contains no perfect cube factors, so $\sqrt[3]{18}$ cannot be simplified further.

15. $\sqrt[3]{\dfrac{7}{8}} = \dfrac{\sqrt[3]{7}}{\sqrt[3]{8}} = \dfrac{\sqrt[3]{7}}{2}$

16. $\sqrt[3]{\dfrac{40}{27}} = \dfrac{\sqrt[3]{40}}{\sqrt[3]{27}} = \dfrac{\sqrt[3]{8 \cdot 5}}{3} = \dfrac{\sqrt[3]{8} \cdot \sqrt[3]{5}}{3} = \dfrac{2\sqrt[3]{5}}{3}$

Work Practice 13–16

Answers
13. $2\sqrt[3]{11}$ **14.** $\sqrt[3]{50}$ **15.** $\dfrac{\sqrt[3]{10}}{3}$ **16.** $\dfrac{3\sqrt[3]{3}}{2}$

Vocabulary and Readiness Check

Use the choices below to fill in each blanks. Not all choices will be used.

$a \cdot b$ $\quad \dfrac{a}{b}$ $\quad \dfrac{\sqrt{a}}{\sqrt{b}}$ $\quad \sqrt{a} \cdot \sqrt{b}$

1. If $\sqrt{a}$ and $\sqrt{b}$ are real numbers, then $\sqrt{a \cdot b} =$ ________.

2. If $\sqrt{a}$ and $\sqrt{b}$ are real numbers, then $\sqrt{\dfrac{a}{b}} =$ ________.

For Exercises 3 and 4, fill in the blanks using the example: $\sqrt{4 \cdot 9} = \sqrt{\underline{4}} \cdot \sqrt{\underline{9}} = \underline{2} \cdot \underline{3} = \underline{6}$.

3. $\sqrt{16 \cdot 25} = \sqrt{\_\_} \cdot \sqrt{\_\_} = \_ \cdot \_ = \_\_$.

4. $\sqrt{36 \cdot 3} = \sqrt{\_\_} \cdot \sqrt{\_\_} = \_ \cdot \sqrt{\_} =$ ________.

True or False: Decide whether each radical is completely simplified.

5. $\sqrt{48} = 2\sqrt{12}$ Completely simplified: ________.

6. $\sqrt[3]{40} = 2\sqrt[3]{5}$ Completely simplified: ________.

8.2 Exercise Set

FOR EXTRA HELP

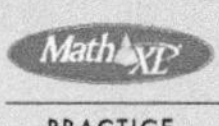
PRACTICE

WATCH

DOWNLOAD

READ

REVIEW

Objective A *Use the product rule to simplify each radical. See Examples 1 through 4.*

1. $\sqrt{20}$ **2.** $\sqrt{44}$ **3.** $\sqrt{50}$ **4.** $\sqrt{28}$ **5.** $\sqrt{33}$

6. $\sqrt{21}$ **7.** $\sqrt{98}$ **8.** $\sqrt{125}$ **9.** $\sqrt{60}$ **10.** $\sqrt{90}$

11. $\sqrt{180}$ **12.** $\sqrt{150}$ **13.** $\sqrt{52}$ **14.** $\sqrt{75}$

Use the product rule to simplify each radical. See Example 5.

15. $3\sqrt{25}$ **16.** $9\sqrt{36}$ **17.** $7\sqrt{63}$

18. $11\sqrt{99}$ **19.** $-5\sqrt{27}$ **20.** $-6\sqrt{75}$

Objective B *Use the quotient rule and the product rule to simplify each radical. See Examples 6 through 8.*

21. $\sqrt{\dfrac{8}{25}}$ **22.** $\sqrt{\dfrac{63}{16}}$ **23.** $\sqrt{\dfrac{27}{121}}$ **24.** $\sqrt{\dfrac{24}{169}}$

25. $\sqrt{\dfrac{9}{4}}$ **26.** $\sqrt{\dfrac{100}{49}}$ **27.** $\sqrt{\dfrac{125}{9}}$ **28.** $\sqrt{\dfrac{27}{100}}$

29. $\sqrt{\dfrac{11}{36}}$ **30.** $\sqrt{\dfrac{30}{49}}$ **31.** $-\sqrt{\dfrac{27}{144}}$ **32.** $-\sqrt{\dfrac{84}{121}}$

Objective C *Simplify each radical. Assume that all variables represent positive numbers. See Examples 9 through 12.*

33. $\sqrt{x^7}$ **34.** $\sqrt{y^3}$ **35.** $\sqrt{x^{13}}$ **36.** $\sqrt{y^{17}}$

37. $\sqrt{36a^3}$ **38.** $\sqrt{81b^5}$ **39.** $\sqrt{96x^4}$ **40.** $\sqrt{40y^{10}}$

41. $\sqrt{\frac{12}{m^2}}$ **42.** $\sqrt{\frac{63}{p^2}}$ **43.** $\sqrt{\frac{9x}{y^{10}}}$ **44.** $\sqrt{\frac{6y^2}{z^{16}}}$

45. $\sqrt{\frac{88}{x^{12}}}$ **46.** $\sqrt{\frac{500}{y^{22}}}$

Objectives A B C **Mixed Practice** *Simplify each radical. See Examples 1 through 12.*

47. $8\sqrt{4}$ **48.** $6\sqrt{49}$ **49.** $\sqrt{\frac{36}{121}}$ **50.** $\sqrt{\frac{25}{144}}$

51. $\sqrt{175}$ **52.** $\sqrt{700}$ **53.** $\sqrt{\frac{20}{9}}$ **54.** $\sqrt{\frac{45}{64}}$

55. $\sqrt{24m^7}$ **56.** $\sqrt{50n^{13}}$ **57.** $\sqrt{\frac{23y^3}{4x^6}}$ **58.** $\sqrt{\frac{41x^5}{9y^8}}$

Objective D *Simplify each radical. See Examples 13 through 16.*

59. $\sqrt[3]{24}$ **60.** $\sqrt[3]{81}$ **61.** $\sqrt[3]{250}$ **62.** $\sqrt[3]{56}$

63. $\sqrt[3]{\frac{5}{64}}$ **64.** $\sqrt[3]{\frac{32}{125}}$ **65.** $\sqrt[3]{\frac{23}{8}}$ **66.** $\sqrt[3]{\frac{37}{27}}$

67. $\sqrt[3]{\frac{15}{64}}$ **68.** $\sqrt[3]{\frac{4}{27}}$ **69.** $\sqrt[3]{80}$ **70.** $\sqrt[3]{108}$

Review

Perform each indicated operation. See Sections 3.4 and 3.5.

71. $6x + 8x$ **72.** $(6x)(8x)$ **73.** $(2x + 3)(x - 5)$

74. $(2x + 3) + (x - 5)$ **75.** $9y^2 - 9y^2$ **76.** $(9y^2)(-8y^2)$

Concept Extensions

Simplify each radical. Assume that all variables represent positive numbers.

77. $\sqrt{x^6y^3}$ **78.** $\sqrt{a^{13}b^{14}}$ **79.** $\sqrt{98x^5y^4}$

80. $\sqrt{27x^8y^{11}}$ **81.** $\sqrt[3]{-8x^6}$ **82.** $\sqrt[3]{27x^{12}}$

83. If a cube is to have a volume of 80 cubic inches, then each side must be $\sqrt[3]{80}$ inches long. Simplify the radical representing the side length.

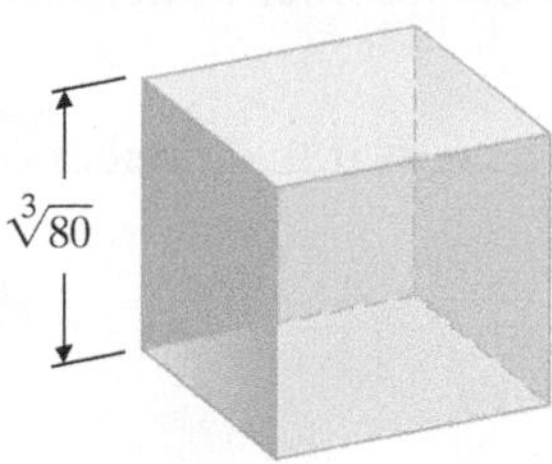

84. Jeannie Boswell is swimming across a 40-foot-wide river, trying to head straight across to the opposite shore. However, the current is strong enough to move her downstream 100 feet by the time she reaches land. (See the figure.) Because of the current, the actual distance she swims is $\sqrt{11{,}600}$ feet. Simplify this radical.

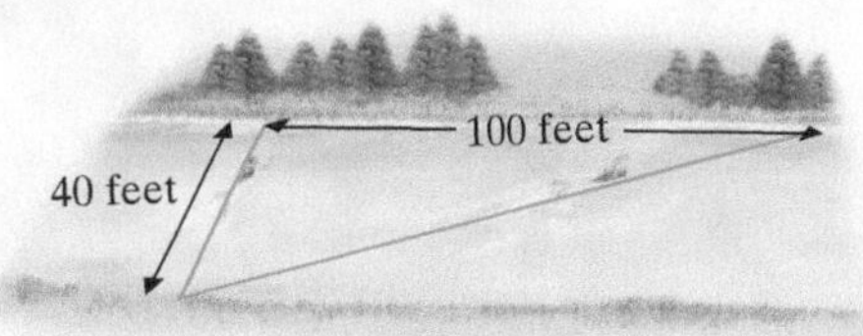

85. By using replacement values for a and b, show that $\sqrt{a^2 + b^2}$ does not equal $a + b$.

86. By using replacement values for a and b, show that $\sqrt{a + b}$ does not equal $\sqrt{a} + \sqrt{b}$.

The length of a side of a cube is given by the expression $\frac{\sqrt{6A}}{6}$, where A is the cube's surface area. Use this expression where necessary for Exercises 87 through 92. Be sure to attach the appropriate units.

87. The surface area of a cube is 120 square inches. Find the exact length of a side of the cube.

88. The surface area of a cube is 594 square feet. Find the exact length of a side of the cube.

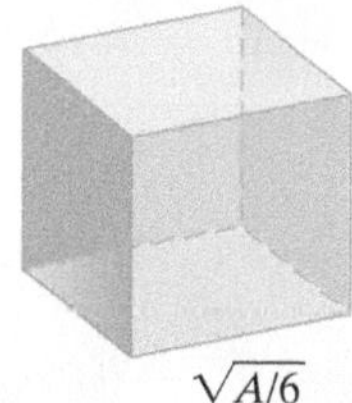

89. The "Water Cube" was the swimming and diving venue for the 2008 Beijing Summer Olympics. It is not actually a cube, because it is only 31 meters high, which is not the same as it is wide and long. However, the roof of it is a square. If area of the roof of the Water Cube is 31,329 square meters, find the dimensions of the roof of the Water Cube.

90. The competition diving pool in the Water Cube at the Beijing Summer Olympics is not a cube either. It has a square footprint, but is only 5 meters deep. If the volume of the diving pool is 3125 cubic meters, find the length and width of the competition diving pool.

91. Rubik's cube, named after its inventor, Erno Rubik, was first imagined by him in 1974, and by 1980 was a worldwide phenomenon. A standard Rubik's cube has a surface area of 30.375 square inches. Find the length of one side of a Rubik's cube. (A few world records are listed below. *Source: Guinness World Records*)

Fastest time to solve 1 Rubik's cube: 9.55 sec by Ron van Bruchem (Netherlands) in 2007.

Most Rubik's cubes solved in 1 hour: 185 by David Calvo (Spain) in 2008.

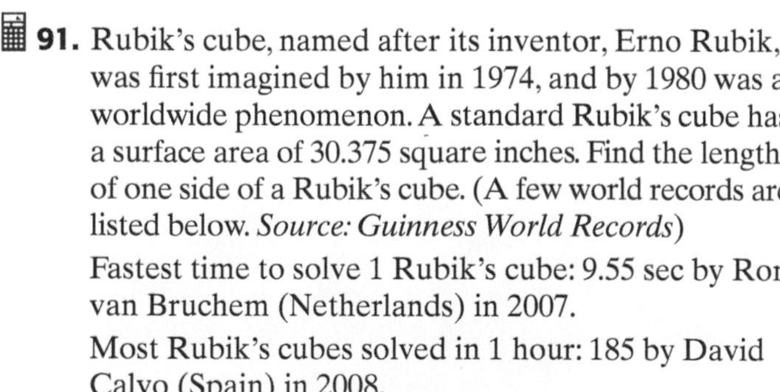

92. The Borg spaceship on *Star Trek: The Next Generation* is in the shape of a cube. Suppose a model of this ship has a surface area of 121 square inches. Find the length of a side of the ship.

The cost C in dollars per day to operate a small delivery service is given by $C = 100\sqrt[3]{n} + 700$, where n is the number of deliveries per day.

93. Find the cost if the number of deliveries is 1000.

94. Approximate the cost if the number of deliveries is 500.

The Mosteller formula for calculating body surface area is $B = \sqrt{\frac{hw}{3600}}$, where B is an individual's body surface area in square meters, h is the individual's height in centimeters, and w is the individual's weight in kilograms. Use this formula in Exercises 95 and 96. Round answers to the nearest tenth.

95. Find the body surface area of a person who is 169 cm tall and weighs 64 kilograms.

96. Approximate the body surface area of a person who is 183 cm tall and weighs 85 kilograms.

8.3 ADDING AND SUBTRACTING RADICALS

Objective A Adding and Subtracting Radicals

Recall that to combine like terms, we use the distributive property.

$$5x + 3x = (5 + 3)x = 8x$$

The distributive property can also be applied to expressions containing the same radicals. For example,

$$5\sqrt{2} + 3\sqrt{2} = (5 + 3)\sqrt{2} = 8\sqrt{2}$$

Also,

$$9\sqrt{5} - 6\sqrt{5} = (9 - 6)\sqrt{5} = 3\sqrt{5}$$

Radical terms such as $5\sqrt{2}$ and $3\sqrt{2}$ are **like radicals,** as are $9\sqrt{5}$ and $6\sqrt{5}$. Like radicals have the same index and the same radicand.

Examples Add or subtract as indicated.

1. $4\sqrt{5} + 3\sqrt{5} = (4 + 3)\sqrt{5} = 7\sqrt{5}$
2. $\sqrt{10} - 6\sqrt{10} = 1\sqrt{10} - 6\sqrt{10} = (1 - 6)\sqrt{10} = -5\sqrt{10}$
3. $2\sqrt{6} + 2\sqrt{5}$ cannot be simplified further since the radicands are not the same.
4. $\sqrt{15} + \sqrt{15} - \sqrt{2} = 1\sqrt{15} + 1\sqrt{15} - \sqrt{2}$
   $= (1 + 1)\sqrt{15} - \sqrt{2}$
   $= 2\sqrt{15} - \sqrt{2}$

   This expression cannot be simplified further since the radicands are not the same.

Work Practice 1–4

PRACTICE 1–4

Add or subtract as indicated.

1. $6\sqrt{11} + 9\sqrt{11}$
2. $\sqrt{7} - 3\sqrt{7}$
3. $\sqrt{2} + \sqrt{2} - \sqrt{15}$
4. $3\sqrt{3} - 3\sqrt{2}$

✓**Concept Check** Which is true?

a. $2 + 3\sqrt{5} = 5\sqrt{5}$

b. $2\sqrt{3} + 2\sqrt{7} = 2\sqrt{10}$

c. $\sqrt{3} + \sqrt{5} = \sqrt{8}$

d. $\sqrt{3} + \sqrt{3} = 3$

e. None of the above is true. In each case, the left-hand side cannot be simplified further.

Objective B Simplifying Square Root Radicals Before Adding or Subtracting

At first glance, it appears that the expression $\sqrt{50} + \sqrt{8}$ cannot be simplified further because the radicands are different. However, the product rule can be used to simplify each radical, and then further simplification might be possible.

Objectives

A Add or Subtract Like Radicals.

B Simplify Square Root Radical Expressions, and Then Add or Subtract Any Like Radicals.

C Simplify Cube Root Radical Expressions, and Then Add or Subtract Any Like Radicals.

Answers

1. $15\sqrt{11}$ 2. $-2\sqrt{7}$ 3. $2\sqrt{2} - \sqrt{15}$ 4. $3\sqrt{3} - 3\sqrt{2}$

✓ **Concept Check Answer**

e

PRACTICE 5–8

Simplify each radical expression.

5. $\sqrt{27} + \sqrt{75}$

6. $3\sqrt{20} - 7\sqrt{45}$

7. $\sqrt{36} - \sqrt{48} - 4\sqrt{3} - \sqrt{9}$

8. $\sqrt{9x^4} - \sqrt{36x^3} + \sqrt{x^3}$

Examples Simplify each radical expression.

5. $\sqrt{50} + \sqrt{8} = \sqrt{25 \cdot 2} + \sqrt{4 \cdot 2}$ Factor radicands.

$= \sqrt{25} \cdot \sqrt{2} + \sqrt{4} \cdot \sqrt{2}$ Use the product rule.

$= 5\sqrt{2} + 2\sqrt{2}$ Simplify $\sqrt{25}$ and $\sqrt{4}$.

$= 7\sqrt{2}$ Add like radicals.

6. $7\sqrt{12} - 2\sqrt{75} = 7\sqrt{4 \cdot 3} - 2\sqrt{25 \cdot 3}$ Factor radicands.

$= 7\sqrt{4} \cdot \sqrt{3} - 2\sqrt{25} \cdot \sqrt{3}$ Use the product rule.

$= 7 \cdot 2\sqrt{3} - 2 \cdot 5\sqrt{3}$ Simplify $\sqrt{4}$ and $\sqrt{25}$.

$= 14\sqrt{3} - 10\sqrt{3}$ Multiply.

$= 4\sqrt{3}$ Subtract like radicals.

7. $\sqrt{25} - \sqrt{27} - 2\sqrt{18} - \sqrt{16}$

$= 5 - \sqrt{9 \cdot 3} - 2\sqrt{9 \cdot 2} - 4$ Factor radicands and simplify $\sqrt{25}$ and $\sqrt{16}$.

$= 5 - \sqrt{9} \cdot \sqrt{3} - 2\sqrt{9} \cdot \sqrt{2} - 4$ Use the product rule.

$= 5 - 3\sqrt{3} - 2 \cdot 3\sqrt{2} - 4$ Simplify $\sqrt{9}$.

$= 1 - 3\sqrt{3} - 6\sqrt{2}$ Write $5 - 4$ as 1 and $2 \cdot 3$ as 6.

8. $2\sqrt{x^2} - \sqrt{25x^5} + \sqrt{x^5}$

$= 2x - \sqrt{25x^4 \cdot x} + \sqrt{x^4 \cdot x}$ Factor radicands so that one factor is a perfect square. Simplify $\sqrt{x^2}$.

$= 2x - \sqrt{25x^4} \cdot \sqrt{x} + \sqrt{x^4} \cdot \sqrt{x}$ Use the product rule.

$= 2x - 5x^2\sqrt{x} + x^2\sqrt{x}$ Write $\sqrt{25x^4}$ as $5x^2$ and $\sqrt{x^4}$ as x^2.

$= 2x - 4x^2\sqrt{x}$ Add like radicals.

Work Practice 5–8

Objective C Simplifying Cube Root Radicals Before Adding or Subtracting

PRACTICE 9

Simplify the radical expression.

$10\sqrt[3]{81p^6} - \sqrt[3]{24p^6}$

Example 9 Simplify the radical expression.

$5\sqrt[3]{16x^3} - \sqrt[3]{54x^3}$

$= 5\sqrt[3]{8x^3 \cdot 2} - \sqrt[3]{27x^3 \cdot 2}$ Factor radicands so that one factor is a perfect cube.

$= 5 \cdot \sqrt[3]{8x^3} \cdot \sqrt[3]{2} - \sqrt[3]{27x^3} \cdot \sqrt[3]{2}$ Use the product rule.

$= 5 \cdot 2x \cdot \sqrt[3]{2} - 3x \cdot \sqrt[3]{2}$ Write $\sqrt[3]{8x^3}$ as $2x$ and $\sqrt[3]{27x^3}$ as $3x$.

$= 10x\sqrt[3]{2} - 3x\sqrt[3]{2}$ Write $5 \cdot 2x$ as $10x$.

$= 7x\sqrt[3]{2}$ Subtract like radicands.

Work Practice 9

Answers

5. $8\sqrt{3}$ **6.** $-15\sqrt{5}$ **7.** $3 - 8\sqrt{3}$ **8.** $3x^2 - 5x\sqrt{x}$ **9.** $28p^2\sqrt[3]{3}$

Vocabulary and Readiness Check

Fill in each blank.

1. Radicals that have the same index and same radicand are called ____________.

2. The expressions $7\sqrt[3]{2x}$ and $-\sqrt[3]{2x}$ are called ____________.

3. $11\sqrt{2} + 6\sqrt{2} =$ ____________
   a. $66\sqrt{2}$ **b.** $17\sqrt{2}$ **c.** $17\sqrt{4}$

4. $\sqrt{5}$ is the same as ____________.
   a. $0\sqrt{5}$ **b.** $1\sqrt{5}$ **c.** $5\sqrt{5}$

5. $\sqrt{5} + \sqrt{5} =$ ____________
   a. $\sqrt{10}$ **b.** 5 **c.** $2\sqrt{5}$

6. $9\sqrt{7} - \sqrt{7} =$ ____________
   a. $8\sqrt{7}$ **b.** 9 **c.** 0

8.3 Exercise Set

FOR EXTRA HELP

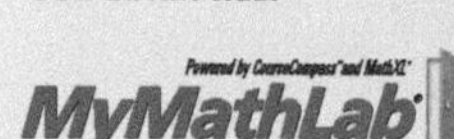

PRACTICE

WATCH

DOWNLOAD

READ

REVIEW

Objective A *Add or subtract as indicated. See Examples 1 through 4.*

1. $4\sqrt{3} - 8\sqrt{3}$

2. $\sqrt{5} - 9\sqrt{5}$

3. $3\sqrt{6} + 8\sqrt{6} - 2\sqrt{6} - 5$

4. $12\sqrt{2} - 3\sqrt{2} + 8\sqrt{2} + 10$

5. $6\sqrt{5} - 5\sqrt{5} + \sqrt{2}$

6. $4\sqrt{3} + \sqrt{5} - 3\sqrt{3}$

7. $2\sqrt{3} + 5\sqrt{3} - \sqrt{2}$

8. $8\sqrt{14} + 2\sqrt{14} + \sqrt{5}$

9. $2\sqrt{2} - 7\sqrt{2} - 6$

10. $5\sqrt{7} + 2 - 11\sqrt{7}$

Objective B *Add or subtract by first simplifying each radical and then combining any like radicals. Assume that all variables represent positive numbers. See Examples 5 through 8.*

11. $\sqrt{12} + \sqrt{27}$

12. $\sqrt{50} + \sqrt{18}$

13. $\sqrt{45} + 3\sqrt{20}$

14. $5\sqrt{32} - \sqrt{72}$

15. $2\sqrt{54} - \sqrt{20} + \sqrt{45} - \sqrt{24}$

16. $2\sqrt{8} - \sqrt{128} + \sqrt{48} + \sqrt{18}$

17. $4x - 3\sqrt{x^2} + \sqrt{x}$

18. $x - 6\sqrt{x^2} + 2\sqrt{x}$

19. $\sqrt{25x} + \sqrt{36x} - 11\sqrt{x}$

20. $\sqrt{9x} - \sqrt{16x} + 2\sqrt{x}$

21. $\sqrt{\frac{5}{9}} + \sqrt{\frac{5}{81}}$

22. $\sqrt{\frac{3}{64}} + \sqrt{\frac{3}{16}}$

23. $\sqrt{\frac{3}{4}} - \sqrt{\frac{3}{64}}$

24. $\sqrt{\frac{2}{25}} + \sqrt{\frac{2}{9}}$

Objectives A B Mixed Practice *See Examples 1 through 8.*

25. $12\sqrt{5} - \sqrt{5} - 4\sqrt{5}$

26. $\sqrt{6} + 3\sqrt{6} + \sqrt{6}$

27. $\sqrt{75} + \sqrt{48}$

28. $2\sqrt{80} - \sqrt{45}$

29. $\sqrt{5} + \sqrt{15}$

30. $\sqrt{5} + \sqrt{5}$

31. $3\sqrt{x^3} - x\sqrt{4x}$

32. $x\sqrt{16x} - \sqrt{x^3}$

33. $\sqrt{8} + \sqrt{9} + \sqrt{18} + \sqrt{81}$

34. $\sqrt{6} + \sqrt{16} + \sqrt{24} + \sqrt{25}$

35. $4 + 8\sqrt{2} - 9$

36. $11 - 5\sqrt{7} - 8$

37. $2\sqrt{45} - 2\sqrt{20}$

38. $5\sqrt{18} + 2\sqrt{32}$

39. $\sqrt{35} - \sqrt{140}$

40. $\sqrt{15} - \sqrt{135}$

41. $6 - 2\sqrt{3} - \sqrt{3}$

42. $8 - \sqrt{2} - 5\sqrt{2}$

43. $3\sqrt{9x} + 2\sqrt{x}$

44. $5\sqrt{2x} + \sqrt{98x}$

45. $\sqrt{9x^2} + \sqrt{81x^2} - 11\sqrt{x}$

46. $\sqrt{100x^2} + 3\sqrt{x} - \sqrt{36x^2}$

47. $\sqrt{3x^3} + 3x\sqrt{x}$

48. $x\sqrt{4x} + \sqrt{9x^3}$

49. $\sqrt{32x^2} + \sqrt{32x^2} + \sqrt{4x^2}$

50. $\sqrt{18x^2} + \sqrt{24x^3} + \sqrt{2x^2}$

51. $\sqrt{40x} + \sqrt{40x^4} - 2\sqrt{10x} - \sqrt{5x^4}$

52. $\sqrt{72x^2} + \sqrt{54x} - x\sqrt{50} - 3\sqrt{2x}$

Objective C *Simplify each radical expression. See Example 9.*

53. $2\sqrt[3]{9} + 5\sqrt[3]{9} - \sqrt[3]{25}$

54. $8\sqrt[3]{4} + 2\sqrt[3]{4} - \sqrt[3]{49}$

55. $2\sqrt[3]{2} - 7\sqrt[3]{2} - 6$

56. $5\sqrt[3]{9} + 2 - 11\sqrt[3]{9}$

57. $\sqrt[3]{81} + \sqrt[3]{24}$

58. $\sqrt[3]{32} + \sqrt[3]{4}$

59. $\sqrt[3]{8} + \sqrt[3]{54} - 5$

60. $\sqrt[3]{64} + \sqrt[3]{14} - 9$

61. $2\sqrt[3]{8x^3} + 2\sqrt[3]{16x^3}$

62. $3\sqrt[3]{27z^3} + 3\sqrt[3]{81z^3}$

63. $12\sqrt[3]{y^7} - y^2\sqrt[3]{8y}$

64. $19\sqrt[3]{z^{11}} - z^3\sqrt[3]{125z^2}$

65. $\sqrt{40x} + x\sqrt[3]{40} - 2\sqrt{10x} - x\sqrt[3]{5}$

66. $\sqrt{72x^2} + \sqrt[3]{54} - x\sqrt{50} - 3\sqrt[3]{2}$

Review

Square each binomial. See Section 3.6.

67. $(x + 6)^2$

68. $(3x + 2)^2$

69. $(2x - 1)^2$

70. $(x - 5)^2$

Concept Extensions

71. In your own words, describe like radicals.

72. In the expression $\sqrt{5} + 2 - 3\sqrt{5}$, explain why 2 and -3 cannot be combined.

73. Find the perimeter of the rectangular picture frame.

74. Find the perimeter of the plot of land.

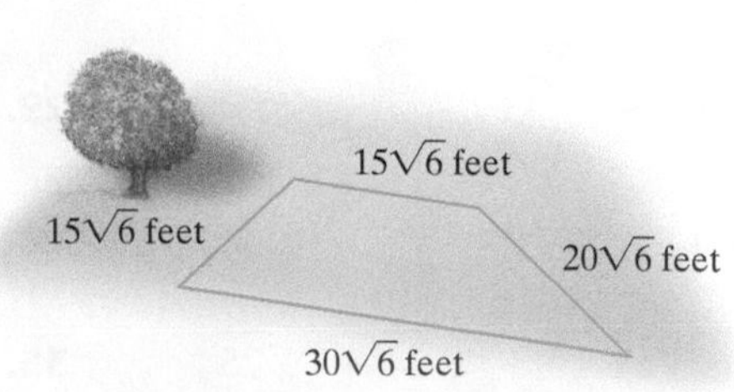

△ **75.** A water trough is to be made of wood. Each of the two triangular end pieces has an area of $\frac{3\sqrt{27}}{4}$ square feet. The two side panels are both rectangular. In simplest radical form, find the total area of the wood needed.

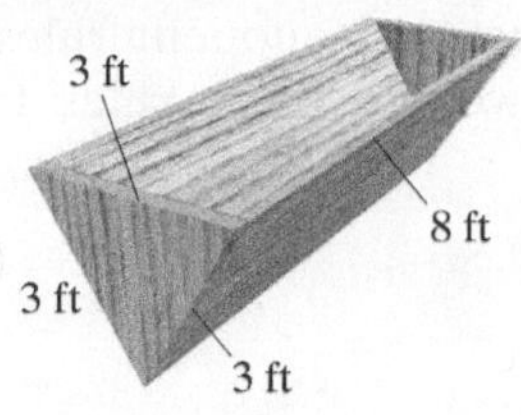

76. Eight wooden braces are to be attached along the diagonals of the vertical sides of a storage bin. Each of four of these diagonals has a length of $\sqrt{52}$ feet, while each of the other four has a length of $\sqrt{80}$ feet. In simplest radical form, find the total length of the wood needed for these braces.

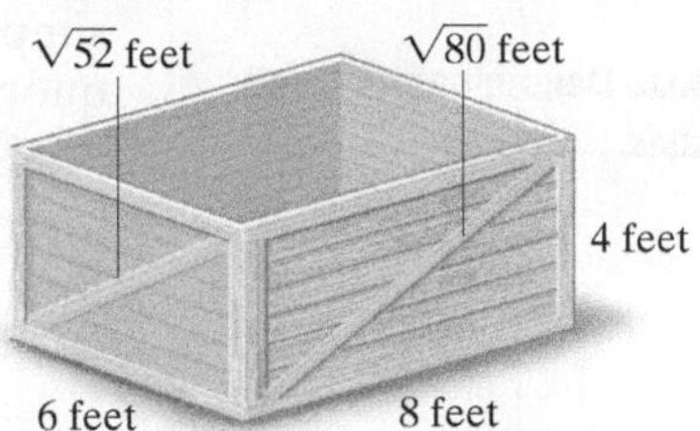

Determine whether each expression can be simplified. If yes, then simplify. See the Concept Check in this section.

77. $4\sqrt{2} + 3\sqrt{2}$

78. $3\sqrt{7} + 3\sqrt{6}$

79. $6 + 7\sqrt{6}$

80. $5x\sqrt{2} + 8x\sqrt{2}$

81. $\sqrt{7} + \sqrt{7} + \sqrt{7}$

82. $6\sqrt{5} - \sqrt{5}$

Simplify.

83. $\sqrt{\frac{x^3}{16}} - x\sqrt{\frac{9x}{25}} + \frac{\sqrt{81x^3}}{2}$

84. $7\sqrt{x^{11}y^7} - x^2y\sqrt{25x^7y^5} + \sqrt{8x^8y^2}$

Objectives

A Multiply Radicals.

B Divide Radicals.

C Rationalize Denominators.

D Rationalize Denominators Using Conjugates.

8.4 MULTIPLYING AND DIVIDING RADICALS

Objective A Multiplying Radicals

In Section 8.2, we used the product and quotient rules for radicals to help us simplify radicals. In this section, we use these rules to simplify products and quotients of radicals.

Product Rule for Radicals

If $\sqrt{a}$ and $\sqrt{b}$ are real numbers, then

$$\sqrt{a}\cdot\sqrt{b} = \sqrt{a\cdot b}$$

In other words, the product of the square roots of two numbers is the square root of the product of the two numbers. For example,

$$\sqrt{3}\cdot\sqrt{2} = \sqrt{3\cdot 2} = \sqrt{6}$$

Examples Multiply. Then simplify each product if possible.

1. $\sqrt{7}\cdot\sqrt{3} = \sqrt{7\cdot 3}$
$= \sqrt{21}$

2. $\sqrt{3}\cdot\sqrt{3} = \sqrt{3\cdot 3} = \sqrt{9} = 3$

3. $\sqrt{3}\cdot\sqrt{15} = \sqrt{45}$ — Use the product rule.
$= \sqrt{9\cdot 5}$ — Factor the radicand.
$= \sqrt{9}\cdot\sqrt{5}$ — Use the product rule.
$= 3\sqrt{5}$ — Simplify $\sqrt{9}$.

4. $\sqrt{2x^3}\cdot\sqrt{6x} = \sqrt{2x^3\cdot 6x}$ — Use the product rule.
$= \sqrt{12x^4}$ — Multiply.
$= \sqrt{4x^4\cdot 3}$ — Write $12x^4$ so that one factor is a perfect square.
$= \sqrt{4x^4}\cdot\sqrt{3}$ — Use the product rule.
$= 2x^2\sqrt{3}$ — Simplify.

Work Practice 1–4

PRACTICE 1–4

Multiply. Then simplify each product if possible.

1. $\sqrt{5}\cdot\sqrt{2}$
2. $\sqrt{7}\cdot\sqrt{7}$
3. $\sqrt{6}\cdot\sqrt{3}$
4. $\sqrt{10x}\cdot\sqrt{2x}$

From Example 2, we found that

$$\sqrt{3}\cdot\sqrt{3} = 3 \quad\text{or}\quad \left(\sqrt{3}\right)^2 = 3$$

This is true in general.

If a is a positive number,

$$\sqrt{a}\cdot\sqrt{a} = a \quad\text{or}\quad (\sqrt{a})^2 = a$$

✓Concept Check Identify the true statement(s).

a. $\sqrt{7}\cdot\sqrt{7} = 7$
b. $\sqrt{2}\cdot\sqrt{3} = 6$
c. $\left(\sqrt{131}\right)^2 = 131$
d. $\sqrt{5x}\cdot\sqrt{5x} = 5x$ (Here x is a positive number.)

When multiplying radical expressions containing more than one term, we use the same techniques we use to multiply other algebraic expressions with more than one term.

Answers
1. $\sqrt{10}$ 2. 7 3. $3\sqrt{2}$ 4. $2x\sqrt{5}$

✓ Concept Check Answers
a, c, d

Example 5 Multiply.

a. $\sqrt{5}(\sqrt{5}-\sqrt{2})$ b. $\sqrt{3x}(\sqrt{x}-5\sqrt{3})$

c. $(\sqrt{x}+\sqrt{2})(\sqrt{x}-\sqrt{7})$

Solution:

a. Using the distributive property, we have

$$\sqrt{5}(\sqrt{5}-\sqrt{2}) = \sqrt{5}\cdot\sqrt{5}-\sqrt{5}\cdot\sqrt{2}$$

$$= 5-\sqrt{10} \quad \text{Since } \sqrt{5}\cdot\sqrt{5}=5 \text{ and } \sqrt{5}\cdot\sqrt{2}=\sqrt{10}$$

b. $\sqrt{3x}(\sqrt{x}-5\sqrt{3}) = \sqrt{3x}\cdot\sqrt{x}-\sqrt{3x}\cdot 5\sqrt{3}$ Use the distributive property.

$= \sqrt{3x\cdot x}-5\sqrt{3x\cdot 3}$ Use the product rule.

$= \sqrt{3\cdot x^2}-5\sqrt{9\cdot x}$ Factor each radicand so that one factor is a perfect square.

$= \sqrt{3}\cdot\sqrt{x^2}-5\cdot\sqrt{9}\cdot\sqrt{x}$ Use the product rule.

$= x\sqrt{3}-5\cdot 3\cdot\sqrt{x}$ Simplify.

$= x\sqrt{3}-15\sqrt{x}$ Simplify.

c. Using the FOIL method of multiplication, we have

$$(\sqrt{x}+\sqrt{2})(\sqrt{x}-\sqrt{7})$$

$$\overset{F}{=\sqrt{x}\cdot\sqrt{x}} - \overset{O}{\sqrt{x}\cdot\sqrt{7}} + \overset{I}{\sqrt{2}\cdot\sqrt{x}} - \overset{L}{\sqrt{2}\cdot\sqrt{7}}$$

$$= x-\sqrt{7x}+\sqrt{2x}-\sqrt{14} \quad \text{Use the product rule.}$$

Work Practice 5

PRACTICE 5

Multiply.

a. $\sqrt{7}(\sqrt{7}-\sqrt{3})$

b. $\sqrt{5x}(\sqrt{x}-3\sqrt{5})$

c. $(\sqrt{x}+\sqrt{5})(\sqrt{x}-\sqrt{3})$

The special product formulas also can be used to multiply expressions containing radicals.

Example 6 Multiply.

a. $(\sqrt{5}-7)(\sqrt{5}+7)$ b. $(\sqrt{7x}+2)^2$

Solution:

a. $(\sqrt{5}-7)(\sqrt{5}+7) = (\sqrt{5})^2-7^2$ Recall that $(a-b)(a+b)=a^2-b^2$.

$= 5-49$

$= -44$

b. $(\sqrt{7x}+2)^2$

$= (\sqrt{7x})^2+2(\sqrt{7x})(2)+(2)^2$ Recall that $(a+b)^2=a^2+2ab+b^2$.

$= 7x+4\sqrt{7x}+4$

Work Practice 6

PRACTICE 6

Multiply.

a. $(\sqrt{3}+8)(\sqrt{3}-8)$

b. $(\sqrt{5x}+4)^2$

Objective B Dividing Radicals

To simplify quotients of rational expressions, we use the quotient rule.

Quotient Rule for Radicals

If $\sqrt{a}$ and $\sqrt{b}$ are real numbers and $b \neq 0$, then

$$\frac{\sqrt{a}}{\sqrt{b}} = \sqrt{\frac{a}{b}}$$

Answers

5. a. $7-\sqrt{21}$ b. $x\sqrt{5}-15\sqrt{x}$ c. $x-\sqrt{3x}+\sqrt{5x}-\sqrt{15}$

6. a. -61 b. $5x+8\sqrt{5x}+16$

PRACTICE 7–9

Divide. Then simplify the quotient if possible.

7. $\dfrac{\sqrt{15}}{\sqrt{3}}$

8. $\dfrac{\sqrt{90}}{\sqrt{2}}$

9. $\dfrac{\sqrt{125x^3}}{\sqrt{5x}}$

Examples Divide. Then simplify the quotient if possible.

7. $\dfrac{\sqrt{14}}{\sqrt{2}} = \sqrt{\dfrac{14}{2}} = \sqrt{7}$

8. $\dfrac{\sqrt{100}}{\sqrt{5}} = \sqrt{\dfrac{100}{5}} = \sqrt{20} = \sqrt{4 \cdot 5} = \sqrt{4} \cdot \sqrt{5} = 2\sqrt{5}$

9. $\dfrac{\sqrt{12x^3}}{\sqrt{3x}} = \sqrt{\dfrac{12x^3}{3x}} = \sqrt{4x^2} = 2x$

Work Practice 7–9

Objective C Rationalizing Denominators

It is sometimes easier to work with radical expressions if the denominator does not contain a radical. To rewrite an expression so that the denominator does not contain a radical expression, we use the fact that we can multiply the numerator and the denominator of a fraction by the same nonzero number without changing the value of the expression. This is the same as multiplying the fraction by 1. For example, to get rid of the radical in the denominator of $\dfrac{\sqrt{5}}{\sqrt{2}}$, we multiply by 1 in the form of $\dfrac{\sqrt{2}}{\sqrt{2}}$. Then

$$\frac{\sqrt{5}}{\sqrt{2}} = \frac{\sqrt{5}}{\sqrt{2}} \cdot 1 = \frac{\sqrt{5}}{\sqrt{2}} \cdot \frac{\sqrt{2}}{\sqrt{2}} = \frac{\sqrt{5} \cdot \sqrt{2}}{\sqrt{2} \cdot \sqrt{2}} = \frac{\sqrt{10}}{2}$$

This process is called **rationalizing** the denominator.

PRACTICE 10

Rationalize the denominator of $\dfrac{5}{\sqrt{3}}$.

Example 10 Rationalize the denominator of $\dfrac{2}{\sqrt{7}}$.

Solution: To rewrite $\dfrac{2}{\sqrt{7}}$ so that there is no radical in the denominator, we multiply by 1 in the form of $\dfrac{\sqrt{7}}{\sqrt{7}}$.

$$\frac{2}{\sqrt{7}} = \frac{2}{\sqrt{7}} \cdot \frac{\sqrt{7}}{\sqrt{7}} = \frac{2 \cdot \sqrt{7}}{\sqrt{7} \cdot \sqrt{7}} = \frac{2\sqrt{7}}{7}$$

Work Practice 10

PRACTICE 11

Rationalize the denominator of $\dfrac{\sqrt{7}}{\sqrt{20}}$.

Example 11 Rationalize the denominator of $\dfrac{\sqrt{5}}{\sqrt{12}}$.

Solution: We can multiply by $\dfrac{\sqrt{12}}{\sqrt{12}}$, but see what happens if we simplify first.

$$\frac{\sqrt{5}}{\sqrt{12}} = \frac{\sqrt{5}}{\sqrt{4 \cdot 3}} = \frac{\sqrt{5}}{2\sqrt{3}}$$

To rationalize the denominator now, we multiply by $\dfrac{\sqrt{3}}{\sqrt{3}}$.

$$\frac{\sqrt{5}}{2\sqrt{3}} = \frac{\sqrt{5}}{2\sqrt{3}} \cdot \frac{\sqrt{3}}{\sqrt{3}} = \frac{\sqrt{5} \cdot \sqrt{3}}{2\sqrt{3} \cdot \sqrt{3}} = \frac{\sqrt{15}}{2 \cdot 3} = \frac{\sqrt{15}}{6}$$

Work Practice 11

Answers

7. $\sqrt{5}$ 8. $3\sqrt{5}$ 9. $5x$ 10. $\dfrac{5\sqrt{3}}{3}$ 11. $\dfrac{\sqrt{35}}{10}$

Example 12 Rationalize the denominator of $\sqrt{\frac{1}{18x}}$.

Solution: First we simplify.

$$\sqrt{\frac{1}{18x}} = \frac{\sqrt{1}}{\sqrt{18x}} = \frac{1}{\sqrt{9}\cdot\sqrt{2x}} = \frac{1}{3\sqrt{2x}}$$

Now to rationalize the denominator, we multiply by $\frac{\sqrt{2x}}{\sqrt{2x}}$.

$$\frac{1}{3\sqrt{2x}} = \frac{1}{3\sqrt{2x}}\cdot\frac{\sqrt{2x}}{\sqrt{2x}} = \frac{1\cdot\sqrt{2x}}{3\sqrt{2x}\cdot\sqrt{2x}} = \frac{\sqrt{2x}}{3\cdot 2x} = \frac{\sqrt{2x}}{6x}$$

Work Practice 12

PRACTICE 12

Rationalize the denominator of $\sqrt{\frac{2}{45x}}$.

Objective D Rationalizing Denominators Using Conjugates

To rationalize a denominator that is a sum or a difference, such as the denominator in

$$\frac{2}{4+\sqrt{3}}$$

we multiply the numerator and the denominator by $4-\sqrt{3}$. The expressions $4+\sqrt{3}$ and $4-\sqrt{3}$ are called conjugates of each other. When a radical expression such as $4+\sqrt{3}$ is multiplied by its conjugate, $4-\sqrt{3}$, the product simplifies to an expression that contains no radicals.

In general, the expressions $a+b$ and $a-b$ are **conjugates** of each other.

$$(a+b)(a-b) = a^2 - b^2$$

$$(4+\sqrt{3})(4-\sqrt{3}) = 4^2 - (\sqrt{3})^2 = 16 - 3 = 13$$

Then

$$\frac{2}{4+\sqrt{3}} = \frac{2(4-\sqrt{3})}{(4+\sqrt{3})(4-\sqrt{3})} = \frac{2(4-\sqrt{3})}{13}$$

Example 13 Rationalize the denominator of $\frac{2}{1+\sqrt{3}}$.

Solution: We multiply the numerator and the denominator of this fraction by the conjugate of $1+\sqrt{3}$, that is, by $1-\sqrt{3}$.

$$\frac{2}{1+\sqrt{3}} = \frac{2(1-\sqrt{3})}{(1+\sqrt{3})(1-\sqrt{3})}$$

$$= \frac{2(1-\sqrt{3})}{1^2-(\sqrt{3})^2}$$

$$= \frac{2(1-\sqrt{3})}{1-3}$$

$$= \frac{2(1-\sqrt{3})}{-2}$$

$$= -\frac{2(1-\sqrt{3})}{2} \quad \frac{a}{-b} = -\frac{a}{b}$$

$$= -1(1-\sqrt{3}) \quad \text{Simplify.}$$

$$= -1+\sqrt{3} \quad \text{Multiply.}$$

Helpful Hint
Don't forget that $(\sqrt{3})^2 = 3$.

Work Practice 13

PRACTICE 13

Rationalize the denominator of $\frac{3}{2+\sqrt{7}}$.

Answers
12. $\frac{\sqrt{10x}}{15x}$ 13. $-2+\sqrt{7}$

PRACTICE 14

Rationalize the denominator of $\frac{\sqrt{2}+5}{\sqrt{2}-1}$.

PRACTICE 15

Rationalize the denominator of $\frac{7}{2-\sqrt{x}}$.

Answers

14. $7+6\sqrt{2}$ **15.** $\frac{7(2+\sqrt{x})}{4-x}$

Example 14 Rationalize the denominator of $\frac{\sqrt{5}+4}{\sqrt{5}-1}$.

Solution:

$$\frac{\sqrt{5}+4}{\sqrt{5}-1} = \frac{(\sqrt{5}+4)(\sqrt{5}+1)}{(\sqrt{5}-1)(\sqrt{5}+1)}$$ Multiply the numerator and denominator by $\sqrt{5}+1$, the conjugate of $\sqrt{5}-1$.

$$= \frac{5+\sqrt{5}+4\sqrt{5}+4}{5-1}$$ Multiply.

$$= \frac{9+5\sqrt{5}}{4}$$ Simplify.

Work Practice 14

Example 15 Rationalize the denominator of $\frac{3}{1+\sqrt{x}}$.

Solution:

$$\frac{3}{1+\sqrt{x}} = \frac{3(1-\sqrt{x})}{(1+\sqrt{x})(1-\sqrt{x})}$$ Multiply the numerator and denominator by $1-\sqrt{x}$, the conjugate of $1+\sqrt{x}$.

$$= \frac{3(1-\sqrt{x})}{1-x}$$

Work Practice 15

Vocabulary and Readiness Check

Fill in each blank.

1. $\sqrt{7} \cdot \sqrt{3} =$ ______
2. $\sqrt{10} \cdot \sqrt{10} =$ ______
3. $\dfrac{\sqrt{15}}{\sqrt{3}} =$ ______
4. The process of eliminating the radical in the denominator of a radical expression is called ______.
5. The conjugate of $2 + \sqrt{3}$ is ______.

8.4 Exercise Set

FOR EXTRA HELP

Objective A *Multiply and simplify. Assume that all variables represent positive real numbers. See Examples 1 through 6.*

1. $\sqrt{8} \cdot \sqrt{2}$
2. $\sqrt{3} \cdot \sqrt{12}$
3. $\sqrt{10} \cdot \sqrt{5}$
4. $\sqrt{2} \cdot \sqrt{14}$

5. $(\sqrt{6})^2$
6. $(\sqrt{10})^2$
7. $\sqrt{2x} \cdot \sqrt{2x}$
8. $\sqrt{5y} \cdot \sqrt{5y}$

9. $(2\sqrt{5})^2$
10. $(3\sqrt{10})^2$
11. $(6\sqrt{x})^2$
12. $(8\sqrt{y})^2$

13. $\sqrt{3x^5} \cdot \sqrt{6x}$
14. $\sqrt{21y^7} \cdot \sqrt{3y}$
15. $\sqrt{2xy^2} \cdot \sqrt{8xy}$
16. $\sqrt{18x^2y^2} \cdot \sqrt{2x^2y}$

17. $\sqrt{6}(\sqrt{5} + \sqrt{7})$
18. $\sqrt{10}(\sqrt{3} - \sqrt{7})$
19. $\sqrt{10}(\sqrt{2} + \sqrt{5})$

20. $\sqrt{6}(\sqrt{3} + \sqrt{2})$
21. $\sqrt{7y}(\sqrt{y} - 2\sqrt{7})$
22. $\sqrt{5b}(2\sqrt{b} + \sqrt{5})$

23. $(\sqrt{3} + 6)(\sqrt{3} - 6)$
24. $(\sqrt{5} + 2)(\sqrt{5} - 2)$
25. $(\sqrt{3} + \sqrt{5})(\sqrt{2} - \sqrt{5})$

26. $(\sqrt{7} + \sqrt{5})(\sqrt{2} - \sqrt{5})$
27. $(2\sqrt{11} + 1)(\sqrt{11} - 6)$
28. $(5\sqrt{3} + 2)(\sqrt{3} - 1)$

29. $(\sqrt{x} + 6)(\sqrt{x} - 6)$
30. $(\sqrt{y} + 5)(\sqrt{y} - 5)$
31. $(\sqrt{x} - 7)^2$

32. $(\sqrt{x} + 4)^2$
33. $(\sqrt{6y} + 1)^2$
34. $(\sqrt{3y} - 2)^2$

Objective B *Divide and simplify. Assume that all variables represent positive real numbers. See Examples 7 through 9.*

35. $\dfrac{\sqrt{32}}{\sqrt{2}}$
36. $\dfrac{\sqrt{40}}{\sqrt{10}}$
37. $\dfrac{\sqrt{21}}{\sqrt{3}}$
38. $\dfrac{\sqrt{55}}{\sqrt{5}}$
39. $\dfrac{\sqrt{90}}{\sqrt{5}}$

40. $\dfrac{\sqrt{96}}{\sqrt{8}}$
41. $\dfrac{\sqrt{75y^5}}{\sqrt{3y}}$
42. $\dfrac{\sqrt{24x^7}}{\sqrt{6x}}$
43. $\dfrac{\sqrt{150}}{\sqrt{2}}$
44. $\dfrac{\sqrt{120}}{\sqrt{3}}$

45. $\dfrac{\sqrt{72y^5}}{\sqrt{3y^3}}$
46. $\dfrac{\sqrt{54x^3}}{\sqrt{2x}}$
47. $\dfrac{\sqrt{24x^3y^4}}{\sqrt{2xy}}$
48. $\dfrac{\sqrt{96x^5y^3}}{\sqrt{3x^2y}}$

Objective C *Rationalize each denominator and simplify. Assume that all variables represent positive real numbers. See Examples 10 through 12.*

49. $\frac{\sqrt{3}}{\sqrt{5}}$

50. $\frac{\sqrt{2}}{\sqrt{3}}$

51. $\frac{7}{\sqrt{2}}$

52. $\frac{8}{\sqrt{11}}$

53. $\frac{1}{\sqrt{6y}}$

54. $\frac{1}{\sqrt{10z}}$

55. $\sqrt{\frac{5}{18}}$

56. $\sqrt{\frac{7}{12}}$

57. $\sqrt{\frac{3}{x}}$

58. $\sqrt{\frac{5}{x}}$

59. $\sqrt{\frac{1}{8}}$

60. $\sqrt{\frac{1}{27}}$

61. $\sqrt{\frac{2}{15}}$

62. $\sqrt{\frac{11}{14}}$

63. $\sqrt{\frac{3}{20}}$

64. $\sqrt{\frac{3}{50}}$

65. $\frac{3x}{\sqrt{2x}}$

66. $\frac{5y}{\sqrt{3y}}$

67. $\frac{8y}{\sqrt{5}}$

68. $\frac{7x}{\sqrt{2}}$

69. $\sqrt{\frac{x}{36y}}$

70. $\sqrt{\frac{z}{49y}}$

71. $\sqrt{\frac{y}{12x}}$

72. $\sqrt{\frac{x}{20y}}$

Objective D *Rationalize each denominator and simplify. Assume that all variables represent positive real numbers. See Examples 13 through 15.*

73. $\frac{3}{\sqrt{2}+1}$

74. $\frac{6}{\sqrt{5}+2}$

75. $\frac{4}{2-\sqrt{5}}$

76. $\frac{2}{\sqrt{10}-3}$

77. $\frac{\sqrt{5}+1}{\sqrt{6}-\sqrt{5}}$

78. $\frac{\sqrt{3}+1}{\sqrt{3}-\sqrt{2}}$

79. $\frac{\sqrt{3}+1}{\sqrt{2}-1}$

80. $\frac{\sqrt{2}-2}{2-\sqrt{3}}$

81. $\frac{5}{2+\sqrt{x}}$

82. $\frac{9}{3+\sqrt{x}}$

83. $\frac{3}{\sqrt{x}-4}$

84. $\frac{4}{\sqrt{x}-1}$

Review

Solve each equation. See Sections 2.3 and 4.6.

85. $x + 5 = 7^2$

86. $2y - 1 = 3^2$

87. $4z^2 + 6z - 12 = (2z)^2$

88. $16x^2 + x + 9 = (4x)^2$

89. $9x^2 + 5x + 4 = (3x + 1)^2$

90. $x^2 + 3x + 4 = (x + 2)^2$

Concept Extensions

△ **91.** Find the area of a rectangular room whose length is $13\sqrt{2}$ meters and width is $5\sqrt{6}$ meters.

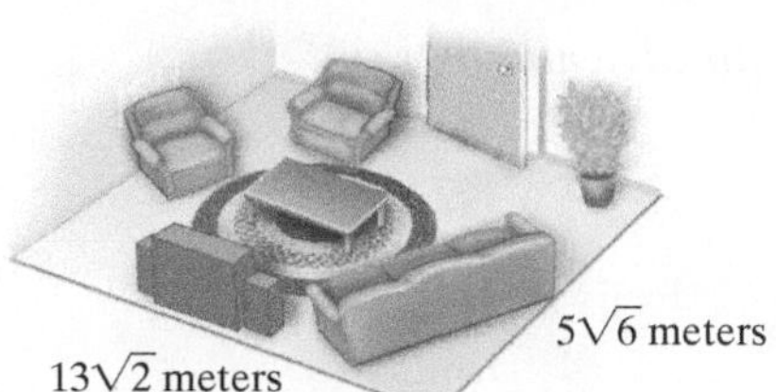

△ **92.** Find the volume of a microwave oven whose length is $\sqrt{3}$ feet, width is $\sqrt{2}$ feet, and height is $\sqrt{2}$ feet.

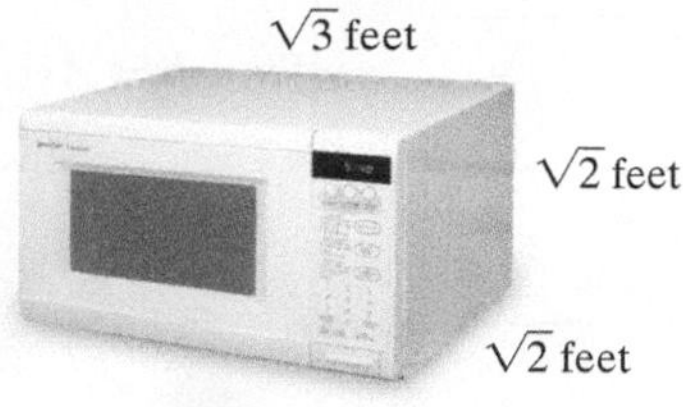

△ **93.** If a circle has area A, then the formula for the radius r of the circle is

$$r = \sqrt{\frac{A}{\pi}}$$

Rationalize the denominator of this expression.

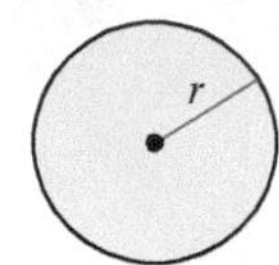

△ **94.** If a round ball has volume V, then the formula for the radius r of the ball is

$$r = \sqrt[3]{\frac{3V}{4\pi}}$$

Simplify this expression by rationalizing the denominator.

Identify each statement as true or false. See the Concept Check in this section.

95. $\sqrt{5} \cdot \sqrt{5} = 5$

96. $\sqrt{5} \cdot \sqrt{3} = 15$

97. $\sqrt{3x} \cdot \sqrt{3x} = 2\sqrt{3x}$

98. $\sqrt{3x} + \sqrt{3x} = 2\sqrt{3x}$

99. $\sqrt{11} + \sqrt{2} = \sqrt{13}$

100. $\sqrt{11} \cdot \sqrt{2} = \sqrt{22}$

101. When rationalizing the denominator of $\frac{\sqrt{2}}{\sqrt{3}}$, explain why both the numerator and the denominator must be multiplied by $\sqrt{3}$.

102. In your own words, explain why $\sqrt{6} + \sqrt{2}$ cannot be simplified further, but $\sqrt{6} \cdot \sqrt{2}$ can be.

103. When rationalizing the denominator of $\frac{\sqrt[3]{2}}{\sqrt[3]{3}}$, explain why both the numerator and the denominator must be multiplied by $\sqrt[3]{9}$.

104. When rationalizing the denominator of $\frac{5}{1 + \sqrt{2}}$, explain why multiplying by $\frac{\sqrt{2}}{\sqrt{2}}$ will not accomplish this, but multiplying by $\frac{1 - \sqrt{2}}{1 - \sqrt{2}}$ will.

It is often more convenient to work with a radical expression whose numerator is rationalized. Rationalize the numerator of each expression by multiplying the numerator and denominator by the conjugate of the numerator.

105. $\frac{\sqrt{3} + 1}{\sqrt{2} - 1}$

106. $\frac{\sqrt{2} - 2}{2 - \sqrt{3}}$

Answers

1. ______
2. ______
3. ______
4. ______
5. ______
6. ______
7. ______
8. ______
9. ______
10. ______
11. ______
12. ______
13. ______
14. ______
15. ______
16. ______
17. ______
18. ______
19. ______
20. ______
21. ______
22. ______

Integrated Review Sections 8.1–8.4

Simplifying Radicals

Simplify. Assume that all variables represent positive numbers.

1. $\sqrt{36}$

2. $\sqrt{48}$

3. $\sqrt{x^4}$

4. $\sqrt{y^7}$

5. $\sqrt{16x^2}$

6. $\sqrt{18x^{11}}$

7. $\sqrt[3]{8}$

8. $\sqrt[4]{81}$

9. $\sqrt[3]{-27}$

10. $\sqrt{-4}$

11. $\sqrt{\frac{11}{9}}$

12. $\sqrt[3]{\frac{7}{64}}$

13. $-\sqrt{16}$

14. $-\sqrt{25}$

15. $\sqrt{\frac{9}{49}}$

16. $\sqrt{\frac{1}{64}}$

17. $\sqrt{a^8b^2}$

18. $\sqrt{x^{10}y^{20}}$

19. $\sqrt{25m^6}$

20. $\sqrt{9n^{16}}$

Add or subtract as indicated.

21. $5\sqrt{7} + \sqrt{7}$

22. $\sqrt{50} - \sqrt{8}$

23. $5\sqrt{2} - 5\sqrt{3}$

24. $2\sqrt{x} + \sqrt{25x} - \sqrt{36x} + 3x$

Multiply and simplify if possible.

25. $\sqrt{2} \cdot \sqrt{15}$

26. $\sqrt{3} \cdot \sqrt{3}$

27. $(2\sqrt{7})^2$

28. $(3\sqrt{5})^2$

29. $\sqrt{3}(\sqrt{11} + 1)$

30. $\sqrt{6}(\sqrt{3} - 2)$

31. $\sqrt{8y} \cdot \sqrt{2y}$

32. $\sqrt{15x^2} \cdot \sqrt{3x^2}$

33. $(\sqrt{x} - 5)(\sqrt{x} + 2)$

34. $(3 + \sqrt{2})^2$

Divide and simplify if possible.

35. $\dfrac{\sqrt{8}}{\sqrt{2}}$

36. $\dfrac{\sqrt{45}}{\sqrt{15}}$

37. $\dfrac{\sqrt{24x^5}}{\sqrt{2x}}$

38. $\dfrac{\sqrt{75a^4b^5}}{\sqrt{5ab}}$

Rationalize each denominator.

39. $\sqrt{\dfrac{1}{6}}$

40. $\dfrac{x}{\sqrt{20}}$

41. $\dfrac{4}{\sqrt{6} + 1}$

42. $\dfrac{\sqrt{2} + 1}{\sqrt{x} - 5}$

23. ______

24. ______

25. ______

26. ______

27. ______

28. ______

29. ______

30. ______

31. ______

32. ______

33. ______

34. ______

35. ______

36. ______

37. ______

38. ______

39. ______

40. ______

41. ______

42. ______

Objectives

A **Solve Radical Equations by Using the Squaring Property of Equality Once.**

B **Solve Radical Equations by Using the Squaring Property of Equality Twice.**

8.5 SOLVING EQUATIONS CONTAINING RADICALS

Objective A Using the Squaring Property of Equality Once

In this section, we solve **radical equations** such as

$$\sqrt{x+3} = 5 \quad \text{and} \quad \sqrt{2x+1} = \sqrt{3x}$$

Radical equations contain variables in the radicand. To solve these equations, we rely on the following squaring property.

> ***The Squaring Property of Equality***
>
> If $a = b$, then $a^2 = b^2$.

Unfortunately, this squaring property does not guarantee that all solutions of the new equation are solutions of the original equation. For example, if we square both sides of the equation

$$x = 2$$

we have

$$x^2 = 4$$

This new equation has two solutions, 2 and -2, while the original equation, $x = 2$, has only one solution. For this reason, we must **always check proposed solutions of radical equations in the original equation.**

PRACTICE 1

Solve: $\sqrt{x-2} = 7$

Example 1 Solve: $\sqrt{x+3} = 5$

Solution: To solve this radical equation, we use the squaring property of equality and square both sides of the equation.

$$\begin{aligned} \sqrt{x+3} &= 5 \\ \left(\sqrt{x+3}\right)^2 &= 5^2 && \text{Square both sides.} \\ x + 3 &= 25 && \text{Simplify.} \\ x &= 22 && \text{Subtract 3 from both sides.} \end{aligned}$$

Check: We replace x with 22 in the original equation.

$$\begin{aligned} \sqrt{x+3} &= 5 && \text{Original equation} \\ \sqrt{22+3} &\stackrel{?}{=} 5 && \text{Let } x = 22. \\ \sqrt{25} &\stackrel{?}{=} 5 \\ 5 &= 5 && \text{True} \end{aligned}$$

Since a true statement results, 22 is the solution.

Work Practice 1

Helpful Hint Don't forget to check the proposed solutions of radical equations in the original equation.

When solving radical equations, if possible, move radicals so that at least one radical is by itself on one side of the equation.

Answer

1. $x = 51$

Example 2 Solve: $\sqrt{x} = \sqrt{5x - 2}$

Solution: Each radical is by itself on one side of the equation. Let's begin solving by squaring both sides.

$$\sqrt{x} = \sqrt{5x - 2} \quad \text{Original equation}$$
$$(\sqrt{x})^2 = \left(\sqrt{5x - 2}\right)^2 \quad \text{Square both sides.}$$
$$x = 5x - 2 \quad \text{Simplify.}$$
$$-4x = -2 \quad \text{Subtract } 5x \text{ from both sides.}$$
$$x = \frac{-2}{-4} = \frac{1}{2} \quad \text{Divide both sides by } -4 \text{ and simplify.}$$

Check: We replace x with $\frac{1}{2}$ in the original equation.

$$\sqrt{x} = \sqrt{5x - 2} \quad \text{Original equation}$$
$$\sqrt{\frac{1}{2}} \stackrel{?}{=} \sqrt{5 \cdot \frac{1}{2} - 2} \quad \text{Let } x = \frac{1}{2}.$$
$$\sqrt{\frac{1}{2}} \stackrel{?}{=} \sqrt{\frac{5}{2} - 2} \quad \text{Multiply.}$$
$$\sqrt{\frac{1}{2}} \stackrel{?}{=} \sqrt{\frac{5}{2} - \frac{4}{2}} \quad \text{Write 2 as } \frac{4}{2}.$$
$$\sqrt{\frac{1}{2}} = \sqrt{\frac{1}{2}} \quad \text{True}$$

This statement is true, so the solution is $\frac{1}{2}$.

Work Practice 2

PRACTICE 2

Solve: $\sqrt{6x - 1} = \sqrt{x}$

Example 3 Solve: $\sqrt{x} + 6 = 4$

Solution: First we write the equation so that the radical is by itself on one side of the equation.

$$\sqrt{x} + 6 = 4$$
$$\sqrt{x} = -2 \quad \text{Subtract 6 from both sides to get the radical by itself.}$$

Normally we would now square both sides. Recall, however, that $\sqrt{x}$ is the principal or nonnegative square root of x so that $\sqrt{x}$ cannot equal -2 and thus this equation has no solution. We arrive at the same conclusion if we continue by applying the squaring property.

$$\sqrt{x} = -2$$
$$(\sqrt{x})^2 = (-2)^2 \quad \text{Square both sides.}$$
$$x = 4 \quad \text{Simplify.}$$

Check: We replace x with 4 in the original equation.

$$\sqrt{x} + 6 = 4 \quad \text{Original equation}$$
$$\sqrt{4} + 6 \stackrel{?}{=} 4 \quad \text{Let } x = 4.$$
$$2 + 6 = 4 \quad \text{False}$$

Since 4 *does not* satisfy the original equation, this equation has no solution.

Work Practice 3

PRACTICE 3

Solve: $\sqrt{x} + 9 = 2$

Example 3 makes it very clear that we *must* check proposed solutions in the original equation to determine if they are truly solutions. If a proposed solution does not work, we say that the value is an **extraneous solution.**

The following steps can be used to solve radical equations containing square roots.

Answers

2. $x = \frac{1}{5}$ **3.** no solution

To Solve a Radical Equation Containing Square Roots

Step 1: Arrange terms so that one radical is by itself on one side of the equation. That is, isolate a radical.

Step 2: Square both sides of the equation.

Step 3: Simplify both sides of the equation.

Step 4: If the equation still contains a radical term, repeat Steps 1 through 3.

Step 5: Solve the equation.

Step 6: Check all solutions in the original equation for extraneous solutions.

PRACTICE 4

Solve: $\sqrt{9y^2 + 2y - 10} = 3y$

Example 4 Solve: $\sqrt{4y^2 + 5y - 15} = 2y$

Solution: The radical is already isolated, so we start by squaring both sides.

$$\sqrt{4y^2 + 5y - 15} = 2y$$

$$\left(\sqrt{4y^2 + 5y - 15}\right)^2 = (2y)^2 \quad \text{Square both sides.}$$

$$4y^2 + 5y - 15 = 4y^2 \quad \text{Simplify.}$$

$$5y - 15 = 0 \quad \text{Subtract } 4y^2 \text{ from both sides.}$$

$$5y = 15 \quad \text{Add 15 to both sides.}$$

$$y = 3 \quad \text{Divide both sides by 5.}$$

Check: We replace y with 3 in the original equation.

$$\sqrt{4y^2 + 5y - 15} = 2y \quad \text{Original equation}$$

$$\sqrt{4 \cdot 3^2 + 5 \cdot 3 - 15} \stackrel{?}{=} 2 \cdot 3 \quad \text{Let } y = 3.$$

$$\sqrt{4 \cdot 9 + 15 - 15} \stackrel{?}{=} 6 \quad \text{Simplify.}$$

$$\sqrt{36} \stackrel{?}{=} 6$$

$$6 = 6 \quad \text{True}$$

This statement is true, so the solution is 3.

Work Practice 4

PRACTICE 5

Solve: $\sqrt{x + 1} - x = -5$

Example 5 Solve: $\sqrt{x + 3} - x = -3$

Solution: First we isolate the radical by adding x to both sides. Then we square both sides.

$$\sqrt{x + 3} - x = -3$$

$$\sqrt{x + 3} = x - 3 \quad \text{Add } x \text{ to both sides.}$$

$$\left(\sqrt{x + 3}\right)^2 = (x - 3)^2 \quad \text{Square both sides.}$$

$$x + 3 = x^2 - 6x + 9 \quad \text{Simplify.}$$

Helpful Hint

Don't forget that $(x - 3)^2 = (x - 3)(x - 3) = x^2 - 6x + 9$.

To solve the resulting quadratic equation, we write the equation in standard form by subtracting x and 3 from both sides.

$$x + 3 = x^2 - 6x + 9$$

$$3 = x^2 - 7x + 9 \quad \text{Subtract } x \text{ from both sides.}$$

$$0 = x^2 - 7x + 6 \quad \text{Subtract 3 from both sides.}$$

$$0 = (x - 6)(x - 1) \quad \text{Factor.}$$

$$0 = x - 6 \quad \text{or} \quad 0 = x - 1 \quad \text{Set each factor equal to zero.}$$

$$6 = x \qquad 1 = x \quad \text{Solve for } x.$$

Answers

4. $y = 5$ **5.** $x = 8$

Check: We replace x with 6 and then x with 1 in the original equation.

Let $x = 6$.	Let $x = 1$.
$\sqrt{x+3} - x = -3$	$\sqrt{x+3} - x = -3$
$\sqrt{6+3} - 6 \stackrel{?}{=} -3$	$\sqrt{1+3} - 1 \stackrel{?}{=} -3$
$\sqrt{9} - 6 \stackrel{?}{=} -3$	$\sqrt{4} - 1 \stackrel{?}{=} -3$
$3 - 6 \stackrel{?}{=} -3$	$2 - 1 \stackrel{?}{=} -3$
$-3 = -3$ True	$1 = -3$ False

Since replacing x with 1 resulted in a false statement, 1 is an extraneous solution. The only solution is 6.

Work Practice 5

Objective B Using the Squaring Property of Equality Twice

If a radical equation contains two radicals, we may need to use the squaring property twice.

Example 6 Solve: $\sqrt{x-4} = \sqrt{x} - 2$

Solution:

$$\sqrt{x-4} = \sqrt{x} - 2$$

$$\left(\sqrt{x-4}\right)^2 = \left(\sqrt{x} - 2\right)^2 \quad \text{Square both sides.}$$

$$x - 4 = x - 4\sqrt{x} + 4$$

$$-8 = -4\sqrt{x} \quad \text{To get the radical term alone, subtract } x \text{ and 4 from both sides.}$$

$$2 = \sqrt{x} \quad \text{Divide both sides by } -4.$$

$$4 = x \quad \text{Square both sides again.}$$

Check the proposed solution in the original equation. The solution is 4.

Work Practice 6

PRACTICE 6

Solve: $\sqrt{x} + 3 = \sqrt{x + 15}$

Helpful Hint

Don't forget:

$$\begin{aligned}(\sqrt{x} - 2)^2 &= (\sqrt{x} - 2)(\sqrt{x} - 2)\\ &= \sqrt{x} \cdot \sqrt{x} - 2\sqrt{x} - 2\sqrt{x} + 4\\ &= x - 4\sqrt{x} + 4\end{aligned}$$

Answer

6. $x = 1$

8.5 Exercise Set

FOR EXTRA HELP MyMathLab

PRACTICE

WATCH

DOWNLOAD

READ

REVIEW

Objective A *Solve each equation. See Examples 1 through 3.*

1. $\sqrt{x} = 9$
2. $\sqrt{x} = 4$
3. $\sqrt{x+5} = 2$
4. $\sqrt{x+12} = 3$
5. $\sqrt{x} - 2 = 5$
6. $4\sqrt{x} - 7 = 5$
7. $3\sqrt{x} + 5 = 2$
8. $3\sqrt{x} + 8 = 5$
9. $\sqrt{x} = \sqrt{3x-8}$
10. $\sqrt{x} = \sqrt{4x-3}$
11. $\sqrt{4x-3} = \sqrt{x+3}$
12. $\sqrt{5x-4} = \sqrt{x+8}$

Solve each equation. See Examples 4 and 5.

13. $\sqrt{9x^2+2x-4} = 3x$
14. $\sqrt{4x^2+3x-9} = 2x$
15. $\sqrt{x} = x - 6$
16. $\sqrt{x} = x - 2$
17. $\sqrt{x+7} = x + 5$
18. $\sqrt{x+5} = x - 1$
19. $\sqrt{3x+7} - x = 3$
20. $x = \sqrt{4x-7} + 1$
21. $\sqrt{16x^2+2x+2} = 4x$
22. $\sqrt{4x^2+3x+2} = 2x$
23. $\sqrt{2x^2+6x+9} = 3$
24. $\sqrt{3x^2+6x+4} = 2$

Objective B *Solve each equation. See Example 6.*

25. $\sqrt{x-7} = \sqrt{x} - 1$
26. $\sqrt{x-8} = \sqrt{x} - 2$
27. $\sqrt{x} + 2 = \sqrt{x+24}$
28. $\sqrt{x} + 5 = \sqrt{x+55}$
29. $\sqrt{x+8} = \sqrt{x} + 2$
30. $\sqrt{x} + 1 = \sqrt{x+15}$

Objectives A B Mixed Practice *Solve each equation. See Examples 1 through 6.*

31. $\sqrt{2x+6} = 4$
32. $\sqrt{3x+7} = 5$
33. $\sqrt{x+6} + 1 = 3$
34. $\sqrt{x+5} + 2 = 5$
35. $\sqrt{x+6} + 5 = 3$
36. $\sqrt{2x-1} + 7 = 1$
37. $\sqrt{16x^2-3x+6} = 4x$
38. $\sqrt{9x^2-2x+8} = 3x$
39. $-\sqrt{x} = -6$
40. $-\sqrt{y} = -8$
41. $\sqrt{x+9} = \sqrt{x} - 3$
42. $\sqrt{x} - 6 = \sqrt{x+36}$
43. $\sqrt{2x+1} + 3 = 5$
44. $\sqrt{3x-1} + 1 = 4$
45. $\sqrt{x} + 3 = 7$
46. $\sqrt{x} + 5 = 10$
47. $\sqrt{4x} = \sqrt{2x+6}$
48. $\sqrt{5x+6} = \sqrt{8x}$
49. $\sqrt{2x+1} = x - 7$
50. $\sqrt{2x+5} = x - 5$
51. $x = \sqrt{2x-2} + 1$
52. $\sqrt{2x-4} + 2 = x$
53. $\sqrt{1-8x} - x = 4$
54. $\sqrt{2x+5} - 1 = x$

Review

Translating *Translate each sentence into an equation and then solve. See Section 2.4.*

55. If 8 is subtracted from the product of 3 and x, the result is 19. Find x.

56. If 3 more than x is subtracted from twice x, the result is 11. Find x.

57. The length of a rectangle is twice the width. The perimeter is 24 inches. Find the length.

58. The length of a rectangle is 2 inches longer than the width. The perimeter is 24 inches. Find the length.

Concept Extensions

Solve each equation.

59. $\sqrt{x-3}+3=\sqrt{3x+4}$

60. $\sqrt{2x+3}=\sqrt{x-2}+2$

61. Explain why proposed solutions of radical equations must be checked in the original equation.

62. Is 8 a solution of the equation $\sqrt{x-4}-5=\sqrt{x+1}$? Explain why or why not.

63. The formula $b=\sqrt{\frac{V}{2}}$ can be used to determine the length b of a side of the base of a square-based pyramid with height 6 units and volume V cubic units.

a. Find the length of the side of the base that produces a pyramid with each volume. (Round to the nearest tenth of a unit.)

V	20	200	2000
b			

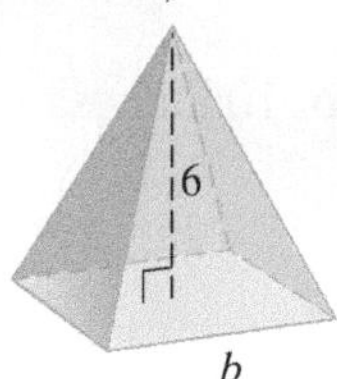

b. Notice in the table that volume V has been increased by a factor of 10 each time. Does the corresponding length b of a side increase by a factor of 10 each time also?

64. The formula $r=\sqrt{\frac{V}{2\pi}}$ can be used to determine the radius r of a cylinder with height 2 units and volume V cubic units.

a. Find the radius needed to manufacture a cylinder with each volume. (Round to the nearest tenth of a unit.)

V	10	100	1000
r			

r

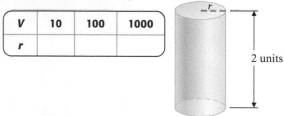

2 units

b. Notice in the table that volume V has been increased by a factor of 10 each time. Does the corresponding radius increase by a factor of 10 each time also?

Graphing calculators can be used to solve equations. To solve $\sqrt{x-2}=x-5$, for example, graph $y_1=\sqrt{x-2}$ and $y_2=x-5$ on the same set of axes. Use the Trace and Zoom features or an Intersect feature to find the point of intersection of the graphs. The x-value of the point is the solution of the equation. Use a graphing calculator to solve the equations below. Approximate solutions to the nearest hundredth.

65. $\sqrt{x-2}=x-5$

66. $\sqrt{x+1}=2x-3$

67. $-\sqrt{x+4}=5x-6$

68. $-\sqrt{x+5}=-7x+1$

Objectives

A **Use the Pythagorean Theorem to Solve Problems.**

B **Solve Problems Using Formulas Containing Radicals.**

8.6 RADICAL EQUATIONS AND PROBLEM SOLVING

Objective A Using the Pythagorean Theorem

Applications of radicals can be found in geometry, finance, science, and other areas of technology. Our first application involves the Pythagorean theorem, which gives a formula that relates the lengths of the three sides of a right triangle. We studied the Pythagorean theorem in Chapter 4, and we review it here.

The Pythagorean Theorem

If a and b are lengths of the legs of a right triangle and c is the length of the hypotenuse, then $a^2 + b^2 = c^2$.

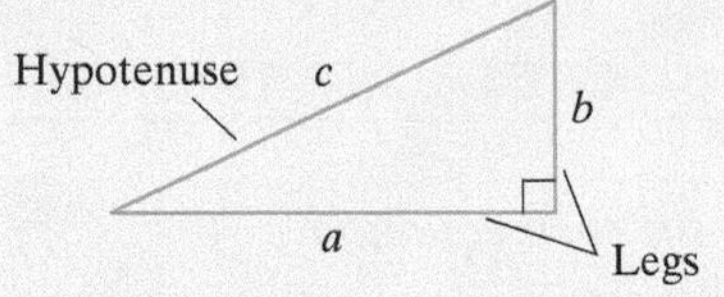

PRACTICE 1

Find the length of the hypotenuse of the right triangle shown.

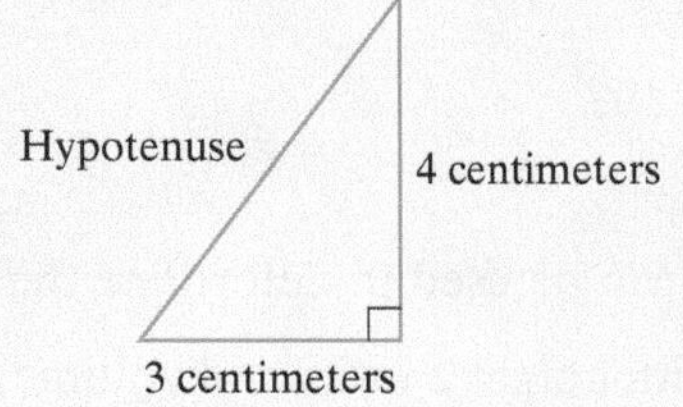

Example 1 Find the length of the hypotenuse of a right triangle whose legs are 6 inches and 8 inches long.

Solution: Because this is a right triangle, we use the Pythagorean theorem. We let $a = 6$ inches and $b = 8$ inches. Length c must be the length of the hypotenuse.

$a^2 + b^2 = c^2$ Use the Pythagorean theorem.

$6^2 + 8^2 = c^2$ Substitute the lengths of the legs.

$36 + 64 = c^2$ Simplify.

$100 = c^2$

6 inches

Hypotenuse

8 inches

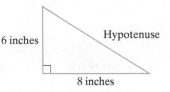

Since c represents a length, we know that c is positive and is the principal square root of 100.

$100 = c^2$

$\sqrt{100} = c$ Use the definition of principal square root.

$10 = c$ Simplify.

The hypotenuse has a length of 10 inches.

Work Practice 1

PRACTICE 2

Find the length of the leg of the right triangle shown. Give the exact length and a two-decimal-place approximation.

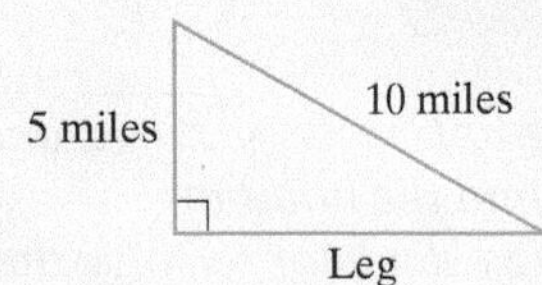

Example 2 Find the length of the leg of the right triangle shown. Give the exact length and a two-decimal-place approximation.

Solution: We let $a = 2$ meters and b be the unknown length of the other leg. The hypotenuse is $c = 5$ meters.

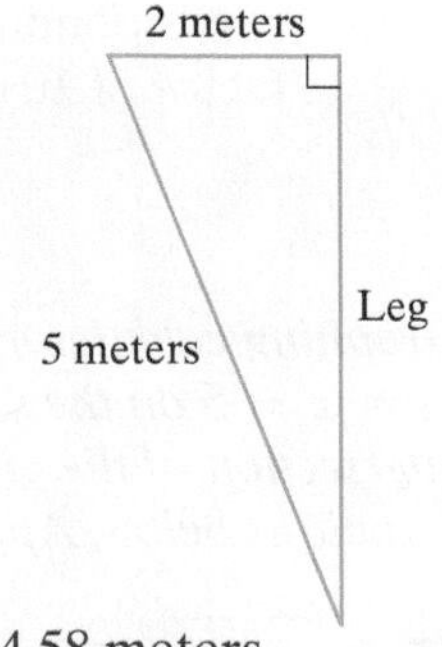

$a^2 + b^2 = c^2$ Use the Pythagorean theorem.

$2^2 + b^2 = 5^2$ Let $a = 2$ and $c = 5$.

$4 + b^2 = 25$

$b^2 = 21$

$b = \sqrt{21} \approx 4.58$ meters

The length of the leg is exactly $\sqrt{21}$ meters or approximately 4.58 meters.

Work Practice 2

Answers

1. 5 cm **2.** $5\sqrt{3}$ mi; 8.66 mi

Example 3 Finding a Distance

A surveyor must determine the distance across a lake at points P and Q as shown in the figure. To do this, she finds a third point, R, perpendicular to line PQ. If the length of $\overline{PR}$ is 320 feet and the length of $\overline{QR}$ is 240 feet, what is the distance across the lake? Approximate this distance to the nearest whole foot.

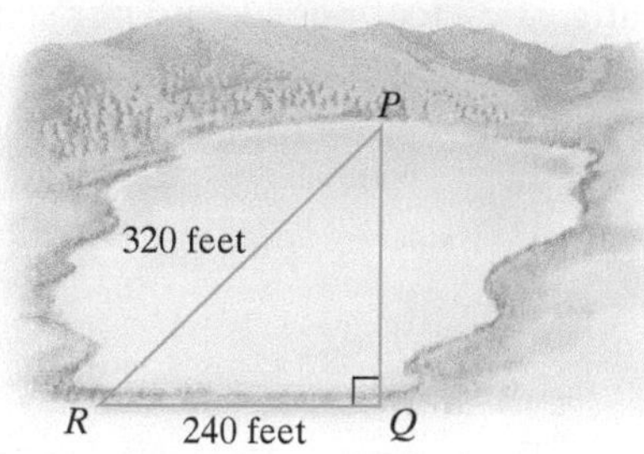

Solution:

1. UNDERSTAND. Read and reread the problem. We will set up the problem using the Pythagorean theorem. By creating a line perpendicular to line PQ, the surveyor deliberately constructed a right triangle. The hypotenuse, $\overline{PR}$, has a length of 320 feet, so we let $c = 320$ in the Pythagorean theorem. The side $\overline{QR}$ is one of the legs, so we let $a = 240$ and $b =$ the unknown length.

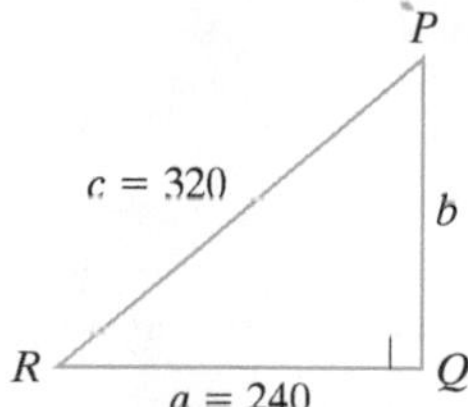

2. TRANSLATE.

$a^2 + b^2 = c^2$ Use the Pythagorean theorem.

$240^2 + b^2 = 320^2$ Let $a = 240$ and $c = 320$.

3. SOLVE.

$57{,}600 + b^2 = 102{,}400$

$b^2 = 44{,}800$ Subtract 57,600 from both sides.

$b = \sqrt{44{,}800}$ Use the definition of principal square root.

$= 80\sqrt{7}$ Simplify.

4. INTERPRET.

Check: See that $240^2 + \left(\sqrt{44{,}800}\right)^2 = 320^2$.

State: The distance across the lake is *exactly* $\sqrt{44{,}800}$ or $80\sqrt{7}$ feet. The surveyor can now use a calculator to find that $80\sqrt{7}$ feet is *approximately* 211.6601 feet, so the distance across the lake is roughly 212 feet.

Work Practice 3

PRACTICE 3

Evan Saacks wants to determine the distance at certain points across a pond on his property. He is able to measure the distances shown on the following diagram. Find how wide the pond is to the nearest tenth of a foot.

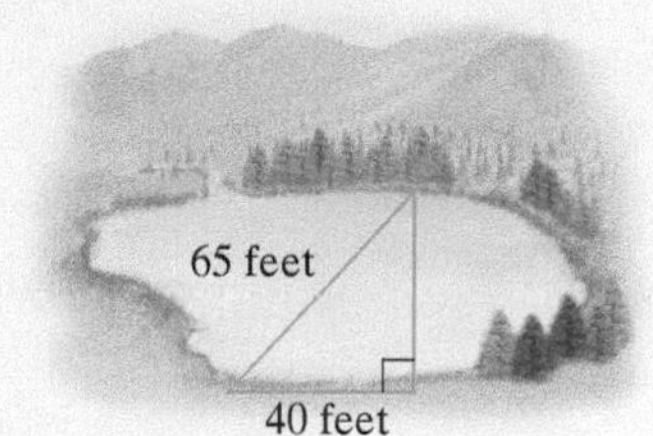

Objective B Using Formulas Containing Radicals

The Pythagorean theorem is an extremely important result in mathematics and should be memorized. But there are other applications involving formulas containing radicals that are not quite as well known, such as the velocity formula used in the next example.

Answer

3. $5\sqrt{105}$ ft ≈ 51.2 ft

PRACTICE 4

Use the formula from Example 4 and find the velocity of an object after it has fallen 20 feet, rounded to the nearest tenth.

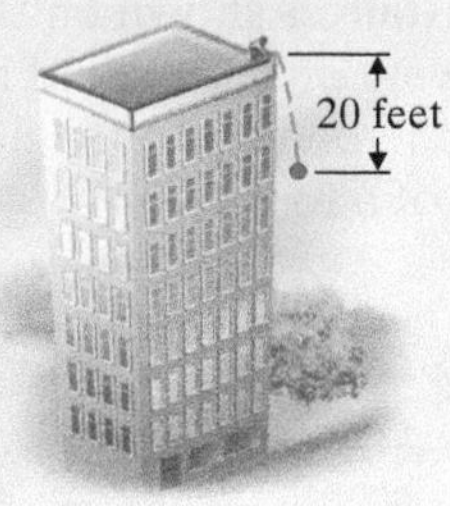

Example 4 Finding the Velocity of an Object

A formula used to determine the velocity v, in feet per second, of an object after it has fallen a certain height (neglecting air resistance) is $v = \sqrt{2gh}$, where g is the acceleration due to gravity and h is the height the object has fallen. On Earth, the acceleration g due to gravity is approximately 32 feet per second per second. Find the velocity of a person after falling 5 feet, rounded to the nearest tenth.

Solution: We are told that $g = 32$ feet per second per second. To find the velocity v when $h = 5$ feet, we use the velocity formula.

$v = \sqrt{2gh}$ Use the velocity formula.

$= \sqrt{2 \cdot 32 \cdot 5}$ Substitute known values.

$= \sqrt{320}$

$= 8\sqrt{5}$ Simplify the radicand.

The velocity of the person after falling 5 feet is *exactly* $8\sqrt{5}$ feet per second, or *approximately* 17.9 feet per second.

Work Practice 4

Answer

4. $16\sqrt{5}$ ft per sec ≈ 35.8 ft per sec

8.6 Exercise Set

FOR EXTRA HELP

MyMathLab

PRACTICE

WATCH

DOWNLOAD

READ

REVIEW

Objective A *Use the Pythagorean theorem to find the length of the unknown side of each right triangle. Give an exact answer and a two-decimal-place approximation. See Examples 1 and 2.*

1.
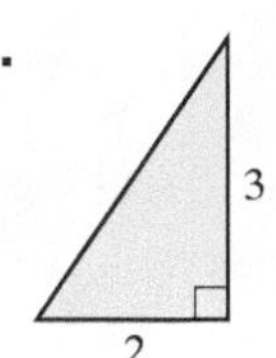

2.
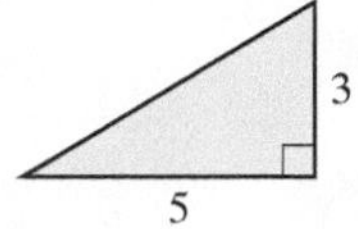

3.
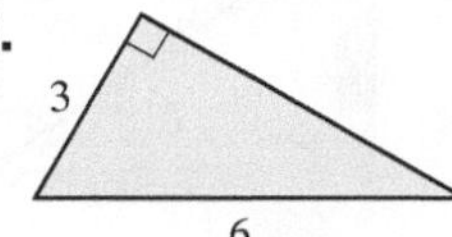

4.
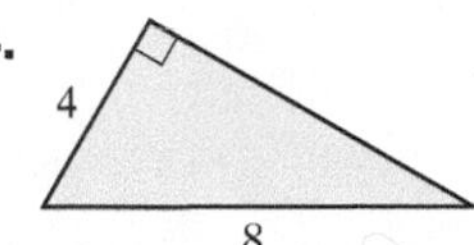

5.
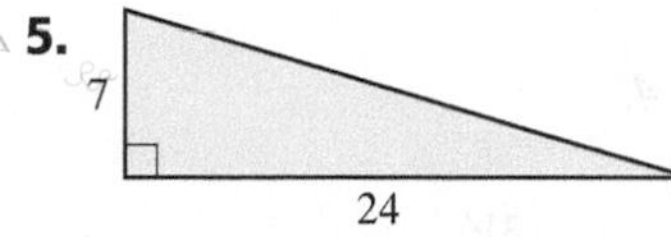

6.
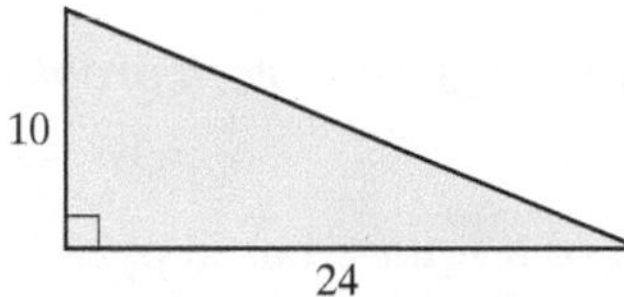

7.
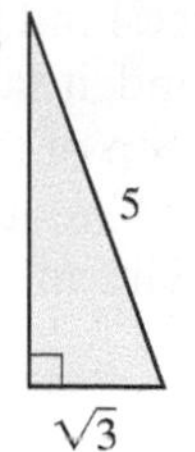

8.
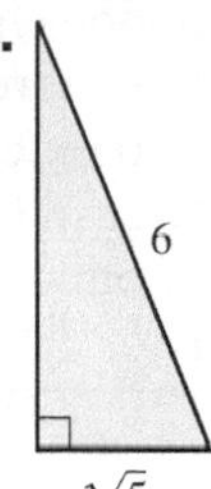

9.
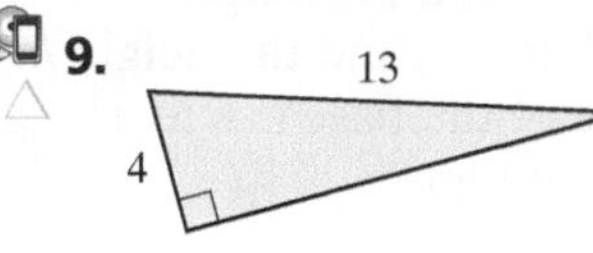

10.
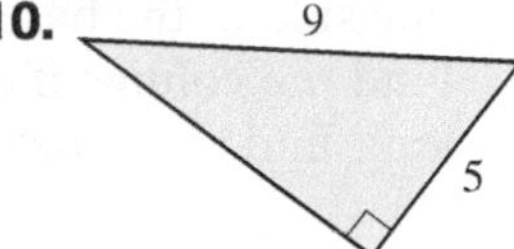

Find the length of the unknown side of each right triangle with sides a, b, and c, where c is the hypotenuse. See Examples 1 and 2. Give an exact answer and a two-decimal-place approximation.

11. $a = 4, b = 5$

12. $a = 2, b = 7$

13. $b = 2, c = 6$

14. $b = 1, c = 5$

15. $a = \sqrt{10}, c = 10$

16. $a = \sqrt{7}, c = \sqrt{35}$

Solve each problem. See Example 3.

17. A wire is used to anchor a 20-foot-tall pole. One end of the wire is attached to the top of the pole. The other end is fastened to a stake five feet away from the bottom of the pole. Find the length of the wire rounded to the nearest tenth of a foot.

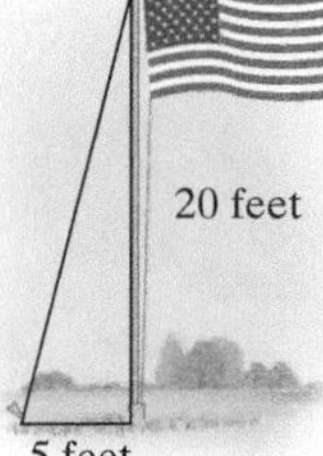

18. Jim Spivey needs to connect two underground pipelines, which are offset by 3 feet, as pictured in the diagram. Neglecting the joints needed to join the pipes, find the length of the shortest possible connecting pipe rounded to the nearest hundredth of a foot.

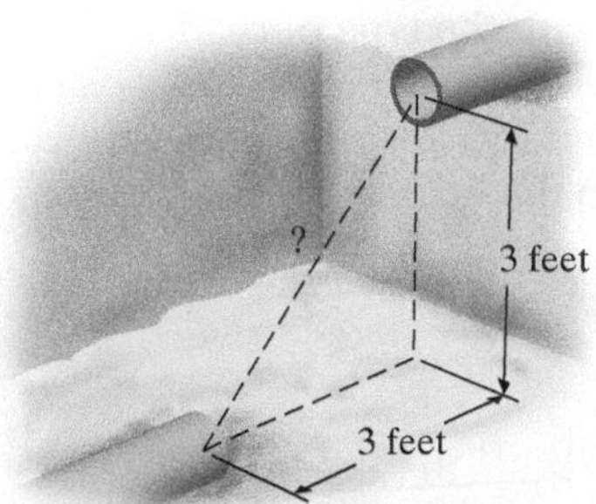

△ **19.** Robert Weisman needs to attach a diagonal brace to a rectangular frame in order to make it structurally sound. If the framework is 6 feet by 10 feet, find how long the brace needs to be to the nearest tenth of a foot.

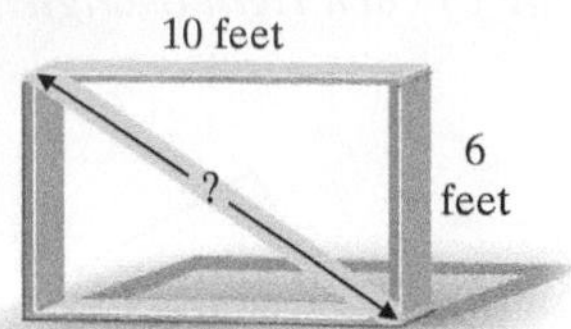

△ **20.** Elizabeth Kaster is flying a kite. She let out 80 feet of string and attached the string to a stake in the ground. The kite is now directly above her brother Mike, who is 32 feet away from the stake. Find the height of the kite to the nearest foot.

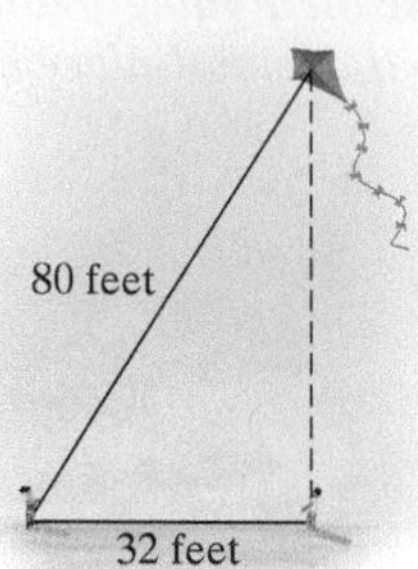

Objective B *Solve each problem. See Example 4.*

△ **21.** For a square-based pyramid, the formula $b = \sqrt{\frac{3V}{h}}$ describes the relationship between the length b of one side of the base, the volume V, and the height h. Find the volume if each side of the base is 6 feet long, and the pyramid is 2 feet high.

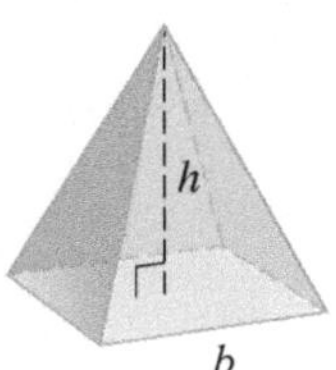

22. The formula $t = \frac{\sqrt{d}}{4}$ relates the distance d, in feet, that an object falls in t seconds, assuming that air resistance does not slow down the object. Find how long, to the nearest hundredth of a second, it takes an object to reach the ground from the top of the Willis Tower in Chicago, a distance of 1730 feet. (*Source:* Council on Tall Buildings and Urban Habitat)

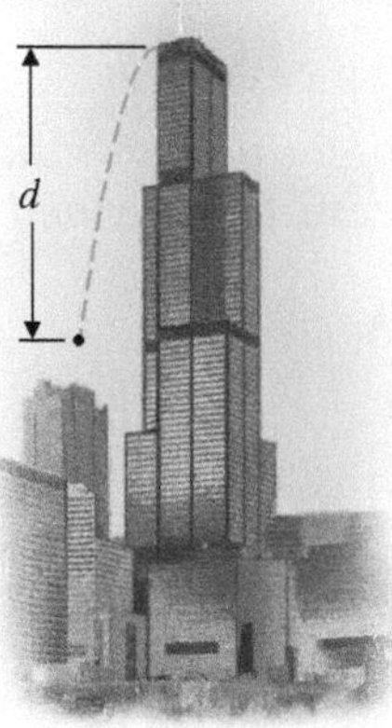

23. Police use the formula $s = \sqrt{30fd}$ to estimate the speed s of a car just before it skidded. In this formula, the speed s is measured in miles per hour, d represents the distance the car skidded in feet, and f represents the coefficient of friction. The value of f depends on the type of road surface, and for wet concrete f is 0.35. Find how fast a car was moving if it skidded 280 feet on wet concrete. Round your result to the nearest mile per hour.

24. The coefficient of friction of a certain dry road is 0.95. Use the formula in Exercise 23 to find how far a car will skid on this dry road if it is traveling at a rate of 60 mph. Round the length to the nearest foot.

25. The formula $v = \sqrt{2.5r}$ can be used to estimate the maximum safe velocity, v, in miles per hour, at which a car can travel if it is driven along a curved road with a **radius of curvature** r in feet. Find the maximum safe speed to the nearest whole number if a cloverleaf exit on an expressway has a radius of curvature of 300 feet.

26. Use the formula from Exercise 25 to find the radius of curvature if the safe velocity is 30 mph.

△ **27.** The maximum distance d in kilometers that you can see from a height of h meters is given by $d = 3.5\sqrt{h}$. Find how far you can see from the top of the Bank One Tower in Indianapolis, a height of 285.4 meters. Round to the nearest tenth of a kilometer. (*Source: World Almanac and Book of Facts*)

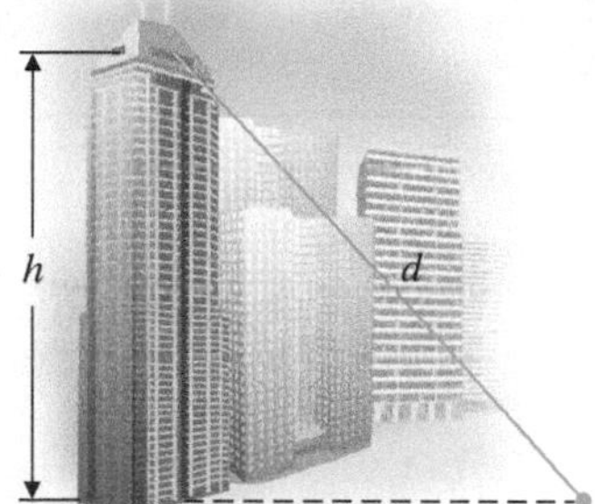

△ **28.** Use the formula from Exercise 27 to find how far you can see from the top of the Chase Tower Building in Houston, Texas, a height of 305 meters. Round to the nearest tenth of a kilometer. (*Source:* Council on Tall Buildings and Urban Habitat)

29. Use the formula from Exercise 27 to find how far you can see from the top of the First Interstate Tower in Houston, Texas, a height of 295.7 meters. Round to the nearest tenth of a kilometer. (*Source:* Council on Tall Buildings and Urban Habitat)

30. Use the formula from Exercise 27 to find how far you can see from the top of the Gas Company Tower in Los Angeles, California, a height of 228.3 m. Round to the nearest tenth of a kilometer. (*Source:* Council on Tall Buildings and Urban Habitat)

Review

Find two numbers whose square is the given number. See Section 8.1.

31. 9 **32.** 25 **33.** 100

34. 49 **35.** 64 **36.** 121

Concept Extensions

For each triangle, find the length of y, then x.

△ **37.**

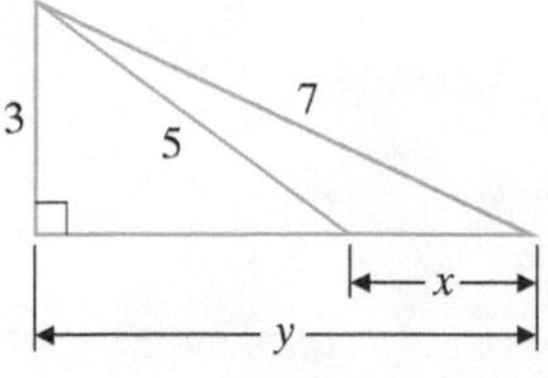

△ **38.**

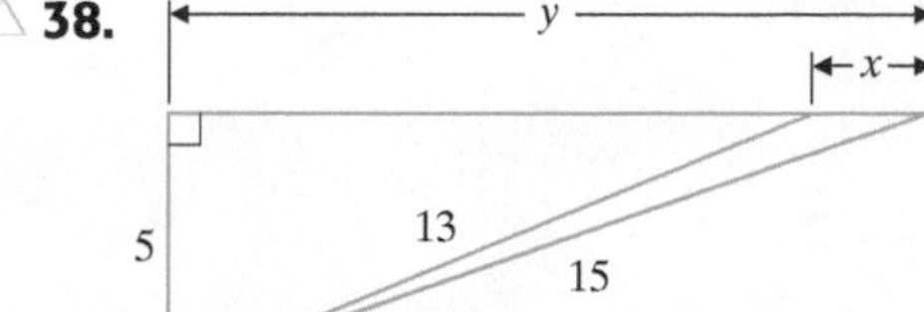

△ **39.** Mike and Sandra Hallahan leave the seashore at the same time. Mike drives northward at a rate of 30 miles per hour, while Sandra drives west at 60 mph. Find how far apart they are after 3 hours to the nearest mile.

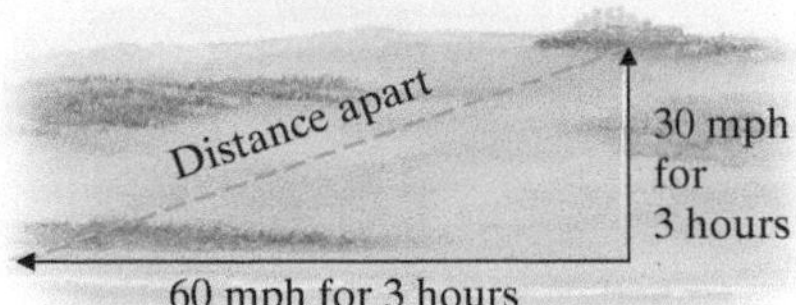

△ **40.** Railroad tracks are invariably made up of relatively short sections of rail connected by expansion joints. To see why this construction is necessary, consider a single rail 100 feet long (or 1200 inches). On an extremely hot day, suppose it expands 1 inch in the hot sun to a new length of 1201 inches. Theoretically, the track would bow upward as pictured.

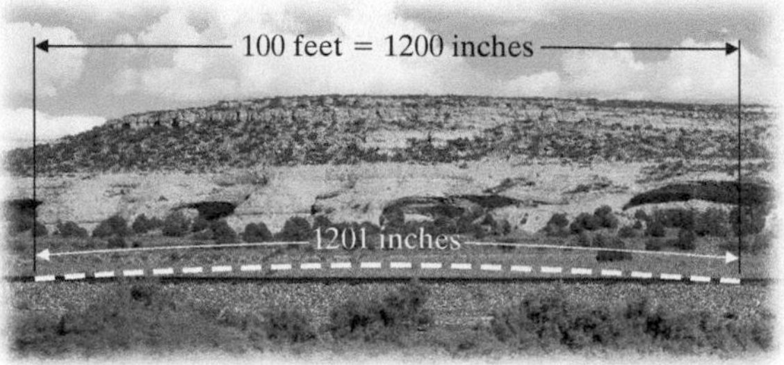

Let us approximate the bulge in the railroad this way.

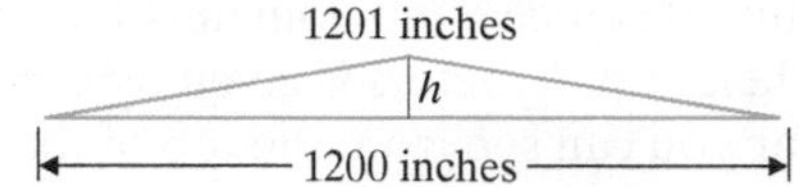

Calculate the height h of the bulge to the nearest tenth of an inch.

41. Based on the results of Exercise 40, explain why railroads use short sections of rail connected by expansion joints.

Chapter 8 Group Activity

Graphing and the Distance Formula
Sections 8.1–8.4

One application of radicals is finding the distance between two points in the coordinate plane. This can be very useful in graphing.

The distance d between two points with coordinates (x_1, y_1) and (x_2, y_2) is given by the **distance formula**

$$d = \sqrt{(x_2 - x_1)^2 + (y_2 - y_1)^2}.$$

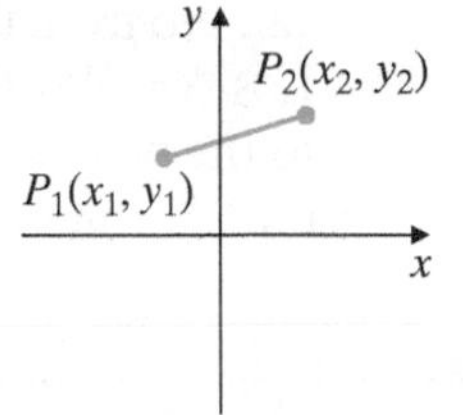

Suppose we want to find the distance between the two points $(-1, 9)$ and $(3, 5)$. We can use the distance formula with $(x_1, y_1) = (-1, 9)$ and $(x_2, y_2) = (3, 5)$. Then we have

$$\begin{aligned} d &= \sqrt{(x_2 - x_1)^2 + (y_2 - y_1)^2} \\ &= \sqrt{[3 - (-1)]^2 + (5 - 9)^2} \\ &= \sqrt{(4)^2 + (-4)^2} \\ &= \sqrt{16 + 16} \\ &= \sqrt{32} = 4\sqrt{2} \end{aligned}$$

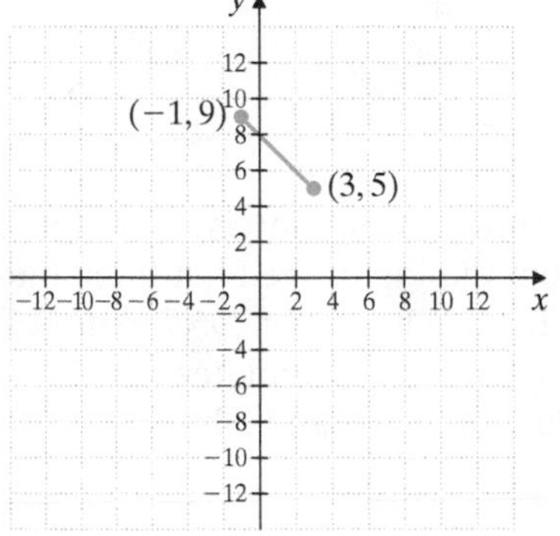

The distance between the two points is exactly $4\sqrt{2}$ units or approximately 5.66 units.

Group Activity

Brainstorm to come up with several disciplines or activities in which the distance formula might be useful. Make up an example that shows how the distance formula would be used in one of the activities on your list. Then present your example to the rest of the class.

Chapter 8 Vocabulary Check

Fill in each blank with one of the words or phrases listed below. Not all choices will be used.

index	radicand	like radicals
rationalizing the denominator	conjugate	leg
principal square root	radical	hypotenuse

1. The expressions $5\sqrt{x}$ and $7\sqrt{x}$ are examples of ____________________.
2. In the expression $\sqrt[3]{45}$, the number 3 is the ____________________, the number 45 is the ____________________, and $\sqrt{}$ is called the ____________________ sign.
3. The ____________________ of $a + b$ is $a - b$.
4. The ____________________ of 25 is 5.
5. The process of eliminating the radical in the denominator of a radical expression is called ____________________.
6. The Pythagorean theorem states that for a right triangle, $(\text{leg})^2 + (\text{leg})^2 = ($____________________$)^2$.

Helpful Hint Are you preparing for your test? Don't forget to take the Chapter 8 Test on page 643. Then check your answers at the back of the text and use the Chapter Test Prep Videos to see the fully worked-out solutions to any of the exercises you want to review.

8 Chapter Highlights

Definitions and Concepts	Examples
Section 8.1 Introduction to Radicals	
The **positive or principal square root** of a positive number a is written as $\sqrt{a}$. The **negative square root** of a is written as $-\sqrt{a}$. $\sqrt{a} = b$ only if $b^2 = a$ and $b > 0$.	$\sqrt{25} = 5$ $\sqrt{100} = 10$ $-\sqrt{9} = -3$ $\sqrt{\frac{4}{49}} = \frac{2}{7}$
A square root of a negative number is not a real number.	$\sqrt{-4}$ is not a real number.
The **cube root** of a real number a is written as $\sqrt[3]{a}$ and $\sqrt[3]{a} = b$ only if $b^3 = a$.	$\sqrt[3]{64} = 4$ $\sqrt[3]{-8} = -2$
The ***n*th root** of a number a is written as $\sqrt[n]{a}$ and $\sqrt[n]{a} = b$ only if $b^n = a$.	$\sqrt[4]{81} = 3$
In $\sqrt[n]{a}$, the natural number n is called the **index,** the symbol $\sqrt{}$ is called a **radical,** and the expression within the radical is called the **radicand.** (*Note:* If the index is even, the radicand must be nonnegative for the root to be a real number.)	$\sqrt[5]{-32} = -2$ index → n in $\sqrt[n]{a}$ ← radicand a
Section 8.2 Simplifying Radicals	
Product Rule for Radicals If $\sqrt{a}$ and $\sqrt{b}$ are real numbers, then $\sqrt{a \cdot b} = \sqrt{a} \cdot \sqrt{b}$	
A square root is in **simplified form** if the radicand contains no perfect square factors other than 1. To simplify a square root, factor the radicand so that one of its factors is a perfect square factor then apply the product rule.	$\sqrt{45} = \sqrt{9 \cdot 5}$ $= \sqrt{9} \cdot \sqrt{5}$ $= 3\sqrt{5}$

(*continued*)

Definitions and Concepts	Examples
Section 8.2 Simplifying Radicals (*continued*)	
QUOTIENT RULE FOR RADICALS If $\sqrt{a}$ and $\sqrt{b}$ are real numbers and $b \neq 0$, then $\sqrt{\frac{a}{b}} = \frac{\sqrt{a}}{\sqrt{b}}$	$\sqrt{\frac{18}{x^6}} = \frac{\sqrt{18}}{\sqrt{x^6}} = \frac{\sqrt{9\cdot 2}}{x^3} = \frac{\sqrt{9}\cdot\sqrt{2}}{x^3} = \frac{3\sqrt{2}}{x^3}$
Section 8.3 Adding and Subtracting Radicals	
Like radicals are radical expressions that have the same index and the same radicand. To **combine like radicals** use the distributive property.	$5\sqrt{2}, -7\sqrt{2}, \sqrt{2}$ $2\sqrt{7} - 13\sqrt{7} = (2 - 13)\sqrt{7} = -11\sqrt{7}$ $\sqrt{8} + \sqrt{50} = 2\sqrt{2} + 5\sqrt{2} = 7\sqrt{2}$
Section 8.4 Multiplying and Dividing Radicals	
The product and quotient rules for radicals may be used to simplify products and quotients of radicals.	Perform each indicated operation and simplify. Multiply. $\sqrt{2}\cdot\sqrt{8} = \sqrt{16} = 4$ $(\sqrt{3x} + 1)(\sqrt{5} - \sqrt{3})$ $= \sqrt{15x} - \sqrt{9x} + \sqrt{5} - \sqrt{3}$ $= \sqrt{15x} - 3\sqrt{x} + \sqrt{5} - \sqrt{3}$ Divide. $\frac{\sqrt{20}}{\sqrt{2}} = \sqrt{\frac{20}{2}} = \sqrt{10}$
The process of eliminating the radical in the denominator of a radical expression is called **rationalizing the denominator.**	Rationalize the denominator. $\frac{5}{\sqrt{11}} = \frac{5\cdot\sqrt{11}}{\sqrt{11}\cdot\sqrt{11}} = \frac{5\sqrt{11}}{11}$
The **conjugate** of $a + b$ is $a - b$.	The conjugate of $2 + \sqrt{3}$ is $2 - \sqrt{3}$.
To rationalize a denominator that is a sum or difference of radicals, multiply the numerator and the denominator by the conjugate of the denominator.	Rationalize the denominator. $\frac{5}{6 - \sqrt{5}} = \frac{5(6 + \sqrt{5})}{(6 - \sqrt{5})(6 + \sqrt{5})}$ $= \frac{30 + 5\sqrt{5}}{36 - 5}$ $= \frac{30 + 5\sqrt{5}}{31}$

Definitions and Concepts	Examples
Section 8.5 Solving Equations Containing Radicals	
To Solve a Radical Equation Containing Square Roots **Step 1.** Get one radical by itself on one side of the equation. **Step 2.** Square both sides of the equation. **Step 3.** Simplify both sides of the equation. **Step 4.** If the equation still contains a radical term, repeat Steps 1 through 3. **Step 5.** Solve the equation. **Step 6.** Check solutions in the original equation.	Solve: $\sqrt{2x-1}-x=-2$ $\sqrt{2x-1}=x-2$ $(\sqrt{2x-1})^2=(x-2)^2$ Square both sides. $2x-1=x^2-4x+4$ $0=x^2-6x+5$ $0=(x-1)(x-5)$ Factor. $x-1=0$ or $x-5=0$ $x=1$ $x=5$ Solve. Check both proposed solutions in the original equation. Here, 5 checks but 1 does not. The only solution is 5.
Section 8.6 Radical Equations and Problem Solving	
Problem-Solving Steps 1. UNDERSTAND. Read and reread the problem.	A rain gutter is to be mounted on the eaves of a house 15 feet above the ground. A garden is adjacent to the house so that the closest a ladder can be placed to the house is 6 feet. How long a ladder is needed for installing the gutter? Let $x=$ the length of the ladder. 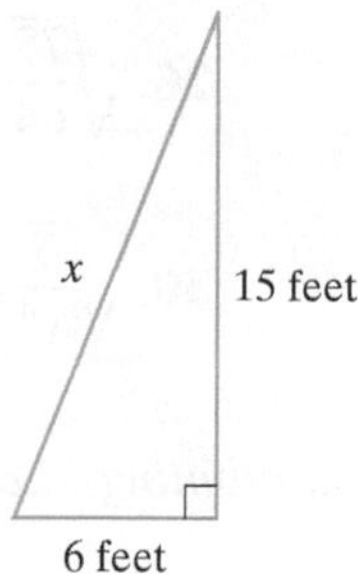 Here, we use the Pythagorean theorem. The unknown length x is the hypotenuse. In words: $(\text{leg})^2 + (\text{leg})^2 = (\text{hypotenuse})^2$
2. TRANSLATE. 3. SOLVE.	Translate: $6^2+15^2=x^2$ $36+225=x^2$ $261=x^2$ $\sqrt{261}=x$ or $x=3\sqrt{29}$
4. INTERPRET.	Check and state. The ladder needs to be $3\sqrt{29}$ feet or approximately 16.2 feet long.

Chapter 8 Review

(8.1) *Find each root.*

1. $\sqrt{81}$

2. $-\sqrt{49}$

3. $\sqrt[3]{27}$

4. $\sqrt[4]{81}$

5. $-\sqrt{\frac{9}{64}}$

6. $\sqrt{\frac{36}{81}}$

7. $\sqrt[4]{16}$

8. $\sqrt[3]{-8}$

9. Which radical(s) is not a real number?
a. $\sqrt{4}$ **b.** $-\sqrt{4}$ **c.** $\sqrt{-4}$ **d.** $\sqrt[3]{-4}$

10. Which radical(s) is not a real number?
a. $\sqrt{-5}$ **b.** $\sqrt[3]{-5}$ **c.** $\sqrt[4]{-5}$ **d.** $\sqrt[5]{-5}$

Find each root. Assume that all variables represent positive numbers.

11. $\sqrt{x^{12}}$

12. $\sqrt{x^8}$

13. $\sqrt{9y^2}$

14. $\sqrt{25x^4}$

(8.2) *Simplify each expression using the product rule. Assume that all variables represent positive numbers.*

15. $\sqrt{40}$

16. $\sqrt{24}$

17. $\sqrt{54}$

18. $\sqrt{88}$

19. $\sqrt{x^5}$

20. $\sqrt{y^7}$

21. $\sqrt{20x^2}$

22. $\sqrt{50y^4}$

23. $\sqrt[3]{54}$

24. $\sqrt[3]{88}$

Simplify each expression using the quotient rule. Assume that all variables represent positive numbers.

25. $\sqrt{\frac{18}{25}}$

26. $\sqrt{\frac{75}{64}}$

27. $-\sqrt{\frac{50}{9}}$

28. $-\sqrt{\frac{12}{49}}$

29. $\sqrt{\frac{11}{x^2}}$

30. $\sqrt{\frac{7}{y^4}}$

31. $\sqrt{\frac{y^5}{100}}$

32. $\sqrt{\frac{x^3}{81}}$

(8.3) *Add or subtract by combining like radicals.*

33. $5\sqrt{2} - 8\sqrt{2}$

34. $\sqrt{3} - 6\sqrt{3}$

35. $6\sqrt{5} + 3\sqrt{6} - 2\sqrt{5} + \sqrt{6}$

36. $-\sqrt{7} + 8\sqrt{2} - \sqrt{7} - 6\sqrt{2}$

Add or subtract by simplifying each radical and then combining like terms. Assume that all variables represent positive numbers.

37. $\sqrt{28} + \sqrt{63} + \sqrt{56}$

38. $\sqrt{75} + \sqrt{48} - \sqrt{16}$

39. $\sqrt{\frac{5}{9}} - \sqrt{\frac{5}{36}}$

40. $\sqrt{\frac{11}{25}} + \sqrt{\frac{11}{16}}$

41. $\sqrt{45x^2} + 3\sqrt{5x^2} - 7x\sqrt{5} + 10$

42. $\sqrt{50x} - 9\sqrt{2x} + \sqrt{72x} - \sqrt{3x}$

(8.4) *Multiply and simplify if possible. Assume that all variables represent positive numbers.*

43. $\sqrt{3} \cdot \sqrt{6}$

44. $\sqrt{5} \cdot \sqrt{15}$

45. $\sqrt{2}(\sqrt{5} - \sqrt{7})$

46. $\sqrt{5}(\sqrt{11} + \sqrt{3})$

47. $(\sqrt{3} + 2)(\sqrt{6} - 5)$

48. $(\sqrt{5} + 1)(\sqrt{5} - 3)$

49. $(\sqrt{x} - 2)^2$

50. $(\sqrt{y} + 4)^2$

Divide and simplify if possible. Assume that all variables represent positive numbers.

51. $\frac{\sqrt{27}}{\sqrt{3}}$

52. $\frac{\sqrt{20}}{\sqrt{5}}$

53. $\frac{\sqrt{160}}{\sqrt{8}}$

54. $\frac{\sqrt{96}}{\sqrt{3}}$

55. $\frac{\sqrt{30x^6}}{\sqrt{2x^3}}$

56. $\frac{\sqrt{54x^5y^2}}{\sqrt{3xy^2}}$

Rationalize each denominator and simplify.

57. $\frac{\sqrt{2}}{\sqrt{11}}$

58. $\frac{\sqrt{3}}{\sqrt{13}}$

59. $\sqrt{\frac{5}{6}}$

60. $\sqrt{\frac{7}{10}}$

61. $\frac{1}{\sqrt{5x}}$

62. $\frac{5}{\sqrt{3y}}$

63. $\sqrt{\frac{3}{x}}$

64. $\sqrt{\frac{6}{y}}$

65. $\frac{3}{\sqrt{5} - 2}$

66. $\frac{8}{\sqrt{10} - 3}$

67. $\frac{\sqrt{2} + 1}{\sqrt{3} - 1}$

68. $\frac{\sqrt{3} - 2}{\sqrt{5} + 2}$

69. $\frac{10}{\sqrt{x} + 5}$

70. $\frac{8}{\sqrt{x} - 1}$

(8.5) *Solve each radical equation.*

71. $\sqrt{2x} = 6$

72. $\sqrt{x + 3} = 4$

73. $\sqrt{x} + 3 = 8$

74. $\sqrt{x} + 8 = 3$

75. $\sqrt{2x + 1} = x - 7$

76. $\sqrt{3x + 1} = x - 1$

77. $\sqrt{x} + 3 = \sqrt{x + 15}$

78. $\sqrt{x - 5} = \sqrt{x} - 1$

(8.6) *Use the Pythagorean theorem to find the length of each unknown side. Give an exact answer and a two-decimal-place approximation.*

79.

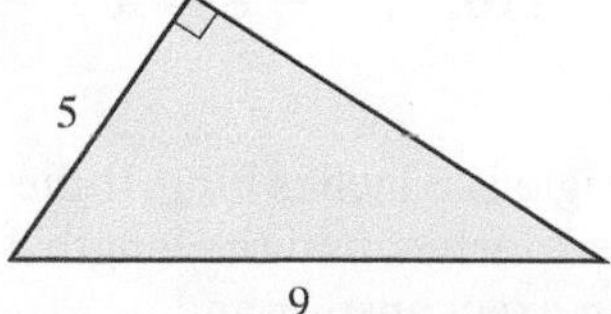

80.

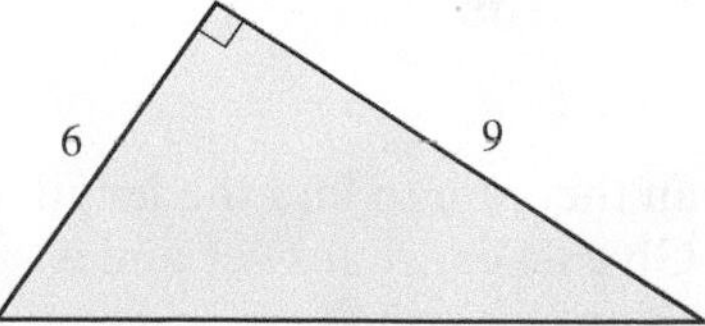

△ 81. Romeo is standing 20 feet away from the wall below Juliet's balcony during a school play. Juliet is on the balcony, 12 feet above the ground. Find how far apart Romeo and Juliet are.

△ 82. The diagonal of a rectangle is 10 inches long. If the width of the rectangle is 5 inches, find the length of the rectangle.

Use the formula $r = \sqrt{\frac{S}{4\pi}}$, *where* $r =$ *the radius of a sphere and* $S =$ *the surface area of the sphere, for Exercises 83 and 84.*

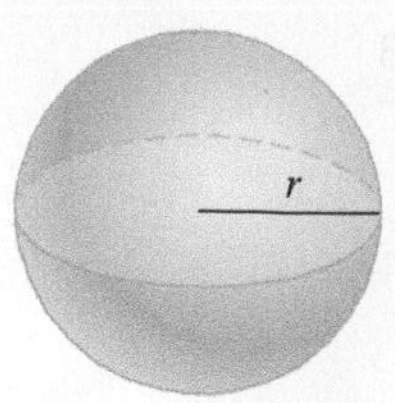

△ **83.** Find the radius of a sphere to the nearest tenth of an inch if the surface area is 72 square inches.

△ **84.** Find the exact surface area of a sphere if its radius is 6 inches. (Do not approximate π.)

Mixed Review

Find each root. Assume all variables represent positive numbers.

85. $\sqrt{144}$ **86.** $-\sqrt[3]{64}$ **87.** $\sqrt{16x^{16}}$ **88.** $\sqrt{4x^{24}}$

Simplify each expression. Assume all variables represent positive numbers.

89. $\sqrt{18x^7}$ **90.** $\sqrt{48y^6}$ **91.** $\sqrt{\frac{y^4}{81}}$ **92.** $\sqrt{\frac{x^9}{9}}$

Add or subtract by simplifying and then combining like terms. Assume all variables represent positive numbers.

93. $\sqrt{12} + \sqrt{75}$ **94.** $\sqrt{63} + \sqrt{28} - \sqrt{9}$

95. $\sqrt{\frac{3}{16}} - \sqrt{\frac{3}{4}}$ **96.** $\sqrt{45x^3} + x\sqrt{20x} - \sqrt{5x^3}$

Multiply and simplify if possible. Assume all variables represent positive numbers.

97. $\sqrt{7} \cdot \sqrt{14}$ **98.** $\sqrt{3}(\sqrt{9} - \sqrt{2})$ **99.** $(\sqrt{2} + 4)(\sqrt{5} - 1)$ **100.** $(\sqrt{x} + 3)^2$

Divide and simplify if possible. Assume all variables represent positive numbers.

101. $\frac{\sqrt{120}}{\sqrt{5}}$ **102.** $\frac{\sqrt{60x^9}}{\sqrt{15x^7}}$

Rationalize each denominator and simplify.

103. $\sqrt{\frac{2}{7}}$ **104.** $\frac{3}{\sqrt{2x}}$

105. $\frac{3}{\sqrt{x} - 6}$ **106.** $\frac{\sqrt{7} - 5}{\sqrt{5} + 3}$

Solve each radical equation.

107. $\sqrt{4x} = 2$ **108.** $\sqrt{x - 4} = 3$ **109.** $\sqrt{4x + 8} + 6 = x$ **110.** $\sqrt{x - 8} = \sqrt{x} - 2$

111. Use the Pythagorean theorem to find the length of the unknown side. Give an exact answer and a two-decimal-place approximation.

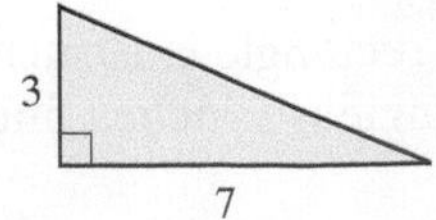

112. The diagonal of a rectangle is 6 inches long. If the width of the rectangle is 2 inches, find the length of the rectangle. Give an exact answer and a two-decimal-place approximation.

Chapter 8 Test

Step-by-step test solutions are found on the Chapter Test Prep Videos available via the Interactive DVD Lecture Series, in MyMathLab or on YouTube (search "MartinGayIntroAlg" and click on "Channels").

Simplify each radical. Indicate if the radical is not a real number. Assume that x represents a positive number.

1. $\sqrt{16}$

2. $\sqrt[3]{125}$

3. $\sqrt[4]{81}$

4. $\sqrt{\frac{9}{16}}$

5. $\sqrt[4]{-81}$

6. $\sqrt{x^{10}}$

Simplify each radical. Assume that all variables represent positive numbers.

7. $\sqrt{54}$

8. $\sqrt{92}$

9. $\sqrt{y^7}$

10. $\sqrt{24x^8}$

11. $\sqrt[3]{27}$

12. $\sqrt[3]{16}$

13. $\sqrt{\frac{5}{16}}$

14. $\sqrt{\frac{y^3}{25}}$

Perform each indicated operation. Assume that all variables represent positive numbers.

15. $\sqrt{13} + \sqrt{13} - 4\sqrt{13}$

16. $\sqrt{18} - \sqrt{75} + 7\sqrt{3} - \sqrt{8}$

17. $\sqrt{\frac{3}{4}} + \sqrt{\frac{3}{25}}$

18. $\sqrt{7} \cdot \sqrt{14}$

19. $\sqrt{2}\left(\sqrt{6} - \sqrt{5}\right)$

Answers

1. ______
2. ______
3. ______
4. ______
5. ______
6. ______
7. ______
8. ______
9. ______
10. ______
11. ______
12. ______
13. ______
14. ______
15. ______
16. ______
17. ______
18. ______
19. ______

20. ____________

21. ____________

22. ____________

23. ____________

24. ____________

25. ____________

26. ____________

27. ____________

28. ____________

29. ____________

30. ____________

31. ____________

20. $(\sqrt{x} + 2)(\sqrt{x} - 3)$ **21.** $\dfrac{\sqrt{50}}{\sqrt{10}}$ **22.** $\dfrac{\sqrt{40x^4}}{\sqrt{2x}}$

Rationalize each denominator. Assume that all variables represent positive numbers.

23. $\sqrt{\dfrac{2}{3}}$ **24.** $\dfrac{8}{\sqrt{5y}}$ **25.** $\dfrac{8}{\sqrt{6} + 2}$ **26.** $\dfrac{1}{3 - \sqrt{x}}$

Solve each radical equation.

27. $\sqrt{x} + 8 = 11$ **28.** $\sqrt{3x - 6} = \sqrt{x + 4}$ **29.** $\sqrt{2x - 2} = x - 5$

△ **30.** Find the length of the unknown leg of the right triangle shown. Give an exact answer.

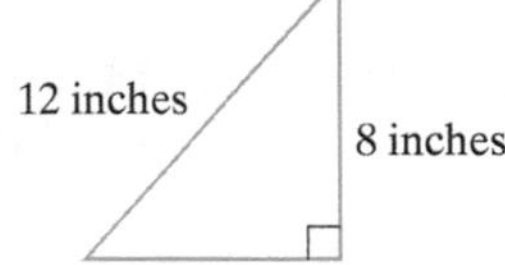

△ **31.** The formula $r = \sqrt{\dfrac{A}{\pi}}$ can be used to find the radius r of a circle given its area A. Use this formula to approximate the radius of the given circle. Round to two decimal places.

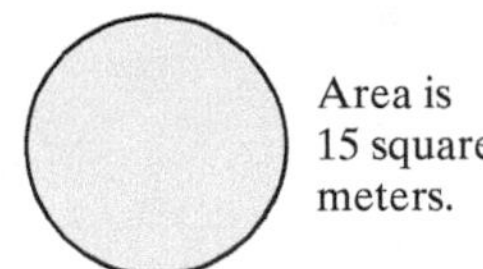

Cumulative Review Chapters 1–8

Multiply.

1. $-2(-14)$

2. $9(-5.2)$

3. $-\frac{2}{3} \cdot \frac{4}{7}$

4. $-3\frac{3}{8} \cdot 5\frac{1}{3}$

5. Solve: $4(2x - 3) + 7 = 3x + 5$

6. Solve: $6y - 11 + 4 + 2y = 8 + 15y - 8y$

7. The circle graph below shows the purpose of trips made by American travelers. Use this graph to answer the questions below.

a. What percent of trips made by American travelers is solely for the purpose of business?

b. What percent of trips made by American travelers is for the purpose of business or combined business/pleasure?

c. On an airplane flight of 253 Americans, how many of these people might we expect to be traveling solely for business?

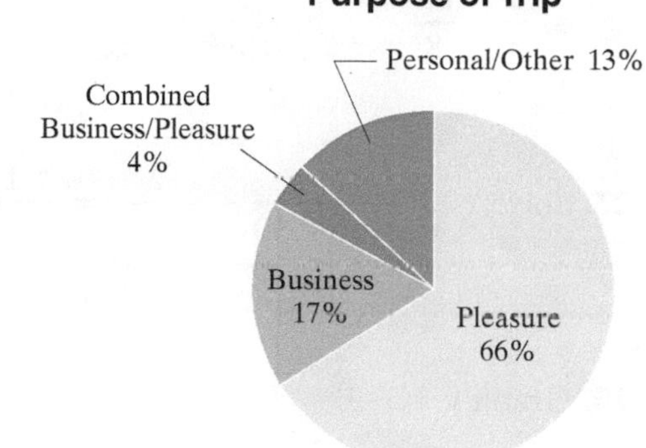

Source: Travel Industry Association of America

8. Simplify each expression.

a. $\frac{4(-3) - (-6)}{-8 + 4}$

b. $\frac{3 + (-3)(-2)^3}{-1 - (-4)}$

9. Write the following numbers in standard form, without exponents.

a. 1.02×10^5

b. 7.358×10^{-3}

c. 8.4×10^7

d. 3.007×10^{-5}

10. Write the following numbers in scientific notation.

a. 7,200,000

b. 0.000308

11. Multiply: $(3x + 2)(2x - 5)$

Answers

1. ______
2. ______
3. ______
4. ______
5. ______
6. ______
7. a. ______
b. ______
c. ______
8. a. ______
b. ______
9. a. ______
b. ______
c. ______
d. ______
10. a. ______
b. ______
11. ______

12. ______
13. ______
14. ______
15. ______
16. ______
17. a. ______
b. ______
c. ______
18. ______
19. ______
20. ______
21. a. ______
b. ______
22. ______
23. ______
24. ______
25. ______
26. ______
27. ______
28. ______
29. ______
30. ______

12. Multiply: $(7x + 1)^2$

13. Factor $xy + 2x + 3y + 6$ by grouping.

14. Factor $xy^2 + 5x - y^2 - 5$ by grouping.

15. Factor: $3x^2 + 11x + 6$

16. Factor: $3x^2 + 15x + 18$

17. Are there any values for x for which each expression is undefined?

a. $\dfrac{x}{x - 3}$

b. $\dfrac{x^2 + 2}{x^2 - 3x + 2}$

c. $\dfrac{x^3 - 6x^2 - 10x}{3}$

18. Simplify: $\dfrac{2x^2 + 7x + 3}{x^2 - 9}$

19. Simplify: $\dfrac{x^2 + 4x + 4}{x^2 + 2x}$

20. Divide: $\dfrac{12x^2y^3}{5} \div \dfrac{3y^3}{x}$

21. Perform each indicated operation.

a. $\dfrac{a}{4} - \dfrac{2a}{8}$ **b.** $\dfrac{3}{10x^2} + \dfrac{7}{25x}$

22. Find an equation of the line with y-intercept $(0, 4)$ and slope of -2.

23. Solve: $\dfrac{4x}{x^2 + x - 30} + \dfrac{2}{x - 5} = \dfrac{1}{x + 6}$

24. Combine like terms to simplify.
$4a^2 + 3a - 2a^2 + 7a - 5$

25. Graph $y = -3$.

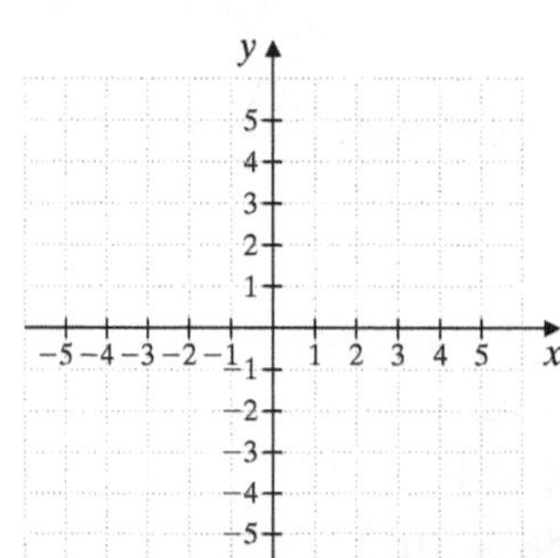

26. Complete the table for the equation $2x + y = 6$.

x	y
0	
	−2
3	

27. Find an equation of the line with y-intercept $(0, -3)$ and slope of $\dfrac{1}{4}$.

28. Find an equation of the line perpendicular to $y = 2x + 4$ and passing through $(1, 5)$.

29. Solve the system:
$$\begin{cases} 3x + 4y = 13 \\ 5x - 9y = 6 \end{cases}$$

30. Solve the system:
$$\begin{cases} \dfrac{x}{2} + y = \dfrac{5}{6} \\ 2x - y = \dfrac{5}{6} \end{cases}$$

31. As part of an exercise program, two students, Louisa and Alfredo, start walking each morning. They live 15 miles away from each other. They decide to meet one day by walking toward one another. After 2 hours they meet. If Louisa walks one mile per hour faster than Alfredo, find both walking speeds.

32. Two streetcars are 11 miles apart and traveling toward each other on parallel tracks. They meet in 12 minutes. Find the speed of each streetcar if one travels 15 miles per hour faster than the other.

Find each root.

33. $\sqrt[3]{1}$ **34.** $\sqrt{121}$ **35.** $\sqrt[3]{-27}$

36. $\sqrt{\frac{1}{4}}$ **37.** $\sqrt[3]{\frac{1}{125}}$ **38.** $\sqrt{\frac{25}{144}}$

Simplify.

39. $\sqrt{54}$ **40.** $\sqrt{63}$ **41.** $\sqrt{200}$ **42.** $\sqrt{500}$

Perform indicated operations. If possible, first simplify each radical.

43. $7\sqrt{12} - 2\sqrt{75}$

44. $(\sqrt{x} + 5)(\sqrt{x} - 5)$

45. $2\sqrt{x^2} - \sqrt{25x^5} + \sqrt{x^5}$

46. $(\sqrt{6} + 2)^2$

47. Rationalize the denominator of $\frac{2}{\sqrt{7}}$.

48. Simplify: $\dfrac{x + 3}{\frac{1}{x} + \frac{1}{3}}$

49. Solve: $\sqrt{x} = \sqrt{5x - 2}$

50. Solve: $\sqrt{x + 4} = \sqrt{3x - 1}$

31. ______
32. ______
33. ______
34. ______
35. ______
36. ______
37. ______
38. ______
39. ______
40. ______
41. ______
42. ______
43. ______
44. ______
45. ______
46. ______
47. ______
48. ______
49. ______
50. ______

9 Quadratic Equations

Beam bridge

Cantilever bridge

Arch bridge

Suspension bridge

Cable-stayed bridge

Truss bridge

Sections

Check Your Progress

An important part of the study of algebra is learning to use methods for solving equations. Starting in Chapter 2, we presented techniques for solving linear equations in one variable. In Chapter 4, we solved quadratic equations in one variable by factoring the quadratic expressions. We now present other methods for solving quadratic equations in one variable.

If you have ever laid down a piece of wood to cross over some water to keep from getting wet, you have constructed a bridge. A bridge is a structure that provides passage over some sort of obstacle: a river, a valley, a road, or even a set of railroad tracks. There are six major types of bridges. They are described below and illustrated above.

In Section 9.1, Exercise 73, you will examine some statistics about the number of bridges along highways in the United States.

Bridge Type	Description
Beam	These bridges have horizontal beams supported at each end by piers.
Cantilever	These are built using cantilevers—horizontal beams that are supported on only one end. Most of these bridges use 2 cantilever arms.
Arch	These are arch shaped and have abutments at each end.
Suspension	These bridges are suspended from cables.
Cable-stayed	These bridges are held up by cables, but less cable is required and the towers holding the cables are proportionately shorter than in suspension bridges.
Truss	These are composed of connected elements. They have a solid deck and a lattice of girders for the sides.

Objectives

A **Use the Quadratic Formula to Solve Quadratic Equations.**

B **Approximate Solutions to Quadratic Equations.**

9.3 SOLVING QUADRATIC EQUATIONS BY THE QUADRATIC FORMULA

Objective A Using the Quadratic Formula

We can use the technique of completing the square to develop a formula to find solutions of any quadratic equation. We develop and use the **quadratic formula** in this section.

Recall that a quadratic equation in **standard form** is

$$ax^2 + bx + c = 0, \quad a \neq 0$$

To develop the quadratic formula, let's complete the square for this quadratic equation in standard form.

First we divide both sides of the equation by the coefficient of x^2 and then get the variable terms alone on one side of the equation.

$$x^2 + \frac{b}{a}x + \frac{c}{a} = 0 \quad \text{Divide by } a\text{; recall that } a \text{ cannot be 0.}$$

$$x^2 + \frac{b}{a}x = -\frac{c}{a} \quad \text{Get the variable terms alone on one side of the equation.}$$

The coefficient of x is $\frac{b}{a}$. Half of $\frac{b}{a}$ is $\frac{b}{2a}$ and $\left(\frac{b}{2a}\right)^2 = \frac{b^2}{4a^2}$. So we add $\frac{b^2}{4a^2}$ to both sides of the equation.

$$x^2 + \frac{b}{a}x + \frac{b^2}{4a^2} = -\frac{c}{a} + \frac{b^2}{4a^2} \quad \text{Add } \frac{b^2}{4a^2} \text{ to both sides.}$$

$$\left(x + \frac{b}{2a}\right)^2 = -\frac{c}{a} + \frac{b^2}{4a^2} \quad \text{Factor the left side.}$$

$$\left(x + \frac{b}{2a}\right)^2 = -\frac{4ac}{4a^2} + \frac{b^2}{4a^2} \quad \text{Multiply } -\frac{c}{a} \text{ by } \frac{4a}{4a} \text{ so that the terms on the right side have a common denominator.}$$

$$\left(x + \frac{b}{2a}\right)^2 = \frac{b^2 - 4ac}{4a^2} \quad \text{Simplify the right side.}$$

Now we use the square root property.

$$x + \frac{b}{2a} = \sqrt{\frac{b^2 - 4ac}{4a^2}} \quad \text{or} \quad x + \frac{b}{2a} = -\sqrt{\frac{b^2 - 4ac}{4a^2}} \quad \text{Use the square root property.}$$

$$x + \frac{b}{2a} = \frac{\sqrt{b^2 - 4ac}}{2a} \qquad x + \frac{b}{2a} = -\frac{\sqrt{b^2 - 4ac}}{2a} \quad \text{Simplify the radical.}$$

$$x = -\frac{b}{2a} + \frac{\sqrt{b^2 - 4ac}}{2a} \qquad x = -\frac{b}{2a} - \frac{\sqrt{b^2 - 4ac}}{2a} \quad \text{Subtract } \frac{b}{2a} \text{ from both sides.}$$

$$x = \frac{-b + \sqrt{b^2 - 4ac}}{2a} \qquad x = \frac{-b - \sqrt{b^2 - 4ac}}{2a} \quad \text{Simplify.}$$

The solutions are $\frac{-b \pm \sqrt{b^2 - 4ac}}{2a}$. This final equation is called the **quadratic formula** and gives the solutions of any quadratic equation.

Quadratic Formula

If a, b, and c are real numbers and $a \neq 0$, a quadratic equation written in the standard form $ax^2 + bx + c = 0$ has solutions

$$x = \frac{-b \pm \sqrt{b^2 - 4ac}}{2a}$$

Helpful Hint

Don't forget that to correctly identify a, b, and c in the quadratic formula, you should write the equation in standard form.

Quadratic Equations in Standard Form

$5x^2 - 6x + 2 = 0$	$a = 5, b = -6, c = 2$
$4y^2 - 9 = 0$	$a = 4, b = 0, c = -9$
$x^2 + x = 0$	$a = 1, b = 1, c = 0$
$\sqrt{2}x^2 + \sqrt{5}x + \sqrt{3} = 0$	$a = \sqrt{2}, b = \sqrt{5}, c = \sqrt{3}$

Example 1 Solve $3x^2 + x - 3 = 0$ using the quadratic formula.

Solution: This equation is in standard form with $a = 3$, $b = 1$, and $c = -3$. By the quadratic formula, we have

$$x = \frac{-b \pm \sqrt{b^2 - 4ac}}{2a}$$

$$x = \frac{-1 \pm \sqrt{1^2 - 4 \cdot 3 \cdot (-3)}}{2 \cdot 3} \quad \text{Let } a = 3, b = 1, \text{ and } c = -3.$$

$$= \frac{-1 \pm \sqrt{1 + 36}}{6} \quad \text{Simplify.}$$

$$= \frac{-1 \pm \sqrt{37}}{6}$$

Check both solutions in the original equation. The solutions are $\frac{-1 + \sqrt{37}}{6}$ and $\frac{-1 - \sqrt{37}}{6}$.

Work Practice 1

PRACTICE 1

Solve $2x^2 - x - 5 = 0$ using the quadratic formula.

Example 2 Solve $2x^2 - 9x = 5$ using the quadratic formula.

Solution: First we write the equation in standard form by subtracting 5 from both sides.

$$2x^2 - 9x = 5$$
$$2x^2 - 9x - 5 = 0$$

Next we note that $a = 2$, $b = -9$, and $c = -5$. We substitute these values into the quadratic formula.

$$x = \frac{-b \pm \sqrt{b^2 - 4ac}}{2a}$$

$$x = \frac{-(-9) \pm \sqrt{(-9)^2 - 4 \cdot 2 \cdot (-5)}}{2 \cdot 2} \quad \text{Substitute in the formula.}$$

$$= \frac{9 \pm \sqrt{81 + 40}}{4} \quad \text{Simplify.}$$

$$= \frac{9 \pm \sqrt{121}}{4} = \frac{9 \pm 11}{4}$$

Continued on next page

PRACTICE 2

Solve $3x^2 + 8x = 3$ using the quadratic formula.

Helpful Hint

Notice that the fraction bar is under the entire numerator $-b \pm \sqrt{b^2 - 4ac}$.

Answers

1. $\frac{1 + \sqrt{41}}{4}$ and $\frac{1 - \sqrt{41}}{4}$

2. $\frac{1}{3}$ and -3

Then,

$$x = \frac{9 - 11}{4} = -\frac{1}{2} \quad \text{or} \quad x = \frac{9 + 11}{4} = 5$$

Check $-\frac{1}{2}$ and 5 in the original equation. Both $-\frac{1}{2}$ and 5 are solutions.

Work Practice 2

The following steps may be useful when solving a quadratic equation by the quadratic formula.

To Solve a Quadratic Equation by the Quadratic Formula

Step 1: Write the quadratic equation in standard form: $ax^2 + bx + c = 0$.

Step 2: If necessary, clear the equation of fractions to simplify calculations.

Step 3: Identify a, b, and c.

Step 4: Replace a, b, and c in the quadratic formula with the identified values, and simplify.

✓Concept Check For the quadratic equation $2x^2 - 5 = 7x$, if $a = 2$ and $c = -5$ in the quadratic formula, the value of b is which of the following?

a. $\frac{7}{2}$ **b.** 7 **c.** -5 **d.** -7

PRACTICE 3

Solve $5x^2 = 2$ using the quadratic formula.

Example 3 Solve $7x^2 = 1$ using the quadratic formula.

Solution: First we write the equation in standard form by subtracting 1 from both sides.

$$7x^2 = 1$$
$$7x^2 - 1 = 0$$

Helpful Hint
$7x^2 - 1 = 0$ can be written as $7x^2 + 0x - 1 = 0$. This form helps you see that $b = 0$.

Next we replace a, b, and c with the identified values: $a = 7, b = 0, c = -1$.

$$x = \frac{0 \pm \sqrt{0^2 - 4 \cdot 7 \cdot (-1)}}{2 \cdot 7} \quad \text{Substitute in the formula.}$$

$$= \frac{\pm\sqrt{28}}{14} \quad \text{Simplify.}$$

$$= \frac{\pm 2\sqrt{7}}{14}$$

$$= \pm\frac{2\sqrt{7}}{2 \cdot 7}$$

$$= \pm\frac{\sqrt{7}}{7}$$

The solutions are $\frac{\sqrt{7}}{7}$ and $-\frac{\sqrt{7}}{7}$.

Work Practice 3

Answer

3. $\frac{\sqrt{10}}{5}$ and $-\frac{\sqrt{10}}{5}$

✓ Concept Check Answer

d

Notice that we could have solved the equation $7x^2 = 1$ in Example 3 by dividing both sides by 7 and then using the square root property. We solved the equation by the quadratic formula to show that this formula can be used to solve any quadratic equation.

Example 4 Solve $x^2 = -x - 1$ using the quadratic formula.

Solution: First we write the equation in standard form.

$$x^2 + x + 1 = 0$$

Next we replace a, b, and c in the quadratic formula with $a = 1$, $b = 1$, and $c = 1$.

$$x = \frac{-1 \pm \sqrt{1^2 - 4\cdot 1\cdot 1}}{2\cdot 1} \quad \text{Substitute in the formula.}$$

$$= \frac{-1 \pm \sqrt{-3}}{2} \quad \text{Simplify.}$$

There is no real number solution because $\sqrt{-3}$ is not a real number.

Work Practice 4

PRACTICE 4

Solve $x^2 = -2x - 3$ using the quadratic formula.

Example 5 Solve $\frac{1}{2}x^2 - x = 2$ using the quadratic formula.

Solution: We write the equation in standard form and then clear the equation of fractions by multiplying both sides by the LCD, 2.

$$\frac{1}{2}x^2 - x = 2$$

$$\frac{1}{2}x^2 - x - 2 = 0 \quad \text{Write in standard form.}$$

$$x^2 - 2x - 4 = 0 \quad \text{Multiply both sides by 2.}$$

Here, $a = 1$, $b = -2$, and $c = -4$, so we substitute these values into the quadratic formula.

$$x = \frac{-(-2) \pm \sqrt{(-2)^2 - 4\cdot 1\cdot(-4)}}{2\cdot 1}$$

$$= \frac{2 \pm \sqrt{20}}{2} = \frac{2 \pm 2\sqrt{5}}{2} \quad \text{Simplify.}$$

$$= \frac{2\left(1 \pm \sqrt{5}\right)}{2} = 1 \pm \sqrt{5} \quad \text{Factor and simplify.}$$

The solutions are $1 - \sqrt{5}$ and $1 + \sqrt{5}$.

Work Practice 5

PRACTICE 5

Solve $\frac{1}{3}x^2 - x = 1$ using the quadratic formula.

Notice that in Example 5, although we cleared the equation of fractions, the coefficients $a = \frac{1}{2}$, $b = -1$, and $c = -2$ will give the same results.

Answers

4. no real solution
5. $\frac{3 + \sqrt{21}}{2}$ and $\frac{3 - \sqrt{21}}{2}$

Helpful Hint

When simplifying an expression such as

$$\frac{3 \pm 6\sqrt{2}}{6}$$

first factor out a common factor from the terms of the numerator and then simplify.

$$\frac{3 \pm 6\sqrt{2}}{6} = \frac{3\left(1 \pm 2\sqrt{2}\right)}{2 \cdot 3} = \frac{1 \pm 2\sqrt{2}}{2}$$

Objective B Approximate Solutions to Quadratic Equations

Sometimes approximate solutions for quadratic equations are appropriate.

PRACTICE 6

Approximate the exact solutions of the quadratic equation in Practice 1. Round the approximations to the nearest tenth.

Example 6 Approximate the exact solutions of the quadratic equation in Example 1. Round the approximations to the nearest tenth.

Solution: From Example 1, we have exact solutions $\frac{-1 \pm \sqrt{37}}{6}$. Thus,

$$\frac{-1 + \sqrt{37}}{6} \approx 0.847127088 \approx 0.8 \text{ to the nearest tenth.}$$

$$\frac{-1 - \sqrt{37}}{6} \approx -1.180460422 \approx -1.2 \text{ to the nearest tenth.}$$

Thus approximate solutions to the quadratic equation in Example 1 are 0.8 and −1.2.

Work Practice 6

Answer

6. $\frac{1 + \sqrt{41}}{4} \approx 1.9, \frac{1 - \sqrt{41}}{4} \approx -1.4$

Vocabulary and Readiness Check

Fill in each blank.

1. The quadratic formula is ______________.

Identify the values of a, b, and c in each quadratic equation.

2. $5x^2 - 7x + 1 = 0$; $a =$ ______________, $b =$ ______________, $c =$ ______________

3. $x^2 + 3x - 7 = 0$; $a =$ ______________, $b =$ ______________, $c =$ ______________

4. $x^2 - 6 = 0$; $a =$ ______________, $b =$ ______________, $c =$ ______________

5. $x^2 + x - 1 = 0$; $a =$ ______________, $b =$ ______________, $c =$ ______________

6. $9x^2 - 4 = 0$; $a =$ ______________, $b =$ ______________, $c =$ ______________

Simplify the following.

7. $\dfrac{-1 \pm \sqrt{1^2 - 4(1)(-2)}}{2(1)}$

8. $\dfrac{-(-5) \pm \sqrt{(-5)^2 - 4(2)(3)}}{2(2)}$

9. $\dfrac{-5 \pm \sqrt{5^2 - 4(1)(2)}}{2(1)}$

10. $\dfrac{-7 \pm \sqrt{7^2 - 4(2)(1)}}{2(2)}$

9.3 Exercise Set

FOR EXTRA HELP

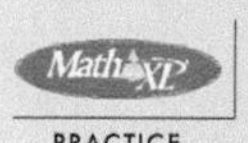

PRACTICE

WATCH

DOWNLOAD

READ

REVIEW

Objective A *Use the quadratic formula to solve each quadratic equation. See Examples 1 through 4.*

1. $x^2 - 3x + 2 = 0$

2. $x^2 - 5x - 6 = 0$

3. $3k^2 + 7k + 1 = 0$

4. $7k^2 + 3k - 1 = 0$

5. $4x^2 - 3 = 0$

6. $25x^2 - 15 = 0$

7. $5z^2 - 4z + 3 = 0$

8. $3x^2 + 2x + 1 = 0$

9. $y^2 = 7y + 30$

10. $y^2 = 5y + 36$

11. $2x^2 = 10$

12. $5x^2 = 15$

13. $m^2 - 12 = m$

14. $m^2 - 14 = 5m$

15. $3 - x^2 = 4x$

16. $10 - x^2 = 2x$

17. $6x^2 + 9x = 2$

18. $3x^2 - 9x = 8$

19. $7p^2 + 2 = 8p$

20. $11p^2 + 2 = 10p$

21. $x^2 - 6x + 2 = 0$

22. $x^2 - 10x + 19 = 0$

23. $2x^2 - 6x + 3 = 0$

24. $5x^2 - 8x + 2 = 0$

25. $3x^2 = 1 - 2x$

26. $5y^2 = 4 - y$

27. $4y^2 = 6y + 1$

28. $6z^2 = 2 - 3z$

29. $20y^2 = 3 - 11y$

30. $2z^2 = z + 3$

31. $x^2 + x + 2 = 0$

32. $k^2 + 2k + 5 = 0$

Use the quadratic formula to solve each quadratic equation. See Example 5.

33. $\frac{m^2}{2} = m + \frac{1}{2}$

34. $\frac{m^2}{2} = 3m - 1$

35. $3p^2 - \frac{2}{3}p + 1 = 0$

36. $\frac{5}{2}p^2 - p + \frac{1}{2} = 0$

37. $4p^2 + \frac{3}{2} = -5p$

38. $4p^2 + \frac{3}{2} = 5p$

39. $5x^2 = \frac{7}{2}x + 1$

40. $2x^2 = \frac{5}{2}x + \frac{7}{2}$

41. $x^2 - \frac{11}{2}x - \frac{1}{2} = 0$

42. $\frac{2}{3}x^2 - 2x - \frac{2}{3} = 0$

43. $5z^2 - 2z = \frac{1}{5}$

44. $9z^2 + 12z = -1$

Objectives A B Mixed Practice *Use the quadratic formula to solve each quadratic equation. Find the exact solutions; then approximate these solutions to the nearest tenth. See Example 6.*

45. $3x^2 = 21$

46. $2x^2 = 26$

47. $x^2 + 6x + 1 = 0$

48. $x^2 + 4x + 2 = 0$

49. $x^2 = 9x + 4$

50. $x^2 = 7x + 5$

51. $3x^2 - 2x - 2 = 0$

52. $5x^2 - 3x - 1 = 0$

Review

Graph the following linear equations in two variables. See Sections 6.2 and 6.3.

53. $y = -3$

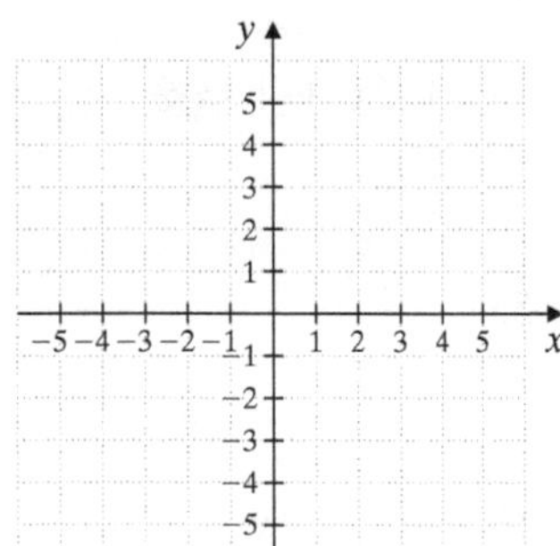

54. $x = 4$

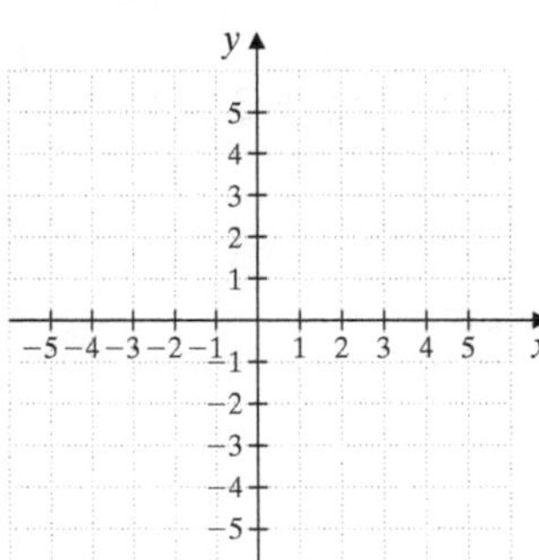

55. $y = 3x - 2$

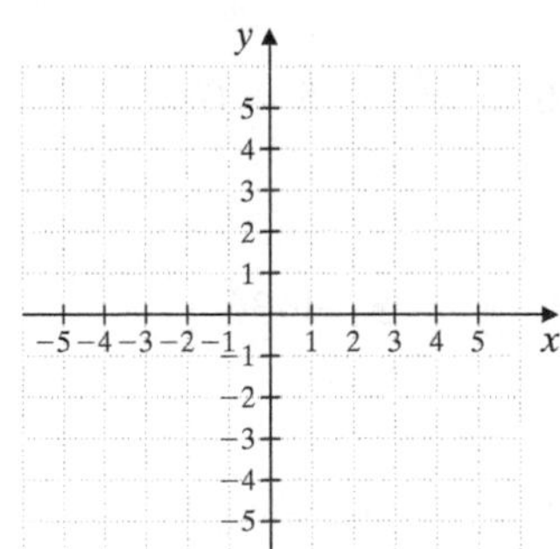

56. $y = 2x + 3$

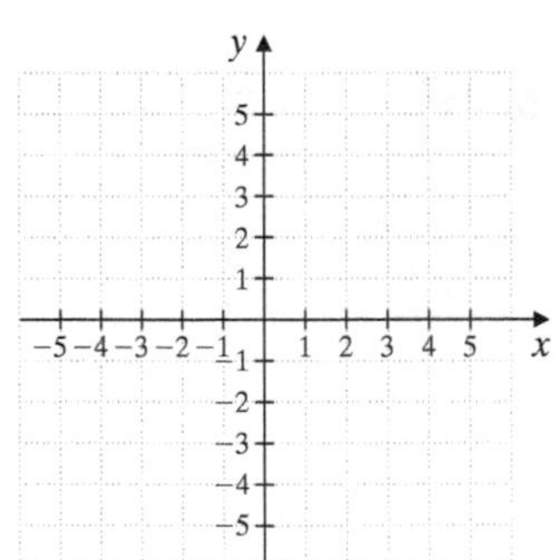

Concept Extensions

Solve. See the Concept Check in this section. For the quadratic equation $5x^2 + 2 = x$, *if* $a = 5$,

57. What is the value of b?

a. $\frac{1}{5}$ **b.** 0 **c.** −1 **d.** 1

58. What is the value of c?

a. 5 **b.** x **c.** −2 **d.** 2

For the quadratic equation $7y^2 = 3y$, *if* $b = 3$,

59. What is the value of a?

a. 7 **b.** −7 **c.** 0 **d.** 1

60. What is the value of c?

a. 7 **b.** 3 **c.** 0 **d.** 1

△ **61.** In a recent year, Nestle created a chocolate bar that the company claimed weighed more than 2 tons. The rectangular bar had a base area of approximately 34.65 square feet, and its length was 0.6 foot shorter than three times its width. Find the length and width of the bar. (*Source:* Nestle)

△ **62.** The area of a rectangular conference room table is 95 square feet. If its length is six feet longer than its width, find the dimensions of the table. Round each dimension to the nearest tenth.

Solve each equation using the quadratic formula.

63. $x^2 + 3\sqrt{2}x - 5 = 0$

64. $y^2 - 2\sqrt{5}y - 1 = 0$

65. Explain how to correctly identify a, b, and c when solving a quadratic equation by the quadratic formula.

66. Explain how the quadratic formula is developed and why it is useful.

Use the quadratic formula and a calculator to solve each equation. Round solutions to the nearest tenth.

67. $7.3z^2 + 5.4z - 1.1 = 0$

68. $1.2x^2 - 5.2x - 3.9 = 0$

A rocket is launched from the top of an 80-foot cliff with an initial velocity of 120 feet per second. The height, h, of the rocket after t seconds is given by the equation $h = -16t^2 + 120t + 80$. *Use this for Exercises 69 and 70.*

69. How long after the rocket is launched will it be 30 feet from the ground? Round to the nearest tenth of a second.

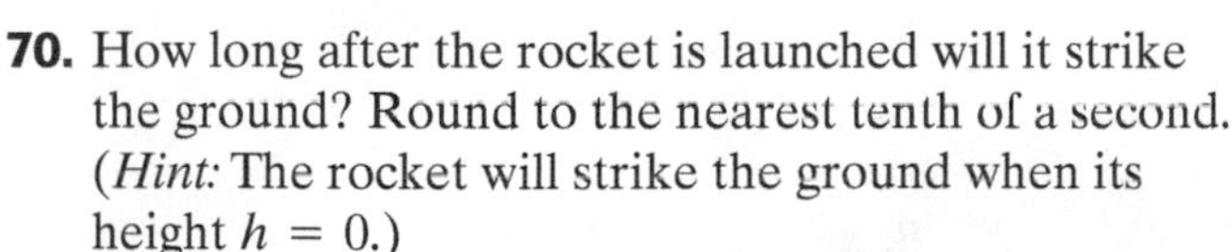

70. How long after the rocket is launched will it strike the ground? Round to the nearest tenth of a second. (*Hint:* The rocket will strike the ground when its height $h = 0$.)

71. The revenues from product sales y (in thousands of dollars) of ABIOMED, Inc., maker of the AbioCor artificial heart, from 2004 through 2008 can be modeled by the equation $y = -587x^2 + 10{,}243x + 26{,}047$, where $x = 0$ represents 2004. Assume that this trend continues and predict the first year in which ABIOMED's revenues from product sales will be \$70,423 thousand. (*Source:* Based on data from ABIOMED Corporation)

72. The average annual salary y (in millions of dollars) for NFL players for the years 2003 through 2007 is approximated by the equation $y = 0.014x^2 + 0.08x + 1.25$, where $x = 0$ represents the year 2003. Assume that this trend continues and predict the year in which the average NFL salary will be approximately \$2.5 million. (*Source:* Based on data from the NFL and *USA Today*)

Integrated Review Sections 9.1–9.3

Summary on Solving Quadratic Equations

Answers

1. ______

2. ______

3. ______

4. ______

5. ______

6. ______

7. ______

8. ______

9. ______

10. ______

11. ______

12. ______

13. ______

14. ______

15. ______

16. ______

17. ______

18. ______

19. ______

20. ______

An important skill in mathematics is learning when to use one technique in favor of another. We now practice this by deciding which method to use when solving quadratic equations. Although both the quadratic formula and completing the square can be used to solve any quadratic equation, the quadratic formula is usually less tedious and thus preferred. The following steps may be used to solve a quadratic equation.

To Solve a Quadratic Equation

Step 1: If the equation is in the form $ax^2 = c$ or $(ax + b)^2 = c$, use the square root property and solve. If not, go to Step 2.

Step 2: Write the equation in standard form: $ax^2 + bx + c = 0$.

Step 3: Try to solve the equation by the factoring method. If not possible, go to Step 4.

Step 4: Solve the equation by the quadratic formula.

Choose and use a method to solve each equation.

1. $5x^2 - 11x + 2 = 0$

2. $5x^2 + 13x - 6 = 0$

3. $x^2 - 1 = 2x$

4. $x^2 + 7 = 6x$

5. $a^2 = 20$

6. $a^2 = 72$

7. $x^2 - x + 4 = 0$

8. $x^2 - 2x + 7 = 0$

9. $3x^2 - 12x + 12 = 0$

10. $5x^2 - 30x + 45 = 0$

11. $9 - 6p + p^2 = 0$

12. $49 - 28p + 4p^2 = 0$

13. $4y^2 - 16 = 0$

14. $3y^2 - 27 = 0$

15. $x^2 - 3x + 2 = 0$

16. $x^2 + 7x + 12 = 0$

17. $(2z + 5)^2 = 25$

18. $(3z - 4)^2 = 16$

19. $30x = 25x^2 + 2$

20. $12x = 4x^2 + 4$

21. $\frac{2}{3}m^2 - \frac{1}{3}m - 1 = 0$

22. $\frac{5}{8}m^2 + m - \frac{1}{2} = 0$

23. $x^2 - \frac{1}{2}x - \frac{1}{5} = 0$

24. $x^2 + \frac{1}{2}x - \frac{1}{8} = 0$

25. $4x^2 - 27x + 35 = 0$

26. $9x^2 - 16x + 7 = 0$

27. $(7 - 5x)^2 = 18$

28. $(5 - 4x)^2 = 75$

29. $3z^2 - 7z = 12$

30. $6z^2 + 7z = 6$

31. $x = x^2 - 110$

32. $x = 56 - x^2$

33. $\frac{3}{4}x^2 - \frac{5}{2}x - 2 = 0$

34. $x^2 - \frac{6}{5}x - \frac{8}{5} = 0$

35. $x^2 - 0.6x + 0.05 = 0$

36. $x^2 - 0.1x - 0.06 = 0$

37. $10x^2 - 11x + 2 = 0$

38. $20x^2 - 11x + 1 = 0$

39. $\frac{1}{2}z^2 - 2z + \frac{3}{4} = 0$

40. $\frac{1}{5}z^2 - \frac{1}{2}z - 2 = 0$

41. Explain how you will decide what method to use when solving quadratic equations.

21. ______
22. ______
23. ______
24. ______
25. ______
26. ______
27. ______
28. ______
29. ______
30. ______
31. ______
32. ______
33. ______
34. ______
35. ______
36. ______
37. ______
38. ______
39. ______
40. ______
41. ______

Chapter 9 Vocabulary Check

Fill in each blank with one of the words or phrases listed below. Some choices may be used more than once and some may not be used at all.

square root	vertex	one	parabola
completing the square	quadratic	zero	

1. If $x^2 = a$, then $x = \sqrt{a}$ or $x = -\sqrt{a}$. This property is called the ________________ property.
2. The graph of $y = x^2$ is called a(n) ________________.
3. The formula $x = \frac{-b}{2a}$ where $y = ax^2 + bx + c$ is called the ________________ formula.
4. The process of solving a quadratic equation by writing it in the form $(x + a)^2 = c$ is called ________________.
5. The formula $x = \frac{-b \pm \sqrt{b^2 - 4ac}}{2a}$ is called the ________________ formula.
6. The lowest point on a parabola that opens upward is called the ________________.
7. The zero-factor property states that if the product of two numbers is zero, then at least one of the two numbers is ________________.

Helpful Hint Are you preparing for your test? Don't forget to take the Chapter 9 Test on page 688. Then check your answers at the back of the text and use the Chapter Test Prep Videos to see the fully worked-out solutions to any of the exercises you want to review.

9 Chapter Highlights

Definitions and Concepts	Examples
Section 9.1 Solving Quadratic Equations by the Square Root Property	
Square Root Property If $x^2 = a$ for $a \geq 0$, then $x = \sqrt{a}$ or $x = -\sqrt{a}$.	Solve the equation. $(x - 1)^2 = 15$ $x - 1 = \sqrt{15}$ or $x - 1 = -\sqrt{15}$ $x = 1 + \sqrt{15}$ $\quad$ $x = 1 - \sqrt{15}$
Section 9.2 Solving Quadratic Equations by Completing the Square	
To Solve a Quadratic Equation by Completing the Square **Step 1.** If the coefficient of x^2 is not 1, divide both sides of the equation by the coefficient. **Step 2.** Get all terms with variables alone on one side. **Step 3.** Complete the square by adding the square of half of the coefficient of x to both sides. **Step 4.** Factor the perfect square trinomial. **Step 5.** Use the square root property to solve.	Solve $2x^2 + 12x - 10 = 0$ by completing the square. $\frac{2x^2}{2} + \frac{12x}{2} - \frac{10}{2} = \frac{0}{2}$ Divide by 2. $x^2 + 6x - 5 = 0$ Simplify. $x^2 + 6x = 5$ Add 5. The coefficient of x is 6. Half of 6 is 3 and $3^2 = 9$. Add 9 to both sides. $x^2 + 6x + 9 = 5 + 9$ $(x + 3)^2 = 14$ Factor. $x + 3 = \sqrt{14}$ or $x + 3 = -\sqrt{14}$ $x = -3 + \sqrt{14}$ $\quad$ $x = -3 - \sqrt{14}$

Definitions and Concepts	Examples

Section 9.3 Solving Quadratic Equations by the Quadratic Formula

QUADRATIC FORMULA

If a, b, and c are real numbers and $a \neq 0$, the quadratic equation $ax^2 + bx + c = 0$ has solutions

$$x = \frac{-b \pm \sqrt{b^2 - 4ac}}{2a}$$

Identify a, b, and c in the quadratic equation

$$4x^2 - 6x = 5$$

First, subtract 5 from both sides.

$$4x^2 - 6x - 5 = 0$$

$a = 4$, $b = -6$, and $c = -5$.

TO SOLVE A QUADRATIC EQUATION BY THE QUADRATIC FORMULA

Step 1. Write the equation in standard form: $ax^2 + bx + c = 0$.

Step 2. If necessary, clear the equation of fractions.

Step 3. Identify a, b, and c.

Step 4. Replace a, b, and c in the quadratic formula with the identified values, and simplify.

Solve $3x^2 - 2x - 2 = 0$.
In this equation, $a = 3$, $b = -2$,and $c = -2$.

$$x = \frac{-(-2) \pm \sqrt{(-2)^2 - 4(3)(-2)}}{2 \cdot 3}$$

$$= \frac{2 \pm \sqrt{4 - (-24)}}{6}$$

$$= \frac{2 \pm \sqrt{28}}{6} = \frac{2 \pm \sqrt{4 \cdot 7}}{6} = \frac{2 \pm 2\sqrt{7}}{6}$$

$$= \frac{2(1 \pm \sqrt{7})}{2 \cdot 3} = \frac{1 \pm \sqrt{7}}{3}$$

Section 9.4 Graphing Quadratic Equations in Two Variables

The graph of a quadratic equation $y = ax^2 + bx + c$, $a \neq 0$, is called a **parabola.** The lowest point on a parabola opening upward or the highest point on a parabola opening downward is called the **vertex.** The vertical line through the vertex is the **line of symmetry.**

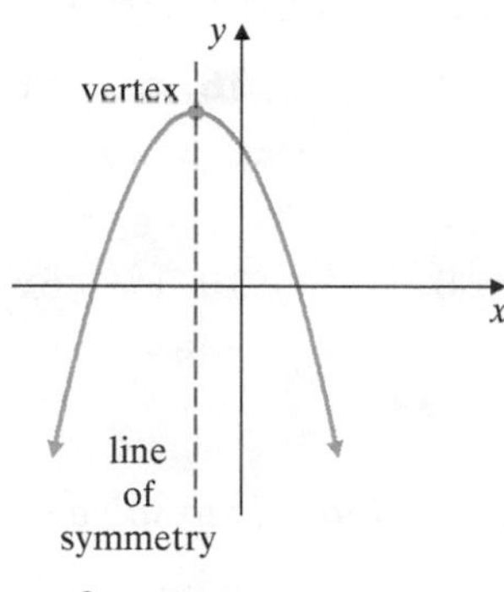

VERTEX FORMULA

The vertex of the parabola $y = ax^2 + bx + c$ has x-coordinate $\frac{-b}{2a}$. To find the corresponding y-coordinate, substitute the x-coordinate into the original equation and solve for y.

Graph: $y = 2x^2 - 6x + 4$
The x-coordinate of the vertex is

$$x = \frac{-b}{2a} = \frac{-(-6)}{2(2)} = \frac{6}{4} = \frac{3}{2}$$

The y-coordinate is

$$y = 2\left(\frac{3}{2}\right)^2 - 6\left(\frac{3}{2}\right) + 4 = 2\left(\frac{9}{4}\right) - 9 + 4 = -\frac{1}{2}$$

The vertex is $\left(\frac{3}{2}, -\frac{1}{2}\right)$.

The y-intercept is

$$y = 2 \cdot 0^2 - 6 \cdot 0 + 4 = 4$$

The x-intercepts are

$$0 = 2x^2 - 6x + 4$$
$$0 = 2(x - 2)(x - 1)$$
$$x = 2 \quad \text{or} \quad x = 1$$

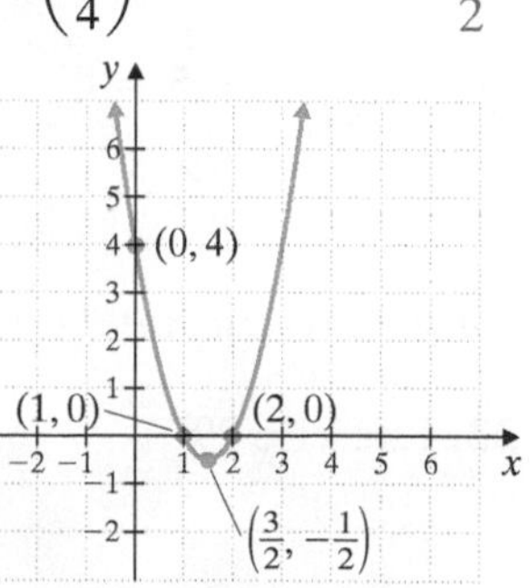

Chapter 9 Review

(9.1) *Solve each quadradic equation by factoring.*

1. $x^2 - 121 = 0$

2. $y^2 - 100 = 0$

3. $3m^2 - 5m = 2$

4. $7m^2 + 2m = 5$

Use the square root property to solve each quadratic equation.

5. $x^2 = 36$

6. $x^2 = 81$

7. $k^2 = 50$

8. $k^2 = 45$

9. $(x - 11)^2 = 49$

10. $(x + 3)^2 = 100$

11. $(4p + 5)^2 = 41$

12. $(3p + 7)^2 = 37$

Solve. For Exercises 13 and 14, use the formula $h = 16t^2$*, where h is the height in feet at time t seconds.*

13. If Kara Washington dives from a height of 100 feet, how long before she hits the water?

14. How long does a 5-mile free-fall take? Round your result to the nearest tenth of a second. (*Hint:* 1 mi = 5280 ft)

(9.2) *Solve each quadratic equation by completing the square.*

15. $x^2 - 9x = -8$

16. $x^2 + 8x = 20$

17. $x^2 + 4x = 1$

18. $x^2 - 8x = 3$

19. $x^2 - 6x + 7 = 0$

20. $x^2 + 6x + 7 = 0$

21. $2y^2 + y - 1 = 0$

22. $4y^2 + 3y - 1 = 0$

(9.3) *Use the quadratic formula to solve each quadratic equation.*

23. $9x^2 + 30x + 25 = 0$

24. $16x^2 - 72x + 81 = 0$

25. $7x^2 = 35$

26. $11x^2 = 33$

27. $x^2 - 10x + 7 = 0$

28. $x^2 + 4x - 7 = 0$

29. $3x^2 + x - 1 = 0$

30. $x^2 + 3x - 1 = 0$

31. $2x^2 + x + 5 = 0$

32. $7x^2 - 3x + 1 = 0$

For the exercise numbers given, approximate the exact solutions to the nearest tenth.

33. Exercise 29

34. Exercise 30

35. The average price of platinum (in dollars per ounce) from 2003 to 2008 is modeled by the equation $y = 8x^2 + 109x + 700$. In this equation, x is the number of years since 2003. Assume that this trend continues and find the year after 2003 in which the price of platinum will be \$2590 per ounce. (*Source:* U.S. Geological Survey, Minerals Information)

36. The average price of silver (in cents per ounce) from 2003 to 2007 is modeled by the equation $y = 26x^2 + 115x + 493$. In this equation, x is the number of years since 2003. Assume that this trend continues and find the year after 2003 in which the price of silver will be 3077 cents per ounce. (*Source:* U.S. Geological Survey, Minerals Information)

(9.4) *Graph each quadratic equation and find and plot any intercepts.*

37. $y = 5x^2$

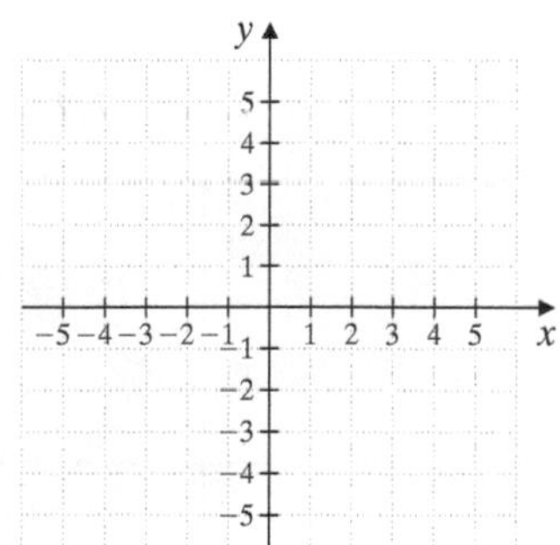

38. $y = -\frac{1}{2}x^2$

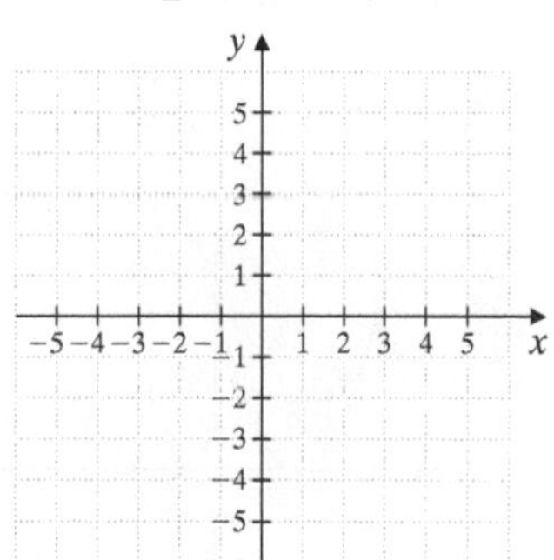

Graph each quadratic equation. Label the vertex and the intercepts with their coordinates.

39. $y = x^2 - 25$

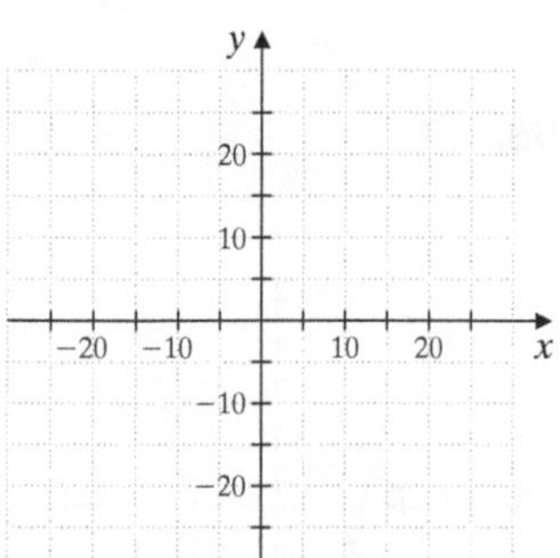

40. $y = x^2 - 36$

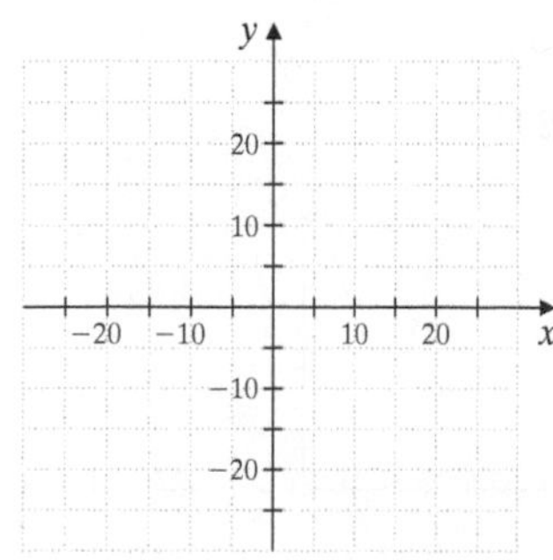

41. $y = x^2 + 3$

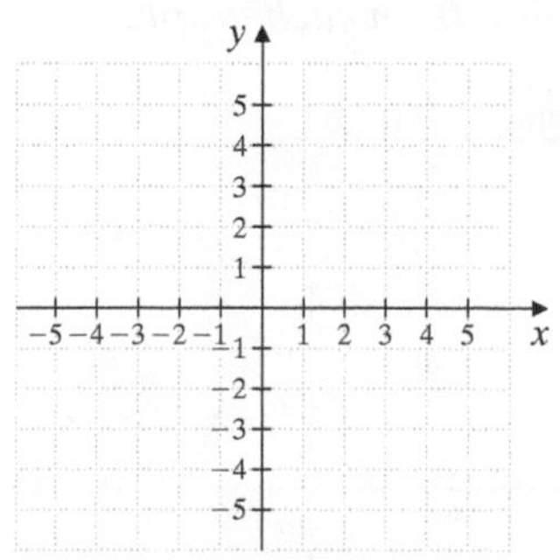

42. $y = x^2 + 8$

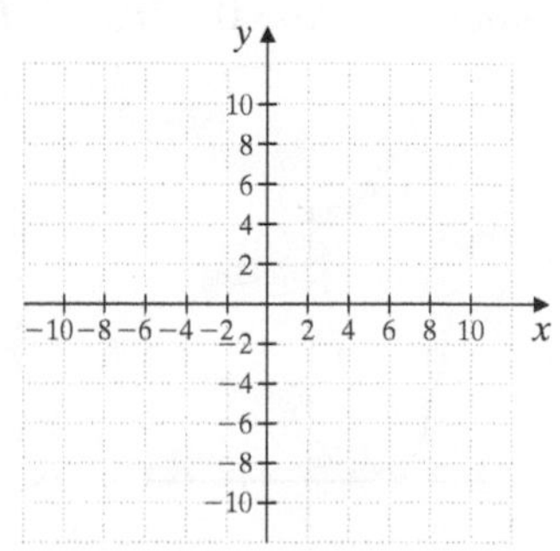

43. $y = -4x^2 + 8$

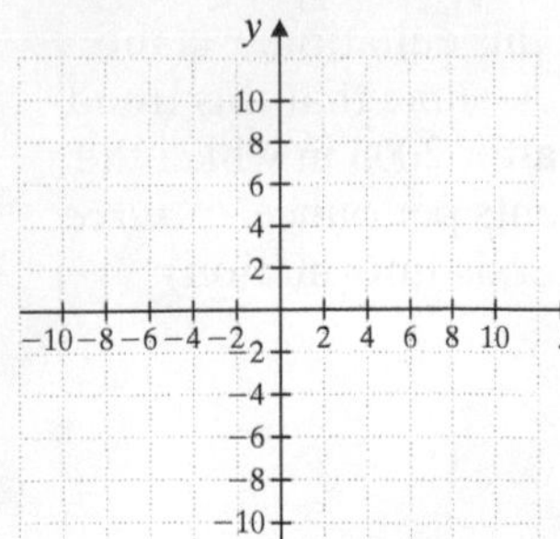

44. $y = -3x^2 + 9$

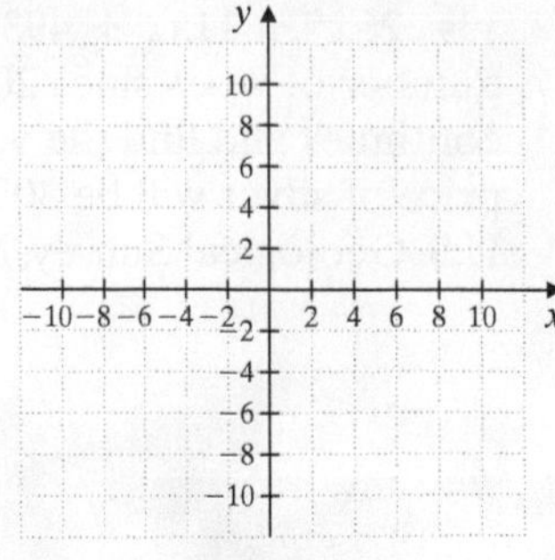

45. $y = x^2 + 3x - 10$

y

20

10

−20 −10 10 20 x

−10

−20

46. $y = x^2 + 3x - 4$

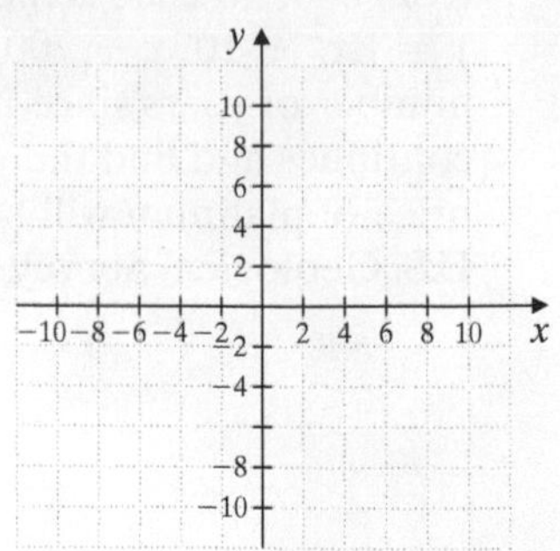

47. $y = -x^2 - 5x - 6$

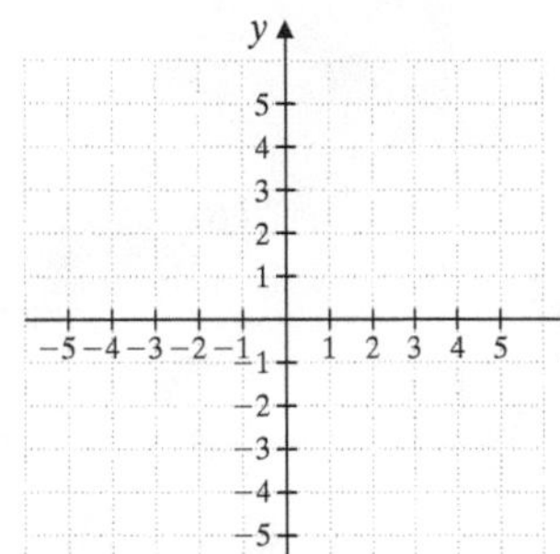

48. $y = 3x^2 - x - 2$

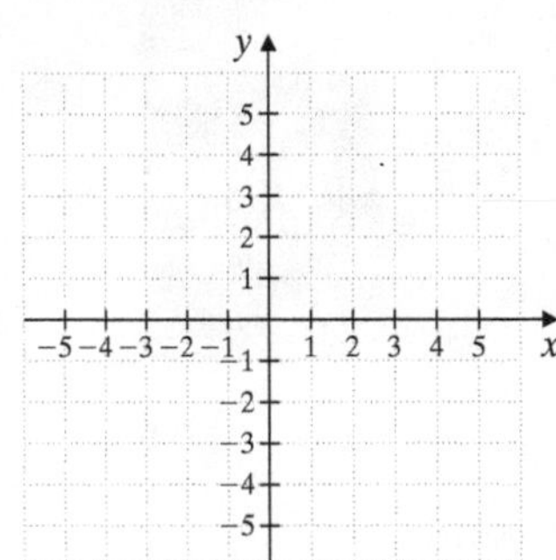

49. $y = 2x^2 - 11x - 6$

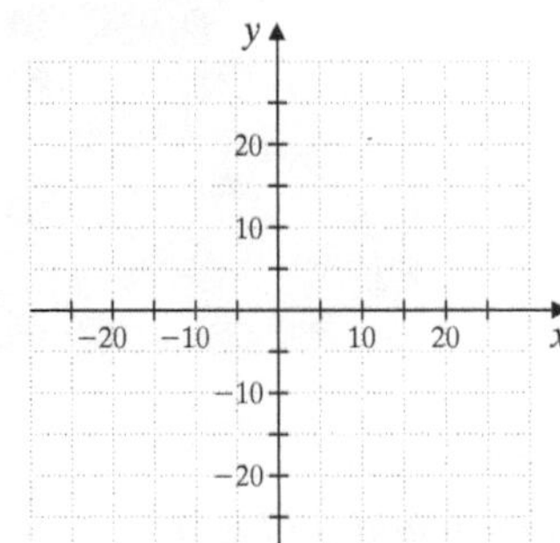

50. $y = -x^2 + 4x + 8$

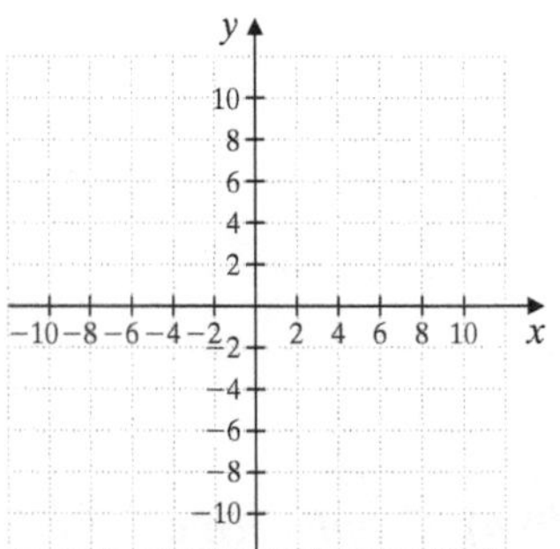

Match each quadratic equation with its graph.

51. $y = 2x^2$

52. $y = -x^2$

53. $y = x^2 + 4x + 4$

54. $y = x^2 + 5x + 4$

A

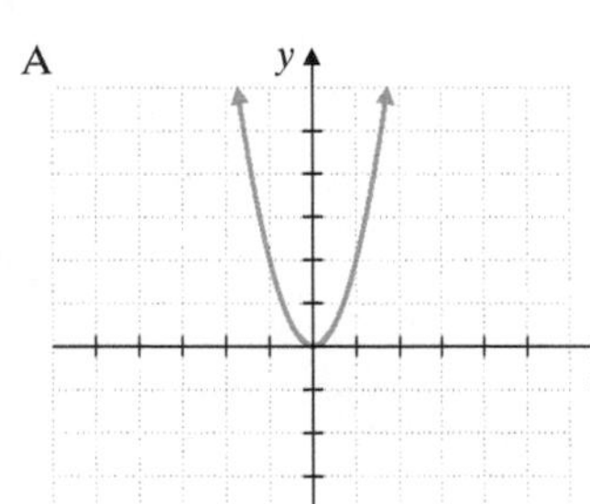

B

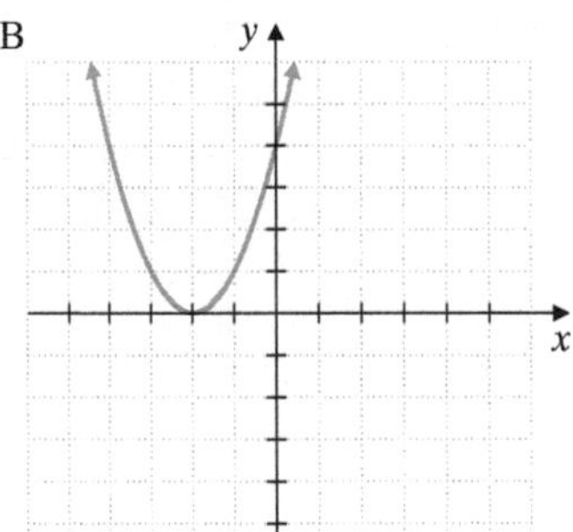

C

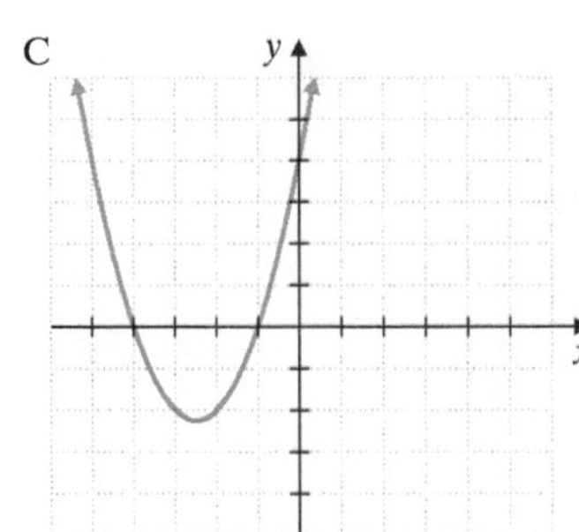

D

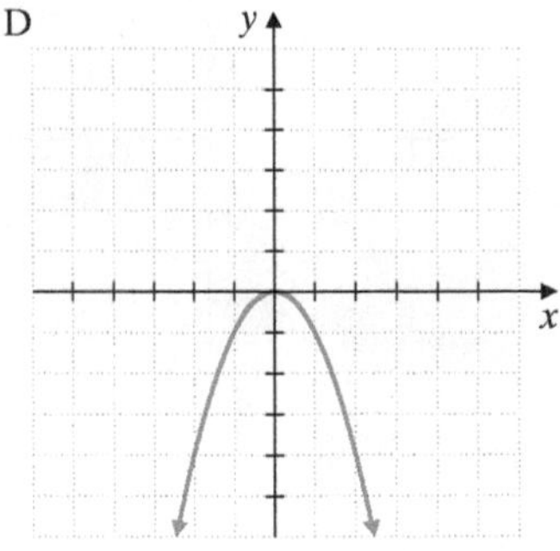

Quadratic equations in the form $y = ax^2 + bx + c$ are graphed below. Determine the number of real solutions for the related equation $0 = ax^2 + bx + c$ from each graph.

55.

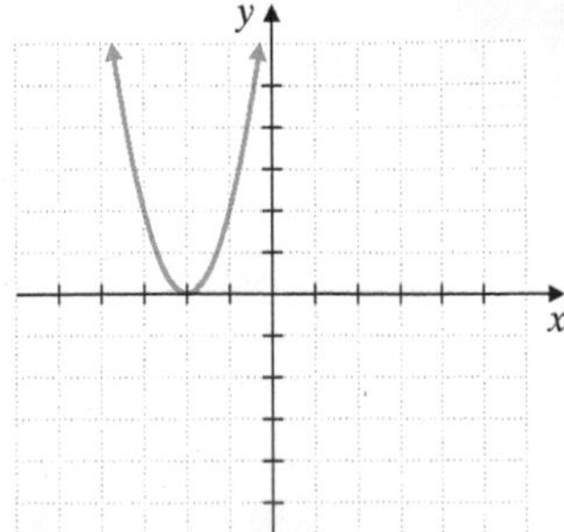

56.

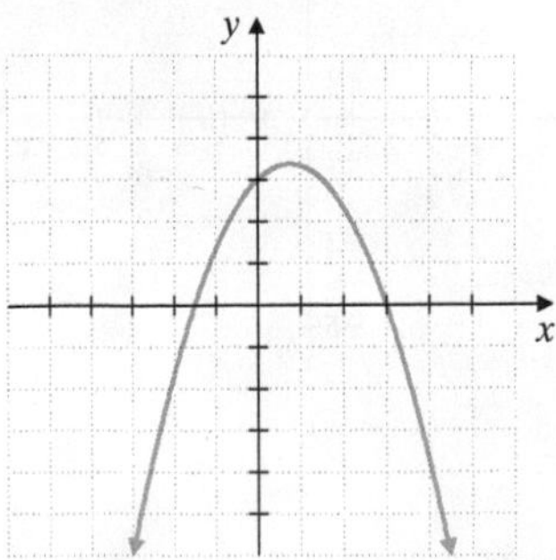

57.

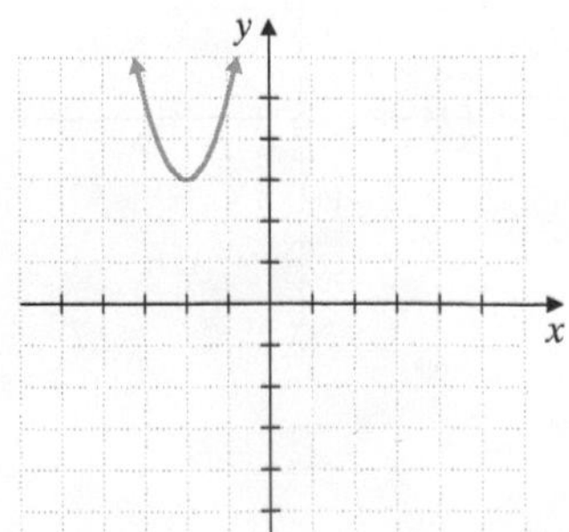

58.

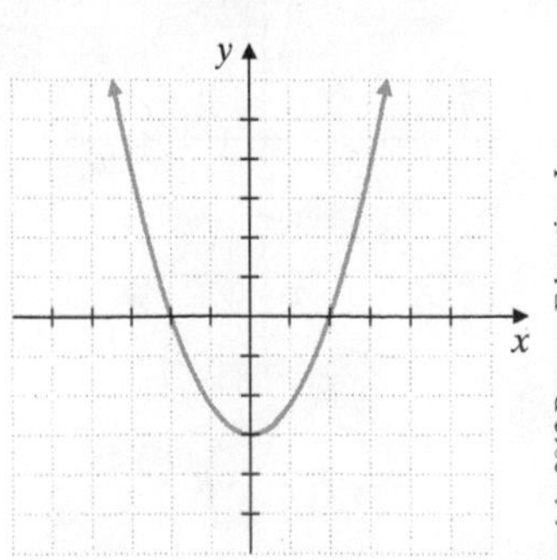

Mixed Review

Use the square root property to solve each quadratic equation.

59. $x^2 = 49$

60. $y^2 = 75$

61. $(x - 7)^2 = 64$

Solve each quadratic equation by completing the square.

62. $x^2 + 4x = 6$

63. $3x^2 + x = 2$

64. $4x^2 - x - 2 = 0$

Use the quadratic formula to solve each quadratic equation.

65. $4x^2 - 3x - 2 = 0$

66. $5x^2 + x - 2 = 0$

67. $4x^2 + 12x + 9 = 0$

68. $2x^2 + x + 4 = 0$

Graph each quadratic equation. Label the vertex and the intercepts with their coordinates.

69. $y = 4 - x^2$

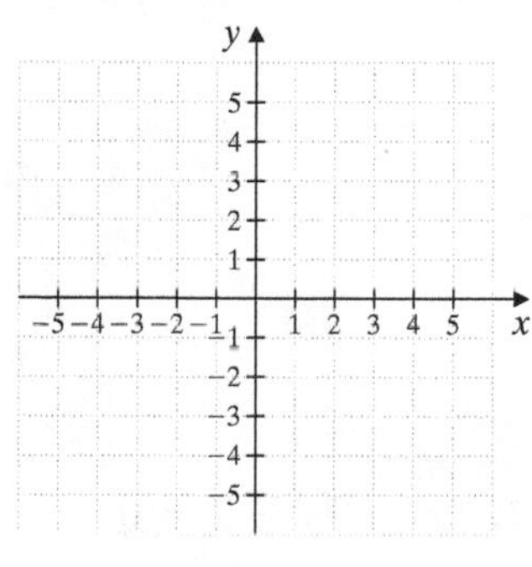

70. $y = x^2 + 4$

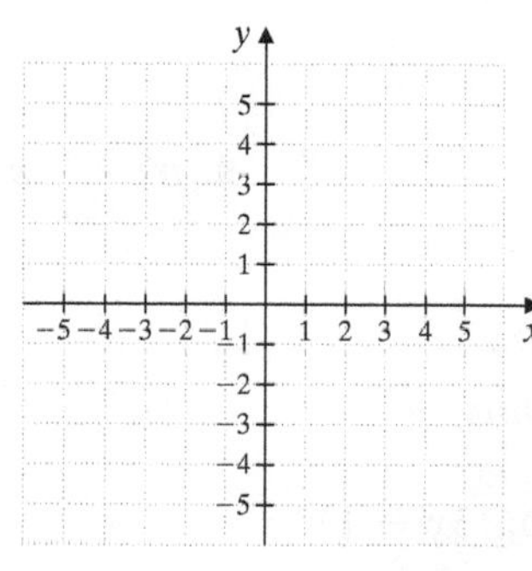

71. $y = x^2 + 6x + 8$

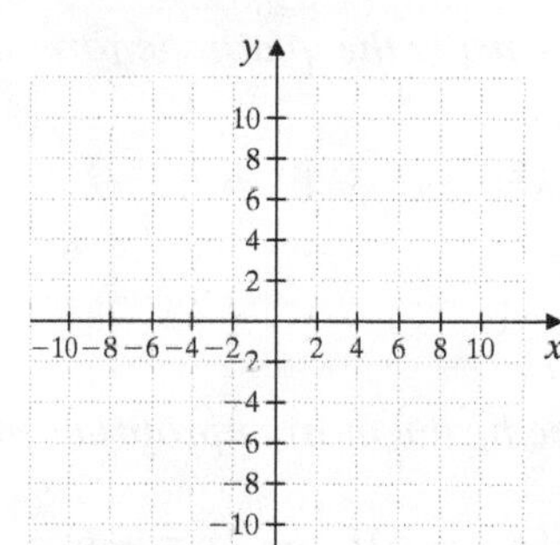

72. $y = x^2 - 2x - 4$

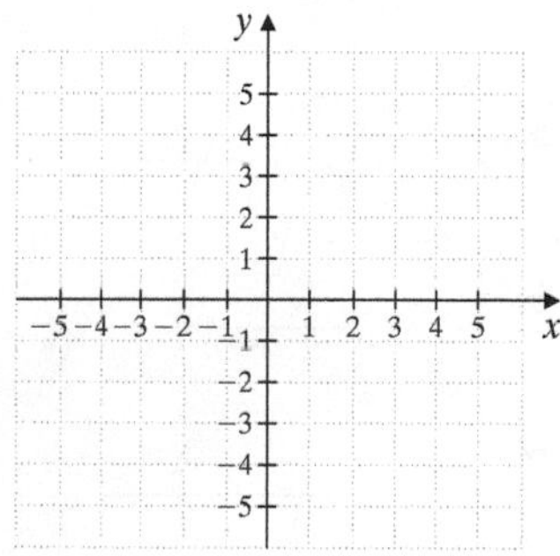

Chapter 9 Test

Step-by-step test solutions are found on the Chapter Test Prep Videos available via the Interactive DVD Lecture Series, in MyMathLab or on YouTube (search "MartinGayIntroAlg" and click on "Channels").

Answers

1. ______
2. ______
3. ______
4. ______
5. ______
6. ______
7. ______
8. ______
9. ______
10. ______
11. ______
12. ______
13. ______
14. ______
15. ______

Solve by factoring.

1. $x^2 - 400 = 0$

2. $2x^2 - 11x = 21$

Solve using the square root property.

3. $5k^2 = 80$

4. $(3m - 5)^2 = 8$

Solve by completing the square.

5. $x^2 - 26x + 160 = 0$

6. $3x^2 + 12x - 4 = 0$

Solve using the quadratic formula.

7. $x^2 - 3x - 10 = 0$

8. $p^2 - \frac{5}{3}p - \frac{1}{3} = 0$

Solve by the most appropriate method.

9. $(3x - 5)(x + 2) = -6$

10. $(3x - 1)^2 = 16$

11. $3x^2 - 7x - 2 = 0$

12. $x^2 - 4x - 5 = 0$

13. $3x^2 - 7x + 2 = 0$

14. $2x^2 - 6x + 1 = 0$

△ **15.** The height of a triangle is 4 times the length of the base. The area of the triangle is 18 square feet. Find the height and base of the triangle.

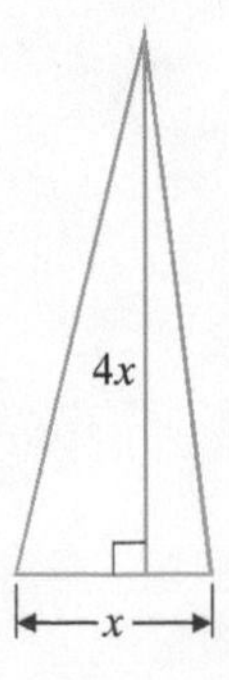

Graph each quadratic equation. Label the vertex and the intercept points with their coordinates.

16. $y = -5x^2$

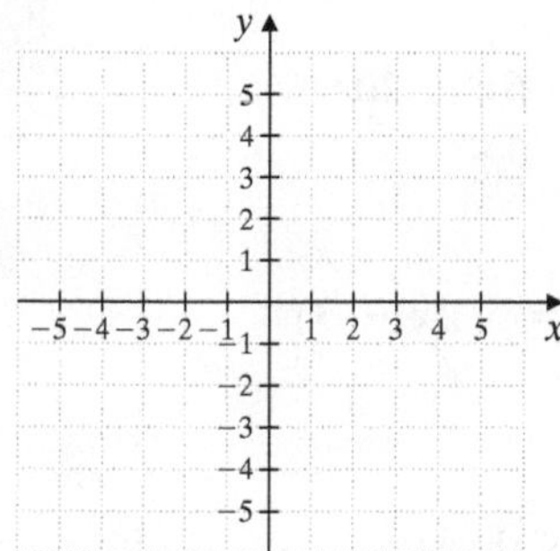

17. $y = x^2 - 4$

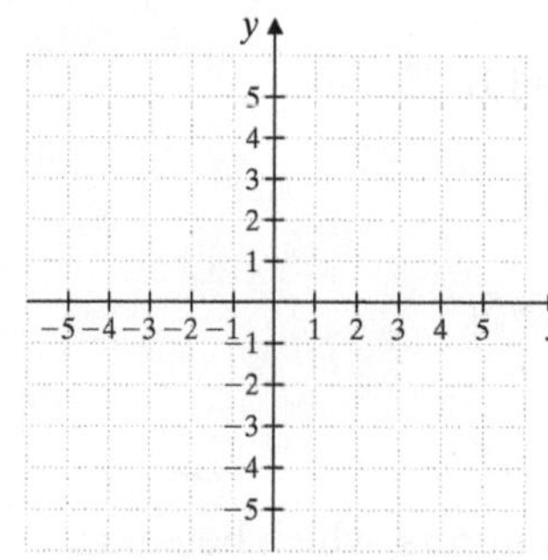

18. $y = x^2 - 7x + 10$

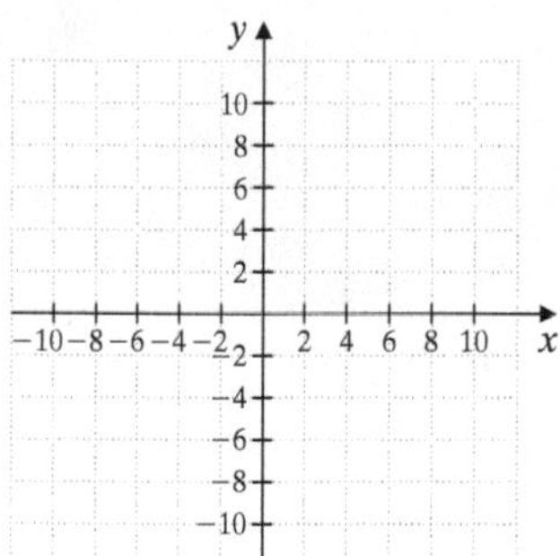

19. $y = 2x^2 + 4x - 1$

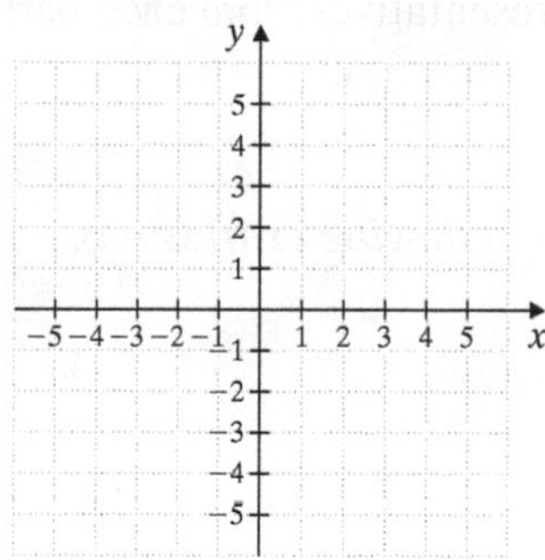

△ **20.** The number of diagonals d that a polygon with n sides has is given by the formula

$$d = \frac{n^2 - 3n}{2}$$

Find the number of sides of a polygon if it has 9 diagonals.

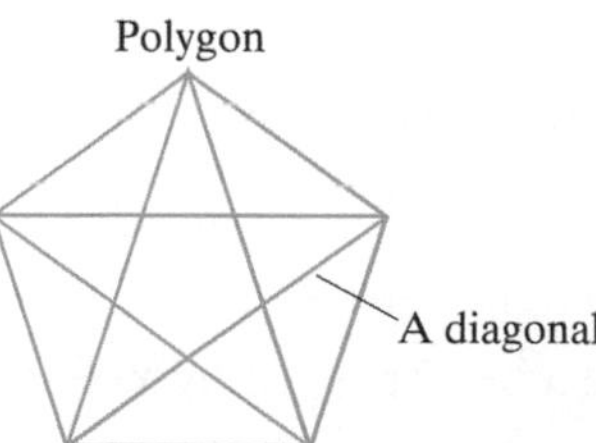

Solve.

21. The highest dive from a diving board by a woman was made by Lucy Wardle of the United States. She dove from a height of 120.75 feet at Ocean Park, Hong Kong, in 1985. To the nearest tenth of a second, how long did the dive take? Use the formula $h = 16t^2$.

16. ______

17. ______

18. ______

19. ______

20. ______

21. ______

Answers

1. ______

2. ______

3. ______

4. ______

5. ______

6. ______

7. ______

8. ______

9. ______

10. ______

11. ______

12. ______

13. ______

14. ______

15. ______

16. ______

17. ______

18. a. ______

b. ______

19. ______

20. ______

21. ______

Cumulative Review Chapters 1–9

Solve each equation.

1. $y + 0.6 = -1.0$

2. $8x - 14 = 6x - 20$

3. $8(2 - t) = -5t$

4. $2(x + 7) = 5(2x - 3)$

5. The 111th Congress, which began at noon on January 3, 2009, had a total of 434 Democrats and Republicans. There were 78 more Democratic representatives than Republican. Find the number of representatives from each party.

6. The sum of three consecutive integers is 438. Find the integers.

Simplify the following expressions.

7. 3^0

8. $\left(\frac{-6x}{y^3}\right)^3$

9. $(5x^3y^2)^0$

10. $\frac{a^2b^7}{(2b^2)^5}$

11. -4^0

12. $\frac{(3y)^2}{y^2}$

13. Multiply: $(3y + 2)^2$

14. Multiply: $(x^2 + 5)(y - 1)$

15. Divide $x^2 + 7x + 12$ by $x + 3$ using long division.

16. Simplify by combining like terms: $2 + 8.1a + a - 6$

17. Factor: $r^2 - r - 42$

18. Find the value of each expression when $x = -4$ and $y = 7$.

a. $\frac{x - y}{7 - x}$ **b.** $x^2 + 2y$

19. Factor: $10x^2 - 13xy - 3y^2$

20. Add: $\frac{1}{x + 2} + \frac{7}{x - 1}$

21. Factor $8x^2 - 14x + 5$ by grouping.

22. Multiply: $\frac{x^2 + 7x}{5x} \cdot \frac{10x + 25}{x^2 - 49}$

23. Factor each binomial.

a. $4x^3 - 49x$ **b.** $162x^4 - 2$

24. Solve: $\frac{2x + 7}{3} = \frac{x - 6}{2}$

25. Solve: $(5x - 1)(2x^2 + 15x + 18) = 0$

26. Simplify each expression by combining like terms.

a. $4x - 3 + 7 - 5x$ **b.** $-6y + 3y - 8 + 8y$

c. $7 + 10.1a - a - 11$ **d.** $2x^2 - 2x$

27. Simplify: $\frac{x^2 + 8x + 7}{x^2 - 4x - 5}$

28. Solve $2x^2 + 5x = 7$.

29. The quotient of a number and 6, minus $\frac{5}{3}$, is the quotient of the number and 2. Find the number.

30. Find the distance between $(-7, 4)$ and $(2, 5)$. (See the Chapter 8 Group Activity.)

31. Complete the table for the equation $y = 3x$.

	x	y
a.	-1	
b.		0
c.		-9

32. Identify the x- and y-intercepts.

a.

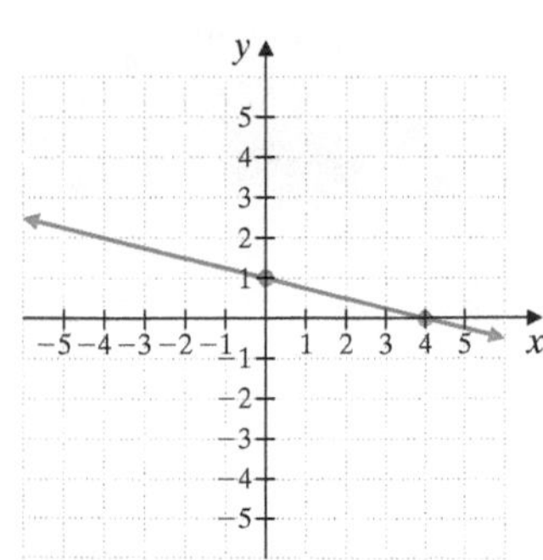

b.

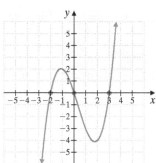

33. Determine whether each pair of lines is parallel, perpendicular, or neither.

a. $y = -\frac{1}{5}x + 1$
$2x + 10y = 3$

b. $x + y = 3$
$-x + y = 4$

c. $3x + y = 5$
$2x + 3y = 6$

34. Determine whether the graphs of $y = 3x + 7$ and $x + 3y = -15$ are parallel lines, perpendicular lines, or neither.

35. Which of the following relations are also functions?

a. $\{(-1, 1), (2, 3), (7, 3), (8, 6)\}$

b. $\{(0, -2), (1, 5), (0, 3), (7, 7)\}$

22. ____________
23. a. ____________
b. ____________
24. ____________
25. ____________
26. a. ____________
b. ____________
c. ____________
d. ____________
27. ____________
28. ____________
29. ____________
30. ____________
31. ____________
32. a. ____________
b. ____________
33. a. ____________
b. ____________
c. ____________
34. ____________
35. a. ____________
b. ____________

36. a. ______

b. ______

c. ______

37. ______

38. ______

39. ______

40. ______

41. ______

42. ______

43. ______

44. ______

45. ______

46. ______

47. ______

48. ______

49. ______

50. ______

36. Add or subtract by first simplifying each radical.

a. $\sqrt{80} + \sqrt{20}$

b. $2\sqrt{98} - 2\sqrt{18}$

c. $\sqrt{32} + \sqrt{121} - \sqrt{12}$

37. Solve the system: $\begin{cases} 2x + y = 10 \\ x = y + 2 \end{cases}$

38. Solve the system. $\begin{cases} 5x + y = 3 \\ y = -5x \end{cases}$

39. Solve the system: $\begin{cases} 2x - y = 7 \\ 8x - 4y = 1 \end{cases}$

40. Solve the system. $\begin{cases} -2x + y = 7 \\ 6x - 3y = -21 \end{cases}$

Find each square root.

41. $\sqrt{36}$

42. $\sqrt{\frac{4}{25}}$

43. $\sqrt{\frac{9}{100}}$

44. $\sqrt{\frac{16}{121}}$

45. Rationalize the denominator of $\frac{2}{1 + \sqrt{3}}$.

46. Rationalize the denominator of $\frac{5}{\sqrt{8}}$.

47. Use the square root property to solve $(x - 3)^2 = 16$.

48. Use the square root property to solve $3(x - 4)^2 = 9$.

49. Solve $\frac{1}{2}x^2 - x = 2$ by using the quadratic formula.

50. Solve $x^2 + 4x = 8$ by using the quadratic formula.

9.5 WEIGHT AND MASS

Objective A Defining and Converting U.S. System Units of Weight

Whenever we talk about how heavy an object is, we are concerned with the object's **weight.** We discuss weight when we refer to a 12-ounce box of Rice Krispies, a 15-pound tabby cat, or a barge hauling 24 tons of garbage.

12 ounces

15 pounds

24 tons of garbage

The most common units of weight in the U.S. measurement system are the **ounce,** the **pound,** and the **ton.** The following is a summary of equivalencies between units of weight:

U.S. Units of Weight	***Unit Fractions***
16 ounces (oz) = 1 pound (lb)	$\frac{16 \text{ oz}}{1 \text{ lb}} = \frac{1 \text{ lb}}{16 \text{ oz}} = 1$
2000 pounds = 1 ton	$\frac{2000 \text{ lb}}{1 \text{ ton}} = \frac{1 \text{ ton}}{2000 \text{ lb}} = 1$

✔**Concept Check** If you were describing the weight of a fully loaded semi-trailer, which type of unit would you use: ounce, pound, or ton? Why?

Unit fractions that equal 1 are used to convert between units of weight in the U.S. system. When converting using unit fractions, recall that the numerator of a unit fraction should contain the units we are converting to and the denominator should contain the original units.

Example 1 Convert 9000 pounds to tons.

Solution: We multiply 9000 lb by a unit fraction that uses the equality

2000 pounds = 1 ton.

Remember, the unit fraction should be $\frac{\text{units to convert to}}{\text{original units}}$ or $\frac{1 \text{ ton}}{2000 \text{ lb}}$.

Continued on next page

Objectives

A **Define U.S. Units of Weight and Convert from One Unit to Another.**

C **Define Metric Units of Mass and Convert from One Unit to Another.**

PRACTICE 1

Convert 6500 pounds to tons.

Answer

1. $3\frac{1}{4}$ tons

✔ **Concept Check Answer**

ton

$$9000 \text{ lb} = \frac{9000 \text{ lb}}{1} \cdot 1 = \frac{9000 \not{\text{lb}}}{1} \cdot \frac{1 \text{ ton}}{2000 \not{\text{lb}}} = \frac{9000 \text{ tons}}{2000} = \frac{9}{2} \text{ tons or } 4\frac{1}{2} \text{ tons}$$

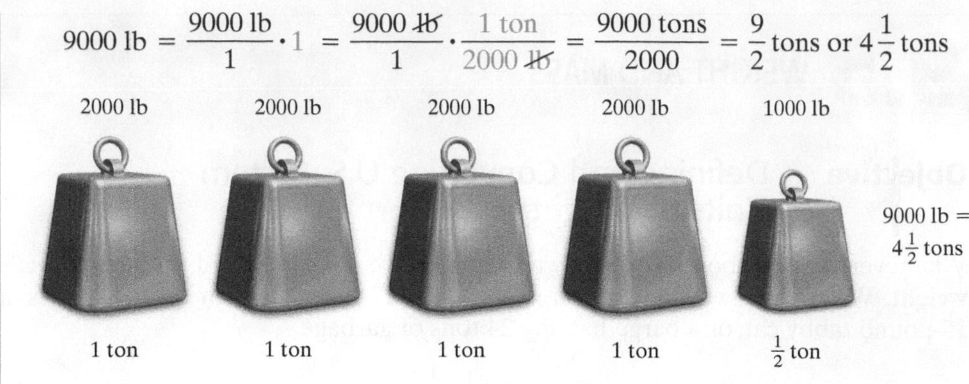

Work Practice 1

PRACTICE 2

Convert 72 ounces to pounds.

Example 2 Convert 3 pounds to ounces.

Solution: We multiply by the unit fraction $\frac{16 \text{ oz}}{1 \text{ lb}}$ to convert from pounds to ounces.

$$3 \text{ lb} = \frac{3 \text{ lb}}{1} \cdot 1 = \frac{3 \not{\text{lb}}}{1} \cdot \frac{16 \text{ oz}}{1 \not{\text{lb}}} = 3 \cdot 16 \text{ oz} = 48 \text{ oz}$$

1 pound 1 pound 1 pound

3 lb = 48 oz

16 ounces 16 ounces 16 ounces

Work Practice 2

As with length, it is sometimes useful to simplify a measurement of weight by writing it in terms of mixed units.

PRACTICE 3

Convert:

47 ounces = _____ lb _____ oz

Example 3 Convert: 33 ounces = _____ lb _____ oz

Solution: Because 16 oz = 1 lb, divide 16 into 33 to see how many pounds are in 33 ounces. The quotient is the number of pounds, and the remainder is the number of ounces. To see why we divide 16 into 33, notice that

$$33 \text{ oz} = 33 \not{\text{oz}} \cdot \frac{1 \text{ lb}}{16 \not{\text{oz}}} = \frac{33}{16} \text{ lb}$$

$$\begin{array}{r} \text{2 lb 1 oz} \\ 16\overline{)33} \\ -32 \\ \hline 1 \end{array}$$

Thus, 33 ounces is the same as 2 lb 1 oz.

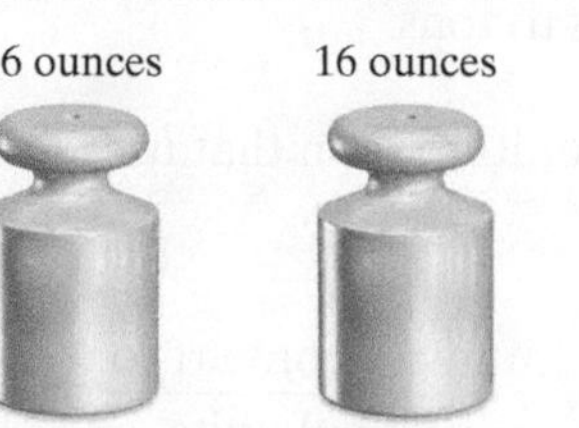

33 oz = 2 lb 1 oz

Work Practice 3

Answers

2. $4\frac{1}{2}$ lb **3.** 2 lb 15 oz

Objective C Defining and Converting Metric System Units of Mass

In scientific and technical areas, a careful distinction is made between **weight** and **mass. Weight** is really a measure of the pull of gravity. The farther from Earth an object gets, the less it weighs. However, **mass** is a measure of the amount of substance in the object and does not change. Astronauts orbiting Earth weigh much less than they weigh on Earth, but they have the same mass in orbit as they do on Earth. Here on Earth, weight and mass are the same, so either term may be used.

The basic unit of mass in the metric system is the **gram.** It is defined as the mass of water contained in a cube 1 centimeter (cm) on each side.

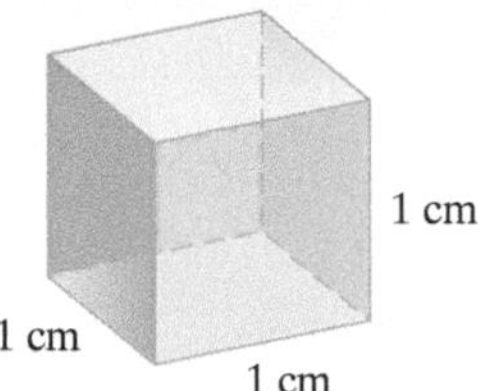

The following examples may help you get a feeling for metric masses:

A tablet contains 200 milligrams of ibuprofen.

A large paper clip weighs approximately 1 gram.

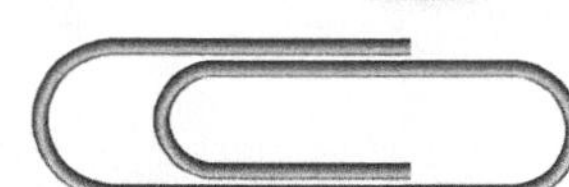

A box of crackers weighs 453 grams.

A kilogram is slightly over 2 pounds. An adult woman may weigh 60 kilograms.

The prefixes for units of mass in the metric system are the same as for units of length, as shown in the following table:

Metric Units of Mass
1 **kilo**gram (kg) = 1000 grams (g)
1 **hecto**gram (hg) = 100 g
1 **deka**gram (dag) = 10 g
1 gram (g) = 1 g
1 **deci**gram (dg) = 1/10 g or 0.1 g
1 **centi**gram (cg) = 1/100 g or 0.01 g
1 **milli**gram (mg) = 1/1000 g or 0.001 g

✓**Concept Check** True or false? A decigram is larger than a dekagram. Explain.

The **milligram,** the **gram,** and the **kilogram** are the three most commonly used units of mass in the metric system.

As with lengths, all units of mass are powers of 10 of the gram, so converting from one unit of mass to another only involves moving the decimal point. To convert

✓ **Concept Check Answer**
false

from one unit of mass to another in the metric system, list the units of mass in order from largest to smallest.

Let's convert 4300 milligrams to grams. To convert from milligrams to grams, we move along the list 3 units to the left.

kg hg dag **g** dg cg **mg**

3 units to the left

This means that we move the decimal point 3 places to the left to convert from milligrams to grams.

4300 mg = 4.3 g

Don't forget, the same conversion can be done with unit fractions.

$$4300 \text{ mg} = \frac{4300 \text{ mg}}{1} \cdot 1 = \frac{4300 \text{ mg}}{1} \cdot \frac{0.001 \text{ g}}{1 \text{ mg}}$$

$$= 4300 \cdot 0.001 \text{ g}$$

$$= 4.3 \text{ g}$$ To multiply by 0.001, move the decimal point 3 places to the left.

To see that this is reasonable, study the diagram:

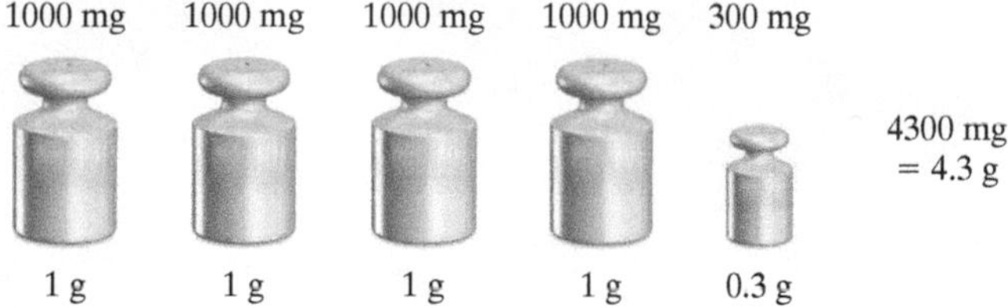

Thus, 4300 mg = 4.3 g

Example 7 Convert 3.2 kg to grams.

Solution: First we convert by using a unit fraction.

Unit fraction

$$3.2 \text{ kg} = 3.2 \text{ kg} \cdot 1 = 3.2 \text{ kg} \cdot \frac{1000 \text{ g}}{1 \text{ kg}} = 3200 \text{ g}$$

Now let's list the units of mass in order from left to right and move from kilograms to grams.

kg hg dag g dg cg mg

3 units to the right

3.200 kg = 3200. g

3 places to the right

1 kg 1 kg 1 kg 0.2 kg

3.2 kg = 3200 g

1000 g 1000 g 1000 g 200 g

Work Practice 7

PRACTICE 7

Convert 3.41 g to milligrams.

Answer

7. 3410 mg

PRACTICE 8

Convert 56.2 cg to grams.

Example 8 Convert 2.35 cg to grams.

Solution: We list the units of mass in a chart and move from centigrams to grams.

kg hg dag g dg cg mg

2 units to the left

02.35 cg = 0.0235 g

2 places to the left

Work Practice 8

Vocabulary and Readiness Check

Use the choices below to fill in each blank.

mass   weight   gram

1. __________ is a measure of the amount of substance in an object. This measure does not change.
2. __________ is the measure of the pull of gravity.
3. The basic unit of mass in the metric system is the __________.

Fill in these blanks with the correct number. Choices for these blanks are not shown in the list of terms above.

4. One pound equals __________ ounces.
5. One ton equals __________ pounds.

9.5 Exercise Set

FOR EXTRA HELP

PRACTICE

WATCH

DOWNLOAD

READ

REVIEW

Objective A *Convert as indicated. See Examples 1 through 3.*

1. 2 pounds to ounces

2. 5 pounds to ounces

3. 5 tons to pounds

4. 7 tons to pounds

5. 18,000 pounds to tons

6. 28,000 pounds to tons

7. 60 ounces to pounds

8. 90 ounces to pounds

9. 3500 pounds to tons

10. 11,000 pounds to tons

11. 12.75 pounds to ounces

12. 9.5 pounds to ounces

13. 4.9 tons to pounds

14. 8.3 tons to pounds

15. $4\frac{3}{4}$ pounds to ounces

16. $9\frac{1}{8}$ pounds to ounces

17. 2950 pounds to the nearest tenth of a ton

18. 51 ounces to the nearest tenth of a pound

19. $\frac{4}{5}$ oz to pounds

20. $\frac{1}{4}$ oz to pounds

21. $5\frac{3}{4}$ lb to ounces

22. $2\frac{1}{4}$ lb to ounces

23. 10 lb 1 oz to ounces

24. 7 lb 6 oz to ounces

25. 89 oz = _____ lb _____ oz

26. 100 oz = _____ lb _____ oz

Objective B *Perform each indicated operation. See Examples 4 through 6.*

27. 34 lb 12 oz + 18 lb 14 oz

28. 6 lb 10 oz + 10 lb 8 oz

29. 3 tons 1820 lb + 4 tons 930 lb

30. 1 ton 1140 lb + 5 tons 1200 lb

31. 5 tons 1050 lb − 2 tons 875 lb

32. 4 tons 850 lb − 1 ton 260 lb

33. 12 lb 4 oz − 3 lb 9 oz

34. 45 lb 6 oz − 26 lb 10 oz

35. 5 lb 3 oz × 6

36. 2 lb 5 oz × 5

37. 6 tons 1500 lb ÷ 5

38. 5 tons 400 lb ÷ 4

Objective C *Convert as indicated. See Examples 7 and 8.*

39. 500 g to kilograms

40. 820 g to kilograms

41. 4 g to milligrams

42. 9 g to milligrams

43. 25 kg to grams

44. 18 kg to grams

45. 48 mg to grams

46. 112 mg to grams

47. 6.3 g to kilograms

48. 4.9 g to kilograms

49. 15.14 g to milligrams

50. 16.23 g to milligrams

51. 6.25 kg to grams

52. 3.16 kg to grams

53. 35 hg to centigrams

54. 4.26 cg to dekagrams

Objective D *Perform each indicated operation. Remember to insert units when writing your answers. See Examples 9 and 10.*

55. 3.8 mg + 9.7 mg

56. 41.6 g + 9.8 g

57. 205 mg + 5.61 g

58. 2.1 g + 153 mg

59. 9 g − 7150 mg

60. 6.13 g − 418 mg

61. 1.61 kg − 250 g

62. 4 kg − 2410 g

63. 5.2 kg × 2.6

64. 4.8 kg × 9.3

65. 17 kg ÷ 8

66. 8.25 g ÷ 6

Objectives A B C D **Mixed Practice** *Solve. Remember to insert units when writing your answers. For Exercises 67 through 74, complete the chart. See Examples 1 through 10.*

	Object	Tons	Pounds	Ounces
67.	Statue of Liberty—weight of copper sheeting	100		
68.	Statue of Liberty—weight of steel	125		
69.	A 12-inch cube of osmium (heaviest metal)		1345	
70.	A 12-inch cube of lithium (lightest metal)		32	

	Object	Grams	Kilograms	Milligrams	Centigrams
71.	Capsule of Amoxicillin (antibiotic)			500	
72.	Tablet of Topamax (epilepsy and migraine uses)			25	
73.	A six-year-old boy		21		
74.	A golf ball	45			

75. A can of 7-Up weighs 336 grams. Find the weight in kilograms of 24 cans.

76. Guy Green normally weighs 73 kg, but he lost 2800 grams after being sick with the flu. Find Guy's new weight.

77. Sudafed is a decongestant that comes in two strengths. Regular strength contains 60 mg of medication. Extra strength contains 0.09 g of medication. How much extra medication is in the extra-strength tablet?

78. A small can of Planters sunflower seeds weighs 177 g. If each can contains 6 servings, find the weight of one serving.

79. Doris Johnson has two open containers of Uncle Ben's rice. If she combines 1 lb 10 oz from one container with 3 lb 14 oz from the other container, how much total rice does she have?

80. Dru Mizel maintains the records of the amount of coal delivered to his department in the steel mill. In January, 3 tons 1500 lb were delivered. In February, 2 tons 1200 lb were delivered. Find the total amount delivered in these two months.

81. Carla Hamtini was amazed when she grew a 28-lb 10-oz zucchini in her garden, but later she learned that the heaviest zucchini ever grown weighed 64 lb 8 oz in Llanharry, Wales, by B. Lavery in 1990. How far below the record weight was Carla's zucchini? (*Source: Guinness World Records*)

82. The heaviest baby born in good health weighed an incredible 22 lb 8 oz. He was born in Italy in September 1955. How much heavier is this than a 7-lb 12-oz baby? (*Source: Guinness World Records*)

83. The smallest baby born in good health weighed only 8.6 ounces, less than a can of soda. She was born in Chicago in December 2004. How much lighter was she than an average baby, who weighs about 7 lb 8 ounces?

84. A large bottle of Hire's Root Beer weighs 1900 grams. If a carton contains 6 large bottles of root beer, find the weight in kilograms of 5 cartons.

85. Three milligrams of preservatives are added to a 0.5-kg box of dried fruit. How many milligrams of preservatives are in 3 cartons of dried fruit if each carton contains 16 boxes?

86. One box of Swiss Miss Cocoa Mix weighs 0.385 kg, but 39 grams of this weight is the packaging. Find the actual weight of the cocoa in 8 boxes.

87. A carton of 12 boxes of Quaker Oats Oatmeal weighs 6.432 kg. Each box includes 26 grams of packaging material. What is the actual weight of the oatmeal in the carton?

88. The supermarket prepares hamburger in 85-gram market packages. When Leo Gonzalas gets home, he divides the package in half before refrigerating the meat. How much will each package weigh?

89. The Shop 'n Bag supermarket chain ships hamburger meat by placing 10 packages of hamburger in a box, with each package weighing 3 lb 4 oz. How much will 4 boxes of hamburger weigh?

90. The Quaker Oats Company ships its 1-lb 2-oz boxes of oatmeal in cartons containing 12 boxes of oatmeal. How much will 3 such cartons weigh?

91. A carton of Del Monte Pineapple weighs 55 lb 4 oz, but 2 lb 8 oz of this weight is due to packaging. Find the actual weight of the pineapple in 4 cartons.

92. The Hormel Corporation ships cartons of canned ham weighing 43 lb 2 oz each. Of this weight, 3 lb 4 oz is due to packaging. Find the actual weight of the ham found in 3 cartons.

Review

Write each fraction as a decimal. See Section 5.5.

93. $\frac{4}{25}$

94. $\frac{3}{5}$

95. $\frac{7}{8}$

96. $\frac{3}{16}$

Concept Extensions

Determine whether the measurement in each statement is reasonable.

97. The doctor prescribed a pill containing 2 kg of medication.

98. A full-grown cat weighs approximately 15 g.

99. A bag of flour weighs 4.5 kg.

100. A staple weighs 15 mg.

101. A professor weighs less than 150 g.

102. A car weighs 2000 mg.

103. Use a unit other than centigram and write a mass that is equivalent to 25 centigrams. (*Hint:* There are many possibilities.)

104. Use a unit other than pound and write a weight that is equivalent to 4000 pounds. (*Hint:* There are many possibilities.)

True or false? See the second Concept Check in this section.

105. A kilogram is larger than a gram.

106. A decigram is larger than a milligram.

107. Why is the decimal point moved to the right when grams are converted to milligrams?

108. To change 8 pounds to ounces, multiply by 16. Why is this the correct procedure?

Objectives

A Define U.S. Units of Capacity and Convert from One Unit to Another.

C Define Metric Units of Capacity and Convert from One Unit to Another.

9.6 CAPACITY

Objective A Defining and Converting U.S. System Units of Capacity

Units of **capacity** are generally used to measure liquids. The number of gallons of gasoline needed to fill a gas tank in a car, the number of cups of water needed in a bread recipe, and the number of quarts of milk sold each day at a supermarket are all examples of using units of capacity. The following summary shows equivalencies between units of capacity:

U.S. Units of Capacity

8 fluid ounces (fl oz) = 1 cup (c)

2 cups = 1 pint (pt)

2 pints = 1 quart (qt)

4 quarts = 1 gallon (gal)

Just as with units of length and weight, we can form unit fractions to convert between different units of capacity. For instance,

$$\frac{2\text{ c}}{1\text{ pt}} = \frac{1\text{ pt}}{2\text{ c}} = 1 \quad\text{and}\quad \frac{2\text{ pt}}{1\text{ qt}} = \frac{1\text{ qt}}{2\text{ pt}} = 1$$

PRACTICE 1

Convert 43 pints to quarts.

Example 1 Convert 9 quarts to gallons.

Solution: We multiply by the unit fraction $\frac{1\text{ gal}}{4\text{ qt}}$.

$$\begin{aligned} 9\text{ qt} &= \frac{9\text{ qt}}{1}\cdot 1 \\ &= \frac{9\text{ qt}}{1}\cdot\frac{1\text{ gal}}{4\text{ qt}} \\ &= \frac{9\text{ gal}}{4} \\ &= 2\frac{1}{4}\text{ gal} \end{aligned}$$

Thus, 9 quarts is the same as $2\frac{1}{4}$ gallons, as shown in the diagram:

Work Practice 1

Answer

1. $21\frac{1}{2}$ qt

Example 2 Convert 14 cups to quarts.

Solution: Our equivalency table contains no direct conversion from cups to quarts. However, from this table we know that

$$1 \text{ qt} = 2 \text{ pt} = \frac{2 \text{ pt}}{1} \cdot 1 = \frac{2 \text{ pt}}{1} \cdot \frac{2 \text{ c}}{1 \text{ pt}} = 4 \text{ c}$$

so 1 qt = 4 c. Now we have the unit fraction $\frac{1 \text{ qt}}{4 \text{ c}}$. Thus,

$$14 \text{ c} = \frac{14 \text{ c}}{1} \cdot 1 = \frac{14 \cancel{\text{c}}}{1} \cdot \frac{1 \text{ qt}}{4 \cancel{\text{c}}} = \frac{14 \text{ qt}}{4} = \frac{7}{2} \text{ qt} \quad \text{or} \quad 3\frac{1}{2} \text{ qt}$$

1 quart + 1 quart + 1 quart + $\frac{1}{2}$ quart

14 cups $= 3\frac{1}{2}$ qt

Work Practice 2

PRACTICE 2

Convert 26 quarts to cups.

✔**Concept Check** If 50 cups is converted to quarts, will the equivalent number of quarts be less than or greater than 50? Explain.

Objective C Defining and Converting Metric System Units of Capacity

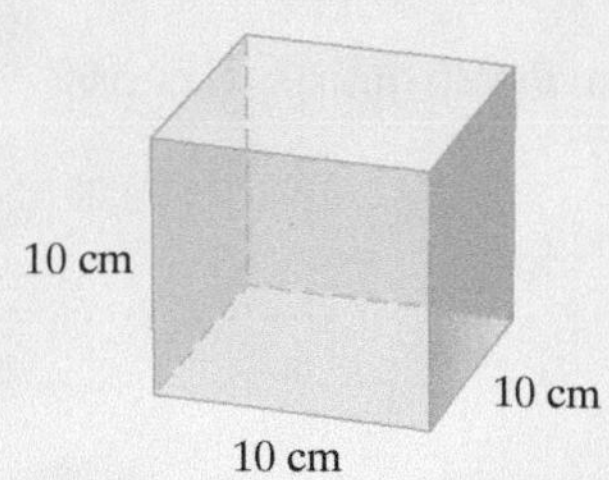

Thus far, we know that the basic unit of length in the metric system is the meter and that the basic unit of mass in the metric system is the gram. What is the basic unit of capacity? The **liter.** By definition, a **liter** is the capacity or volume of a cube measuring 10 centimeters on each side.

The following examples may help you get a feeling for metric capacities:

One liter of liquid is slightly more than one quart.

Many soft drinks are packaged in 2-liter bottles.

1 liter 1 quart

The metric system was designed to be a consistent system. Once again, the prefixes for metric units of capacity are the same as for metric units of length and mass, as summarized in the following table:

Metric Units of Capacity
1 **kilo**liter (kl) = 1000 liters (L)
1 **hecto**liter (hl) = 100 L
1 **deka**liter (dal) = 10 L
1 liter (L) = 1 L
1 **deci**liter (dl) = 1/10 L or 0.1 L
1 **centi**liter (cl) = 1/100 L or 0.01 L
1 **milli**liter (ml) = 1/1000 L or 0.001 L

2 liters

The **milliliter** and the **liter** are the two most commonly used metric units of capacity.

Converting from one unit of capacity to another involves multiplying by powers of 10 or moving the decimal point to the left or to the right. Listing units of capacity in order from largest to smallest helps to keep track of how many places to move the decimal point when converting.

Let's convert 2.6 liters to milliliters. To convert from liters to milliliters, we move along the chart 3 units to the right.

kl hl dal **L** dl cl **ml**

3 units to the right

Answer

4. 20 gal 2 qt

This means that we move the decimal point 3 places to the right to convert from liters to milliliters.

2.600 L = 2600. ml

This same conversion can be done with unit fractions.

$$\begin{aligned} 2.6 \text{ L} &= \frac{2.6 \text{ L}}{1} \cdot 1 \\ &= \frac{2.6 \cancel{\text{L}}}{1} \cdot \frac{1000 \text{ ml}}{1 \cancel{\text{L}}} \\ &= 2.6 \cdot 1000 \text{ ml} \\ &= 2600 \text{ ml} \end{aligned}$$

To multiply by 1000, move the decimal point 3 places to the right.

To visualize the result, study the diagram below:

Thus, 2.6 L = 2600 ml.

Example 5 Convert 3210 ml to liters.

Solution: Let's use the unit fraction method first.

$$3210 \text{ ml} = \frac{3210 \text{ ml}}{1} \cdot 1 = 3210 \cancel{\text{ml}} \cdot \overbrace{\frac{1 \text{ L}}{1000 \cancel{\text{ml}}}}^{\text{Unit fraction}} = 3.21 \text{ L}$$

Now let's list the unit measures in order from left to right and move from milliliters to liters.

kl hl dal L dl cl ml

3 units to the left

3210 ml = 3.210 L, the same results as before and shown below in the diagram.

3 places to the left

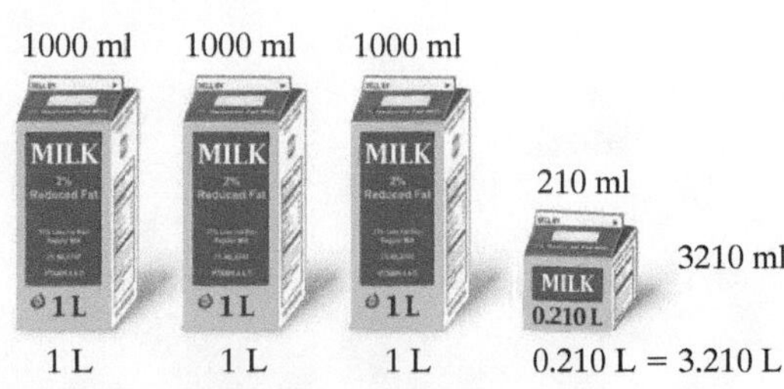

Work Practice 5

PRACTICE 5

Convert 2100 ml to liters.

Answer

5. 2.1 L

PRACTICE 6

Convert 2.13 dal to liters.

Example 6 Convert 0.185 dl to milliliters.

Solution: We list the unit measures in order from left to right and move from deciliters to milliliters.

kl hl dal L dl cl ml

2 units to the right

0.185 dl = 18.5 ml

2 places to the right

Work Practice 6

Vocabulary and Readiness Check

Use the choices below to fill in each blank. Some choices may be used more than once.

cups	pints	liter
quarts	fluid ounces	capacity

1. Units of ____________ are generally used to measure liquids.
2. The basic unit of capacity in the metric system is the ____________.
3. One cup equals 8 ____________.
4. One quart equals 2 ____________.
5. One pint equals 2 ____________.
6. One quart equals 4 ____________.
7. One gallon equals 4 ____________.

9.6 Exercise Set

FOR EXTRA HELP

PRACTICE

WATCH
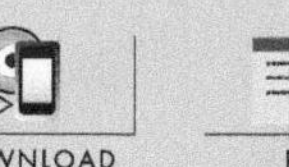
DOWNLOAD

READ

REVIEW

Objective A *Convert each measurement as indicated. See Examples 1 and 2.*

1. 32 fluid ounces to cups
2. 16 quarts to gallons
3. 8 quarts to pints
4. 9 pints to quarts
5. 14 quarts to gallons
6. 11 cups to pints
7. 80 fluid ounces to pints
8. 18 pints to gallons
9. 2 quarts to cups
10. 3 pints to fluid ounces
11. 120 fluid ounces to quarts
12. 20 cups to gallons
13. 42 cups to quarts
14. 7 quarts to cups
15. $4\frac{1}{2}$ pints to cups
16. $6\frac{1}{2}$ gallons to quarts
17. 5 gal 3 qt to quarts
18. 4 gal 1 qt to quarts
19. $\frac{1}{2}$ cup to pints
20. $\frac{1}{2}$ pint to quarts
21. 58 qt = _____ gal _____ qt
22. 70 qt = _____ gal _____ qt
23. 39 pt = _____ gal _____ qt _____ pt
24. 29 pt = _____ gal _____ qt _____ pt
25. $2\frac{3}{4}$ gallons to pints
26. $3\frac{1}{4}$ quarts to cups

Objective B *Perform each indicated operation. See Examples 3 and 4.*

27. 5 gal 3 qt + 7 gal 3 qt
28. 2 gal 2 qt + 9 gal 3 qt
29. 1 c 5 fl oz + 2 c 7 fl oz

30. 2 c 3 fl oz + 2 c 6 fl oz

31. 3 gal − 1 gal 3 qt

32. 2 pt − 1 pt 1 c

33. 3 gal 1 qt − 1 qt 1 pt

34. 3 qt 1 c − 1 c 4 fl oz

35. 8 gal 2 qt × 2

36. 6 gal 1 pt × 2

37. 9 gal 2 qt ÷ 2

38. 5 gal 6 fl oz ÷ 2

Objective C *Convert as indicated. See Examples 5 and 6.*

39. 5 L to milliliters

40. 8 L to milliliters

41. 0.16 L to kiloliters

42. 0.127 L to kiloliters

43. 5600 ml to liters

44. 1500 ml to liters

45. 3.2 L to centiliters

46. 1.7 L to centiliters

47. 410 L to kiloliters

48. 250 L to kiloliters

49. 64 ml to liters

50. 39 ml to liters

51. 0.16 kl to liters

52. 0.48 kl to liters

53. 3.6 L to milliliters

54. 1.9 L to milliliters

Objective D *Perform each indicated operation. Remember to insert units when writing your answers. See Examples 7 and 8.*

55. 3.4 L + 15.9 L

56. 18.5 L + 4.6 L

57. 2700 ml + 1.8 L

58. 4.6 L + 1600 ml

59. 8.6 L − 190 ml

60. 4.8 L − 283 ml

61. 17,500 ml − 0.9 L

62. 6850 ml − 0.3 L

63. 480 ml × 8

64. 290 ml × 6

65. 81.2 L ÷ 0.5

66. 5.4 L ÷ 3.6

Objectives A B C D **Mixed Practice** *Solve. Remember to insert units when writing your answers. For Exercises 67 through 70, complete the chart.*

	Capacity	Cups	Gallons	Quarts	Pints
67.	An average-size bath of water		21		
68.	A dairy cow's daily milk yield				38
69.	Your kidneys filter about this amount of blood every minute	4			
70.	The amount of water needed in a punch recipe	2			

71. Mike Schaferkotter drank 410 ml of Mountain Dew from a 2-liter bottle. How much Mountain Dew remains in the bottle?

72. The Werners' Volvo has a 54.5-L gas tank. Only 3.8 liters of gasoline still remain in the tank. How much is needed to fill it?

73. Margie Phitts added 354 ml of Prestone dry gas to the 18.6 L of gasoline in her car's tank. Find the total amount of gasoline in the tank.

74. Chris Peckaitis wishes to share a 2-L bottle of Coca-Cola equally with 7 of his friends. How much will each person get?

75. A garden tool engine requires a 30-to-1 gas-to-oil mixture. This means that $\frac{1}{30}$ of a gallon of oil should be mixed with 1 gallon of gas. Convert $\frac{1}{30}$ gallon to fluid ounces. Round to the nearest tenth.

76. Henning's Supermarket sells homemade soup in 1 qt 1 pt containers. How much soup is contained in three such containers?

77. Can 5 pt 1 c of fruit punch and 2 pt 1 c of ginger ale be poured into a 1-gal container without it overflowing?

78. Three cups of prepared Jell-O are poured into 6 dessert dishes. How many fluid ounces of Jell-O are in each dish?

79. Stanley Fisher paid \$14 to fill his car with 44.3 liters of gasoline. Find the price per liter of gasoline to the nearest thousandth of a dollar.

80. A student carelessly misread the scale on a cylinder in the chemistry lab and added 40 cl of water to a mixture instead of 40 ml. Find the excess amount of water.

Review

Write each fraction in simplest form. See Section 4.2.

81. $\frac{20}{25}$ **82.** $\frac{75}{100}$ **83.** $\frac{27}{45}$ **84.** $\frac{56}{60}$ **85.** $\frac{72}{80}$ **86.** $\frac{18}{20}$

Concept Extensions

Determine whether the measurement in each statement is reasonable.

87. Clair took a dose of 2 L of cough medicine to cure her cough.

88. John drank 250 ml of milk for lunch.

89. Jeannie likes to relax in a tub filled with 3000 ml of hot water.

90. Sarah pumped 20 L of gasoline into her car yesterday.

Solve. See the Concept Checks in this section.

91. If 70 pints are converted to gallons, will the equivalent number of gallons be less than or greater than 70? Explain why.

92. If 30 gallons are converted to quarts, will the equivalent number of quarts be less than or greater than 30? Explain why.

93. Explain how to estimate the following operation: Add 986 ml to 6.9 L.

94. Explain how to borrow in order to subtract 1 gal 2 qt from 3 gal 1 qt.

95. Find the number of fluid ounces in 1 gallon.

96. Find the number of fluid ounces in 1.5 gallons.

A cubic centimeter (cc) is the amount of space that a volume of 1 ml occupies. Because of this, we will say that 1 cc = 1 ml.

A common syringe is one with a capacity of 3 cc. Use the diagram and give the measurement indicated by each arrow.

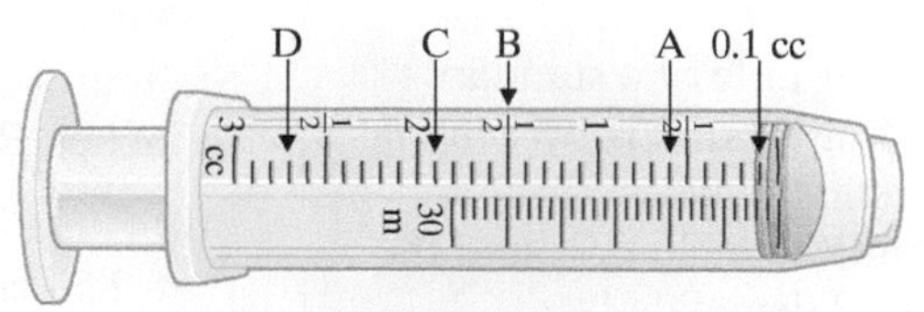

97. B **98.** A **99.** D **100.** C

In order to measure small dosages, such as for insulin, u-100 syringes are used. For these syringes, 1 cc has been divided into 100 equal units (u). Use the diagram and give the measurement indicated by each arrow in units (u) and then in cubic centimeters. Use 100 u = 1 cc.

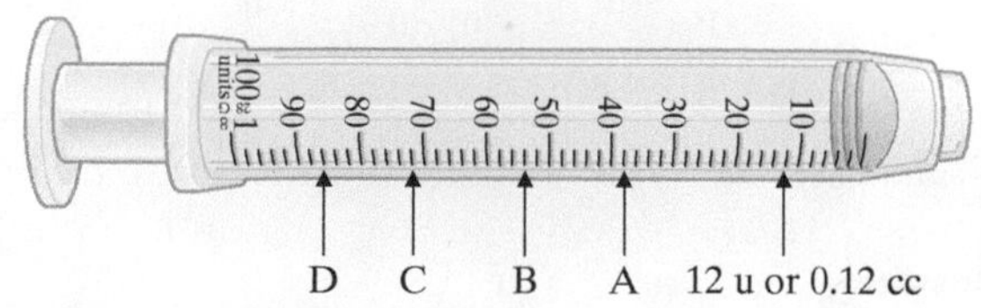

101. B **102.** A

103. D **104.** C

Objective

A Convert Between the U.S. and Metric Systems.

B Convert Temperatures from Degrees Celsius to Degrees Fahrenheit.

C Convert Temperatures from Degrees Fahrenheit to Degrees Celsius.

9.7 TEMPERATURE AND CONVERSIONS BETWEEN THE U.S. AND METRIC SYSTEMS

Objective A Converting Between the U.S. and Metric Systems

The metric system probably had its beginnings in France in the 1600s, but it was the Metric Act of 1866 that made the use of this system legal (but not mandatory) in the United States. Other laws have followed that allow for a slow, but deliberate, transfer to the modernized metric system. In April 2001, for example, the U.S. Stock Exchanges completed their change to decimal trading instead of fractions. By the end of 2009, all products sold in Europe (with some exceptions) were required to have only metric units on their labels. (*Source:* U.S. Metric Association and National Institute of Standards and Technology)

You may be surprised at the number of everyday items we use that are already manufactured in metric units. We easily recognize 1L and 2L soda bottles, but what about the following?

Pencil leads (0.5 mm or 0.7 mm)
Camera film (35 mm)
Sporting events (5-km or 10-km races)
Medicines (500-mg capsules)
Labels on retail goods (dual-labeled since 1994)

1 yard

1 meter

1 quart 1 liter

1 pound 1 kilogram

Since the United States has not completely converted to the metric system, we need to practice converting from one system to the other. Below is a table of mostly approximate conversions.

Length:

Metric	U.S. System
1 m	≈ 1.09 yd
1 m	≈ 3.28 ft
1 km	≈ 0.62 mi
2.54 cm	= 1 in.
0.30 m	≈ 1 ft
1.61 km	≈ 1 mi

Capacity:

Metric	U.S. System
1 L	≈ 1.06 qt
1 L	≈ 0.26 gal
3.79 L	≈ 1 gal
0.95 L	≈ 1 qt
29.57 ml	≈ 1 fl oz

Weight (mass):

Metric	U.S. System
1 kg	≈ 2.20 lb
1 g	≈ 0.04 oz
0.45 kg	≈ 1 lb
28.35 g	≈ 1 oz

There are many ways to perform these metric-to-U.S. conversions. We will do so by using unit fractions.

PRACTICE 1

The center hole of a standard-sized compact disc is 1.5 centimeters in diameter. Convert this length to inches. Round the result to 2 decimal places.

Example 1 Compact Discs

Standard-sized compact discs are 12 centimeters in diameter. Convert this length to inches. Round the result to two decimal places. (*Source:* usByte.com)

Solution: From our length conversion table, we know that 2.54 cm = 1 in. This fact gives us two unit fractions: $\frac{2.54 \text{ cm}}{1 \text{ in.}}$ and $\frac{1 \text{ in.}}{2.54 \text{ cm}}$. We use the unit fraction with cm in the denominator so that these units divide out.

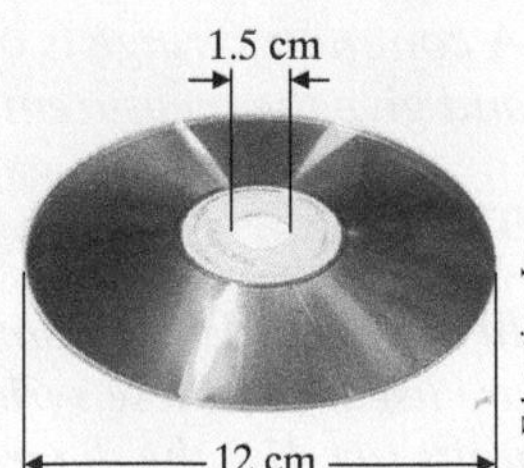

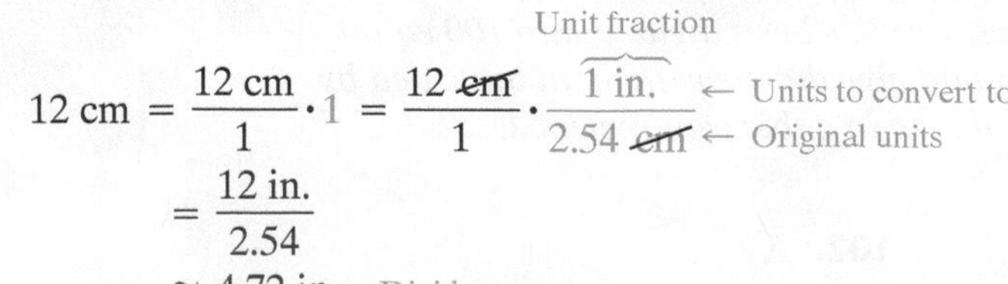

$$12 \text{ cm} = \frac{12 \text{ cm}}{1} \cdot 1 = \frac{12 \text{ cm}}{1} \cdot \overbrace{\frac{1 \text{ in.}}{2.54 \text{ cm}}}^{\text{Unit fraction}} \begin{matrix} \leftarrow \text{Units to convert to} \\ \leftarrow \text{Original units} \end{matrix}$$

$$= \frac{12 \text{ in.}}{2.54}$$

$$\approx 4.72 \text{ in.} \quad \text{Divide.}$$

Answer
1. 0.59 in.

Thus, the diameter of a standard compact disc is exactly 12 cm or approximately 4.72 inches. For a dimension this size, you can use a ruler to check. Another method is to approximate. Our result, 4.72 in., is close to 5 inches. Since 1 in. is about 2.5 cm, then 5 in. is about 5(2.5 cm) = 12.5 cm, which is close to 12 cm.

Work Practice 1

Example 2 Liver

The liver is your largest internal organ. It weighs about 3.5 pounds in a grown man. Convert this weight to kilograms. Round to the nearest tenth. (*Source: Some Body!* by Dr. Pete Rowan)

Solution:

$$3.5 \text{ lb} \approx \frac{3.5 \not{\text{lb}}}{1} \cdot \overbrace{\frac{0.45 \text{ kg}}{1 \not{\text{lb}}}}^{\text{Unit fraction}} = 3.5(0.45 \text{ kg}) \approx 1.6 \text{ kg}$$

Thus 3.5 pounds are approximately 1.6 kilograms. From the table of conversions, we know that 1 kg ≈ 2.2 lb. So that means 0.5 kg ≈ 1.1 lb and after adding, we have 1.5 kg ≈ 3.3 lb. Our result is reasonable.

Work Practice 2

PRACTICE 2

A full-grown human heart weighs about 8 ounces. Convert this weight to grams. If necessary, round your result to the nearest tenth of a gram.

Example 3 Postage Stamp

Australia converted to the metric system in 1973. In that year, four postage stamps were issued to publicize this conversion. One such stamp is shown. Let's check the mathematics on the stamp by converting 7 fluid ounces to milliliters. Round to the nearest hundred.

Solution:

$$7 \text{ fl oz} \approx \frac{7 \not{\text{fl oz}}}{1} \cdot \overbrace{\frac{29.57 \text{ ml}}{1 \not{\text{fl oz}}}}^{\text{Unit fraction}} = 7(29.57 \text{ ml}) = 206.99 \text{ ml}$$

Rounded to the nearest hundred, 7 fl oz ≈ 200 ml.

Work Practice 3

PRACTICE 3

Convert 237 ml to fluid ounces. Round to the nearest whole fluid ounce.

Now that we have practiced converting between two measurement systems, let's practice converting between two temperature scales.

Temperature When Gabriel Fahrenheit and Anders Celsius independently established units for temperature scales, each based his unit on the heat of water the moment it boils compared to the moment it freezes. One degree Celsius is $\frac{1}{100}$ of the difference in heat. One degree Fahrenheit is $\frac{1}{180}$ of the difference in heat. Celsius arbitrarily labeled the temperature at the freezing point at 0°C, making the boiling point 100°C; Fahrenheit labeled the freezing point 32°F, making the boiling point 212°F. Water boils at 212°F or 100°C.

By comparing the two scales in the figure, we see that a 20°C day is as warm as a 68°F day. Similarly, a sweltering 104°F day in the Mojave desert corresponds to a 40°C day.

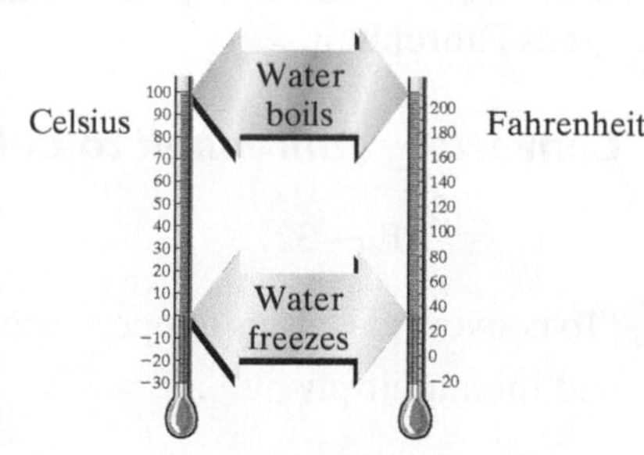

Answers

2. 226.8 g 3. 8 fl oz

✓**Concept Check** Which of the following statements is correct? Explain.

a. 6°C is below the freezing point of water.

b. 6°F is below the freezing point of water.

Objective B Converting Degrees Celsius to Degrees Fahrenheit

To convert from Celsius temperatures to Fahrenheit temperatures, see the box below. In this box, we use the symbol F to represent degrees Fahrenheit and the symbol C to represent degrees Celsius.

Converting Celsius to Fahrenheit

$$F = \frac{9}{5}C + 32 \quad \text{or} \quad F = 1.8C + 32$$

(To convert to Fahrenheit temperature, multiply the Celsius temperature by $\frac{9}{5}$ or 1.8, and then add 32.)

PRACTICE 4

Convert 60°C to degrees Fahrenheit.

Example 4 Convert 15°C to degrees Fahrenheit.

Solution:

$$\begin{aligned} F &= \frac{9}{5}C + 32 \\ &= \frac{9}{5} \cdot 15 + 32 && \text{Replace C with 15.} \\ &= 27 + 32 && \text{Simplify.} \\ &= 59 && \text{Add.} \end{aligned}$$

Thus, 15°C is equivalent to 59°F.

Work Practice 4

PRACTICE 5

Convert 32°C to degrees Fahrenheit.

Example 5 Convert 29°C to degrees Fahrenheit.

Solution:

$$\begin{aligned} F &= 1.8C + 32 \\ &= 1.8 \cdot 29 + 32 && \text{Replace C with 29.} \\ &= 52.2 + 32 && \text{Multiply 1.8 by 29.} \\ &= 84.2 && \text{Add.} \end{aligned}$$

Therefore, 29°C is the same as 84.2°F.

Work Practice 5

Objective C Converting Degrees Fahrenheit to Degrees Celsius

To convert from Fahrenheit temperatures to Celsius temperatures, see the box below. The symbol C represents degrees Celsius and the symbol F represents degrees Fahrenheit.

Converting Fahrenheit to Celsius

$$C = \frac{5}{9}(F - 32)$$

(To convert to Celsius temperature, subtract 32 from the Fahrenheit temperature, and then multiply by $\frac{5}{9}$.)

Answers

4. 140°F **5.** 89.6°F

✓ **Concept Check Answers**

b.

Example 6 Convert 59°F to degrees Celsius.

Solution: We evaluate the formula $C = \frac{5}{9}(F - 32)$ when F is 59.

$$C = \frac{5}{9}(F - 32)$$
$$= \frac{5}{9} \cdot (59 - 32) \quad \text{Replace F with 59.}$$
$$= \frac{5}{9} \cdot (27) \quad \text{Subtract inside parentheses.}$$
$$= 15 \quad \text{Multiply.}$$

Therefore, 59°F is the same temperature as 15°C.

Work Practice 6

PRACTICE 6

Convert 68°F to degrees Celsius.

Example 7 Convert 114°F to degrees Celsius. If necessary, round to the nearest tenth of a degree.

Solution:
$$C = \frac{5}{9}(F - 32)$$
$$= \frac{5}{9}(114 - 32) \quad \text{Replace F with 114.}$$
$$= \frac{5}{9} \cdot (82) \quad \text{Subtract inside parentheses.}$$
$$\approx 45.6 \quad \text{Multiply.}$$

Therefore, 114°F is approximately 45.6°C.

Work Practice 7

PRACTICE 7

Convert 113°F to degrees Celsius. If necessary, round to the nearest tenth of a degree.

Example 8 Body Temperature

Normal body temperature is 98.6°F. What is this temperature in degrees Celsius?

Solution: We evaluate the formula $C = \frac{5}{9}(F - 32)$ when F is 98.6.

$$C = \frac{5}{9}(F - 32)$$
$$= \frac{5}{9}(98.6 - 32) \quad \text{Replace F with 98.6.}$$
$$= \frac{5}{9} \cdot (66.6) \quad \text{Subtract inside parentheses.}$$
$$= 37 \quad \text{Multiply.}$$

Therefore, normal body temperature is 37°C.

Work Practice 8

PRACTICE 8

During a bout with the flu, Albert's temperature reaches 102.8°F. What is his temperature measured in degrees Celsius? Round to the nearest tenth of a degree.

✓**Concept Check** Clarissa must convert 40°F to degrees Celsius. What is wrong with her work shown below?

$F = 1.8 \cdot C + 32$
$F = 1.8 \cdot 40 + 32$
$F = 72 + 32$
$F = 104$

Answers

6. 20°C **7.** 45°C **8.** 39.3°C

✓ **Concept Check Answer**

She used the conversion for Celsius to Fahrenheit instead of Fahrenheit to Celsius.

9.7 Exercise Set

FOR EXTRA HELP

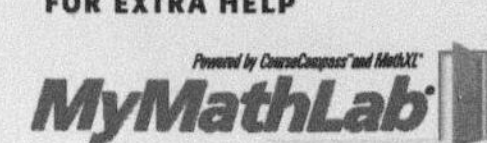
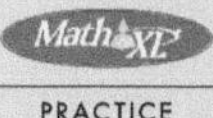
PRACTICE

WATCH

DOWNLOAD

READ

REVIEW

Note: Because approximations are used, your answers may vary slightly from the answers given in the back of the book.

Objective A *Convert as indicated. If necessary, round answers to two decimal places. See Examples 1 through 3.*

1. 756 milliliters to fluid ounces

2. 18 liters to quarts

3. 86 inches to centimeters

4. 86 miles to kilometers

5. 1000 grams to ounces

6. 100 kilograms to pounds

7. 93 kilometers to miles

8. 9.8 meters to feet

9. 14.5 liters to gallons

10. 150 milliliters to fluid ounces

11. 30 pounds to kilograms

12. 15 ounces to grams

Fill in the chart. Give exact answers or round to 1 decimal place. See Examples 1 through 3.

		Meters	Yards	Centimeters	Feet	Inches
13.	The Height of a Woman				5	
14.	Statue of Liberty Length of Nose	1.37				
15.	Leaning Tower of Pisa		60			
16.	Blue Whale		36			

Solve. If necessary, round answers to two decimal places. See Examples 1 through 3.

17. The balance beam for female gymnasts is 10 centimeters wide. Convert this width to inches.

18. In men's gymnastics, the rings are 250 centimeters from the floor. Convert this height to inches, then to feet.

19. In many states, the maximum speed limit for recreational vehicles is 50 miles per hour. Convert this to kilometers per hour.

20. In some states, the speed limit is 70 miles per hour. Convert this to kilometers per hour.

21. Ibuprofen comes in 200-milligram tablets. Convert this to ounces. (Round your answer to this exercise to 3 decimal places.)

22. Vitamin C tablets come in 500-milligram caplets. Convert this to ounces.

23. A stone is a unit in the British customary system. Use the conversion 14 pounds = 1 stone to check the equivalencies in this 1973 Australian stamp. Is 100 kilograms approximately 15 stone 10 pounds?

24. Convert 5 feet 11 inches to centimeters and check the conversion on this 1973 Australian stamp. Is it correct?

25. The Monarch butterfly migrates annually between the northern United States and central Mexico. The trip is about 4500 km long. Convert this to miles.

26. There is a species of African termite that builds nests up to 18 ft high. Convert this to meters.

27. A $3\frac{1}{2}$-inch diskette is not really $3\frac{1}{2}$ inches. To find its actual width, convert this measurement to centimeters, then to millimeters. Round the result to the nearest ten.

28. The average two-year-old is 84 centimeters tall. Convert this to feet and inches.

29. For an average adult, the weight of the right lung is greater than the weight of the left lung. If the right lung weighs 1.5 pounds and the left lung weighs 1.25 pounds, find the difference in grams. (*Source: Some Body!*)

30. The skin of an average adult weighs 9 pounds and is the heaviest organ. Find the weight in grams. (*Source: Some Body!*)

31. A fast sneeze has been clocked at about 167 kilometers per hour. Convert this to miles per hour. Round to the nearest whole.

32. A Boeing 747 has a cruising speed of about 980 kilometers per hour. Convert this to miles per hour. Round to the nearest whole.

33. The General Sherman giant sequoia tree has a diameter of about 8 meters at its base. Convert this to feet. (*Source: Fantastic Book of Comparisions*)

34. The largest crater on the near side of the moon is Billy Crater. It has a diameter of 303 kilometers. Convert this to miles. (*Source: Fantastic Book of Comparisions*)

35. The total length of the track on a CD is about 4.5 kilometers. Convert this to miles. Round to the nearest whole mile.

36. The distance between Mackinaw City, Michigan, and Cheyenne, Wyoming, is 2079 kilometers. Convert this to miles. Round to the nearest whole mile.

37. A doctor orders a dosage of 5 ml of medicine every 4 hours for 1 week. How many fluid ounces of medicine should be purchased? Round up to the next whole fluid ounce.

38. A doctor orders a dosage of 12 ml of medicine every 6 hours for 10 days. How many fluid ounces of medicine should be purchased? Round up to the next whole fluid ounce.

Without actually converting, choose the most reasonable answer.

39. This math book has a height of about _____.

a. 28 mm **b.** 28 cm
c. 28 m **d.** 28 km

40. A mile is _____ a kilometer.

a. shorter than **b.** longer than
c. the same length as

41. A liter has _____ capacity than a quart.

a. less **b.** greater
c. the same

42. A foot is _____ a meter.

a. shorter than **b.** longer than
c. the same length as

43. A kilogram weighs _____ a pound.

a. the same as **b.** less than
c. greater than

44. A football field is 100 yards, which is about _____.

a. 9 m **b.** 90 m
c. 900 m **d.** 9000 m

45. An $8\frac{1}{2}$-ounce glass of water has a capacity of about _____.

a. 250 L **b.** 25 L
c. 2.5 L **d.** 250 ml

46. A 5-gallon gasoline can has a capacity of about _____.

a. 19 L **b.** 1.9 L
c. 19 ml **d.** 1.9 ml

47. The weight of an average man is about _____.

a. 700 kg **b.** 7 kg
c. 0.7 kg **d.** 70 kg

48. The weight of a pill is about _____.

a. 200 kg **b.** 20 kg
c. 2 kg **d.** 200 mg

Objectives **B C Mixed Practice** *Convert as indicated. When necessary, round to the nearest tenth of a degree. See Examples 4 through 8.*

49. 77°F to degrees Celsius

50. 86°F to degrees Celsius

51. 104°F to degrees Celsius

52. 140°F to degrees Celsius

53. 50°C to degrees Fahrenheit

54. 80°C to degrees Fahrenheit

55. 115°C to degrees Fahrenheit

56. 225°C to degrees Fahrenheit

57. 20°F to degrees Celsius

58. 26°F to degrees Celsius

59. 142.1°F to degrees Celsius

60. 43.4°F to degrees Celsius

61. 92°C to degrees Fahrenheit

62. 75°C to degrees Fahrenheit

63. 12.4°C to degrees Fahrenheit

64. 48.6°C to degrees Fahrenheit

65. The hottest temperature ever recorded in the United States, in Death Valley, was 134°F. Convert this temperature to degrees Celsius. (*Source:* National Climatic Data Center)

66. The hottest temperature ever recorded in the United States in January was 95°F in Los Angeles. Convert this temperature to degrees Celsius. (*Source:* National Climatic Data Center)

67. A weather forecaster in Caracas predicts a high temperature of 27°C. Find this measurement in degrees Fahrenheit.

68. While driving to work, Alan Olda notices a temperature of 18°C flash on the local bank's temperature display. Find the corresponding temperature in degrees Fahrenheit.

69. At Mack Trucks' headquarters, the room temperature is to be set at 70°F, but the thermostat is calibrated in degrees Celsius. Find the temperature to be set.

70. The computer room at Merck, Sharp, and Dohm is normally cooled to 66°F. Find the corresponding temperature in degrees Celsius.

71. In a European cookbook, a recipe requires the ingredients for caramels to be heated to 118°C, but the cook has access only to a Fahrenheit thermometer. Find the temperature in degrees Fahrenheit that should be used to make the caramels.

72. The ingredients for divinity should be heated to 127°C, but the candy thermometer that Myung Kim has is calibrated to degrees Fahrenheit. Find how hot he should heat the ingredients.

73. The temperature of Earth's core is estimated to be 4000°C. Find the corresponding temperature in degrees Fahrenheit.

74. In 2005, the average temperature of the Earth's surface was 58.1°F, the second warmest in recorded history. Convert this temperature to degrees Celsius.

Review

Perform the indicated operations. See Section 1.7.

75. $6 \cdot 4 + 5 \div 1$

76. $10 \div 2 + 9(8)$

77. $3[(1 + 5) \cdot (8 - 6)]$

78. $5[(18 - 8) - 9]$

Concept Extensions

Determine whether the measurement in each statement is reasonable.

79. A 72°F room feels comfortable.

80. Water heated to 110°F will boil.

81. Josiah has a fever if a thermometer shows his temperature to be 40°F.

82. An air temperature of 20°F on a Vermont ski slope can be expected in the winter.

83. When the temperature is 30°C outside, an overcoat is needed.

84. An air-conditioned room at 60°C feels quite chilly.

85. Barbara has a fever when a thermometer records her temperature at 40°C.

86. Water cooled to 32°C will freeze.

Body surface area (BSA) is often used to calculate dosages for some drugs. BSA is calculated in square meters using a person's weight and height.

$$\text{BSA} = \sqrt{\frac{(\text{weight in kg}) \times (\text{height in cm})}{3600}}$$

For Exercises 87 through 92, calculate the BSA for each person. Round to the nearest hundredth. You will need to use the square root key on your calculator.

87. An adult whose height is 182 cm and weight is 90 kg.

88. An adult whose height is 157 cm and weight is 63 kg.

89. A child whose height is 40 in. and weight is 50 kg. (*Hint:* Don't forget to first convert inches to centimeters.)

90. A child whose height is 26 in. and weight is 13 kg. (*Hint:* Don't forget to first convert inches to centimeters.)

91. An adult whose height is 60 in. and weight is 150 lb.

92. An adult whose height is 69 in. and weight is 172 lb.

93. On February 17, 1995, in the Tokamak Fusion Test Reactor at Princeton University, the highest temperature produced in a laboratory was achieved. This temperature was 918,000,000°F. Convert this temperature to degrees Celsius. Round your answer to the nearest ten million degrees. (*Source: Guinness World Records*)

94. The hottest-burning substance known is carbon subnitride. Its flame at one atmospheric pressure reaches 9010°F. Convert this temperature to degrees Celsius. (*Source: Guinness World Records*)

95. In your own words, describe how to convert from degrees Celsius to degrees Fahrenheit.

96. In your own words, describe how to convert from degrees Fahrenheit to degrees Celsius.

Group Activity

Map Reading

Sections 9.1, 9.4, and 9.7

Materials:

- ruler
- string
- calculator

This activity may be completed by working in groups or individually.

Investigate the route you would take from Santa Rosa, New Mexico, to San Antonio, New Mexico. Use the map in the figure to answer the following questions. You may find that using string to match the roads on the map is useful when measuring distances.

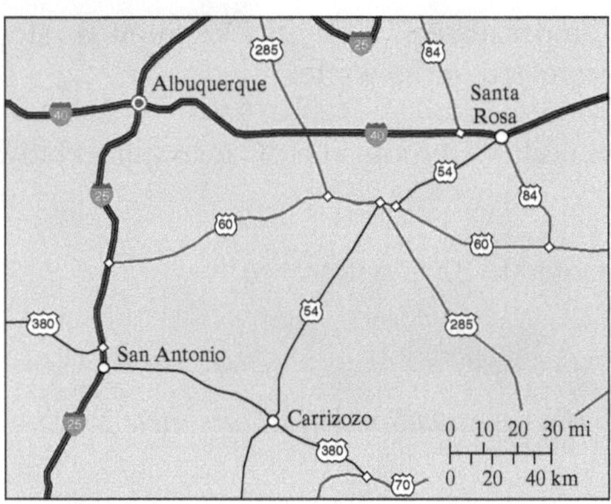

1. How many miles is it from Santa Rosa to San Antonio via Interstate 40 and Interstate 25? Convert this distance to kilometers.
2. How many miles is it from Santa Rosa to San Antonio via U.S. 54 and U.S. 380? Convert this distance to kilometers.
3. Assume that the speed limit on Interstates 40 and 25 is 65 miles per hour. How long would the trip take if you took this route and traveled 65 miles per hour the entire trip?
4. At what average speed would you have to travel on the U.S. routes to make the trip from Santa Rosa to San Antonio in the same amount of time that it would take on the interstate routes? Do you think this speed is reasonable on this route? Explain your reasoning.
5. Discuss in general the factors that might affect your decision between the different routes.
6. Explain which route you would choose in this case and why.

Chapter 9 Vocabulary Check

Fill in each blank with one of the words or phrases listed below.

transversal	line segment	obtuse	straight	adjacent	right	volume	area
acute	perimeter	vertical	supplementary	ray	angle	line	complementary
vertex	mass	unit fractions	gram	weight	meter	liter	surface area

1. ______________ is a measure of the pull of gravity.
2. ______________ is a measure of the amount of substance in an object. This measure does not change.
3. The basic unit of length in the metric system is the ______________.
4. To convert from one unit of length to another, ______________ may be used.
5. The ______________ is the basic unit of mass in the metric system.
6. The ______________ is the basic unit of capacity in the metric system.
7. A(n) ______________ is a piece of a line with two end points.
8. Two angles that have a sum of 90° are called ______________ angles.
9. A(n) ______________ is a set of points extending indefinitely in two directions.
10. The ______________ of a polygon is the distance around the polygon.
11. A(n) ______________ is made up of two rays that share the same end point. The common end point is called the ______________.
12. ______________ measures the amount of surface of a region.
13. A(n) ______________ is a part of a line with one end point. A ray extends indefinitely in one direction.
14. A line that intersects two or more lines at different points is called a(n) ______________.
15. An angle that measures 180° is called a(n) ______________ angle.
16. The measure of the space of a solid is called its ______________.
17. When two lines intersect, four angles are formed. Two of these angles that are opposite each other are called ______________ angles.
18. Two of the angles from #17 that share a common side are called ______________ angles.
19. An angle whose measure is between 90° and 180° is called a(n) ______________ angle.
20. An angle that measures 90° is called a(n) ______________ angle.
21. An angle whose measure is between 0° and 90° is called a(n) ______________ angle.
22. Two angles that have a sum of 180° are called ______________ angles.
23. The ______________ of a polyhedron is the sum of the areas of the faces of the polyhedron.

Helpful Hint Are you preparing for your test? Don't forget to take the Chapter 9 Test on page 683. Then check your answers at the back of the text and use the Chapter Test Prep Video CD to see the fully worked-out solutions to any of the exercises you want to review.

9 Chapter Highlights

Definitions and Concepts	Examples
Section 9.1 Lines and Angles	
A **line** is a set of points extending indefinitely in two directions. A line has no width or height, but it does have length. We name a line by any two of its points.	Line AB or $\overleftrightarrow{AB}$
A **line segment** is a piece of a line with two end points.	Line segment AB or $\overline{AB}$

(continued)

Definitions and Concepts	Examples
Section 9.1 Lines and Angles (*continued*)	
A **ray** is a part of a line with one end point. A ray extends indefinitely in one direction.	Ray AB or $\overrightarrow{AB}$ 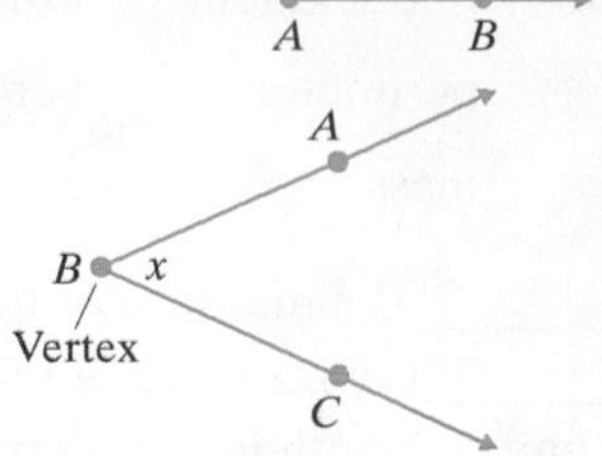
An **angle** is made up of two rays that share the same end point. The common end point is called the **vertex.**	
Section 9.2 Perimeter	
PERIMETER FORMULAS	Find the perimeter of the rectangle.
Rectangle: $P = 2l + 2w$	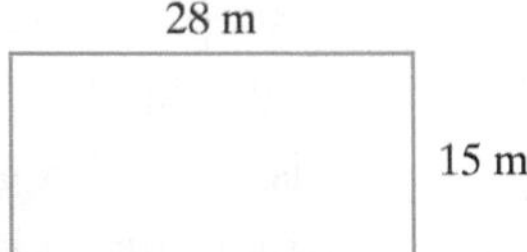
Square: $P = 4s$	$P = 2l + 2w$
Triangle: $P = a + b + c$	$= 2 \cdot 28$ meters $+ 2 \cdot 15$ meters
Circumference of a Circle: $C = 2\pi r$ or $C = \pi d$	$= 56$ meters $+ 30$ meters $= 86$ meters
where $\pi \approx 3.14$ or $\pi \approx \frac{22}{7}$	The perimeter is 86 meters.
Section 9.3 Area, Volume, and Surface Area	
AREA FORMULAS	Find the area of the square.
Rectangle: $A = lw$	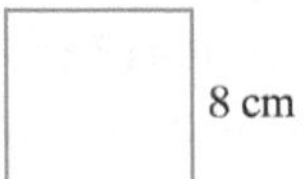
Square: $A = s^2$	$A = s^2$
Triangle: $A = \frac{1}{2}bh$	$= (8 \text{ centimeters})^2$
Parallelogram: $A = bh$	$= 64$ square centimeters
Trapezoid: $A = \frac{1}{2}(b + B)h$	The area of the square is 64 square centimeters.
Circle: $A = \pi r^2$	
VOLUME FORMULAS	Find the volume of the sphere. Use $\frac{22}{7}$ for π.
Rectangular Solid: $V = lwh$	
Cube: $V = s^3$	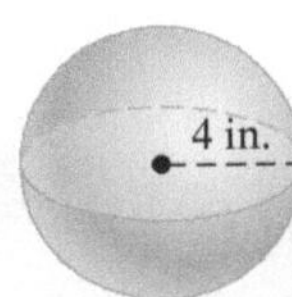
Sphere: $V = \frac{4}{3}\pi r^3$	
Right Circular Cylinder: $V = \pi r^2 h$	$V = \frac{4}{3}\pi r^3$
Cone: $V = \frac{1}{3}\pi r^2 h$	$\approx \frac{4}{3} \cdot \frac{22}{7} \cdot (4 \text{ inches})^3$
Square-Based Pyramid: $V = \frac{1}{3}s^2 h$	$= \frac{4 \cdot 22 \cdot 64}{3 \cdot 7}$ cubic inches
SURFACE AREA FORMULAS: See page 620.	$= \frac{5632}{21}$ or $268\frac{4}{21}$ cubic inches

Definitions and Concepts	Examples
Section 9.4 Linear Measurement	

To convert from one unit of length to another, multiply by a **unit fraction** in the form

$$\frac{\text{units to convert to}}{\text{original units}}$$

$\frac{12 \text{ inches}}{1 \text{ foot}}, \frac{1 \text{ foot}}{12 \text{ inches}}, \frac{3 \text{ feet}}{1 \text{ yard}}$

LENGTH: U.S. SYSTEM OF MEASUREMENT

12 inches (in.) = 1 foot (ft)
3 feet = 1 yard (yd)
5280 feet = 1 mile (mi)

Convert 6 feet to inches.

$$6 \text{ ft} = \frac{6 \text{ ft}}{1} \cdot 1$$
$$= \frac{6 \cancel{\text{ft}}}{1} \cdot \frac{12 \text{ in.}}{1 \cancel{\text{ft}}} \quad \begin{matrix} \leftarrow \text{units to convert to} \\ \leftarrow \text{original units} \end{matrix}$$
$$= 6 \cdot 12 \text{ in.}$$
$$= 72 \text{ in.}$$

LENGTH: METRIC SYSTEM OF MEASUREMENT

The basic unit of length in the metric system is the **meter.** A meter is slightly longer than a yard.

Metric Units of Length

1 **kilo**meter (km) = 1000 meters (m)
1 **hecto**meter (hm) = 100 m
1 **deka**meter (dam) = 10 m
1 meter (m) = 1 m
1 **deci**meter (dm) = 1/10 m or 0.1 m
1 **centi**meter (cm) = 1/100 m or 0.01 m
1 **milli**meter (mm) = 1/1000 m or 0.001 m

Convert 3650 centimeters to meters.

$$3650 \text{ cm} = 3650 \text{ cm} \cdot 1$$
$$= \frac{3650 \cancel{\text{cm}}}{1} \cdot \frac{0.01 \text{ m}}{1 \cancel{\text{cm}}} = 36.5 \text{ m}$$

or

km hm dam m dm cm mm
2 units to the left

3650 cm = 36.5 m
2 places to the left

Section 9.5 Weight and Mass

Weight is really a measure of the pull of gravity. **Mass** is a measure of the amount of substance in an object and does not change.

WEIGHT: U.S. SYSTEM OF MEASUREMENT

16 ounces (oz) = 1 pound (lb)
2000 pounds = 1 ton

Convert 5 pounds to ounces.

$$5 \text{ lb} = 5 \text{ lb} \cdot 1 = \frac{5 \cancel{\text{lb}}}{1} \cdot \frac{16 \text{ oz}}{1 \cancel{\text{lb}}} = 80 \text{ oz}$$

MASS: METRIC SYSTEM OF MEASUREMENT

The **gram** is the basic unit of mass in the metric system. It is the mass of water contained in a cube 1 centimeter on each side. A paper clip weighs about 1 gram.

Metric Units of Mass

1 **kilo**gram (kg) = 1000 grams (g)
1 **hecto**gram (hg) = 100 g
1 **deka**gram (dag) = 10 g
1 gram (g) = 1 g
1 **deci**gram (dg) = 1/10 g or 0.1 g
1 **centi**gram (cg) = 1/100 g or 0.01 g
1 **milli**gram (mg) = 1/1000 g or 0.001 g

Convert 260 grams to kilograms.

$$260 \text{ g} = \frac{260 \text{ g}}{1} \cdot 1 = \frac{260 \cancel{\text{g}}}{1} \cdot \frac{1 \text{ kg}}{1000 \cancel{\text{g}}} = 0.26 \text{ kg}$$

or

kg hg dag g dg cg mg
3 units to the left

260 g = 0.26 kg
3 places to the left

Definitions and Concepts	Examples

Section 9.6 Capacity

CAPACITY: U.S. SYSTEM OF MEASUREMENT

8 fluid ounces (fl oz) = 1 cup (c)
2 cups = 1 pint (pt)
2 pints = 1 quart (qt)
4 quarts = 1 gallon (gal)

Convert 5 pints to gallons.

1 gal = 4 qt = 8 pt

$$5 \text{ pt} = 5 \text{ pt} \cdot 1 = \frac{5 \cancel{\text{pt}}}{1} \cdot \frac{1 \text{ gal}}{8 \cancel{\text{pt}}} = \frac{5}{8} \text{ gal}$$

CAPACITY: METRIC SYSTEM OF MEASUREMENT

The **liter** is the basic unit of capacity in the metric system. It is the capacity or volume of a cube measuring 10 centimeters on each side. A liter of liquid is slightly more than 1 quart.

Metric Units of Capacity
1 **kilo**liter (kl) = 1000 liters (L)
1 **hecto**liter (hl) = 100 L
1 **deka**liter (dal) = 10 L
1 liter (L) = 1 L
1 **deci**liter (dl) = 1/10 L or 0.1 L
1 **centi**liter (cl) = 1/100 L or 0.01 L
1 **milli**liter (ml) = 1/1000 L or 0.001 L

Convert 1.5 liters to milliliters.

$$1.5 \text{ L} = \frac{1.5 \text{ L}}{1} \cdot 1 = \frac{1.5 \cancel{\text{L}}}{1} \cdot \frac{1000 \text{ ml}}{1 \cancel{\text{L}}} = 1500 \text{ ml}$$

or

kl hl dal L dl cl ml

3 units to the right

1.500 L = 1500 ml

3 places to the right

Section 9.7 Temperature and Conversions Between the U.S. and Metric Systems

To convert between systems, use approximate unit fractions.

Convert 7 feet to meters.

$$7 \text{ ft} \approx \frac{7 \cancel{\text{ft}}}{1} \cdot \frac{0.30 \text{ m}}{1 \cancel{\text{ft}}} = 2.1 \text{ m}$$

Convert 8 liters to quarts.

$$8 \text{ L} \approx \frac{8 \cancel{\text{L}}}{1} \cdot \frac{1.06 \text{ qt}}{1 \cancel{\text{L}}} = 8.48 \text{ qt}$$

Convert 363 grams to ounces.

$$363 \text{ g} \approx \frac{363 \cancel{\text{g}}}{1} \cdot \frac{0.04 \text{ oz}}{1 \cancel{\text{g}}} = 14.52 \text{ oz}$$

CELSIUS TO FAHRENHEIT

$$F = \frac{9}{5}C + 32 \quad \text{or} \quad F = 1.8C + 32$$

Convert 35°C to degrees Fahrenheit.

$$F = \frac{9}{5} \cdot 35 + 32 = 63 + 32 = 95$$

35°C = 95°F

FAHRENHEIT TO CELSIUS

$$C = \frac{5}{9}(F - 32)$$

Convert 50°F to degrees Celsius.

$$C = \frac{5}{9} \cdot (50 - 32) = \frac{5}{9} \cdot (18) = 10$$

50°F = 10°C

Appendix E

Tables

E.1 TABLE OF SQUARES AND SQUARE ROOTS

n	n^2	$\sqrt{n}$	n	n^2	$\sqrt{n}$
1	1	1.000	51	2601	7.141
2	4	1.414	52	2704	7.211
3	9	1.732	53	2809	7.280
4	16	2.000	54	2916	7.348
5	25	2.236	55	3025	7.416
6	36	2.449	56	3136	7.483
7	49	2.646	57	3249	7.550
8	64	2.828	58	3364	7.616
9	81	3.000	59	3481	7.681
10	100	3.162	60	3600	7.746
11	121	3.317	61	3721	7.810
12	144	3.464	62	3844	7.874
13	169	3.606	63	3969	7.937
14	196	3.742	64	4096	8.000
15	225	3.873	65	4225	8.062
16	256	4.000	66	4356	8.124
17	289	4.123	67	4489	8.185
18	324	4.243	68	4624	8.246
19	361	4.359	69	4761	8.307
20	400	4.472	70	4900	8.367
21	441	4.583	71	5041	8.426
22	484	4.690	72	5184	8.485
23	529	4.796	73	5329	8.544
24	576	4.899	74	5476	8.602
25	625	5.000	75	5625	8.660
26	676	5.099	76	5776	8.718
27	729	5.196	77	5929	8.775
28	784	5.292	78	6084	8.832
29	841	5.385	79	6241	8.888
30	900	5.477	80	6400	8.944
31	961	5.568	81	6561	9.000
32	1024	5.657	82	6724	9.055
33	1089	5.745	83	6889	9.110
34	1156	5.831	84	7056	9.165
35	1225	5.916	85	7225	9.220
36	1296	6.000	86	7396	9.274
37	1369	6.083	87	7569	9.327
38	1444	6.164	88	7744	9.381
39	1521	6.245	89	7921	9.434
40	1600	6.325	90	8100	9.487
41	1681	6.403	91	8281	9.539
42	1764	6.481	92	8464	9.592
43	1849	6.557	93	8649	9.644
44	1936	6.633	94	8836	9.695
45	2025	6.708	95	9025	9.747
46	2116	6.782	96	9216	9.798
47	2209	6.856	97	9409	9.849
48	2304	6.928	98	9604	9.899
49	2401	7.000	99	9801	9.950
50	2500	7.071	100	10,000	10.000

E.2 TABLE OF PERCENT, DECIMAL, AND FRACTION EQUIVALENTS

Percent, Decimal, and Fraction Equivalents

Percent	Decimal	Fraction
1%	0.01	$\frac{1}{100}$
5%	0.05	$\frac{1}{20}$
10%	0.1	$\frac{1}{10}$
12.5% or $12\frac{1}{2}$%	0.125	$\frac{1}{8}$
$16.\overline{6}$% or $16\frac{2}{3}$%	$0.1\overline{6}$	$\frac{1}{6}$
20%	0.2	$\frac{1}{5}$
25%	0.25	$\frac{1}{4}$
30%	0.3	$\frac{3}{10}$
$33.\overline{3}$% or $33\frac{1}{3}$%	$0.\overline{3}$	$\frac{1}{3}$
37.5% or $37\frac{1}{2}$%	0.375	$\frac{3}{8}$
40%	0.4	$\frac{2}{5}$
50%	0.5	$\frac{1}{2}$
60%	0.6	$\frac{3}{5}$
62.5% or $62\frac{1}{2}$%	0.625	$\frac{5}{8}$
$66.\overline{6}$% or $66\frac{2}{3}$%	$0.\overline{6}$	$\frac{2}{3}$
70%	0.7	$\frac{7}{10}$
75%	0.75	$\frac{3}{4}$
80%	0.8	$\frac{4}{5}$
$83.\overline{3}$% or $83\frac{1}{3}$%	$08.\overline{3}$	$\frac{5}{6}$
87.5% or $87\frac{1}{2}$%	0.875	$\frac{7}{8}$
90%	0.9	$\frac{9}{10}$
100%	1.0	1
110%	1.1	$1\frac{1}{10}$
125%	1.25	$1\frac{1}{4}$
$133.\overline{3}$% or $133\frac{1}{3}$%	$1.\overline{3}$	$1\frac{1}{3}$
150%	1.5	$1\frac{1}{2}$
$166.\overline{6}$% or $166\frac{2}{3}$%	$1.\overline{6}$	$1\frac{2}{3}$
175%	1.75	$1\frac{3}{4}$
200%	2.0	2

Contents of Student Resources

Student Resources

Study Skills Builders

Attitude and Study Tips

STUDY SKILLS BUILDER 1

Have You Decided to Complete This Course Successfully?

Ask yourself if one of your current goals is to complete this course successfully.

If it is not a goal of yours, ask yourself why. One common reason is fear of failure. Amazingly enough, fear of failure alone can be strong enough to keep many of us from doing our best in any endeavor.

Another common reason is that you simply haven't taken the time to think about or write down your goals for this course. To help accomplish this, answer the questions below.

Exercises

1. Write down your goal(s) for this course.

2. Now list steps you will take to make sure your goal(s) in Exercise 1 are accomplished.

3. Rate your commitment to this course with a number between 1 and 5. Use the diagram below to help.

High Commitment		Average Commitment		Not Committed at All
5	4	3	2	1

4. If you have rated your personal commitment level (from the exercise above) as a 1, 2, or 3, list the reasons why this is so. Then determine whether it is possible to increase your commitment level to a 4 or 5.

Good luck, and don't forget that a positive attitude will make a big difference.

STUDY SKILLS BUILDER 2

Tips for Studying for an Exam

To prepare for an exam, try the following study techniques:

- Start the study process days before your exam.
- Make sure that you are up-to-date on your assignments.
- If there is a topic that you are unsure of, use one of the many resources that are available to you. For example,

  See your instructor.

  View a lecture video on the topic.

  Visit a learning resource center on campus.

  Read the textbook material and examples on the topic.
- Reread your notes and carefully review the Chapter Highlights at the end of any chapter.
- Work the review exercises at the end of the chapter.
- Find a quiet place to take the Chapter Test found at the end of the chapter. Do not use any resources when taking this sample test. This way, you will have a clear indication of how prepared you are for your exam. Check your answers and use the Chapter Test Prep Videos to make sure that you correct any missed exercises.

Good luck, and keep a positive attitude.

Exercises

Let's see how you did on your last exam.

1. How many days before your last exam did you start studying for that exam?
2. Were you up-to-date on your assignments at that time or did you need to catch up on assignments?
3. List the most helpful text supplement (if you used one).
4. List the most helpful campus supplement (if you used one).
5. List your process for preparing for a mathematics test.
6. Was this process helpful? In other words, were you satisfied with your performance on your exam?
7. If not, what changes can you make in your process that will make it more helpful to you?

STUDY SKILLS BUILDER 3

What to Do the Day of an Exam

Your first exam may be soon. On the day of an exam, don't forget to try the following:

- Allow yourself plenty of time to arrive.
- Read the directions on the test carefully.
- Read each problem carefully as you take your test. Make sure that you answer the question asked.
- Watch your time and pace yourself so that you may attempt each problem on your test.
- Check your work and answers.
- ***Do not turn your test in early.*** If you have extra time, spend it double-checking your work.

Good luck!

Exercises

Answer the following questions based on your most recent mathematics exam, whenever that was.

1. How soon before class did you arrive?
2. Did you read the directions on the test carefully?
3. Did you make sure you answered the question asked for each problem on the exam?
4. Were you able to attempt each problem on your exam?
5. If your answer to Exercise 4 is no, list reasons why.
6. Did you have extra time on your exam?
7. If your answer to Exercise 6 is yes, describe how you spent that extra time.

STUDY SKILLS BUILDER 4

Are You Satisfied with Your Performance on a Particular Quiz or Exam?

If not, don't forget to analyze your quiz or exam and look for common errors. Were most of your errors a result of:

- *Carelessness?* Did you turn in your quiz or exam before the allotted time expired? If so, resolve to use any extra time to check your work.
- *Running out of time?* Answer the questions you are sure of first. Then attempt the questions you are unsure of, and delay checking your work until all questions have been answered.
- *Not understanding a concept?* If so, review that concept and correct your work so that you make sure you understand it before the next quiz or the final exam.
- *Test conditions?* When studying for a quiz or exam, make sure you place yourself in conditions similar to test conditions. For example, before your next quiz or exam, take a sample test without the aid of your notes or text.

(For a sample test, see your instructor or use the Chapter Test at the end of each chapter.)

Exercises

1. Have you corrected all your previous quizzes and exams?
2. List any errors you have found common to two or more of your graded papers.
3. Is one of your common errors not understanding a concept? If so, are you making sure you understand all the concepts for the next quiz or exam?
4. Is one of your common errors making careless mistakes? If so, are you now taking all the time allotted to check over your work so that you can minimize the number of careless mistakes?
5. Are you satisfied with your grades thus far on quizzes and tests?
6. If your answer to Exercise 5 is no, are there any more suggestions you can make to your instructor or yourself to help? If so, list them here and share these with your instructor.

STUDY SKILLS BUILDER 5

How Are You Doing?

If you haven't done so yet, take a few moments and think about how you are doing in this course. Are you working toward your goal of successfully completing this course? Is your performance on homework, quizzes, and tests satisfactory? If not, you might want to see your instructor to see if he/she has any suggestions on how you can improve your performance. Reread Section 1.1 for ideas on places to get help with your mathematics course.

Exercises

Answer the following.

1. List any textbook supplements you are using to help you through this course.
2. List any campus resources you are using to help you through this course.
3. Write a short paragraph describing how you are doing in your mathematics course.
4. If improvement is needed, list ways that you can work toward improving your situation as described in Exercise 3.

STUDY SKILLS BUILDER 6

Are You Preparing for Your Final Exam?

To prepare for your final exam, try the following study techniques:

- Review the material that you will be responsible for on your exam. This includes material from your textbook, your notebook, and any handouts from your instructor.
- Review any formulas that you may need to memorize.
- Check to see if your instructor or mathematics department will be conducting a final exam review.
- Check with your instructor to see whether final exams from previous semesters/quarters are available to students for review.
- Use your previously taken exams as a practice final exam. To do so, rewrite the test questions in mixed order on blank sheets of paper. This will help you prepare for exam conditions.
- If you are unsure of a few concepts, see your instructor or visit a learning lab for assistance. Also, view the video segment of any troublesome sections.
- If you need further exercises to work, try the Cumulative Reviews at the end of the chapters.

Once again, good luck! I hope you are enjoying this textbook and your mathematics course.

Organizing Your Work

STUDY SKILLS BUILDER 7

Learning New Terms

Many of the terms used in this text may be new to you. It will be helpful to make a list of new mathematical terms and symbols as you encounter them and to review them frequently. Placing these new terms (including page references) on 3×5 index cards might help you later when you're preparing for a quiz.

Exercises

1. Name one way you might place a word and its definition on a 3×5 card.

2. How do new terms stand out in this text so that they can be found?

STUDY SKILLS BUILDER 8

Are You Organized?

Have you ever had trouble finding a completed assignment? When it's time to study for a test, are your notes neat and organized? Have you ever had trouble reading your own mathematics handwriting? (Be honest—I have.)

When any of these things happens, it's time to get organized. Here are a few suggestions:

- Write your notes and complete your homework assignments in a notebook with pockets (spiral or ring binder).
- Take class notes in this notebook, and then follow the notes with your completed homework assignment.
- When you receive graded papers or handouts, place them in the notebook pocket so that you will not lose them.
- Mark (possibly with an exclamation point) any note(s) that seem extra important to you.
- Mark (possibly with a question mark) any notes or homework that you are having trouble with.
- See your instructor or a math tutor to help you with the concepts or exercises that you are having trouble understanding.
- If you are having trouble reading your own handwriting, *slow down* and write your mathematics work clearly!

Exercises

1. Have you been completing your assignments on time?

2. Have you been correcting any exercises you may be having difficulty with?

3. If you are having trouble with a mathematical concept or correcting any homework exercises, have you visited your instructor, a tutor, or your campus math lab?

4. Are you taking lecture notes in your mathematics course? (By the way, these notes should include worked-out examples solved by your instructor.)

5. Is your mathematics course material (handouts, graded papers, lecture notes) organized?

6. If your answer to Exercise 5 is no, take a moment and review your course material. List at least two ways that you might better organize it.

STUDY SKILLS BUILDER 9

Organizing a Notebook

It's never too late to get organized. If you need ideas about organizing a notebook for your mathematics course, try some of these:

- Use a spiral or ring binder notebook with pockets and use it for mathematics only.
- Start each page by writing the book's section number you are working on at the top.
- When your instructor is lecturing, take notes. *Always* include any examples your instructor works for you.
- Place your worked-out homework exercises in your notebook immediately after the lecture notes from that section. This way, a section's worth of material is together.
- Homework exercises: Attempt and check all assigned homework.
- Place graded quizzes in the pockets of your notebook or a special section of your binder.

Exercises

Check your notebook organization by answering the following questions.

1. Do you have a spiral or ring binder notebook for your mathematics course only?
2. Have you ever had to flip through several sheets of notes and work in your mathematics notebook to determine what section's work you are in?
3. Are you now writing the textbook's section number at the top of each notebook page?
4. Have you ever lost or had trouble finding a graded quiz or test?
5. Are you now placing all your graded work in a dedicated place in your notebook?
6. Are you attempting all of your homework and placing all of your work in your notebook?
7. Are you checking and correcting your homework in your notebook? If not, why not?
8. Are you writing in your notebook the examples your instructor works for you in class?

STUDY SKILLS BUILDER 10

How Are Your Homework Assignments Going?

It is very important in mathematics to keep up with homework. Why? Many concepts build on each other. Often your understanding of a day's concepts depends on an understanding of the previous day's material.

Remember that completing your homework assignment involves a lot more than attempting a few of the problems assigned.

To complete a homework assignment, remember these four things:

- Attempt all of it.
- Check it.
- Correct it.
- If needed, ask questions about it.

Exercises

Take a moment and review your completed homework assignments. Answer the questions below based on this review.

1. Approximate the fraction of your homework you have attempted.
2. Approximate the fraction of your homework you have checked (if possible).
3. If you are able to check your homework, have you corrected it when errors have been found?
4. When working homework, if you do not understand a concept, what do you do?

MyMathLab and MathXL

STUDY SKILLS BUILDER 11

Tips for Turning In Your Homework on Time

It is very important to keep up with your mathematics homework assignments. Why? Many concepts in mathematics build upon each other.

Remember these four tips to help ensure your work is completed on time:

- Know the assignments and due dates set by your instructor.
- Do not wait until the last minute to submit your homework.
- Set a goal to submit your homework 6–8 hours before the scheduled due date in case you have unexpected technology trouble.
- Schedule enough time to complete each assignment.

Following the tips above will also help you avoid potentially losing points for late or missed assignments.

Exercises

Take a moment to consider your work on your homework assignments to date and answer the following questions:

1. What percentage of your assignments have you turned in on time?

2. Why might it be a good idea to submit your homework 6–8 hours before the scheduled deadline?

3. If you have missed submitting any homework by the due date, list some of the reasons why this occurred.

4. What steps do you plan to take in the future to ensure your homework is submitted on time?

STUDY SKILLS BUILDER 12

Tips for Doing Your Homework Online

Practice is one of the main keys to success in any mathematics course. Did you know that MyMathLab/MathXL provides you with **immediate feedback** for each exercise? If you are incorrect, you are given hints to work the exercise correctly. You have **unlimited practice opportunities** and can rework any exercises you have trouble with until you master them, and submit homework assignments unlimited times before the deadline.

Remember these success tips when doing your homework online:

- Attempt all assigned exercises.
- Write down (neatly) your step-by-step work for each exercise before entering your answer.
- Use the immediate feedback provided by the program to help you check and correct your work for each exercise.
- Rework any exercises you have trouble with until you master them.
- Work through your homework assignment as many times as necessary until you are satisfied.

Exercises

Take a moment to think about your homework assignments to date and answer the following:

1. Have you attempted all assigned exercises?

2. Of the exercises attempted, have you also written out your work before entering your answer—so that you can check it?

3. Are you familiar with how to enter answers using the MathXL player so that you avoid answer entry type errors?

4. List some ways the immediate feedback and practice supports have helped you with your homework. If you have not used these supports, how do you plan to use them with the success tips above on your next assignment?

STUDY SKILLS BUILDER 13

Organizing Your Work

Have you ever used any readily available paper (such as the back of a flyer, another course assignment, post-its, etc.) to work out homework exercises before entering the answer in MathXL? To save time, have you ever entered answers directly into MathXL without working the exercises on paper? When it's time to study, have you ever been unable to find your completed work or read and follow your own mathematics handwriting?

When any of these things happen, it's time to get organized. Here are some suggestions:

- Write your step-by-step work for each homework exercise, (neatly) on lined, loose-leaf paper and keep this in a 3-ring binder.
- Refer to your step-by-step work when you receive feedback that your answer is incorrect in MathXL. Double-check against the steps and hints provided by the program and correct your work accordingly.
- Keep your written homework with your class notes for that section.
- Identify any exercises you are having trouble with and ask questions about them.
- Keep all graded quizzes and tests in this binder as well to study later.

If you follow the suggestions above, you and your instructor or tutor will be able to follow your steps and correct any mistakes. You will have a written copy of your work to refer to later to ask questions and study for tests.

Exercises

1. Why is it important that you write out your step-by-step work on homework exercises and keep a hard copy of all work submitted online?
2. If you have gotten an incorrect answer, are you able to follow your steps and find your error?
3. If you were asked today to review your previous homework assignments and first test, could you find them? If not, list some ways you might better organize your work.

STUDY SKILLS BUILDER 14

Getting Help with Your Homework Assignments

There are many helpful resources available to you through MathXL to help you work through any homework exercises you may have trouble with. It is important that you know what these resources are and know when and how to use them.

Let's review these features found in the homework exercises:

- **Help Me Solve This**—provides step-by-step help for the exercise you are working. You must work an additional exercise of the same type (without this help) before you can get credit for having worked it correctly.
- **View an Example**—allows you to view a correctly worked exercise similar to the one you are having trouble with. You can go back to your original exercise and work it on your own.
- **E-Book**—allows you to read examples from your text and find similar exercises.
- **Video**—your text author, Elayn Martin-Gay, works an exercise similar to the one you need help with. **Not all exercises have an accompanying video clip.
- **Ask My Instructor**—allows you to email your instructor for help with an exercise.

Exercises

1. How does the "Help Me Solve This" feature work?
2. If the "View an Example" feature is used, is it necessary to work an additional problem before continuing the assignment?
3. When might be a good time to use the "Video" feature? Do all exercises have an accompanying video clip?
4. Which of the features above have you used? List those you found the most helpful to you.
5. If you haven't used the features discussed, list those you plan to try on your next homework assignment.

STUDY SKILLS BUILDER 15

Tips for Preparing for an Exam

Did you know that you can rework your previous homework assignments in MyMathLab and MathXL? This is a great way to prepare for tests. To do this, open a previous homework assignment and click "similar exercise." This will generate new exercises similar to the homework you have submitted. You can then rework the exercises and assignments until you feel confident that you understand them.

To prepare for an exam, follow these tips:

- Review your written work for your previous homework assignments along with your class notes.
- Identify any exercises or topics that you have questions on or have difficulty understanding.
- Rework your previous assignments in MyMathLab and MathXL until you fully understand them and can do them without help.
- Get help for any topics you feel unsure of or for which you have questions.

Exercises

1. Are your current homework assignments up to date and is your written work for them organized in a binder or notebook? If the answer is no, it's time to get organized. For tips on this, see Study Skills Builder 13—Organizing Your Work.
2. How many days in advance of an exam do you usually start studying?
3. List some ways you think that practicing previous homework assignments can help you prepare for your test.
4. List two or three resources you can use to get help for any topics you are unsure of or have questions on.

Good luck!

STUDY SKILLS BUILDER 16

How Well Do You Know the Resources Available to You in MyMathLab?

There are many helpful resources available to you in MyMathLab. Let's take a moment to locate and explore a few of them now. Go into your MyMathLab course, and visit the multimedia library, tools for success, and E-book.

Let's see what you found.

Exercises

1. List the resources available to you in the Multimedia Library.
2. List the resources available to you in the Tools for Success folder.
3. Where did you find the English/Spanish Audio Glossary?
4. Can you view videos from the E-Book?
5. Did you find any resources you did not know about? If so, which ones?
6. Which resources have you used most often or found most helpful?

Additional Help Inside and Outside Your Textbook

STUDY SKILLS BUILDER 17

How Well Do You Know Your Textbook?

The questions below will help determine whether you are familiar with your textbook. For additional information, see Section 1.1 in this text.

1. What does the icon mean?
2. What does the icon mean?
3. What does the △ icon mean?
4. Where can you find a review for each chapter? What answers to this review can be found in the back of your text?
5. Each chapter contains an overview of the chapter along with examples. What is this feature called?
6. Each chapter contains a review of vocabulary. What is this feature called?
7. There are practice exercises that are contained in this text. What are they and how can they be used?
8. This text contains a student section in the back entitled Student Resources. List the contents of this section and how they might be helpful.
9. What exercise answers are available in this text? Where are they located?

STUDY SKILLS BUILDER 18

Are You Familiar with Your Textbook Supplements?

Below is a review of some of the student supplements available for additional study. Check to see if you are using the ones most helpful to you.

- Chapter Test Prep Videos. These videos provide video clip solutions to the Chapter Test exercises in this text. You will find this extremely useful when studying for tests or exams.
- Interactive DVD Lecture Series. These are keyed to each section of the text. The material is presented by me, Elayn Martin-Gay, and I have placed a [video icon] by the exercises in the text that I have worked on the video.
- The *Student Solutions Manual*. This contains worked-out solutions to odd-numbered exercises as well as Practice Exercises and every exercise in the Integrated Reviews, Chapter Reviews, Chapter Tests, and Cumulative Reviews.
- Pearson Tutor Center. Mathematics questions may be phoned, faxed, or e-mailed to this center.
- MyMathLab is a text-specific online course. MathXL is an online homework, tutorial, and assessment system. Take a moment and determine whether these are available to you.

As usual, your instructor is your best source of information.

Exercises

Let's see how you are doing with textbook supplements.

1. Name one way the Lecture Videos can be helpful to you.
2. Name one way the Chapter Test Prep Video can help you prepare for a chapter test.
3. List any textbook supplements that you have found useful.
4. Have you located and visited a learning resource lab located on your campus?
5. List the textbook supplements that are currently housed in your campus's learning resource lab.

STUDY SKILLS BUILDER 19

Are You Getting All the Mathematics Help That You Need?

Remember that, in addition to your instructor, there are many places to get help with your mathematics course. For example:

- This text has an accompanying video lesson for every section, and the Chapter Test Prep videos provide worked-out solutions to every Chapter Test exercise.
- The back of the book contains answers to odd-numbered exercises.
- A *Student Solutions Manual* is available that contains worked-out solutions to odd-numbered exercises as well as solutions to Practice Exercises and every exercise in the Integrated Reviews, Chapter Reviews, Chapter Tests, and Cumulative Reviews.
- Don't forget to check with your instructor for other local resources available to you, such as a tutoring center.

Exercises

1. List items you find helpful in the text and all student supplements to this text.
2. List all the campus help that is available to you for this course.
3. List any help (besides the textbook) from Exercises 1 and 2 above that you are using.
4. List any help (besides the textbook) that you feel you should try.
5. Write a goal for yourself that includes trying everything you listed in Exercise 4 during the next week.

Bigger Picture—Study Guide Outline

Simplifying Expressions and Solving Equations

I. Simplifying Expressions

A. Real Numbers

1. Add: (Sec. 1.4)

$-1.7 + (-0.21) = -1.91$ Adding like signs. Add absolute values. Attach common sign.

$-7 + 3 = -4$ Adding different signs. Subtract absolute values. Attach the sign of the number with the larger absolute value.

2. Subtract: Add the first number to the opposite of the second number. (Sec. 1.5)

$17 - 25 = 17 + (-25) = -8$

3. Multiply or divide: Multiply or divide the two numbers as usual. If the signs are the same, the answer is positive. If the signs are different, the answer is negative. (Sec. 1.6)

$-10 \cdot 3 = -30, \quad -81 \div (-3) = 27$

B. Exponents (Sec. 3.1, 3.2)

$x^7 \cdot x^5 = x^{12};\ (x^7)^5 = x^{35};\ \frac{x^7}{x^5} = x^2;\ x^0 = 1;\ 8^{-2} = \frac{1}{8^2} = \frac{1}{64}$

C. Polynomials

1. Add: Combine like terms. (Sec. 3.4)

$$(3y^2 + 6y + 7) + (9y^2 - 11y - 15) = 3y^2 + 6y + 7 + 9y^2 - 11y - 15$$
$$= 12y^2 - 5y - 8$$

2. Subtract: Change the sign of the terms of the polynomial being subtracted, then add. (Sec. 3.4)

$$(3y^2 + 6y + 7) - (9y^2 - 11y - 15) = 3y^2 + 6y + 7 - 9y^2 + 11y + 15$$
$$= -6y^2 + 17y + 22$$

3. Multiply: Multiply each term of one polynomial by each term of the other polynomial. (Sec. 3.5)

$$(x + 5)(2x^2 - 3x + 4) = x(2x^2 - 3x + 4) + 5(2x^2 - 3x + 4)$$
$$= 2x^3 - 3x^2 + 4x + 10x^2 - 15x + 20$$
$$= 2x^3 + 7x^2 - 11x + 20$$

4. Divide: (Sec. 3.7)

a. To divide by a monomial, divide each term of the polynomial by the monomial.

$$\frac{8x^2 + 2x - 6}{2x} = \frac{8x^2}{2x} + \frac{2x}{2x} - \frac{6}{2x} = 4x + 1 - \frac{3}{x}$$

b. To divide by a polynomial other than a monomial, use long division.

$$\begin{array}{r} x - 6 + \dfrac{40}{2x+5} \\ 2x + 5\overline{)2x^2 - 7x + 10} \\ \underline{-2x^2 \mp 5x} \\ -12x + 10 \\ \underline{\pm 12x \pm 30} \\ 40 \end{array}$$

D. Factoring Polynomials

See the Chapter 4 Integrated Review for steps.

$$3x^4 - 78x^2 + 75 = 3(x^4 - 26x^2 + 25) \quad \text{Factor out GCF—always first step.}$$
$$= 3(x^2 - 25)(x^2 - 1) \quad \text{Factor trinomial.}$$
$$= 3(x + 5)(x - 5)(x + 1)(x - 1) \quad \text{Factor further—each difference of squares.}$$

E. Rational Expressions

1. **Simplify:** Factor the numerator and denominator. Then remove factors of 1 by dividing out common factors in the numerator and denominator. (Sec. 5.1)

$$\frac{x^2 - 9}{7x^2 - 21x} = \frac{(x + 3)(x - 3)}{7x(x - 3)} = \frac{x + 3}{7x}$$

2. **Multiply:** Multiply numerators, then multiply denominators. (Sec. 5.2)

$$\frac{5z}{2z^2 - 9z - 18} \cdot \frac{22z + 33}{10z} = \frac{5 \cdot z}{(2z + 3)(z - 6)} \cdot \frac{11(2z + 3)}{2 \cdot 5 \cdot z} = \frac{11}{2(z - 6)}$$

3. **Divide:** First fraction times the reciprocal of the second fraction. (Sec. 5.2)

$$\frac{14}{x + 5} \div \frac{x + 1}{2} = \frac{14}{x + 5} \cdot \frac{2}{x + 1} = \frac{28}{(x + 5)(x + 1)}$$

4. **Add or subtract:** Must have same denominator. If not, find the LCD and write each fraction as an equivalent fraction with the LCD as denominator. (Sec. 5.4)

$$\frac{9}{10} - \frac{x + 1}{x + 5} = \frac{9(x + 5)}{10(x + 5)} - \frac{10(x + 1)}{10(x + 5)}$$
$$= \frac{9x + 45 - 10x - 10}{10(x + 5)} = \frac{-x + 35}{10(x + 5)}$$

F. Radicals

1. **Simplify square roots:** If possible, factor the radicand so that one factor is a perfect square. Then use the product rule and simplify. (Sec. 8.2)

$$\sqrt{75} = \sqrt{25 \cdot 3} = \sqrt{25} \cdot \sqrt{3} = 5\sqrt{3}$$

2. **Add or subtract:** Only like radicals (same index and radicand) can be added or subtracted. (Sec. 8.3)

$$8\sqrt{10} - \sqrt{40} + \sqrt{5} = 8\sqrt{10} - 2\sqrt{10} + \sqrt{5} = 6\sqrt{10} + \sqrt{5}$$

3. **Multiply or divide:** $\sqrt{a} \cdot \sqrt{b} = \sqrt{ab}$; $\frac{\sqrt{a}}{\sqrt{b}} = \sqrt{\frac{a}{b}}$. (Sec. 8.4)

$$\sqrt{11} \cdot \sqrt{3} = \sqrt{33}; \frac{\sqrt{140}}{\sqrt{7}} = \sqrt{\frac{140}{7}} = \sqrt{20} = \sqrt{4 \cdot 5} = 2\sqrt{5}$$

4. **Rationalizing the denominator:** (Sec. 8.4)

   a. If denominator is one term,

$$\frac{5}{\sqrt{11}} = \frac{5 \cdot \sqrt{11}}{\sqrt{11} \cdot \sqrt{11}} = \frac{5\sqrt{11}}{11}$$

   b. If denominator is two terms, multiply by 1 in the form of $\frac{\text{conjugate of denominator}}{\text{conjugate of denominator}}$.

$$\frac{13}{3 + \sqrt{2}} = \frac{13}{3 + \sqrt{2}} \cdot \frac{3 - \sqrt{2}}{3 - \sqrt{2}} = \frac{13(3 - \sqrt{2})}{9 - 2} = \frac{39 - 13\sqrt{2}}{7}$$

II. Solving Equations and Inequalities

A. Linear Equations: Power on variable is 1 and there are no variables in denominator. (Sec. 2.3)

$7(x-3)=4x+6$ Linear equation. (If fractions, multiply by LCD.)

$7x-21=4x+6$ Use the distributive property.

$7x=4x+27$ Add 21 to both sides.

$3x=27$ Subtract $4x$ from both sides.

$x=9$ Divide both sides by 3.

B. Linear Inequalities: Same as linear equation except if you multiply or divide by a negative number, then reverse direction of inequality. (Sec. 2.7)

$-4x+11\leq-1$ Linear inequality.

$-4x\leq-12$ Subtract 11 from both sides.

$\frac{-4x}{-4}\geq\frac{-12}{-4}$ Divide both sides by -4 and reverse the direction of the inequality symbol.

$x\geq3$ Simplify.

C. Quadratic and Higher Degree Equations: Solve: first write the equation in standard form (one side is 0).

1. If the polynomial on one side factors, solve by factoring. (Sec. 4.6)

2. If the polynomial does not factor, solve by the quadratic formula. (Sec. 9.3)

By factoring:

$$x^2+x=6$$
$$x^2+x-6=0$$
$$(x-2)(x+3)=0$$
$$x-2=0 \text{ or } x+3=0$$
$$x=2 \quad \text{or} \quad x=-3$$

By quadratic formula:

$$x^2+x=5$$
$$x^2+x-5=0$$
$$a=1, b=1, c=-5$$
$$x=\frac{-1\pm\sqrt{1^2-4(1)(-5)}}{2\cdot1}$$
$$=\frac{-1\pm\sqrt{21}}{2}$$

D. Equations with Rational Expressions: Make sure the proposed solution does not make any denominator 0. (Sec. 5.5)

$\frac{3}{x}-\frac{1}{x-1}=\frac{4}{x-1}$ Equation with rational expressions.

$x(x-1)\cdot\frac{3}{x}-x(x-1)\cdot\frac{1}{x-1}=x(x-1)\cdot\frac{4}{x-1}$ Multiply through by $x(x-1)$.

$3(x-1)-x\cdot1=x\cdot4$ Simplify.

$3x-3-x=4x$ Use the distributive property.

$-3=2x$ Simplify and move variable terms to right side.

$-\frac{3}{2}=x$ Divide both sides by 2.

E. Proportions: An equation with two ratios equal. Set cross products equal, then solve. Make sure the proposed solution does not make any denominator 0. (Sec. 5.6)

$$\frac{5}{x}=\frac{9}{2x-3}$$

$5(2x-3)=9\cdot x$ Set cross products equal.

$10x-15=9x$ Multiply.

$x=15$ Write equation with variable terms on one side and constants on the other.

F. Equations with Radicals: To solve, isolate a radical, then square both sides. You may have to repeat this. Check possible solution in the original equation. (Sec. 8.5)

$$\sqrt{x + 49} + 7 = x$$

$$\sqrt{x + 49} = x - 7 \qquad \text{Subtract 7 from both sides.}$$

$$x + 49 = x^2 - 14x + 49 \qquad \text{Square both sides.}$$

$$0 = x^2 - 15x \qquad \text{Set terms equal to 0.}$$

$$0 = x(x - 15) \qquad \text{Factor.}$$

~~$x = 0$~~ or $x = 15$ Set each factor equal to 0 and solve.

Practice Final Exam

Step-by-step test solutions are found on the Chapter Test Prep Videos available via the Interactive DVD Lecture Series, in MyMathLab or on YouTube (search "MartinGayIntroAlg" and click on "Channels").

1. ______
2. ______
3. ______
4. ______
5. ______
6. ______
7. ______
8. ______
9. ______
10. ______
11. ______
12. ______
13. ______
14. ______
15. ______
16. ______
17. ______

Preparing for your Final Exam? Take this Practice Final and watch the full video solutions to any of the exercises you want to review. You will find the Practice Final video in the Video Lecture Series. The video also provides you with an overview to help you approach different problem types just as you will need to do on a Final Exam. To build your own study guide use the Bigger Picture feature in the text. See Appendix A.1 for an example.

Evaluate.

1. -3^4

2. 4^{-3}

3. $6[5 + 2(3 - 8) - 3]$

Perform the indicated operations and simplify if possible.

4. $(5x^3 + x^2 + 5x - 2) - (8x^3 - 4x^2 + x - 7)$

5. $(4x - 2)^2$

6. $(3x + 7)(x^2 + 5x + 2)$

Factor.

7. $6t^2 - t - 5$

8. $3x^3 - 21x^2 + 30x$

9. $180 - 5x^2$

10. $3a^2 + 3ab - 7a - 7b$

11. $x - x^5$

Simplify. Write answers with positive exponents only.

12. $\left(\dfrac{4x^2y^3}{x^3y^{-4}}\right)^2$

13. $\dfrac{5 - \dfrac{1}{y^2}}{\dfrac{1}{y} + \dfrac{2}{y^2}}$

Perform the indicated operations and simplify if possible.

14. $\dfrac{x^2 - 13x + 42}{x^2 + 10x + 21} \div \dfrac{x^2 - 4}{x^2 + x - 6}$

15. $\dfrac{5a}{a^2 - a - 6} - \dfrac{2}{a - 3}$

Solve each equation or inequality.

16. $4(n - 5) = -(4 - 2n)$

17. $x(x + 6) = 7$

18. $3x - 5 \geq 7x + 3$

19. $2x^2 - 6x + 1 = 0$

20. $\frac{4}{y} - \frac{5}{3} = -\frac{1}{5}$

21. $\frac{5}{y+1} = \frac{4}{y+2}$

22. $\frac{a}{a-3} = \frac{3}{a-3} - \frac{3}{2}$

23. $\sqrt{2x - 2} = x - 5$

Graph the following.

24. $5x - 7y = 10$

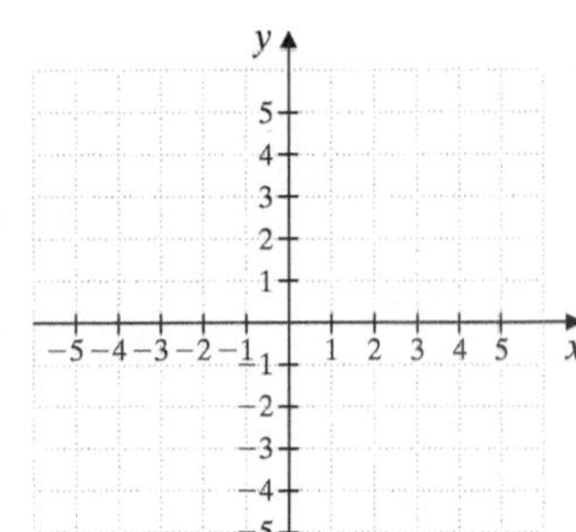

25. $y = -1$

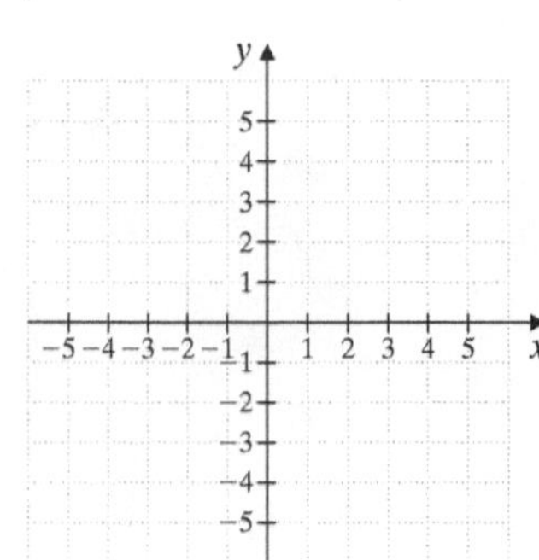

26. $y \geq -4x$

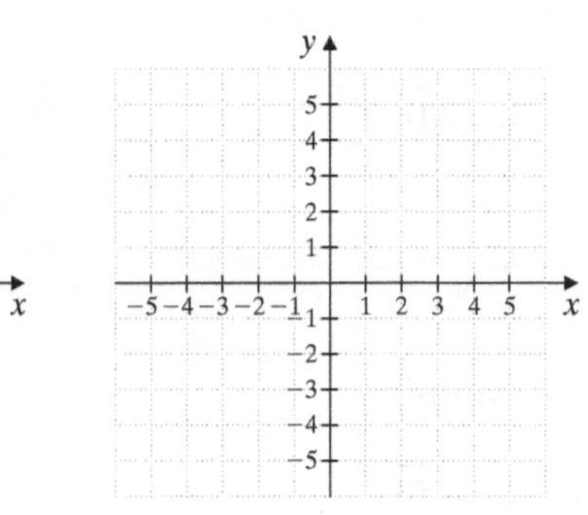

Find the slope of each line.

27. through $(6, -5)$ and $(-1, 2)$

28. $-3x + y = 5$

Write equations of the following lines. Write each equation in standard form.

29. through $(2, -5)$ and $(1, 3)$

30. slope $\frac{1}{8}$; y-intercept $(0, 12)$

Solve each system of equations.

31. $\begin{cases} 3x - 2y = -14 \\ y = x + 5 \end{cases}$

32. $\begin{cases} 4x - 6y = 7 \\ -2x + 3y = 0 \end{cases}$

Answer the questions about functions.

33. If $f(x) = x^3 - x$, find
a. $f(-1)$ **b.** $f(0)$ **c.** $f(4)$

18. ______
19. ______
20. ______
21. ______
22. ______
23. ______
24. ______
25. ______
26. ______
27. ______
28. ______
29. ______
30. ______
31. ______
32. ______
33. a. ______
b. ______
c. ______

34. ______________

35. ______________

36. ______________

37. ______________

38. ______________

39. ______________

40. ______________

41. ______________

42. ______________

43. ______________

44. ______________

45. ______________

46. ______________

47. ______________

48. ______________

34. Determine whether the relation is also a function. If a function, find its domain and range.

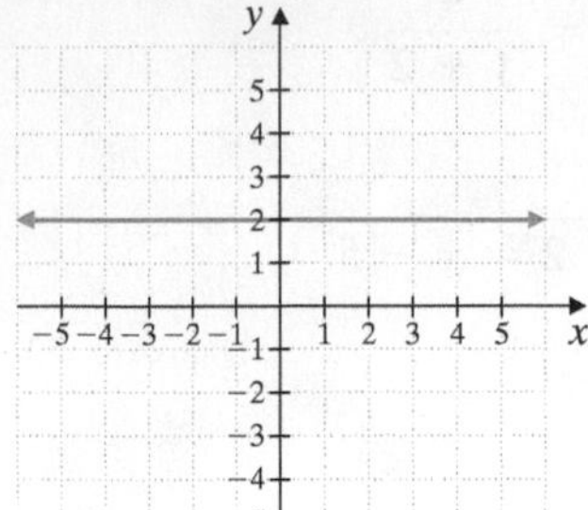

Evaluate.

35. $\sqrt{16}$

36. $\sqrt[3]{125}$

37. $\sqrt{\dfrac{9}{16}}$

Simplify.

38. $\sqrt{54}$

39. $\sqrt{24x^8}$

Perform the indicated operations and simplify if possible.

40. $\sqrt{18} - \sqrt{75} + 7\sqrt{3} - \sqrt{8}$

41. $\dfrac{\sqrt{40x^4}}{\sqrt{2x}}$

42. $\sqrt{2}\left(\sqrt{6} - \sqrt{5}\right)$

Rationalize each denominator.

43. $\dfrac{8}{\sqrt{5y}}$

44. $\dfrac{8}{\sqrt{6} + 2}$

Solve each application.

45. One number plus five times its reciprocal is equal to six. Find the number.

46. Some states have a single area code for the entire state. Two such states have area codes where one is double the other. If the sum of these integers is 1203, find the two area codes.

47. Two hikers start at opposite ends of the St. Tammany Trails and walk toward each other. The trail is 36 miles long and they meet in 4 hours. If one hiker is twice as fast as the other, find both hiking speeds.

48. Find the amount of a 12% saline solution a lab assistant should add to 80 cc (cubic centimeters) of a 22% saline solution in order to have a 16% solution.

Answers to Selected Exercises

Chapter R Prealgebra Review

Section R.1

Vocabulary and Readiness Check **1.** prime factorization **3.** prime **5.** factor

Exercise Set R.1 **1.** 1, 3, 9 **3.** 1, 2, 3, 4, 6, 8, 12, 24 **5.** 1, 2, 3, 6, 7, 14, 21, 42 **7.** 1, 2, 4, 5, 8, 10, 16, 20, 40, 80 **9.** 1, 19 **11.** prime **13.** composite **15.** prime **17.** composite **19.** composite **21.** $2\cdot3\cdot3$ **23.** $2\cdot2\cdot5$ **25.** $2\cdot2\cdot2\cdot7$ **27.** $3\cdot3\cdot3\cdot3$ **29.** $2\cdot2\cdot3\cdot5\cdot5$ **31.** $2\cdot2\cdot3\cdot7\cdot7$ **33.** d **35.** 12 **37.** 42 **39.** 60 **41.** 35 **43.** 36 **45.** 80 **47.** 360 **49.** 72 **51.** 120 **53.** 42 **55.** 48 **57.** 360 **59. a.** $2\cdot2\cdot2\cdot5$ **b.** $2\cdot2\cdot2\cdot5$ **c.** answers may vary **61.** every 35 days **63.** 2520

Section R.2

Vocabulary and Readiness Check **1.** fraction; denominator; numerator **3.** simplest form **5.** $\frac{a\cdot c}{b\cdot d}$ **7.** $\frac{a\cdot d}{b\cdot c}$ **9.** least common denominator (LCD)

Exercise Set R.2 **1.** 1 **3.** 10 **5.** 13 **7.** 0 **9.** undefined **11.** $\frac{21}{30}$ **13.** $\frac{4}{18}$ **15.** $\frac{16}{20}$ **17.** $\frac{1}{2}$ **19.** $\frac{2}{3}$ **21.** $\frac{3}{7}$ **23.** $\frac{3}{5}$ **25.** $\frac{4}{5}$ **27.** $\frac{11}{8}$ **29.** $\frac{30}{61}$ **31.** $\frac{8}{11}$ **33.** $\frac{3}{8}$ **35.** $\frac{1}{2}$ **37.** $\frac{6}{7}$ **39.** 15 **41.** $18\frac{20}{27}$ **43.** $2\frac{28}{29}$ **45.** 1 **47.** $\frac{11}{60}$ **49.** $\frac{23}{21}$ **51.** $\frac{65}{21}$ **53.** $1\frac{3}{4}$ **55.** $5\frac{1}{6}$ **57.** $\frac{9}{35}$ **59.** $\frac{1}{3}$ **61.** $\frac{1}{6}$ **63.** $\frac{3}{80}$ **65.** $\frac{5}{66}$ **67.** $48\frac{1}{15}$ **69.** 37 **71.** $10\frac{5}{11}$ **73.** $\frac{7}{5}$ **75.** $7\frac{1}{12}$ **77.** $\frac{17}{18}$ **79.** incorrect; $\frac{12}{24}=\frac{2\cdot2\cdot3}{2\cdot2\cdot2\cdot3}=\frac{1}{2}$ **81.** incorrect; $\frac{2}{7}+\frac{9}{7}=\frac{11}{7}$ **83.** answers may vary **85.** $\frac{1}{12}$ **87.** $\frac{6}{11}$ **89.** $7\frac{13}{20}$ in. **91. a.** $\frac{21}{100}$ **b.** $\frac{1}{2}$ **c.** multiplexes **d.** $\frac{1}{2}$ **93.** $\frac{6}{55}$ sq m

Section R.3

Vocabulary and Readiness Check **1.** decimal **3.** vertically **5.** Percent **7.** percent **9.** right

Exercise Set R.3 **1.** $\frac{6}{10}$ **3.** $\frac{186}{100}$ **5.** $\frac{114}{1000}$ **7.** $\frac{1231}{10}$ **9.** 6.83 **11.** 27.0578 **13.** 6.5 **15.** 15.22 **17.** 0.12 **19.** 0.2646 **21.** 1.68 **23.** 5.8 **25.** 56.431 **27.** 67.5 **29.** 70 **31.** 598.23 **33.** 43.274 **35.** 840 **37.** 84.97593 **39.** 0.6 **41.** 0.23 **43.** 0.595 **45.** 98,207.2 **47.** 12.35 **49.** 0.75 **51.** $0.\overline{3}\approx0.33$ **53.** 0.4375 **55.** $0.\overline{54}\approx0.55$ **57.** $4.8\overline{3}\approx4.83$ **59.** 0.28 **61.** 0.031 **63.** 1.35 **65.** 2 **67.** 0.9655 **69.** 0.001 **71.** 0.158 **73.** 68% **75.** 87.6% **77.** 100% **79.** 50% **81.** 192% **83.** 0.4% **85.** 78.1% **87.** 0.005; $\frac{1}{200}$ **89.** 0.142; $\frac{71}{500}$ **91. a.** tenths **b.** thousandths **c.** ones **93.** answers may vary **95.** 182.6 lb **97. a.** 52.9% **b.** 52.86% **99.** b, d **101.** 4% **103.** network systems and data communication analysts **105.** 0.35 **107.** answers may vary

Chapter R Vocabulary Check **1.** factor **2.** multiple **3.** composite number **4.** percent **5.** equivalent **6.** improper fraction **7.** prime number **8.** simplified **9.** proper fraction **10.** mixed number

Chapter R Review **1.** $2\cdot3\cdot7$ **2.** $2\cdot2\cdot2\cdot2\cdot2\cdot5\cdot5$ **3.** 60 **4.** 42 **5.** 60 **6.** 70 **7.** $\frac{15}{24}$ **8.** $\frac{40}{60}$ **9.** $\frac{2}{5}$ **10.** $\frac{3}{20}$ **11.** 2 **12.** 1 **13.** $\frac{8}{77}$ **14.** $\frac{11}{20}$ **15.** $\frac{1}{20}$ **16.** $\frac{11}{18}$ **17.** $14\frac{11}{32}$ **18.** $\frac{1}{2}$ **19.** $20\frac{17}{30}$ **20.** $2\frac{6}{7}$ **21.** $\frac{11}{20}$ sq mi **22.** $\frac{5}{16}$ sq m **23.** $\frac{181}{100}$ **24.** $\frac{35}{1000}$ **25.** 95.118 **26.** 36.785 **27.** 13.38 **28.** 691.573 **29.** 91.2 **30.** 46.816 **31.** 28.6 **32.** 230 **33.** 0.77 **34.** 25.6 **35.** 0.5 **36.** 0.375 **37.** $0.\overline{36}\approx0.364$ **38.** $0.8\overline{3}\approx0.833$ **39.** 0.29 **40.** 0.014 **41.** 39% **42.** 120% **43.** 0.683 **44.** b

Chapter R Test **1.** $2\cdot2\cdot2\cdot3\cdot3$ **2.** 180 **3.** $\frac{25}{60}$ **4.** $\frac{3}{4}$ **5.** $\frac{12}{25}$ **6.** $\frac{13}{10}$ **7.** $\frac{53}{40}$ **8.** $\frac{18}{49}$ **9.** $\frac{1}{20}$ **10.** $\frac{29}{36}$ **11.** $4\frac{8}{9}$ **12.** $2\frac{5}{22}$ **13.** 55 **14.** $13\frac{13}{20}$ **15.** 45.11 **16.** 65.88 **17.** 12.688 **18.** 320 **19.** 23.73 **20.** 0.875 **21.** $0.1\overline{6}\approx0.167$ **22.** 0.632 **23.** 9% **24.** 75% **25.** $\frac{3}{4}$ **26.** $\frac{1}{200}$ **27.** $\frac{49}{200}$ **28.** $\frac{199}{200}$ **29.** $\frac{1}{8}$ sq ft **30.** $\frac{63}{64}$ sq cm

Chapter 1 Real Numbers and Introduction to Algebra

Section 1.2

Vocabulary and Readiness Check **1.** whole **3.** inequality **5.** real **7.** 0 **9.** absolute value

Exercise Set 1.2 **1.** $<$ **3.** $>$ **5.** $=$ **7.** $<$ **9.** $32<212$ **11.** $30\le45$ **13.** true **15.** false **17.** true **19.** false **21.** $20\le25$ **23.** $6>0$ **25.** $-12<-10$ **27.** $7<11$ **29.** $5\ge4$ **31.** $15\ne-2$ **33.** 14,494; −282 **35.** −28,000 **37.** 475; −195 **39.**

41. **43.**

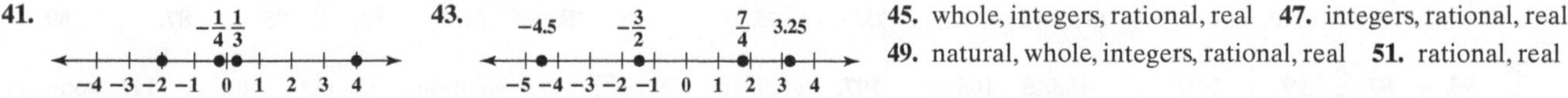

45. whole, integers, rational, real **47.** integers, rational, real **49.** natural, whole, integers, rational, real **51.** rational, real

53. false **55.** true **57.** false **59.** false **61.** 8.9 **63.** 20 **65.** $\frac{9}{2}$ **67.** $\frac{12}{13}$ **69.** $>$ **71.** $=$ **73.** $<$ **75.** $<$
77. 905 thousand $>$ 823 thousand, or 905,000 $>$ 823,000 **79.** decreased by 24 or -24 **81.** 49 million $>$ 16 million, or 49,000,000 $>$ 16,000,000 **83.** 38 million pounds less, or -38 million **85.** $-0.04 > -26.7$ **87.** sun **89.** sun **91.** answers may vary

Section 1.3

Calculator Explorations **1.** 125 **3.** 59,049 **5.** 30 **7.** 9857 **9.** 2376

Vocabulary and Readiness Check **1.** base; exponent **3.** multiplication **5.** subtraction **7.** expression **9.** expression; variables **11.** equation

Exercise Set 1.3 **1.** 243 **3.** 27 **5.** 1 **7.** 5 **9.** 49 **11.** $\frac{16}{81}$ **13.** $\frac{1}{125}$ **15.** 1.44 **17.** 0.343 **19.** 5^2 sq m **21.** 17 **23.** 20 **25.** 12 **27.** 21 **29.** 45 **31.** 0 **33.** $\frac{2}{7}$ **35.** 30 **37.** 2 **39.** $\frac{7}{18}$ **41.** $\frac{27}{10}$ **43.** $\frac{7}{5}$ **45.** 32 **47.** $\frac{23}{27}$ **49.** 9 **51.** 1 **53.** 1 **55.** 11 **57.** 8 **59.** 45 **61.** 27 **63.** 132 **65.** $\frac{37}{18}$ **67.** solution **69.** not a solution **71.** not a solution **73.** solution **75.** not a solution **77.** solution **79.** $x + 15$ **81.** $x - 5$ **83.** $\frac{x}{4}$ **85.** $3x + 22$ **87.** $1 + 2 = 9 \div 3$ **89.** $3 \neq 4 \div 2$ **91.** $5 + x = 20$ **93.** $7.6x = 17$ **95.** $13 - 3x = 13$ **97.** no; answers may vary **99. a.** 64 **b.** 43 **c.** 19 **d.** 22 **101.** 14 in., 12 sq in. **103.** 14 in., 9.01 sq in. **105.** Rectangles with the same perimeter can have different areas. **107.** $(20 - 4) \cdot 4 \div 2$ **109. a.** expression **b.** equation **c.** equation **d.** expression **e.** expression **111.** answers may vary **113.** answers may vary, for example, $-2(5) - 1$.

Section 1.4

Vocabulary and Readiness Check **1.** 0 **3.** *a*

Exercise Set 1.4 **1.** 3 **3.** -14 **5.** 1 **7.** -12 **9.** -5 **11.** -12 **13.** -4 **15.** 7 **17.** -2 **19.** 0 **21.** -19 **23.** 31 **25.** -47 **27.** -2.1 **29.** 38 **31.** -13.1 **33.** $\frac{1}{4}$ **35.** $-\frac{3}{16}$ **37.** $-\frac{13}{10}$ **39.** -8 **41.** -8 **43.** -59 **45.** -9 **47.** 5 **49.** 11 **51.** -18 **53.** 19 **55.** -7 **57.** -26 **59.** -6 **61.** 2 **63.** 0 **65.** -6 **67.** -2 **69.** 7 **71.** 7.9 **73.** $5z$ **75.** $\frac{2}{3}$ **77.** -70 **79.** 3 **81.** 19 **83.** -10 **85.** $0 + (-215) + (-16) = -231$; 231 ft below the surface **87.** 107°F **89.** -95 m **91.** -21 **93.** $-\$6.9$ million **95.** July **97.** October **99.** 4.7°F **101.** answers may vary **103.** -3 **105.** -22 **107.** true **109.** false **111.** answers may vary

Section 1.5

Vocabulary and Readiness Check **1.** $a + (-b)$; b **3.** $-10 - (-14)$; d

Exercise Set 1.5 **1.** -10 **3.** -5 **5.** 19 **7.** 11 **9.** -8 **11.** -11 **13.** 37 **15.** 5 **17.** -71 **19.** 0 **21.** $\frac{2}{11}$ **23.** -6.4 **25.** 4.1 **27.** $-\frac{1}{6}$ **29.** $-\frac{11}{12}$ **31.** 8.92 **33.** -8.92 **35.** 13 **37.** -5 **39.** -1 **41.** -23 **43.** -26 **45.** -24 **47.** 3 **49.** -45 **51.** -4 **53.** 13 **55.** 6 **57.** 9 **59.** -9 **61.** $\frac{7}{5}$ **63.** -7 **65.** 21 **67.** $\frac{1}{4}$ **69.** not a solution **71.** not a solution **73.** solution **75.** 265°F **77.** 35,653 ft **79.** 30° **81.** -308 ft **83.** 19,852 ft **85.** 130° **87.** $-5 + x$ **89.** $-20 - x$ **91.** $-4.4°$, $2.6°$, $12°$, $23.5°$, $15.3°$ **93.** May **95.** answers may vary **97.** 16 **99.** -20 **101.** true; answers may vary **103.** false; answers may vary **105.** negative, $-30{,}387$

Integrated Review **1.** negative **2.** negative **3.** positive **4.** 0 **5.** positive **6.** 0 **7.** positive **8.** positive **9.** $-\frac{1}{7}; \frac{1}{7}$ **10.** $\frac{12}{5}; \frac{12}{5}$ **11.** 3; 3 **12.** $-\frac{9}{11}; \frac{9}{11}$ **13.** -42 **14.** 10 **15.** 2 **16.** -18 **17.** -7 **18.** -39 **19.** -2 **20.** -9 **21.** -3.4 **22.** -9.8 **23.** $-\frac{25}{28}$ **24.** $-\frac{5}{24}$ **25.** -4 **26.** -24 **27.** 6 **28.** 20 **29.** 6 **30.** 61 **31.** -6 **32.** -16 **33.** -19 **34.** -13 **35.** -4 **36.** -1 **37.** $\frac{13}{20}$ **38.** $-\frac{29}{40}$ **39.** 4 **40.** 9 **41.** -1 **42.** -3 **43.** 8 **44.** 10 **45.** 47 **46.** $\frac{2}{3}$

Section 1.6

Calculator Explorations **1.** 38 **3.** -441 **5.** 490 **7.** 54,499 **9.** 15,625

Vocabulary and Readiness Check **1.** negative **3.** positive **5.** 0 **7.** 0

Exercise Set 1.6 **1.** -24 **3.** -2 **5.** 50 **7.** -45 **9.** $\frac{3}{10}$ **11.** -7 **13.** -15 **15.** 0 **17.** 16 **19.** -16 **21.** $\frac{9}{16}$ **23.** -0.49 **25.** $\frac{3}{2}$ **27.** $-\frac{1}{14}$ **29.** $-\frac{11}{3}$ **31.** $\frac{1}{0.2}$ **33.** -9 **35.** -4 **37.** 0 **39.** undefined **41.** $-\frac{18}{7}$ **43.** 160 **45.** 64 **47.** $-\frac{8}{27}$ **49.** 3 **51.** -15 **53.** -125 **55.** -0.008 **57.** $\frac{2}{3}$ **59.** $\frac{20}{27}$ **61.** 0.84 **63.** -40 **65.** 81 **67.** -1 **69.** -121 **71.** -1 **73.** -19 **75.** 90 **77.** -84 **79.** -5 **81.** $-\frac{9}{2}$ **83.** 18 **85.** 17 **87.** -20 **89.** 16 **91.** 2 **93.** $-\frac{34}{7}$ **95.** 0 **97.** $\frac{6}{5}$ **99.** $\frac{3}{2}$ **101.** $-\frac{5}{38}$ **103.** 3 **105.** -1 **107.** undefined **109.** $-\frac{22}{9}$ **111.** solution **113.** not a solution **115.** solution

117. $-71 \cdot x$ or $-71x$ **119.** $-16 - x$ **121.** $-29 + x$ **123.** $\frac{x}{-33}$ or $x \div (-33)$ **125.** $3 \cdot (-4) = -12$; a loss of 12 yd **127.** $5(-20) = -100$; a depth of 100 ft **129.** true **131.** false **133.** $-162°$F **135.** answers may vary **137.** $1, -1$; answers may vary **139.** $\frac{0}{5} - 7 = -7$ **141.** $-8(-5) + (-1) = 39$

Section 1.7

Vocabulary and Readiness Check **1.** commutative property of addition **3.** distributive property **5.** associative property of addition **7.** opposites or additive inverses

Exercise Set 1.7 **1.** $16 + x$ **3.** $y \cdot (-4)$ **5.** yx **7.** $13 + 2x$ **9.** $x \cdot (yz)$ **11.** $(2 + a) + b$ **13.** $(4a) \cdot b$ **15.** $a + (b + c)$ **17.** $17 + b$ **19.** $24y$ **21.** y **23.** $26 + a$ **25.** $-72x$ **27.** s **29.** $-\frac{5}{2}x$ **31.** $4x + 4y$ **33.** $9x - 54$ **35.** $6x + 10$ **37.** $28x - 21$ **39.** $18 + 3x$ **41.** $-2y + 2z$ **43.** $-y - \frac{5}{3}$ **45.** $5x + 20m + 10$ **47.** $8m - 4n$ **49.** $-5x - 2$ **51.** $-r + 3 + 7p$ **53.** $3x + 4$ **55.** $-x + 3y$ **57.** $6r + 8$ **59.** $-36x - 70$ **61.** $-1.6x - 2.5$ **63.** $4(1 + y)$ **65.** $11(x + y)$ **67.** $-1(5 + x)$ **69.** $30(a + b)$ **71.** commutative property of multiplication **73.** associative property of addition **75.** commutative property of addition **77.** associative property of multiplication **79.** identity element for addition **81.** distributive property **83.** multiplicative inverse property **85.** identity element for multiplication **87.** $-8; \frac{1}{8}$ **89.** $-x; \frac{1}{x}$ **91.** $2x; -2x$ **93.** false **95.** no **97.** yes **99.** yes **101.** yes **103. a.** commutative property of addition **b.** commutative property of addition **c.** associative property of addition **105.** answers may vary **107.** answers may vary

Section 1.8

Vocabulary and Readiness Check **1.** expression **3.** combine like term **5.** like; unlike **7.** -7 **9.** 1 **11.** 17 **13.** like **15.** unlike **17.** like

Exercise Set 1.8 **1.** $15y$ **3.** $13w$ **5.** $-7b - 9$ **7.** $-m - 6$ **9.** -8 **11.** $7.2x - 5.2$ **13.** $k - 6$ **15.** $-15x + 18$ **17.** $4x - 3$ **19.** $5x^2$ **21.** -11 **23.** $1.3x + 3.5$ **25.** $5y + 20$ **27.** $-2x - 4$ **29.** $-10x + 15y - 30$ **31.** $-3x + 2y - 1$ **33.** $7d - 11$ **35.** 16 **37.** $x + 5$ **39.** $x + 2$ **41.** $2k + 10$ **43.** $-3x + 5$ **45.** $2x + 14$ **47.** $3y + \frac{5}{6}$ **49.** $-22 + 24x$ **51.** $0.9m + 1$ **53.** $10 - 6x - 9y$ **55.** $-x - 38$ **57.** $5x - 7$ **59.** $10x - 3$ **61.** $-4x - 9$ **63.** $-4m - 3$ **65.** $2x - 4$ **67.** $\frac{3}{4}x + 12$ **69.** $12x - 2$ **71.** $8x + 48$ **73.** $x - 10$ **75.** balanced **77.** balanced **79.** answers may vary **81.** $(18x - 2)$ ft **83.** $(15x + 23)$ in. **85.** answers may vary

Chapter 1 Vocabulary Check **1.** inequality symbols **2.** equation **3.** absolute value **4.** variable **5.** opposites **6.** numerator **7.** solution **8.** reciprocals **9.** base; exponent **10.** numerical coefficient **11.** denominator **12.** grouping symbols **13.** term **14.** like terms **15.** unlike terms

Chapter 1 Review **1.** $<$ **2.** $>$ **3.** $>$ **4.** $>$ **5.** $<$ **6.** $>$ **7.** $=$ **8.** $=$ **9.** $>$ **10.** $<$ **11.** $4 \geq -3$ **12.** $6 \neq 5$ **13.** $0.03 < 0.3$ **14.** $155 < 400$ **15. a.** 1, 3 **b.** 0, 1, 3 **c.** $-6, 0, 1, 3$ **d.** $-6, 0, 1, 1\frac{1}{2}, 3, 9.62$ **e.** π **f.** all numbers in set **16. a.** 2, 5 **b.** 2, 5 **c.** $-3, 2, 5$ **d.** $-3, -1.6, 2, 5, \frac{11}{2}, 15.1$ **e.** $\sqrt{5}, 2\pi$ **f.** all numbers in set **17.** Friday **18.** Wednesday **19.** c **20.** b **21.** 37 **22.** 41 **23.** $\frac{18}{7}$ **24.** 80 **25.** $20 - 12 = 2 \cdot 4$ **26.** $\frac{9}{2} > -5$ **27.** 18 **28.** 108 **29.** 5 **30.** 24 **31.** $63°$ **32.** $105°$ **33.** solution **34.** not a solution **35.** 9 **36.** $-\frac{2}{3}$ **37.** -2 **38.** 7 **39.** -11 **40.** -17 **41.** $-\frac{3}{16}$ **42.** -5 **43.** -13.9 **44.** 3.9 **45.** -14 **46.** -11.5 **47.** 5 **48.** -11 **49.** -19 **50.** 4 **51.** a **52.** a **53.** \$51 **54.** \$54 **55.** $-\frac{1}{6}$ **56.** $\frac{5}{3}$ **57.** -48 **58.** 28 **59.** 3 **60.** -14 **61.** -36 **62.** 0 **63.** undefined **64.** $-\frac{1}{2}$ **65.** commutative property of addition **66.** identity element for multiplication **67.** distributive property **68.** additive inverse property **69.** associative property of addition **70.** commutative property of multiplication **71.** distributive property **72.** associative property of multiplication **73.** multiplicative inverse property **74.** identity element for addition **75.** commutative property of addition **76.** distributive property **77.** $6x$ **78.** $-11.8z$ **79.** $4x - 2$ **80.** $2y + 3$ **81.** $3n - 18$ **82.** $4w - 6$ **83.** $-6x + 7$ **84.** $-0.4y + 2.3$ **85.** $3x - 7$ **86.** $5x + 5.6$ **87.** $<$ **88.** $>$ **89.** -15.3 **90.** -6 **91.** -80 **92.** -5 **93.** $-\frac{1}{4}$ **94.** 0.15 **95.** 16 **96.** 16 **97.** -5 **98.** 9 **99.** $-\frac{5}{6}$ **100.** undefined **101.** $16x - 41$ **102.** $18x - 12$

Chapter 1 Test **1.** $|-7| > 5$ **2.** $9 + 5 \geq 4$ **3.** -5 **4.** -11 **5.** -14 **6.** -39 **7.** 12 **8.** -2 **9.** undefined **10.** -8 **11.** $-\frac{1}{3}$ **12.** $4\frac{5}{8}$ **13.** $\frac{51}{40}$ **14.** -32 **15.** -48 **16.** 3 **17.** 0 **18.** $>$ **19.** $>$ **20.** $>$ **21.** $=$ **22. a.** 1, 7 **b.** 0, 1, 7 **c.** $-5, -1, 0, 1, 7$ **d.** $-5, -1, \frac{1}{4}, 0, 1, 7, 11.6$ **e.** $\sqrt{7}, 3\pi$ **f.** $-5, -1, \frac{1}{4}, 0, 1, 7, 11.6, \sqrt{7}, 3\pi$ **23.** 40 **24.** 12 **25.** 22 **26.** -1 **27.** associative property of addition **28.** commutative property of multiplication **29.** distributive property **30.** multiplicative inverse **31.** 9 **32.** -3 **33.** second down **34.** yes **35.** $17°$ **36.** \$420 **37.** $y - 10$ **38.** $5.9x + 1.2$ **39.** $-2x + 10$ **40.** $-15y + 1$

Chapter 2 Equations, Inequalities, and Problem Solving

Section 2.1

Vocabulary and Readiness Check **1.** expression **3.** equation **5.** expression; equation **7.** Equivalent **9.** 2 **11.** 12 **13.** 17

Exercise Set 2.1 **1.** 3 **3.** -2 **5.** -14 **7.** 0.5 **9.** $\frac{1}{4}$ **11.** $\frac{5}{12}$ **13.** -3 **15.** -9 **17.** -10 **19.** 2 **21.** -7 **23.** -1 **25.** -9 **27.** -12 **29.** $-\frac{1}{2}$ **31.** 11 **33.** 21 **35.** 25 **37.** -3 **39.** -0.7 **41.** 11 **43.** 13 **45.** -30 **47.** -0.4 **49.** -7 **51.** $-\frac{1}{3}$ **53.** -17.9 **55.** $(10 - x)$ ft **57.** $(180 - x)°$ **59.** $n - 28{,}000$ **61.** $7x$ sq mi **63.** $\frac{8}{5}$ **65.** $\frac{1}{2}$ **67.** -9 **69.** x **71.** y **73.** x **75.** answers may vary **77.** 4 **79.** answers may vary **81.** $(173 - 3x)°$ **83.** answers may vary **85.** -145.478

Section 2.2

Vocabulary and Readiness Check **1.** multiplication **3.** equation; expression **5.** Equivalent **7.** 9 **9.** 2 **11.** −5

Exercise Set 2.2 **1.** 4 **3.** 0 **5.** 12 **7.** −12 **9.** 3 **11.** 2 **13.** 0 **15.** 6.3 **17.** 10 **19.** −20 **21.** 0 **23.** −9 **25.** 1 **27.** −30 **29.** 3 **31.** $\frac{10}{9}$ **33.** −1 **35.** −4 **37.** $-\frac{1}{2}$ **39.** 0 **41.** 4 **43.** $-\frac{1}{14}$ **45.** 0.21 **47.** 5 **49.** 6 **51.** −5.5 **53.** −5 **55.** 0 **57.** −3 **59.** $-\frac{9}{28}$ **61.** $\frac{14}{3}$ **63.** −9 **65.** −2 **67.** $\frac{11}{2}$ **69.** $-\frac{1}{4}$ **71.** $\frac{9}{10}$ **73.** $-\frac{17}{20}$ **75.** −16 **77.** $2x + 2$ **79.** $2x + 2$ **81.** $5x + 20$ **83.** $7x - 12$ **85.** $12z + 44$ **87.** 1 **89.** −48 **91.** answers may vary **93.** answers may vary **95.** 2

Section 2.3

Calculator Explorations **1.** solution **3.** not a solution **5.** solution

Vocabulary and Readiness Check **1.** equation **3.** expression **5.** expression **7.** equation

Exercise Set 2.3 **1.** −6 **3.** 3 **5.** 1 **7.** $\frac{3}{2}$ **9.** 0 **11.** −1 **13.** 4 **15.** −4 **17.** −3 **19.** 2 **21.** 50 **23.** 1 **25.** $\frac{7}{3}$ **27.** 0.2 **29.** all real numbers **31.** no solution **33.** no solution **35.** all real numbers **37.** 18 **39.** $\frac{19}{9}$ **41.** $\frac{14}{3}$ **43.** 13 **45.** 4 **47.** all real numbers **49.** $-\frac{3}{5}$ **51.** −5 **53.** 10 **55.** no solution **57.** 3 **59.** −17 **61.** $\frac{7}{5}$ **63.** $-\frac{1}{50}$ **65.** $(6x - 8)$ m **67.** $-8 - x$ **69.** $-3 + 2x$ **71.** $9(x + 20)$ **73. a.** all real numbers **b.** answers may vary **c.** answers may vary **75.** a **77.** b **79.** c **81.** answers may vary **83. a.** $x + x + x + 2x + 2x = 28$ **b.** $x = 4$ **c.** $x = 4$ cm; $2x$ cm $= 8$ cm **85.** answers may vary **87.** 15.3 **89.** −0.2

Integrated Review **1.** 6 **2.** −17 **3.** 12 **4.** −26 **5.** −3 **6.** −1 **7.** $\frac{27}{2}$ **8.** $\frac{25}{2}$ **9.** 8 **10.** −64 **11.** 2 **12.** −3 **13.** 5 **14.** −1 **15.** 2 **16.** 2 **17.** −2 **18.** −2 **19.** $-\frac{5}{6}$ **20.** $\frac{1}{6}$ **21.** 1 **22.** 6 **23.** 4 **24.** 1 **25.** $\frac{9}{5}$ **26.** $-\frac{6}{5}$ **27.** all real numbers **28.** all real numbers **29.** 0 **30.** −1.6 **31.** $\frac{4}{19}$ **32.** $-\frac{5}{19}$ **33.** $\frac{7}{2}$ **34.** $-\frac{1}{4}$ **35.** no solution **36.** no solution **37.** $\frac{7}{6}$ **38.** $\frac{1}{15}$

Section 2.4

Vocabulary and Readiness Check **1.** $2x; 2x - 31$ **3.** $x + 5; 2(x + 5)$ **5.** $20 - y; \frac{20 - y}{3}$ or $(20 - y) \div 3$

Exercise Set 2.4 **1.** $2x + 7 = x + 6; -1$ **3.** $3x - 6 = 2x + 8; 14$ **5.** −25 **7.** $-\frac{3}{4}$ **9.** 3 in.; 6 in.; 16 in. **11.** 1st piece: 5 in.; 2nd piece: 10 in.; 3rd piece: 25 in. **13.** Texas: 30 million pounds; New Mexico: 45 million pounds **15.** 172 mi **17.** 25 mi **19.** 1st angle: 37.5°; 2nd angle: 37.5°; 3rd angle: 105° **21.** *A*: 60°; *B*: 120°; *C*: 120°; *D*: 60° **23.** $3x + 3$ **25.** $x + 2; x + 4; 2x + 4$ **27.** $x + 1; x + 2; x + 3; 4x + 6$ **29.** $x + 2; x + 4; 2x + 6$ **31.** 234, 235 **33.** Belgium: 32; France: 33; Spain: 34 **35.** 5 ft, 12 ft **37.** Maglev: 361 mph; TGV: 357.2 mph **39.** 43°, 137° **41.** 58°, 60°, 62° **43.** 1 **45.** 280 mi **47.** USC: 38; Penn State: 24 **49.** Montana: 56 counties; California: 58 counties **51.** Neptune: 8 moons; Uranus: 21 moons; Saturn: 18 moons **53.** −16 **55.** Sahara: 3,500,000 sq mi; Gobi: 500,000 sq mi **57.** Australia: 6; Germany: 7; Korea: 8 **59.** Chambliss: 1,220,854; Martin: 905,637 **61.** 34.5°; 34.5°; 111° **63.** Eagles: *Their Greatest Hits, 1971–1975* **65.** *Thriller*: $27 million; *The Wall*: $23 million **67.** answers may vary **69.** 34 **71.** 225π **73.** 15 ft by 24 ft **75.** 5400 chirps per hour; 129,600 chirps per day; 47,304,000 chirps per year **77.** answers may vary **79.** answers may vary **81.** c

Section 2.5

Exercise Set 2.5 **1.** $h = 3$ **3.** $h = 3$ **5.** $h = 20$ **7.** $c = 12$ **9.** $r = 2.5$ **11.** $h = \frac{f}{5g}$ **13.** $w = \frac{V}{lh}$ **15.** $y = 7 - 3x$ **17.** $R = \frac{A - P}{PT}$ **19.** $A = \frac{3V}{h}$ **21.** $a = P - b - c$ **23.** $h = \frac{S - 2\pi r^2}{2\pi r}$ **25.** 120 ft **27. a.** area: 480 sq in.; perimeter: 120 in. **b.** frame: perimeter; glass: area **29. a.** area: 103.5 sq ft; perimeter: 41 ft **b.** baseboard: perimeter; carpet: area **31.** −10°C **33.** 6.25 hr **35.** length: 78 ft; width: 52 ft **37.** 18 ft, 36 ft, 48 ft **39.** 137.5 mi **41.** 61.5°F **43.** 60 chirps per minute **45.** increases **47.** 96 piranhas **49.** 2 bags **51.** one 16-in. pizza **53.** 4.65 min **55.** 13 in. **57.** 2.25 hr **59.** 12,090 ft **61.** 50°C **63.** 515,509.5 cu in. **65.** 449 cu in. **67.** 333°F **69.** 0.32 **71.** 2.00 or 2 **73.** 17% **75.** 720% **77.** $V = G(N - R)$ **79.** multiplies the volume by 8; answers may vary **81.** $53\frac{1}{3}$ **83.** ○ = (△ − □)/■ **85.** 44.3 sec **87.** $P = 3{,}200{,}000$ **89.** $V = 113.1$

Section 2.6

Vocabulary and Readiness Check **1.** no **3.** yes

Exercise Set 2.6 **1.** 11.2 **3.** 55% **5.** 180 **7.** 4% **9.** 9990 **11.** discount: $1480; new price: $17,020 **13.** $46.58 **15.** 50% **17.** 30% **19.** $104 **21.** $42,500 **23.** 2 gal **25.** 7 lb **27.** 4.6 **29.** 50 **31.** 30% **33.** 71% **35.** 181,155 **37.** 56%, 7%, 28%, 2% **39.** 75% **41.** $3900 **43.** 300% **45.** mark-up: $0.11; new price: $2.31 **47.** 400 oz **49.** 52.3% **51.** 120 employees **53.** decrease: $64; sale price: $192 **55.** 854 thousand Scoville units **57.** 361 college students **59.** 400 oz **61.** > **63.** = **65.** > **67.** no; answers may vary **69.** 9.6% **71.** 26.9%; yes **73.** 17.1%

Section 2.7

Vocabulary and Readiness Check **1.** expression **3.** inequality **5.** equation **7.** −5 **9.** 4.1

Exercise Set 2.7 **1.** −1 **3.** $\frac{1}{2}$ **5.** 4 **7.** −2

9. -1 3 **11.** 0 2 **13.** $\{x \mid x \geq -5\}$ -5

15. $\{y \mid y < 9\}$ 9 **17.** $\{x \mid x > -3\}$ -3 **19.** $\{x \mid x \leq 1\}$ 1

21. $\{x \mid x < -3\}$ -3 **23.** $\{x \mid x \geq -2\}$ -2 **25.** $\{x \mid x < 0\}$ 0

27. $\left\{y \,\middle|\, y \geq -\frac{8}{3}\right\}$ $-\frac{8}{3}$ **29.** $\{y \mid y > 3\}$ 3 **31.** $\{x \mid x > -15\}$ **33.** $\{x \mid x \geq -11\}$

35. $\left\{x \,\middle|\, x > \frac{1}{4}\right\}$ **37.** $\{y \mid y \geq -12\}$ **39.** $\{z \mid z < 0\}$ **41.** $\{x \mid x > -3\}$ **43.** $\left\{x \,\middle|\, x \geq -\frac{2}{3}\right\}$ **45.** $\{x \mid x \leq -2\}$ **47.** $\{x \mid x > -13\}$

49. $\{x \mid x \leq -8\}$ **51.** $\{x \mid x > 4\}$ **53.** $\left\{x \,\middle|\, x \leq \frac{5}{4}\right\}$ **55.** $\left\{x \,\middle|\, x > \frac{8}{3}\right\}$ **57.** $\{x \mid x \geq 0\}$ **59.** all numbers greater than -10 **61.** 35 cm

63. at least 193 **65.** 86 people **67.** 35 min **69.** 81 **71.** 1 **73.** $\frac{49}{64}$ **75.** about 3200 **77.** 2006 and 2007 **79.** 2005 **81.** $>$ **83.** $\geq$

85. when multiplying or dividing by a negative number **87.** final exam score $\geq$ 78.5

Chapter 2 Vocabulary Check **1.** linear equation in one variable **2.** equivalent equations **3.** formula **4.** linear inequality in one variable **5.** all real numbers **6.** no solution **7.** the same **8.** reversed

Chapter 2 Review **1.** 4 **2.** -3 **3.** 6 **4.** -6 **5.** 0 **6.** -9 **7.** -23 **8.** 28 **9.** b **10.** a **11.** b **12.** c **13.** -12 **14.** 4 **15.** 0 **16.** -7 **17.** 0.75 **18.** -3 **19.** -6 **20.** -1 **21.** -1 **22.** $\frac{3}{2}$ **23.** $-\frac{1}{5}$ **24.** 7 **25.** $3x + 3$ **26.** $2x + 6$ **27.** -4 **28.** -4 **29.** 2 **30.** -3 **31.** no solution **32.** no solution **33.** $\frac{3}{4}$ **34.** $-\frac{8}{9}$ **35.** 20 **36.** $-\frac{6}{23}$ **37.** $\frac{23}{7}$ **38.** $-\frac{2}{5}$ **39.** 102 **40.** 0.25 **41.** 6665.5 in. **42.** short piece: 4 ft; long piece: 8 ft **43.** Harvard: 80; Cornell: 39 **44.** $-39, -38, -37$ **45.** 3 **46.** -4 **47.** $w = 9$ **48.** $h = 4$ **49.** $m = \frac{y - b}{x}$ **50.** $s = \frac{r + 5}{vt}$ **51.** $x = \frac{2y - 7}{5}$ **52.** $y = \frac{2 + 3x}{6}$ **53.** $\pi = \frac{C}{D}$ **54.** $\pi = \frac{C}{2r}$ **55.** 15 m **56.** 18 ft by 12 ft **57.** 1 hr and 20 min **58.** 40°C **59.** 20% **60.** 70% **61.** 110 **62.** 1280 **63.** mark-up: \$209; new price: \$2109 **64.** 50,844 **65.** 40% solution: 10 gal; 10% solution: 20 gal **66.** 1.9% increase **67.** 18% **68.** swerving into another lane **69.** 966 customers **70.** no; answers may vary **71.** -2 **72.** 0 5 **73.** $\{x \mid x \leq 1\}$ **74.** $\{x \mid x > -5\}$ **75.** $\{x \mid x \leq 10\}$ **76.** $\{x \mid x < -4\}$ **77.** $\{x \mid x < -4\}$ **78.** $\{x \mid x \leq 4\}$ **79.** $\{y \mid y > 9\}$ **80.** $\{y \mid y \geq -15\}$ **81.** $\left\{x \,\middle|\, x < \frac{7}{4}\right\}$ **82.** $\left\{x \,\middle|\, x \leq \frac{19}{3}\right\}$ **83.** \$2500 **84.** score must be less than 83 **85.** 4 **86.** -14 **87.** $-\frac{3}{2}$ **88.** 21 **89.** all real numbers **90.** no solution **91.** -13 **92.** shorter piece: 4 in.; longer piece: 19 in. **93.** $h = \frac{3V}{A}$ **94.** 22.1 **95.** 160 **96.** 20% **97.** $\{x \mid x > 9\}$ 9 **98.** $\{x \mid x > -4\}$ -4 **99.** $\{x \mid x \leq 0\}$ 0

Chapter 2 Test **1.** -5 **2.** 8 **3.** $\frac{7}{10}$ **4.** 0 **5.** 27 **6.** $-\frac{19}{6}$ **7.** 3 **8.** $\frac{3}{11}$ **9.** 0.25 **10.** $\frac{25}{7}$ **11.** no solution **12.** 21 **13.** 7 gal **14.** $x = 6$ **15.** $h = \frac{V}{\pi r^2}$ **16.** $y = \frac{3x - 10}{4}$ **17.** $\{x \mid x \leq -2\}$ -2 **18.** $\{x \mid x < 4\}$ 4 **19.** $\{x \mid x \leq -8\}$ **20.** $\{x \mid x \geq 11\}$ **21.** $\left\{x \,\middle|\, x > \frac{2}{5}\right\}$ **22.** 552 **23.** 40% **24.** 401, 802 **25.** New York: 754; Georgia: 58

Cumulative Review **1.** True; Sec. 1.2, Ex. 3 **2.** False **3.** True; Sec. 1.2, Ex. 4 **4.** True **5.** False; Sec. 1.2, Ex. 5 **6.** True **7.** True; Sec. 1.2, Ex. 6 **8.** True **9. a.** $<$ **b.** $=$ **c.** $>$ **d.** $<$ **e.** $>$; Sec. 1.2, Ex. 13 **10. a.** 5 **b.** 8 **c.** $\frac{2}{3}$ **11.** $\frac{8}{3}$; Sec. 1.3, Ex. 6 **12.** 33 **13.** -19; Sec. 1.4, Ex. 6 **14.** -10 **15.** 8; Sec. 1.4, Ex. 7 **16.** 10 **17.** -0.3; Sec. 1.4, Ex. 8 **18.** 0 **19. a.** -12 **b.** -3; Sec. 1.5, Ex. 7 **20. a.** 5 **b.** $\frac{2}{3}$ **c.** a **d.** -3 **21. a.** 0 **b.** -24 **c.** 90; Sec. 1.6, Ex. 7 **22. a.** -11.1 **b.** $-\frac{1}{5}$ **c.** $\frac{3}{4}$ **23. a.** -6 **b.** 7 **c.** -5; Sec. 1.6, Ex. 10 **24. a.** -0.36 **b.** $\frac{6}{17}$ **25.** $15 - 10z$; Sec. 1.7, Ex. 8 **26.** $2x^3 - 6x^2 + 8x$ **27.** $3x + 17$; Sec. 1.7, Ex. 12 **28.** $2x + 8$ **29. a.** unlike **b.** like **c.** like **d.** like **e.** like; Sec. 1.8, Ex. 2 **30. a.** -4 **b.** 9 **c.** $\frac{10}{63}$ **31.** $-2x - 1$; Sec. 1.8, Ex. 15 **32.** $-15x - 2$ **33.** 17; Sec. 2.1, Ex. 1 **34.** $-\frac{1}{6}$ **35.** -10; Sec. 2.2, Ex. 7 **36.** 3 **37.** 0; Sec. 3, Ex. 4 **38.** 72 **39.** Republicans: 178; Democrats: 256; Sec. 2.4, Ex. 4 **40.** 5 **41.** 79.2 yr; Sec. 2.5, Ex. 1 **42.** 6 **43.** 87.5%; Sec. 2.6, Ex. 1 **44.** $\frac{C}{2\pi} = r$ **45.** $-\frac{9}{10}$; Sec. 2.2, Ex. 10 **46.** $\{x \mid x > 5\}$ **47.** -1 Sec. 2.7, Ex. 2 **48.** $\{x \mid x \leq -10\}$ **49.** $\{x \mid x \geq 1\}$; Sec. 2.7, Ex. 9 **50.** $\{x \mid x \leq -3\}$

Chapter 3 Exponents and Polynomials

Section 3.1

Vocabulary and Readiness Check **1.** exponent **3.** add **5.** 1 **7.** exponent: 2; base: 3 **9.** exponent: 2; base: 4 **11.** exponent: 2; base: x

Exercise Set 3.1 **1.** 49 **3.** -5 **5.** -16 **7.** 16 **9.** $\frac{1}{27}$ **11.** 112 **13.** 4 **15.** 135 **17.** 150 **19.** $\frac{32}{5}$ **21.** x^7 **23.** $(-3)^{12}$ **25.** $15y^5$ **27.** $x^{19}y^6$ **29.** $-72m^3n^8$ **31.** $-24z^{20}$ **33.** $20x^5$ sq ft **35.** x^{36} **37.** p^8q^8 **39.** $8a^{15}$ **41.** $x^{10}y^{15}$ **43.** $49a^4b^{10}c^2$ **45.** $\frac{r^9}{s^9}$ **47.** $\frac{m^9p^9}{n^9}$ **49.** $\frac{4x^2z^2}{y^{10}}$

51. $64z^{10}$ sq dm **53.** $27y^{12}$ cu ft **55.** x^2 **57.** -64 **59.** p^6q^5 **61.** $\frac{y^3}{2}$ **63.** 1 **65.** 1 **67.** -7 **69.** 2 **71.** -81 **73.** $\frac{1}{64}$ **75.** b^6 **77.** a^9 **79.** $-16x^7$ **81.** $a^{11}b^{20}$ **83.** $26m^9n^7$ **85.** z^{40} **87.** $64a^3b^3$ **89.** $36x^2y^2z^6$ **91.** $3x$ **93.** $81x^2y^2$ **95.** 9 **97.** $\frac{y^{15}}{8x^{12}}$ **99.** $2x^2y$ **101.** 2 **103.** $\frac{x^{18}}{4y^{22}}$ **105.** $-b^5$ **107.** -2 **109.** 5 **111.** -7 **113.** c **115.** e **117.** answers may vary **119.** answers may vary **121.** 343 cu m **123.** volume **125.** answers may vary **127.** answers may vary **129.** x^{9a} **131.** a^{5b} **133.** x^{5a}

Section 3.2

Calculator Explorations **1.** 5.31 EE 3 **3.** 6.6 EE −9 **5.** 1.5×10^{13} **7.** 8.15×10^{19}

Vocabulary and Readiness Check **1.** $\frac{1}{x^3}$ **3.** scientific notation **5.** $\frac{5}{x^2}$ **7.** y^6 **9.** $4y^3$

Exercise Set 3.2 **1.** $\frac{1}{64}$ **3.** $\frac{7}{x^3}$ **5.** -64 **7.** $\frac{5}{6}$ **9.** p^3 **11.** $\frac{q^4}{p^5}$ **13.** $\frac{1}{x^3}$ **15.** z^3 **17.** $\frac{4}{9}$ **19.** $\frac{1}{9}$ **21.** $-p^4$ **23.** -2 **25.** x^4 **27.** p^4 **29.** m^{11} **31.** r^6 **33.** $\frac{1}{x^{15}y^9}$ **35.** $\frac{1}{x^4}$ **37.** $\frac{1}{a^2}$ **39.** $4k^3$ **41.** $3m$ **43.** $-\frac{4a^5}{b}$ **45.** $-\frac{6}{7y^2z^5}$ **47.** $\frac{27a^6}{b^{12}}$ **49.** $\frac{a^{30}}{b^{12}}$ **51.** $\frac{1}{x^{10}y^6}$ **53.** $\frac{z^2}{4}$ **55.** $\frac{x^{11}}{81}$ **57.** $\frac{49a^4}{b^6}$ **59.** $-\frac{3m^7}{n^4}$ **61.** $a^{24}b^8$ **63.** 200 **65.** x^9y^{19} **67.** $-\frac{y^8}{8x^2}$ **69.** $\frac{25b^{33}}{a^{16}}$ **71.** $\frac{27}{z^3x^6}$ cu in. **73.** 7.8×10^4 **75.** 1.67×10^{-6} **77.** 6.35×10^{-3} **79.** 1.16×10^6 **81.** 2.4×10^3 **83.** 0.0000000008673 **85.** 0.033 **87.** 20,320 **89.** 700,000,000 **91.** 1.84×10^{11} **93.** 155,000,000,000 **95.** 35,000 **97.** 0.000036 **99.** 0.000000000000000028 **101.** 0.0000005 **103.** 200,000 **105.** 2.7×10^9 gal **107.** $-2x + 7$ **109.** $2y - 10$ **111.** $-x - 4$ **113.** 90,000,000; 9×10^7 **115.** 1,000,000,000; 1×10^9 **117.** 440,000,000; 4.4×10^8 **119.** no; answers may vary **121.** $9a^{13}$ **123.** -5 **125.** answers may vary **127. a.** 1.3×10^1 **b.** 4.4×10^7 **c.** 6.1×10^{-2} **129.** answers may vary **131.** $\frac{1}{x^{9s}}$ **133.** a^{4m+5}

Section 3.3

Vocabulary and Readiness Check **1.** binomial **3.** trinomial **5.** constant

Exercise Set 3.3 **1.** 1; $-3x$; 5 **3.** -5; 3.2; 1; -5 **5.** 1; binomial **7.** 3; none of these **9.** 6; trinomial **11.** 4; binomial **13. a.** -6 **b.** -11 **15. a.** -2 **b.** 4 **17. a.** -15 **b.** -10 **19.** 184 ft **21.** 595.84 ft **23.** 164 thousand **25.** 371.95 million wireless subscribers **27.** $-11x$ **29.** $23x^3$ **31.** $16x^2 - 7$ **33.** $12x^2 - 13$ **35.** $7s$ **37.** $-1.1y^2 + 4.8$ **39.** $\frac{5}{6}x^4 - 7x^3 - 19$ **41.** $\frac{3}{20}x^3 + 6x^2 - \frac{13}{20}x - \frac{1}{10}$ **43.** $4x^2 + 7x + x^2 + 5x$; $5x^2 + 12x$ **45.** $5x + 3 + 4x + 3 + 2x + 6 + 3x + 7x$; $21x + 12$ **47.** 2, 1, 1, 0; 2 **49.** 4, 0, 4, 3; 4 **51.** $9ab - 11a$ **53.** $4x^2 - 7xy + 3y^2$ **55.** $-3xy^2 + 4$ **57.** $14y^3 - 19 - 16a^2b^2$ **59.** $7x^2 + 0x + 3$ **61.** $x^3 + 0x^2 + 0x - 64$ **63.** $5y^3 + 0y^2 + 2y - 10$ **65.** $2y^4 + 0y^3 + 0y^2 + 8y + 0y^0$ or $2y^4 + 0y^3 + 0y^2 + 8y + 0$ **67.** $6x^5 + 0x^4 + x^3 + 0x^2 - 3x + 15$ **69.** $10x + 19$ **71.** $-x + 5$ **73.** answers may vary **75.** answers may vary **77.** x^{13} **79.** a^3b^{10} **81.** $2y^{20}$ **83.** answers may vary **85.** answers may vary **87.** $11.1x^2 - 7.97x + 10.76$

Section 3.4

Vocabulary and Readiness Check **1.** $-14y$ **3.** $7x$ **5.** $5m^2 + 2m$

Exercise Set 3.4 **1.** $12x + 12$ **3.** $-3x^2 + 10$ **5.** $-3x^2 + 4$ **7.** $-y^2 - 3y - 1$ **9.** $7.9x^3 + 4.4x^2 - 3.4x - 3$ **11.** $\frac{1}{2}m^2 - \frac{7}{10}m + \frac{13}{16}$ **13.** $8t^2 - 4$ **15.** $15a^3 + a^2 - 3a + 16$ **17.** $-x + 14$ **19.** $5x^2 + 2y^2$ **21.** $-2x + 9$ **23.** $2x^2 + 7x - 16$ **25.** $2x^2 + 11x$ **27.** $-0.2x^2 + 0.2x - 2.2$ **29.** $\frac{2}{5}z^2 - \frac{3}{10}z + \frac{7}{20}$ **31.** $-2z^2 - 16z + 6$ **33.** $2u^5 - 10u^2 + 11u - 9$ **35.** $5x - 9$ **37.** $4x - 3$ **39.** $11y + 7$ **41.** $-2x^2 + 8x - 1$ **43.** $14x + 18$ **45.** $3a^2 - 6a + 11$ **47.** $3x - 3$ **49.** $7x^2 - 4x + 2$ **51.** $7x^2 - 2x + 2$ **53.** $4y^2 + 12y + 19$ **55.** $-15x + 7$ **57.** $-2a - b + 1$ **59.** $3x^2 + 5$ **61.** $6x^2 - 2xy + 19y^2$ **63.** $8r^2s + 16rs - 8 + 7r^2s^2$ **65.** $(x^2 + 7x + 4)$ ft **67.** $\left(\frac{19}{2}x + 3\right)$ units **69.** $(3y^2 + 4y + 11)$ m **71.** $-6.6x^2 - 1.8x - 1.8$ **73.** $6x^2$ **75.** $-12x^8$ **77.** $200x^3y^2$ **79.** 2; 2 **81.** 4; 3; 3; 4 **83.** b **85.** e **87. a.** $4z$ **b.** $3z^2$ **c.** $-4z$ **d.** $3z^2$; answers may vary **89. a.** m^3 **b.** $3m$ **c.** $-m^3$ **d.** $-3m$; answers may vary **91.** $874x^2 + 66x + 25{,}376$

Section 3.5

Vocabulary and Readiness Check **1.** distributive **3.** $(5y - 1)(5y - 1)$ **5.** x^8 **7.** cannot simplify **9.** x^{14} **11.** $2x^7$ **13.** $99y^4$ **15.** $20y^2$

Exercise Set 3.5 **1.** $24x^3$ **3.** x^4 **5.** $-28n^{10}$ **7.** $-12.4x^{12}$ **9.** $-\frac{2}{15}y^3$ **11.** $-24x^8$ **13.** $6x^2 + 15x$ **15.** $7x^3 + 14x^2 - 7x$ **17.** $-2a^2 - 8a$ **19.** $6x^3 - 9x^2 + 12x$ **21.** $12a^5 + 45a^2$ **23.** $-6a^4 + 4a^3 - 6a^2$ **25.** $6x^5y - 3x^4y^3 + 24x^2y^4$ **27.** $-4x^3y + 7x^2y^2 - xy^3 - 3y^4$ **29.** $4x^4 - 3x^3 + \frac{1}{2}x^2$ **31.** $x^2 + 7x + 12$ **33.** $a^2 + 5a - 14$ **35.** $x^2 + \frac{1}{3}x - \frac{2}{9}$ **37.** $12x^4 + 25x^2 + 7$ **39.** $12x^2 - 29x + 15$ **41.** $1 - 7a + 12a^2$ **43.** $4y^2 - 16y + 16$ **45.** $x^3 - 5x^2 + 13x - 14$ **47.** $x^4 + 5x^3 - 3x^2 - 11x + 20$ **49.** $10a^3 - 27a^2 + 26a - 12$ **51.** $49x^2y^2 - 14xy^2 + y^2$ **53.** $12x^2 - 64x - 11$ **55.** $2x^3 + 10x^2 + 11x - 3$ **57.** $2x^4 + 3x^3 - 58x^2 + 4x + 63$ **59.** $8.4y^7$ **61.** $-3x^3 - 6x^2 + 24x$ **63.** $2x^2 + 39x + 19$ **65.** $x^2 - \frac{2}{7}x - \frac{3}{49}$ **67.** $9y^2 + 30y + 25$ **69.** $a^3 - 2a^2 - 18a + 24$ **71.** $(4x^2 - 25)$ sq yd **73.** $(6x^2 - 4x)$ sq in. **75.** $5a + 15a = 20a$; $5a - 15a = -10a$; $5a \cdot 15a = 75a^2$; $\frac{5a}{15a} = \frac{1}{3}$ **77.** $-3y^5 + 9y^4$, cannot be simplified; $-3y^5 - 9y^4$, cannot be simplified; $-3y^5 \cdot 9y^4 = -27y^9$; $\frac{-3y^5}{9y^4} = -\frac{y}{3}$ **79. a.** $6x + 12$ **b.** $9x^2 + 36x + 35$; answers may vary **81.** $13x - 7$ **83.** $30x^2 - 28x + 6$ **85.** $-7x + 5$ **87.** $x^2 + 3x$ **89.** $x + 2x^2$; $x(1 + 2x)$ **91.** $11a$ **93.** $25x^2 + 4y^2$ **95. a.** $a^2 - b^2$ **b.** $4x^2 - 9y^2$ **c.** $16x^2 - 49$ **d.** answers may vary

Section 3.6

Vocabulary and Readiness Check **1.** false **3.** false

Exercise Set 3.6 **1.** $x^2 + 7x + 12$ **3.** $x^2 + 5x - 50$ **5.** $5x^2 + 4x - 12$ **7.** $4y^2 - 25y + 6$ **9.** $6x^2 + 13x - 5$ **11.** $6y^3 + 4y^2 + 42y + 28$ **13.** $x^2 + \frac{1}{3}x - \frac{2}{9}$ **15.** $0.08 - 2.6a + 15a^2$ **17.** $2x^2 + 9xy - 5y^2$ **19.** $x^2 + 4x + 4$ **21.** $4a^2 - 12a + 9$ **23.** $9a^2 - 30a + 25$ **25.** $x^4 + x^2 + 0.25$ **27.** $y^2 - \frac{4}{7}y + \frac{4}{49}$ **29.** $4x^2 - 4x + 1$ **31.** $25x^2 + 90x + 81$ **33.** $9x^2 - 42xy + 49y^2$ **35.** $16m^2 + 40mn + 25n^2$ **37.** $25x^8 - 30x^4 + 9$ **39.** $a^2 - 49$ **41.** $x^2 - 36$ **43.** $9x^2 - 1$ **45.** $x^4 - 25$ **47.** $4y^4 - 1$ **49.** $16 - 49x^2$ **51.** $9x^2 - \frac{1}{4}$ **53.** $81x^2 - y^2$ **55.** $4m^2 - 25n^2$ **57.** $a^2 + 9a + 20$ **59.** $a^2 - 14a + 49$ **61.** $12a^2 - a - 1$ **63.** $x^2 - 4$ **65.** $9a^2 + 6a + 1$ **67.** $4x^2 + 3xy - y^2$ **69.** $\frac{1}{9}a^4 - 49$ **71.** $6b^2 - b - 35$ **73.** $x^4 - 100$ **75.** $16x^2 - 25$ **77.** $25x^2 - 60xy + 36y^2$ **79.** $4r^2 - 9s^2$ **81.** $(4x^2 + 4x + 1)$ sq ft **83.** $\frac{5b^5}{7}$ **85.** $-\frac{2a^{10}}{b^5}$ **87.** $\frac{2y^8}{3}$ **89.** c **91.** d **93.** 2 **95.** $(x^4 - 3x^2 + 1)$ sq m **97.** $(24x^2 - 32x + 8)$ sq m **99.** answers may vary **101.** answers may vary

Integrated Review **1.** $35x^5$ **2.** $-32y^9$ **3.** -16 **4.** 16 **5.** $2x^2 - 9x - 5$ **6.** $3x^2 + 13x - 10$ **7.** $3x - 4$ **8.** $4x + 3$ **9.** $7x^6y^2$ **10.** $\frac{10b^6}{7}$ **11.** $144m^{14}n^{12}$ **12.** $64y^{27}z^{30}$ **13.** $16y^2 - 9$ **14.** $49x^2 - 1$ **15.** $\frac{y^{45}}{x^{63}}$ **16.** $\frac{1}{64}$ **17.** $\frac{x^{27}}{27}$ **18.** $\frac{r^{58}}{16s^{14}}$ **19.** $2x^2 - 2x - 6$ **20.** $6x^2 + 13x - 11$ **21.** $2.5y^2 - 6y - 0.2$ **22.** $8.4x^2 - 6.8x - 4.2$ **23.** $2y^2 - 6y - 1$ **24.** $6z^2 + 2z + \frac{11}{2}$ **25.** $x^2 + 8x + 16$ **26.** $y^2 - 18y + 81$ **27.** $2x + 8$ **28.** $2y - 18$ **29.** $7x^2 - 10xy + 4y^2$ **30.** $-a^2 - 3ab + 6b^2$ **31.** $x^3 + 2x^2 - 16x + 3$ **32.** $x^3 - 2x^2 - 5x - 2$ **33.** $6x^2 - x - 70$ **34.** $20x^2 + 21x - 5$ **35.** $2x^3 - 19x^2 + 44x - 7$ **36.** $5x^3 + 9x^2 - 17x + 3$ **37.** $4x^2 - \frac{25}{81}$ **38.** $144y^2 - \frac{9}{49}$

Section 3.7

Vocabulary and Readiness Check **1.** dividend; quotient; divisor **3.** a^2 **5.** y

Exercise Set 3.7 **1.** $12x^3 + 3x$ **3.** $4x^3 - 6x^2 + x + 1$ **5.** $5p^2 + 6p$ **7.** $-\frac{3}{2x} + 3$ **9.** $-3x^2 + x - \frac{4}{x^3}$ **11.** $-1 + \frac{3}{2x} - \frac{7}{4x^4}$ **13.** $x + 1$ **15.** $2x + 3$ **17.** $2x + 1 + \frac{7}{x - 4}$ **19.** $3a^2 - 3a + 1 + \frac{2}{3a + 2}$ **21.** $4x + 3 - \frac{2}{2x + 1}$ **23.** $2x^2 + 6x - 5 - \frac{2}{x - 2}$ **25.** $x + 6$ **27.** $x^2 + 3x + 9$ **29.** $-3x + 6 - \frac{11}{x + 2}$ **31.** $2b - 1 - \frac{6}{2b - 1}$ **33.** $ab - b^2$ **35.** $4x + 9$ **37.** $x + 4xy - \frac{y}{2}$ **39.** $2b^2 + b + 2 - \frac{12}{b + 4}$ **41.** $y^2 + 5y + 10 + \frac{24}{y - 2}$ **43.** $-6x - 12 - \frac{19}{x - 2}$ **45.** $x^3 - x^2 + x$ **47.** 3 **49.** -4 **51.** $3x$ **53.** $9x$ **55.** $(3x^3 + x - 4)$ ft **57.** $(2x + 5)$ m **59.** answers may vary **61.** c

Chapter 3 Vocabulary Check **1.** term **2.** FOIL **3.** trinomial **4.** degree of a polynomial **5.** binomial **6.** coefficient **7.** degree of a term **8.** monomial **9.** polynomials **10.** distributive

Chapter 3 Review **1.** base: 3; exponent: 2 **2.** base: -5; exponent: 4 **3.** base: 5; exponent: 4 **4.** base: x; exponent: 6 **5.** 512 **6.** 36 **7.** -36 **8.** -65 **9.** 1 **10.** 1 **11.** y^9 **12.** x^{14} **13.** $-6x^{11}$ **14.** $-20y^7$ **15.** x^8 **16.** y^{15} **17.** $81y^{24}$ **18.** $8x^9$ **19.** x^5 **20.** z^7 **21.** $\frac{x^3y^4}{4}$ **22.** $\frac{x^6y^6}{4}$ **23.** $40a^{19}$ **24.** $36x^3$ **25.** $-a^9$ **26.** $-x^7$ **27.** 3 **28.** 9 **29.** b **30.** c **31.** $\frac{1}{49}$ **32.** $-\frac{1}{49}$ **33.** $\frac{2}{x^4}$ **34.** $\frac{1}{16x^4}$ **35.** 125 **36.** $\frac{9}{4}$ **37.** $\frac{17}{16}$ **38.** $\frac{1}{42}$ **39.** r **40.** y^3 **41.** c^4 **42.** $\frac{x^3}{y^3}$ **43.** $\frac{a^2}{5b^7c^3}$ **44.** $\frac{b^3}{5a^6c^7}$ **45.** $\frac{9}{x^6y^{13}}$ **46.** $\frac{3a^{10}}{b^{10}}$ **47.** 2.7×10^{-4} **48.** 8.868×10^{-1} **49.** 8.08×10^7 **50.** 8.68×10^5 **51.** 1.27×10^8 **52.** 1.5×10^5 **53.** 867,000 **54.** 0.00386 **55.** 0.00086 **56.** 893,600 **57.** 1,431,280,000,000,000 **58.** 0.0000000001 **59.** 0.016 **60.** 400,000,000,000 **61.** 5 **62.** 2 **63.** 5 **64.** 6 **65.** 4000 ft; 3984 ft; 3856 ft; 3600 ft **66.** 22; 78; 154.02; 400 **67.** $2a^2$ **68.** $-4y$ **69.** $15a^2 + 4a$ **70.** $22x^2 + 3x + 6$ **71.** $-6a^2b - 3b^2 - q^2$ **72.** cannot be combined **73.** $8x^2 + 3x + 6$ **74.** $2x^5 + 3x^4 + 4x^3 + 9x^2 + 7x + 6$ **75.** $-7y^2 - 1$ **76.** $-6m^7 - 3x^4 + 7m^6 - 4m^2$ **77.** $-x^2 - 6xy - 2y^2$ **78.** $x^6 + 4xy + 2y^2$ **79.** $-5x^2 + 5x + 1$ **80.** $-2x^2 - x + 20$ **81.** $6x + 30$ **82.** $9x - 63$ **83.** $8a + 28$ **84.** $54a - 27$ **85.** $-7x^3 - 35x$ **86.** $-32y^3 + 48y$ **87.** $-2x^3 + 18x^2 - 2x$ **88.** $-3a^3b - 3a^2b - 3ab^2$ **89.** $-6a^4 + 8a^2 - 2a$ **90.** $42b^4 - 28b^2 + 14b$ **91.** $2x^2 - 12x - 14$ **92.** $6x^2 - 11x - 10$ **93.** $4a^2 + 27a - 7$ **94.** $42a^2 + 11a - 3$ **95.** $x^4 + 7x^3 + 4x^2 + 23x - 35$ **96.** $x^6 + 2x^5 + x^2 + 3x + 2$ **97.** $x^4 + 4x^3 + 4x^2 - 16$ **98.** $x^6 + 8x^4 + 16x^2 - 16$ **99.** $x^3 + 21x^2 + 147x + 343$ **100.** $8x^3 - 60x^2 + 150x - 125$ **101.** $x^2 + 14x + 49$ **102.** $x^2 - 10x + 25$ **103.** $9x^2 - 42x + 49$ **104.** $16x^2 + 16x + 4$ **105.** $25x^2 - 90x + 81$ **106.** $25x^2 - 1$ **107.** $49x^2 - 16$ **108.** $a^2 - 4b^2$ **109.** $4x^2 - 36$ **110.** $16a^4 - 4b^2$ **111.** $(9x^2 - 6x + 1)$ sq m **112.** $(5x^2 - 3x - 2)$ sq mi **113.** $\frac{1}{7} + \frac{3}{x} + \frac{7}{x^2}$ **114.** $-a^2 + 3b - 4$ **115.** $a + 1 + \frac{6}{a - 2}$ **116.** $4x + \frac{7}{x + 5}$ **117.** $a^2 + 3a + 8 + \frac{22}{a - 2}$ **118.** $3b^2 - 4b - \frac{1}{3b - 2}$ **119.** $2x^3 - x^2 + 2 - \frac{1}{2x - 1}$ **120.** $-x^2 - 16x - 117 - \frac{684}{x - 6}$ **121.** $\left(5x - 1 + \frac{20}{x^2}\right)$ ft **122.** $(7a^3b^6 + a - 1)$ units **123.** 27 **124.** $-\frac{1}{8}$ **125.** $4x^4y^7$ **126.** $\frac{2x^6}{3}$ **127.** $\frac{27a^{12}}{b^6}$ **128.** $\frac{x^{16}}{16y^{12}}$ **129.** $9a^2b^8$

Answers to Selected Exercises

130. $2y^2 - 10$ **131.** $11x - 5$ **132.** $5x^2 + 3x - 2$ **133.** $5y^2 - 3y - 1$ **134.** $6x^2 + 11x - 10$ **135.** $28x^3 + 12x$ **136.** $28x^2 - 71x + 18$
137. $x^3 + x^2 - 18x + 18$ **138.** $25x^2 + 40x + 16$ **139.** $36x^2 - 9$ **140.** $4a - 1 + \frac{2}{a^2} - \frac{5}{2a^3}$ **141.** $x - 3 + \frac{25}{x + 5}$ **142.** $2x^2 + 7x + 5 + \frac{19}{2x - 3}$

Chapter 3 Test **1.** 32 **2.** 81 **3.** -81 **4.** $\frac{1}{64}$ **5.** $-15x^{11}$ **6.** y^5 **7.** $\frac{1}{r^5}$ **8.** $\frac{16y^{14}}{x^2}$ **9.** $\frac{1}{6xy^8}$ **10.** 5.63×10^5 **11.** 8.63×10^{-5} **12.** 0.0015
13. 62,300 **14.** 0.036 **15. a.** 4, 3; 7, 3; 1, 4; -2, 0 **b.** 4 **16.** $-2x^2 + 12x + 11$ **17.** $16x^3 + 7x^2 - 3x - 13$ **18.** $-3x^3 + 5x^2 + 4x + 5$
19. $x^3 + 8x^2 + 3x - 5$ **20.** $3x^3 + 22x^2 + 41x + 14$ **21.** $6x^4 - 9x^3 + 21x^2$ **22.** $3x^2 + 16x - 35$ **23.** $9x^2 - \frac{1}{25}$ **24.** $16x^2 - 16x + 4$
25. $64x^2 + 48x + 9$ **26.** $x^4 - 81b^2$ **27.** 1001 ft; 985 ft; 857 ft; 601 ft **28.** $(4x^2 - 9)$ sq in. **29.** $\frac{x}{2y} + \frac{1}{4} - \frac{7}{8y}$ **30.** $x + 2$
31. $9x^2 - 6x + 4 - \frac{16}{3x + 2}$

Cumulative Review **1. a.** 11, 112 **b.** 0, 11, 112 **c.** $-3, -2, 0, 11, 112$ **d.** $-3, -2, 0, \frac{1}{4}, 11, 112$ **e.** $\sqrt{2}$ **f.** $-2, 0, \frac{1}{4}, 112, -3, 11, \sqrt{2}$; Sec. 1.2, Ex. 11
2. a. 7.2 **b.** 0 **c.** $\frac{1}{2}$ **3. a.** 9 **b.** 125 **c.** 16 **d.** 7 **e.** $\frac{9}{49}$ **f.** 0.36; Sec. 1.3, Ex. 1 **4. a.** $\frac{1}{4}$ **b.** $2\frac{5}{12}$ **5.** $\frac{1}{4}$; Sec. 1.3, Ex. 4 **6.** $\frac{3}{25}$ **7. a.** $x + 3$
b. $3x$ **c.** $7.3 \div x$ or $\frac{7.3}{x}$ **d.** $10 - x$ **e.** $5x + 7$; Sec. 1.3, Ex. 9 **8.** 41 **9.** 6.7; Sec. 1.4, Ex. 10 **10.** no **11. a.** $\frac{1}{2}$ **b.** 9; Sec. 1.5, Ex. 8
12. a. -33 **b.** 5 **13.** 3; Sec. 1.6, Ex. 11a **14.** -8 **15.** -70; Sec. 1.6, Ex. 11d **16.** 150 **17.** $15x + 10$; Sec. 1.8, Ex. 8 **18.** $-6x + 9$
19. $-2y - 0.6z + 2$; Sec. 1.8, Ex. 9 **20.** $-4x^3 + 24x - 4x$ **21.** $-9x - y + 2z - 6$; Sec. 1.8, Ex. 10 **22.** $4xy - 6y + 2$ **23.** $a = 19$; Sec. 2.1, Ex. 6
24. $x = -\frac{1}{2}$ **25.** $y = 140$; Sec. 2.2, Ex. 4 **26.** $j = \frac{12}{5}$ **27.** $x = 4$; Sec. 2.3, Ex. 5 **28.** $x = 1$ **29.** 10; Sec. 2.4, Ex. 2 **30.** $(x + 7) - 2x$ or $-x + 7$
31. 40 ft; Sec. 2.5, Ex. 2 **32.** undefined **33.** 800; Sec. 2.6, Ex. 2 **34.** 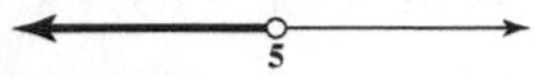

35. 

$\{x \mid x \le 4\}$;
Sec. 2.7, Ex. 7 **36. a.** 25 **b.** -25 **c.** 50 **37. a.** x^{11} **b.** $\frac{t^4}{16}$ **c.** $81y^{10}$; Sec. 3.1, Ex. 33 **38.** z^4 **39.** $\frac{b^3}{27a^6}$; Sec. 3.2, Ex. 10 **40.** $-15x^{16}$
41. $\frac{1}{25y^6}$; Sec. 3.2, Ex. 13 **42.** $\frac{1}{9}$ **43.** $10x^3$; Sec. 3.3, Ex. 8 **44.** $4y^2 - 8$ **45.** $5x^2 - 3x - 3$; Sec. 3.3, Ex. 9 **46.** $100x^4 - 9$
47. $7x^3 + 14x^2 + 35x$; Sec. 3.5, Ex. 4 **48.** $100x^4 + 60x^2 + 9$ **49.** $3x^3 - 4 + \frac{1}{x}$; Sec. 3.7. Ex. 2

Chapter 4 Factoring Polynomials

Section 4.1

Vocabulary and Readiness Check **1.** factors **3.** least **5.** false **7.** $2 \cdot 7$ **9.** 3 **11.** 5

Exercise Set 4.1 **1.** 4 **3.** 6 **5.** 1 **7.** y^2 **9.** z^7 **11.** xy^2 **13.** 7 **15.** $4y^3$ **17.** $5x^2$ **19.** $3x^3$ **21.** $9x^2y$ **23.** $10a^6b$ **25.** $3(a + 2)$
27. $15(2x - 1)$ **29.** $x^2(x + 5)$ **31.** $2y^3(3y + 1)$ **33.** $2x(16y - 9x)$ **35.** $4(x - 2y + 1)$ **37.** $3x(2x^2 - 3x + 4)$ **39.** $a^2b^2(a^5b^4 - a + b^3 - 1)$
41. $5xy(x^2 - 3x + 2)$ **43.** $4(2x^5 + 4x^4 - 5x^3 + 3)$ **45.** $\frac{1}{3}x(x^3 + 2x^2 - 4x^4 + 1)$ **47.** $(x^2 + 2)(y + 3)$ **49.** $(y + 4)(z + 3)$
51. $(z^2 - 6)(r + 1)$ **53.** $-1(x + 7)$ **55.** $-1(2 - z)$ **57.** $-1(-3a + b - 2)$ **59.** $(x + 2)(x^2 + 5)$ **61.** $(x + 3)(5 + y)$
63. $(3x - 2)(2x^2 + 5)$ **65.** $(5m^2 + 6n)(m + 1)$ **67.** $(y - 4)(2 + x)$ **69.** $(2x + 1)(x^2 + 4)$ **71.** not factorable by grouping
73. $(x - 2y)(4x - 3)$ **75.** $(5q - 4p)(q - 1)$ **77.** $2(2y - 7)(3x^2 - 1)$ **79.** $3(2a + 3b^2)(a + b)$ **81.** $x^2 + 7x + 10$ **83.** $b^2 - 3b - 4$
85. 2, 6 **87.** $-1, -8$ **89.** $-2, 5$ **91.** $-8, 3$ **93.** d **95.** factored **97.** not factored **99. a.** 22,752 thousand bales **b.** 18,960 thousand bales
c. $-1264(x^2 - 4x - 15)$ or $1264(-x^2 + 4x + 15)$ **101.** $4x^2 - \pi x^2$; $x^2(4 - \pi)$ **103.** $(x^3 - 1)$ units **105.** answers may vary
107. answers may vary

Section 4.2

Vocabulary and Readiness Check **1.** true **3.** false **5.** $+5$ **7.** -3 **9.** $+2$

Exercise Set 4.2 **1.** $(x + 6)(x + 1)$ **3.** $(y - 9)(y - 1)$ **5.** $(x - 3)(x - 3)$ or $(x - 3)^2$ **7.** $(x - 6)(x + 3)$ **9.** $(x + 10)(x - 7)$
11. prime **13.** $(x + 5y)(x + 3y)$ **15.** $(a^2 - 5)(a^2 + 3)$ **17.** $(m + 13)(m + 1)$ **19.** $(t - 2)(t + 12)$ **21.** $(a - 2b)(a - 8b)$
23. $2(z + 8)(z + 2)$ **25.** $2x(x - 5)(x - 4)$ **27.** $(x - 4y)(x + y)$ **29.** $(x + 12)(x + 3)$ **31.** $(x - 2)(x + 1)$ **33.** $(r - 12)(r - 4)$
35. $(x + 2y)(x - y)$ **37.** $3(x + 5)(x - 2)$ **39.** $3(x - 18)(x - 2)$ **41.** $(x - 24)(x + 6)$ **43.** prime **45.** $(x - 5)(x - 3)$
47. $6x(x + 4)(x + 5)$ **49.** $4y(x^2 + x - 3)$ **51.** $(x - 7)(x + 3)$ **53.** $(x + 5y)(x + 2y)$ **55.** $2(t + 8)(t + 4)$ **57.** $x(x - 6)(x + 4)$
59. $2t^3(t - 4)(t - 3)$ **61.** $5xy(x - 8y)(x + 3y)$ **63.** $3(m - 9)(m - 6)$ **65.** $-1(x - 11)(x - 1)$ **67.** $\frac{1}{2}(y - 11)(y + 2)$
69. $x(xy - 4)(xy + 5)$ **71.** $2x^2 + 11x + 5$ **73.** $15y^2 - 17y + 4$ **75.** $9a^2 + 23ab - 12b^2$ **77.** $x^2 + 5x - 24$ **79.** answers may vary
81. $2x^2 + 28x + 66$; $2(x + 3)(x + 11)$ **83.** $-16(t - 5)(t + 1)$ **85.** $\left(x + \frac{1}{4}\right)\left(x + \frac{1}{4}\right)$ or $\left(x + \frac{1}{4}\right)^2$ **87.** $(x + 1)(z - 10)(z + 7)$
89. 15; 28; 39; 48; 55; 60; 63; 64 **91.** 9; 12; 21 **93.** $(x^n + 10)(x^n - 2)$

Section 4.3

Vocabulary and Readiness Check **1.** d **3.** c

Exercise Set 4.3 **1.** $x + 4$ **3.** $10x - 1$ **5.** $4x - 3$ **7.** $(2x + 3)(x + 5)$ **9.** $(y - 1)(8y - 9)$ **11.** $(2x + 1)(x - 5)$ **13.** $(4r - 1)(5r + 8)$ **15.** $(10x + 1)(x + 3)$ **17.** $(3x - 2)(x + 1)$ **19.** $(3x - 5y)(2x - y)$ **21.** $(3m - 5)(5m + 3)$ **23.** $(x - 4)(x - 5)$ **25.** $(2x + 11)(x - 9)$ **27.** $(7t + 1)(t - 4)$ **29.** $(3a + b)(a + 3b)$ **31.** $(7p + 1)(7p - 2)$ **33.** $(6x - 7)(3x + 2)$ **35.** prime **37.** $(8x + 3)(3x + 4)$ **39.** $x(3x + 2)(4x + 1)$ **41.** $3(7b + 5)(b - 3)$ **43.** $(3z + 4)(4z - 3)$ **45.** $2y^2(3x - 10)(x + 3)$ **47.** $(2x - 7)(2x + 3)$ **49.** $3(x^2 - 14x + 21)$ **51.** $(4x + 9y)(2x - 3y)$ **53.** $-1(x - 6)(x + 4)$ **55.** $x(4x + 3)(x - 3)$ **57.** $(4x - 9)(6x - 1)$ **59.** $b(8a - 3)(5a + 3)$ **61.** $2x(3x + 2)(5x + 3)$ **63.** $2y(3y + 5)(y - 3)$ **65.** $5x^2(2x - y)(x + 3y)$ **67.** $-1(2x - 5)(7x - 2)$ **69.** $p^2(4p - 5)(4p - 5)$ or $p^2(4p - 5)^2$ **71.** $-1(2x + 1)(x - 5)$ **73.** $-4(12x - 1)(x - 1)$ **75.** $(2t^2 + 9)(t^2 - 3)$ **77.** prime **79.** $a(6a^2 + b^2)(a^2 + 6b^2)$ **81.** $x^2 - 16$ **83.** $x^2 + 4x + 4$ **85.** $4x^2 - 4x + 1$ **87.** no **89.** $4x^2 + 21x + 5$; $(4x + 1)(x + 5)$ **91.** $\left(2x + \frac{1}{2}\right)\left(2x + \frac{1}{2}\right)$ or $\left(2x + \frac{1}{2}\right)^2$ **93.** $(y - 1)^2(4x + 5)(x + 5)$ **95.** 2; 14 **97.** 2 **99.** answers may vary

Section 4.4

Vocabulary and Readiness Check **1.** a **3.** b

Exercise Set 4.4 **1.** $(x + 3)(x + 2)$ **3.** $(y + 8)(y - 2)$ **5.** $(8x - 5)(x - 3)$ **7.** $(5x^2 - 3)(x^2 + 5)$ **9. a.** 9, 2 **b.** $9x + 2x$ **c.** $(2x + 3)(3x + 1)$ **11. a.** $-20, -3$ **b.** $-20x - 3x$ **c.** $(3x - 4)(5x - 1)$ **13.** $(3y + 2)(7y + 1)$ **15.** $(7x - 11)(x + 1)$ **17.** $(5x - 2)(2x - 1)$ **19.** $(2x - 5)(x - 1)$ **21.** $(2x + 3)(2x + 3)$ or $(2x + 3)^2$ **23.** $(2x + 3)(2x - 7)$ **25.** $(5x - 4)(2x - 3)$ **27.** $x(2x + 3)(x + 5)$ **29.** $2(8y - 9)(y - 1)$ **31.** $(2x - 3)(3x - 2)$ **33.** $3(3a + 2)(6a - 5)$ **35.** $a(4a + 1)(5a + 8)$ **37.** $3x(4x + 3)(x - 3)$ **39.** $y(3x + y)(x + y)$ **41.** prime **43.** $6(a + b)(4a - 5b)$ **45.** $p^2(15p + q)(p + 2q)$ **47.** $(7 + x)(5 + x)$ or $(x + 7)(x + 5)$ **49.** $(6 - 5x)(1 - x)$ or $(5x - 6)(x - 1)$ **51.** $x^2 - 4$ **53.** $y^2 + 8y + 16$ **55.** $81z^2 - 25$ **57.** $16x^2 - 24x + 9$ **59.** $10x^2 + 45x + 45$; $5(2x + 3)(x + 3)$ **61.** $(x^n + 2)(x^n + 3)$ **63.** $(3x^n - 5)(x^n + 7)$ **65.** answers may vary

Section 4.5

Calculator Explorations

	$x^2 - 2x + 1$	$x^2 - 2x - 1$	$(x - 1)^2$
$x = 5$	16	14	16
$x = -3$	16	14	16
$x = 2.7$	2.89	0.89	2.89
$x = -12.1$	171.61	169.61	171.61
$x = 0$	1	-1	1

Vocabulary and Readiness Check **1.** perfect square trinomial **3.** perfect square trinomial **5.** $(x + 5y)^2$ **7.** false **9.** 8^2 **11.** $(11a)^2$ **13.** $(6p^2)^2$

Exercise Set 4.5 **1.** yes **3.** no **5.** yes **7.** no **9.** no **11.** yes **13.** $(x + 11)^2$ **15.** $(x - 8)^2$ **17.** $(4a - 3)^2$ **19.** $(x^2 + 2)^2$ **21.** $2(n - 7)^2$ **23.** $(4y + 5)^2$ **25.** $(xy - 5)^2$ **27.** $m(m + 9)^2$ **29.** prime **31.** $(3x - 4y)^2$ **33.** $(x + 2)(x - 2)$ **35.** $(9 + p)(9 - p)$ or $-1(p + 9)(p - 9)$ **37.** $-1(2r + 1)(2r - 1)$ **39.** $(3x + 4)(3x - 4)$ **41.** prime **43.** $-1(6 + x)(6 - x)$ or $(x + 6)(x - 6)$ **45.** $(m^2 + 1)(m + 1)(m - 1)$ **47.** $(x + 13y)(x - 13y)$ **49.** $2(3r + 2)(3r - 2)$ **51.** $x(3y + 2)(3y - 2)$ **53.** $16x^2(x + 2)(x - 2)$ **55.** $xy(y - 3z)(y + 3z)$ **57.** $4(3x - 4y)(3x + 4y)$ **59.** $9(4 - 3x)(4 + 3x)$ **61.** $(5y - 3)(5y + 3)$ **63.** $(11m + 10n)(11m - 10n)$ **65.** $(xy - 1)(xy + 1)$ **67.** $\left(x - \frac{1}{2}\right)\left(x + \frac{1}{2}\right)$ **69.** $\left(7 - \frac{3}{5}m\right)\left(7 + \frac{3}{5}m\right)$ **71.** $(9a + 5b)(9a - 5b)$ **73.** $(x + 7y)^2$ **75.** $2(4n^2 - 7)^2$ **77.** $x^2(x^2 + 9)(x + 3)(x - 3)$ **79.** $pq(8p + 9q)(8p - 9q)$ **81.** 6 **83.** -2 **85.** $\frac{1}{5}$ **87.** $\left(x - \frac{1}{3}\right)^2$ **89.** $(x + 2 + y)(x + 2 - y)$ **91.** $(b - 4)(a + 4)(a - 4)$ **93.** $(x + 3 + 2y)(x + 3 - 2y)$ **95.** $(x^n + 10)(x^n - 10)$ **97.** 8 **99.** answers may vary **101.** $(x + 6)$ **103.** $a^2 + 2ab + b^2$ **105. a.** 2560 ft **b.** 1920 ft **c.** 13 sec **d.** $16(13 - t)(13 + t)$ **107. a.** 1456 ft **b.** 816 ft **c.** 10 sec **d.** $16(10 + t)(10 - t)$

Integrated Review **1.** $(x - 3)(x + 4)$ **2.** $(x - 8)(x - 2)$ **3.** $(x + 1)^2$ **4.** $(x - 3)^2$ **5.** $(x + 2)(x - 3)$ **6.** $(x + 2)(x - 1)$ **7.** $(x + 3)(x - 2)$ **8.** $(x + 3)(x + 4)$ **9.** $(x - 5)(x - 2)$ **10.** $(x - 6)(x + 5)$ **11.** $2(x - 7)(x + 7)$ **12.** $3(x - 5)(x + 5)$ **13.** $(x + 3)(x + 5)$ **14.** $(y - 7)(3 + x)$ **15.** $(x + 8)(x - 2)$ **16.** $(x - 7)(x + 4)$ **17.** $4x(x + 7)(x - 2)$ **18.** $6x(x - 5)(x + 4)$ **19.** $2(3x + 4)(2x + 3)$ **20.** $3(2a - b)(4a + 5b)$ **21.** $(2a + b)(2a - b)$ **22.** $(x + 5y)(x - 5y)$ **23.** $(4 - 3x)(7 + 2x)$ **24.** $(5 - 2x)(4 + x)$ **25.** prime **26.** prime **27.** $(3y + 5)(2y - 3)$ **28.** $(4x - 5)(x + 1)$ **29.** $9x(2x^2 - 7x + 1)$ **30.** $4a(3a^2 - 6a + 1)$ **31.** $(4a - 7)^2$ **32.** $(5p - 7)^2$ **33.** $(7 - x)(2 + x)$ **34.** $(3 + x)(1 - x)$ **35.** $3x^2y(x + 6)(x - 4)$ **36.** $2xy(x + 5y)(x - y)$ **37.** $3xy(4x^2 + 81)$ **38.** $2xy^2(3x^2 + 4)$ **39.** $2xy(1 + 6x)(1 - 6x)$ **40.** $2x(x - 3)(x + 3)$ **41.** $(x + 6)(x + 2)(x - 2)$ **42.** $(x - 2)(x + 6)(x - 6)$ **43.** $2a^2(3a + 5)$ **44.** $2n(2n - 3)$ **45.** $(3x - 1)(x^2 + 4)$ **46.** $(x - 2)(x^2 + 3)$ **47.** $6(x + 2y)(x + y)$ **48.** $2(x + 4y)(6x - y)$ **49.** $(x + y)(5 + x)$ **50.** $(x - y)(7 + y)$ **51.** $(7t - 1)(2t - 1)$ **52.** prime **53.** $-1(3x + 5)(x - 1)$ **54.** $-1(7x - 2)(x + 3)$ **55.** $(1 - 10a)(1 + 2a)$ **56.** $(1 + 5a)(1 - 12a)$ **57.** $(x + 3)(x - 3)(x - 1)(x + 1)$ **58.** $(x + 3)(x - 3)(x + 2)(x - 2)$ **59.** $(x - 15)(x - 8)$ **60.** $(y + 16)(y + 6)$ **61.** $(5p - 7q)^2$ **62.** $(4a - 7b)^2$ **63.** prime **64.** $(7x + 3y)(x + 3y)$ **65.** $-1(x - 5)(x + 6)$ **66.** $-1(x - 2)(x - 4)$ **67.** $(3r - 1)(s + 4)$ **68.** $(x - 2)(x^2 + 1)$ **69.** $(x - 2y)(4x - 3)$ **70.** $(2x - y)(2x + 7z)$ **71.** $(x + 12y)(x - 3y)$ **72.** $(3x - 2y)(x + 4y)$ **73.** $(x^2 + 2)(x + 4)(x - 4)$ **74.** $(x^2 + 3)(x + 5)(x - 5)$ **75.** answers may vary **76.** yes; $9(x^2 + 9y^2)$

Section 4.6

Vocabulary and Readiness Check **1.** quadratic **3.** $3, -5$

Exercise Set 4.6 **1.** $2, -1$ **3.** $6, 7$ **5.** $-9, -17$ **7.** $0, -6$ **9.** $0, 8$ **11.** $-\frac{3}{2}, \frac{5}{4}$ **13.** $\frac{7}{2}, -\frac{2}{7}$ **15.** $\frac{1}{2}, -\frac{1}{3}$ **17.** $-0.2, -1.5$ **19.** $9, 4$ **21.** $-4, 2$ **23.** $0, 7$ **25.** $0, -20$ **27.** $4, -4$ **29.** $8, -4$ **31.** $-3, 12$ **33.** $\frac{7}{3}, -2$ **35.** $\frac{8}{3}, -9$ **37.** $0, -\frac{1}{2}, \frac{1}{2}$ **39.** $\frac{17}{2}$ **41.** $\frac{3}{4}$ **43.** $-\frac{1}{2}, \frac{1}{2}$ **45.** $-\frac{3}{2}, -\frac{1}{2}, 3$ **47.** $-5, 3$ **49.** $-\frac{5}{6}, \frac{6}{5}$ **51.** $2, -\frac{4}{5}$ **53.** $-\frac{4}{3}, 5$ **55.** $-4, 3$ **57.** $0, 8, 4$ **59.** -7 **61.** $0, \frac{3}{2}$ **63.** $0, 1, -1$ **65.** $-6, \frac{4}{3}$ **67.** $\frac{6}{7}, 1$ **69.** $\frac{47}{45}$ **71.** $\frac{17}{60}$ **73.** $\frac{7}{10}$ **75.** didn't write equation in standard form; should be $x = 4$ or $x = -2$ **77.** answers may vary, for example, $(x - 6)(x + 1) = 0$ **79.** answers may vary, for example, $x^2 - 12x + 35 = 0$ **81. a.** 300; 304; 276; 216; 124; 0; -156 **b.** 5 sec **c.** 304 ft **83.** $0, \frac{1}{2}$ **85.** $0, -15$

Section 4.7

Exercise Set 4.7 **1.** width: x; length: $x + 4$ **3.** x and $x + 2$ if x is an odd integer **5.** base: x; height: $4x + 1$ **7.** 11 units **9.** 15 cm, 13 cm, 22 cm, 70 cm **11.** base: 16 mi; height: 6 mi **13.** 5 sec **15.** width: 5 cm; length: 6 cm **17.** 54 diagonals **19.** 10 sides **21.** -12 or 11 **23.** 14, 15 **25.** 13 feet **27.** 5 in. **29.** 12 mm, 16 mm, 20 mm **31.** 10 km **33.** 36 ft **35.** 9.5 sec **37.** 20% **39.** length: 15 mi; width: 8 mi **41.** 105 units **43.** 1.9 million or 1,900,000 **45.** 1.9 million or 1,900,000 **47.** 2003 **49.** answers may vary **51.** 8 m **53.** 10 and 15 **55.** width of pool: 29 m; length of pool: 35 m

Chapter 4 Vocabulary Check **1.** quadratic equation **2.** Factoring **3.** greatest common factor **4.** perfect square trinomial **5.** hypotenuse **6.** leg **7.** hypotenuse

Chapter 4 Review **1.** $2x - 5$ **2.** $2x^4 + 1 - 5x^3$ **3.** $5(m + 6)$ **4.** $4x(5x^2 + 3x + 6)$ **5.** $(2x + 3)(3x - 5)$ **6.** $(x + 1)(5x - 1)$ **7.** $(x - 1)(3x + 2)$ **8.** $(a + 3b)(3a + b)$ **9.** $(2a + b)(5a + 7b)$ **10.** $(3x + 5)(2x - 1)$ **11.** $(x + 4)(x + 2)$ **12.** $(x - 8)(x - 3)$ **13.** prime **14.** $(x - 6)(x + 1)$ **15.** $(x + 4)(x - 2)$ **16.** $(x + 6y)(x - 2y)$ **17.** $(x + 5y)(x + 3y)$ **18.** $2(3 - x)(12 + x)$ **19.** $4(8 + 3x - x^2)$ **20.** $5y(y - 6)(y - 4)$ **21.** $-48, 2$ **22.** factor out the GCF, 3 **23.** $(2x + 1)(x + 6)$ **24.** $(2x + 3)(2x - 1)$ **25.** $(3x + 4y)(2x - y)$ **26.** prime **27.** $(2x + 3)(x - 13)$ **28.** $(6x + 5y)(3x - 4y)$ **29.** $5y(2y - 3)(y + 4)$ **30.** $3y(4y - 1)(5y - 2)$ **31.** $5x^2 - 9x - 2$; $(5x + 1)(x - 2)$ **32.** $16x^2 - 28x + 6$; $2(4x - 1)(2x - 3)$ **33.** yes **34.** no **35.** no **36.** yes **37.** yes **38.** no **39.** yes **40.** no **41.** $(x + 9)(x - 9)$ **42.** $(x + 6)^2$ **43.** $(2x + 3)(2x - 3)$ **44.** $(3t + 5s)(3t - 5s)$ **45.** prime **46.** $(n - 9)^2$ **47.** $3(r + 6)^2$ **48.** $(3y - 7)^2$ **49.** $5m^6(m + 1)(m - 1)$ **50.** $(2x - 7y)^2$ **51.** $3y(x + y)^2$ **52.** $(4x^2 + 1)(2x + 1)(2x - 1)$ **53.** $-6, 2$ **54.** $-11, 7$ **55.** $0, -1, \frac{2}{7}$ **56.** $-\frac{1}{5}, -3$ **57.** $-7, -1$ **58.** $-4, 6$ **59.** -5 **60.** $2, 8$ **61.** $\frac{1}{3}$ **62.** $-\frac{2}{7}, \frac{3}{8}$ **63.** $0, 6$ **64.** $5, -5$ **65.** $x^2 - 9x + 20 = 0$ **66.** $x^2 + 2x + 1 = 0$ **67.** c **68.** d **69.** 9 units **70.** 8 units, 13 units, 16 units, 10 units **71.** width: 20 in.; length: 25 in. **72.** 36 yd **73.** 19 and 20 **74.** 20 and 22 **75. a.** 17.5 sec and 10 sec; answers may vary **b.** 27.5 sec **76.** 32 cm **77.** $6(x + 4)$ **78.** $7(x - 9)$ **79.** $(4x - 3)(11x - 6)$ **80.** $(x - 5)(2x - 1)$ **81.** $(3x - 4)(x^2 + 2)$ **82.** $(y + 2)(x - 1)$ **83.** $2(x + 4)(x - 3)$ **84.** $3x(x - 9)(x - 1)$ **85.** $(2x + 9)(2x - 9)$ **86.** $2(x + 3)(x - 3)$ **87.** $(4x - 3)^2$ **88.** $5(x + 2)^2$ **89.** $-\frac{7}{2}, 4$ **90.** $-3, 5$ **91.** $0, -7, -4$ **92.** $3, 2$ **93.** $0, 16$ **94.** 19 in.; 8 in.; 21 in. **95.** length: 6 in.; width: 2 in.

Chapter 4 Test **1.** $3x(3x - 1)$ **2.** $(x + 7)(x + 4)$ **3.** $(7 + m)(7 - m)$ **4.** $(y + 11)^2$ **5.** $(x^2 + 4)(x + 2)(x - 2)$ **6.** $(a + 3)(4 - y)$ **7.** prime **8.** $(y - 12)(y + 4)$ **9.** $(a + b)(3a - 7)$ **10.** $(3x - 2)(x - 1)$ **11.** $5(6 + x)(6 - x)$ **12.** $3x(x - 5)(x - 2)$ **13.** $(6t + 5)(t - 1)$ **14.** $(x - 7)(y - 2)(y + 2)$ **15.** $x(1 + x^2)(1 + x)(1 - x)$ **16.** $(x + 12y)(x + 2y)$ **17.** $3, -9$ **18.** $-7, 2$ **19.** $-7, 1$ **20.** $0, \frac{3}{2}, -\frac{4}{3}$ **21.** $0, 3, -3$ **22.** $-3, 5$ **23.** $0, \frac{5}{2}$ **24.** 17 ft **25.** width: 6 units; length: 9 units **26.** 7 sec **27.** hypotenuse: 25 cm; legs: 15 cm, 20 cm **28.** 8.25 sec

Cumulative Review **1. a.** $9 \leq 11$ **b.** $8 > 1$ **c.** $3 \neq 4$; Sec. 1.2, Ex. 7 **2. a.** $>$ **b.** $<$ **3.** solution; Sec. 1.3, Ex. 8 **4.** 102 **5.** -12; Sec. 1.5, Ex. 5a **6.** -102 **7. a.** $\frac{3}{4}$ **b.** -24 **c.** 1; Sec. 1.6, Ex. 16 **8.** -98 **9.** $5x + 7$; Sec. 1.8, Ex. 4 **10.** $19 - 6x$ **11.** $-4a - 1$; Sec. 1.8, Ex. 5 **12.** $-13x - 21$ **13.** $7.3x - 6$; Sec. 1.8, Ex. 7 **14.** 2 **15.** -11; Sec. 2.2, Ex. 3 **16.** 28 **17.** every real number; Sec. 2.3, Ex. 7 **18.** 33 **19.** $l = \frac{V}{wh}$; Sec. 2.5, Ex. 5 **20.** $y = \frac{-3x - 7}{2}$ or $y = -\frac{3}{2}x - \frac{7}{2}$ **21.** 5^{18}; Sec. 3.1, Ex. 16 **22.** 30 **23.** y^{16}; Sec. 3.1, Ex. 17 **24.** y^{10} **25.** $16x^6$; Sec. 3.2, Ex. 9 **26.** $\frac{1}{9}$ **27.** $\frac{y^{18}}{z^{36}}$; Sec. 3.2, Ex. 11 **28.** x^4 **29.** $\frac{1}{x^{19}}$; Sec. 3.2, Ex. 12 **30.** $25a^9$ **31.** $4x$; Sec. 3.3, Ex. 6 **32.** $\frac{5}{6}x - 77$ **33.** $13x^2 - 2$; Sec. 3.3, Ex. 7 **34.** $-0.5x + 1.2$ **35.** $4x^2 - 4xy + y^2$; Sec. 3.5, Ex. 8 **36.** $9x^2 - 42xy + 49y^2$ **37.** $t^2 + 4t + 4$; Sec. 3.6, Ex. 5 **38.** $x^2 - 26x + 169$ **39.** $x^4 - 14x^2y + 49y^2$; Sec. 3.6, Ex. 8 **40.** $49x^2 + 14xy + y^2$ **41.** $2xy - 4 + \frac{1}{2y}$; Sec. 3.7, Ex. 3 **42.** $(z^2 + 7)(z + 1)$ **43.** $(x + 3)(5 + y)$; Sec. 4.1, Ex. 9 **44.** $2x(x + 7)(x - 6)$ **45.** $(x^2 + 2)(x^2 + 3)$; Sec. 4.2, Ex. 7 **46.** $(-4x + 1)(x + 6)$ or $-1(4x - 1)(x + 6)$ **47.** $2(x - 2)(3x + 5)$; Sec. 4.4, Ex. 2 **48.** $x(3y + 4)(3y - 4)$ **49.** 3 sec; Sec. 4.7, Ex. 1 **50.** $9, 4$

Chapter 5 Rational Expressions

Section 5.1

Vocabulary and Readiness Check **1.** rational expression **3.** -1 **5.** 2 **7.** $\frac{-a}{b}; \frac{a}{-b}$ **9.** yes **11.** no

Exercise Set 5.1 **1.** $\frac{7}{4}$ **3.** $-\frac{8}{3}$ **5.** $-\frac{11}{2}$ **7. a.** \$403 **b.** \$7 **c.** decrease; answers may vary **9.** $x = 0$ **11.** $x = -2$ **13.** $x = \frac{5}{2}$ **15.** $x = 0, x = -2$ **17.** none **19.** $x = 6, x = -1$ **21.** $x = -2, x = -\frac{7}{3}$ **23.** 1 **25.** -1 **27.** $\frac{1}{4(x + 2)}$ **29.** $\frac{1}{x + 2}$ **31.** can't simplify

33. -5 **35.** $\frac{7}{x}$ **37.** $\frac{1}{x-9}$ **39.** $5x+1$ **41.** $\frac{x^2}{x-2}$ **43.** $7x$ **45.** $\frac{x+5}{x-5}$ **47.** $\frac{x+2}{x+4}$ **49.** $\frac{x+2}{2}$ **51.** $-(x+2)$ **53.** $\frac{x+1}{x-1}$ **55.** $x+y$ **57.** $\frac{5-y}{2}$ **59.** $\frac{2y+5}{3y+4}$ **61.** $\frac{-(x-10)}{x+8}; \frac{-x+10}{x+8}; \frac{x-10}{-(x+8)}; \frac{x-10}{-x-8}$ **63.** $\frac{-(5y-3)}{y-12}; \frac{-5y+3}{y-12}; \frac{5y-3}{-(y-12)}; \frac{5y-3}{-y+12}$ **65.** correct **67.** correct **69.** $\frac{3}{11}$ **71.** $\frac{4}{3}$ **73.** $\frac{117}{40}$ **75.** correct **77.** incorrect; $\frac{1+2}{1+3}=\frac{3}{4}$ **79.** answers may vary **81.** answers may vary **83.** 400 mg **85.** $C = 78.125$; medium **87.** 65.3%

Section 5.2

Vocabulary and Readiness Check **1.** reciprocals **3.** $\frac{a \cdot d}{b \cdot c}$ **5.** $\frac{6}{7}$

Exercise Set 5.2 **1.** $\frac{21}{4y}$ **3.** x^4 **5.** $-\frac{b^2}{6}$ **7.** $\frac{x^2}{10}$ **9.** $\frac{1}{3}$ **11.** $\frac{m+n}{m-n}$ **13.** $\frac{x+5}{x}$ **15.** $\frac{(x+2)(x-3)}{(x-4)(x+4)}$ **17.** $\frac{2x^4}{3}$ **19.** $\frac{12}{y^6}$ **21.** $x(x+4)$ **23.** $\frac{3(x+1)}{x^3(x-1)}$ **25.** m^2-n^2 **27.** $-\frac{x+2}{x-3}$ **29.** $\frac{x+2}{x-3}$ **31.** $\frac{5}{6}$ **33.** $\frac{3x}{8}$ **35.** $\frac{3}{2}$ **37.** $\frac{3x+4y}{2(x+2y)}$ **39.** $\frac{2(x+2)}{x-2}$ **41.** $-\frac{y(x+2)}{4}$ **43.** $\frac{(a+5)(a+3)}{(a+2)(a+1)}$ **45.** $\frac{5}{x}$ **47.** $\frac{2(n-8)}{3n-1}$ **49.** 1440 **51.** 5 **53.** 81 **55.** 73 **57.** 56.7 **59.** 1,201,500 sq ft **61.** 244.9 miles/hour **63.** 1 **65.** $-\frac{10}{9}$ **67.** $-\frac{1}{5}$ **69.** true **71.** false; $\frac{x^2+3x}{20}$ **73.** $\frac{2}{9(x-5)}$ sq ft **75.** $\frac{x}{2}$ **77.** $\frac{5a(2a+b)(3a-2b)}{b^2(a-b)(a+2b)}$ **79.** answers may vary **81.** 1510 euros

Section 5.3

Vocabulary and Readiness Check **1.** $\frac{9}{11}$ **3.** $\frac{a+c}{b}$ **5.** $\frac{5-(6+x)}{x}$

Exercise Set 5.3 **1.** $\frac{a+9}{13}$ **3.** $\frac{3m}{n}$ **5.** 4 **7.** $\frac{y+10}{3+y}$ **9.** $5x+3$ **11.** $\frac{4}{a+5}$ **13.** $\frac{1}{x-6}$ **15.** $4x^3$ **17.** $8x(x+2)$ **19.** $(x+3)(x-2)$ **21.** $3(x+6)$ **23.** $5(x-6)^2$ **25.** $6(x+1)^2$ **27.** $x-8$ or $8-x$ **29.** $(x-1)(x+4)(x+3)$ **31.** $(3x+1)(x+1)(x-1)(2x+1)$ **33.** $2x^2(x+4)(x-4)$ **35.** $\frac{6x}{4x^2}$ **37.** $\frac{24b^2}{12ab^2}$ **39.** $\frac{9y}{2y(x+3)}$ **41.** $\frac{9ab+2b}{5b(a+2)}$ **43.** $\frac{x^2+x}{x(x+4)(x+2)(x+1)}$ **45.** $\frac{18y-2}{30x^2-60}$ **47.** $2x$ **49.** $\frac{x+3}{2x-1}$ **51.** $x+1$ **53.** $\frac{3}{x}$ **55.** $\frac{3x+1}{5x+1}$ **57.** $\frac{29}{21}$ **59.** $-\frac{5}{12}$ **61.** $\frac{7}{30}$ **63.** d **65.** answers may vary **67.** $\frac{20}{x-2}$ m **69.** answers may vary **71.** 95,304 Earth days **73.** answers may vary **75.** answers may vary

Section 5.6

Vocabulary and Readiness Check **1.** c **3.** $\frac{1}{x}; \frac{1}{x} - 3$ **5.** $z+5; \frac{1}{z+5}$ **7.** $2y; \frac{11}{2y}$

Exercise Set 5.6 **1.** 4 **3.** $\frac{50}{9}$ **5.** -3 **7.** $\frac{14}{9}$ **9.** 123 lb **11.** 165 cal **13.** $y = 21.25$ **15.** $y = 5\frac{5}{7}$ ft **17.** 2 **19.** -3 **21.** $2\frac{2}{9}$ hr **23.** $1\frac{1}{2}$ min **25.** trip to park rate: r; to park time: $\frac{12}{r}$; return trip rate: r; return time: $\frac{18}{r} = \frac{12}{r} + 1$; $r = 6$ mph **27.** 1st portion: 10 mph; cooldown: 8 mph **29.** 360 sq ft **31.** 2 **33.** \$108.00 **35.** 20 mph **37.** $y = 37\frac{1}{2}$ ft **39.** 41 mph; 51 mph **41.** 5 **43.** 217 mph **45.** 9 gal **47.** 8 mph **49.** 2.2 mph; 3.3 mph **51.** 3 hr **53.** $26\frac{2}{3}$ ft **55.** 216 nuts **57.** $666\frac{2}{3}$ mi **59.** 20 hr **61.** car: 70 mph; motorcycle: 60 mph **63.** $5\frac{1}{4}$ hr **65.** 8 **67.** one car: 64 mph; second car: 50 mph **69.** 510 mph **71.** $x = 5$ **73.** $x = 13.5$ **75.** $\frac{1}{2}$ **77.** $\frac{3}{7}$ **79.** faster pump: 28 min; slower pump: 84 min **81.** answers may vary **83.** $R = \frac{D}{T}$ **85.** 3.75 min

Chapter 5 Vocabulary Check **1.** rational expression **2.** complex fraction **3.** $\frac{-a}{b}; \frac{a}{-b}$ **4.** denominator **5.** simplifying **6.** reciprocals **7.** least common denominator **8.** unit **9.** ratio **10.** proportion **11.** cross products **12.** rate

Chapter 5 Review **1.** $x = 2, x = -2$ **2.** $x = \frac{5}{2}, x = -\frac{3}{2}$ **3.** $\frac{4}{3}$ **4.** $\frac{11}{12}$ **5.** $\frac{2}{x}$ **6.** $\frac{3}{x}$ **7.** $\frac{1}{x-5}$ **8.** $\frac{1}{x+1}$ **9.** $\frac{x(x-2)}{x+1}$ **10.** $\frac{5(x-5)}{x-3}$ **11.** $\frac{x-3}{x-5}$ **12.** $\frac{x}{x+4}$ **13.** $\frac{x+a}{x-c}$ **14.** $\frac{x+5}{x-3}$ **15.** $\frac{3x^2}{y}$ **16.** $-\frac{9x^2}{8}$ **17.** $\frac{x-3}{x+2}$ **18.** $-\frac{2x(2x+5)}{(x-6)^2}$ **19.** $\frac{x+3}{x-4}$ **20.** $\frac{4x}{3y}$ **21.** $(x-6)(x-3)$ **22.** $\frac{2}{3}$ **23.** $\frac{1}{2}$ **24.** $\frac{3(x+2)}{3x+y}$ **25.** $\frac{1}{x+2}$ **26.** $\frac{1}{x-3}$ **27.** $\frac{2(x-5)}{3x^2}$ **28.** $\frac{2x+1}{2x^2}$ **29.** $14x$ **30.** $(x-8)(x+8)(x+3)$ **31.** $\frac{10x^2y}{14x^3y}$ **32.** $\frac{36y^2x}{16y^3x}$ **33.** $\frac{x^2-3x-10}{(x+2)(x-5)(x+9)}$ **34.** $\frac{3x^2+4x-15}{(x+2)^2(x+3)}$ **35.** $\frac{4y+30x^2}{5x^2y}$ **36.** $-\frac{2(x-5)}{(x-3)(x-1)}$ **37.** $-\frac{2(x+1)}{x+3}$ **38.** $\frac{5(x+1)}{(x+4)(x-2)(x-1)}$ **39.** $\frac{x-4}{3x}$ **40.** $-\frac{x}{x-1}$ **41.** 30 **42.** 3, −4 **43.** no solution **44.** 5 **45.** $\frac{9}{7}$ **46.** −6, 1 **47.** $x = 9$ **48.** no solution **49.** 675 parts **50.** \$33.75 **51.** 3 **52.** 2 **53.** fast car speed: 30 mph; slow car speed: 20 mph **54.** 20 mph **55.** $17\frac{1}{2}$ hr **56.** $8\frac{4}{7}$ days **57.** $x = 15$ **58.** $x = 6$ **59.** $-\frac{7}{18y}$ **60.** $\frac{6}{7}$ **61.** $\frac{3y-1}{2y-1}$ **62.** $-\frac{7+2x}{2x}$ **63.** $\frac{1}{2x}$ **64.** $\frac{x(x-3)}{x+7}$ **65.** $\frac{x-4}{x+4}$ **66.** $\frac{(x-9)(x+8)}{(x+5)(x+9)}$ **67.** $\frac{1}{x-6}$ **68.** $\frac{2x+1}{4x}$ **69.** $\frac{2}{(x+3)(x-2)}$ **70.** $-\frac{3x}{(x+2)(x-3)}$ **71.** $\frac{1}{2}$ **72.** no solution **73.** 1 **74.** $1\frac{5}{7}$ days **75.** $x = 6$ **76.** $x = 12$ **77.** $\frac{3}{10}$ **78.** $\frac{2}{3}$

Chapter 5 Test **1.** $x = -1, x = -3$ **2. a.** \$115 **b.** \$103 **3.** $\frac{3}{5}$ **4.** $\frac{1}{x+6}$ **5.** −1 **6.** $-\frac{1}{x+y}$ **7.** $\frac{2m(m+2)}{m-2}$ **8.** $\frac{a+2}{a+5}$ **9.** $\frac{(x-6)(x-7)}{(x+7)(x+2)}$ **10.** 15 **11.** $\frac{y-2}{4}$ **12.** $-\frac{1}{2x+5}$ **13.** $\frac{3a-4}{(a-3)(a+2)}$ **14.** $\frac{3}{x-1}$ **15.** $\frac{2(x+3)(x+5)}{x(x^2+4x+1)}$ **16.** $\frac{x^2+2x+35}{(x+9)(x+2)(x-5)}$ **17.** $\frac{4y^2+13y-15}{(y+5)(y+1)(y+4)}$ **18.** $\frac{30}{11}$ **19.** −6 **20.** no solution **21.** no solution **22.** −2, 5 **23.** $\frac{xz}{2y}$ **24.** $b - a$ **25.** $\frac{5y^2-1}{y+2}$ **26.** 1 or 5 **27.** 30 mph **28.** $6\frac{2}{3}$ hr **29.** $x = 12$ **30.** 18 bulbs

Cumulative Review **1. a.** $\frac{15}{x} = 4$ **b.** $12 - 3 = x$ **c.** $4x + 17 = 21$; Sec. 1.3, Ex. 10 **2. a.** $12 - x = -45$ **b.** $12x = -45$ **c.** $x - 10 = 2x$ **3. a.** −12 **b.** −9; Sec. 1.4, Ex. 12 **4. a.** −8 **b.** −17 **5.** distributive property; Sec. 1.7, Ex. 15 **6.** commutative property of addition

7. associative property of addition; Sec. 1.7, Ex. 16 **8.** associative property of multiplication **9.** $x = -4$; Sec. 2.1, Ex. 7 **10.** $x = 0$ **11.** shorter piece, 2 ft; longer piece, 8 ft; Sec. 2.4, Ex. 3 **12.** 190, 192 **13.** $\frac{y-b}{m} = x$; Sec. 2.5, Ex. 6 **14.** $x = \frac{2y+6}{3}$ **15.** $x \leq -10$; 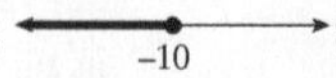; Sec. 2.7, Ex. 4 **16.** $\{x \mid x < -1\}$ **17.** x^3; Sec. 3.1, Ex. 24 **18.** 1 **19.** 256; Sec. 3.1, Ex. 25 **20.** $x^{15}y^6$ **21.** -27; Sec. 3.1, Ex. 26 **22.** $x^{18}y^4$ **23.** $2x^4y$; Sec. 3.1, Ex. 27 **24.** $-15a^5b^2$ **25.** $\frac{2}{x^3}$; Sec. 3.2, Ex. 2 **26.** $\frac{1}{49}$ **27.** $\frac{1}{16}$; Sec. 3.2, Ex. 4 **28.** $\frac{5}{z^7}$ **29.** $10x^4 + 30x$; Sec. 3.5, Ex. 5 **30.** $x^2 + 18x + 81$ **31.** $-15x^4 - 18x^3 + 3x^2$; Sec. 3.5, Ex. 6 **32.** $4x^2 - 1$ **33.** $4x^2 - 4x + 6 - \frac{11}{2x+3}$; Sec. 3.7, Ex. 7 **34.** $4x^2 + 16x + 55 + \frac{222}{x-4}$ **35.** $(x+3)(x+4)$; Sec. 4.2, Ex. 1 **36.** $-2(a+1)(a-6)$ **37.** $(5x+2y)^2$; Sec. 4.5, Ex. 5 **38.** $(x+2)(x-2)$ **39.** $x = 11, x = -2$; Sec. 4.6, Ex. 4 **40.** $-2, \frac{1}{3}$ **41.** $\frac{2}{5}$; Sec. 5.2, Ex. 2 **42.** $\frac{x+5}{2x^3}$ **43.** $3x - 5$; Sec. 5.3, Ex. 3 **44.** $7x^4(x^2 - x + 1)$ **45.** $\frac{3}{x-2}$; Sec. 5.4, Ex. 2 **46.** $(2x+3)^2$ **47.** $t = 5$; Sec. 5.5, Ex. 2 **48.** $\frac{30}{x+3}$ **49.** $2\frac{1}{10}$ hr; Sec. 5.6, Ex. 6 **50.** $\frac{4m+2n}{m+n}$ or $\frac{2(2m+n)}{m+n}$

Chapter 6 Graphing Equations and Inequalities

Section 6.1

Vocabulary and Readiness Check **1.** *x*-axis **3.** origin **5.** *x*-coordinate; *y*-coordinate **7.** solution

Exercise Set 6.1 **1.** France **3.** France, U.S., Spain, China **5.** 43 million **7.** 71,000 **9.** 2005; 78,100 **11.** 50 **13.** from 1984 to 1986 **15.** 1994 **17.**

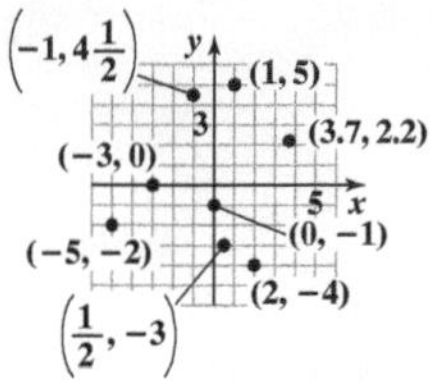

(1, 5) and (3.7, 2.2) are in quadrant I, $\left(-1, 4\frac{1}{2}\right)$ is in quadrant II, $(-5, -2)$ is in quadrant III, $(2, -4)$ and $\left(\frac{1}{2}, -3\right)$ are in quadrant IV, $(-3, 0)$ lies on the *x*-axis, $(0, -1)$ lies on the *y*-axis **19.** (0, 0) **21.** (3, 2) **23.** $(-2, -2)$ **25.** $(2, -1)$ **27.** $(0, -3)$ **29.** (1, 3) **31.** $(-3, -1)$ **33. a.** (2003, 9.17), (2004, 9.22), (2005, 8.83), (2006, 9.14), (2007, 9.63), (2008, 9.79) **b.** In the year 2006, the domestic box office was $9.14 billion.

c.

d. answers may vary

35. a. (0.50, 10), (0.75, 12), (1.00, 15), (1.25, 16), (1.50, 18), (1.50, 19), (1.75, 19), (2.00, 20) **b.** When Minh studied 1.25 hours, her quiz score was 16. **c.**

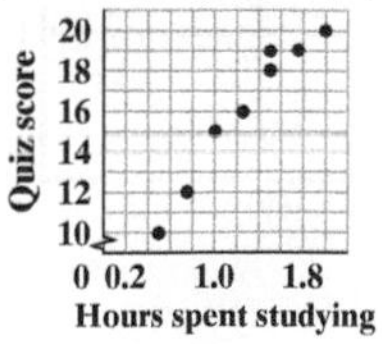

d. answers may vary **37.** $(-4, -2), (4, 0)$ **39.** $(-8, -5), (16, 1)$ **41.** $0; 7; -\frac{2}{7}$ **43.** 2; 2; 5 **45.** $0; -3; 2$ **47.** 2; 6; 3 **49.** $-12; 5; -6$ **51.** $\frac{5}{7}; \frac{5}{2}; -1$ **53.** $0; -5; -2$ **55.** $2; 1; -6$

57. a. 13,000; 21,000; 29,000 **b.** 45 desks **59. a.** 5.59; 5.99; 6.39 **b.** 2005 **c.** 2013 **61.** $y = 5 - x$ **63.** $y = \frac{5-2x}{4}$ **65.** $y = -2x$ **67.** false **69.** true **71.** negative; negative **73.** positive; negative **75.** 0; 0 **77.** y **79.** no; answers may vary **81.** answers may vary **83.** answers may vary **85.** $(4, -7)$ **87.** 26 units **89.** $47 billion; $53 billion; $59 billion; $63 billion

Section 6.2

Calculator Explorations **1.**

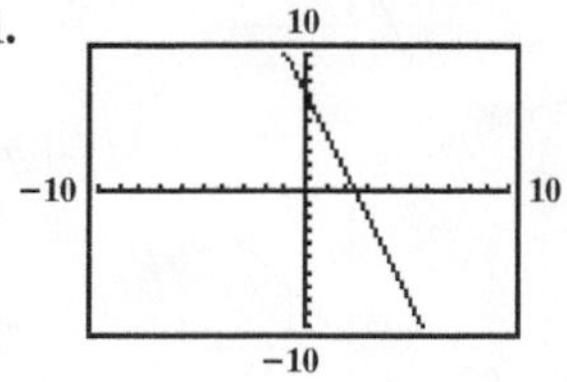

3.

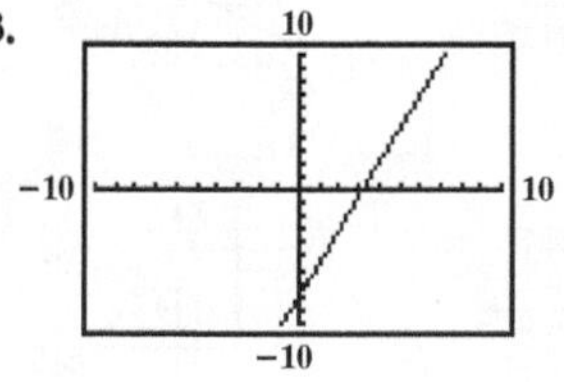

5.

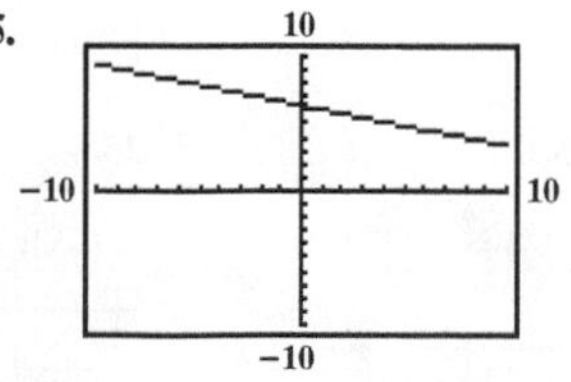

Exercise Set 6.2 **1.** $6; -2; 5$

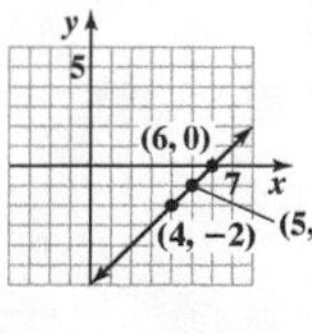

3. $-4; 0; 4$

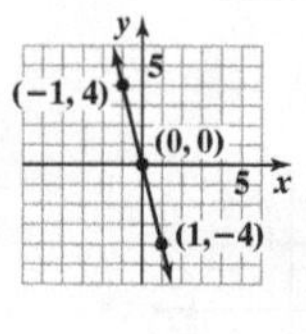

5. $0; 2; -1$

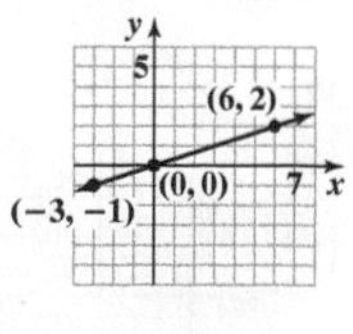

7. $3; -1; -5$

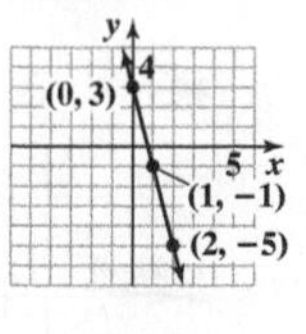

9.
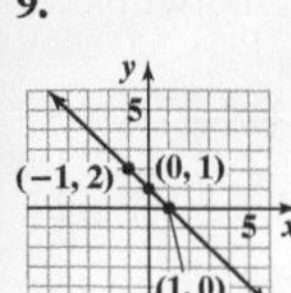

11.
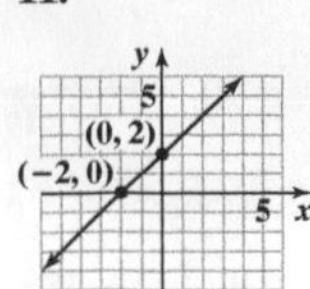

13.
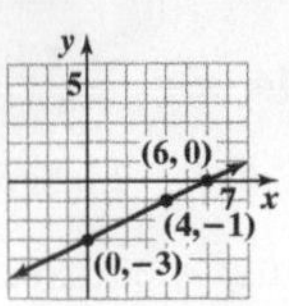

15.
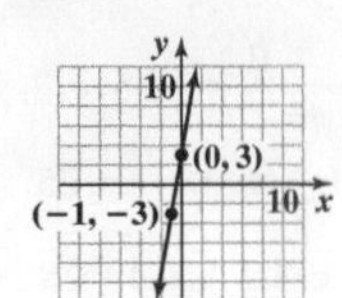

17.
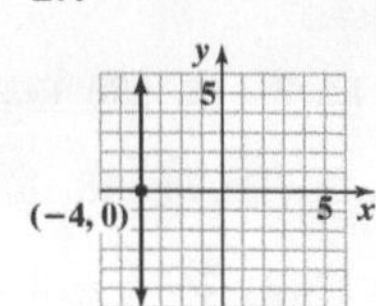

19.
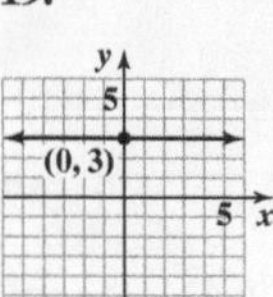

21.
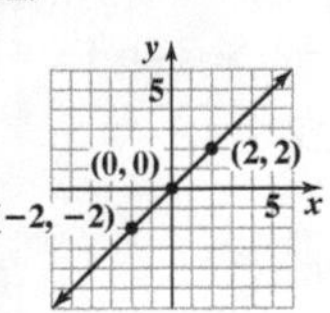

23.
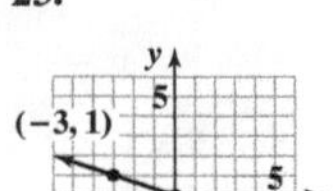

25.
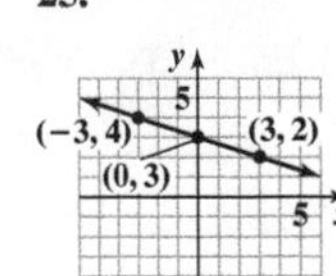

27.
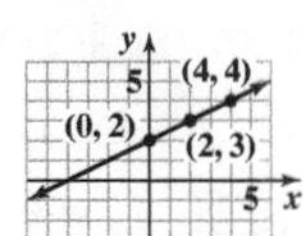

29.
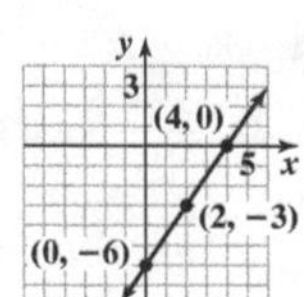

31.
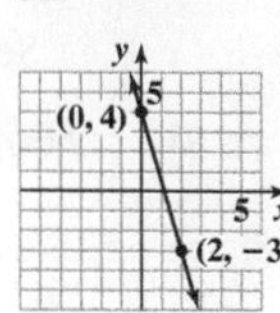

33. a.
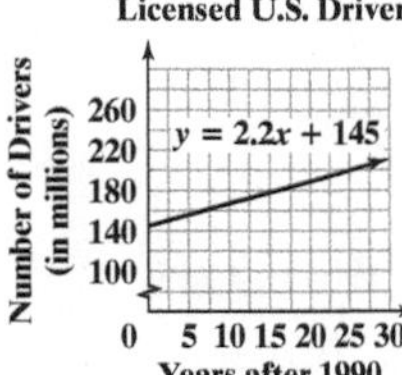

b. yes; answers may vary **35. a.**
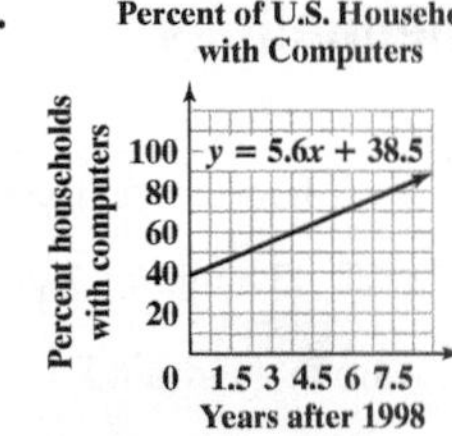

b. (5, 66.5)
c. In 2003, 66.5% of American households had at least one computer.

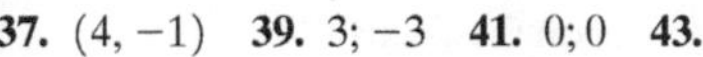
37. (4, −1) **39.** 3; −3 **41.** 0; 0 **43.**
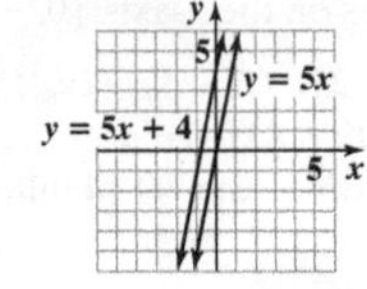

45.
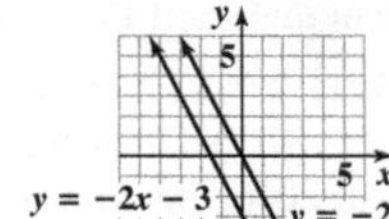

47. 0; 1; 1; 4; 4
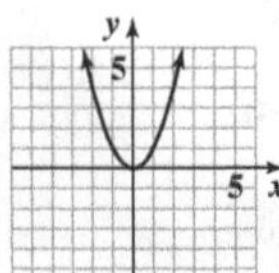

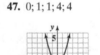

49. $x + y = 12$; 9 cm **51.** yes; answers may vary

Section 6.3

Calculator Explorations **1.**
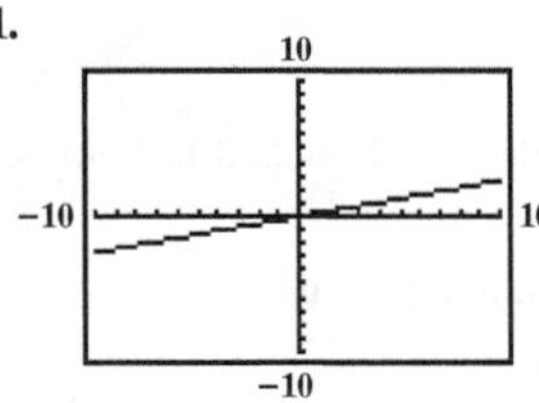

3.
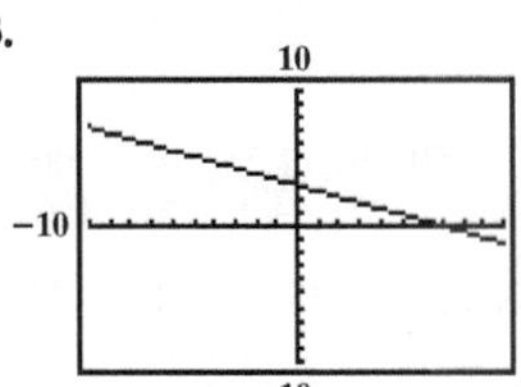

5.
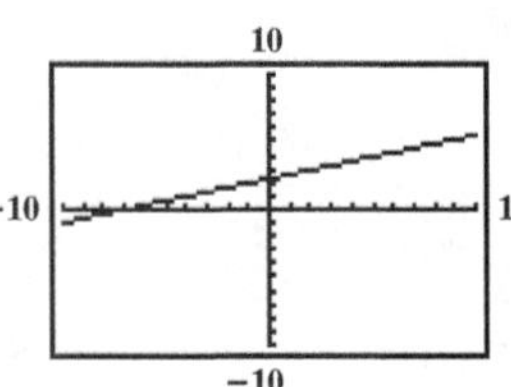

Vocabulary and Readiness Check **1.** linear **3.** horizontal **5.** y-intercept **7.** y; x **9.** false **11.** true

Exercise Set 6.3 **1.** (−1, 0); (0, 1) **3.** (−2, 0); (2, 0); (0, −2) **5.** (−2, 0); (1, 0); (3, 0); (0, 3) **7.** (−1, 0); (1, 0); (0, 1); (0, −2)

9.
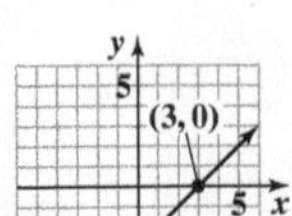

11.
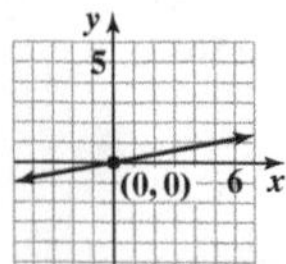

13.
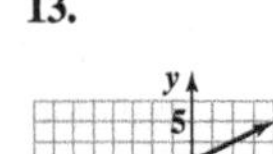

15.
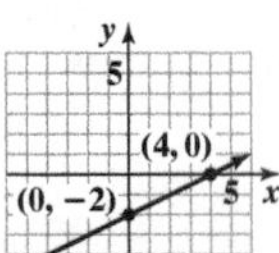

17.

19.
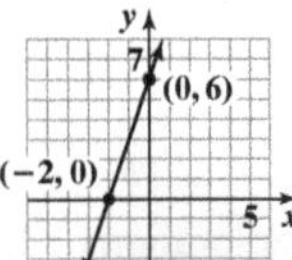

21.
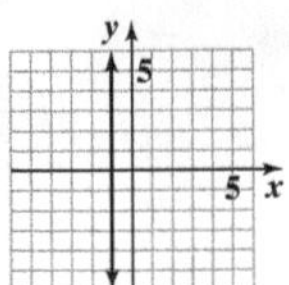

23.
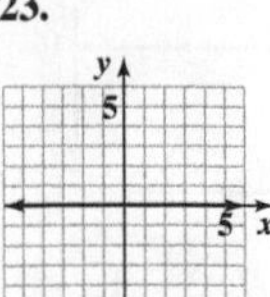

25.
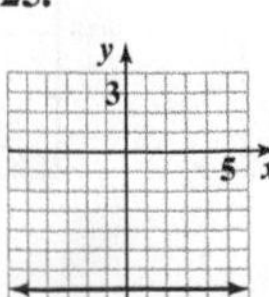

27.
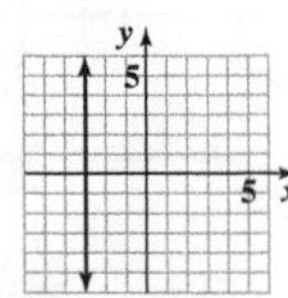

29.
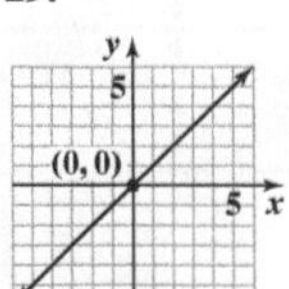

31.
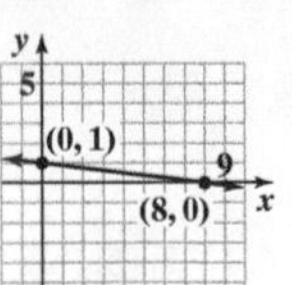

33.
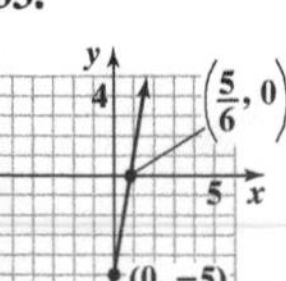

35.
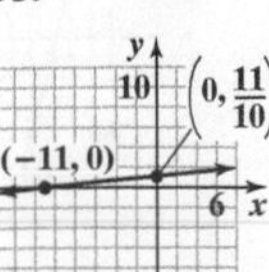

37.
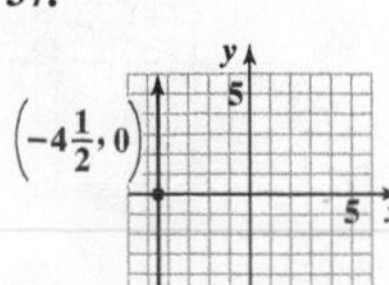

39.
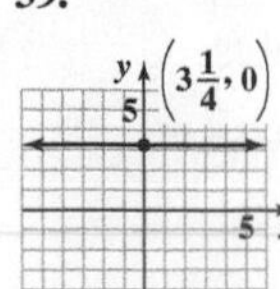

41.
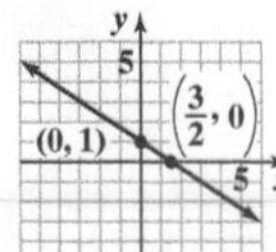

43.
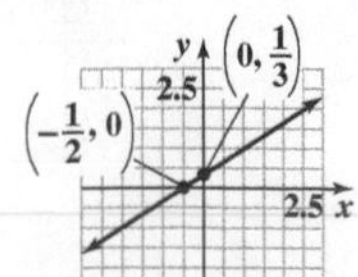

45. $\frac{3}{2}$ **47.** 6 **49.** $-\frac{6}{5}$ **51.** c **53.** a **55.** infinite **57.** 0 **59.** answers may vary **61.** (0, 200); no chairs and 200 desks are manufactured. **63.** 300 chairs **65.** $y = -4$ **67. a.** (31.1, 0) **b.** 31.1 years after 2003, there may be no newspaper circulation.

Section 6.4

Calculator Explorations **1.**

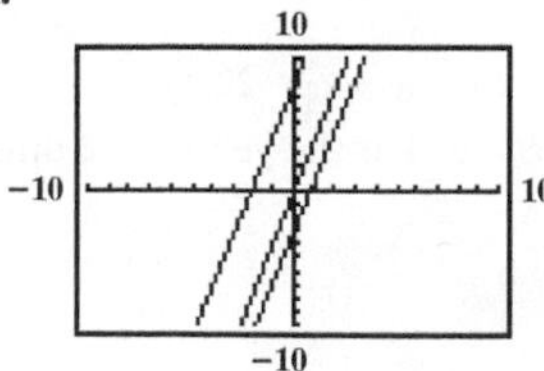

3.

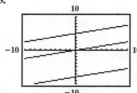

10

−10 10

−10

Vocabulary and Readiness Check **1.** slope **3.** 0 **5.** positive **7.** $y; x$ **9.** positive **11.** 0 **13.** downward **15.** vertical

Exercise Set 6.4 **1.** $m = -1$ **3.** $m = -\frac{1}{4}$ **5.** $m = 0$ **7.** undefined slope **9.** $m = -\frac{4}{3}$ **11.** $m = \frac{5}{2}$ **13.** line 1 **15.** line 2 **17.** $m = 5$ **19.** $m = -0.3$ **21.** $m = -2$ **23.** undefined slope **25.** $m = \frac{2}{3}$ **27.** undefined slope **29.** $m = \frac{1}{2}$ **31.** $m = 0$ **33.** $m = -\frac{3}{4}$ **35.** $m = 4$ **37.** neither **39.** neither **41.** parallel **43.** perpendicular **45. a.** 1 **b.** −1 **47. a.** $\frac{9}{11}$ **b.** $-\frac{11}{9}$ **49.** $\frac{3}{5}$ **51.** 12.5% **53.** 40% **55.** 37%; 35% **57.** $m = \frac{5}{4}$; Every 4 years, there are/should be 5 million more U.S. households with televisions. **59.** $m = 0.15$; Every year, the median age of U.S. automobiles increases by 0.15 year. **61.** $y = 2x - 14$ **63.** $y = -6x - 11$ **65.** d **67.** b **69.** e **71.** $m = \frac{1}{2}$ **73.** answers may vary **75.** 29.5 **77.** 1999; 28.3 mi per gal **79.** from 2006 to 2007 **81.** $x = 20$ **83. a.** (2004, 2025), (2007, 2208) **b.** 61 **c.** For the years 2004 through 2007, the number of heart transplants increased at a rate of 61 per year. **85.** Opposite sides are parallel since their slopes are equal, so the figure is a parallelogram. **87.** 2.0625 **89.** −1.6 **91.** The line becomes steeper.

Section 6.5

Calculator Explorations **1.**

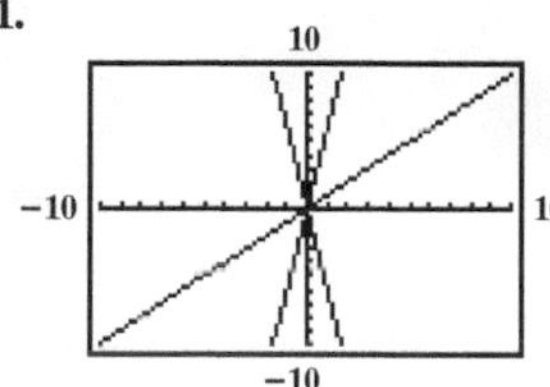

3.

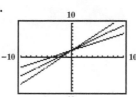

10

−10 10

−10

Vocabulary and Readiness Check **1.** slope-intercept; $m; b$ **3.** point-slope **5.** slope- intercept **7.** horizontal

Exercise Set 6.5 **1.**

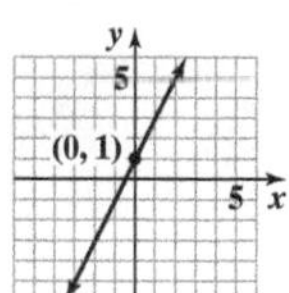

3.

y 14 (0, 5) 6 x

5.

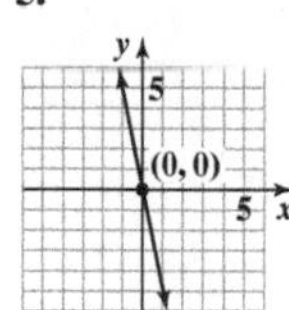

7.

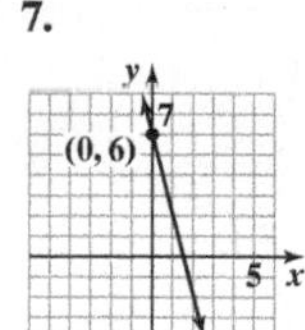

9.

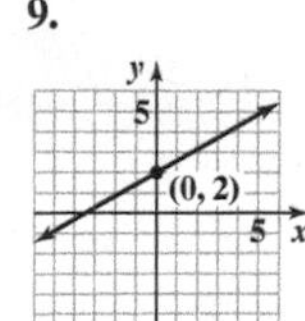

11.

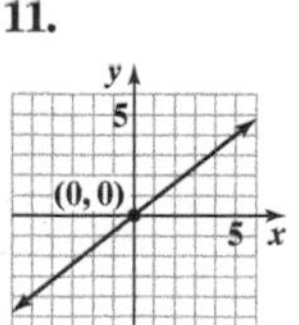

13. $y = 5x + 3$ **15.** $y = -4x - \frac{1}{6}$ **17.** $y = \frac{2}{3}x$ **19.** $y = -8$ **21.** $y = -\frac{1}{5}x + \frac{1}{9}$ **23.** $-6x + y = -10$ **25.** $8x + y = -13$ **27.** $3x - 2y = 27$ **29.** $x + 2y = -3$ **31.** $2x - y = 4$ **33.** $8x - y = -11$ **35.** $4x - 3y = -1$ **37.** $8x + 13y = 0$ **39.** $y = -\frac{1}{2}x + \frac{5}{3}$ **41.** $y = -x + 17$ **43.** $x = -\frac{3}{4}$ **45.** $y = x + 16$ **47.** $y = -5x + 7$ **49.** $y = 2$ **51.** $y = \frac{3}{2}x$ **53.** $y = -3$ **55.** $y = -\frac{4}{7}x - \frac{18}{7}$ **57. a.** (0, 302), (4, 322) **b.** $y = 5x + 302$ **c.** 312 million **59. a.** $s = 32t$ **b.** 128 ft/sec **61. a.** $y = 90{,}000x + 83{,}000$ **b.** 533,000 vehicles **63. a.** $y = -40x + 5700$ **b.** 5420 cinema sites **65. a.** $S = -1000p + 13{,}000$ **b.** 9500 Fun Noodles **67.** −1 **69.** 5 **71.** b **73.** d **75.** $3x - y = -5$ **77.** $x + 3y = 5$

Integrated Review **1.** $m = 2$ **2.** $m = 0$ **3.** $m = -\frac{2}{3}$ **4.** slope is undefined

5.

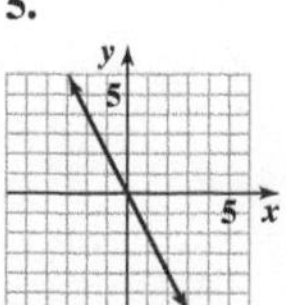

6.

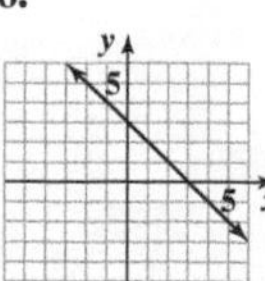

7.

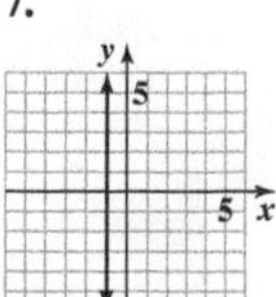

8.

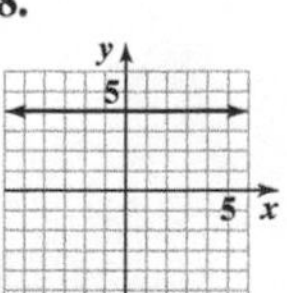

9.
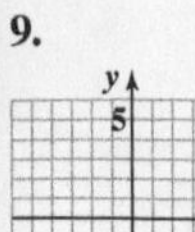

10.
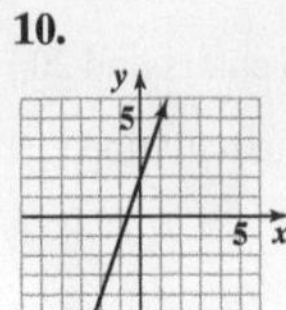

11.
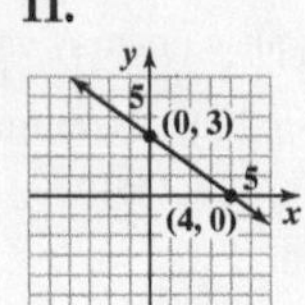

12.
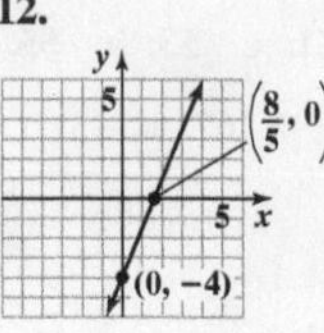

13. $m = 3$ **14.** $m = -6$ **15.** $m = -\frac{7}{2}$ **16.** $m = 2$ **17.** undefined slope **18.** $m = 0$ **19.** $y = 2x - \frac{1}{3}$ **20.** $y = -4x - 1$ **21.** $-x + y = -2$ **22.** neither **23.** perpendicular **24. a.** (2002, 2133); (2007, 3478) **b.** 269 **c.** For the years 2002 through 2007, the amount of yogurt produced increased at a rate of 269 million pounds per year.

Chapter 6 Vocabulary Check **1.** solution **2.** y-axis **3.** linear **4.** x-intercept **5.** standard **6.** y-intercept **7.** function **8.** slope-intercept **9.** domain **10.** range **11.** relation **12.** point-slope **13.** y **14.** x-axis **15.** x **16.** slope **17.** direct **18.** inverse

Chapter 6 Review **1–6.**

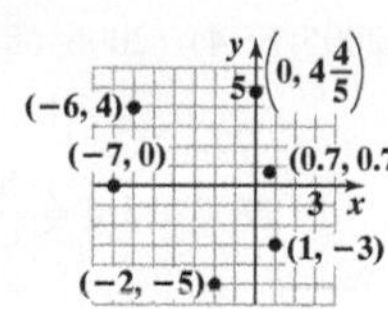

7. (7, 44) **8.** $\left(-\frac{13}{3}, -8\right)$ **9.** −3; 1; 9 **10.** 5; 5; 5 **11.** 0; 10; −10 **12. a.** 2005; 2500; 7000 **b.** 886 compact disc holders

13.

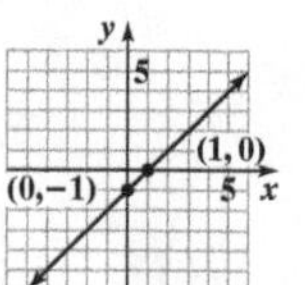

14.

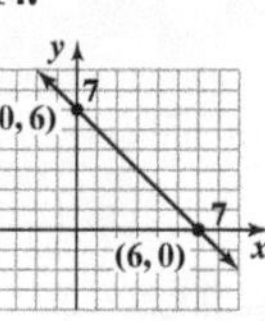

15.

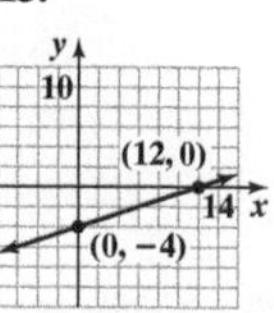

16.

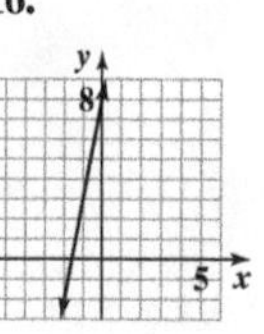

17.

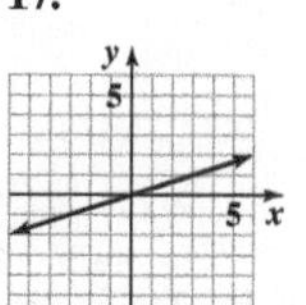

18.

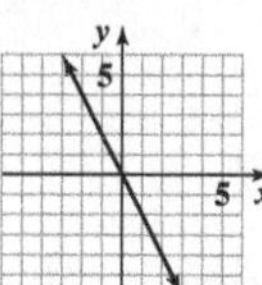

19. (4, 0); (0, −2) **20.** (−2, 0); (2, 0); (0, 2); (0, −2) **21.**

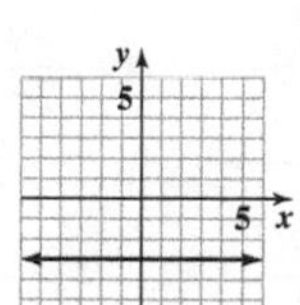

22.

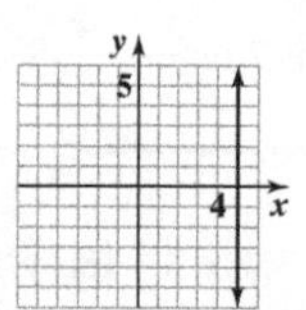

23. (12, 0), (0, −4) **24.** (−2, 0), (0, 8) **25.** $m = -\frac{3}{4}$ **26.** $m = \frac{1}{5}$ **27.** d **28.** b **29.** c **30.** a **31.** $m = \frac{3}{4}$ **32.** $m = \frac{5}{3}$ **33.** $m = 4$ **34.** $m = -1$ **35.** $m = 3$ **36.** $m = \frac{1}{2}$ **37.** $m = 0$ **38.** undefined slope **39.** perpendicular **40.** parallel **41.** neither **42.** perpendicular **43.** $m = 0.025$; Every 1 year, 0.025 million (25,000) more students graduate with a bachelor's degree. **44.** $m = 600$; Every 1 year, 600 more people get a kidney transplant. **45.** $m = \frac{1}{6}$; $\left(0, \frac{1}{6}\right)$ **46.** $m = -3$; (0, 7) **47.** $y = -5x + \frac{1}{2}$ **48.** $y = \frac{2}{3}x + 6$ **49.** d **50.** c **51.** a **52.** b **53.** $-4x + y = -8$ **54.** $3x + y = -5$ **55.** $-3x + 5y = 17$ **56.** $x + 3y = 6$ **57.** $y = -14x + 21$ **58.** $y = -\frac{1}{2}x + 4$ **59.** no **60.** yes **61.** yes **62.** yes **63.** no **64.** yes **65.** 6 **66.** 10 **67.** 5 **68.** 7

69.

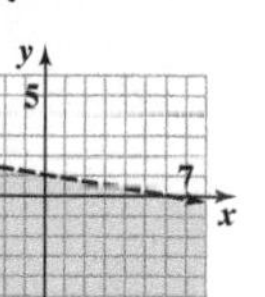

70.

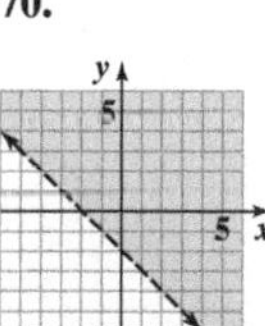

71.

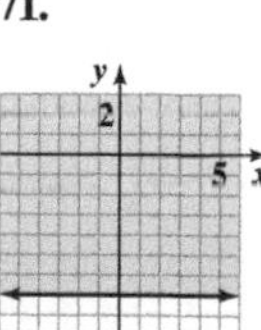

72.

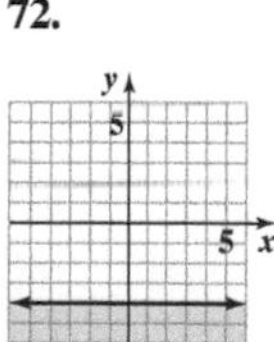

73.

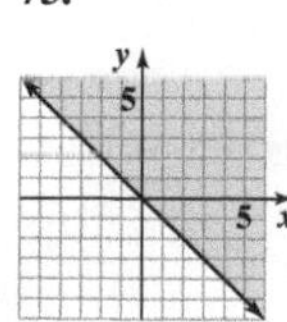

74.

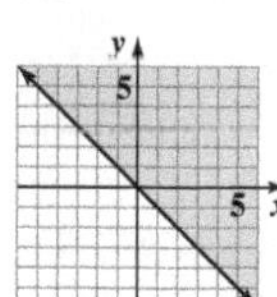

75. $y = 110$ **76.** $y = \frac{1}{2}$ **77.** $y = \frac{100}{27}$ **78.** $y = 700$ **79.** \$3960 **80.** $4\frac{4}{5}$ in. **81.** 7; −1; −3 **82.** 0; −3; −2 **83.** (3, 0); (0, −2) **84.** (−2, 0); (0, 10) **85.**

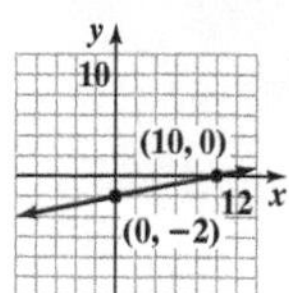

86.

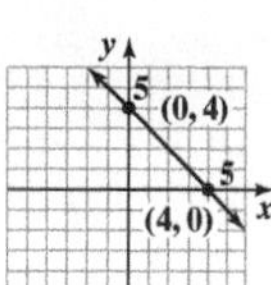

87.

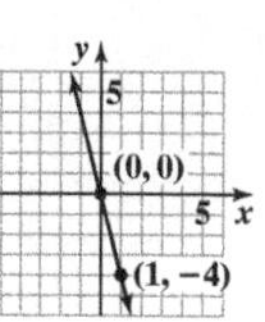

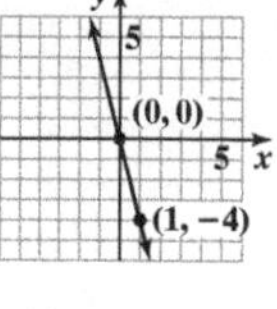

88.

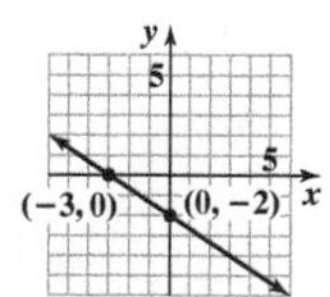

89.

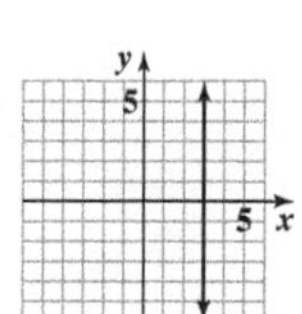

90.

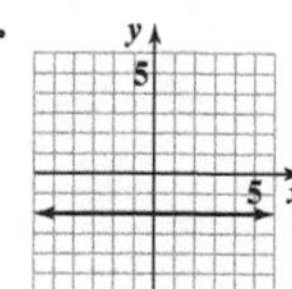

91. $m = -1$ **92.** $m = \frac{11}{7}$ **93.** $m = 2$ **94.** $m = -\frac{1}{3}$ **95.** $m = \frac{2}{3}$; (0, −5) **96.** $m = -6$; (0, 2) **97.** $5x + y = 8$ **98.** $3x - y = -6$ **99.** $4x + y = -3$ **100.** $5x + y = 16$

Chapter 6 Test **1.** (1, 1) **2.** (−4, 17) **3.** $m = \frac{2}{5}$ **4.** $m = 0$ **5.** $m = -1$ **6.** $m = -7$ **7.** $m = 3$ **8.** undefined slope

9.

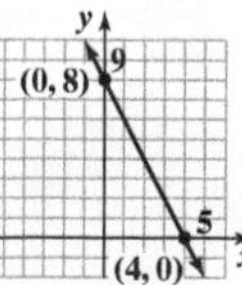

10.

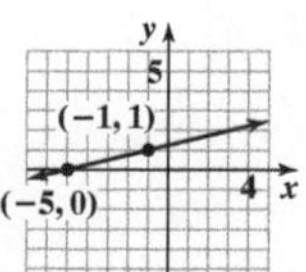

11.

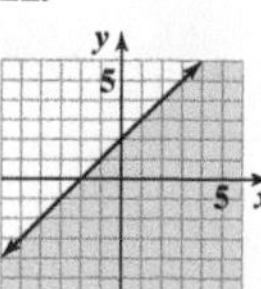

12.

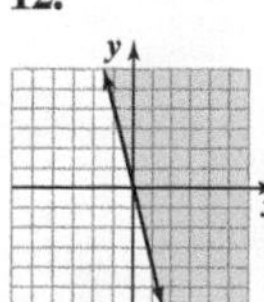

13.

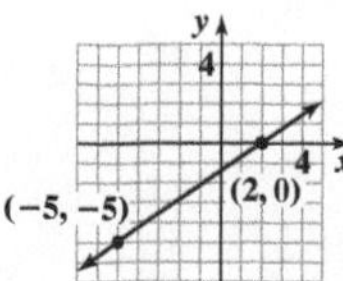

14.

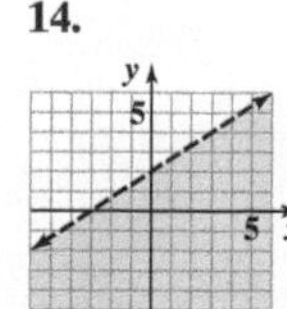

15. 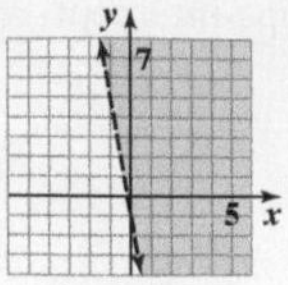

16. 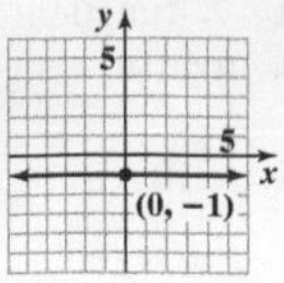

17. neither **18.** $x + 4y = 10$ **19.** $7x + 6y = 0$ **20.** $8x + y = 11$ **21.** $x - 8y = -96$ **22.** yes **23.** no **24.** function; domain: all real numbers; range: all real numbers **25.** function; domain: all real numbers; range: {2} **26. a.** −8 **b.** −3.6 **c.** −4 **27. a.** 0 **b.** 0 **c.** 60 **28.** $x + 2y = 21$; $x = 5$ m **29. a.** (2003, 66.0); (2004, 65.4); (2005, 65.4); (2006, 65.6); (2007, 64.9); (2008, 63.7); (2009, 62.1)

b. 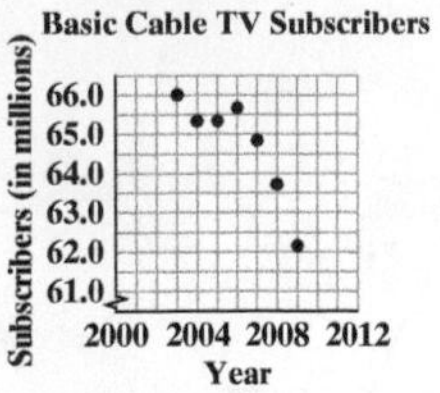

30. $m = -28$; For every 1 year, 28 million fewer movie tickets are sold. **31.** $y = 28$ **32.** $y = \frac{8}{9}$

Cumulative Review **1.** 27; Sec. 1.3, Ex. 2 **2.** $\frac{25}{7}$ **3.** 51; Sec. 1.3, Ex. 5 **4.** 23 **5.** 20,602 ft; Sec. 1.5, Ex. 10 **6.** $0.8x - 36$ **7.** $2x + 6$; Sec. 1.8, Ex. 16 **8.** $-15\left(x + \frac{2}{3}\right) = -15x - 10$ **9.** $(x - 4) \div 7$ or $\frac{x - 4}{7}$; Sec. 1.8, Ex. 17 **10.** $\frac{-9}{2x}$ **11.** $5 + (x + 1) = 6 + x$; Sec. 1.8, Ex. 18 **12.** $-86 - x$ **13.** 6; Sec. 2.2, Ex. 1 **14.** −24 **15.** 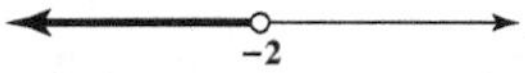

$\{x \mid x < -2\}$; Sec. 2.7, Ex. 6 **16.** $\left\{x \middle| x \le \frac{8}{3}\right\}$ **17. a.** 2; trinomial **b.** 1; binomial **c.** 3; none of these; Sec. 3.3, Ex. 3 **18.** $y = \frac{6 - x}{2}$ **19.** $-4x^2 + 6x + 2$; Sec. 3.4, Ex. 2 **20.** $4x - 4$ **21.** $9y^2 + 6y + 1$; Sec. 3.6, Ex. 4 **22.** $x^2 - 24x + 144$ **23.** $3a(-3a^4 + 6a - 1)$; Sec. 4.1, Ex. 5 **24.** $4(x + 3)(x - 3)$ **25.** $(x - 2)(x + 6)$; Sec. 4.2, Ex. 3 **26.** $(3x + y)(x - 7y)$ **27.** $(4x - 1)(2x - 5)$; Sec. 4.3, Ex. 2 **28.** $(18x - 1)(x + 2)$ **29.** $x = 11, x = -2$; Sec. 4.6, Ex. 4 **30.** $x = 0, x = 1$ **31.** 1; Sec. 5.2, Ex. 7 **32.** $\frac{x + 5}{2x^3}$ **33.** $\frac{12ab^2}{27a^2b}$; Sec. 5.3, Ex. 9a **34.** $\frac{7x^2}{14x^3}$ **35.** $\frac{2m + 1}{m + 1}$; Sec. 5.4, Ex. 5 **36.** $\frac{x + 5}{x - 6}$ **37.** $x = -3, x = -2$; Sec. 5.5, Ex. 3 **38.** $x = -2, x = \frac{1}{3}$ **39.** $\frac{x + 1}{x + 2y}$; Sec. 5.7, Ex. 5 **40.** $\frac{6x - 2y}{x - 4y}$ or $\frac{2(3x - y)}{x - 4y}$ **41. a.** (0, 12) **b.** (2, 6) **c.** (−1, 15); Sec. 6.1, Ex. 5 **42.** 0; 5; −2

43. 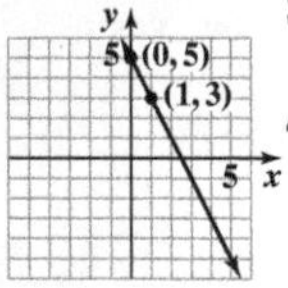

Sec. 6.2, Ex. 1 **44.** $\frac{1}{5}$ **45.** $\frac{2}{3}$; Sec. 6.4, Ex. 3 **46.** undefined slope **47.** $y = -2x + 3$; Sec. 6.5, Ex. 4 **48.** $m = \frac{2}{5}$, y-intercept: (0, −2) **49. a.** 1; (2, 1) **b.** 1; (−2, 1) **c.** −3; (0, −3); Sec. 6.6, Ex. 7 **50.** $3x - 2y = 0$

Chapter 8 Roots and Radicals

Section 8.1

Calculator Explorations **1.** 2.449 **3.** 3.317 **5.** 9.055 **7.** 3.420 **9.** 2.115 **11.** 1.783

Vocabulary and Readiness Check **1.** principal **3.** square root **5.** power **7.** false **9.** true

Exercise Set 8.1 **1.** 4 **3.** $\frac{1}{5}$ **5.** -10 **7.** not a real number **9.** -11 **11.** $\frac{3}{5}$ **13.** 30 **15.** 12 **17.** $\frac{1}{10}$ **19.** 0.5 **21.** 5 **23.** -4 **25.** -2 **27.** $\frac{1}{2}$ **29.** -5 **31.** 2 **33.** 9 **35.** not a real number **37.** $-\frac{3}{4}$ **39.** -5 **41.** 1 **43.** 2.646 **45.** 6.083 **47.** 11.662 **49.** $\sqrt{2} \approx 1.41$; 126.90 ft **51.** m **53.** x^2 **55.** $3x^4$ **57.** $9x$ **59.** ab^2 **61.** $4a^3b^2$ **63.** a^2b^6 **65.** $-2xy^9$ **67.** $\frac{x^3}{6}$ **69.** $\frac{5y}{3}$ **71.** $25 \cdot 2$ **73.** $16 \cdot 2$ or $4 \cdot 8$ **75.** $4 \cdot 7$ **77.** $9 \cdot 3$ **79.** a, b **81.** 7 mi **83.** 3.1 in. **85.** 3 **87.** 10 **89.** 4, 5 **91.** 8, 9 **93.** 6.1 sec **95.** answers may vary **97.** 1; 1.7; 2; 3

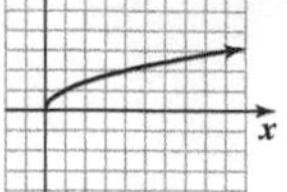

99. $|x|$ **101.** $|x + 2|$ **103.** (2, 0); answers may vary **105.** $(-4, 0)$; answers may vary

Section 8.2

Vocabulary and Readiness Check **1.** $\sqrt{a} \cdot \sqrt{b}$ **3.** 16; 25; 4; 5; 20 **5.** false

Exercise Set 8.2 **1.** $2\sqrt{5}$ **3.** $5\sqrt{2}$ **5.** $\sqrt{33}$ **7.** $7\sqrt{2}$ **9.** $2\sqrt{15}$ **11.** $6\sqrt{5}$ **13.** $2\sqrt{13}$ **15.** 15 **17.** $21\sqrt{7}$ **19.** $-15\sqrt{3}$ **21.** $\frac{2\sqrt{2}}{5}$ **23.** $\frac{3\sqrt{3}}{11}$ **25.** $\frac{3}{2}$ **27.** $\frac{5\sqrt{5}}{3}$ **29.** $\frac{\sqrt{11}}{6}$ **31.** $-\frac{\sqrt{3}}{4}$ **33.** $x^3\sqrt{x}$ **35.** $x^6\sqrt{x}$ **37.** $6a\sqrt{a}$ **39.** $4x^2\sqrt{6}$ **41.** $\frac{2\sqrt{3}}{m}$ **43.** $\frac{3\sqrt{x}}{y^5}$ **45.** $\frac{2\sqrt{22}}{x^6}$ **47.** 16 **49.** $\frac{6}{11}$ **51.** $5\sqrt{7}$ **53.** $\frac{2\sqrt{5}}{3}$ **55.** $2m^3\sqrt{6m}$ **57.** $\frac{y\sqrt{23y}}{2x^3}$ **59.** $2\sqrt[3]{3}$ **61.** $5\sqrt[3]{2}$ **63.** $\frac{\sqrt[3]{5}}{4}$ **65.** $\frac{\sqrt[3]{23}}{2}$ **67.** $\frac{\sqrt[3]{15}}{4}$ **69.** $2\sqrt[3]{10}$ **71.** $14x$ **73.** $2x^2 - 7x - 15$ **75.** 0 **77.** $x^3y\sqrt{y}$ **79.** $7x^2y^2\sqrt{2x}$ **81.** $-2x^2$ **83.** $2\sqrt[3]{10}$ in. **85.** answers may vary **87.** $2\sqrt{5}$ in. **89.** 177 m by 177 m **91.** 2.25 in. **93.** $1700 **95.** 1.7 sq m

Section 8.3

Vocabulary and Readiness Check **1.** like radicals **3.** $17\sqrt{2}$; b **5.** $2\sqrt{5}$; c

Exercise Set 8.3 **1.** $-4\sqrt{3}$ **3.** $9\sqrt{6} - 5$ **5.** $\sqrt{5} + \sqrt{2}$ **7.** $7\sqrt{3} - \sqrt{2}$ **9.** $-5\sqrt{2} - 6$ **11.** $5\sqrt{3}$ **13.** $9\sqrt{5}$ **15.** $4\sqrt{6} + \sqrt{5}$ **17.** $x + \sqrt{x}$ **19.** 0 **21.** $\frac{4\sqrt{5}}{9}$ **23.** $\frac{3\sqrt{3}}{8}$ **25.** $7\sqrt{5}$ **27.** $9\sqrt{3}$ **29.** $\sqrt{5} + \sqrt{15}$ **31.** $x\sqrt{x}$ **33.** $5\sqrt{2} + 12$ **35.** $8\sqrt{2} - 5$ **37.** $2\sqrt{5}$ **39.** $-\sqrt{35}$ **41.** $6 - 3\sqrt{3}$ **43.** $11\sqrt{x}$ **45.** $12x - 11\sqrt{x}$ **47.** $x\sqrt{3x} + 3x\sqrt{x}$ **49.** $8x\sqrt{2} + 2x$ **51.** $2x^2\sqrt{10} - x^2\sqrt{5}$ **53.** $7\sqrt[3]{9} - \sqrt[3]{25}$ **55.** $-5\sqrt[3]{2} - 6$ **57.** $5\sqrt[3]{3}$ **59.** $-3 + 3\sqrt[3]{2}$ **61.** $4x + 4x\sqrt[3]{2}$ **63.** $10y^2\sqrt[3]{y}$ **65.** $x\sqrt[3]{5}$ **67.** $x^2 + 12x + 36$ **69.** $4x^2 - 4x + 1$ **71.** answers may vary **73.** $8\sqrt{5}$ in. **75.** $\left(48 + \frac{9\sqrt{3}}{2}\right)$ sq ft **77.** yes; $7\sqrt{2}$ **79.** no **81.** yes; $3\sqrt{7}$ **83.** $\frac{83x\sqrt{x}}{20}$

Section 8.4

Vocabulary and Readiness Check **1.** $\sqrt{21}$ **3.** $\sqrt{\frac{15}{3}}$ or $\sqrt{5}$ **5.** $2 - \sqrt{3}$

Exercise Set 8.4 **1.** 4 **3.** $5\sqrt{2}$ **5.** 6 **7.** $2x$ **9.** 20 **11.** $36x$ **13.** $3x^3\sqrt{2}$ **15.** $4xy\sqrt{y}$ **17.** $\sqrt{30} + \sqrt{42}$ **19.** $2\sqrt{5} + 5\sqrt{2}$ **21.** $y\sqrt{7} - 14\sqrt{y}$ **23.** -33 **25.** $\sqrt{6} - \sqrt{15} + \sqrt{10} - 5$ **27.** $16 - 11\sqrt{11}$ **29.** $x - 36$ **31.** $x - 14\sqrt{x} + 49$ **33.** $6y + 2\sqrt{6y} + 1$ **35.** 4 **37.** $\sqrt{7}$ **39.** $3\sqrt{2}$ **41.** $5y^2$ **43.** $5\sqrt{3}$ **45.** $2y\sqrt{6}$ **47.** $2xy\sqrt{3y}$ **49.** $\frac{\sqrt{15}}{5}$ **51.** $\frac{7\sqrt{2}}{2}$ **53.** $\frac{\sqrt{6y}}{6y}$ **55.** $\frac{\sqrt{10}}{6}$ **57.** $\frac{\sqrt{3x}}{x}$ **59.** $\frac{\sqrt{2}}{4}$ **61.** $\frac{\sqrt{30}}{15}$ **63.** $\frac{\sqrt{15}}{10}$ **65.** $\frac{3\sqrt{2x}}{2}$ **67.** $\frac{8y\sqrt{5}}{5}$ **69.** $\frac{\sqrt{xy}}{6y}$ **71.** $\frac{\sqrt{3xy}}{6x}$ **73.** $3\sqrt{2} - 3$ **75.** $-8 - 4\sqrt{5}$ **77.** $\sqrt{30} + 5 + \sqrt{6} + \sqrt{5}$ **79.** $\sqrt{6} + \sqrt{3} + \sqrt{2} + 1$ **81.** $\frac{10 - 5\sqrt{x}}{4 - x}$ **83.** $\frac{3\sqrt{x} + 12}{x - 16}$ **85.** 44 **87.** 2 **89.** 3 **91.** $130\sqrt{3}$ sq m **93.** $\frac{\sqrt{A\pi}}{\pi}$ **95.** true **97.** false **99.** false **101.** answers may vary **103.** answers may vary **105.** $\frac{2}{\sqrt{6} - \sqrt{2} - \sqrt{3} + 1}$

Integrated Review **1.** 6 **2.** $4\sqrt{3}$ **3.** x^2 **4.** $y^3\sqrt{y}$ **5.** $4x$ **6.** $3x^5\sqrt{2x}$ **7.** 2 **8.** 3 **9.** -3 **10.** not a real number **11.** $\frac{\sqrt{11}}{3}$ **12.** $\frac{\sqrt[3]{7}}{4}$ **13.** -4 **14.** -5 **15.** $\frac{3}{7}$ **16.** $\frac{1}{8}$ **17.** a^4b **18.** x^5y^{10} **19.** $5m^3$ **20.** $3n^8$ **21.** $6\sqrt{7}$ **22.** $3\sqrt{2}$ **23.** cannot be simplified **24.** $\sqrt{x} + 3x$ **25.** $\sqrt{30}$ **26.** 3 **27.** 28 **28.** 45 **29.** $\sqrt{33} + \sqrt{3}$ **30.** $3\sqrt{2} - 2\sqrt{6}$ **31.** $4y$ **32.** $3x^2\sqrt{5}$ **33.** $x - 3\sqrt{x} - 10$ **34.** $11 + 6\sqrt{2}$ **35.** 2 **36.** $\sqrt{3}$ **37.** $2x^2\sqrt{3}$ **38.** $ab^2\sqrt{15a}$ **39.** $\frac{\sqrt{6}}{6}$ **40.** $\frac{x\sqrt{5}}{10}$ **41.** $\frac{4\sqrt{6} - 4}{5}$ **42.** $\frac{\sqrt{2x} + 5\sqrt{2} + \sqrt{x} + 5}{x - 25}$

Section 8.5

Exercise Set 8.5 **1.** 81 **3.** -1 **5.** 49 **7.** no solution **9.** 4 **11.** 2 **13.** 2 **15.** 9 **17.** -3 **19.** $-1, -2$ **21.** no solution **23.** $0, -3$ **25.** 16 **27.** 25 **29.** 1 **31.** 5 **33.** -2 **35.** no solution **37.** 2 **39.** 36 **41.** no solution **43.** $\frac{3}{2}$ **45.** 16 **47.** 3 **49.** 12 **51.** 3, 1 **53.** -1 **55.** $3x - 8 = 19$; $x = 9$ **57.** $2(2x) + 2x = 24$; length = 8 in. **59.** 4, 7 **61.** answers may vary **63. a.** 3.2, 10, 31.6 **b.** no **65.** 7.30 **67.** 0.76

Section 8.6

Exercise Set 8.6 **1.** $\sqrt{13}$; 3.61 **3.** $3\sqrt{3}$; 5.20 **5.** 25 **7.** $\sqrt{22}$; 4.69 **9.** $3\sqrt{17}$; 12.37 **11.** $\sqrt{41}$; 6.40 **13.** $4\sqrt{2}$; 5.66 **15.** $3\sqrt{10}$; 9.49 **17.** 20.6 ft **19.** 11.7 ft **21.** 24 cu ft **23.** 54 mph **25.** 27 mph **27.** 59.1 km **29.** 60.2 km **31.** 3, −3 **33.** 10, −10 **35.** 8, −8 **37.** $y = 2\sqrt{10}$; $x = 2\sqrt{10} - 4$ **39.** 201 miles **41.** answers may vary

Chapter 8 Vocabulary Check **1.** like radicals **2.** index; radicand; radical **3.** conjugate **4.** principal square root **5.** rationalizing the denominator **6.** hypotenuse

Chapter 8 Review **1.** 9 **2.** -7 **3.** 3 **4.** 3 **5.** $-\frac{3}{8}$ **6.** $\frac{2}{3}$ **7.** 2 **8.** -2 **9.** c **10.** a, c **11.** x^6 **12.** x^4 **13.** $3y$ **14.** $5x^2$ **15.** $2\sqrt{10}$ **16.** $2\sqrt{6}$ **17.** $3\sqrt{6}$ **18.** $2\sqrt{22}$ **19.** $x^2\sqrt{x}$ **20.** $y^3\sqrt{y}$ **21.** $2x\sqrt{5}$ **22.** $5y^2\sqrt{2}$ **23.** $3\sqrt[3]{2}$ **24.** $2\sqrt[3]{11}$ **25.** $\frac{3\sqrt{2}}{5}$ **26.** $\frac{5\sqrt{3}}{8}$ **27.** $-\frac{5\sqrt{2}}{3}$

28. $-\frac{2\sqrt{3}}{7}$ **29.** $\frac{\sqrt{11}}{x}$ **30.** $\frac{\sqrt{7}}{y^2}$ **31.** $\frac{y^2\sqrt{y}}{10}$ **32.** $\frac{x\sqrt{x}}{9}$ **33.** $-3\sqrt{2}$ **34.** $-5\sqrt{3}$ **35.** $4\sqrt{5} + 4\sqrt{6}$ **36.** $-2\sqrt{7} + 2\sqrt{2}$ **37.** $5\sqrt{7} + 2\sqrt{14}$ **38.** $9\sqrt{3} - 4$ **39.** $\frac{\sqrt{5}}{6}$ **40.** $\frac{9\sqrt{11}}{20}$ **41.** $10 - x\sqrt{5}$ **42.** $2\sqrt{2x} - \sqrt{3x}$ **43.** $3\sqrt{2}$ **44.** $5\sqrt{3}$ **45.** $\sqrt{10} - \sqrt{14}$ **46.** $\sqrt{55} + \sqrt{15}$ **47.** $3\sqrt{2} - 5\sqrt{3} + 2\sqrt{6} - 10$ **48.** $2 - 2\sqrt{5}$ **49.** $x - 4\sqrt{x} + 4$ **50.** $y + 8\sqrt{y} + 16$ **51.** 3 **52.** 2 **53.** $2\sqrt{5}$ **54.** $4\sqrt{2}$ **55.** $x\sqrt{15x}$ **56.** $3x^2\sqrt{2}$ **57.** $\frac{\sqrt{22}}{11}$ **58.** $\frac{\sqrt{39}}{13}$ **59.** $\frac{\sqrt{30}}{6}$ **60.** $\frac{\sqrt{70}}{10}$ **61.** $\frac{\sqrt{5x}}{5x}$ **62.** $\frac{5\sqrt{3y}}{3y}$ **63.** $\frac{\sqrt{3x}}{x}$ **64.** $\frac{\sqrt{6y}}{y}$ **65.** $3\sqrt{5} + 6$ **66.** $8\sqrt{10} + 24$ **67.** $\frac{\sqrt{6} + \sqrt{2} + \sqrt{3} + 1}{2}$ **68.** $\sqrt{15} - 2\sqrt{3} - 2\sqrt{5} + 4$ **69.** $\frac{10\sqrt{x} - 50}{x - 25}$ **70.** $\frac{8\sqrt{x} + 8}{x - 1}$ **71.** 18 **72.** 13 **73.** 25 **74.** no solution **75.** 12 **76.** 5 **77.** 1 **78.** 9 **79.** $2\sqrt{14}$; 7.48 **80.** $3\sqrt{13}$; 10.82 **81.** $4\sqrt{34}$ ft; 23.32 ft **82.** $5\sqrt{3}$ in.; 8.66 in. **83.** 2.4 in. **84.** 144π sq in. **85.** 12 **86.** −4 **87.** $4x^8$ **88.** $2x^{12}$ **89.** $3x^3\sqrt{2x}$ **90.** $4y^3\sqrt{3}$ **91.** $\frac{y^2}{9}$ **92.** $\frac{x^4\sqrt{x}}{3}$ **93.** $7\sqrt{3}$ **94.** $5\sqrt{7} - 3$ **95.** $-\frac{\sqrt{3}}{4}$ **96.** $4x\sqrt{5x}$ **97.** $7\sqrt{2}$ **98.** $3\sqrt{3} - \sqrt{6}$ **99.** $\sqrt{10} - \sqrt{2} + 4\sqrt{5} - 4$ **100.** $x + 6\sqrt{x} + 9$ **101.** $2\sqrt{6}$ **102.** $2x$ **103.** $\frac{\sqrt{14}}{7}$ **104.** $\frac{3\sqrt{2x}}{2x}$ **105.** $\frac{3\sqrt{x} + 18}{x - 36}$ **106.** $\frac{\sqrt{35} - 3\sqrt{7} - 5\sqrt{5} + 15}{-4}$ **107.** 1 **108.** 13 **109.** 14 **110.** 9 **111.** $\sqrt{58}$; 7.62 **112.** $4\sqrt{2}$ in.; 5.66 in.

Chapter 8 Test **1.** 4 **2.** 5 **3.** 3 **4.** $\frac{3}{4}$ **5.** not a real number **6.** x^5 **7.** $3\sqrt{6}$ **8.** $2\sqrt{23}$ **9.** $y^3\sqrt{y}$ **10.** $2x^4\sqrt{6}$ **11.** 3 **12.** $2\sqrt[3]{2}$ **13.** $\frac{\sqrt{5}}{4}$ **14.** $\frac{y\sqrt{y}}{5}$ **15.** $-2\sqrt{13}$ **16.** $\sqrt{2} + 2\sqrt{3}$ **17.** $\frac{7\sqrt{3}}{10}$ **18.** $7\sqrt{2}$ **19.** $2\sqrt{3} - \sqrt{10}$ **20.** $x - \sqrt{x} - 6$ **21.** $\sqrt{5}$ **22.** $2x\sqrt{5x}$ **23.** $\frac{\sqrt{6}}{3}$ **24.** $\frac{8\sqrt{5y}}{5y}$ **25.** $4\sqrt{6} - 8$ **26.** $\frac{3 + \sqrt{x}}{9 - x}$ **27.** 9 **28.** 5 **29.** 9 **30.** $4\sqrt{5}$ in. **31.** 2.19 m

Cumulative Review **1.** 28; Sec. 1.6, Ex. 3 **2.** −46.8 **3.** $-\frac{8}{21}$; Sec. 1.6, Ex. 4 **4.** −18 **5.** 2; Sec. 2.3, Ex. 1 **6.** 15 **7. a.** 17% **b.** 21% **c.** 43 American travelers; Sec. 2.6, Ex. 3 **8. a.** $\frac{3}{2}$ **b.** 9 **9. a.** 102,000 **b.** 0.007358 **c.** 84,000,000 **d.** 0.00003007; Sec. 3.2, Ex. 18 **10. a.** 7.2×10^6 **b.** 3.08×10^{-4} **11.** $6x^2 - 11x - 10$; Sec. 3.5; Ex. 7b **12.** $49x^2 + 14x + 1$ **13.** $(y + 2)(x + 3)$; Sec. 4.1; Ex. 10 **14.** $(y^2 + 5)(x - 1)$ **15.** $(3x + 2)(x + 3)$; Sec. 4.3, Ex. 1 **16.** $3(x + 2)(x + 3)$ **17. a.** $x = 3$ **b.** $x = 2, x = 1$ **c.** none; Sec. 5.1, Ex. 2 **18.** $\frac{2x + 1}{x - 3}$ **19.** $\frac{x + 2}{x}$; Sec. 5.1, Ex. 5 **20.** $\frac{4x^3}{5}$ **21. a.** 0 **b.** $\frac{15 + 14x}{50x^2}$; Sec. 5.4, Ex. 1 **22.** $y = -2x + 4$ **23.** $-\frac{17}{5}$; Sec. 5.5, Ex. 4 **24.** $2a^2 + 1$… 5 **25.**

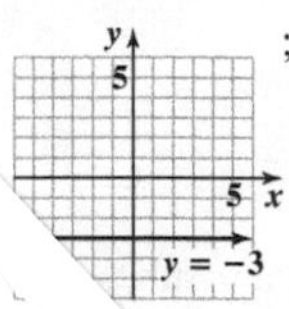

; Sec. 6.3, Ex. 7 **26.** 6; 4; 0 **27.** $y = \frac{1}{4}x - 3$; Sec. 6.5, Ex. 3 **28.** $y = -\frac{1}{2}x + \frac{11}{2}$

29. (3, 1); Sec. 7.3, Ex. 5 **30.** $(\frac{}{3}, \frac{1}{})$ **31.** Alfredo: 3.25 mph; Louisa: 4.25 mph; Sec. 7.4, Ex. 3 **32.** 20 mph, 35 mph **33.** 1; Sec. 8.1, Ex. 6 **34.** 11 **35.** −3; Sec. 8.1, Ex. 7 **36.** $\frac{1}{2}$ **37.** $\frac{1}{5}$; Sec. 8.1, Ex. 8 **38.** $\frac{5}{12}$ **39.** $3\sqrt{6}$; Sec. 8.2, Ex. 1 **40.** $3\sqrt{7}$ **41.** $10\sqrt{2}$; Sec. 8.2, Ex. 3 **42.** $10\sqrt{5}$ **43.** $4\sqrt{3}$; Sec. 8.3, Ex. 6 **44.** $x - 25$ **45.** $2x - 4x^2\sqrt{x}$; Sec. 8.3, Ex. 8 **46.** $10 + 4\sqrt{6}$ **47.** $\frac{2\sqrt{7}}{7}$; Sec. 8.4, Ex. 10 **48.** $3x$ **49.** $\frac{1}{2}$; Sec. 8.5, Ex. 2 **50.** $\frac{5}{2}$

Chapter 9 Quadratic Equations

Section 9.3

Vocabulary and Readiness Check **1.** $x = \dfrac{-b \pm \sqrt{b^2 - 4ac}}{2a}$ **3.** 1; 3; −7 **5.** 1; 1; −1 **7.** −2, 1 **9.** $\dfrac{-5 \pm \sqrt{17}}{2}$

Exercise Set 9.3 **1.** 2, 1 **3.** $\dfrac{-7 \pm \sqrt{37}}{6}$ **5.** $\pm\dfrac{\sqrt{3}}{2}$ **7.** no real solution **9.** 10, −3 **11.** $\pm\sqrt{5}$ **13.** −3, 4 **15.** $-2 \pm \sqrt{7}$ **17.** $\dfrac{-9 \pm \sqrt{129}}{12}$ **19.** $\dfrac{4 \pm \sqrt{2}}{7}$ **21.** $3 \pm \sqrt{7}$ **23.** $\dfrac{3 \pm \sqrt{3}}{2}$ **25.** $\dfrac{1}{3}, -1$ **27.** $\dfrac{3 \pm \sqrt{13}}{4}$ **29.** $\dfrac{1}{5}, -\dfrac{3}{4}$ **31.** no real solution **33.** $1 \pm \sqrt{2}$ **35.** no real solution **37.** $-\dfrac{1}{2}, -\dfrac{3}{4}$ **39.** $\dfrac{7 \pm \sqrt{129}}{20}$ **41.** $\dfrac{11 \pm \sqrt{129}}{4}$ **43.** $\dfrac{1 \pm \sqrt{2}}{5}$ **45.** $\pm\sqrt{7}$; −2.6, 2.6 **47.** $-3 \pm 2\sqrt{2}$; −5.8, −0.2 **49.** $\dfrac{9 \pm \sqrt{97}}{2}$; 9.4, −0.4 **51.** $\dfrac{1 \pm \sqrt{7}}{3}$; 1.2, −0.5 **53.** $y = -3$ **55.** $y = 3x - 2$ **57.** c **59.** b **61.** width: 3.5 ft; length: 9.9 ft **63.** $\dfrac{-3\sqrt{2} \pm \sqrt{38}}{2}$ **65.** answers may vary **67.** −0.9, 0.2 **69.** 7.9 sec **71.** 2012

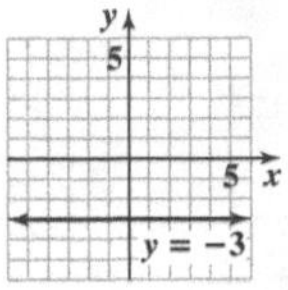

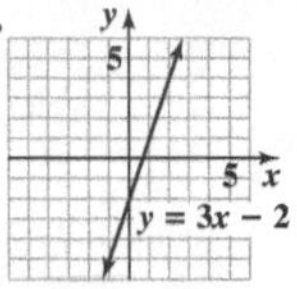

Integrated Review **1.** $2, \dfrac{1}{5}$ **2.** $\dfrac{2}{5}, -3$ **3.** $1 \pm \sqrt{2}$ **4.** $3 \pm \sqrt{2}$ **5.** $\pm 2\sqrt{5}$ **6.** $\pm 6\sqrt{2}$ **7.** no real solution **8.** no real solution **9.** 2 **10.** 3 **11.** $p = 3$ **12.** $\dfrac{7}{2}$ **13.** ±2 **14.** ±3 **15.** 1, 2 **16.** −3, −4 **17.** 0, −5 **18.** $\dfrac{8}{3}, 0$ **19.** $\dfrac{3 \pm \sqrt{7}}{5}$ **20.** $\dfrac{3 \pm \sqrt{5}}{2}$ **21.** $\dfrac{3}{2}, -1$ **22.** $\dfrac{2}{5}, -2$ **23.** $\dfrac{5 \pm \sqrt{105}}{20}$ **24.** $\dfrac{-1 \pm \sqrt{3}}{4}$ **25.** $5, \dfrac{7}{4}$ **26.** $1, \dfrac{7}{9}$ **27.** $\dfrac{-7 \pm 3\sqrt{2}}{-5}, \dfrac{7 \pm 3\sqrt{2}}{5}$ **28.** $\dfrac{-5 \pm 5\sqrt{3}}{-4}, \dfrac{5 \pm 5\sqrt{3}}{4}$ **29.** $\dfrac{7 \pm \sqrt{193}}{6}$ **30.** $\dfrac{-7 \pm \sqrt{193}}{12}$ **31.** 11, −10 **32.** 7, −8 **33.** $4, -\dfrac{2}{3}$ **34.** $2, -\dfrac{4}{5}$ **35.** 0.5, 0.1 **36.** 0.3, −0.2 **37.** $\dfrac{11 \pm \sqrt{41}}{20}$ **38.** $\dfrac{11 \pm \sqrt{41}}{40}$ **39.** $\dfrac{4 \pm \sqrt{10}}{2}$ **40.** $\dfrac{5 \pm \sqrt{185}}{4}$ **41.** answers may vary

Chapter 9 Vocabulary Check **1.** square root **2.** parabola **3.** vertex **4.** completing the square **5.** quadratic **6.** vertex **7.** zero

Chapter 9 Review **1.** ± 11 **2.** ± 10 **3.** $-\frac{1}{3}, 2$ **4.** $\frac{5}{7}, -1$ **5.** ± 6 **6.** ± 9 **7.** $\pm 5\sqrt{2}$ **8.** $\pm 3\sqrt{5}$ **9.** 4, 18 **10.** 7, -13 **11.** $\frac{-5 \pm \sqrt{41}}{4}$ **12.** $\frac{-7 \pm \sqrt{37}}{3}$ **13.** 2.5 sec **14.** 40.6 sec **15.** 1, 8 **16.** $-10, 2$ **17.** $-2 \pm \sqrt{5}$ **18.** $4 \pm \sqrt{19}$ **19.** $3 \pm \sqrt{2}$ **20.** $-3 \pm \sqrt{2}$ **21.** $\frac{1}{2}, -1$ **22.** $\frac{1}{4}, -1$ **23.** $-\frac{5}{3}$ **24.** $\frac{9}{4}$ **25.** $\pm\sqrt{5}$ **26.** $\pm\sqrt{3}$ **27.** $5 \pm 3\sqrt{2}$ **28.** $-2 \pm \sqrt{11}$ **29.** $\frac{-1 \pm \sqrt{13}}{6}$ **30.** $\frac{-3 \pm \sqrt{13}}{2}$ **31.** no real solution **32.** no real solution **33.** 0.4, -0.8 **34.** 0.3, -3.3 **35.** 2013 **36.** 2011

37.
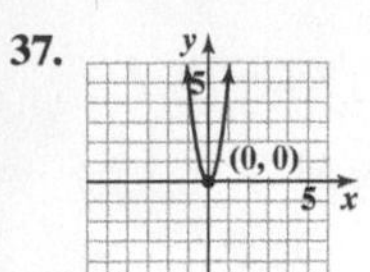

38.
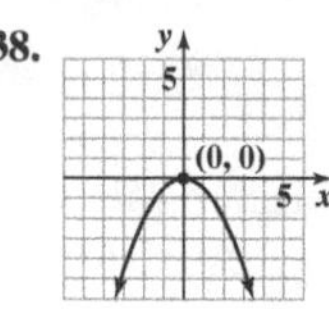

39.
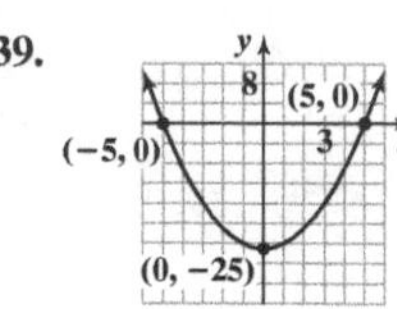

40.
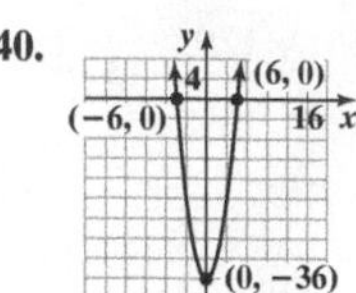

41.
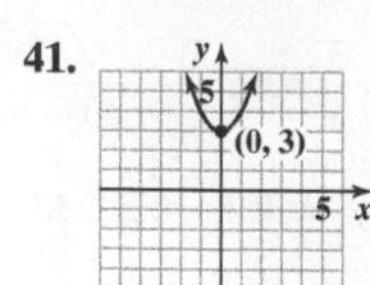

42.
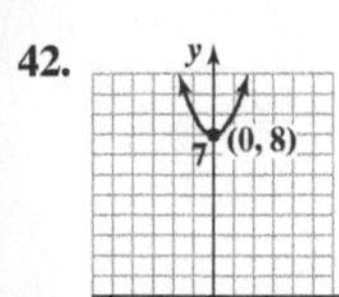

43.
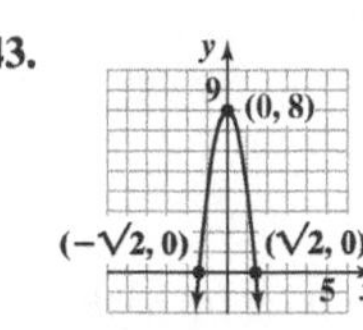

44.
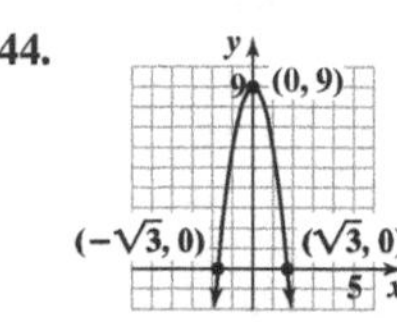

45.
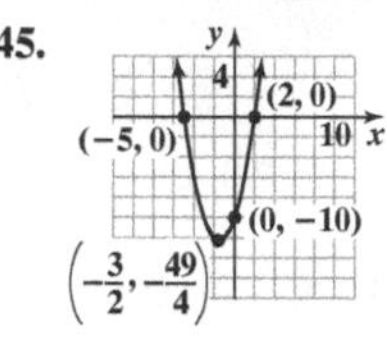

46.
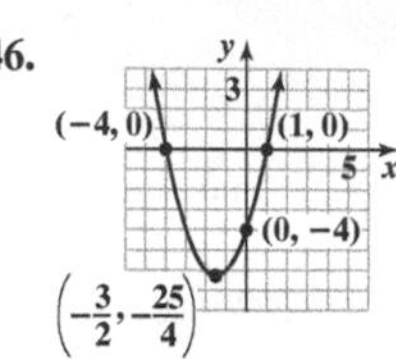

47.
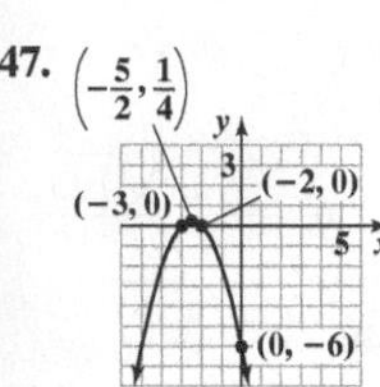

48.
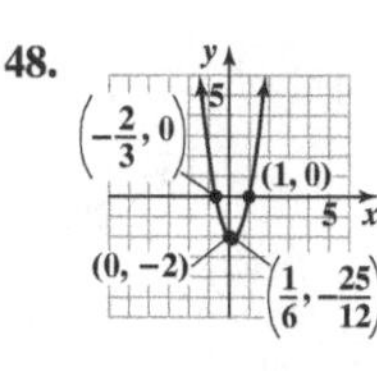

49.
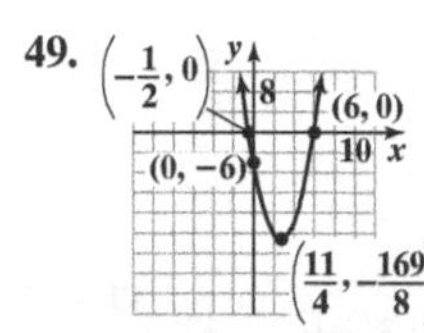

50.
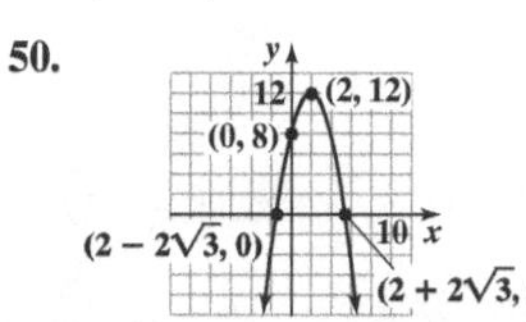

51. A **52.** D **53.** B **54.** C **55.** one real solution **56.** two real solutions **57.** no real solution **58.** two real solutions **59.** ± 7 **60.** $\pm 5\sqrt{3}$ **61.** 15, -1 **62.** $-2 \pm \sqrt{10}$ **63.** $\frac{2}{3}, -1$ **64.** $\frac{1 \pm \sqrt{33}}{8}$ **65.** $\frac{3 \pm \sqrt{41}}{8}$ **66.** $\frac{-1 \pm \sqrt{41}}{10}$ **67.** $-\frac{3}{2}$ **68.** no real solution

69.
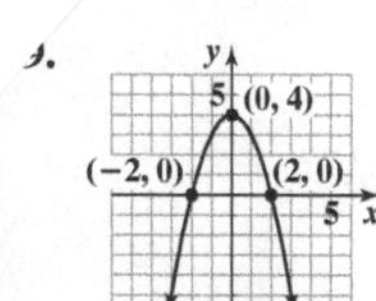

70.
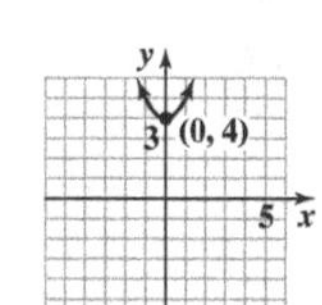

71.
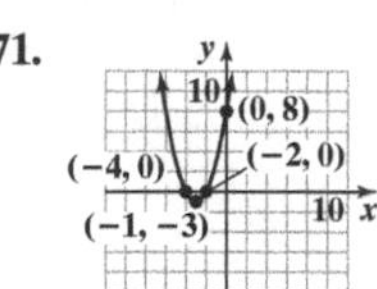

72.
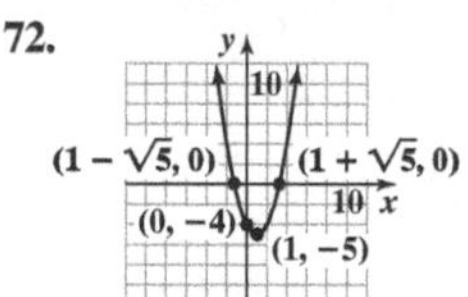

Chapter 9 Test **1.** ± 20 **2.** $-\frac{3}{2}, 7$ **3.** ± 4 **4.** $\frac{5 \pm 2\sqrt{2}}{3}$ **5.** 10, 16 **6.** $-2 \pm \frac{4\sqrt{3}}{3}$ **7.** $-2, 5$ **8.** $\frac{5 \pm \sqrt{37}}{6}$ **9.** 1, $-\frac{4}{3}$ **10.** $-1, \frac{5}{3}$ **11.** $\frac{7 \pm \sqrt{73}}{6}$ **12.** $-1, 5$ **13.** 2, $\frac{1}{3}$ **14.** $\frac{3 \pm \sqrt{7}}{2}$ **15.** base: 3 ft; height: 12 ft

16.
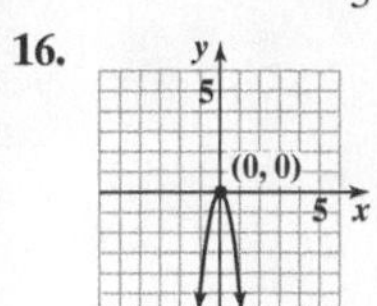

17.
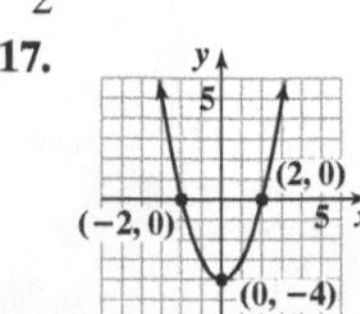

18.
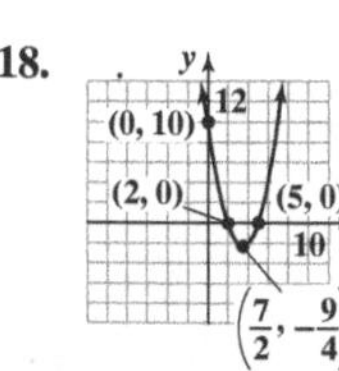

19.
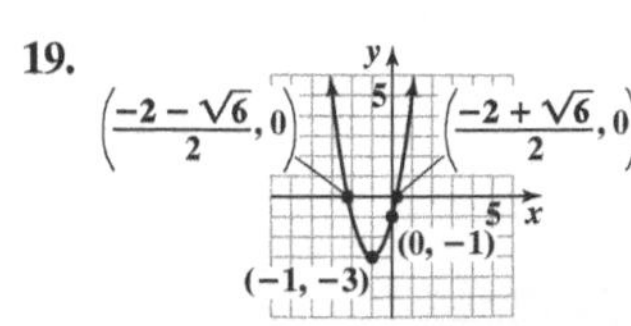

20. 6 sides **21.** 2.7 sec

Cumulative Review **1.** -1.6; Sec. 2.1, Ex. 2 **2.** -3 **3.** $\frac{16}{3}$; Sec. 2.3, Ex. 2 **4.** $\frac{29}{8}$ **5.** Democratic: 256; Republican: 178; Sec. 2.4, Ex. 4 **6.** 145, 146, 147 **7.** 1; Sec. 3.1, Ex. 28 **8.** $-\frac{216x^3}{y^9}$ **9.** 1; Sec. 3.1, Ex. 29 **10.** $\frac{a^2}{32b^3}$ **11.** -1; Sec. 3.1, Ex. 30 **12.** 9 **13.** $9y^2 + 12y + 4$; Sec. 3.6, Ex. 15 **14.** $x^2y - x^2 + 5y - 5$ **15.** $x + 4$; Sec. 3.7, Ex. 4 **16.** $9.1a - 4$ **17.** $(r + 6)(r - 7)$; Sec. 4.2, Ex. 4 **18. a.** -1 **b.** 30 **19.** $(2x - 3y)(5x + y)$; Sec. 4.3, Ex. 4 **20.** $\frac{8x + 13}{(x + 2)(x - 1)}$ **21.** $(2x - 1)(4x - 5)$; Sec. 4.4, Ex. 1 **22.** $\frac{2x + 5}{x - 7}$ **23. a.** $x(2x + 7)(2x - 7)$; Sec. 4.5, Ex. 16 **b.** $2(9x^2 + 1)(3x + 1)(3x - 1)$; Sec. 4.5, Ex. 17 **24.** -32 **25.** $\frac{1}{5}, -\frac{3}{2}, -6$; Sec. 4.6, Ex. 8 **26. a.** $-x + 4$ **b.** $5y - 8$ **c.** $9.1a - 4$ **d.** $2x^2 - 2x$ **27.** $\frac{x + 7}{x - 5}$; Sec. 5.1, Ex. 4 **28.** $-\frac{7}{2}, 1$ **29.** -5; Sec. 5.6, Ex. 5 **30.** $\sqrt{82}$ units **31. a.** -3 **b.** 0 **c.** -3; Sec. 6.1, Ex. 6 **32. a.** x-int: (4, 0); y-int: (0, 1) **b.** x-int: $(-2, 0)$, $(0, 0)$, $(3, 0)$; y-int: (0, 0) **33. a.** parallel **b.** perpendicular **c.** neither; Sec. 6.4, Ex. 7 **34.** perpendicular **35. a.** function **b.** not a function; Sec. 6.6, Ex. 2 **36. a.** $6\sqrt{5}$ **b.** $8\sqrt{2}$ **c.** $11 - 2\sqrt{3} + 4\sqrt{2}$ **37.** (4, 2); Sec. 7.2, Ex. 1 **38.** no solution

39. no solution; Sec. 7.3, Ex. 3 **40.** infinite number of solutions **41.** 6; Sec. 8.1, Ex. 1 **42.** $\frac{2}{5}$ **43.** $\frac{3}{10}$; Sec. 8.1, Ex. 3 **44.** $\frac{4}{11}$ **45.** $-1 + \sqrt{3}$; Sec. 8.4, Ex. 13 **46.** $\frac{5\sqrt{2}}{4}$ **47.** 7, −1; Sec. 9.1, Ex. 5 **48.** $4 \pm \sqrt{3}$ **49.** $1 \pm \sqrt{5}$; Sec. 9.3, Ex. 5 **50.** $-2 \pm 2\sqrt{3}$

Section 9.5

Vocabulary and Readiness Check **1.** Mass **3.** gram **5.** 2000

Exercise Set 9.5 **1.** 32 oz **3.** 10,000 lb **5.** 9 tons **7.** $3\frac{3}{4}$ lb **9.** $1\frac{3}{4}$ tons **11.** 204 oz **13.** 9800 lb **15.** 76 oz **17.** 1.5 tons **19.** $\frac{1}{20}$ lb **21.** 92 oz **23.** 161 oz **25.** 5 lb 9 oz **27.** 53 lb 10 oz **29.** 8 tons 750 lb **31.** 3 tons 175 lb **33.** 8 lb 11 oz **35.** 31 lb 2 oz **37.** 1 ton 700 lb **39.** 0.5 kg **41.** 4000 mg **43.** 25,000 g **45.** 0.048 g **47.** 0.0063 kg **49.** 15,140 mg **51.** 6250 g **53.** 350,000 cg **55.** 13.5 mg **57.** 5.815 g or 5815 mg **59.** 1850 mg or 1.85 g **61.** 1360 g or 1.36 kg **63.** 13.52 kg **65.** 2.125 kg **67.** 200,000; 3,200,000 **69.** $\frac{269}{400}$ or 0.6725; 21,520 **71.** 0.5; 0.0005; 50 **73.** 21,000; 21,000,000; 2,100,000 **75.** 8.064 kg **77.** 30 mg **79.** 5 lb 8 oz **81.** 35 lb 14 oz **83.** 6 lb 15.4 oz **85.** 144 mg **87.** 6.12 kg **89.** 130 lb **91.** 211 lb **93.** 0.16 **95.** 0.875 **97.** no **99.** yes **101.** no **103.** answers may vary; for example, 250 mg or 0.25 g **105.** true **107.** answers may vary

Section 9.6

Vocabulary and Readiness Check **1.** capacity **3.** fluid ounces **5.** cups **7.** quarts

Exercise Set 9.6 **1.** 4 c **3.** 16 pt **5.** $3\frac{1}{2}$ gal **7.** 5 pt **9.** 8 c **11.** $3\frac{3}{4}$ qt **13.** $10\frac{1}{2}$ qt **15.** 9 c **17.** 23 qt **19.** $\frac{1}{4}$ pt **21.** 14 gal 2 qt **23.** 4 gal 3 qt 1 pt **25.** 22 pt **27.** 13 gal 2 qt **29.** 4 c 4 fl oz **31.** 1 gal 1 qt **33.** 2 gal 3 qt 1 pt **35.** 17 gal **37.** 4 gal 3 qt **39.** 5000 ml **41.** 0.00016 kl **43.** 5.6 L **45.** 320 cl **47.** 0.41 kl **49.** 0.064 L **51.** 160 L **53.** 3600 ml **55.** 19.3 L **57.** 4.5 L or 4500 ml **59.** 8410 ml or 8.41 L **61.** 16,600 ml or 16.6 L **63.** 3840 ml **65.** 162.4 L **67.** 336; 84; 168 **69.** $\frac{1}{4}$; 1; 2 **71.** 1.59 L **73.** 18.954 L **75.** 4.3 fl oz **77.** yes **79.** $0.316 **81.** $\frac{4}{5}$ **83.** $\frac{3}{5}$ **85.** $\frac{9}{10}$ **87.** no **89.** no **91.** less than; answers may vary **93.** answers may vary **95.** 128 fl oz **97.** 1.5 cc **99.** 2.7 cc **101.** 54 u or 0.54 cc **103.** 86 u or 0.86 cc

Section 9.7

Exercise Set 9.7 **1.** 25.57 fl oz **3.** 218.44 cm **5.** 40 oz **7.** 57.66 mi **9.** 3.77 gal **11.** 13.5 kg **13.** 1.5; 1[illegible] 50; 60 **15.** 55; 5500; 180; 2160 **17.** 3.94 in. **19.** 80.5 kph **21.** 0.008 oz **23.** yes **25.** 2790 mi **27.** 90 mm **29.** 112.[illegible] **31.** 104 mph **33.** 26.24 ft **35.** 3 mi **37.** 8 fl oz **39.** b **41.** b **43.** c **45.** d **47.** d **49.** 25°C **51.** 40°C **53.** 122°F **55.** 2[illegible] **57.** −6.7°C **59.** 61.2°C **61.** 197.6°F **63.** 54.3°F **65.** 56.7°C **67.** 80.6°F **69.** 21.1°C **71.** 244.4°F **73.** 7232°F **75.** 29 [illegible] 36 **79.** yes **81.** no **83.** no **85.** yes **87.** 2.13 sq m **89.** 1.19 sq m **91.** 1.69 sq m **93.** 510,000,000°C **95.** answers may vary

Chapter 9 Vocabulary Check **1.** Weight **2.** Mass **3.** meter **4.** unit fractions **5.** gram **6.** liter **7.** line segment **8.** complementary **9.** line **10.** perimeter **11.** angle; vertex **12.** Area **13.** ray **14.** transversal **15.** straight **16.** volume **17.** vertical **18.** adjacent **19.** obtuse **20.** right **21.** acute **22.** supplementary **23.** surface area

Practice Final Exam **1.** −81 **2.** $\frac{1}{64}$ **3.** −48 **4.** $-3x^3 + 5x^2 + 4x + 5$ **5.** $16x^2 - 16x + 4$ **6.** $3x^3 + 22x^2 + 41x + 14$ **7.** $(6t + 5)(t - 1)$ **8.** $3x(x - 5)(x - 2)$ **9.** $5(6 + x)(6 - x)$ **10.** $(a + b)(3a - 7)$ **11.** $x(1 - x)(1 + x)(1 + x^2)$ **12.** $\frac{16y^{14}}{x^2}$ **13.** $\frac{5y^2 - 1}{y + 2}$ **14.** $\frac{(x - 6)(x - 7)}{(x + 7)(x + 2)}$ **15.** $\frac{3a - 4}{(a - 3)(a + 2)}$ **16.** 8 **17.** −7, 1 **18.** $\{x | x \le -2\}$ **19.** $\frac{3 \pm \sqrt{7}}{2}$ **20.** $\frac{30}{11}$ **21.** −6 **22.** no solution **23.** 9

24.

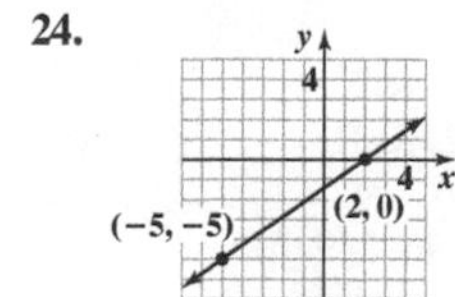

25.

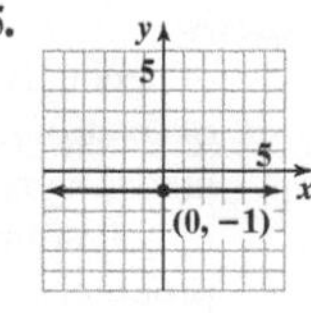

26.

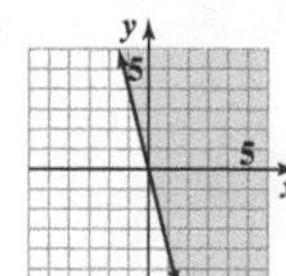

27. $m = -1$ **28.** $m = 3$ **29.** $8x + y = 11$ **30.** $x - 8y = -96$ **31.** $(-4, 1)$ **32.** no solution **33. a.** 0 **b.** 0 **c.** 60 **34.** function; domain: all real numbers; range: {2} **35.** 4 **36.** 5 **37.** $\frac{3}{4}$ **38.** $3\sqrt{6}$ **39.** $2x^4\sqrt{6}$ **40.** $\sqrt{2} + 2\sqrt{3}$ **41.** $2x\sqrt{5x}$ **42.** $2\sqrt{3} - \sqrt{10}$ **43.** $\frac{8\sqrt{5y}}{5y}$ **44.** $4\sqrt{6} - 8$ **45.** 5 or 1 **46.** 401, 802 **47.** 3 mph; 6 mph **48.** 120 cc

Index

O

P

Q

R

Photo Credits

Chapter R **CO** Andy Z./Shutterstock

Chapter 1 **p. 5** Creatas Images/Thinkstock **p. 10** Tim Davis/Corbis; Jovannig/Dreamstime **p. 22** ElementalImaging/iStockphoto **p. 35** ELEN/Shutterstock **p. 38** Smellme/Dreamstime; MidkhatIzmaylov/Shutterstock; Sean Nel/Shutterstock; Sgcallaway1994/Dreamstime **p. 47** Oversnap/iStockphoto; Donald Gargano/Shutterstock **p. 59** Stockbyte/Thinkstock

Chapter 2 **CO** Mirceax/Dreamstime **p. 99** Astikhin/Dreamstime; Xbrandonx/Dreamstime **p. 102** Jeppo75/Dreamstime; Dmitryp/Dreamstime **p. 127** Nantela/Dreamstime **p. 128** Thielandrzej/Dreamstime; ES James/Shutterstock **p. 130** Yuri Arcurs/Shutterstock **p. 136** Ewg3D/iStockphoto **p. 138** William D. Fergus McNeill/iStockphoto **p. 148** Steve Geer/iStockphoto **p. 150** Kim Gunkelist2/iStockphoto **p. 155** Cynthia Farmer/Shutterstock **p. 156** Steve Debenpor/iStockphoto **p. 161** ericsphotography/iStockphoto; Daniel Yordanov/Shutterstock **p. 180** S. Borisov/Shutterstock

Chapter 3 **CO** Bakaleev Aleksey/iStockphoto **p. 208** Haak78/Shutterstock; NASA **p. 228** TebNad/Shutterstock; AVAVA/Shutterstock **p. 258** Paolo Vairo/Shutterstock; Giovanni Benintende/Shutterstock **p. 259** Jabiru/Dreamstime

Chapter 4 **p. 277** Comstock **p. 304** Katrina Brown/Fotolia; Holgs/Dreamstime; Sborisov/Dreamstime **p. 315** Vulkanette/Dreamstime

Chapter 5 **CO** Debby Wong/Shutterstock; Ken Durden/Shutterstock **p. 353** Matt Grant/Shutterstock; Macie J. Noskowski/iStockphoto **p. 365** Gabor Izso/iStockphoto **p. 388** Rainerplendl/Dreamstime **p. 398** Sideline/Dreamstime

Chapter 6 **CO** Gudella/Dreamstime **p. 422** Stockbyte/Getty Images **p. 432** Anton Prado Photo/Shutterstock **p. 433** Willee Cole/Shutterstock **p. 442** Sean Locke/iStockphoto **p. 447** AVAVA/Shutterstock; Webphotographer/iStockphoto **p. 466** Scott Cramer/iStockphoto **p. 474** Jim Pickerell/Stock Connection; Alexey Fiodorov/iStockphoto **p. 479** Teresa Pigeon/iStockphoto **p. 485** Michael Shake/Shutterstock; Gresei/Dreamstime **p. 486** Fotovampir/Dreamstime

Chapter 7 **CO** Kirk Peart Professional Imaging/Shutterstock **p. 559** Kirk Peart Professional Imaging/Shutterstock; Fotografia, Inc./iStockphoto **p. 567** Mangostock/Shutterstock; Doxa Digital/iStockphoto **p. 570** Paha_l/Dreamstime **p. 576** Ken Inness/Shutterstock; Olaf Loose/iStockphoto **p. 577** Iwikoz6/Dreamstime **p. 588** Thomas Barrat/Shutterstock

Chapter 8 **CO** Lion_beat/Dreamstime **p. 599** Cpurdy/Dreamstime **p. 607** Empire331/Dreamstime; MaxFX/Shutterstock **p. 608** Steve Cole/iStockphoto

Chapter 9 **CO** Pavelk/Shutterstock; Brendan Howard/Shutterstock; Alexander Chaiken/Shutterstock; Stas Volik/Shutterstock; Gewre/Dreamstime; Liza1979/Shutterstock **p. 652** Brasil2/iStockphoto **p. 654** Thomas Trotscher/iStockphoto; Daivaluk/Dreamstime **p. 669** Sebastian Kaulitzki/Shutterstock **p. 681** Tony Acevedo/National Astronomy and Ionosphere Center **p. 685** Olesia Ru & Ivan Ru/Shutterstock